COMPLETE VOLUME

University Physics
THIRD EDITION

by

FRANCIS WESTON SEARS

Dartmouth College

and

MARK W. ZEMANSKY

The City College of the
City University of New York

ADDISON-WESLEY PUBLISHING COMPANY

READING, MASSACHUSETTS • PALO ALTO • LONDON • DON MILLS, ONTARIO

This book is in the

ADDISON-WESLEY SERIES IN PHYSICS

Preface

University Physics is available in one complete volume or as two separate parts: Part 1 covers the subjects of mechanics, heat, and sound; Part 2 includes electricity and magnetism, light, and atomic physics. The total number of topics is small enough so that the complete text may be taught in two semesters. The text is intended for students of science and engineering who are taking a course in calculus concurrently and to whom calculus is still a new tool.

The emphasis is on physical principles; historical background and practical applications have been given a place of secondary importance.

Three systems of units are used: the British gravitational system because it is the one used in engineering work throughout the country; the cgs system because some familiarity with it is essential for any intelligent reading of the literature of physics; and the mks system because of its increasing use in electricity and magnetism, as well as because it seems destined eventually to supplant the cgs system. The symbols and terminology, with few exceptions, are those recommended by the Committee on Letter Symbols and Abbreviations of the American Association of Physics Teachers as listed in the American Standard, ASA-Z10, published in 1947.

The main features of the preceding editions have been retained in the third. The supplementary problems that appeared at the end of the second edition have been incorporated with the problems that follow each chapter. Many figures have been redrawn to achieve greater uniformity and clarity, and many of the optical ray diagrams have been reproduced in white on black. Numerous illustrative problems are worked out in the body of the text; in each of them, all physical quantities are expressed by numerics along with the appropriate units. The general level of sophistication has been raised and calculus has been used a little more, but mathematical difficulties have *not* been increased. Throughout the book, boldface symbols have been used for vectors and both the vector product and the scalar product have been used extensively.

A new treatment of relative velocity has been introduced to serve as a better introduction to the ideas of relativity. With the aid of Brehme diagrams (*American Journal of Physics*, July 1962), very simple derivations of the Lorentz-Einstein transformation equations are given, and length contraction and time dilation are explained. The treatment of motion in an accelerated frame has been considerably expanded in order to explain the concepts of apparent weight and weightlessness. More space has been devoted to the motion of a satellite, and to the effect of the earth's rotation on the apparent weight of an object.

The entire chapter on work and energy has been rewritten to provide a better background for the study of electricity. In the chapter on momentum the relativistic relation between mass and velocity is derived with the aid of Brehme diagrams and from this the mass-energy relationship is obtained.

Other new topics include: plasticity, Lissajous figures, circulation in hydrodynamics, Poiseuille's equation, zeroth law of thermodynamics, temperature variation of expansion coefficients and of heat capacities, and the meaning and applications of entropy changes.

In preparing this revision the authors have referred constantly to the many letters and reviews sent to the publishers by colleagues and friends. We have tried to incorporate most of the suggestions based upon actual teaching experience and have rejected only those which would have required too much space or would have involved too great a departure from normal practice. It is with a feeling of sincere gratitude that we acknowledge the help we have received from the following teachers of physics: Robert A. Kromhout, Robert J. Lee, Gerald P. Lietz, James A. Richards, Jr., T. L. Rokoske, Richard C. Sapp, M. Russell Wehr, Gilbert B. Weingourt, Lester V. Whitney, Jack Willis, and R. E. Worley.

Hanover and New York   F. W. S.
January 1963   M. W. Z.

Contents

1 COMPOSITION AND RESOLUTION OF VECTORS

1–1 The fundamental indefinables of mechanics 1
1–2 Standards and units 1
1–3 Symbols for physical quantities 5
1–4 Force 6
1–5 Graphical representation of forces. Vectors 7
1–6 Vector addition. Resultant of a set of forces 8
1–7 Resultant of parallel and antiparallel forces 11
1–8 Components of a vector 12
1–9 Resultant by rectangular resolution 14
1–10 Vector difference 16

2 EQUILIBRIUM OF A PARTICLE

2–1 Introduction 20
2–2 Equilibrium. Newton's first law 20
2–3 Discussion of Newton's first law of motion 23
2–4 Stable, unstable, and neutral equilibrium 24
2–5 Newton's third law of motion 24
2–6 Equilibrium of a particle 26
2–7 Friction 33

3 EQUILIBRIUM OF A RIGID BODY

3–1 Moment of a force 44
3–2 Vector product. Vector moment 47
3–3 The second condition of equilibrium 48
3–4 Resultant of parallel forces 53
3–5 Center of gravity 54
3–6 Couples 57

4 RECTILINEAR MOTION. SPECIAL RELATIVITY

4 1 Motion 64
4–2 Average velocity 64
4–3 Instantaneous velocity 65
4–4 Average and instantaneous acceleration 68
4–5 Velocity and coordinate by integration 71
4–6 Uniformly accelerated motion 74
4–7 Freely falling bodies 76

Contents

4–8 Rectilinear motion with variable acceleration 79
4–9 Relative velocity 81
4–10 Graphical representation of events relative to moving coordinate systems 85
4–11 The Lorentz-Einstein transformation 88

5 NEWTON'S SECOND LAW. GRAVITATION

5–1 Introduction 99
5–2 Newton's second law. Mass 99
5–3 Systems of units 101
5–4 Newton's law of universal gravitation 103
5–5 Mass and weight 105
5–6 Applications of Newton's second law 108

6 MOTION IN A PLANE

6–1 Motion in a plane 124
6–2 Average and instantaneous velocity 124
6–3 Average and instantaneous acceleration 126
6–4 Components of acceleration 127
6–5 Motion of a projectile 129
6–6 Circular motion 135
6–7 Centripetal force 138
6–8 Motion in a vertical circle 141
6–9 Motion of a satellite 145
6–10 Effect of the earth's rotation on g 148

7 WORK AND ENERGY

7–1 Introduction 156
7–2 Work 157
7–3 Kinetic energy 161
7–4 Gravitational potential energy 162
7–5 Elastic potential energy 169
7–6 Conservative and dissipative forces 171
7–7 Internal work 172
7–8 Internal potential energy 173
7–9 Power 175
7–10 Power and velocity 176

8 IMPULSE AND MOMENTUM

8–1 Impulse and momentum 182
8–2 Conservation of linear momentum 186
8–3 Elastic and inelastic collisions 187
8–4 Inelastic collisions 188
8–5 Elastic collisions 190
8–6 Recoil 192
8–7 Principles of rocket propulsion 194
8–8 Relativistic change of mass with velocity 195
8–9 Mass and energy 199
8–10 Relativistic force transformation 202
8–11 Transverse and longitudinal mass 204

9 ROTATION

9–1   Introduction 211
9–2   Angular velocity 211
9–3   Angular acceleration 213
9–4   Rotation with variable angular acceleration 214
9–5   Rotation with constant angular acceleration 214
9–6   Relation between angular and linear velocity and acceleration 216
9–7   Torque and angular acceleration. Moment of inertia 217
9–8   Calculation of moments of inertia 220
9–9   Kinetic energy, work, and power 225
9–10 Angular momentum 227
9–11 Rotation about a moving axis. The top and the gyroscope 231

10 ELASTICITY

10–1   Stress 244
10–2   Strain 247
10–3   Elasticity and plasticity 248
10–4   Elastic modulus 249
10–5   The force constant 253

11 HARMONIC MOTION

11–1   Introduction 256
11–2   Elastic restoring forces 256
11–3   Definitions 257
11–4   Equations of simple harmonic motion 258
11–5   Motion of a body suspended from a coil spring 265
11–6   The simple pendulum 267
11–7   Lissajous' figures 268
11–8   Angular harmonic motion 271
11–9   The physical pendulum 271
11–10 Center of oscillation 272

12 HYDROSTATICS

12–1   Introduction 280
12–2   Pressure in a fluid 281
12–3   The hydrostatic paradox 283
12–4   Pressure gauges 284
12–5   Vacuum pumps 285
12–6   Archimedes' principle 287
12–7   Forces against a dam 290

13 SURFACE TENSION

13–1   Surface tension 296
13–2   Surface tension and surface energy 299
13–3   Pressure difference across a surface film 300

13–4 Minimal surfaces 302
13–5 Contact angle 304
13–6 Capillarity 306

14 HYDRODYNAMICS AND VISCOSITY

14–1 Introduction 309
14–2 The equation of continuity 311
14–3 Bernoulli's equation 311
14–4 Applications of Bernoulli's equation 313
14–5 Viscosity 317
14–6 Poiseuille's law 320
14–7 Stokes' law 322
14–8 Dynamic lift 323
14–9 Reynolds number 327

15 TEMPERATURE-EXPANSION

15–1 Concept of temperature 334
15–2 Thermometers 337
15–3 The establishment of a temperature scale 339
15–4 The celsius, rankine, and fahrenheit scales 343
15–5 Expansion of solids and liquids 345
15–6 Thermal stresses 348

16 HEAT AND HEAT MEASUREMENTS

16–1 Heat, a form of energy 352
16–2 Units of heat. The mechanical equivalent of heat 353
16–3 Heat capacity 354
16–4 The measurement of heat capacity 355
16–5 Experimental values of heat capacities 357
16–6 Change of phase 360

17 TRANSFER OF HEAT

17–1 Conduction 368
17–2 Heat flow through a compound wall 371
17–3 Radial heat flow in a sphere or cylinder 372
17–4 Convection 372
17–5 Radiation 375
17–6 The complete radiator or blackbody 376
17–7 Planck's law 380
17–8 Wien's displacement law and Stefan's law 382
17–9 Heat transfer by radiation 383
17–10 Newton's law of cooling 384

18 THERMAL PROPERTIES OF MATTER

18–1 Equations of state 389
18–2 The ideal gas 389
18–3 pVT-surface for an ideal gas 394
18–4 pVT-surface for a real substance 395
18–5 Critical point and triple point 398
18–6 Effect of dissolved substances on freezing and boiling points 404
18–7 Humidity 404
18–8 The Wilson cloud chamber and the bubble chamber 406

19 THE LAWS OF THERMODYNAMICS

19–1   Work in thermodynamics 411
19–2   Work in changing the volume 412
19–3   Work and heat 413
19–4   The first law of thermodynamics 414
19–5   Adiabatic process 416
19–6   Isochoric process 416
19–7   Isothermal process 416
19–8   Isobaric process 417
19–9   Throttling process 417
19–10 Differential form of the first law 419
19–11 Internal energy of a gas 419
19–12 Heat capacities of an ideal gas 420
19–13 Adiabatic process of an ideal gas 422
19–14 The conversion of heat into work 425
19–15 The gasoline engine 428
19–16 The diesel engine 429
19–17 The steam engine 429
19–18 The second law of thermodynamics 430
19–19 The refrigerator 431
19–20 The Carnot cycle 433
19–21 The kelvin temperature scale 435
19–22 Absolute zero 437
19–23 Entropy 438
19–24 The principle of the increase of entropy 440

20 MOLECULAR PROPERTIES OF MATTER

20–1   Molecular theory of matter 446
20–2   Avogadro's number 449
20–3   Equation of state of an ideal gas 451
20–4   Molar heat capacity of a gas 456
20–5   The principle of equipartition of energy 457
20–6   Distribution of molecular speeds 459
20–7   Experimental measurement of molecular speeds 461
20–8   Collision cross section. Mean free path 463
20–9   Viscosity of a gas 466
20–10 The Clausius and van der Waals equations of state 468

20–11 Crystals   470
20–12 Heat capacity of a crystal   473

21 TRAVELING WAVES

21–1   Introduction   477
21–2   Mathematical representation of a traveling wave   479
21–3   Calculation of the speed of a transverse pulse   481
21–4   Calculation of the speed of a longitudinal pulse   483
21–5   Adiabatic character of a longitudinal wave   485
21–6   Waves in a canal   488

22 VIBRATING BODIES

22–1   Boundary conditions for a string   494
22–2   Stationary waves in a string   495
22–3   Vibration of a string fixed at both ends   498
22–4   Demonstration of the harmonic series in a vibrating string   499
22–5   Resonance   500
22–6   Interference of longitudinal waves   501
22–7   Stationary longitudinal waves   502
22–8   Vibrations of organ pipes   505
22–9   Vibrations of rods and plates   506

23 ACOUSTICAL PHENOMENA

23–1   Pressure variations in a sound wave   510
23–2   Intensity   510
23–3   Intensity level and loudness   511
23–4   Quality and pitch   513
23–5   Spherical waves   515
23–6   Radiation from a piston. Diffraction   515
23–7   Radiating efficiency of a sound source   519
23–8   Beats   520
23–9   The Doppler effect   521
23–10 The relativistic Doppler effect   524

24 COULOMB'S LAW

24–1   Electric charges   529
24–2   Atomic structure   530
24–3   The leaf electroscope and the electrometer   532
24–4   Conductors and insulators   533
24–5   Charging by induction   533
24–6   Coulomb's law   535

25 THE ELECTRIC FIELD, GAUSS'S LAW

25–1   The electric field   540
25–2   Calculation of electric intensity   542

25–3 Lines of force 548
25–4 Gauss's law 549
25–5 Applications of Gauss's law 553

26 POTENTIAL

26–1 Line integral of electric intensity 566
26–2 Electrical potential energy 568
26–3 Potential 569
26–4 Calculation of potential differences 570
26–5 Potential in terms of charge distribution 574
26–6 Potential gradient 575
26–7 Field of a dipole 576
26–8 The Millikan oil drop experiment 580
26–9 The electron volt. Relativistic variation of mass with velocity 582
26–10 The cathode ray oscilloscope 583
26–11 Sharing of charge by conductors 587
26–12 The Van de Graaff generator 588

27 CAPACITANCE, PROPERTIES OF DIELECTRICS

27–1 Capacitors 594
27–2 The parallel-plate capacitor 594
27–3 Capacitors in series and parallel 596
27–4 Energy of a charged capacitor 599
27–5 Effect of a dielectric 601
27–6 Molecular theory of induced charges on a dielectric 603
27–7 Polarization 605
27–8 Susceptibility, permittivity, and dielectric coefficient 605
27–9 Displacement 608

28 CURRENT, RESISTANCE, AND ELECTROMOTIVE FORCE

28–1 Current 614
28–2 Resistivity 617
28–3 Resistance 620
28–4 Electromotive force 623
28–5 Terminal voltage of a source 627
28–6 Current-voltage diagrams 634
28–7 Power and work in electrical circuits 635
28–8 Thermoelectricity 640
28–9 Applications of the fundamental thermocouple equation 642

29 DIRECT-CURRENT CIRCUITS AND INSTRUMENTS

29–1 Resistors in series and in parallel 649
29–2 Kirchhoff's rules 652
29–3 Ammeters and voltmeters 654
29–4 The Wheatstone bridge 657
29–5 The ohmmeter 658

29–6   The potentiometer   659
29–7   The *R-C* series circuit. 659
29–8   The sweep circuit 662
29–9   Displacement current   663

30   THE MAGNETIC FIELD

30–1   Magnetism   671
30–2   Charges, currents, and relativity. 672
30–3   Experimental study of magnetic fields 676
30–4   Lines of induction. Magnetic flux 678
30–5   Orbits of charged particles in magnetic fields 679
30–6   Thomson's measurement of e/m 681
30–7   Positive rays 683
30–8   Isotopes   685
30–9   Mass spectroscopy   686
30–10 Atomic weights. The atomic mass unit   687
30–11 The cyclotron 688

31   MAGNETIC FORCES ON CURRENT-CARRYING CONDUCTORS

31–1   Force on a current-carrying conductor   694
31–2   The Hall effect. 695
31–3   Force and torque on a complete circuit. Magnetic moment   696
31–4   The spinning electron   698
31–5   The galvanometer   699
31–6   The pivoted-coil galvanometer 701
31–7   The ballistic galvanometer   702
31–8   The direct-current motor   702
31–9   The electromagnetic pump 704

32   MAGNETIC FIELD OF A CURRENT

32–1   Magnetic field of a current-carrying circuit. The Biot law 708
32–2   Magnetic field of a long straight conductor   709
32–3   Force between parallel conductors. The ampere and the coulomb   . . 711
32–4   Magnetic field of a circular turn   713
32–5   Ampere's law 715
32–6   Applications of Ampere's law 716
32–7   Magnetic field of a displacement current 719

33   INDUCED ELECTROMOTIVE FORCE

33–1   Motional electromotive force   725
33–2   Induced electric fields   726
33–3   Induced electromotive force. The Faraday law 729
33–4   Lenz's law 731
33–5   The search coil   735
33–6   Galvanometer damping 736

33–7 Eddy currents 737
33–8 The betatron 739
33–9 Mutual inductance 741
33–10 Self-inductance 743
33–11 Energy associated with an inductor 744
33–12 The *R-L* circuit 745
33–13 The *L-C* circuit 746
33–14 The *R-L-C* circuit 748

34 MAGNETIC PROPERTIES OF MATTER

34–1 Equivalent surface currents 757
34–2 Molecular theory of dia- and paramagnetism 759
34–3 Magnetization. Magnetic intensity 761
34–4 Magnetic susceptibility, permeability, and magnetic coefficient 762
34–5 Ferromagnetism 765
34–6 Magnetization of iron. Magnetic domains 766
34–7 Hysteresis 769
34–8 Magnetic poles 772
34–9 Demagnetizing fields 775
34–10 The magnetic field of the earth 777
34–11 The magnetic circuit 778

35 ALTERNATING CURRENTS

35–1 Introduction 783
35–2 Circuits containing resistance, inductance, or capacitance 783
35–3 The *R-L-C* series circuit 788
35–4 Average and root-mean-square values. AC instruments 790
35–5 Power in AC circuits 793
35–6 Series resonance 796
35–7 Circuits in parallel 797
35–8 The transformer 798

36 ELECTROMAGNETIC WAVES

36–1 Introduction 804
36–2 Propagation of an electromagnetic wave 804
36–3 Electromagnetic waves in matter 811
36–4 The Poynting vector 811
36–5 Sinusoidal waves 815
36–6 Stationary waves 817
36–7 Radiation of electromagnetic waves from an antenna 819

37 THE NATURE AND PROPAGATION OF LIGHT

37–1 The nature of light 823
37–2 Sources of light 824
37–3 Waves, wavefronts, and rays 827
37–4 The speed of light 830

37–5   The laws of reflection and refraction 832
37–6   Index of refraction 834

38   REFLECTION AND REFRACTION AT PLANE SURFACES

38–1   Huygens' principle 838
38–2   Derivation of the law of reflection from Huygens' principle 840
38–3   Derivation of Snell's law from Huygens' principle 841
38–4   Total internal reflection 843
38–5   Refraction by a prism 845
38–6   Dispersion 847
38–7   The rainbow 848

39   IMAGES FORMED BY A SINGLE REFLECTION OR REFRACTION

39–1   Introduction 852
39–2   Reflection at a plane mirror 852
39–3   Reflection at a spherical mirror 855
39–4   Sign conventions 857
39–5   Focal point and focal length 860
39–6   Graphical methods 862
39–7   Refraction at a plane surface 864
39–8   Refraction at a spherical surface 866
39–9   Summary 869

40   LENSES AND OPTICAL INSTRUMENTS

40–1   Images as objects 872
40–2   The thin lens 873
40–3   Diverging lenses 877
40–4   Graphical methods 879
40–5   Images as objects for lenses 880
40–6   Lens aberrations 881
40–7   The eye 881
40–8   The magnifier 884
40–9   The camera 885
40–10 The projection lantern 886
40–11 The microscope 887
40–12 The telescope 888

41   INTERFERENCE AND DIFFRACTION

41–1   Principles of interference. Coherent sources 895
41–2   Young's double slit and Pohl's mica sheet 898
41–3   Intensity distribution in interference fringes 902
41–4   Phase change in reflection. Lloyd's mirror 903
41–5   The Michelson interferometer 905
41–6   The Michelson-Morley experiment 907
41–7   Interference in thin films. Newton's rings 911
41–8   Thin coatings on glass 913

41–9   Fresnel diffraction.   917
41–10   Fraunhofer diffraction by a single slit   920
41–11   The plane diffraction grating   923
41–12   Diffraction of x-rays by a crystal   927
41–13   The resolving power of optical instruments   928

42 POLARIZATION

42–1   Polarization   934
42–2   Polarization by reflection.   935
42–3   Double refraction   937
42–4   Polarization by double refraction   939
42–5   Percentage polarization. Malus' law   940
42–6   The scattering of light   942
42–7   Circular and elliptic polarization   944
42 8   Production of colors by polarized light.   946
42–9   Optical stress analysis   947
42–10   Study of crystals by convergent polarized light   949
42–11   Optical activity   949

43 ATOMS, ELECTRONS, AND PHOTONS

43–1   Conduction in gases   952
43–2   Thermionic emission   953
43–3   The triode   956
43–4   The photoelectric effect   957
43–5   Line spectra   959
43–6   The Bohr atom   961
43–7   Deuterium   966
43–8   Wave mechanics   967
43–9   The electron microscope   968
43–10   Absorption spectra   970
43–11   The laser   973
43–12   Band spectra   974
43–13   The x-ray tube   975
43–14   X-ray spectra   976

44 RADIOACTIVITY AND NUCLEAR PHYSICS

44–1   Natural radioactivity   982
44–2   Alpha particles   983
44–3   Rutherford's scattering experiment   984
44–4   Beta particles   986
44–5   Gamma rays   987
44–6   Radioactive transformations   988
44–7   Artificial nuclear disintegration   991
44–8   Cosmic rays. The positron   992
44–9   Neutrons and mesons.   994
44–10   Nuclear stability   997
44–11   Nuclear fission.   999
44–12   Thermonuclear reactions   1000

Answers to Odd-Numbered Problems 1002

Natural Trigonometric Functions 1013

Common Logarithms 1014

Periodic Table of the Elements 1016

Fundamental Constants 1017

Conversion Factors 1018

Index 1019

CHAPTER 1

Composition and Resolution of Vectors

1-1 The fundamental indefinables of mechanics

Physics has been called the science of measurement. To quote from Lord Kelvin (1824–1907), "I often say that when you can measure what you are speaking about, and express it in numbers, you know something about it; but when you cannot express it in numbers, your knowledge is of a meagre and unsatisfactory kind; it may be the beginning of knowledge, but you have scarcely, in your thoughts, advanced to the stage of *Science*, whatever the matter may be."

A definition of a quantity in physics must provide a set of rules for calculating it in terms of other quantities that can be measured. Thus, when momentum is defined as the product of "mass" and "velocity," the rule for calculating momentum is contained within the definition, and all that is necessary is to know how to measure mass and velocity. The definition of velocity is given in terms of length and time, but there are no simpler or more fundamental quantities in terms of which length and time may be expressed. *Length and time are two of the indefinables of mechanics.* It has been found possible to express all the quantities of mechanics in terms of only three indefinables. The third may be taken to be "mass" or "force" with equal justification. *We shall choose mass as the third indefinable of mechanics.*

In geometry, the fundamental indefinable is the "point." The geometer asks his disciple to build any picture of a point in his mind, provided the picture is consistent with what the geometer *says* about the point. In physics, the situation is not so subtle. Physicists from all over the world have international committees at whose meetings the rules of measurement of the indefinables are adopted. The rule for measuring an indefinable takes the place of a definition.

1-2 Standards and units

The set of rules for measuring the indefinables of mechanics is determined by an international committee called the *General Conference on Weights and Measures*, to which all the major countries send delegates. One of the chief functions of the Conference is to decide on a standard for each indefinable. A standard may be an actual object, in which case its main characteristic must be *durability*. Thus in 1889 when the meter bar of platinum-iridium alloy was chosen as the standard of length, it was felt that this alloy was particularly stable in its chemical structure. If, instead of platinum-iridium, a glass bar had been chosen, its length would have changed throughout the years because of the unavoidable crystallization that glass undergoes as it

TABLE 1–1

STANDARDS AND UNITS (AS OF 1963)

	Standard	Device for using standard for measuring	Unit
Length	Wavelength of orange-red light from krypton-86	Optical interferometer	One meter = 1,650,763.73 wavelengths
Time	Tropical year 1900	Pendulum clock (soon, an atomic clock)	One second = 1/31,556,925.9747 of tropical year 1900
Mass	Platinum-iridium cylinder, one kilogram	Equal-arm balance	One kilogram

ages. Although platinum-iridium is an unusually stable alloy, the preservation of a bar of this material as a world standard entails a number of cumbersome provisions, such as making a large number of replicas for all the major countries and comparing these replicas with the world standard at periodic intervals.

On October 14, 1960, the General Conference changed the standard of length to an *atomic constant*, namely, the *wavelength of the orange-red light emitted by the individual atoms of krypton-86* in a tube filled with krypton gas in which an electrical discharge is maintained. The standard of mass is the mass of a *cylinder of platinum-iridium*, designated as *one kilogram*, and kept at the International Bureau of Weights and Measures at Sèvres, near Paris. Before 1960, the standard of time was the time between successive appearances of the sun overhead, averaged over a year and known as a mean solar day. This has now been changed to what is known as the *tropical year 1900*, that is, the time it took the sun to move from a certain point in the heavens, known as the *vernal equinox*, back to the same point in 1900. The three standards are listed in Table 1–1.

After the choice of a standard, the next step is to decide upon an instrument and a technique for comparing the standard with an unknown. Consider, for example, the distance x between the two mirrors, A and B, of the device, called an *etalon*, shown in Fig. 1–1(a). To find the number of wavelengths of orange-red light of krypton-86 in the distance x requires the use of an *optical interferometer*, one type of which, due to Michelson, is shown in Fig. 1–1(b). A movable mirror M on the Michelson interferometer is first made to coincide in position with A on the etalon. Then the mirror is moved slowly to coincide with B, during which time gradations of orange and black, known as *interference fringes*, move past the cross-hair in the field of view of a telescope and are counted. The motion of one complete fringe corresponds to a motion of mirror M of exactly one-half a wavelength. A length known as *one meter* is defined in this way as

1 meter = 1,650,763.73 wavelengths of orange-red light of krypton-86.

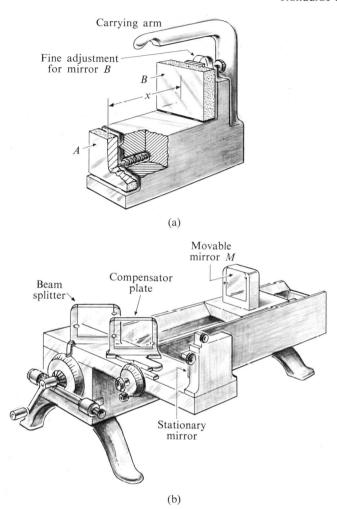

Fig. 1–1. (a) Etalon and (b) Michelson interferometer for use in measuring the distance x in terms of the wavelength of light.

Other units of length frequently used in pure science are:

1 angstrom unit	$= 1\ A$	$= 10^{-10}$ m (used by spectroscopists),
1 nanometer	$= 1$ nm	$= 10^{-9}$ m (used by optical designers),
1 micron	$= 1\ \mu$	$= 10^{-6}$ m (used commonly in biology),
1 millimeter	$= 1$ mm	$= 10^{-3}$ m $\rbrace$ (used the most often),
1 centimeter	$= 1$ cm	$= 10^{-2}$ m
1 kilometer	$= 1$ km	$= 10^{3}$ m (a common European unit of distance).

The words "nanometer" and "kilometer" are both accented on the *first* syllable, *not* the second, just like the words "millimeter" and "centimeter." The prefix "nano" is pronounced "nanno." Units of length used in everyday life and in engineering in both the United States and the United Kingdom are defined as follows:

$$1 \text{ inch} = 1 \text{ in} = \begin{cases} 41{,}929.399 \text{ wavelengths of Kr light,} \\ 2.54 \text{ cm,} \end{cases}$$

$$
\begin{aligned}
1 \text{ foot} &= 1 \text{ ft} \doteq 12 \text{ in,} \\
1 \text{ yard} &= 1 \text{ yd} = 3 \text{ ft,} \\
1 \text{ mile} &= 1 \text{ mi} = 5280 \text{ ft.}
\end{aligned}
$$

The standard of time has been mentioned as the tropical year 1900. The subdivision of this year into smaller time intervals was accomplished with the aid of two natural clocks and one type of laboratory clock:

(1) The nightly motion of the stars across the heavens enables the daily rotation of the earth about its axis to serve as a repeating time interval into which the tropical year may be subdivided.

(2) The nightly motion of the moon across the heavens provides another naturally recurring time interval connected with the motion of the moon around the earth.

(3) The recurring swings of a pendulum, protected from air currents and maintained at constant temperature, pressure, and humidity, and controlled so that the length of the swing is always the same, are assumed to take place in equal time intervals.

The way in which these three clocks were used to subdivide the tropical year 1900 is a long and extremely complicated story. The time based on this year is used in the *Nautical ephemeris*, a book of tables which enables the navigator to find his position in terms of measurements on the stars. The unit of time used throughout the world is called the *second* and is defined to be

$$1 \text{ second} = 1 \text{ sec} = \frac{1}{31{,}556{,}925.9747} \text{ of tropical year 1900.}$$

The suggestion has been made and is under discussion now (1963) that a natural time unit available in all laboratories in all parts of the world, similar to the natural wavelength unit of krypton light, be adopted as a world standard. One of the most convenient natural time units is the periodic time in a vibratory process that may easily be stimulated in a beam of individual cesium atoms. All the bureaus of standards of the world are experimenting with the cesium clock. This clock is used by our own National Bureau of Standards to control the time signals broadcast over station WWV. Using the second, defined as a fraction of the tropical year 1900, the time interval between vibrations in the cesium atom has been found to be

$$1 \text{ Cs time interval} = \frac{1}{9{,}192{,}631{,}770} \text{ sec.}$$

It is highly probable that, within very few years, the vibration time in a cesium atom will be the world standard of time, and the second will be *defined* as the time for 9,192,631,770 cesium vibrations.

TABLE 1–2

PREFIXES FOR POWERS OF TEN

Power of ten	10^{-12}	10^{-9}	10^{-6}	10^{-3}	10^{-2}	10^3	10^6	10^9	10^{12}
Prefix	pico-	nano-	micro-	milli-	centi-	kilo-	mega-	giga-	tera-
Abbreviation	p	n	μ	m	c	k	M	G	T

Common units of time are:

$$
\begin{aligned}
1 \text{ nanosecond} &= 1 \text{ nsec} = 10^{-9} \text{ sec,} \\
1 \text{ microsecond} &= 1 \text{ } \mu\text{sec} = 10^{-6} \text{ sec,} \\
1 \text{ millisecond} &= 1 \text{ msec} = 10^{-3} \text{ sec,} \\
1 \text{ minute} &= 1 \text{ min} = 60 \text{ sec,} \\
1 \text{ hour} &= 1 \text{ hr} = 3600 \text{ sec,} \\
1 \text{ day} &= 1 \text{ day} = 86{,}400 \text{ sec.}
\end{aligned}
$$

The device used to subdivide the standard of mass, the kilogram, into equal sub-masses is the equal-arm balance, which will be discussed in Chapter 5. Frequently used units of mass are:

$$
\begin{aligned}
1 \text{ microgram} &= 1 \text{ } \mu\text{gm} = 10^{-9} \text{ kgm} \\
1 \text{ milligram} &= 1 \text{ mgm} = 10^{-6} \text{ kgm} \\
1 \text{ gram} &= 1 \text{ gm} = 10^{-3} \text{ kgm} \\
1 \text{ pound mass} &= 1 \text{ lbm} = 0.45359237 \text{ kgm}
\end{aligned}
$$

It will be found useful to memorize the prefixes and abbreviations for the various powers of ten, which are collected in Table 1–2. (The prefix "giga" is pronounced "jeega.")

1–3 Symbols for physical quantities

We shall adopt the convention that an algebraic symbol representing a physical quantity, such as F, p, or v, stands for both a *number* and a *unit*. For example, F might represent a force of 10 lb, p a pressure of 15 lb/ft^2, and v a velocity of 15 ft/sec.
When we write

$$x = v_0 t + \tfrac{1}{2}at^2,$$

if x is in feet, then the terms $v_0 t$ and $\tfrac{1}{2}at^2$ must be in feet also. Suppose t is in seconds. Then the units of v_0 must be ft/sec and those of a must be ft/sec^2. (The factor $\tfrac{1}{2}$ is a *pure number*, without units.) As a numerical example, let $v_0 = 10$ ft/sec, $a = 4$ ft/sec^2, $t = 10$ sec. Then the preceding equation would be written

$$x = 10 \frac{\text{ft}}{\text{sec}} \times 10 \text{ sec} + \tfrac{1}{2} \times 4 \frac{\text{ft}}{\text{sec}^2} \times 100 \text{ sec}^2.$$

The units are treated like algebraic symbols. The sec's cancel in the first term and the sec^2's in the second, and

$$x = 100 \text{ ft} + 200 \text{ ft} = 300 \text{ ft}.$$

The beginning student will do well to include the units of all physical quantities, as well as their magnitudes, in all his calculations. This will be done consistently in the numerical examples throughout the book.

1–4 Force

Mechanics is the branch of physics which deals with the motion of material bodies and with the forces that bring about the motion. Since motion is best described by the methods of calculus and many readers of this book are just beginning their study of this subject, we shall postpone a discussion of motion until Chapter 4, and start with a study of forces.

When we push or pull on a body, we are said to exert a *force* on it. Forces can also be exerted by inanimate objects: a stretched spring exerts forces on the bodies to which its ends are attached, compressed air exerts a force on the walls of its container, a locomotive exerts a force on the train it is drawing. The force of which we are most aware in our daily lives is the force of gravitational attraction exerted on every body by the earth, and is called the *weight* of the body. Gravitational forces (and electrical and magnetic forces also) can act through empty space without contact. In this respect they differ from the forces mentioned above, where the body doing the pushing or pulling must make contact with the body being pushed or pulled.

We are not yet in a position to show how a unit of force can be defined in terms of the units of mass, length, and time. This will be done in Chapter 5. For the present, a unit of force can be defined as follows. We select as a standard body the standard pound, defined in the preceding section as a certain fraction (approximately 0.454) of a standard kilogram. The force with which the earth attracts this body, at some specified point on the earth's surface, is then a perfectly definite, reproducible force and is called a force of *one pound* (avoirdupois). A particular point on the earth's surface must be specified, since the attraction of the earth for a given body varies slightly from one point to another. If great precision is not required it suffices to take any point at sea level and 45° latitude.

In order that an unknown force can be compared with the force unit, and thereby measured, some measurable effect produced by a force must be used. One such effect is to alter the dimensions or shape of a body on which the force is exerted; another is to alter the state of motion of the body. Both of these effects are used in the measurement of forces. In this chapter we shall consider only the former; the latter will be discussed in Chapter 5.

The instrument most commonly used to measure forces is the spring balance, which consists of a coil spring enclosed in a case for protection and carrying at one end a pointer that moves over a scale. A force exerted on the balance changes the length of the spring. The balance can be calibrated as follows. The standard pound is first suspended from the balance at sea level and 45° latitude and the position of the pointer is marked 1 lb. Any number of duplicates of the standard can then be prepared by suspending a body from the balance and adding or removing material until the index again stands at 1 lb. Then when two, three, or more of these are suspended simultaneously from the balance the force stretching it is 2 lb, 3 lb, etc., and the corresponding positions of the pointer can be labeled 2 lb, 3 lb, etc. This procedure makes no assumption about the elastic properties of the spring except that the force exerted on it is always the same when the pointer stands at the same position. The calibrated balance can then be used to measure an unknown force.

1–5 Graphical representation of forces. Vectors

Suppose we are to slide a box along the floor by pulling it with a string or pushing it with a stick, as in Fig. 1–2. That is, we are to slide it by exerting a force on it. The point of view which we now adopt is that the motion of the box is caused not by the *objects* which push or pull on it, but by the *forces* which these exert. For concreteness, assume the magnitude of the push or pull to be 10 lb. It is clear that simply to write "10 lb" on the diagram would not completely describe the force, since it would not indicate the direction in which the force was acting. One might write "10 lb, 30° above horizontal to the right," or "10 lb, 45° below horizontal to the right," but all the above information may be conveyed more briefly if we adopt the convention of representing a force by an arrow. The length of the arrow, to some chosen scale, indicates the size or *magnitude* of the force, and the direction in which the arrow points indicates the *direction* of the force. Thus Fig. 1–3 is the force diagram corresponding to Fig. 1–2. (There are other forces acting on the box, but these are not shown in the figure.)

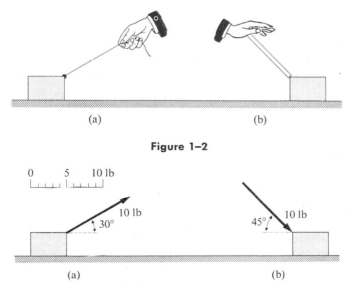

(a)   (b)

Figure 1–2

(a)   (b)

Figure 1–3

Force is not the only physical quantity which requires the specification of a direction in space as well as a magnitude. For example, the velocity of an aircraft is not completely specified by stating that it is 300 miles per hour; we need to know the direction also. The concept of volume, on the other hand, has no direction associated with it.

Quantities like volume, which involve a magnitude only, are called *scalars*. Those like force and velocity, which involve both a magnitude and a direction in space, are called *vector quantities*. Any vector quantity can be represented by an arrow, and this arrow is called a vector (or if a more specific statement is needed, a force vector or a velocity vector).

Some vector quantities, of which force is one, are not *completely* specified by their magnitude and direction alone. Thus the effect of a force depends also on its *line of action* and its *point of application*. (The line of action is a line of indefinite length, of which the force vector is a segment.) For example, if one is pushing horizontally against a door, the effectiveness of a force of given magnitude and direction depends on the distance of its line of action from the hinges. If a body is deformable, as all bodies are to a greater or lesser extent, the deformation depends on the point of application of the force. However, since many actual objects are deformed only very slightly by the forces acting on them, we shall assume for the present that all objects considered are perfectly rigid. The point of application of a given force acting on a rigid body may be transferred to any other point on the line of action without altering the effect of the force. Thus *a force applied to a rigid body may be regarded as acting anywhere along its line of action.*

A vector quantity is represented by a letter in bold-face type. The same letter in ordinary type represents the magnitude of the quantity. Thus the magnitude of a force **F** is represented by *F*.

1–6 Vector addition.   Resultant of a set of forces

The sciences of arithmetic and algebra deal with pure numbers. Similarly, in the science of *vector analysis*, another branch of pure mathematics, a vector is considered simply as an arrow or a "directed line segment," without any physical significance. However, just as the laws of arithmetic and algebra are found to describe certain operations that can be carried out with some physical quantities, so the laws of vector algebra are found to represent some (but not all) aspects of the behavior of other physical quantities.

For example, two (mathematical) vectors are considered equal, by definition, if they have the same magnitude and direction. Thus in Fig. 1–4 the vectors **A**, **B**, and **C** are all equal. It follows that in mathematics a given vector may be moved around at will, provided its length and direction are not changed. However, if the vectors in Fig. 1–4 represent forces acting on a body, the forces are not physically equivalent, since they have different points of application and different lines of action.

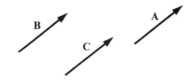

Fig. 1–4. The vectors **A**, **B**, and **C** are mathematically equal.

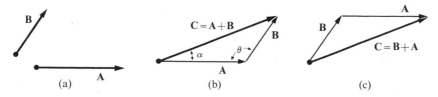

Fig. 1–5. Vector **C** is the vector sum of vectors **A** and **B**. **C** = **A** + **B** = **B** + **A**.

The *vector sum* of two (mathematical) vectors is defined as follows. Let **A** and **B** in Fig. 1–5(a) be two given vectors. Draw the vectors as in (b) at any convenient point, with the initial point of **B** at the endpoint of **A**. The vector sum **C** is then defined as the vector from the initial point of **A** to the endpoint of **B**. The symbol for vector addition is the same as for algebraic addition, and we write

$$\mathbf{C} = \mathbf{A} + \mathbf{B}.$$

Alternatively, the given vectors can be drawn as in Fig. 1–5(c), with the initial point of **A** at the endpoint of **B**. The vector **C** has the same magnitude and direction as in (b) and hence the two vector sums are mathematically equal. The order in which the vectors are added is therefore immaterial, and vector addition obeys the same commutative law as algebraic addition:

$$\mathbf{A} + \mathbf{B} = \mathbf{B} + \mathbf{A}.$$

The magnitude and direction of the vector sum **C** can be found from measurements on a carefully drawn diagram. They can also be computed by the methods of trigonometry. Thus if θ represents the angle between vectors **A** and **B**, as in Fig. 1–5(b), the magnitude of **C** is given by

$$C^2 = A^2 + B^2 - 2AB\cos\theta.$$

The angle α between **C** and **A** can be found from the relation

$$\frac{\sin\alpha}{B} = \frac{\sin\theta}{C}.$$

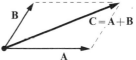

Fig. 1–6. Parallelogram method for obtaining the vector sum of two vectors.

Another useful method of finding the sum of two vectors is shown in Fig. 1–6, where vectors **A** and **B** are both drawn from a common point. The vector sum **C** is the concurrent diagonal of a parallelogram of which the given vectors form two sides.

Figure 1–7 illustrates a special case in which two vectors are parallel, as in (a), or antiparallel, as in (b). If they are parallel, the magnitude of the vector sum **C**

Fig. 1–7. Vector sum of (a) two parallel vectors, (b) two antiparallel vectors.

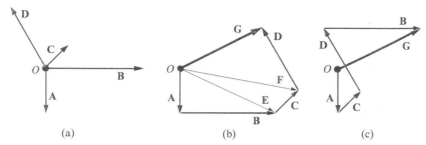

(a)   (b)   (c)

Fig. 1–8.   Polygon method of vector addition.

equals the sum of the magnitudes of **A** and **B**. If they are antiparallel, the magnitude
of the vector sum equals the difference of the magnitudes of **A** and **B**. (The vectors
in Fig. 1–7 have been displaced slightly sidewise from their line of action to show them
more clearly. Actually, all vectors lie along the same geometrical line.)

   When more than two vectors are to be added, we may first find the vector sum
of any two, add this vectorially to the third, and so on. This process is illustrated
in Fig. 1–8, which shows in part (a) four vectors **A**, **B**, **C**, and **D**. In Fig. 1–8(b),
vectors **A** and **B** are first added by the triangle method, giving a vector sum **E**; vectors
E and **C** are then added by the same process to obtain the vector sum **F**; finally, **F** and
D are added to obtain the vector sum

$$\mathbf{G} = \mathbf{A} + \mathbf{B} + \mathbf{C} + \mathbf{D}.$$

Evidently the vectors **E** and **F** need not have been drawn; we need only draw
the given vectors in succession, with the tail of each at the head of the one preceding
it, and complete the polygon by a vector **G** from the tail of the first to the
head of the last vector. The order in which the vectors are drawn makes no
difference, as shown in Fig. 1–8(c).

   Now consider the following physical problem. Two forces, represented by the
vectors $\mathbf{F}_1$ and $\mathbf{F}_2$ in Fig. 1–9, are simultaneously applied at the same point A of a

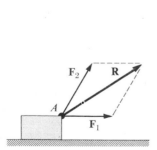

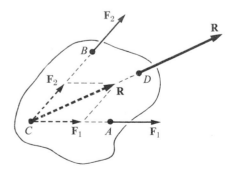

Fig. 1–9.   A force represented by the vector
R, equal to the vector sum of $\mathbf{F}_1$ and $\mathbf{F}_2$,
produces the same effect as the forces $\mathbf{F}_1$
and $\mathbf{F}_2$ acting simultaneously.

Fig. 1–10.   Method of finding the resultant
R of two coplanar forces $\mathbf{F}_1$ and $\mathbf{F}_2$ having
different points of application.

body. Is it possible to produce the same effect by applying a single force at A, and if so, what should be its magnitude and direction? The question can be answered only by experiment, and experimental results show that a single force, represented in magnitude, direction, and line of action by the vector sum $\mathbf{R}$ of the original forces, is in all respects equivalent to them. This single force is called the *resultant* of the original forces. Hence the mathematical process of *vector addition* of two force vectors corresponds to the physical operation of finding the *resultant* of two forces, simultaneously applied at a given point.

Consider next the more general case in which two forces are applied at different points of a rigid body, as in Fig. 1–10, where the points of application of forces $\mathbf{F}_1$ and $\mathbf{F}_2$ are at A and B. We shall consider only the special case in which the forces lie in the same plane, or are *coplanar*. Since a force applied to a rigid body can be displaced along its line of action, let the forces be transferred to point C, where their action lines intersect. (The point of intersection may lie outside the body on which the forces act; see Fig. 2–9.) The resultant $\mathbf{R}$ is then obtained as in Fig. 1–9, and this force, applied at any point on its line of action, such as point D, is physically equivalent to forces $\mathbf{F}_1$ and $\mathbf{F}_2$ acting simultaneously.

The vector sum of $\mathbf{F}_1$ and $\mathbf{F}_2$ can also be obtained by the construction of Fig. 1–5, where the vectors are drawn tail-to-head at any convenient point. The vector sum then has the same magnitude and direction as the resultant $\mathbf{R}$, but not necessarily the same line of action. This again illustrates that although a mathematical vector may be displaced in any way (retaining its original magnitude and direction) a force acting on a rigid body can be displaced only along its action line.

The resultant of more than two coplanar forces can be found by a repetition of the process in Fig. 1–10. We first find the resultant of any two forces, then combine this with a third, and so on. Since vectors obey the commutative law of addition, the order in which they are added makes no difference.

1–7 Resultant of parallel and antiparallel forces

When two forces having different lines of action are parallel or antiparallel, the construction shown in Fig. 1–10 breaks down, since the lines of action of the forces do not intersect (or intersect only at infinity). The magnitude, direction, and line of action of the resultant can be found, however, by the following artifice.

Figure 1–11 shows the parallel forces $\mathbf{F}_1$ and $\mathbf{F}_2$ applied at points A and B. Let us apply at A and B the auxiliary forces $\mathbf{P}_1$ and $\mathbf{P}_2$, having equal magnitudes, opposite directions, and the same line of action AB. The resultant of these forces is zero, and they have no effect on the motion of the body on which they act. Forces $\mathbf{F}_1$ and $\mathbf{P}_1$ can now be combined to form the resultant $\mathbf{Q}_1$, and forces $\mathbf{F}_2$ and $\mathbf{P}_2$ can be combined to form the resultant $\mathbf{Q}_2$. The action lines of $\mathbf{Q}_1$ and $\mathbf{Q}_2$ intersect at point C, and when $\mathbf{Q}_1$ and $\mathbf{Q}_2$ are transferred to this point we get the final resultant $\mathbf{R}$. It is easy to show by similar triangles that (a) $\mathbf{R}$ is parallel to $\mathbf{F}_1$ and $\mathbf{F}_2$, (b) the magnitude of $\mathbf{R}$ equals the sum of the magnitudes of $\mathbf{F}_1$ and $\mathbf{F}_2$, and (c) the line of action of $\mathbf{R}$ divides the line AB into segments OA and OB whose lengths are inversely proportional to the magnitudes of $\mathbf{F}_1$ and $\mathbf{F}_2$, or $OA/OB = F_2/F_1$.

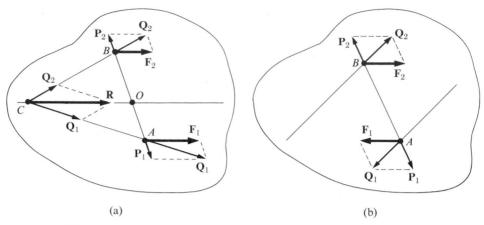

Fig. 1–11. (a) Construction for finding the resultant **R** of the parallel forces F_1 and F_2. (b) The method of part (a) breaks down when F_1 and F_2 are equal in magnitude and anti-parallel.

The method just described may also be used to reduce two *unequal antiparallel* forces to a single force and to determine the position of the line of action of the resultant. More than two parallel or antiparallel forces may also be treated in the same way, but one exception of the utmost importance stands out: *two antiparallel forces that are equal in magnitude*, as shown in Fig. 1–11(b). When the two colinear forces P_1 and P_2 are applied to the rigid body and the resultants $Q_1 = F_1 + P_1$ and $Q_2 = F_2 + P_2$ are constructed, they are found to be also equal and anti-parallel! *Two forces that are equal in magnitude, oppositely directed, and not colinear constitute an irreducible entity,* called a *couple.* The properties of couples will be discussed in Section 3–6, after the concept of the *moment of a force* has been introduced.

1–8 Components of a vector

Any two vectors whose vector sum equals a given vector are called the *components* of that vector. In Fig. 1–6, for example, vectors **A** and **B** are components of the vector **C**. Evidently, a given vector has an infinite number of pairs of possible components. If the *directions* of the components are specified, however, the problem of finding the components, or of *resolving* the vector into components, has a unique solution. Thus suppose we are given the vector **A** in Fig. 1–12(a) and we wish to resolve it into components in the directions of the lines *Op* and *Oq*. From the tip of vector **A** draw the dotted construction lines parallel to *Op* and *Oq*, forming a parallelogram. Vectors A_p and A_q, from *O* to the points of intersection of the construction lines with *Op* and *Oq*, are then the desired components, since they are in the specified directions and the given vector is their vector sum.

The special case in which the specified directions are at right angles to each other is of particular importance. In Fig. 1–12(b), lines *Ox* and *Oy* are the axes of a rectangular coordinate system. The parallelogram obtained by drawing the dotted

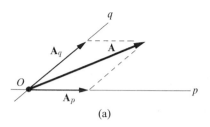

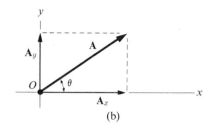

(a)   (b)

Fig. 1–12. (a) Vectors $\mathbf{A}_p$ and $\mathbf{A}_q$ are the components of $\mathbf{A}$ in the directions Op and Oq. (b) Vectors $\mathbf{A}_x$ and $\mathbf{A}_y$ are the rectangular components of $\mathbf{A}$ in the directions of the x- and y-axes.

construction lines from the tip of vector $\mathbf{A}$ then becomes a rectangle, and the components $\mathbf{A}_x$ and $\mathbf{A}_y$ are called the *rectangular components* of $\mathbf{A}$.

The magnitudes of the rectangular components of a vector are easily computed. If θ is the angle which the vector $\mathbf{A}$ makes with the x-axis, then

$$A_x = A \cos \theta, \qquad A_y = A \sin \theta,$$

where A, A_x, and A_y are the *magnitudes* of the corresponding vectors.

It is customary to refer to the rectangular component of a vector in a given direction simply as its component in that direction, and in this sense the magnitude of the component of a vector $\mathbf{A}$ in a direction making an angle θ with that of the vector is equal to $A \cos \theta$. Thus in Fig. 1–13 the component of $\mathbf{A}$ in the direction Oc is the vector $\mathbf{A}_c$, and its component in the direction Ob is the vector $\mathbf{A}_b$. If the angle θ is 90°, as for the direction Od, $\cos \theta = 0$ and the component is zero. If the angle is zero, $\cos \theta = 1$ and the component is equal to the vector.

The application of the concepts above to a physical problem is illustrated in Fig. 1–14, where a force $\mathbf{F}$ is exerted on a body at point O. The rectangular components of $\mathbf{F}$ in the directions Ox and Oy are $\mathbf{F}_x$ and $\mathbf{F}_y$, and it is found that simultaneous applications of the forces $\mathbf{F}_x$ and $\mathbf{F}_y$, as in Fig. 1–14(b), is equivalent in all respects to the effect of the original force. *Any force can be replaced by its rectangular components.*

Fig. 1–13. Vectors $\mathbf{A}_b$ and $\mathbf{A}_c$ are the components of $\mathbf{A}$ in the directions Ob and Oc. The component along Od, perpendicular to $\mathbf{A}$, is zero, and the component along Oa is equal to $\mathbf{A}$. In general, the magnitude of the component equals $A \cos \theta$.

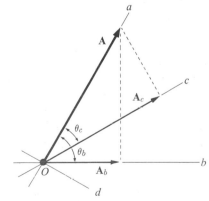

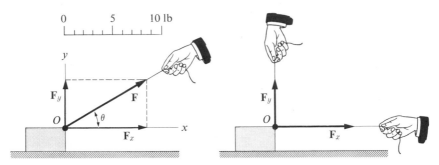

Fig. 1–14. The inclined force **F** may be replaced by its rectangular components F_x and F_y. $F_x = F \cos \theta$, $F_y = F \sin \theta$.

As a numerical example, let

$$F = 10 \text{ lb}, \qquad \theta = 30°.$$

Then

$$F_x = F \cos \theta = 10 \text{ lb} \times 0.866 = 8.66 \text{ lb},$$

$$F_y = F \sin \theta = 10 \text{ lb} \times 0.500 = 5.00 \text{ lb},$$

and the effect of the original 10-lb force is equivalent to the simultaneous application of a horizontal force of 8.66 lb and a lifting force of 5.00 lb.

1–9 Resultant by rectangular resolution

Although the polygon method is a satisfactory graphical one for finding the resultant of a number of forces, it is awkward for computation because one must, in general, solve a number of oblique triangles. Therefore the usual analytical method of finding the resultant is first to resolve all forces into rectangular components along any convenient pair of axes and then combine these into a single resultant. This makes it possible to work with *right* triangles only.

Figure 1–15(a) shows three concurrent forces F_1, F_2, and F_3, whose resultant we wish to find. Let a pair of rectangular axes be constructed in any arbitrary direction. Simplification results if one axis coincides with one of the forces, which is always possible. In Fig. 1–15(b), the x-axis coincides with F_1. Let us first resolve each of the given forces into x- and y-components. According to the usual conventions of analytic geometry, x-components toward the right are considered positive and those toward the left, negative. Upward y-components are positive and downward y-components are negative.

Force F_1 lies along the x-axis and need not be resolved. The components of F_2 are $F_{2x} = F_2 \cos \theta$, $F_{2y} = F_2 \sin \theta$. Both of these are positive, and F_{2x} has been slightly displaced upward to show it more clearly. The components of F_3 are $F_{3x} = F_3 \cos \phi$, $F_{3y} = F_3 \sin \phi$. Both of these are negative.

We now imagine F_2 and F_3 to be removed and replaced by their rectangular components. To indicate this, the vectors F_2 and F_3 are crossed out lightly. All of the

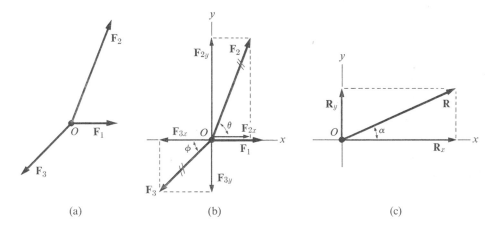

            (a)   (b)   (c)

Fig. 1–15. Vector **R**, the resultant of F_1, F_2, and F_3, is obtained by the method of rectangular resolution. The magnitudes of the rectangular components of **R** are $R_x = \sum F_x$, $R_y = \sum F_y$.

x-components can now be combined into a single force $\mathbf{R}_x$ whose magnitude equals the algebraic sum of the magnitudes of the x-components, or $\sum F_x$, and all of the y-components can be combined into a single force $\mathbf{R}_y$ of magnitude $\sum F_y$:

$$R_x = \sum F_x, \qquad R_y = \sum F_y.$$

Finally, these can be combined as in part (c) of the figure to form the resultant **R** whose magnitude, since $\mathbf{R}_x$ and $\mathbf{R}_y$ are perpendicular to each other, is

$$R = \sqrt{R_x^2 + R_y^2}\,.$$

The angle α between **R** and the x-axis can now be found from any one of its trigonometric functions. For example, $\tan \alpha = R_y/R_x$.

EXAMPLE. In Fig. 1–15, let $F_1 = 120$ lb, $F_2 = 200$ lb, $F_3 = 150$ lb, $\theta = 60°$, $\phi = 45°$. The computations can be arranged systematically as follows:

Force	Angle	x-component	y-component
$F_1 = 120$ lb	0	$+120$ lb	0
$F_2 = 200$ lb	60°	$+100$ lb	$+173$ lb
$F_3 = 150$ lb	45°	-106 lb	-106 lb
		$\sum F_x = +114$ lb	$\sum F_y = +67$ lb

$$R = \sqrt{(114 \text{ lb})^2 + (67 \text{ lb})^2} = 132 \text{ lb}, \qquad \alpha = \tan^{-1}\frac{67 \text{ lb}}{114 \text{ lb}} = \tan^{-1} 0.588 = 30.4°.$$

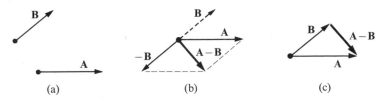

(a)   (b)   (c)

Fig. 1–16.   The vector difference **A** − **B** is found in part (b) by the parallelogram method and in part (c) by the triangle method.

1–10 Vector difference

It is sometimes necessary to subtract one vector from another.   The process of subtracting one *algebraic* quantity from another is equivalent to adding the negative of the quantity to be subtracted.   That is,

$$a - b = a + (-b).$$

Similarly, the process of subtracting one *vector* quantity from another is equivalent to adding (vectorially) the negative of the vector to be subtracted, where the negative of a given vector is defined as a vector of the same length but in the opposite direction. That is, if **A** and **B** are two vectors,

$$\mathbf{A} - \mathbf{B} = \mathbf{A} + (-\mathbf{B}).$$

Vector subtraction is illustrated in Fig. 1–16.   The given vectors are shown in part (a).   In part (b), the vector sum of **A** and −**B**, or the vector difference **A** − **B**, is found by the parallelogram method.   Part (c) shows a second method; vectors **A** and **B** are drawn from a common origin, and the vector difference **A** − **B** is the vector from the tip of **B** to the tip of **A**.   The vector difference **A** − **B** is therefore seen to be the vector that must be added to **B** in order to give **A**, since

$$\mathbf{B} + (\mathbf{A} - \mathbf{B}) = \mathbf{A}.$$

Vector differences may also be found by the method of rectangular resolution. Both vectors are resolved into x- and y-components.   The difference between the x-components is the x-component of the desired vector difference, and the difference between the y-components is the y-component of the vector difference.

Vector subtraction is not often used when dealing with forces, but we shall use it frequently in connection with velocities and accelerations.

A WORD ABOUT PROBLEMS

To obtain a benefit commensurate with the time expended, problem-solving should be considered as much more than merely substituting numbers for the symbols in a formula or fitting together the pieces of a jigsaw puzzle. To merely thumb through the book until you find a formula that seems to fit, or a worked-out example that resembles the problem, is a waste of time and effort. One purpose which problems can serve is to enable you to find out for yourself whether or not you understand the assigned material, after having listened to a lecture and studied the text. Do your studying *before* you tackle the problems, instead of beginning with the problems and not referring to your book or lecture notes until you find yourself stymied. No problem assignment of reasonable length can hope to cover *every* important point, and you will miss a great deal if you read only enough to enable you to "do" your problems.

Every problem involves one or more general physical laws or definitions. After reading the statement of a problem, ask yourself what these laws or definitions are and be sure that you know them. This means that you should be able to state them to yourself clearly and explicitly, and not be satisfied with the comforting feeling that you "understand" Newton's second law although you can't quite put it in so many words.

Nearly every quantity of physical interest is expressed in terms of a unit of that quantity (some quantities are pure numbers). No answer is complete unless the proper units are given.

Unless otherwise stated, the numerical data given in the problems are to be assumed correct to three significant figures (for example, 2 ft implies 2.00 ft). Numerical answers should therefore be rounded off to 3 significant figures. That is, if long division leads to the result 6.574938 . . . ft/sec, give the answer as 6.57 ft/sec. This is automatically taken care of if you use a slide rule.

Answers are provided to about half the problems, and are rounded off to two or three significant figures.

One of the best ways of making sure you understand the principles covered by a particular problem is to work it backwards. That is, if the problem gives x and asks you to compute y, then make up another problem in which y is given and x is to be found. Another helpful procedure is to ask yourself how the result would be altered if the given conditions had been somewhat different. Suppose the friction force had been 10 lb instead of 5 lb? Suppose the slope of the plane had been 60° instead of 30°?

Helpful advice on the techniques of studying and of solving problems will be found in *How to Study Physics* by Chapman and *How to Study, How to Solve* by Dadourian (published by Addison-Wesley).

Problems

1-1. Find graphically the magnitude and direction of the resultant of the three forces in Fig. 1-17. Use the polygon method.

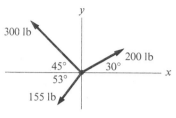

Figure 1-17

1-2. Two men and a boy want to push a crate in the direction marked x in Fig. 1-18. The two men push with forces F_1 and F_2 whose magnitudes and directions are indicated in the figure. Find the magnitude and direction of the smallest force which the boy should exert.

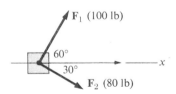

Figure 1-18

1-3. Find graphically the resultant of two 10-lb forces applied at the same point: (a) when the angle between the forces is 30°; (b) when the angle between them is 130°. Use any convenient scale.

1-4. Two men pull horizontally on ropes attached to a post, the angle between the ropes being 45°. If man A exerts a force of 150 lb and man B a force of 100 lb, find the magnitude of the resultant force and the angle it makes with A's pull. Solve: (a) graphically, by the parallelogram method, and (b) graphically, by the triangle method. Let 1 in. = 50 lb in (a) and (b).

1-5. Find graphically the vector sum $A + B$ and the vector difference $A - B$ in Fig. 1-19.

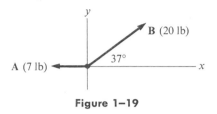

Figure 1-19

1-6. Vector A is 2 in. long and is 60° above the x-axis in the first quadrant. Vector B is 2 in. long and is 60° below the x-axis in the fourth quadrant. Find graphically (a) the vector sum $A + B$, and (b) the vector differences $A - B$ and $B - A$.

1-7. (a) Find graphically the horizontal and vertical components of a 40-lb force the direction of which is 50° above the horizontal to the right. Let $\frac{1}{16}$ in. = 1 lb. (b) Check your results by calculating the components.

1-8. A box is pushed along the floor as in Fig. 1-2 by a force of 40 lb making an angle of 30° with the horizontal. Using a scale of 1 in. = 10 lb, find the horizontal and vertical components of the force by the graphical method. Check your results by calculating the components.

1-9. A block is dragged up an inclined plane of slope angle 20° by a force F making an angle of 30° with the plane. (a) How large a force F is necessary in order that the component F_x parallel to the plane shall be 16 lb? (b) How large will the component F_y then be? Solve graphically, letting 1 in. = 8 lb.

1-10. The three forces shown in Fig. 1-17 act on a body located at the origin. (a) Find the x- and y-components of each of the three forces. (b) Use the method of rectangular resolution to find the resultant of the forces. (c) Find the magnitude and direction of a fourth force which must be added to make the resultant force zero. Indicate the fourth force by a diagram.

1–11. Use the method of rectangular resolution to find the resultant of the following set of forces and the angle it makes with the horizontal: 200 lb, along the x-axis toward the right; 300 lb, 60° above the x-axis to the right; 100 lb, 45° above the x-axis to the left; 200 lb, vertically down.

1–12. A vector **A** of length 10 units makes an angle of 30° with a vector **B** of length 6 units. Find the magnitude of the vector difference **A** − **B** and the angle it makes with vector **A**: (a) by the parallelogram method; (b) by the triangle method; (c) by the method of rectangular resolution.

1–13. Two forces, F_1 and F_2, act at a point. The magnitude of F_1 is 8 lb and its direction is 60° above the x-axis in the first quadrant. The magnitude of F_2 is 5 lb and its direction is 53° below the x-axis in the fourth quadrant. (a) What are the horizontal and vertical components of the resultant force? (b) What is the magnitude of the resultant? (c) What is the magnitude of the vector difference $F_1 - F_2$?

1–14. Two forces, F_1 and F_2, act upon a body in such a manner that the resultant force **R** has a magnitude equal to that of F_1 and makes an angle of 90° with F_1. Let $F_1 = R = 10$ lb. Find the magnitude of the second force, and its direction (relative to F_1).

1–15. The resultant of four forces is 1000 lb in the direction 30° west of north. Three of the forces are 400 lb, 60° north of east; 300 lb, south; and 400 lb, 53° west of south. Find the rectangular components of the fourth force.

1–16. The velocity of an airplane relative to the surface of the earth, v_{PE}, equals the vector sum of its velocity relative to the air, v_{PA}, and the velocity of the air relative to the earth, v_{AE}. Thus

$$v_{PE} = v_{PA} + v_{AE}.$$

(a) Find graphically the magnitude and direction of the velocity v_{PE} if the velocity v_{PA} is 100 mi/hr due north, and if the wind velocity v_{AE} is 40 mi/hr from east to west. Let 1 cm = 20 mi/hr. (b) Find the direction of the velocity v_{PA} if its magnitude is 100 mi/hr, if the direction of v_{PE} is due north, and if v_{AE} is 40 mi/hr from east to west. What is then the magnitude of v_{PE}?

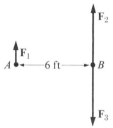

Figure 1–20

1–17. (a) Find graphically the magnitude, direction, and line of action of the parallel forces F_1 and F_2 in Fig. 1–20, if the magnitudes of F_1 and F_2 are 4 lb and 10 lb, respectively. (b) Find graphically the magnitude, direction, and line of action of the antiparallel forces F_1 and F_3 in Fig. 1–20, if the magnitude of F_3 is 10 lb.

Equilibrium of a Particle

CHAPTER 2

2–1 Introduction

The science of mechanics is based on three natural laws which were clearly stated for the first time by Sir Isaac Newton (1643–1727) and were published in 1686 in his *Philosophiae Naturalis Principia Mathematica* ("The Mathematical Principles of Natural Science"). It should not be inferred, however, that the science of mechanics began with Newton. Many men had preceded him in this field, the most outstanding being Galileo Galilei (1564–1642), who in his studies of accelerated motion had laid much of the groundwork for Newton's three laws.

In this chapter we shall make use of only two of Newton's laws, the first and the third. Newton's second law will be discussed in Chapter 5.

2–2 Equilibrium. Newton's first law

One effect of a force is to alter the dimensions or shape of a body on which the force acts; another is to alter the state of motion of the body.

The motion of a body can be considered as made up of its motion as a whole, or its *translational* motion, together with any *rotational* motion the body may have. In the most general case, a single force acting on a body produces a change in both its translational and rotational motion. However, when several forces act on a body

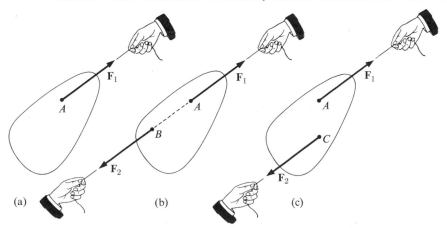

(a) (b) (c)

Fig. 2–1. A rigid body acted on by two forces is in equilibrium if the forces are equal in magnitude, opposite in direction, and have the same line of action, as in part (b).

simultaneously, their effects can compensate one another, with the result that there is no change in either the translational or rotational motion. When this is the case, the body is said to be in *equilibrium*. This means that (1) the body as a whole either remains at rest or moves in a straight line with constant speed, and (2) that the body is either not rotating at all or is rotating at a constant rate.

Let us consider some (idealized) experiments from which the laws of equilibrium can be deduced. Figure 2-1 represents a flat, rigid object of arbitrary shape on a level surface having negligible friction. If a single force F_1 acts on the body, as in Fig. 2-1(a), and if the body is originally at rest, it at once starts to move and to rotate clockwise. If originally in motion, the effect of the force is to change the translational motion of the body in magnitude or direction (or both) and to increase or decrease its rate of rotation. In either case, the body does not remain in equilibrium.

Equilibrium can be maintained, however, by the application of a second force F_2 as in Fig. 2-1(b), provided that F_2 is *equal in magnitude* to F_1, is *opposite in direction* to F_1, and has the *same line of action* as F_1. The resultant of F_1 and F_2 is then zero. If the lines of action of the two forces are not the same, as in Fig. 2-1(c), the body will be in translational but not in rotational equilibrium. (The forces then form a couple.)

Strictly speaking, we should say that the forces F_1 and F_2 are equal in *absolute* magnitude and opposite in sign, or that one equals the negative of the other. That is,

$$F_2 = -F_1.$$

Then if R represents the resultant of F_1 and F_2,

$$R = F_1 + F_2 = F_1 - F_1 = 0.$$

For brevity, we shall often speak of two forces as simply being "equal and opposite," meaning that their absolute magnitudes are equal and that one is the negative of the other.

In Fig. 2-2(a), a body is acted on by three nonparallel coplanar forces, F_1, F_2, and F_3. Any force applied to a rigid body may be regarded as acting anywhere along its line of action. Therefore, let any two of the force vectors, say F_1 and F_2, be transferred to the point of intersection of their lines of action and their resultant R obtained as in Fig. 2-2(b). The forces are now reduced to two, R and F_3, and for equilibrium these must (1) be equal in magnitude, (2) be opposite in direction, and (3) have the same line of action. It follows from the first two conditions that the resultant of the three forces is zero. The third condition can be fulfilled only if the line of action of F_3 passes through the point of intersection of the lines of action of F_1 and F_2. In other words, the three forces must be *concurrent*.

The construction in Fig. 2-2 provides a satisfactory graphical method for the solution of problems in equilibrium. For an analytical solution, it is usually simpler to deal with the rectangular components of the forces. We have shown that the magnitudes of the rectangular components of the resultant R of any set of coplanar forces are

$$R_x = \Sigma F_x, \qquad R_y = \Sigma F_y.$$

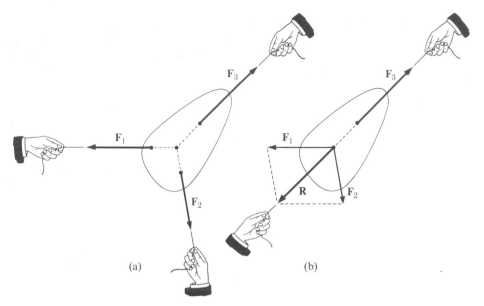

Fig. 2–2. When a body acted on by three nonparallel coplanar forces is in equilibrium, the forces are concurrent and the resultant of any two is equal in absolute magnitude and opposite in direction (or sign) to the third.

When a body is in equilibrium, the resultant of all of the forces acting on it is zero. Both rectangular components are then zero and hence, for a body in equilibrium,

$$\mathbf{R} = 0, \quad \text{or} \quad \Sigma F_x = 0, \quad \Sigma F_y = 0.$$

These equations are called the *first condition of equilibrium*.

The *second condition of equilibrium* is an equation to be developed in Chapter 3 that is a mathematical statement of the following facts:

(a) When a rigid body is in equilibrium under the action of only two forces, they must have the same line of action.

(b) When a rigid body is in equilibrium under the action of three nonparallel forces, they must be concurrent.

The first condition of equilibrium ensures that a body shall be in translational equilibrium; the second, that it be in rotational equilibrium. The statement that a body is in complete equilibrium when both conditions are satisfied is the essence of *Newton's first law of motion*. Newton did not state his first law in exactly these words. His original statement (translated from the Latin in which the *Principia* was written) reads:

"Every body continues in its state of rest, or of uniform motion in a straight line, unless it is compelled to change that state by forces impressed on it."

Although rotational motion was not explicitly mentioned by Newton, it is clear from his work that he fully understood the conditions that the forces must satisfy when the rotation is zero or is constant.

2–3 Discussion of Newton's first law of motion

Newton's first law of motion is not as self-evident as it may seem. In the first place, this law asserts that in the absence of any impressed force a body either remains at rest or moves uniformly in a straight line. It follows that *once a body has been set in motion it is no longer necessary to exert a force on it to maintain it in motion.* This assertion appears to be contradicted by everyday experience. Suppose we exert a force with the hand to move a book along a level table top. After the book has left our hand, and we are no longer exerting a force on it, it does *not* continue to move indefinitely, but slows down and eventually comes to rest. If we wish to keep it moving uniformly we must continue to exert some forward force on it. But this force is required only because a frictional force is exerted on the sliding book by the table top, in a direction opposite to the motion of the book. The smoother the surfaces of book and table, the smaller the frictional force and the smaller the force we must exert to keep the book moving. The first law asserts that if the frictional force could be eliminated completely, no forward force at all would be required to keep the book moving, once it had been set in motion. More than that, however, the law implies that if the *resultant* force on the book is zero, as it is when the frictional force is balanced by an equal forward force, the book also continues to move uniformly. In other words, *zero resultant force is equivalent to no force at all.*

In the second place, the first law defines by implication what is known as an *inertial reference system.* To understand what is meant by this term we must recognize that the motion of a given body can be specified only with respect to, or relative to, some other body. Its motion relative to one body may be very different from that relative to another. Thus a passenger in an aircraft which is making its take-off run may continue at rest relative to the aircraft but be moving faster and faster relative to the earth.

A *reference system* means a set of coordinate axes attached to (or moving with) some specified body or bodies. Suppose we consider a reference system attached to the aircraft referred to above. Everyone knows that during the take-off run, while the aircraft is going faster and faster, a passenger feels the back of his seat pushing him forward, although he remains at rest relative to a reference system attached to the aircraft. Newton's first law does not therefore correctly describe the situation; a forward force *does* act on the passenger, but nevertheless (relative to the aircraft) he remains at rest.

Suppose, on the other hand, that the passenger is standing in the aisle on roller skates. He then starts to move *backward*, relative to the aircraft, when the take-off run begins, even though no backward force acts on him. Newton's first law again does not correctly describe the facts.

We can now define an inertial reference system as one relative to which a body *does* remain at rest or move uniformly in a straight line when no force (or no resultant force) acts on it. That is, *an inertial reference system is one in which Newton's first law correctly describes the motion of a body not acted on by any force.*

An aircraft making its take-off run is evidently *not* an inertial system. For many purposes, a reference system attached to the earth can be considered an inertial system, although we shall show in a later chapter that because of the earth's rotation and its other motions this is not exactly true. Newton himself believed that it was possible to conceive of a reference system in a state of "absolute rest," anchored in some way to empty space. When Newton referred to a state of rest or uniform motion he was using such a system as a reference system. The principles of relativity have led us to believe that the concepts of "absolute rest" and "absolute motion" have no physical meaning. The best solution seems to be to select a reference system at rest relative to the so-called *fixed stars*, stars that are so far away that their motions relative to one another cannot be detected. Newton's first law appears to describe correctly the motions of bodies relative to this system, and it may therefore be considered an inertial system.

Thirdly, Newton's first law contains a qualitative definition of the concept of *force*, or at any rate of one aspect of the force concept, as "that which changes the state of motion of a body." (This does not mean that forces do not produce other effects also, such as changing the length of a coil spring.) When a body at rest relative to the earth is observed to start moving, or when a moving body speeds up, slows down, or changes its direction, we can conclude that a force is acting on it. This effect of a force can be used to define the ratio of two forces and to define a unit force, and we shall show in Chapter 5 how this is done.

2–4 Stable, unstable, and neutral equilibrium

When a body in equilibrium is displaced slightly, the magnitudes, directions, and lines of action of the forces acting on it may all change. If the forces in the displaced position are such as to return the body to its original position, the equilibrium is *stable*. If the forces act to increase the displacement still further, the equilibrium is *unstable*. If the body is still in equilibrium in the displaced position the equilibrium is *neutral*. Whether a given equilibrium state is stable, unstable, or neutral can be determined only by considering other states slightly displaced from the first.

A right circular cone on a level surface affords an example of the three types of equilibrium. When the cone rests on its base, as in Fig. 2–3(a), the equilibrium is stable. When balanced on its apex, as in part (b), the equilibrium is unstable. When resting on its side, as in part (c), the equilibrium is neutral.

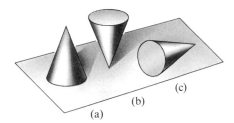

Fig. 2–3. (a) Stable, (b) unstable, and (c) neutral equilibrium.

2–5 Newton's third law of motion

Any given force is but one aspect of a mutual interaction between *two* bodies. It is found that *whenever one body exerts a force on another, the second always exerts on the first a force which is equal in absolute magnitude, opposite in direction (or sign), and has the same line of action.* A single, isolated force is therefore an impossibility.

---

* This statement must be modified when forces of electromagnetic origin are considered. It is correct, however, for any of the forces we shall encounter in Mechanics.

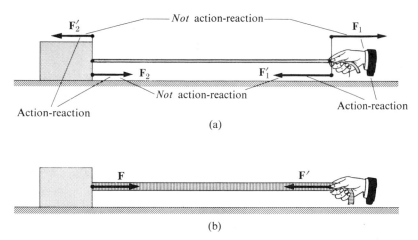

(a)

(b)

Fig. 2-4. (a) Forces $\mathbf{F}_1$ and $\mathbf{F}'_1$ form one action-reaction pair, and forces $\mathbf{F}_2$ and $\mathbf{F}'_2$ another. $\mathbf{F}_1$ is *always* equal to $\mathbf{F}'_1$, $\mathbf{F}_2$ is *always* equal to $\mathbf{F}'_2$. $\mathbf{F}_1$ and $\mathbf{F}'_2$ are equal only if the rope is in equilibrium, and force $\mathbf{F}'_2$ is *not* the reaction to $\mathbf{F}_1$. (Actually all forces lie along the rope.) (b) If the rope is in equilibrium it can be considered to transmit a force from the man to the block, and vice versa.

The two forces involved in every interaction between two bodies are often called an "action" and a "reaction," but this does not imply any difference in their nature, or that one force is the "cause" and the other its "effect." *Either* force may be con-sidered the "action," and the other the "reaction" to it.

This property of forces was stated by Newton in his *third law of motion*. In his own words, *"To every action there is always opposed an equal reaction: or, the mutual actions of two bodies upon each other are always equal, and directed to contrary parts."*

As an example, suppose that a man pulls on one end of a rope attached to a block, as in Fig. 2-4. The weight of the block and the force exerted on it by the surface are not shown. The block may or may not be in equilibrium. The resulting action-reaction pairs of forces are indicated in the figure. (Actually, the lines of action of all the forces lie along the rope. The force vectors have been offset from this line to show them more clearly.) Vector $\mathbf{F}_1$ represents the force exerted on the rope by the man. Its reaction is the equal and opposite force $\mathbf{F}'_1$ exerted on the man by the rope. Vector $\mathbf{F}_2$ represents the force exerted on the block by the rope. The reaction to it is the equal and opposite force $\mathbf{F}'_2$, exerted on the rope by the block.

$$\mathbf{F}'_1 = -\mathbf{F}_1, \qquad \mathbf{F}'_2 = -\mathbf{F}_2.$$

It is very important to realize that the forces $\mathbf{F}_1$ and $\mathbf{F}'_2$, although they are opposite in direction and have the same line of action, do *not* constitute an action-reaction pair. For one thing, both of these forces act on the *same* body (the rope) while an action and its reaction necessarily act on *different* bodies. Furthermore, the forces $\mathbf{F}_1$ and $\mathbf{F}'_2$ are not *necessarily* equal in magnitude. If the block and rope are moving to the right with increasing speed, the rope is not in equilibrium and F_1 is greater than F_2'. Only in the special case when the rope remains at rest or moves with constant speed are the forces F_1 and F_2' equal in magnitude, but this is an example of Newton's *first* law, not his *third*. Even when the speed of the rope is changing, however, the action-reaction forces F_1 and F_1' are equal in magnitude to *each other*, and the action-reaction forces F_2 and F_2' are equal in magnitude to *each other*, although then F_1 is not equal to F_2'.

In the special case when the rope is in equilibrium, and when no forces act on it except those at its ends, F_2' equals F_1 by Newton's *first* law. Since F_2 *always* equals F_2', by Newton's *third* law, then in this special case F_2 also equals F_1 and the force exerted on the block by the rope is equal to the force exerted on the rope by the man. The rope can therefore be considered to "transmit" to the block, without change, the force exerted on it by the man. This point of view is often useful, but it is important to remember that it applies only under the restricted conditions above.

If we adopt this point of view, the rope itself need not be considered and we have the simpler force diagram of Fig. 2–4(b), where the man is considered to exert a force F directly on the block. The reaction is the force F' exerted by the block on the man. The only effect of the rope is to transmit these forces from one body to the other.

A body, like the rope in Fig. 2–4, which is subjected to pulls at its ends is said to be in *tension*. The tension at any point equals the force exerted at that point. Thus in Fig. 2–4(a) the tension at the right-hand end of the rope equals the magnitude of F_1 (or of F_1') and the tension at the left-hand end equals the magnitude of F_2 (or of F_2'). If the rope is in equilibrium and if no forces act except at its ends, as in Fig. 2–4(b), the tension is the same at both ends. If, for example, in Fig. 2–4(b) the magnitudes of F and F' are each 50 lb, the tension in the rope is 50 lb (*not* 100 lb).

2–6 Equilibrium of a particle

The materials found in nature and the processes which occur are rarely simple. As a first step in dealing with a problem of nature it is necessary to *idealize* the material and to make *simplifying assumptions* concerning the processes. Suppose, for example, a baseball is thrown into the air and it is desired to calculate where it lands and with what velocity. The first step in treating this problem consists in idealizing the baseball by ignoring the details of its surface and all departures from sphericity during its motion. In other words, we replace the baseball by an ideal object, i.e., a rigid smooth sphere. The next step is to ignore the rotation of the baseball and the forces brought into play by the air dragged around by the rotating ball. A further step is to regard as negligible the buoyancy and the resistance of the air. We are then left with a problem quite different from the original one; in fact we may be accused of having robbed the problem of almost all of its reality. This is true, but what remains approximates the original problem at low velocities, and has the virtue that it is amenable to simple mathematical treatment, whereas the original problem at high velocities would require the most advanced methods.

In general, the forces acting on a rigid body do not all pass through one point, that is, they are *noncurrent* and, as a result, the rigid body undergoes rotational as well as translational motion. There are, however, many situations of great interest where the rotation of a body is of only minor consequence and is not pertinent in the solution of the problem. The planetary motion, for example, of the earth about the sun taking place under the action of the gravitational force between the two bodies may be studied alone without regard to the earth's rotation. *A body whose rotation is ignored as irrelevant is called a particle. A particle may be so small that it is an approximation to a point, or it may be of any size, provided that the action lines of all the forces acting on it intersect in one point.*

In the remainder of this chapter, we shall limit ourselves to examples and problems involving the equilibrium of particles only. It is surprising how many situations of interest and importance in engineering, in the life and earth sciences, and in everyday life involve the equilibrium of particles. In many of these, it is important to know how to calculate one or two of the forces acting on a particle when the others are given. In order to do this, it is best to adhere scrupulously to the following rules.

(1) Make a simple line sketch of the apparatus or structure, showing dimensions and angles.

(2) Choose some object (like a knot in a rope, for example) as the particle in equilibrium. Draw a separate diagram of this object and show by arrows (use a colored pencil) *all* of the forces exerted *on* it by other bodies. This is called the *force diagram* or *free-body* diagram. When a system is composed of several particles, it may be necessary to construct a separate free-body diagram for each.

Do *not* show, in the free-body diagram of a chosen particle, any of the forces exerted *by* it. These forces (which are the reactions to the forces acting *on* the chosen particle) all act *on other bodies* and appear in the free-body diagrams of those bodies.

(3) Construct a set of rectangular axes and resolve any inclined forces into rectangular components. Cross out lightly those forces which have been resolved.

(4) Set the algebraic sum of all *x*-forces (or force components) equal to zero, and the algebraic sum of all *y*-forces (or components) equal to zero. This provides two independent equations which can be solved simultaneously for two unknown quantities (which may be forces, angles, distances, etc.).

A force which will be encountered in many problems is the *weight* of a body, that is, the force of gravitational attraction exerted on the body by the earth. We shall show in the next chapter that the line of action of this force always passes through a point called the *center of gravity* of the body.

The force of gravitational attraction exerted on a body by the earth is but one aspect of a mutual interaction between the earth and the body. That is, the earth attracts the body and at the same time the body attracts the earth. The force exerted on the earth by the body is opposite in direction and equal in magnitude to the force exerted on the body by the earth. Thus if a body weighs 10 lb (that is, if the earth pulls down on it with a force of 10 lb) the body pulls up on the earth with an equal force of 10 lb. The equal and opposite forces exerted on body and earth are another example of an action-reaction pair.

EXAMPLE 1.   To begin with a simple example, consider the body in Fig. 2–5(a), hanging at rest from the ceiling by a vertical cord. Part (b) of the figure is the free-body diagram for the body. The forces on it are its weight $\mathbf{w}_1$ and the upward force $\mathbf{T}_1$ exerted on it by the cord. If we take the x-axis horizontal and the y-axis vertical, there are no x-components of force, and the y-components are the forces $\mathbf{w}_1$ and $\mathbf{T}_1$. Then from the condition that $\Sigma F_y = 0$, we have

$$\Sigma F_y = T_1 - w_1 = 0,$$

$$T_1 = w_1.   \text{(1st law)}$$

In order that both forces have the same line of action, the center of gravity of the body must lie vertically below the point of attachment of the cord.

Let us emphasize again that the forces $\mathbf{w}_1$ and T_1 are *not* an action-reaction pair, although they are equal in magnitude, opposite in direction, and have the same line of action. The weight $\mathbf{w}_1$ is a force of attraction exerted on the body by the earth. Its reaction is an equal and opposite force of attraction exerted on the earth by the body. This reaction is one of the set of forces acting *on the earth*, and therefore it does not appear in the free-body diagram of the suspended block.

The reaction to the force $\mathbf{T}_1$ is an equal downward force, $\mathbf{T}_1'$, exerted *on the cord* by the suspended body:

$$T_1 = T_1'.   \text{(3rd law)}$$

The force $\mathbf{T}_1'$ is shown in part (c), which is the free-body diagram of the cord. The other forces on the cord are its own weight $\mathbf{w}_2$ and the upward force $\mathbf{T}_2$ exerted on its upper end by the ceiling. Since the cord is also in equilibrium,

$$\Sigma F_y = T_2 - w_2 - T_1' = 0,$$

$$T_2 = w_2 + T_1'.   \text{(1st law)}$$

The reaction to $\mathbf{T}_2$ is the downward force $\mathbf{T}_2'$ in part (d), exerted on the ceiling by the cord:

$$T_2 = T_2'.   \text{(3rd law)}$$

As a numerical example, let the body weigh 20 lb and the cord weigh 1 lb. Then

$$T_1 = w_1 = 20 \text{ lb},$$

$$T_1' = T_1 = 20 \text{ lb},$$

$$T_2 = w_2 + T_1'$$

$$= 1 \text{ lb} + 20 \text{ lb} = 21 \text{ lb},$$

$$T_2' = T_2 = 21 \text{ lb}.$$

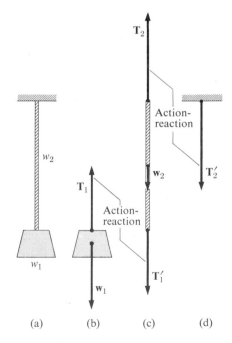

(a)   (b)   (c)   (d)

Fig. 2–5. (a) Block hanging at rest from vertical cord. (b) The block is isolated and *all* forces acting *on* it are shown. (c) Forces on the cord. (d) Downward force on the ceiling. Lines connect action-reaction pairs.

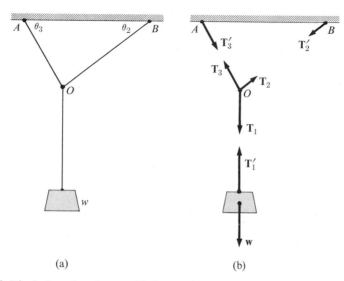

(a)   (b)

Fig. 2–6. (a) Block hanging in equilibrium. (b) Forces acting on the block, on the knot, and on the ceiling.

If the weight of the cord were so small as to be negligible, then in effect no forces would act on it except at its ends. The forces T_2 and T_2' would then each equal 20 lb and, as explained earlier, the cord could be considered to transmit a 20-lb force from one end to the other without change. We could then consider the upward pull of the cord on the block as an "action" and the downward pull on the ceiling as its "reaction." The tension in the cord would then be 20 lb.

EXAMPLE 2.   In Fig. 2–6(a), a block of weight w hangs from a cord which is knotted at O to two other cords fastened to the ceiling. We wish to find the tensions in these three cords. The weights of the cords are negligible.
In order to use the conditions of equilibrium to compute an unknown force, we must consider some body which is in equilibrium and on which the desired force acts. The hanging block is one such body and, as shown in the preceding example, the tension in the vertical cord supporting the block is equal to the weight of the block. The inclined cords do not exert forces on the block, but they do act on the knot at O. Hence we consider the *knot* as a particle in equilibrium whose own weight is negligible.
The free-body diagrams for the block and the knot are shown in Fig. 2–6(b), where T_1, T_2, and T_3 represent the forces exerted *on the knot* by the three cords and T_1', T_2', and T_3' are the reactions to these forces.
Consider first the hanging block. Since it is in equilibrium,

$$T_1' = w. \qquad \text{(1st law)}$$

Since T_1 and T_1' form an action-reaction pair,

$$T_1' = T_1. \qquad \text{(3rd law)}$$

Hence

$$T_1 = w.$$

To find the forces T_2 and T_3, we resolve these forces (see Fig. 2–7) into rectangular components. Then, from Newton's *first* law,

$$\sum F_x = T_2 \cos \theta_2 - T_3 \cos \theta_3 = 0,$$

$$\sum F_y = T_2 \sin \theta_2 + T_3 \sin \theta_3 - T_1 = 0.$$

As a numerical example, let

$$w = 50 \text{ lb}, \qquad \theta_2 = 30°, \qquad \theta_3 = 60°.$$

Then $T_1 = 50$ lb, and from the two preceding equations,

$$T_2 = 25 \text{ lb}, \qquad T_3 = 43.3 \text{ lb}.$$

Finally, we know from Newton's *third* law that the inclined cords exert on the ceiling the forces T_2' and T_3', equal and opposite to T_2 and T_3, respectively.

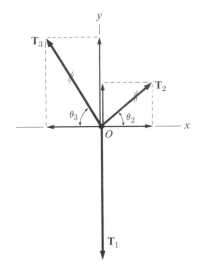

Fig. 2–7. Forces on the knot O in Fig. 2–6, resolved into x- and y-components.

EXAMPLE 3.   Figure 2–8(a) shows a strut AB, pivoted at end A, attached to a wall by a cable, and carrying a load w at end B. The weights of the strut and of the cable are negligible.

Figure 2–8(b) shows the forces acting on the strut: T_1 is the force exerted by the vertical cable, T_2 is the force exerted by the inclined cable, and C is the force exerted by the pivot. Force T_1 is known both in magnitude and in direction, force T_2 is known in direction only, and neither the magnitude nor the direction of C is known. However, the forces T_1 and T_2 must intersect at the outer end of the strut, and since the strut is in equilibrium under three forces, the line of action of force C must also pass through the outer end of the strut. In other words, the direction of force C is along the line of the strut.

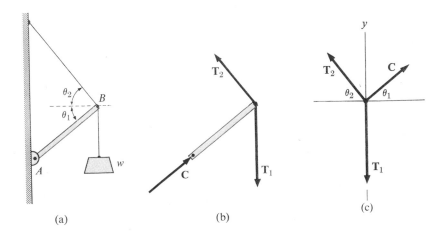

Figure 2–8

Hence the resultant of T_1 and T_2 is also along this line and the strut, in effect, is acted on by forces at its ends, directed toward each other along the line of the strut. The effect of these forces is to compress the strut, and it is said to be in *compression*.

If the forces acting on a strut are not all applied at its ends, the direction of the resultant force at the ends is not along the line of the strut. This is illustrated in the next example.

In Fig. 2–8(c), the force **C** has been transferred along its line of action to the point of intersection B of the three forces. The force diagram for a particle at B is exactly like that of Fig. 2–7, and the problem is solved in the same way. The conditions of equilibrium provide two independent equations among the five quantities T_1, T_2, C, θ_1, and θ_2. Hence if any three are known, the others may be calculated.

EXAMPLE 4. In Fig. 2–9 a ladder, which is in equilibrium, leans against a vertical frictionless wall. The forces on the ladder are (1) its weight **w**, (2) the force F_1 exerted on the ladder by the vertical wall and which is perpendicular to the wall if there is no friction, and (3) the force F_2 exerted by the ground on the base of the ladder. The force **w** is known in magnitude and in direction, the force F_1 is known in direction only, and the force F_2 is unknown in both magnitude and direction. As in the preceding example, the ladder is in equilibrium under three forces, *which must be concurrent*. Since the lines of action of F_1 and **w** are known, their point of intersection (point O) can be located. The line of action of F_2 must then pass through this point also. Note that neither the direction of F_1 nor that of F_2 lies along the line of the ladder. In part (b) the forces have been transferred to the point of intersection of their lines of action, and applying the equations for the equilibrium of a particle at this point, we get

$$\Sigma F_x = F_2 \cos \theta - F_1 = 0, \qquad (2\text{–}1)$$

$$\Sigma F_y = F_2 \sin \theta - w = 0. \qquad (2\text{–}2)$$

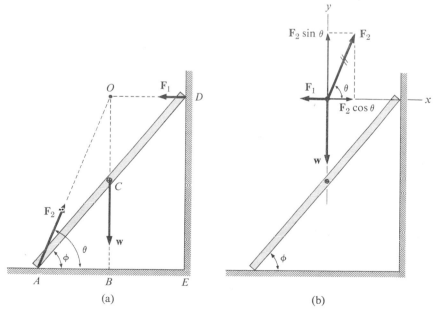

(a)   (b)

Fig. 2–9. Forces on a ladder leaning against a vertical frictionless wall.

As a numerical example, suppose the ladder weighs 80 lb, is 20 ft long, has its center of gravity at its center, and makes an angle $\phi = 53°$ with the ground. We wish to find the angle θ and the forces $\mathbf{F}_1$ and $\mathbf{F}_2$. To calculate θ, we first find the lengths of AB and BO. From the right triangle ABC, we have

$$\overline{AB} = \overline{AC} \cos \phi = 10 \text{ ft} \times 0.60 = 6.0 \text{ ft,}$$

and from the right triangle AED,

$$\overline{DE} = \overline{AD} \sin \phi = 20 \text{ ft} \times 0.80 = 16 \text{ ft.}$$

Then, from the right triangle AOB, since $\overline{OB} = \overline{DE}$, we have

$$\tan \theta = \frac{\overline{OB}}{\overline{AB}} = \frac{16 \text{ ft}}{6.0 \text{ ft}} = 2.67.$$

Then

$$\theta = 69.5°, \qquad \sin \theta = 0.937, \qquad \cos \theta = 0.350.$$

$$F_2 = \frac{w}{\sin \theta} = \frac{80 \text{ lb}}{0.937} = 85.5 \text{ lb,}$$

and from Eq. (2–1),

$$F_1 = F_2 \cos \theta = 85.5 \text{ lb} \times 0.350 = 30 \text{ lb.}$$

The ladder presses against the wall and the ground with forces which are equal and opposite to $\mathbf{F}_1$ and $\mathbf{F}_2$, respectively.

In the next chapter we shall explain another method of solving this problem, using the concept of the *moment* of a force.

EXAMPLE 5.   In Fig. 2–10, block A of weight w_1 rests on a frictionless inclined plane of slope angle θ. The center of gravity of the block is at its center. A flexible cord is attached to the center of the right face of the block, passes over a frictionless pulley, and is attached to a second block B of weight w_2. The weight of the cord and friction in the pulley are

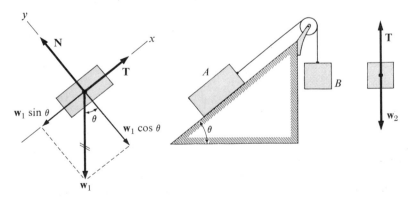

Fig. 2–10.   Forces on a block in equilibrium on a frictionless inclined plane.

negligible. If w_1 and θ are given, find the weight w_2 for which the system is in equilibrium, that is, for which it remains at rest or moves in either direction at constant speed.

The free-body diagrams for the two blocks are shown at the left and right. The forces on block B are its weight w_2 and the force T exerted on it by the cord. Since it is in equilibrium,

$$T = w_2. \quad \text{(1st law)} \tag{2–3}$$

Block A is acted on by its weight w_1, the force T exerted on it by the cord, and the force N exerted on it by the plane. We can use the same symbol T for the force exerted on each block by the cord because, as explained in Section 2–5, these forces are equivalent to an action-reaction pair and have the same magnitude. The force N, if there is no friction, is perpendicular or *normal* to the surface of the plane. Since the lines of action of w_1 and T intersect at the center of gravity of the block, the line of action of N passes through this point also. It is simplest to choose x- and y-axes parallel and perpendicular to the surface of the plane, because then only the weight w_1 needs to be resolved into components. The conditions of equilibrium give

$$\sum F_x = T - w_1 \sin \theta = 0, \quad \left.\right\} \quad \text{(1st law)} \tag{2–4}$$
$$\sum F_y = N - w_1 \cos \theta = 0. \quad \tag{2–5}$$

Thus if $w_1 = 100$ lb and $\theta = 30°$, we have from Eqs. (2–3) and (2–4),

$$w_2 = T = w_1 \sin \theta = 100 \text{ lb} \times 0.500 = 50 \text{ lb},$$

and from Eq. (2–5),

$$N = w_1 \cos \theta = 100 \text{ lb} \times 0.866 = 86.6 \text{ lb}.$$

Note carefully that *in the absence of friction* the same weight w_2 of 50 lb is required whether the system remains at rest or moves with constant speed in *either* direction. This is not the case when friction is present.

2–7 Friction

Whenever the surface of one body slides over that of another, *each* body exerts a frictional force on the other, parallel to the surfaces. The force *on* each body is opposite to the direction of its motion relative to the other. Thus when a block slides from left to right along the surface of a table, a frictional force to the left acts on the block and an equal force toward the right acts on the table. Frictional forces may also act when there is no relative motion. A horizontal force on a heavy packing case resting on the floor may not be enough to set the case in motion, because of an equal and opposite frictional force exerted on the case by the floor.

The origin of these frictional forces is not fully understood, and the study of them is an important field of research. When one unlubricated metal slides over another, there appears to be an actual momentary welding of the metals together at the "high spots" where they make contact. The observed friction force is the force required to break these tiny welds. The mechanism of the friction force between two blocks of wood, or between two bricks, must be quite different.

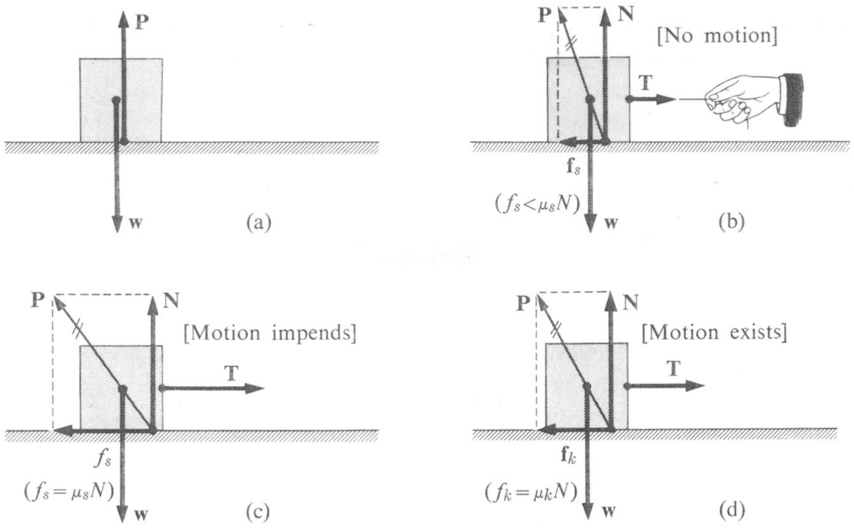

Fig. 2–11. The magnitude of the friction force **f** is less than or equal to $\mu_s N$ when there is no relative motion, and is equal to $\mu_k N$ when motion exists.

In Fig. 2–11(a) a block is at rest on a horizontal surface, in equilibrium under the action of its weight **w** and the upward force **P** exerted on it by the surface. The lines of action of **w** and **P** have been displaced slightly to show these forces more clearly.

Suppose now that a cord is attached to the block as in Fig. 2–11(b) and the tension **T** in the cord is gradually increased. Provided the tension is not too great, the block remains at rest. The force **P** exerted on the block by the surface is inclined toward the left as shown, since the three forces **P**, **w**, and **T** must be concurrent. The component of **P** parallel to the surface is called the *force of static friction*, **f**$_s$. The other component, **N**, is the *normal* force exerted on the block by the surface. From the conditions of equilibrium, the force of static friction **f**$_s$ equals the force **T**, and the normal force **N** equals the weight **w**.

As the force **T** is increased further, a limiting value is reached at which the block breaks away from the surface and starts to move. In other words, there is a certain maximum value which the force of static friction **f**$_s$ can have. Figure 2–11(c) is the force diagram when **T** is just below its limiting value and motion impends. If the force **T** exceeds this limiting value, the block is no longer in equilibrium.

For a given pair of surfaces, the magnitude of the maximum value of **f**$_s$ is nearly proportional to that of the normal force **N**. The actual force of static friction can therefore have any magnitude between zero (when there is no applied force parallel to the surface) and a maximum value proportional to N or equal to $\mu_s N$. The factor μ_s is called the *coefficient of static friction*. Thus,

$$f_s \leqq \mu_s N. \tag{2–6}$$

The equality sign holds only when the applied force **T**, parallel to the surface, has such a value that motion is about to start [Fig. 2–11(c)]. When **T** is less than this value [Fig. 2–11(b)], the inequality sign holds and the magnitude of the friction force must be computed from the conditions of equilibrium.

As soon as sliding begins, it is found that the friction force decreases. This new friction force, for a given pair of surfaces, is also nearly proportional to the magnitude of the normal force. The proportionality factor, μ_k, is called the *coefficient of sliding friction* or *kinetic* friction. Thus, when the block is in motion, the force of sliding or kinetic friction is given by

$$f_k = \mu_k N. \tag{2–7}$$

This is illustrated in Fig. 2–11(d).

The coefficients of static and sliding friction depend primarily on the nature of the surfaces in contact, being relatively large if the surfaces are rough and small if they are smooth. The coefficient of sliding friction varies somewhat with the relative velocity, but for simplicity we shall assume it to be independent of velocity. It is also nearly independent of the contact area. However, since two real surfaces actually touch each other only at a relatively small number of high spots, the true contact area is very different from the over-all area. Equations (2–6) and (2–7) are useful empirical relations, but do not represent fundamental physical laws like Newton's laws. Typical numerical values are given in Table 2–1.

TABLE 2–1

COEFFICIENTS OF FRICTION

Materials	Static, μ_s	Kinetic, μ_k
Steel on steel	0.74	0.57
Aluminum on steel	0.61	0.47
Copper on steel	0.53	0.36
Brass on steel	0.51	0.44
Zinc on cast iron	0.85	0.21
Copper on cast iron	1.05	0.29
Glass on glass	0.94	0.4
Copper on glass	0.68	0.53
Teflon on teflon	0.04	0.04
Teflon on steel	0.04	0.04

In Table 2–1, the coefficients of friction only of solids are listed. Liquids and gases show frictional effects also, but the simple equation $f = \mu N$ does not hold. It will be shown in Chapter 14 that there exists a property of liquids and gases called *viscosity* which determines the friction force between two surfaces sliding over each other with a layer of liquid or gas between them. Gases have the lowest viscosities of all materials at normal temperatures, and therefore, to reduce friction to a value close to zero, it is convenient to have an object slide on a layer of gas.

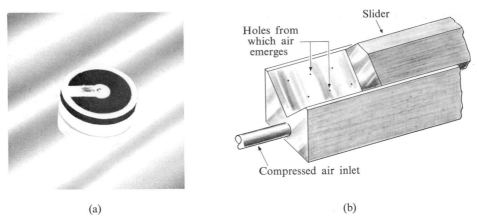

Slider

Holes from
which air
emerges

Compressed air inlet

(a)   (b)

Fig. 2–12. (a) A disk top of metal, bottom of dry ice, slides on a layer of carbon dioxide gas over an aluminum sheet. (b) An object that can slide in a V-shaped groove over an air cushion provided through many small openings.

Two methods for doing this are shown in Fig. 2–12. In Fig. 2–12(a) there is a picture of a composite disk the top part of metal, and the white bottom part composed of solid carbon dioxide, known familiarly as dry ice. For carbon dioxide to exist as a liquid, the pressure must be about five times atmospheric pressure. Hence, under ordinary atmospheric pressure, an influx of heat will convert carbon dioxide directly from solid to gas. The disk is placed on a large smooth aluminum plate. Since the dry ice is at a temperature of about $-78°C$ and the aluminum plate is almost at room temperature, heat flows from the plate to the dry ice, which evaporates and supplies the gas on which the disc rides.

In Fig. 2–12(b) there is depicted a carefully machined V-shaped trough, first developed at the California Institute of Technology, in which a nicely fitting object may slide on a cushion of air supplied through many small openings which communicate to a compressed air manifold. Friction is reduced in this way to an incredibly small amount.

EXAMPLE 1. In Fig. 2–11, suppose that the block weighs 20 lb, that the tension T can be increased to 8 lb before the block starts to slide, and that a force of 4 lb will keep the block moving at constant speed once it has been set in motion. Find the coefficients of static and kinetic friction.

From Fig. 2–11(c) and the data above, we have

$$\left.\begin{array}{l} \sum F_y = N - w = N - 20 \text{ lb} = 0, \\ \sum F_x = T - f_s = 8 \text{ lb} - f_s = 0, \end{array}\right\} \quad \text{(1st law)}$$

$$f_s = \mu_s N \quad \text{(motion impends)}.$$

Hence

$$\mu_s = \frac{f_s}{N} = \frac{8 \text{ lb}}{20 \text{ lb}} = 0.40.$$

From Fig. 2–11(d), we have

$$\sum F_y = N - w = N - 20 \text{ lb} = 0,$$
$$\sum F_x = T - f_k = 4 \text{ lb} - f_k = 0,$$

(1st law)

$$f_k = \mu_k N \quad \text{(motion exists)}.$$

Hence

$$\mu_k = \frac{f_k}{N} = \frac{4 \text{ lb}}{20 \text{ lb}} = 0.20.$$

EXAMPLE 2.   What is the friction force if the block in Fig. 2–11(b) is at rest on the surface and a horizontal force of 5 lb is exerted on it?
We have

$$\sum F_x = T - f_s = 5 \text{ lb} - f_s = 0, \qquad \text{(1st law)}$$
$$f_s = 5 \text{ lb}.$$

Note that in this case

$$f_s < \mu_s N.$$

EXAMPLE 3.   What force **T**, at an angle of 30° above the horizontal, is required to drag a block weighing 20 lb to the right at constant speed, as in Fig. 2–13, if the coefficient of kinetic friction between block and surface is 0.20?

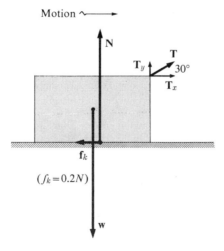

Fig. 2–13.   Forces on a block being dragged to the right on a level surface at constant speed.

The forces on the block are shown in the diagram.   From the first condition of equilibrium,

$$\sum F_x = T \cos 30° - 0.2N = 0,$$
$$\sum F_y = T \sin 30° + N - 20 \text{ lb} = 0.$$

Simultaneous solution gives

$$T = 4.15 \text{ lb},$$

$$N = 17.9 \text{ lb}.$$

Note that in this example the normal force **N** is not equal to the weight of the block, but is less than the weight by the vertical component of the force **T**.

EXAMPLE 4.   In Fig. 2–14, a block has been placed on an inclined plane and the slope angle θ of the plane has been adjusted until the block slides down the plane at constant speed, once it has been set in motion.   Find the angle θ.

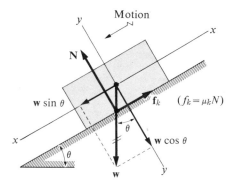

Fig. 2–14.   Forces on a block sliding down an inclined plane (with friction) at constant speed.

The forces on the block are its weight **w** and the normal and frictional components of the force exerted by the plane.   Take axes perpendicular and parallel to the surface of the plane.   Then

$$\left. \begin{array}{l} \sum F_x = \mu_k N - w \sin \theta = 0, \\ \sum F_y = N - w \cos \theta = 0. \end{array} \right\} \quad \text{(1st law)}$$

Hence

$$\mu_k N = w \sin \theta, \qquad N = w \cos \theta.$$

Dividing the former by the latter, we get

$$\mu_k = \tan \theta.$$

It follows that a block, regardless of its weight, slides down an inclined plane with constant speed if the tangent of the slope angle of the plane equals the coefficient of kinetic friction.   Measurement of this angle then provides a simple experimental method for determining the coefficient of kinetic friction.

Problems

Section 2–6 should be read carefully before beginning the solution of problems in this chapter. If difficulties arise, they will not result from any complicated mathematics or from a failure to remember the "formula" (after all, the only "formulas" are $\sum F_x = 0, \sum F_y = 0$) but rather from (1) a failure to *select some one body to talk about*, and (2) a failure to *recognize precisely what forces are exerted* **on** *the selected body*. Once the forces acting on the body have been clearly and correctly shown in a force diagram, the physics of the problem is finished; the rest of the computations might be (and in practice often are) turned over to a machine.

2–1. Imagine that you are holding a book weighing 4 lb at rest on the palm of your hand. Complete the following sentences.

(a) A downward force of magnitude 4 lb is exerted on the book by _____.

(b) An upward force of magnitude _____ is exerted on _____ by the hand.

(c) Is the upward force (b) the reaction to the downward force (a)?

(d) The reaction to force (a) is a force of magnitude _____, exerted on _____ by _____. Its direction is _____.

(e) The reaction to force (b) is a force of magnitude _____, exerted on _____ by _____. Its direction is _____.

(f) That the forces (a) and (b) are equal and opposite is an example of Newton's _____ law.

(g) That forces (b) and (e) are equal and opposite is an example of Newton's _____ law.

Suppose now that you exert an upward force of magnitude 5 lb on the book.

(h) Does the book remain in equilibrium?

(i) Is the force exerted on the book by the hand equal and opposite to the force exerted on the book by the earth?

(j) Is the force exerted on the book by the earth equal and opposite to the force exerted on the earth by the book?

(k) Is the force exerted on the book by the hand equal and opposite to the force exerted on the hand by the book?

Finally, suppose that you snatch your hand away while the book is moving upward.

(l) How many forces then act on the book?

(m) Is the book in equilibrium?

(n) What balances the downward force exerted on the book by the earth?

2–2. A block is given a push along a table top, and slides off the edge of the table. (a) What force or forces are exerted on it while it is falling from the table to the floor? (b) What is the reaction to each force, that is, on what body and by what body is the reaction exerted? Neglect air resistance.

2–3. Two 10-lb weights are suspended at opposite ends of a rope which passes over a light frictionless pulley. The pulley is attached to a chain which goes to the ceiling. (a) What is the tension in the rope? (b) What is the tension in the chain?

2–4. In Fig. 2–6, let the weight of the hanging block be 50 lb. Find the tensions T_2 and T_3, (a) if $\theta_2 = \theta_3 = 60°$, (b) if $\theta_2 = \theta_3 = 10°$, (c) if $\theta_2 = 60°$, $\theta_3 = 0$, and (d) if $AB = 10$ ft, $AO = 6$ ft, $OB = 8$ ft.

2–5. Find the tension in each cord in Fig. 2–15 if the weight of the suspended body is 200 lb.

2–6. Find the tension T in the cable, and the magnitude and direction of the force C exerted on the strut by the pivot in the arrangements in Fig. 2–16. Let the weight of the suspended object in each case be 1000 lb. Neglect the weight of the strut.

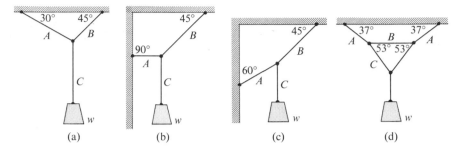

Figure 2–15

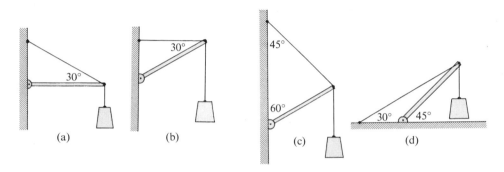

Figure 2–16

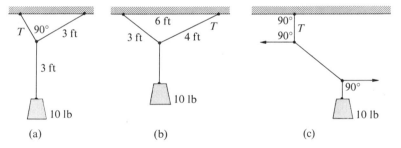

Figure 2–17

2–7. (a) In which of the arrangements in Fig. 2–17 can the tension T be computed, if the only quantities known are those explicitly given? (b) For each case in which insufficient information is given, state one additional quantity, a knowledge of which would permit solution.

2–8. A horizontal boom 8 ft long is hinged to a vertical wall at one end, and a 500-lb body hangs from its outer end.

The boom is supported by a guy wire from its outer end to a point on the wall directly above the boom. (a) If the tension in this wire is not to exceed 1000 lb, what is the minimum height above the boom at which it may be fastened to the wall? (b) By how many pounds would the tension be increased if the wire were fastened 1 ft below this point, the boom remaining horizontal? Neglect weight of boom.

2-9. One end of a rope 50 ft long is attached to an automobile. The other end is fastened to a tree. A man exerts a force of 100 lb at the midpoint of the rope, pulling it 2 ft to the side. What is the force exerted on the automobile?

2-10. Find the largest weight w which can be supported by the structure in Fig. 2-18 if the maximum tension the upper rope can withstand is 1000 lb and the maximum compression the strut can withstand is 2000 lb. The vertical rope is strong enough to carry any load required. Neglect the weight of the strut.

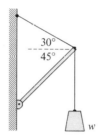

Figure 2-18

⨉ 2-11. (a) Block A in Fig. 2-19 weighs 100 lb. The coefficient of static friction between the block and the surface on which it rests is 0.30. The weight w is 20 lb and the system is in equilibrium. Find the friction force exerted on block A. (b) Find the maximum weight w for which the system will remain in equilibrium.

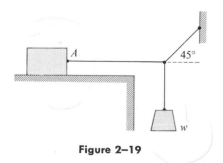

Figure 2-19

2-12. A block hangs from a cord 10 ft long. A second cord is tied to the midpoint of the first, and a horizontal pull

equal to half the weight of the block is exerted on it, the second cord being always kept horizontal. (a) How far will the block be pulled to one side? (b) How far will it be lifted?

2-13. A flexible chain of weight w hangs between two hooks at the same height, as shown in Fig. 2-20. At each end the chain makes an angle θ with the horizontal. (a) What is the magnitude and direction of the force $\mathbf{F}$ exerted by the chain on the hook at the left? (b) What is the tension $\mathbf{T}$ in the chain at its lowest point?

Figure 2-20

2-14. A 30-lb block is pulled at constant speed up a frictionless inclined plane by a weight of 10 lb hanging from a cord attached to the block and passing over a frictionless pulley at the top of the plane. (See Fig. 2-10.) Find (a) the slope angle of the plane, (b) the tension in the cord, and (c) the normal force exerted on the block by the plane.

2-15. (a) A block rests upon a rough horizontal surface. A horizontal force $\mathbf{T}$ is applied to the block and is slowly increased from zero. Draw a graph with T along the x-axis and the friction force f along the y-axis, starting at $T = 0$ and showing the region of no motion, the point where motion impends, and the region where motion exists. (b) A block of weight w rests on a rough horizontal plank. The slope angle of the plank θ is gradually increased until the block starts to slip. Draw two graphs, both with θ along the x-axis. In one graph show the ratio of the normal force to the weight N/w as a function of θ. In the second graph, show the ratio of the friction force to the weight f/w. Indicate the region of no motion, the point where motion impends, and the region where motion exists.

2–16. A block weighing 20 lb rests on a horizontal surface. The coefficient of static friction between block and surface is 0.40 and the coefficient of sliding friction is 0.20. (a) How large is the friction force exerted on the block? (b) How great will the friction force be if a horizontal force of 5 lb is exerted on the block? (c) What is the minimum force which will start the block in motion? (d) What is the minimum force which will keep the block in motion once it has been started? (e) If the horizontal force is 10 lb, how great is the friction force?

2–17. A block is pulled to the right at constant velocity by a 10-lb force acting 30° above the horizontal. The coefficient of sliding friction between the block and the surface is 0.5. What is the weight of the block?

2–18. A block weighing 14 lb is placed on an inclined plane and connected to a 10-lb block by a cord passing over a small frictionless pulley, as in Fig. 2–10. The coefficient of sliding friction between the block and the plane is 1/7. For what two values of θ will the system move with constant velocity?
[*Hint:* $\cos \theta = \sqrt{1 - \sin^2 \theta}$.]

2–19. A block weighing 100 lb is placed on an inclined plane of slope angle 30° and is connected to a second hanging block of weight w by a cord passing over a small frictionless pulley, as in Fig. 2–10. The coefficient of static friction is 0.40 and the coefficient of sliding friction is 0.30. (a) Find the weight w for which the 100-lb block moves up the plane at constant speed. (b) Find the weight w for which it moves down the plane at constant speed. (c) For what range of values of w will the block remain at rest?

2–20. What force P at an angle ϕ above the horizontal is needed to drag a box of weight w at constant speed along a level floor if the coefficient of sliding friction between box and floor is μ?

2–21. A safe weighing 600 lb is to be lowered at constant speed down skids 8 ft long, from a truck 4 ft high. If the coefficient of sliding friction between safe and skids is 0.30, (a) will the safe need to be pulled down or held back? (b) How great a force parallel to the plane is needed?

2–22. If a force of 86 lb parallel to the surface of a 20° inclined plane will push a 120-lb block up the plane at constant speed, (a) what force parallel to the plane will push it down at constant speed? (b) What is the coefficient of sliding friction?   .394

2–23. Block A in Fig. 2–21 weighs 4 lb and block B weighs 8 lb. The coefficient of sliding friction between all surfaces is 0.25. Find the force P necessary to drag block B to the left at constant speed (a) if A rests on B and moves with it, (b) if A is held at rest, and (c) if A and B are connected by a light flexible cord passing around a fixed frictionless pulley.

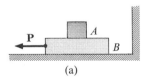

(a)

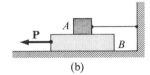

(b)

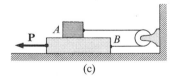

(c)

Figure 2–21

2–24. Block A, of weight w, slides down an inclined plane S of slope angle 37° at constant velocity while the plank B, also of weight w, rests on top of A. The plank is attached by a cord to the top of the

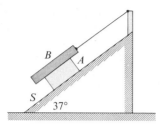

Figure 2–22

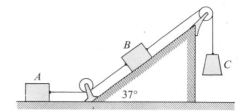

Figure 2–23

plane (Fig. 2–22). (a) Draw a diagram of all the forces acting on block A. (b) If the coefficient of kinetic friction is the same between the surfaces A and B and between S and A, determine its value.

2–25. Two blocks, A and B, are placed as in Fig. 2–23 and connected by ropes to block C. Both A and B weigh 20 lb and the coefficient of sliding friction between each block and the surface is 0.5. Block C descends with constant velocity. (a) Draw two separate force diagrams showing the forces acting on A and B. (b) Find the tension in the rope connecting blocks A and B. (c) What is the weight of block C?

CHAPTER 3

Equilibrium of a Rigid Body

3–1 Moment of a force

In Fig. 3–1 we have reproduced a figure from Chapter 1 in which it is shown how to find graphically the resultant $\mathbf{R}$ of two forces $\mathbf{F}_1$ and $\mathbf{F}_2$ acting at arbitrary points A and B of a rigid body. Methods were described in Chapter 1 for calculating the *magnitude* and *direction* of $\mathbf{R}$. The *line of action* of $\mathbf{R}$, which must pass through point C, can be specified by giving the coordinates of another point on the line or by specifying the perpendicular distance from the line to a point O, arbitrarily chosen as an origin.

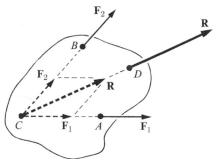

Fig. 3–1. Method of finding the resultant $\mathbf{R}$ of two coplanar forces $\mathbf{F}_1$ and $\mathbf{F}_2$ having different points of application.

In Fig. 3–2, the two coplanar forces $\mathbf{F}_1$ and $\mathbf{F}_2$ are shown acting at points A and B, respectively, of a rigid body whose outline has not been drawn, since it is irrelevant. An arbitrary point O is shown in the same plane, and the perpendicular distances l_1, l_2, and l are indicated from O to the action lines of $\mathbf{F}_1$, $\mathbf{F}_2$, and $\mathbf{R}$. It is desired to specify the position of the action line of $\mathbf{R}$ by calculating l.

Let r be the distance from O to C. Taking components in a direction perpendicular to line OC, we have

$$R \sin \theta = F_1 \sin \phi_1 + F_2 \sin \phi_2.$$

When both sides are multiplied by r, we get

$$Rr \sin \theta = F_1 r \sin \phi_1 + F_2 r \sin \phi_2.$$

Now, it will be seen from Fig. 3–2 that

$$r \sin \theta = l, \qquad r \sin \phi_1 = l_1, \qquad r \sin \phi_2 = l_2,$$

and therefore

$$lR = l_1 F_1 + l_2 F_2. \tag{3–1}$$

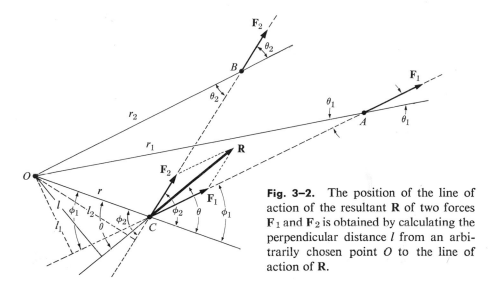

Fig. 3–2. The position of the line of action of the resultant **R** of two forces $\mathbf{F}_1$ and $\mathbf{F}_2$ is obtained by calculating the perpendicular distance l from an arbitrarily chosen point O to the line of action of **R**.

This is the desired equation giving the perpendicular distance l from the origin O to the line of action of **R**, in terms of the forces $\mathbf{F}_1$ and $\mathbf{F}_2$ and the perpendicular distances from O to their lines of action. Note that the equation is a relation among three expressions, *each one the product* of a force and the perpendicular distance from an arbitrarily chosen point to its line of action.

The perpendicular distances l, l_1, l_2 from an arbitrarily chosen origin O to the action lines of **R**, $\mathbf{F}_1$, $\mathbf{F}_2$ are called the *moment* arms (or *lever arms*) of the forces **R**, $\mathbf{F}_1$, $\mathbf{F}_2$, and the products lR, l_1F_1, l_2F_2 are called the *moments* of the forces about point O. The moment of a force (also called a *torque* from the Latin word *torquere*, to twist) is thus the product of the magnitude of the force and the perpendicular distance from an arbitrarily chosen origin and the action line of the force. Representing the moment by capital Greek gamma, Γ, Eq. (3–1) becomes

$$\Gamma = \Gamma_1 + \Gamma_2, \tag{3–2}$$

and expresses the fact that *the moment of the resultant of two forces is the sum of the moments of the two forces*, a statement known as *Varignon's theorem.*

The moment of a force or the torque about a chosen point has an important physical significance. It is a measure of the "twisting ability" or "rotational effect" of a force applied along the given action line. In Fig. 3–2, the effect of force $\mathbf{F}_1$ and its moment arm l_1 is such as to produce counterclockwise rotation about an *axis* through the point O and perpendicular to the plane of the diagram. If however, the point O were chosen to the right of the figure, the effect of $\mathbf{F}_1$ and its new moment arm would be to produce clockwise rotation about a perpendicular axis through O. If the point O were chosen *on* the action line of $\mathbf{F}_1$, both the moment arm and the moment would be zero, and there would be no rotational effect.

In accord with the usual conventions of analytic geometry, we shall consider counterclockwise moments to be positive and clockwise moments to be negative.

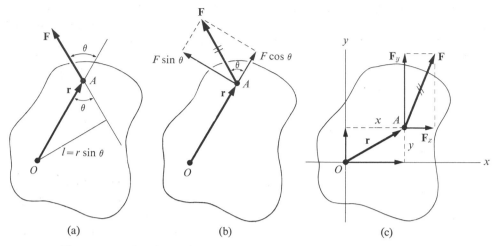

Fig. 3–3. The moment Γ of the force $\mathbf{F}$ about an axis through O can be expressed as (a) $\Gamma = F(r \sin \theta)$, (b) $\Gamma = (F \sin \theta)r$, (c) $\Gamma = xF_y - yF_x$.

If the line of action of a force does not lie in a plane perpendicular to an axis, the force can be resolved into components parallel and perpendicular to the axis. The component parallel to the axis contributes nothing to the moment about the axis; therefore, with the understanding that $\mathbf{F}$ represents the component in a plane perpendicular to the axis, the moment of *any* force about an axis is given by

$$\Gamma = lF,$$

where l is the perpendicular distance from the axis to the line of action of $\mathbf{F}$.

The unit of moment or torque is the product of the unit of force and the unit of length. Thus if the unit of force is 1 lb and the unit of length is 1 ft, the unit of torque is 1 lb·ft (the dot has the significance of the multiplication sign). A force of 1 lb, at a perpendicular distance of 1 ft from an axis, has a moment of 1 lb·ft about the axis, etc.

As defined here, the moment of a force is a *scalar* quantity, since it is the product of two scalars. The *vector moment* of a force is defined in the next section.

The moment of a force about an axis can also be expressed as follows. Figure 3–3(a) shows a force $\mathbf{F}$ and its moment arm l about an axis through O perpendicular to the plane of the diagram. Let $\mathbf{r}$ be the vector from O to A, the point of application of $\mathbf{F}$, and let θ be the angle between $\mathbf{r}$ and $\mathbf{F}$. The moment arm l is then equal to the magnitude of the rectangular component of $\mathbf{r}$ perpendicular to the line of action of $\mathbf{F}$:

$$l = r \sin \theta.$$

The moment of $\mathbf{F}$ about the axis is therefore

$$\Gamma = F \times (r \sin \theta) = rF \sin \theta.$$

In Fig. 3–3(b), the force **F** has been resolved into rectangular components of magnitude $F \sin \theta$ and $F \cos \theta$, perpendicular and parallel to **r**. The component $F \cos \theta$ has no moment about the axis because its line of action passes through the axis. The moment arm of the component $F \sin \theta$ is the length of the vector **r**, since this is the perpendicular distance from the axis to the line of action of this component. The moment about the axis is therefore

$$\Gamma = (F \sin \theta) \times r = rF \sin \theta.$$

We can therefore consider the moment either as the product of the force **F** and the length of the component of **r** perpendicular to **F**, as in Fig. 3–3(a), or as the product of the component of **F** perpendicular to **r** and the length of **r**, as in Fig. 3–3(b).

A third method of expressing the moment of a force is illustrated in Fig. 3–3(c). The force **F** and the vector **r** are both resolved into components in the directions of an arbitrary pair of x- and y-axes. The magnitudes of the components of **r** are equal to the coordinates x and y of the point of application of **F**. The moment of the component $\mathbf{F}_y$ about an axis through O is $+xF_y$, and the moment of the component $\mathbf{F}_x$ is $-yF_x$. The resultant moment is therefore

$$\Gamma = xF_y - yF_x.$$

3–2 Vector product.   Vector moment

The processes of *vector addition* and *vector subtraction* were described in Section 1–4. We must now consider another process of vector algebra, that of *vector multiplication,* or the product of two vectors. Two such products are defined in vector analysis. One, called the scalar product, will be discussed in Chapter 7. The other, known as the *vector product,* is defined as a vector whose magnitude equals the product of the magnitudes of the vectors and the sine of the angle between them. The direction of the vector product is perpendicular to the plane of the vectors.

The vector product of vectors **A** and **B** is written **A** × **B** and is also called the *cross product.* If θ is the angle between the vectors, the *magnitude* of **A** × **B** is $AB \sin \theta$.

The direction in which the vector product **A** × **B** points is defined as follows. Figure 3–4 shows the vectors **A** and **B** drawn from a common point O. Imagine a right-hand screw with its axis perpendicular to the plane of **A** and **B** and let the screw be *turned* in the same way the first vector (**A**) turns when it is rotated through the smallest angle (θ) that will bring it into parallelism with the second vector (**B**). The vector product **A** × **B** then points in the direction of *advance* of the screw. Thus if one looks down on the plane of the vectors **A** and **B** in Fig. 3–4, rotation of vector **A** counterclockwise through the angle θ will bring **A** into parallelism with **B** and a right-hand screw turned in this way would advance upward as shown.

The vector product **B** × **A** has the same *magnitude* as **A** × **B** but points in the *opposite direction.* The first vector (**B**) must be rotated clockwise as seen from above in Fig. 3–4 to bring it into parallelism with the second vector (**A**). A right-hand

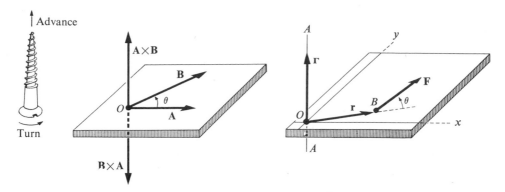

Fig. 3–4. Vector products of vectors A and B. The product **A × B** points upward, while **B × A** points downward. The magnitude of both products is $AB \sin \theta$, but **B × A = −A × B**.

Fig. 3–5. The vector moment **Γ** of the force **F** about the axis *AA* is **Γ = r × F**.

screw turned in this way would advance downward, so the vector **B × A** points downward. Thus **B × A** is the negative of **A × B**:

$$\mathbf{B \times A} = -\mathbf{A \times B}.$$

That is, the vector product is not commutative.

The vector product of two vectors is zero when the vectors are parallel, since then $\sin \theta = 0$. If two vectors are mutually perpendicular, the magnitude of their vector product equals the product of their magnitudes, since then $\sin \theta = 1$.

We now show how the moment of a force about an axis can be correlated with a vector product. Figure 3–5 shows a force **F** in the xy-plane whose point of application is at *B*. The line *AA* is an axis perpendicular to the plane containing **F**. The vector **r** is perpendicular to the axis from *O* to *B*, and therefore lies in the xy-plane. The *vector moment* **Γ** of the force **F** about the axis is defined as the vector product of **r** and **F**:

$$\mathbf{\Gamma = r \times F}. \tag{3–3}$$

The vector **Γ** is perpendicular to the plane of **r** and **F** and it points upward in Fig. 3–5. Its magnitude is

$$\Gamma = rF \sin \theta.$$

But $rF \sin \theta$ equals the *scalar* moment of the force **P** about the axis *AA*. Hence *the **magnitude** of the vector moment of a force about an axis is equal to the scalar moment of the force.*

3–3 The second condition of equilibrium

We saw in Section 2–2 that when a body is acted upon by any number of coplanar forces, the forces can always be reduced to two, as in Fig. 2–2. If the body is in equilibrium, these forces (a) must be equal in magnitude and opposite in direction, and (b) must have the same line of action.

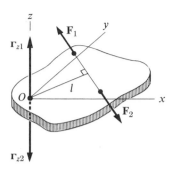

Fig. 3–6. If the two forces F_1 and F_2, in the xy-plane, are in equilibrium, their resultant moment about any z-axis is zero.

If the xy-plane is taken as the plane in which the forces lie, requirement (a) is satisfied by the *first condition of equilibrium:*

$$\sum F_x = 0, \qquad \sum F_y = 0.$$

Requirement (b), which is the second condition of equilibrium, can be simply expressed in terms of the moments of the forces. Figure 3–6 again shows a flat object in the xy-plane, acted on by two forces F_1 and F_2. If the object is in equilibrium, the magnitudes of F_1 and F_2 are equal and both have the same line of action. Hence they have the same moment arm, of length l, about an axis perpendicular to the xy-plane and passing through any arbitrary point O. Let us call this axis the z-axis. The vector moment Γ_{z1} of the force F_1 points upward along the z-axis, and the vector moment Γ_{z2} of the force F_2 points downward. Since the magnitudes of these moments are equal, *the resultant vector moment is zero.* The necessary and sufficient condition, therefore, that two equal and opposite forces in the xy-plane have the same line of action is that the magnitude of their resultant moment about a z-axis through any point shall be zero. The second condition of equilibrium, for this case, can therefore be expressed as

$$\sum \Gamma_z = 0.$$

It is not necessary to first reduce a set of coplanar forces to two forces in order to calculate the sum of their moments. Making use of Varignon's theorem, Eq. (3–2), we need only calculate the moment of each force separately and then add these moments algebraically. Thus if a body is in equilibrium under the action of any number of coplanar forces, the algebraic sum of the moments of these forces about any arbitrary axis perpendicular to the plane is zero.

The most general conditions that must be satisfied by the forces on a body in equilibrium can now be stated in two simple vector equations: (1) *the resultant F of all external forces acting on the body is zero, and* (2) *the resultant vector moment Γ of all external forces, about any axis, is zero:*

$$F = 0, \qquad \Gamma = 0. \qquad\qquad (3\text{–}4)$$

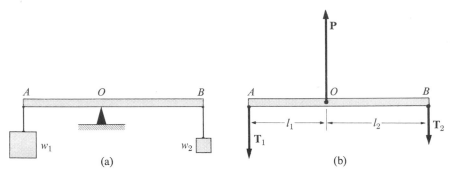

Fig. 3–7. A rod in equilibrium under three parallel forces.

The first condition ensures that the translational motion of the body does not change; the second, that its rotational motion does not change.

The vector equations above are equivalent to the six scalar equations

$$\Sigma F_x = 0, \qquad \Sigma F_y = 0, \qquad \Sigma F_z = 0,$$
$$\Sigma \Gamma_x = 0, \qquad \Sigma \Gamma_y = 0, \qquad \Sigma \Gamma_z = 0.$$

If the forces all lie in the same plane, their vector moment is zero about any axis in the plane. If, for example, the forces lie in the xy-plane, then $\Sigma F_z = 0$, $\Sigma \Gamma_x = 0$, $\Sigma \Gamma_y = 0$. Thus a system of forces in space must satisfy *six* equations if the forces are in equilibrium, while a system of coplanar forces must satisfy only *three*.

Newton's *third* law provides the connecting link between the forces on any number of rigid bodies that interact with one another; therefore, in principle, any problem involving a system made up of any number of rigid bodies in equilibrium can now be solved.

EXAMPLE 1.   A rigid rod whose own weight is negligible (Fig. 3–7) is pivoted at point O and carries a body of weight w_1 at end A. Find the weight w_2 of a second body which must be attached at end B if the rod is to be in equilibrium, and find the force exerted on the rod by the pivot at O.

Figure 3–7(b) is the free-body diagram of the rod. The forces T_1 and T_2 are equal respectively to w_1 and w_2. The conditions of equilibrium, taking moments about a z-axis through O, perpendicular to the diagram, give

$$\Sigma F_y = P - T_1 - T_2 = 0, \qquad \text{(1st condition)}$$
$$\Sigma \Gamma_z = l_1 T_1 - l_2 T_2 = 0. \qquad \text{(2nd condition)}$$

Let $l_1 = 3$ ft, $l_2 = 4$ ft, $w_1 = 4$ lb. Then, from the equations above,

$$T_2 = w_2 = 3 \text{ lb}, \qquad P = 7 \text{ lb}.$$

To illustrate that the resultant moment about *any* z-axis is zero, let us compute moments about an axis through point A.   Then

$$\Sigma \Gamma_z = l_1 P - (l_1 + l_2) T_2 = 3 \text{ ft} \times 7 \text{ lb} - 7 \text{ ft} \times 3 \text{ lb} = 0.$$

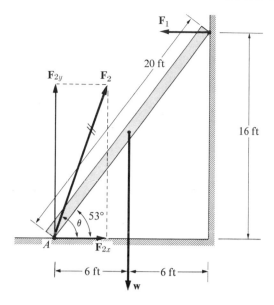

Fig. 3–8. Forces on a ladder in equilibrium, leaning against a frictionless wall.

The axis about which moments are computed need not pass through a point on the rod. To verify this, let the reader calculate the resultant moment about a z-axis through a point 1 ft to the left of A and 1 ft above it.

EXAMPLE 2.   Figure 3–8 illustrates a problem that has already been solved in Example 4 at the end of Section 2–6. A ladder 20 ft long, weighing 80 lb, with its center of gravity at its center, in equilibrium, leans against a vertical frictionless wall and makes an angle of 53° with the horizontal. We wish to find the magnitudes and directions of the forces F_1 and F_2.

If the wall is frictionless, F_1 is horizontal. The direction of F_2 is unknown (except in special cases, its direction does *not* lie along the ladder). Instead of considering its magnitude and direction as unknowns, it is simpler to resolve the force F_2 into x- and y-components and solve for these. The magnitude and direction of F_2 may then be computed. The first condition of equilibrium therefore provides the equations

$$\left. \begin{array}{l} \sum F_x = F_{2x} - F_1 = 0, \\ \sum F_y = F_{2y} - 80 \text{ lb} - 0. \end{array} \right\} \quad \text{(1st condition)}$$

In writing the second condition, moments may be computed about an axis through any point. The resulting equation is simplest if we select a point through which two or more forces pass, since these forces then do not appear in the equation. Let us therefore take moments about an axis through point A:

$$\sum \Gamma_z = 16 \text{ ft} \times F_1 - 6 \text{ ft} \times 80 \text{ lb} = 0. \quad \text{(2nd condition)}$$

From the second equation, $F_{2y} = 80$ lb, and from the third,

$$F_1 = \frac{480 \text{ lb·ft}}{16 \text{ ft}} = 30 \text{ lb.}$$

Then from the first equation,

$$F_{2x} = 30 \text{ lb.}$$

Hence

$$F_2 = \sqrt{(80 \text{ lb})^2 + (30 \text{ lb})^2} = 85.5 \text{ lb,}$$

$$\theta = \tan^{-1}\frac{80 \text{ lb}}{30 \text{ lb}} = 69.5°.$$

This method is simpler than that used in Section 2–5, since it is unnecessary to locate the point of intersection of the concurrent forces, F_1, F_2, and w.

EXAMPLE 3.   Figure 3–9 illustrates a problem that has already been solved, in part, in Example 3 at the end of Section 2–7. (a) What force T, at an angle of 30° above the horizontal, is required to drag a block weighing 20 lb to the right at constant speed along a level surface, if the coefficient of sliding friction between block and surface is 0.20? (b) Determine the line of action of the normal force N exerted on the block by the surface. The block is 1 ft high, 2 ft long, and its center of gravity is at its center.

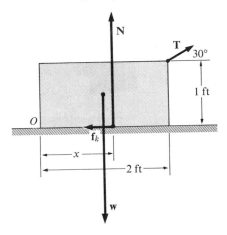

Figure 3–9

From the first condition of equilibrium,

$$\left.\begin{aligned}\Sigma F_x &= T\cos 30° - f_k = T\cos 30° - 0.2N = 0,\\ \Sigma F_y &= T\sin 30° + N - 20 \text{ lb} = 0.\end{aligned}\right\} \quad \text{(1st condition)}$$

Let x represent the distance from point O to the line of action of N, and take moments about an axis through O. Then, from the second condition of equilibrium,

$$\Sigma\Gamma_z = 2 \text{ ft} \times T\sin 30° - 1 \text{ ft} \times T\cos 30° + x \times N - 1 \text{ ft} \times 20 \text{ lb} = 0. \quad \text{(2nd condition)}$$

From the first two equations, we get

$$T = 4.15 \text{ lb}, \qquad N = 17.9 \text{ lb},$$

and from the third equation,

$$x = 1.08 \text{ ft}.$$

The line of action of **N** therefore lies 0.08 ft to the right of the center of gravity.

3–4 Resultant of parallel forces

The direction of the resultant of a set of parallel forces is the same as that of the forces, and its magnitude equals the sum of their magnitudes. A graphical method for finding the *line of action* of the resultant was described in Section 1–5, but it is often more convenient to find it from the condition that the moment of the resultant about any axis is equal to the sum of the moments of the forces about the same axis.

Consider the parallel forces F_1 and F_2 in Fig. 3–10. Point O is any arbitrary point and the x-axis has been taken at right angles to the direction of the forces. The forces have no x-components, so the magnitude of the resultant is

$$R = \Sigma F_y = F_1 + F_2.$$

If x_1 and x_2 are the perpendicular distances from O to the lines of action of the forces, the sum of their moments about a z-axis through O is

$$\Sigma \Gamma_z = x_1 F_1 + x_2 F_2.$$

Let $\bar{x}$ represent the distance from O to the line of action of the resultant. The moment of the resultant is then

$$\bar{x} R = \bar{x}(F_1 + F_2),$$

and since this equals the resultant moment, we have

$$\bar{x}(F_1 + F_2) = x_1 F_1 + x_2 F_2.$$

Therefore

$$\bar{x} = \frac{x_1 F_1 + x_2 F_2}{F_1 + F_2}.$$

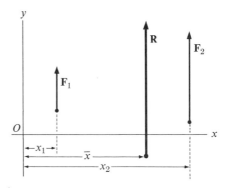

Fig. 3–10. Vector **R** represents the resultant of the parallel forces F_1 and F_2 in magnitude, direction, and line of action.

The resultant of any number of parallel forces is found in the same way. The magnitude of the resultant is

$$R = \Sigma F$$

and, if the forces are perpendicular to the x-axis, the x-coordinate of its line of action is

$$\bar{x} = \frac{\Sigma x F}{\Sigma F} = \frac{\Sigma x F}{R}.$$

EXAMPLE. When a body is in equilibrium under the action of three forces, the resultant of any two is equal and opposite to the third and has the same line of action. Show that these conditions are satisfied by the three parallel forces in Fig. 3–7(b).

It was shown in Example 1 at the end of Section 3–3 that if $l_1 = 3$ ft, $l_2 = 4$ ft, and $T_1 = 4$ lb, then $T_2 = 3$ lb and $P = 7$ lb.

Let us first find the resultant of $\mathbf{T}_1$ and $\mathbf{T}_2$. Take the x-axis along the rod with origin at point A. The magnitude of the resultant is

$$R = \Sigma F = -4\,\text{lb} - 3\,\text{lb} = -7\,\text{lb}.$$

The coordinate of its line of action is

$$\bar{x} = \frac{\Sigma xF}{\Sigma F} = \frac{0 \times 4\,\text{lb} - 7\,\text{ft} \times 3\,\text{lb}}{-7\,\text{lb}} = 3\,\text{ft}.$$

Hence the resultant of $\mathbf{T}_1$ and $\mathbf{T}_2$ is equal and opposite to $\mathbf{P}$ and has the same line of action.

The resultant of $\mathbf{P}$ and $\mathbf{T}_2$ has a magnitude

$$R = \Sigma F = 7\,\text{lb} - 3\,\text{lb} = 4\,\text{lb}.$$

The coordinate of its line of action is

$$\bar{x} = \frac{\Sigma xF}{\Sigma F} = \frac{3\,\text{ft} \times 7\,\text{lb} - 7\,\text{ft} \times 3\,\text{lb}}{4\,\text{lb}} = 0,$$

so the resultant of $\mathbf{P}$ and $\mathbf{T}_2$ is equal and opposite to $\mathbf{T}_1$ and has the same line of action.

3–5 Center of gravity

Every particle of matter in a body is attracted by the earth, and the single force which we call the *weight* of the body is the resultant of all these forces of attraction. The direction of the force on each particle is toward the center of the earth, but the distance to the earth's center is so great that for all practical purposes the forces can be considered parallel to one another. Hence *the weight of a body is the resultant of a large number of parallel forces.*

Figure 3–11(a) shows a thin flat object of arbitrary shape in the xy-plane, the y-axis being vertical. Let the body be subdivided into a large number of small particles of weights w_1, w_2, etc., and let the coordinates of these particles be x_1 and y_1, x_2 and y_2, etc. The magnitude of the total weight w of the object is

$$w = w_1 + w_2 + \cdots = \Sigma w_i. \tag{3–5}$$

(The symbol Σw_i means that the subscript i is to be taken successively as 1, 2, 3, etc., the resulting terms to be summed over all values of i.)

The x-coordinate of the line of action of $\mathbf{w}$ is

$$\bar{x} = \frac{x_1 w_1 + x_2 w_2 + \cdots}{w_1 + w_2 + \cdots} = \frac{\Sigma x_i w_i}{\Sigma w_i} = \frac{\Sigma x_i w_i}{w}. \tag{3–6}$$

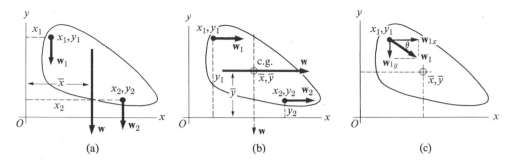

Fig. 3-11. The body's weight **w** is the resultant of a large number of parallel forces. The line of action of **w** always passes through the center of gravity.

Now let the object and the reference axes be rotated 90° clockwise or (which amounts to the same thing) let us consider the gravitational forces to be rotated 90° counterclockwise as in Fig. 3-11(b). The total weight **w** is unaltered and the y-coordinate of its line of action is

$$\bar{y} = \frac{y_1 w_1 + y_2 w_2 + \cdots}{w_1 + w_2 + \cdots} = \frac{\sum y_i w_i}{\sum w_i} = \frac{\sum y_i w_i}{w}. \qquad (3-7)$$

The point of intersection of the lines of action of **w** in Fig. 3-11(b) has the coordinates $\bar{x}$ and $\bar{y}$ and is called the *center of gravity* of the object.

The line of action of **w** always passes through the center of gravity, whatever the orientation of the object. To prove this, we show that the moment of **w** about an axis through the center of gravity is always zero. In Fig. 3-11(c), the pull of gravity makes an arbitrary angle θ with the x-axis. The weight w_1 of the particle at $x_1 y_1$ has been resolved into x- and y-components of magnitudes $w_{1x} = w_1 \cos \theta$ and $w_{1y} = w_1 \sin \theta$. The moment of w_1 about an axis through the center of gravity is

$$\Gamma_1 = (\bar{x} - x_1) w_1 \sin \theta - (y_1 - \bar{y}) w_1 \cos \theta.$$

The resultant moment of the weights of all particles is

$$\Gamma = \sum(\bar{x} - x_i) w_i \sin \theta - \sum(y_i - \bar{y}) w_i \cos \theta$$
$$= \sin \theta(\sum \bar{x} w_i - \sum x_i w_i) - \cos \theta(\sum y_i w_i - \sum \bar{y} w_i).$$

But from Eqs. (3-3) and (3-4),

$$\sum \bar{x} w_i = \sum x_i w_i, \qquad \sum y_i w_i = \sum \bar{y} w_i.$$

Hence

$$\Gamma = 0,$$

and since the resultant moment of the weight about an axis through the center of gravity is zero, the line of action of the weight must pass through the center of gravity, regardless of the value of the angle θ.

Note that the center of gravity of a body does not represent the point of application of the body's weight; all we can say is that *the line of action of the weight always passes through this point.*

All real bodies are three-dimensional, and the z-coordinate of the center of gravity is given by an expression of the same form as those above:

$$\bar{z} = \frac{z_1 w_1 + z_2 w_2 + \cdots}{w_1 + w_2 + \cdots} = \frac{\sum z_i w_i}{\sum w_i} = \frac{\sum z_i w_i}{w}. \tag{3–8}$$

If the positions of the centers of gravity of each of a number of bodies have been determined, the coordinates of the center of gravity of the combination can be computed from Eqs. (3–6) and (3–7), letting w_1, w_2, etc., be the weights of the bodies and x_1 and y_1, x_2 and y_2, etc., be the coordinates of the center of gravity of each.

Symmetry considerations are often useful in finding the position of the center of gravity. Thus the center of gravity of a homogeneous sphere, cube, circular disc, or rectangular plate is at its center. That of a cylinder or right circular cone is on the axis of symmetry, and so on.

EXAMPLE 1.   Locate the center of gravity of the machine part in Fig. 3–12, consisting of a disc 2 inches in diameter and 1 inch long, and a rod 1 inch in diameter and 6 inches long, constructed of a homogeneous material.

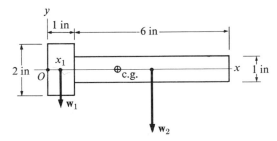

Figure 3–12

By symmetry, the center of gravity lies on the axis and the center of gravity of each part is midway between its ends. The volume of the disc is π in³ and that of the rod is $3\pi/2$ in³. Since the weights of the two parts are proportional to their volumes,

$$\frac{w \, (\text{disc})}{w \, (\text{rod})} = \frac{w_1}{w_2} = \frac{\pi}{3\pi/2} = \frac{2}{3}.$$

Take the origin O at the left face of the disc, on the axis. Then $x_1 = 0.5$ in., $x_2 = 4.0$ in., and

$$\bar{x} = \frac{0.5 \text{ in.} \times w_1 + 4.0 \text{ in.} \times \frac{3}{2}w_1}{w_1 + \frac{3}{2}w_1} = 2.6 \text{ in.}$$

The center of gravity is on the axis, 2.6 in. to the right of O.

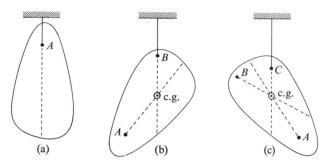

Fig. 3–13.   Method of locating the center of gravity of a flat object.

The center of gravity of a flat object can be located experimentally as shown in Fig. 3–13.   In part (a) the body is suspended from some arbitrary point A.   When allowed to come to equilibrium, the center of gravity must lie on a vertical line through A.   When the object is suspended from a second point B, as in part (b), the center of gravity lies on a vertical line through B and hence lies at the point of intersection of this line and the first.   If the object is now suspended from a third point C, as in part (c), a vertical line through C will be found to pass through the point of intersection of the first two lines.

3–6 Couples

It often happens that the forces on a body reduce to two forces of equal magnitude and opposite direction, having lines of action which are parallel but which do not coincide.   Such a pair of forces was introduced in Section 1–7 and is called a *couple*. A common example is afforded by the forces on a compass needle in the earth's magnetic field.   The north and south poles of the needle are acted on by equal forces, one toward the north and the other toward the south, as shown in Fig. 3–14.   Except when the needle points in the N-S direction, the two forces do not have the same line of action.

Figure 3–15 shows a couple consisting of two forces $\mathbf{F}_1$ and $\mathbf{F}_2$ in the xy-plane. The magnitude of each force is F, the perpendicular distances of their lines of action from point O are x_1 and x_2, and the perpendicular distance between their action

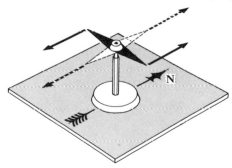

Fig. 3–14.   The forces on the poles of a compass needle form a couple.

lines is $l = x_2 - x_1$. The magnitude of the resultant **R** of the forces is

$$R = F - F = 0.$$

The fact that the resultant force is zero means that a couple has no effect in producing translation as a whole of the body on which it acts. The only effect of a couple is to produce rotation.

The vector moment of the force $\mathbf{F}_2$ points upward and its magnitude is

$$\Gamma_{z2} = x_2 F.$$

The vector moment of $\mathbf{F}_1$ points downward and its magnitude is

$$\Gamma_{z1} = x_1 F.$$

The magnitude of the resultant vector moment is

$$\Gamma_2 = \Gamma_{z2} - \Gamma_{z1} = (x_2 - x_1)F = lF.$$

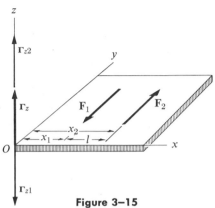

Figure 3–15

Since the distances x_1 and x_2 do not appear in the result, we conclude that *the moment of a couple is the same about all axes perpendicular to the plane of the forces forming the couple and is equal to the product of the magnitude of either force and the perpendicular distance between their lines of action.* The vector moment of a couple can accordingly be drawn through any point. In contrast to the vector representing a force, the line of action of the vector representing the moment of a couple has no physical significance.

A body acted on by a couple can be kept in equilibrium only by another couple of the same moment and in the opposite direction. As an example, the ladder in Fig. 3–8 can be considered as acted on by two couples, one formed by the forces $\mathbf{F}_{2y}$ and $\mathbf{w}$, the other by the forces $\mathbf{F}_{2x}$ and $\mathbf{F}_1$. The moment of the first couple is

$$\Gamma_1 = 6 \text{ ft} \times 80 \text{ lb} = 480 \text{ lb·ft.}$$

The moment of the second couple is

$$\Gamma_2 = 16 \text{ ft} \times 30 \text{ lb} = 480 \text{ lb·ft.}$$

The first moment is clockwise and the second is counterclockwise.

Problems

Section 2–6 and the note at the beginning of the problems in Chapter 2 are equally applicable to these problems. The only difference is that now we have a third "formula," $\Sigma\Gamma$ (about any axis) $= 0$.

3–1. A force F in the xy-plane has components of magnitudes F_x and F_y, respectively. The coordinates of its point of application are x,y. The magnitude of the moment of the force about the z-axis is $M_z = xF_y - yF_x$. Show that this equation is correct if the point x,y lies in any one of the four quadrants, and also that it is correct if the direction of the force F is in any one of the four quadrants.

3–2. You are given (a) a meter stick through which a number of holes have been bored so that its center of gravity is not at its center, (b) a knife edge on which the meter stick can be pivoted, (c) a body whose weight is known to be w, and (d) a spool of thread. Using this equipment only, explain with the aid of a diagram how you would determine the weight of the meter stick.

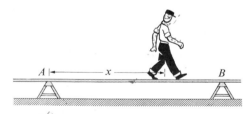

Figure 3–16

3–3. A uniform plank 30 ft long, weighing 80 lb, rests symmetrically on two supports 16 ft apart, as shown in Fig. 3–16. A boy weighing 128 lb starts at point A and walks toward the right. (a) Construct in the same diagram two graphs showing the upward forces F_A and F_B exerted on the plank at points A and B, as functions of the coordinate x of the boy. Let 1 inch $= 50$ lb vertically, and 1 inch $= 5$ ft horizontally. (b) Find from your diagram how far beyond point B the boy can walk before the plank tips. (c) How far from

the right end of the plank should support B be placed in order that the boy can just walk to the end of the plank without causing it to tip?

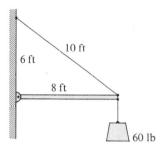

Figure 3–17

3–4. The strut in Fig. 3–17 weighs 40 lb and its center of gravity is at its center. Find (a) the tension in the cable and (b) the horizontal and vertical components of the force exerted on the strut at the wall.

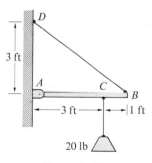

Figure 3–18

3–5. Find the tension in the cable BD in Fig. 3–18, and the horizontal and vertical components of the force exerted on the strut AB at pin A, (a) by using the first and second conditions of equilibrium $(\Sigma F_x = 0, \Sigma F_y = 0, \Sigma\Gamma = 0)$, taking moments about an axis through point A perpendicular to the plane of the diagram, and (b) by using the second condition of equilibrium only, taking moments first about an axis through A, then about an axis through B, and finally about an axis through D. The weight of the strut can be neglected. (c) Represent the computed forces by vectors in a diagram drawn to scale, and show that the lines of action of the forces exerted on the strut at points A, B, and C intersect at a common point.

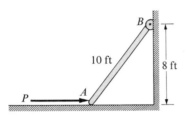

Figure 3–19

✷ 3–6. End A of the bar AB in Fig. 3–19 rests on a frictionless horizontal surface, while end B is hinged. A horizontal force P of 12 lb is exerted on end A. Neglect the weight of the bar. What are the horizontal and vertical components of the force exerted by the bar on the hinge at B?

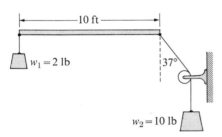

Figure 3–20

✷ 3–7. A single force is to be applied to the bar in Fig. 3–20 to maintain it in equilibrium in the position shown. The weight of the bar can be neglected. (a) What are the x- and y-components of the required force? (b) What is the tangent of the angle which the force must make with the bar? (c) What is the magnitude of the required force? (d) Where should the force be applied?

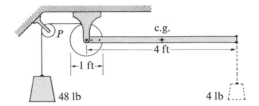

Figure 3–21

3–8. A circular disk 1 ft in diameter, pivoted about a horizontal axis through its center, has a cord wrapped around its rim. The cord passes over a frictionless pulley P and is attached to a body of weight 48 lb. A uniform rod 4 ft long is fastened to the disk with one end at the center of the disk   The apparatus is in equilibrium, with the rod horizontal, as shown in Fig. 3–21. (a) What is the weight of the rod? (b) What is the new equilibrium direction of the rod when a second body weighing 4 lb is suspended from the outer end of the rod, as shown by the dotted line?

3–9. A roller whose diameter is 20 in. weighs 72 lb.   What horizontal force is necessary to pull the roller over a brick 2 in. high when (a) the force is applied at the center, (b) at the top?

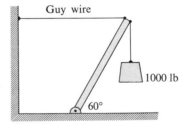

Figure 3–22

3–10. The boom in Fig. 3–22 is uniform and weighs 500 lb. Find the tension in the guy wire, and the horizontal and vertical components of the force exerted on the boom at its lower end.

3–11. Two ladders, 20 ft and 15 ft long, respectively, are hinged at point A and tied together by a horizontal rope 3 ft above the floor, as in Fig. 3–23.   The

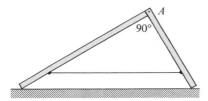

Figure 3–23

ladders weigh 80 lb and 60 lb, respectively, and the center of gravity of each is at its center. If the floor is frictionless, find (a) the upward force at the bottom of each ladder, (b) the tension in the rope, and (c) the force which one ladder exerts on the other at point *A*. (d) If a load of 200 lb is now suspended from point *A*, find the tension in the rope.

3–12. A uniform ladder 20 ft long rests against a vertical frictionless wall with its lower end 12 ft from the wall. The ladder weighs 80 lb. The coefficient of static friction between the foot of the ladder and the ground is 0.40. A man weighing 160 lb climbs slowly up the ladder. (a) What is the maximum frictional force which the ground can exert on the ladder at its lower end? (b) What is the actual frictional force when the man has climbed 10 ft along the ladder? (c) How far along the ladder can the man climb before the ladder starts to slip?

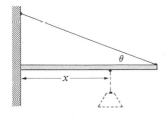

Figure 3–24

3–13. One end of a meter stick is placed against a vertical wall, as in Fig. 3–24. The other end is held by a light cord making an angle θ with the stick. The coefficient of static friction between the end of the meter stick and the wall is 0.30.

(a) What is the maximum value the angle θ can have if the stick is to remain in equilibrium? (b) Let the angle θ be 10°. A body of the same weight as the meter stick is suspended from the stick as shown by dotted lines, at a distance x from the wall. What is the minimum value of x for which the stick will remain in equilibrium? (c) When $\theta = 10°$, how large must the coefficient of static friction be so that the body can be attached at the left end of the stick without causing it to slip?

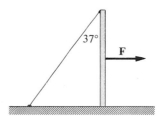

Figure 3–25

3–14. One end of a post weighing 100 lb rests on a rough horizontal surface with $\mu_s = 0.3$. The upper end is held by a rope fastened to the surface and making an angle of 37° with the post, as in Fig. 3–25. A horizontal force **F** is exerted on the post as shown. (a) If the force **F** is applied at the midpoint of the post, what is the largest value it can have without causing the post to slip? (b) How large can the force be, without causing the post to slip, if its height above the surface equals $\frac{9}{10}$ of the length of the post?

3–15. A uniform smooth rod of length l and weight w rests at equilibrium in a smooth semispherical bowl of radius R, as shown in Fig. 3–26, where $R < l/2 <$

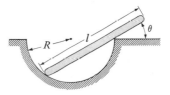

Figure 3–26

2R. If θ is the angle of equilibrium and P is the force exerted by the edge of the bowl on the rod, prove that (a) $P = (l/4R)w$, (b) $\cos 2\theta/\cos \theta = l/4R$.

3–16. A door 7 ft high and 3 ft wide is hung from hinges 6 ft apart and 6 inches from the top and bottom of the door. The door weighs 60 lb, its center of gravity is at its center, and each hinge carries half the weight of the door. Find the horizontal component of the force exerted on the door at each hinge.

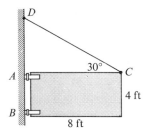

Figure 3–27

3–17. A gate 8 ft long and 4 ft high weighs 80 lb. Its center of gravity is at its center, and it is hinged at A and B. To relieve the strain on the top hinge a wire CD is connected as shown in Fig. 3–27. The tension in CD is increased until the horizontal force at hinge A is zero. (a) What is the tension in the wire CD? (b) What is the magnitude of the horizontal component of force at hinge B? (c) What is the combined vertical force exerted by hinges A and B?

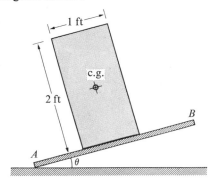

Figure 3–28

3–18. A uniform rectangular block, 2 ft high and 1 ft wide, rests on a plank AB, as in Fig. 3–28. The coefficient of static friction between block and plank is 0.40. (a) In a diagram drawn to scale, show the line of action of the resultant normal force exerted on the block by the plank when the angle $\theta = 15°$. (b) If end B of the plank is slowly raised, will the block start to slide down the plank before it tips over? Find the angle θ at which it starts to slide, or at which it tips. (c) What would be the answer to part (b) if the coefficient of static friction were 0.60? If it were 0.50?

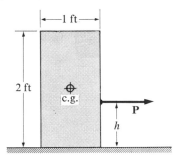

Figure 3–29

3–19. A rectangular block 1 ft wide and 2 ft high is dragged to the right along a level surface at constant speed by a horizontal force $\mathbf{P}$, as shown in Fig. 3–29. The coefficient of sliding friction is 0.40, the block weighs 50 lb, and its center of gravity is at its center. (a) Find the magnitude of the force $\mathbf{P}$. (b) Find the position of the line of action of the normal force N exerted on the block by the surface, if the height $h = 6$ inches. (c) Find the value of h at which the block just starts to tip.

⁂3–20. A garage door is mounted on an overhead rail as in Fig. 3–30. The wheels at A and B have rusted so that they do not roll, but slide along the track. The coefficient of sliding friction is 0.5. The distance between the wheels is 4 ft, and each is 1 ft in from the vertical sides of the door. The door is symmetrical and weighs 160 lb. It is pushed to the left at constant velocity by a horizontal force $\mathbf{P}$. (a) If the dis-

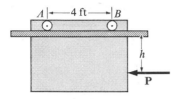

Figure 3–30

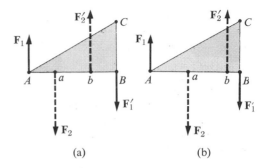

(a)   (b)

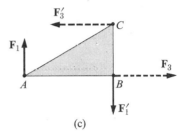

(c)

Figure 3–32

tance h is 3 ft, what is the vertical component of the force exerted on each wheel by the track? (b) Find the maximum value h can have without causing one wheel to leave the track.

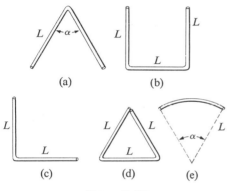

(a)   (b)

(c)   (d)   (e)

Figure 3–31

3–21. The objects in Fig. 3–31 are constructed of wire bent into the shapes shown. Find the position of the center of gravity of each.

3–22. Figure 3–32 is a top view of a triangular flat plate ABC resting on a horizontal frictionless surface. The length of side AB is 20 cm and that of CB is 15 cm. The plate is acted on by a couple consisting of the horizontal forces F_1 and F_1', each of magnitude 150 units. (a) In part (a) of the figure, the plate is kept in equilibrium by a second couple consisting of the forces F_2 and F_2'. Find the magnitude of each if the length $ab = 10$ cm. (b) Show that the plate is still in equilibrium (that is, the first and second conditions of equilibrium are satisfied) if the couple formed by F_2 and F_2' is displaced to the right, as in part (b). (c) Can equilibrium be maintained by the couple formed by the forces F_3 and F_3' in part (c) of the diagram? If so, find the magnitude of each. (d) Show in a diagram how the plate could be kept in equilibrium by a couple consisting of two forces perpendicular to side AC and applied at corners A and C. Find the magnitude of the required forces.

3–23. Where is the center of gravity of the system earth-moon?

CHAPTER 4

Rectilinear Motion. Special Relativity

4–1 Motion

At the beginning of Chapter 1 it was stated that mechanics deals with the relations of force, matter, and motion. The preceding chapters have been concerned with forces, and we are now ready to discuss the mathematical methods of describing motion. This branch of mechanics is called *kinematics*.

Motion may be defined as a *continuous change of position*. In most actual motions, different points in a body move along different paths. The complete motion is known if we know how each point in the body moves, so to begin with we consider only a moving point, or a very small body called a *particle*.

The position of a particle is conveniently specified by its projections onto the three axes of a rectangular coordinate system. As the particle moves along any path in space, its projections move in straight lines along the three axes. The actual motion can be reconstructed from the motions of these three projections, so we shall begin by discussing the motion of a single particle along a straight line, or *rectilinear motion*.

4–2 Average velocity

Consider a particle moving along the *x*-axis, as in Fig. 4–1(a). The curve in Fig. 4–1(b) is a graph of its coordinate *x* plotted as a function of time *t*. At a time t_1 the

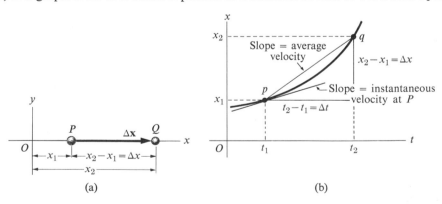

(a)   (b)

Fig. 4–1. (a) Particle moving on the *x*-axis. (b) Coordinate-time graph of the motion. The average velocity between t_1 and t_2 equals the slope of the chord *pq*. The instantaneous velocity at *p* equals the slope of the tangent at *p*.

particle is at point P in Fig. 4–1(a), where its coordinate is x_1, and at a later time t_2 it is at point Q, whose coordinate is x_2. The corresponding points on the coordinate-time graph in part (b) are lettered p and q.

The *displacement* of a particle as it moves from one point of its path to another is defined as the vector Δx drawn from the first point to the second. Thus in Fig. 4–1(a) the vector PQ, of magnitude $x_2 - x_1 = \Delta x$, is the displacement. The *average velocity* of the particle is defined as the ratio of the displacement to the time interval $t_2 - t_1 = \Delta t$. We shall represent average velocity by the symbol $\bar{\mathbf{v}}$ (the bar signifying an average value):

$$\bar{\mathbf{v}} = \frac{\Delta \mathbf{x}}{\Delta t}.$$

Average velocity is a vector, since the ratio of a vector to a scalar is itself a vector. Its direction is the same as that of the displacement vector. The *magnitude* of the average velocity is

$$\bar{v} = \frac{x_2 - x_1}{t_2 - t_1} = \frac{\Delta x}{\Delta t}. \tag{4–1}$$

In Fig. 4–1(b), the average velocity is represented by the slope of the chord pq (due allowance being made for the scales to which x and t are plotted), since the slope is the ratio of the "rise," $x_2 - x_1$ or Δx, to the "run," $t_2 - t_1$ or Δt.

Equation (4–1) can be cleared of fractions and written

$$x_2 - x_1 = \bar{v}(t_2 - t_1). \tag{4–2}$$

Since our time-measuring device can be started at any instant, we can let $t_1 = 0$ and let t_2 be any arbitrary time t. Then if x_0 is the coordinate when $t = 0$ (x_0 is called the *initial position*), and x is the coordinate at time t, Eq. (4–2) becomes

$$x - x_0 = \bar{v}t. \tag{4–3}$$

If the particle is at the origin when $t = 0$, then $x_0 = 0$ and Eq. (4–3) simplifies further to

$$x = \bar{v}t. \tag{4–4}$$

4–3 Instantaneous velocity

The velocity of a particle at some one instant of time, or at some one point of its path, is called its *instantaneous velocity*. This concept requires careful definition.

Suppose we wish to find the instantaneous velocity of the particle in Fig. 4–1 at the point P. The *average* velocity between points P and Q is associated with the entire displacement Δx, and with the entire time interval Δt. Imagine the second point Q to be taken closer and closer to the first point P, and let the average velocity be computed over these shorter and shorter displacements and time intervals. The instantaneous velocity at the first point can then be defined as the *limiting value* of the average velocity when the second point is taken closer and closer to the first. Although the displacement then becomes extremely small, the time interval by which it must be divided becomes small also and the quotient is not necessarily a small quantity.

In the Leibniz notation of calculus, the limiting value of $\Delta x/\Delta t$, as Δt approaches zero, is written dx/dt and is called the *derivative* of x with respect to t. Then if **v** represents the instantaneous velocity, its magnitude v is

$$v = \lim_{\Delta t \to 0} \frac{\Delta x}{\Delta t} = \frac{dx}{dt}. \qquad (4\text{–}5)$$

That is, the *velocity* is the *time rate of change of coordinate.*

Instantaneous velocity is also a vector, whose direction is the limiting direction of the displacement vector $\Delta \mathbf{x}$. Since Δt is necessarily positive, it follows that v has the same algebraic sign as Δx. Hence a positive velocity indicates motion toward the right along the x-axis, if we use the usual convention of signs.

As point Q approaches point P in Fig. 4–1(a), point q approaches point p in Fig. 4–1(b). In the limit, the slope of the chord pq equals the slope of the *tangent* to the curve at point p, due allowance being made for the scales to which x and t are plotted. *The instantaneous velocity at any point of a coordinate-time graph therefore equals the slope of the tangent to the graph at that point.* If the tangent slopes upward to the right, its slope is positive, the velocity is positive, and the motion is toward the right. If the tangent slopes downward to the right, the velocity is negative. At a point where the tangent is horizontal, its slope is zero and the velocity is zero.

If the unit of length is 1 meter and the unit of time is 1 second, the unit of velocity is 1 *meter per second* (1 m/sec). In the engineering system, the unit of velocity is 1 *foot per second* (1 ft/sec). Other common units are 1 *centimeter per second* (1 cm/sec), 1 *mile per hour* (1 mi/hr), and 1 *knot* (1 knot = 1 nautical mile per hour).

The term *speed* has two different meanings. It is sometimes used to mean the *magnitude* of the instantaneous velocity. In this sense, two automobiles traveling at 50 mi/hr, one north and the other south, are both said to have a speed of 50 mi/hr. In another sense, the *average speed* of a body means the total length of path covered, divided by the elapsed time. Thus if an automobile travels a total distance of 90 miles in 3 hours, its average speed is said to be 30 mi/hr even if the trip starts and ends at the same point. The average *velocity*, in the latter case, would be zero, since the displacement is zero.

EXAMPLE. Suppose that the motion of the particle in Fig. 4–1 is described by the equation

$$x = a + bt^2,$$

where $a = 20$ cm and $b = 4$ cm/sec^2. Let $t_1 = 2$ sec and $t_2 = 3$ sec, so that the time interval $t_2 - t_1 = \Delta t = 1$ sec. The coordinate of the particle at time t_1 is

$$x_1 = 20 \text{ cm} + 4 \frac{\text{cm}}{\text{sec}^2} (2 \text{ sec})^2 = 36 \text{ cm}.$$

At time t_2, the coordinate is

$$x_2 = 20 \text{ cm} + 4 \frac{\text{cm}}{\text{sec}^2} (3 \text{ sec})^2 = 56 \text{ cm}.$$

The displacement in the time interval is

$$x_2 - x_1 = \Delta x = 56 \text{ cm} - 36 \text{ cm} = 20 \text{ cm},$$

and the average velocity is

$$\bar{v} = \frac{\Delta x}{\Delta t} = \frac{20 \text{ cm}}{1 \text{ sec}} = 20 \frac{\text{cm}}{\text{sec}}.$$

This corresponds to the slope of the chord pq in Fig. 4–1(b).

If the time interval is shortened from 1 sec to 0.1 sec, so that $t_2 = 2.1$ sec,

$$x_2 = 20 \text{ cm} + 4 \frac{\text{cm}}{\text{sec}^2} (2.1 \text{ sec})^2 = 37.64 \text{ cm},$$

$$x_2 - x_1 = \Delta x = 1.64 \text{ cm},$$

$$\bar{v} = \frac{\Delta x}{\Delta t} = \frac{1.64 \text{ cm}}{0.1 \text{ sec}} = 16.4 \frac{\text{cm}}{\text{sec}}.$$

If the interval is reduced still further to 0.01 sec, $t_2 = 2.01$ sec, and

$$x_2 = 36.1604 \text{ cm}, \qquad \Delta x = 0.1604 \text{ cm},$$

$$\bar{v} = \frac{\Delta x}{\Delta t} = \frac{0.1604 \text{ cm}}{0.01 \text{ sec}} = 16.04 \frac{\text{cm}}{\text{sec}}.$$

As the time interval is shortened, the average velocity seems to be approaching a limit of exactly 16 cm/sec. To verify this, we calculate the instantaneous velocity at time $t = 2$ sec:

$$v = \frac{dx}{dt} = \frac{d}{dt} (a + bt^2) = 2bt,$$

and when $t = 2$ sec:

$$v = 2 \times 4 \frac{\text{cm}}{\text{sec}^2} \times 2 \text{ sec} = 16 \frac{\text{cm}}{\text{sec}}.$$

This corresponds to the slope of the tangent at point p in Fig. 4–1(b).

From the purely mathematical viewpoint, there is no restriction on the values that may be assigned to t in an equation such as $x = a + bt^2$. In practically all physical problems, however, the equation that expresses the coordinate of a particle as a function of time is valid only within a certain time interval, or over a certain *domain* of the quantity t. For example, if a ball is thrown vertically upward and strikes the earth 10 sec later, and if we set $t = 0$ at the instant the ball is thrown, the equation giving its height as a function of t is valid only in the domain of t from $t = 0$ to $t = 10$ sec.

4–4 Average and instantaneous acceleration

Except in certain special cases, the velocity of a moving body changes continuously as the motion proceeds. When this is the case the body is said to move with *accelerated motion*, or to have an *acceleration*.

Figure 4–2(a) shows a particle moving along the x-axis. The vector $\mathbf{v}_1$ represents its instantaneous velocity at point P, and the vector $\mathbf{v}_2$ represents its instantaneous velocity at point Q. Figure 4–2(b) is a graph of the instantaneous velocity v plotted as a function of time, points p and q corresponding to P and Q in part (a).

The *average acceleration* of the particle as it moves from P to Q is defined as the ratio of the change in velocity to the elapsed time.

$$\bar{\mathbf{a}} = \frac{\mathbf{v}_2 - \mathbf{v}_1}{t_2 - t_1} = \frac{\Delta \mathbf{v}}{\Delta t}, \qquad (4\text{–}6)$$

where t_1 and t_2 are the times corresponding to the velocities $\mathbf{v}_1$ and $\mathbf{v}_2$. Since $\mathbf{v}_1$ and $\mathbf{v}_2$ are vectors, the quantity $\mathbf{v}_2 - \mathbf{v}_1$ is a *vector difference* and must be found by the methods explained in Section 1–10. However, since in rectilinear motion both vectors lie in the same straight line, the magnitude of the vector difference in this special case equals the difference between the magnitudes of the vectors. The more general case, in which $\mathbf{v}_1$ and $\mathbf{v}_2$ are not in the same direction, will be considered in Chapter 6.

In Fig. 4–2(b), the magnitude of the average acceleration is represented by the slope of the chord pq.

The *instantaneous acceleration* of a body, that is, its acceleration at some one instant of time or at some one point of its path, is defined in the same way as instantaneous velocity. Let the second point Q in Fig. 4–2(a) be taken closer and closer to the first point P, and let the average acceleration be computed over shorter and shorter intervals of time. The instantaneous acceleration at the first point is defined as the limiting value of the average acceleration when the second point is taken closer and closer to the first:

$$\boxed{a = \lim_{\Delta t \to 0} \frac{\Delta v}{\Delta t} = \frac{dv}{dt}.} \qquad (4\text{–}7)$$

That is, the *acceleration* is the *time rate of change of velocity*.

The direction of the instantaneous acceleration is the limiting direction of the vector change in velocity, $\Delta \mathbf{v}$.

Instantaneous acceleration plays an important part in the laws of mechanics. Average acceleration is less frequently used. Hence from now on when the term "acceleration" is used we shall understand it to mean instantaneous acceleration.

The definition of acceleration just given applies to motion along any path, straight or curved. When a particle moves in a curved path the *direction* of its velocity changes and this change in direction also gives rise to an acceleration, as will be explained in Chapter 6.

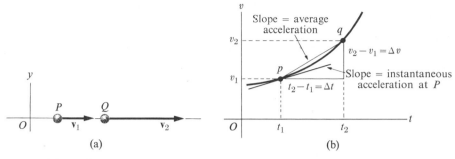

Fig. 4–2. (a) Particle moving on the x-axis. (b) Velocity-time graph of the motion. The average acceleration between t_1 and t_2 equals the slope of the chord pq. The instantaneous acceleration at p equals the slope of the tangent at p.

As point Q approaches point P in Fig. 4–2(a), point q approaches point p in Fig. 4–2(b) and the slope of the chord pq approaches the slope of the tangent to the velocity-time graph at point p. *The instantaneous acceleration at any point of the graph therefore equals the slope of the tangent to the graph at that point.*

Since $v = dx/dt$, it follows that

$$a = \frac{dv}{dt} = \frac{d}{dt}\left(\frac{dx}{dt}\right) = \frac{d^2x}{dt^2}.$$

The acceleration is therefore the *second* derivative of the coordinate with respect to time.

If the unit of velocity is 1 meter per second and the unit of time is 1 second, the unit of acceleration is 1 meter per second per second (1 m/sec/sec). This is usually written as 1 m/sec², and is read "meter per second squared." Other common units of acceleration are 1 foot per second squared (1 ft/sec²) and 1 centimeter per second squared (1 cm/scc²).

When the absolute value of the magnitude of the velocity of a body is decreasing (in other words, when the body is slowing down), the body is said to be *decelerated* or to have a *deceleration*.

EXAMPLE. Suppose that the velocity of the particle in Fig. 4–2 is given by the equation

$$v = m + nt^2,$$

where $m = 10$ cm/sec and $n = 2$ cm/sec³. Let $t_1 = 2$ sec and $t_2 = 5$ sec. The velocity at time t_1 is

$$v_1 = 10\,\frac{\text{cm}}{\text{sec}} + 2\,\frac{\text{cm}}{\text{sec}^3} \times (2\ \text{sec})^2 = 18\,\frac{\text{cm}}{\text{sec}}.$$

The velocity at time t_2 is

$$v_2 = 10\,\frac{\text{cm}}{\text{sec}} + 2\,\frac{\text{cm}}{\text{sec}^3}\,(5\ \text{sec})^2 = 60\,\frac{\text{cm}}{\text{sec}}.$$

The average acceleration in this time interval is

$$\bar{a} = \frac{v_2 - v_1}{t_2 - t_1} = \frac{\Delta v}{\Delta t} = \frac{42 \text{ cm/sec}}{3 \text{ sec}} = 14 \frac{\text{cm}}{\text{sec}^2}.$$

This corresponds to the slope of the chord pq in Fig. 4–2(b).
  The instantaneous acceleration at any time t is

$$a = \frac{dv}{dt} = \frac{d}{dt}(m + nt^2) = 2nt,$$

and when $t = t_1 = 2$ sec,

$$a = 2 \times 2 \frac{\text{cm}}{\text{sec}^3} \times 2 \text{ sec} = 8 \frac{\text{cm}}{\text{sec}^2}.$$

This corresponds to the slope of the tangent at point p in Fig. 4–2(b).

  In the preceding discussion, we have considered the coordinate x, the velocity v, and the acceleration a to be functions of the time t.   That is, as shown schematically in Fig. 4–3, to every value of t within a certain domain, there correspond values of x, v, and a.   It follows that to every value of the coordinate x there correspond values of v and a, so that the velocity and acceleration are functions of x as well as of t. Similarly, the acceleration a is a function of v as well as of x and t. (Except in special cases, the *forms* of these functions are all different.)   Each of the four quantities in Fig. 4–3 thus has a derivative with respect to each of the others, although *names* are given only to the derivatives dx/dt (the velocity) and dv/dt (the acceleration).   An important relation between these derivatives can be obtained by applying the chain rule to the acceleration:

$$a = \frac{dv}{dt} = \frac{dv}{dx}\frac{dx}{dt}.$$

  But dx/dt equals the velocity v, so

$$a = v \frac{dv}{dx}, \qquad (4\text{–}8)$$

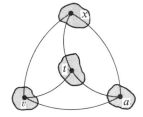

Fig. 4–3.   Each of the quantities x, v, a, and t is a function of each of the others.

which expresses the acceleration in terms of the velocity v and its *space* rate of change, dv/dx.

  EXAMPLE.   Suppose that the velocity of a particle moving on the x-axis is given by $v = k \ln x$, where k is a constant.   Then

$$\frac{dv}{dx} = \frac{k}{x},$$

and the acceleration, expressed as a function of x, is

$$a = v \frac{dv}{dx} = k^2 \frac{\ln x}{x}.$$

4–5 Velocity and coordinate by integration

If the coordinate of a particle moving on the x-axis is given as a function of time, the velocity can be found by differentiation, from the definition $v = dx/dt$. A second differentiation gives the acceleration, since $a = dv/dt$. We now consider the converse process: given the acceleration, to find the velocity and the coordinate. This can be done by the methods of *integral* calculus. We shall discuss first the indefinite and then the definite integral.

Suppose that we are given the acceleration as a function of time,* that is, $a = a(t)$. Since the acceleration is the derivative of the velocity with respect to time, the velocity is a *primitive* or *antiderivative* of the acceleration. In the notation of Leibniz, we write

$$\frac{dv}{dt} = a(t),$$

$$dv = a(t)\, dt,$$

$$v = \int a(t)\, dt + C_1, \tag{4–9}$$

where C_1 is an arbitrary constant.

When the integral above has been evaluated, we have expressed the velocity v as a function of t, or, $v = v(t)$. But the velocity is the derivative of the coordinate with respect to time, so the coordinate is an antiderivative of the velocity. Thus

$$\frac{dx}{dt} = v(t),$$

$$dx = v(t)\, dt,$$

$$x = \int v(t)\, dt + C_2, \tag{4–10}$$

where C_2 is a second arbitrary constant. Evaluation of the integral then leads to the expression for the coordinate x as a function of time, or, $x = x(t)$.

If the acceleration is given as a function of x, we can use Eq. (4–8):

$$v\frac{dv}{dx} = a(x),$$

$$\int v\, dv = \int a(x)\, dx,$$

$$\frac{v^2}{2} = \int a(x)\, dx + C_3. \tag{4–11}$$

---

* A question of notation arises here. In mathematics, one writes $a = f(t)$, not $a = a(t)$. But as shown in Fig. 4–3, there are six functional relationships between the quantities x, v, a, and t, and the symbol $f(t)$ standing alone does not make it clear whether one is considering x, v, or a as a function of t. Also, if one were to write $a = f(t)$ and also $a = f(x)$, it is not clear that the *form* of the function $f(t)$ is different from that of the function $f(x)$. We shall therefore depart from the mathematical nomenclature and instead of writing $\int f(t)\, dt$ we will write $\int a(t)\, dt$, or sometimes for brevity merely $\int a\, dt$. The reader should understand that to evaluate the integral, $a(t)$ or a is to be replaced by the appropriate function of t. In the same way, in an integral such as $\int v(x)\, dx$ or $\int v\, dx$, one is to replace $v(x)$ or v by the appropriate function of x.

If the acceleration is given as a function of the velocity, we may proceed in either of two ways:

(1)

$$\frac{dv}{dt} = a(v),$$

$$\int \frac{dv}{a(v)} = t + C_4, \qquad (4\text{–}12)$$

or (2)

$$v \frac{dv}{dx} = a(v),$$

$$\int \frac{v\, dv}{a(v)} = x + C_5. \qquad (4\text{–}13)$$

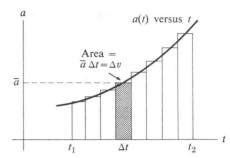

Fig. 4–4.   The interval between t_1 and t_2 is subdivided into strips of width Δt, and a step function is constructed whose height in each interval equals the average acceleration $\bar{a}$ in that interval.

We consider next the definite integral. Suppose first that the acceleration a is given as a function of time, and let the curve in Fig. 4–4 be the graph of a versus t. Let the interval between times t_1 and t_2 be subdivided into strips of width Δt, and construct the *step function* whose height, in each interval, equals the average acceleration $\bar{a}$ in that interval. The change in velocity Δv, in each interval, equals the product of the average acceleration $\bar{a}$ and the time interval Δt,

$$\Delta v = \bar{a}\, \Delta t,$$

and this in turn equals the *area* of the corresponding rectangle, such as the one shaded.

Let v_1 and v_2 be the velocities at times t_1 and t_2. The *total* change in velocity, between t_1 and t_2, equals the sum of the changes in each interval. That is,

$$v_2 - v_1 = \sum \Delta v = \sum \bar{a}\, \Delta t.$$

The sum $\sum \bar{a}\, \Delta t$ equals the *total area* under the step function.

Now let the time intervals be taken shorter and shorter, so that $\Delta t \to 0$. The change in velocity is still equal to the sum of the Δv's, so

$$v_2 - v_1 = \lim_{\Delta t \to 0} \sum \bar{a}\, \Delta t.$$

But the limit of the sum $\sum \bar{a}\, \Delta t$ equals the definite integral of $a\, dt$ between the limits of t_1 and t_2, and this in turn equals the area under the graph of a versus t. Therefore

$$v_2 - v_1 = \int_{t_1}^{t_2} a\, dt. \qquad (4\text{–}14)$$

That is, *the change in velocity, in any time interval, is equal to the area between an acceleration-time graph and the time axis*, bounded by vertical lines at the beginning and end of the interval.

In the same way, the area under a velocity-time graph can be subdivided into vertical strips of width Δt, and a step function constructed whose height, in each interval, equals the average velocity $\bar{v}$ in that interval. The displacement Δx, in each interval, equals the product of the average velocity $\bar{v}$ and the time interval Δt, and the total displacement $x_2 - x_1$ during the interval from t_1 to t_2 equals the sum of the changes in each interval:

$$x_2 - x_1 = \sum \Delta x = \sum \bar{v} \, \Delta t.$$

In the limit, as $\Delta t \to 0$, the sum becomes equal to the integral of $v \, dt$ between t_1 and t_2, and equal to the area under the velocity-time graph. Thus

$$x_2 - x_1 = \int_{t_1}^{t_2} v \, dt. \qquad (4\text{--}15)$$

The displacement in any time interval is therefore equal to the area between a velocity-time graph and the time axis, bounded by vertical lines at the beginning and end of the interval.

This method of finding displacements is most useful when a particle moves in some arbitrary way, as in the graph of Fig. 4–5. Its total displacement in the time interval from t_1 to t_2 is the *algebraic* sum of the shaded areas, where an area above the axis is considered positive and one below the axis, negative. (When the velocity graph lies above the axis the particle is moving to the right; when it lies below the axis the particle is moving to the left.) We cannot write any simple algebraic expression for the velocity or the area, but if the graph is plotted on cross-section paper, the *area* can be found with reasonable precision by counting squares and estimating fractions of a square.

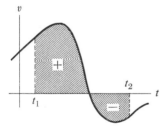

Fig. 4–5. The total displacement in the time interval $t_2 - t_1$ is the *algebraic* sum of the shaded areas.

These principles are at the basis of *inertial navigation.* An instrument called an *accelerometer* in an aircraft or a submarine measures the acceleration at each instant. This information is fed to a computer which, in effect, measures the area under the *a-t* graph and gives the velocity at each instant. A second computer then measures the area under the *v-t* graph and thus determines the distance moved.

If the acceleration is given as a function of x, we proceed as follows. The change in velocity in a time interval Δt is

$$\Delta v = \bar{a} \, \Delta t.$$

Also, since the displacement $\Delta x = \bar{v}\,\Delta t$, the time interval $\Delta t = \Delta x/\bar{v}$, and hence

$$\Delta v = \bar{a}\,\frac{\Delta x}{\bar{v}}, \qquad \text{or} \qquad \bar{v}\,\Delta v = \bar{a}\,\Delta x.$$

When both sides are summed over any interval, we get $\sum \bar{v}\,\Delta v = \sum \bar{a}\,\Delta x$.

In the limit, as the intervals Δv and Δx approach zero, the sums become integrals and

$$\int_{v_1}^{v_2} v\,dv = \int_{x_1}^{x_2} a\,dx. \tag{4–16}$$

The same relation can be obtained from Eq. (4–8), writing it as

$$v\,dv = a\,dx$$

and then integrating both sides between the appropriate limits.

The integral on the right side of Eq. (4–16) can be evaluated only when a is known as a function of x. The left-hand side, however, can always be evaluated, and we have

$$\tfrac{1}{2}v_2^2 - \tfrac{1}{2}v_1^2 = \int_{x_1}^{x_2} a\,dx. \tag{4–17}$$

4–6 Uniformly accelerated motion

The simplest type of accelerated motion is that in which the acceleration is *constant*, and is referred to as *uniformly accelerated motion*. In the absence of air resistance, a body near the earth's surface falls with very nearly constant acceleration. In other instances, such as the acceleration or deceleration of an automobile, the acceleration is often nearly constant, or if not, it is often considered constant as a first approximation. If the acceleration $a = a(t) = $ constant, then from Eq. (4–9),

$$v = \int a(t)\,dt + C_1 = a \int dt + C_1 = at + C_1.$$

Although the integration constant C_1 is completely arbitrary from the purely *mathematical* viewpoint, if our equation is to describe some particular *physical* problem, we must select from all possible values of C_1 the particular value that fits our problem. It is *customary*, although not *necessary*, to express C_1 in terms of the velocity v_0 at the time $t = 0$. The velocity v_0 is called the *initial velocity*. When we substitute $v = v_0$ and $t = 0$ in the preceding equation, we find that $C_1 = v_0$. Hence this equation is usually written as

$$v = v_0 + at. \tag{4–18}$$

We now have the velocity as a function of time, $v = v(t) = v_0 + at$, so from Eq. (4–10),

$$x = \int v(t)\,dt + C_2 = \int (v_0 + at)\,dt + C_2$$

$$= v_0 \int dt + a \int t\,dt + C_2 = v_0 t + \tfrac{1}{2}at^2 + C_2,$$

where C_2 is a second integration constant. Let x_0 (the *initial position*) be the coordinate at time $t = 0$. Then $C_2 = x_0$ and

$$x = x_0 + v_0 t + \tfrac{1}{2} a t^2. \tag{4-19}$$

The acceleration can also be considered as a function of x: $a = a(x) = $ constant. Then from Eq. (4–11),

$$\int v \, dv = \int a(x) \, dx + C_3 = a \int dx + C_3, \qquad \frac{v^2}{2} = ax + C_3.$$

If v_0 is the velocity when $x = x_0$, then

$$C_3 = \frac{v_0^2}{2} - ax_0$$

and

$$\frac{v^2}{2} = ax + \frac{v_0^2}{2} - ax_0,$$

$$v^2 = v_0^2 + 2a(x - x_0), \tag{4-20}$$

which expresses v as a function of x. This equation can also be obtained algebraically by eliminating t between Eqs. (4–18) and (4–19).

Thus for the special case in which

$$a = a(t) = a(x) = \text{constant},$$

we have found that

$$v = v(t) = v_0 + at, \tag{4-18}$$

$$x = x(t) = x_0 + v_0 t + \tfrac{1}{2} a t^2, \tag{4-19}$$

$$v = v(x) = \sqrt{v_0^2 + 2a(x - x_0)},$$

or

$$v^2 = v_0^2 + 2a(x - x_0). \tag{4-20}$$

The preceding equations are the *equations of motion with constant acceleration*. They can also be derived using the definite integral. Thus in Eq. (4–14) let $t_1 = 0$, $t_2 = t$, $v_1 = v_0$, and $v_2 = v$. Then if a is constant,

$$v - v_0 = at,$$

which is Eq. (4–18). Similarly, we have from Eq. (4–15),

$$x - x_0 = \int_0^t (v_0 + at) \, dt = v_0 t + \tfrac{1}{2} a t^2,$$

which is Eq. (4–19). Equation (4–16) yields

$$\tfrac{1}{2} v^2 - \tfrac{1}{2} v_0^2 = a(x - x_0),$$

which is Eq. (4–20).

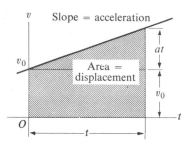

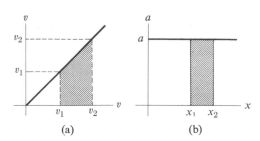

Fig. 4–6. Velocity-time graph of uniformly accelerated motion.

Fig. 4–7. Graphs to show that (a) $\int_{v_1}^{v_2} v \, dv$ equals (b) $\int_{x_1}^{x_2} a \, dx$.

The methods of calculus are not necessary to derive the equations of motion with constant acceleration. We begin by constructing the velocity-time graph of Fig. 4–6. Let v_0 be the velocity at time $t = 0$. The *acceleration* equals the *slope* of a v-t graph, and if the acceleration is *constant*, the slope is constant. That is, the graph is a straight line of constant slope a. The general equation of a straight line has the form $y = mx + b$, which becomes in this case

$$v = at + v_0.$$

The *displacement* equals the *area* under a v-t graph. In Fig. 4–6, this area is subdivided into a rectangle and a triangle. The area of the rectangle is $v_0 t$ and that of the triangle is $\frac{1}{2} \times t \times at = \frac{1}{2}at^2$. Hence the displacement is

$$x - x_0 = v_0 t + \tfrac{1}{2}at^2.$$

Equation (4–16) means that the area under a graph of v versus v equals that under a graph of a versus x. As shown in Fig. 4–7, the area under the graph (a) equals $\frac{1}{2}v_2^2 - \frac{1}{2}v_1^2$, and that under graph (b), if a is constant, equals $a(x_2 - x_1)$. Hence

$$\tfrac{1}{2}v_2^2 - \tfrac{1}{2}v_1^2 = a(x_2 - x_1).$$

4–7 Freely falling bodies

The most common example of motion with (nearly) constant acceleration is that of a body falling toward the earth. In the absence of air resistance it is found that all bodies, regardless of their size or weight, fall with the same acceleration at the same point on the earth's surface, and if the distance covered is not too great, the acceleration remains constant throughout the fall. The effect of air resistance and the decrease in acceleration with altitude will be neglected. This idealized motion is spoken of as "free fall," although the term includes rising as well as falling.

The acceleration of a freely falling body is called the acceleration due to gravity, or the acceleration of gravity, and is denoted by the letter g. At or near the earth's surface its magnitude is approximately 32 ft/sec², 9.8 m/sec², or 980 cm/sec². More precise values, and small variations with latitude and elevation, will be considered later.

NOTE. The quantity "g" is sometimes referred to simply as "gravity," or as "the force of gravity," both of which are incorrect. "Gravity" is a phenomenon, and the "force of gravity" means the force with which the earth attracts a body, otherwise known as the weight of the body. The letter "g" represents the *acceleration* caused by the force resulting from the phenomenon of gravity.

———————————

EXAMPLE 1. A body is released from rest and falls freely. Compute its position and velocity after 1, 2, 3, and 4 seconds. Take the origin O at the elevation of the starting point, the y-axis vertical, and the upward direction as positive.

The initial coordinate y_0 and the initial velocity v_0 are both zero. The acceleration is downward, in the negative y-direction, so $a = -g = -32$ ft/sec^2.

From Eqs. (4–19) and (4–18),

$$y = v_0 t + \tfrac{1}{2}at^2 = 0 - \tfrac{1}{2}gt^2$$

$$= -16\frac{\text{ft}}{\text{sec}^2} \times t^2,$$

$$v = v_0 + at = 0 - gt$$

$$= -32\frac{\text{ft}}{\text{sec}^2} \times t.$$

When $t = 1$ sec,

$$y = -16\frac{\text{ft}}{\text{sec}^2} \times 1\ \text{sec}^2 = -16\ \text{ft},$$

$$v = -32\frac{\text{ft}}{\text{sec}^2} \times 1\ \text{sec} = -32\frac{\text{ft}}{\text{sec}}.$$

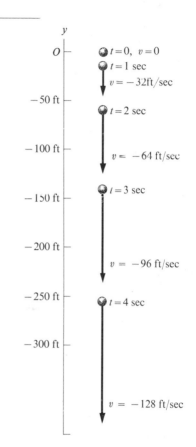

Fig. 4–8. Position and velocity of a freely falling body.

The body is therefore 16 ft below the origin (y is negative) and has a downward velocity (v is negative) of magnitude 32 ft/sec.

The position and velocity at 2, 3, and 4 sec are found in the same way. The results are illustrated in Fig. 4–8.

EXAMPLE 2. A ball is thrown (nearly) vertically upward from the cornice of a tall building, leaving the thrower's hand with a speed of 48 ft/sec and just missing the cornice on the way down. (See Fig. 4–9. The dotted line does not represent the actual path of the body.) Find (a) the position and velocity of the ball, 1 sec and 4 sec after leaving the thrower's hand; (b) the velocity when the ball is 20 ft above its starting point; (c) the maximum height reached and the time at which it is reached. Take the origin at the elevation at which the ball leaves the thrower's hand, the y-axis vertical and positive upward.

The initial position y_0 is zero. The initial velocity v_0 is $+48$ ft/sec, and the acceleration is -32 ft/sec^2.   The velocity at any time is

$$v = v_0 + at = 48 \frac{\text{ft}}{\text{sec}} - 32 \frac{\text{ft}}{\text{sec}^2} \times t. \quad (4\text{--}21)$$

The coordinate at any time is

$$y = v_0 t + \tfrac{1}{2}at^2 = 48 \frac{\text{ft}}{\text{sec}} \times t - 16 \frac{\text{ft}}{\text{sec}^2} \times t^2.$$

The velocity at any coordinate is

$$v^2 = v_0^2 + 2ay = \left(48 \frac{\text{ft}}{\text{sec}}\right)^2 - 64 \frac{\text{ft}}{\text{sec}^2} \times y.$$
$$(4\text{--}22)$$

(a) When $t = 1$ sec,

$$y = +32 \text{ ft}, \qquad v = +16 \frac{\text{ft}}{\text{sec}}.$$

The ball is 32 ft above the origin (y is positive) and it has an upward velocity (v is positive) of 16 ft/sec.   When $t = 4$ sec,

$$y = -64 \text{ ft}, \qquad v = -80 \frac{\text{ft}}{\text{sec}}.$$

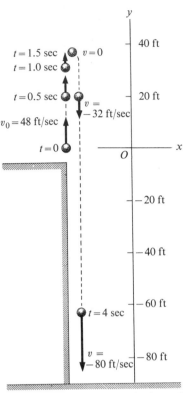

Fig. 4–9. Position and velocity of a body thrown vertically upward.

The ball has passed its highest point and is 64 ft *below* the origin (y is negative).   It has a *downward* velocity (v is negative) of magnitude 80 ft/sec.   Note that it is not necessary to find the highest point reached, or the time at which it was reached.   The equations of motion give the position and velocity at *any* time, whether the ball is on the way up or the way down.

(b) When the ball is 20 ft above the origin,

$$y = +20 \text{ ft}$$

and

$$v^2 = 1024 \frac{\text{ft}^2}{\text{sec}^2}, \qquad v = \pm 32 \frac{\text{ft}}{\text{sec}}.$$

The ball passes this point twice, once on the way up and again on the way down.   The velocity on the way up is $+32$ ft/sec, and on the way down it is -32 ft/sec.

(c) At the highest point, $v = 0$.   Hence

$$y = +36 \text{ ft}.$$

The time can now be found either from Eq. (4–21), setting $v = 0$, or from Eq. (4–22), setting $y = 36$ ft.   From either equation, we get

$$t = 1.5 \text{ sec}.$$

Figure 4–10 is a "multiflash" photograph of a freely falling golf ball. This photograph was taken with the aid of the ultra-high-speed stroboscopic light source developed by Dr. Harold E. Edgerton of the Massachusetts Institute of Technology. By means of this source a series of intense flashes of light can be produced. The interval between successive flashes is controllable at will, and the duration of each flash is so short (a few millionths of a second) that there is no blur in the image of even a rapidly moving body. The camera shutter is left open during the entire motion, and as each flash occurs the position of the ball at that instant is recorded on the photographic film.

The equally spaced light flashes subdivide the motion into equal time intervals Δt. Since the time intervals are all equal, the velocity of the ball between any two flashes is directly proportional to the separation of its corresponding images in the photograph. If the velocity were constant, the images would be equally spaced. The increasing separation of the images during the fall shows that the velocity is continually increasing or the motion is accelerated. By comparing two successive displacements of the ball, the *change* in velocity in the corresponding time interval can be found. Careful measurements, preferably on an enlarged print, show that this change in velocity is the same in each time interval. In other words, the motion is one of *constant acceleration*.

4–8 Rectilinear motion with variable acceleration

Motion with constant acceleration approximates the motion of some falling bodies, and of cars and of airplanes at

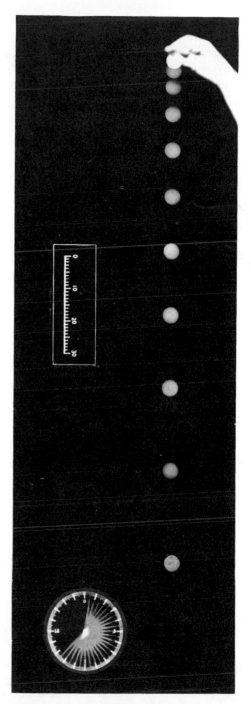

Fig. 4–10. Multiflash photograph (retouched) of freely falling golf ball.

the start of their journey.   There are many important types of motion, however, in which the acceleration is variable, and it is worth while to develop the technique of dealing with such cases. Consider, for example, the motion of a body in the positive x-direction with an acceleration whose direction is opposite that of the velocity and whose magnitude is proportional to the speed. For such a motion

$$a = -kv,$$

where k is a constant. If the initial speed is v_0, how do the speed and the distance vary with the time?

Since $a = dv/dt$, we have

$$\frac{dv}{dt} = -kv, \quad \text{or} \quad \frac{dv}{v} = -k\,dt,$$

and since $v = v_0$ when $t = 0$,

$$\int_{v_0}^{v} \frac{dv}{v} = -k \int_0^t dt.$$

Integration yields the result

$$\ln \frac{v}{v_0} = -kt,$$

which may be written as

$$v = v_0 e^{-kt}, \tag{4-23}$$

showing that the velocity decays exponentially with the time.   Exponential curves are found frequently in many diverse fields of physics.   The decrease in activity of a radioactive substance, the discharge of a capacitor, and the dying out of mechanical, acoustical, and electrical oscillations are all described by exponential equations. Equation (4-23) shows that an infinite time would be required to reduce the speed to zero.

To find the distance x as a function of the time, we replace v by dx/dt.   Thus

$$\frac{dx}{dt} = v_0 e^{-kt}.$$

Suppose that $x = 0$ when $t = 0$.   Then

$$\int_0^x dx = v_0 \int_0^t e^{-kt}\,dt,$$

and

$$x = -\frac{v_0}{k}[e^{-kt}]_0^t ,$$

$$x = \frac{v_0}{k}(1 - e^{-kt}). \tag{4-24}$$

It follows from this equation that although an infinite time is necessary for the body to come to rest, in this infinite time the body will have gone only a finite distance v_0/k.

Other examples of variable acceleration will be found in the problems at the end of this chapter and also in Chapter 5.

4–9 Relative velocity

The position, velocity, and acceleration of a particle can be specified only in relation to some reference coordinate system. The coordinate system may itself be moving relative to some other system, and so on indefinitely. Thus when we speak of "the velocity of an automobile," we usually mean its velocity relative to a coordinate system attached to, and moving with, the surface of the earth. But the earth is rotating about its axis and revolving about the sun, the sun is in motion relative to other stars, and so on.

The principles of *relativity*, as developed by Einstein and others, are concerned with the descriptions of the motion of a given particle relative to two different reference systems that are themselves in motion relative to each other. However, these principles go far beyond the mere statement that "all motion is relative," which is an obvious fact that has been recognized since the beginning of the science of mechanics.

For concreteness, let us imagine that two flatcars A and B are moving on parallel tracks as in Fig. 4–11, and that a pair of rectangular x- and y-axes is attached to each. Car B is moving to the right, relative to A, and A is moving to the left, relative to B. At time $t = 0$ the origins O_A and O_B are opposite each other. At some later time t the origins are displaced as in the diagram, with O_B lying to the right of O_A and O_A lying the same distance to the left of O_B.

The x-coordinate of the origin O_B, relative to the coordinate system attached to car A, is represented by x_{BA}. The x-coordinate of the origin O_A, relative to the system attached to B, is represented by x_{AB}. Evidently,

$$x_{AB} = -x_{BA}.$$

The velocity of system B, relative to A, is defined as the rate of change of the distance x_{BA}, and the velocity of A, relative to B, is defined as the rate of change of x_{AB}:

$$v_{BA} = \frac{dx_{BA}}{dt}, \qquad v_{AB} = \frac{dx_{AB}}{dt}.$$

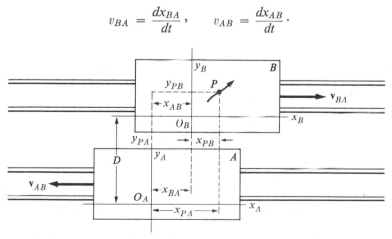

Fig. 4–11. Two flatcars A and B moving with relative velocity $v_{AB} = v_{BA}$.

Since $x_{BA} = -x_{AB}$, it follows that

$$v_{BA} = -v_{AB}. \tag{4-25}$$

The relative velocities v_{BA} and v_{AB} are represented by the equal and opposite vectors in Fig. 4–11.

Note that nothing need be said about the velocities of A and B relative to the *earth*, or to any other system. The distance x_{BA} would increase if A were at rest, relative to the earth, and B were moving to the right, or if B were at rest while A moved to the left. Or, A and B might be moving in opposite directions, relative to the earth, or both might be moving to the right, relative to the earth, with B traveling faster than A. In fact, A and B might be space platforms far removed from any other reference system. We are concerned only with the velocity of one relative to the other.

Consider next the particle P in Fig. 4–11. Its x-coordinate relative to system B is x_{PB}. Its x-coordinate relative to system A is

$$x_{PA} = x_{PB} + x_{BA}. \tag{4-26}$$

When this equation is solved for x_{PB}, and x_{BA} is replaced with $-x_{AB}$, we get

$$x_{PB} = x_{PA} + x_{AB}.$$

Comparison with Eq. (4–26) shows that either equation can be obtained from the other by interchanging the subscripts A and B. This is only to be expected, because there is no essential difference between the systems.

If the relative velocity v_{BA} is *constant*, then

$$x_{BA} = v_{BA}t,$$

and

$$x_{PA} = x_{PB} + v_{BA}t. \tag{4-27}$$

In Fig. 4–11, the x-axes are displaced by a distance D for clarity. For *mathematical* simplicity, let us imagine the x-axes to overhang the cars, so that they coincide. The y-coordinate of P is then the same in both systems, and if particle P lies above the xy-plane its z-coordinate is also the same in both.

The equations relating the coordinates of an event in system A to those of the same event in system B are known as the *Galilean-Newtonian transformation equations*, for two systems A and B in *uniform* relative motion. For completeness, we can also include the equation

$$t_A = t_B, \tag{4-28}$$

because one of the implied postulates of Newtonian mechanics is that the same time scale is applicable to all reference systems. It is primarily on this point, as we shall see, that the postulates of special relativity differ from those of classical mechanics.

Now suppose that P moves in some way, relative to car B. Its x-velocity relative to B is dx_{PB}/dt, and on differentiating Eq. (4–26) with respect to t, we see that its x-velocity relative to A, or dx_{PA}/dt, is

$$\frac{dx_{PA}}{dt} = \frac{dx_{PB}}{dt} + \frac{dx_{BA}}{dt},$$

or

$$(v_{PA})_x = (v_{PB})_x + v_{BA}. \tag{4–29}$$

Because the y- and z-coordinates of P are the same in both systems, the y- and z-components of velocity will be equal in the two systems.

The notation is cumbersome, but three subscripts are necessary in order to be specific. That is, we wish to describe the velocity *of* something (particle P) relative to some *reference system* (A or B) and in some specified *direction* (x, y, or z).

In the preceding analysis, the relative motion of the systems was in the direction of the x-axis and the velocity v_{BA}, in Eq. (4–29), is itself an x-velocity. If the relative velocity of the systems is in some arbitrary direction relative to the axes (the axes themselves remaining parallel to each other), the relative velocity $\mathbf{v}_{BA}$ will have y- and z-components as well as an x-component, and we will have three equations like Eq. (4–29), one for each component. These can be considered as the components of the general vector equation for the addition of relative velocities,

$$\boxed{\mathbf{v}_{PA} = \mathbf{v}_{PB} + \mathbf{v}_{BA}.} \tag{4–30}$$

That is, *the vector velocity of a particle P, relative to system A, is the vector sum of the velocity of the particle relative to system B, and the velocity of system B relative to system A.*

The sequence of subscripts on the right-hand side of Eq. (4–30) can be kept in mind by what has been called the "domino rule." That is, the second letter in the first subscript must be matched by the first letter in the second subscript. The subscripts on the left-hand side are the first and last letters in the sequence on the right. This rule can be extended to any number of systems in relative motion. Thus suppose that P represents a puck sliding over the surface of car B in Fig. 4–11, and that a flea F crawls over the surface of the puck. The velocity of the flea relative to car A is then

$$\mathbf{v}_{FA} = \mathbf{v}_{FP} + \mathbf{v}_{PB} + \mathbf{v}_{BA}.$$

If the velocity of A relative to the earth is v_{AE}, the velocity of the flea relative to the earth is

$$\mathbf{v}_{FE} = \mathbf{v}_{FP} + \mathbf{v}_{PB} + \mathbf{v}_{BA} + \mathbf{v}_{AE}.$$

EXAMPLE 1.   An automobile driver A, traveling relative to the earth at 65 mi/hr on a straight level road, is ahead of motorcycle officer B traveling in the same direction at 80 mi/hr. What is the velocity of B relative to A?

If the subscript E refers to the earth, we have

$$v_{AE} = 65 \text{ mi/hr}, \qquad v_{BE} = 80 \text{ mi/hr},$$

and we wish to find v_{BA}.

From the rule for combining velocities, we have

$$v_{BA} = v_{BE} + v_{EA}.$$

But

$$v_{EA} = -v_{AE},$$

so

$$v_{BA} = v_{BE} - v_{AE}$$
$$= 80 \text{ mi/hr} - 65 \text{ mi/hr} = 15 \text{ mi/hr},$$

and the officer is overtaking the driver at 15 mi/hr.

EXAMPLE 2.   How would the relative velocity be altered if B were ahead of A?

Not at all. The relative *positions* of the bodies does not matter. The velocity of B relative to A is still $+15$ mi/hr, but he is now pulling ahead of A at this rate.

EXAMPLE 3.   The compass of an aircraft indicates that it is headed due north, and its airspeed indicator shows that it is moving relative to the air at 120 mi/hr. If there is a wind of 50 mi/hr from west to east, what is the velocity of the aircraft relative to the earth?

Let subscript A refer to the aircraft, and subscript B to the moving air. Subscript E refers to the earth. We have given

$$\mathbf{v}_{AB} = 120 \text{ mi/hr, due north}$$
$$\mathbf{v}_{BE} = 50 \text{ mi/hr, due east},$$

and we wish to find the magnitude and direction of $\mathbf{v}_{AE}$:

$$\mathbf{v}_{AE} = \mathbf{v}_{AB} + \mathbf{v}_{BE}.$$

The three relative velocities are shown in Fig. 4–12. It follows from this diagram that

$$\mathbf{v}_{AE} = 130 \text{ mi/hr, } 22.5° \text{ E of N.}$$

EXAMPLE 4.   In what direction should the pilot head in order to travel due north? What will then be his velocity relative to the earth? The magnitude of his airspeed and the wind velocity are the same as in the preceding example.

We now have given:

$$\mathbf{v}_{AB} = 120 \text{ mi/hr, direction unknown,}$$
$$\mathbf{v}_{BE} = 50 \text{ mi/hr, due east,}$$

and we wish to find $\mathbf{v}_{AE}$, whose magnitude is unknown but whose direction is due north. (Note that both this and the preceding example require us to determine two unknown quantities. In the former example, these were the *magnitude and direction of* $\mathbf{v}_{AE}$. In this example, the unknowns are the *direction* of v_{AB} and the *magnitude* of v_{AE}.)

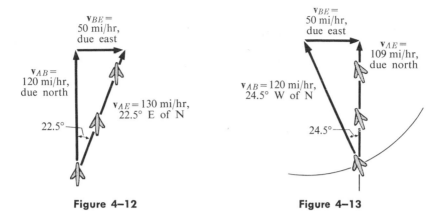

Figure 4–12   Figure 4–13

The three relative velocities must still satisfy the *vector equation*

$$\mathbf{v}_{AE} = \mathbf{v}_{AB} + \mathbf{v}_{BE}.$$

The problem can be solved graphically as follows. First construct the vector $\mathbf{v}_{BE}$ (see Fig. 4–13), known in magnitude and direction. At the head of this vector draw a construction line of indefinite length, in the known direction of $\mathbf{v}_{AE}$. With the tail of $\mathbf{v}_{BE}$ as a center, construct a circular arc of radius equal to the known magnitude of $\mathbf{v}_{AB}$. Vectors $\mathbf{v}_{AB}$ and $\mathbf{v}_{AE}$ may then be drawn from the point of intersection of this arc and the construction line, to the ends of the vector $\mathbf{v}_{BE}$. We find on solving the right triangle that the magnitude of $\mathbf{v}_{AE}$ is 109 mi/hr and the direction of $\mathbf{v}_{AB}$ is 24.5° W of N. That is, the pilot should head 24.5° W of N, and his ground speed will be 109 mi/hr.

4–10 Graphical representation of events relative to moving coordinate systems

The motion of a particle relative to each of two systems, in uniform motion relative to each other, can be represented graphically in a single diagram. We shall consider only the case in which all velocities are in the x-direction. The diagram will be useful as an aid in introducing the principles of *special relativity*.

Consider first a particle moving on the x-axis of some coordinate system, such as the particle P in Fig. 4–1(a). A specification of the coordinate x of the particle, and of the time t at which it has this coordinate, is said to determine an *event*. (In the general case, we must specify three space coordinates, and the time.) Then if we plot x vertically and t horizontally, as in Fig. 4–1(b), every point in the xt-plane corresponds to a *possible* event.

The locus of events in the xt-plane that represent the coordinate of a given particle at various times is called in relativity the *world line* of the particle. Thus the curve in Fig. 4–1(b) is the world line of particle P. In Fig. 4–14(a), the horizontal line is the world line of a stationary particle and the slanting line is the world line of a particle moving to the right with constant velocity. At time t_1 the coordinate of the moving particle is x_1, and the quantities x_1 and t_1 specify event E_1. Similarly, x_2 and t_2 specify event E_2. The events are separated in *space* by a distance $\Delta x = x_2 - x_1$, and they are separated in *time* by an interval $\Delta t = t_2 - t_1$.

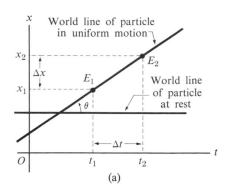
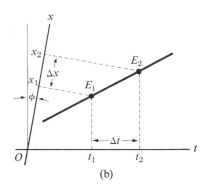

Fig. 4–14. (a) World lines of particles at rest and in motion on a *rectangular xt*-diagram. (b) World line of a moving particle when *x*- and *t*-axes are not at right angles.

The velocity of the particle, as explained earlier, is

$$v = \frac{\Delta x}{\Delta t} = \tan \theta, \tag{4–31}$$

due allowances being made for the scales on the *x*- and *t*-axes. If the scales are the *same*, so that a unit of length and a unit of time are represented by equal distances on the *x*- and *t*-axes, the tangent of the angle θ, as measured in the diagram, is numerically equal to the velocity.

It is conventional, but not necessary, that the *x*- and *t*-axes be constructed at right angles to each other. The events E_1 and E_2 in Fig. 4–14(a) can equally well be represented as in Fig. 4–14(b), the coordinates of the events being obtained by dropping perpendiculars to the *x*- and *t*-axes.

It was pointed out by R. W. Brehme in 1962 that when two systems A and B are in *uniform* relative motion, that is, when the relative velocities v_{BA} and v_{AB} are *constant*, the *t*- and *x*-coordinates of an event, relative to *both* systems, can be shown in a *single* diagram by making use of the type of graph in Fig. 4–14(b). We construct *two* space axes A and B on opposite sides of, and making equal angles with, the normal to the *t*-axis, as in Fig. 4–15(a). Event E_1, occurring at time t_1, occurs at coordinate x_{1A} in the A-system and at coordinate x_{1B} in the B-system. Event E_2 occurs at the same time t_1, and E_1 and E_2 are called *simultaneous* events. They are separated in space, in the A-system, by the distance $x_{2A} - x_{1A}$, and in the B-system by the distance $x_{2B} - x_{1B}$. Events E_1 and E_3 occur at the same point x_{1B} in the B-system. They are separated in time by $t_3 - t_1$, and in the A-system by the distance $x_{3A} - x_{1A}$.

The world line of a particle at rest in the A-system is a line perpendicular to the A-axis, as in Fig. 4–15(b), and that of a particle at rest in the B-system is a line perpendicular to the B-axis. Consider in particular the world line of the origin O_B of the set of B-axes in Fig. 4–11. If L is the length of this line at time t, it can be seen from Fig. 4–15(b) that

$$L \sin 2\phi = x_{BA}, \qquad L \cos \phi = t.$$

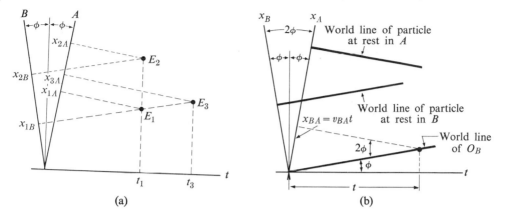

Fig. 4–15. Brehme diagrams for finding coordinates of events relative to each of two systems A and B in uniform relative motion.

Since the velocity v_{BA} is constant,

$$v_{BA} = \frac{x_{BA}}{t} = \frac{L \sin 2\phi}{L \cos \phi} = \frac{2 \sin \phi \cos \phi}{\cos \phi}.$$

Hence

$$v_{BA} = 2 \sin \phi,$$

a relation which determines the angle ϕ at which the A- and B-axes must be constructed.

In constructing a diagram to scale, the scale factors along the x- and t-axes must be taken into account. Thus if the unit of v_{BA} is 1 m/sec, and one inch along the t-axis represents k_t seconds, while one inch along the x-axes represents k_x meters,

$$k_t L \cos \phi = t, \qquad k_x L \sin 2\phi = x_{BA},$$

and

$$\sin \phi = \frac{1}{2} \frac{k_t}{k_x} v_{BA}.$$

For example, if $k_t = 1$ sec, $k_x = 10$ m, and $v_{BA} = 5$ m/sec,

$$\sin \phi = \frac{1}{2} \frac{1 \text{ sec}}{10 \text{ m}} 5 \frac{\text{m}}{\text{sec}} = 0.25,$$

$$\phi = 14.5°.$$

Figure 4–16 shows the world line of a particle P moving in the x-direction with constant velocity. Events E_1 and E_2 correspond to two positions of the particle.

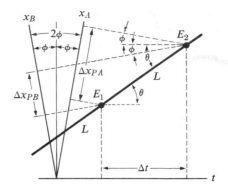

Fig. 4–16.   World line of a particle moving in the x-direction with constant velocity.

The time interval between the events is Δt, and the displacements in systems A and B are Δx_{PA} and Δx_{PB}. We have

$$\Delta x_{PA} = L \sin (\theta + \phi), \qquad \Delta x_{PB} = L \sin (\theta - \phi), \qquad \Delta t = L \cos \theta.$$

The velocities of the particle relative to the two systems are

$$v_{PA} = \frac{\Delta x_{PA}}{\Delta t} = \frac{\sin (\theta + \phi)}{\cos \theta} = \tan \theta \cos \phi + \sin \phi,$$

$$v_{PB} = \frac{\Delta x_{PB}}{\Delta t} = \frac{\sin (\theta - \phi)}{\cos \theta} = \tan \theta \cos \phi - \sin \phi.$$

These equations should be compared with Eq. (4–31) for the velocity of a particle in the conventional x-t diagram. It follows from them that

$$v_{PA} - v_{PB} = 2 \sin \phi = v_{BA},$$

or

$$v_{PA} = v_{PB} + v_{BA}. \tag{4–32}$$

The diagram therefore provides a simple geometrical method of deriving Eq. (4–29). The subscript x has been omitted in Eq. (4–32) since we are considering motion only along the x-axis.

4–11 The Lorentz-Einstein transformation

It can be seen from the construction in Fig. 4–16 that there is no finite velocity as viewed in one system that has the same value in another system moving uniformly relative to the first. This is because no line segment in Fig. 4–16 has *equal* projections on the A- and B-axes. (The only exception is the perpendicular bisector of the angle between the axes, but this corresponds to an *infinite* velocity.) The Michelson-Morley experiment, however, which will be described in the chapter on interference, shows that there *is* one finite velocity whose measured value is the same in all systems, namely, the velocity of light, c. Hence something must be fundamentally wrong with the hypotheses that were made in the preceding analysis and in the construction of Fig. 4–16. It was recognized by Einstein that the error lay in the assumption that a single, universal value of the time t is applicable to all systems. That is, *the time t_A associated with an event by an observer in system A is not necessarily the same as the time t_B associated with the same event by an observer in system B, if B is moving relative to A.*

The relations between the times t_A and t_B can best be described geometrically, in terms of the correct way of constructing the Brehme diagram for two systems in relative motion. Figure 4–17 shows how this is done. In addition to the *space* axes A and B, we must construct *two time* axes, and in such a way that the *time* axis of A is perpendicular to the *space* axis of B and the *time* axis of B is perpendicular to the *space* axis of A. The angle between the time axes is therefore equal to that between the space axes, and for simplicity we represent this angle by α instead of by 2ϕ, as in the preceding diagrams. We also make one other change and plot the product ct along the time axes, where c is the speed of light, instead of t itself.

This means that if a length of one inch along the space axes *in the diagram* corresponds to a distance of, say, one meter traversed by a moving body, the same length of one inch along the time axis corresponds to a product ct of one meter. Since $c = 3 \times 10^8$ m/sec, then if $ct = 1$ m, $t = 3.3 \times 10^{-9}$ sec, and one inch on the time axis corresponds to 3.3×10^{-9} sec.

Then the event E_1 in Fig. 4–17, which occurs at the coordinate x_{1A} and the time t_{1A}, in system A, occurs at the coordinate x_{1B} and the time t_{1B} in system B.

Events E_1 and E_2, which are *simultaneous* in system A, are not simultaneous in system B but occur at times t_{1B} and t_{2B}. Events E_1 and E_3 occur at the same point x_{1B} in system B, but are separated by *different* time intervals in systems A and B.

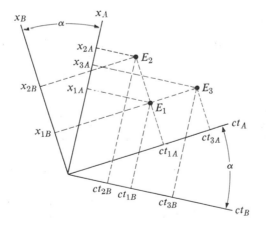

Fig. 4–17. Brehme diagram for two systems in relative motion.

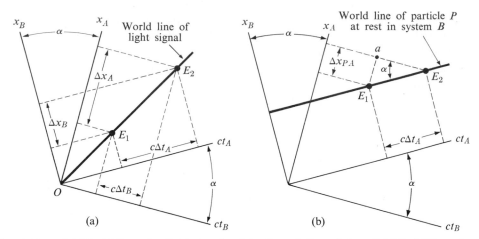

Fig. 4–18. (a) World line of a light signal originating at the origin. (b) World line of a particle P at rest in system B.

The world line of a light signal originating at the origin is the line bisecting the angle between the space and time axes of either system. If we consider two events E_1 and E_2 along this line, then by symmetry, as will be seen from Fig. 4–18(a),

$$\Delta x_A = c\,\Delta t_A, \qquad \Delta x_B = c\,\Delta t_B.$$

The velocity of the signal in the A-system is

$$v_A = \frac{\Delta x_A}{\Delta t_A} = c,$$

and the velocity in the B-system is

$$v_B = \frac{\Delta x_B}{\Delta t_B} = c.$$

Thus if the *time* intervals, in systems A and B, are related to the *space* intervals in the way shown in Fig. 4–18, *the velocity of a light signal is the same in both systems.* Conversely, since we find experimentally that the velocity *is* the same in both systems, we are forced to conclude that the times in the two systems must be related as shown.

Let us now find what the angle α should be. Figure 4–18(b) shows two events E_1 and E_2 on the world line of a particle P at rest in the B-system of Fig. 4–11. The velocity of P relative to the A-system, v_{PA}, is therefore equal to v_{BA}. But we see from the triangle E_1E_2a that

$$\Delta x_{PA} = c\,\Delta t_A \sin \alpha.$$

Hence

$$v_{PA} = \frac{\Delta x_{PA}}{\Delta t_A} = c \sin \alpha,$$

and since $v_{PA} = v_{BA}$,

$$v_{BA} = c \sin \alpha, \qquad \sin \alpha = \frac{v_{BA}}{c}.$$

That is, the sine of the angle α equals the ratio of the relative velocity of systems A and B to the velocity of light. It follows that

$$\cos \alpha = \sqrt{1 - \sin^2 \alpha} = \sqrt{1 - v_{BA}^2/c^2}.$$

We next derive the relativistic transformation equations that connect the coordinate and time of an event, relative to system A, with those relative to system B. In Fig. 4–19, let L represent the length of a construction line from the origin O to an event E. Then

$$x_A = L \sin (\theta + \alpha),$$

$$x_B = L \sin \theta,$$

$$\text{(4-33)}$$

$$ct_A = L \cos \theta,$$

$$ct_B = L \cos (\theta + \alpha).$$

It follows from these equations that

$$x_A = \frac{x_B + ct_B \sin \alpha}{\cos \alpha}$$

$$= \frac{x_B + v_{BA}t_B}{\sqrt{1 - v_{BA}^2/c^2}}, \quad \text{(4-34)}$$

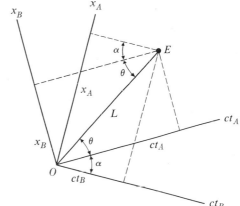

Fig. 4–19. Construction for obtaining the Lorentz transformation equation.

$$ct_A = \frac{ct_B + x_B \sin \alpha}{\cos \alpha} = \frac{ct_B + v_{BA}x_B/c}{\sqrt{1 - v_{BA}^2/c^2}}. \qquad \text{(4-35)}$$

These should be compared with the corresponding Galilean-Newtonian equations, Eqs. (4–27) and (4–28). They reduce to these equations if the relative velocity v_{BA} is small compared with c (or if $c = \infty$).

Note that the coordinate of an event, in system A, depends on the time t_B of the event, as well as on the relative velocity, and that the time of an event, in system A, depends on its coordinate x_B.

The y- and z-coordinates of an event are the same in systems A and B, provided of course that the relative velocity of the systems is in the x-direction.

Equations (4–34) and (4–35), together with those for the y- and z-coordinates, are called the *Lorentz-Einstein transformation equations* of special relativity. They were developed by Lorentz for the special case of electric and magnetic fields as seen by observers in relative motion, before they were generalized by Einstein.

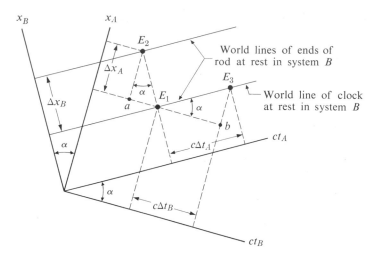

Fig. 4–20.   Construction for calculating length contraction and time dilation.

One of the unexpected consequences of special relativity is that the length of a rod, measured in a system relative to which the rod is moving longitudinally, is less than its length measured in a system in which it is at rest. Suppose the cart B in Fig. 4–11 carries with it a rod, parallel to the x-axis. The world lines of the ends of the rod are then at right angles to the x_B-axis of a Brehme diagram and the length of the rod, as measured in B's system, is represented by Δx_B in Fig. 4–20.

To measure the length of the rod in A's system, two of A's assistants note the positions of the ends of the rod, on their own x-axis, *at the same instant on their own time scale.* Thus events E_1 and E_2 in Fig. 4–20 represent the ends of the rod at times that are *simultaneous* in system A. The distance Δx_A between the x_A-coordinates of E_1 and E_2 is the length of the rod as measured in system A. It can be seen from the triangle $E_1 E_2 a$ that

$$\Delta x_A = \Delta x_B \cos \alpha = \Delta x_B \sqrt{1 - v_{BA}^2/c^2}, \tag{4–36}$$

and hence that Δx_A is *less* than Δx_B.

It is left to the reader to construct the appropriate diagram and show that if a rod is at rest in A's system, its length as measured in B's system is *less* than that measured in A's system. These apparently contradictory results are, however, entirely consistent. *Each* observer finds that the measured length of a rod, in motion relative to him, is less than when it is at relative rest. This phenomenon is known as *length contraction.*

Now suppose that a clock is mounted at one end of the rod, and that E_1 and E_3 in Fig. 4–20 are two events on its world line. Let Δt_B be the elapsed time between E_1 and E_3, as indicated by the clock. Two of A's assistants record the times of their own clocks as the clock in system B passes them, and the difference Δt_A between their clock readings is the elapsed time between E_1 and E_3 in system A.

It can be seen from the triangle $E_1 E_3 b$ in Fig. 4-20 that

$$c \, \Delta t_B = c \, \Delta t_A \cos \alpha,$$

or

$$\Delta t_A = \frac{\Delta t_B}{\cos \alpha} = \frac{\Delta t_B}{\sqrt{1 - v_{BA}^2 / c^2}}. \qquad (4\text{-}37)$$

Hence the elapsed time according to A's clocks, Δt_A, is *greater* than the elapsed time Δt_B indicated by the clock at rest in system B.

Again it is left to the reader to construct the appropriate diagram and show that for a clock at rest in system A the elapsed time as indicated by clocks in system B is greater than that indicated by the clock in system A. *Each* observer finds that a time interval as measured by his clocks is *greater* than that indicated by a clock in relative motion. This phenomenon is known as *time dilation*.

Problems

4–1. A ball is released from rest and rolls down an inclined plane, requiring 4 sec to cover a distance of 100 cm. (a) What was its acceleration in $\mathrm{cm/sec^2}$? (b) How many centimeters would it have fallen vertically in the same time?

4–2. The "reaction time" of the average automobile driver is about 0.7 sec. (The reaction time is the interval between the perception of a signal to stop and the application of the brakes.) If an automobile can decelerate at 16 $\mathrm{ft/sec^2}$, compute the total distance covered in coming to a stop after a signal is observed: (a) from an initial velocity of 30 mi/hr, (b) from an initial velocity of 60 mi/hr.

4–3. At the instant the traffic lights turn green, an automobile that has been waiting at an intersection starts ahead with a constant acceleration of 6 $\mathrm{ft/sec^2}$. At the same instant a truck, traveling with a constant velocity of 30 ft/sec, overtakes and passes the automobile. (a) How far beyond its starting point will the automobile overtake the truck? (b) How fast will it be traveling?

4–4. The engineer of a passenger train traveling at 100 ft/sec sights a freight train whose caboose is 600 ft ahead on the same track. The freight train is traveling in the same direction as the passenger train with a velocity of 30 ft/sec. The engineer of the passenger train immediately applies the brakes, causing a constant deceleration of 4 $\mathrm{ft/sec^2}$, while the freight train continues with constant speed. (a) Will there be a collision? (b) If so, where will it take place?

4–5. A sled starts from rest at the top of a hill and slides down with a constant acceleration. The sled is 140 ft from the top of the hill 2 sec after passing a point which is 92 ft from the top. Four seconds after passing the 92-ft point it is 198 ft from the top, and 6 sec after passing the point it is 266 ft from the top. (a) What is the average velocity of the sled during each of the 2-sec intervals after passing the 92-ft point? (b) What is the acceleration of the sled? (c) What was the velocity of the sled when it passed the 92-ft point? (d) How long did it take to go from the top to the 92-ft point? (e) How far did the sled go during the first sec after passing the 92-ft point? (f) How long does it take the sled to go from the 92-ft point to the midpoint between the 92-ft and the 140-ft mark? (g) What is the velocity of the sled as it passes the midpoint in part (f)?

4–6. A subway train starts from rest at a station and accelerates at a rate of 4 ft/sec^2 for 10 sec. It then runs at constant speed for 30 sec, and decelerates at 8 ft/sec^2 until it stops at the next station. Find the *total* distance covered.

4–7. A body starts from rest, moves in a straight line with constant acceleration, and covers a distance of 64 ft in 4 sec. (a) What was the final velocity? (b) How long a time was required to cover half the total distance? (c) What was the distance covered in one-half the total time? (d) What was the velocity when half the total distance had been covered? (e) What was the velocity after one-half the total time?

4–8. The speed of an automobile going north is reduced from 45 to 30 mi/hr in a distance of 264 ft. Find (a) the magnitude and direction of the acceleration, assuming it to be constant, (b) the elapsed time, (c) the distance in which the car can be brought to rest from 30 mi/hr, assuming the acceleration of part (a).

4–9. An automobile and a truck start from rest at the same instant, with the automobile initially at some distance behind the truck. The truck has a constant acceleration of 4 ft/sec^2 and the automobile an acceleration of 6 ft/sec^2. The automobile overtakes the truck after the truck has moved 150 ft. (a) How long does it take the auto to overtake the truck? (b) How far was the auto behind the truck initially? (c) What is the velocity of each when they are abreast?

4–10. (a) With what velocity must a ball be thrown vertically upward in order to rise to a height of 50 ft? (b) How long will it be in the air?

4–11. A ball is thrown vertically downward from the top of a building, leaving the thrower's hand with a velocity of 30 ft/sec. (a) What will be its velocity after falling for 2 sec? (b) How far will it fall in 2 sec? (c) What will be its velocity after falling 30 ft? (d) If it moved a distance of 3 ft while in the thrower's hand,

find its acceleration while in his hand. (e) If the ball was released at a point 120 ft above the ground, in how many seconds will it strike the ground? (f) What will be its velocity when it strikes?

4–12. A balloon, rising vertically with a velocity of 16 ft/sec, releases a sandbag at an instant when the balloon is 64 ft above the ground. (a) Compute the position and velocity of the sandbag at the following times after its release: $\frac{1}{4}$ sec, $\frac{1}{2}$ sec, 1 sec, 2 sec. (b) How many seconds after its release will the bag strike the ground? (c) With what velocity will it strike?

4–13. A stone is dropped from the top of a tall cliff, and 1 sec later a second stone is thrown vertically downward with a velocity of 60 ft/sec. How far below the top of the cliff will the second stone overtake the first?

4–14. A ball dropped from the cornice of a building takes 0.25 sec to pass a window 9 ft high. How far is the top of the window below the cornice?

4–15. A ball is thrown nearly vertically upward from a point near the cornice of a tall building. It just misses the cornice on the way down, and passes a point 160 ft below its starting point 5 sec after it leaves the thrower's hand. (a) What was the initial velocity of the ball? (b) How high did it rise above its starting point? (c) What were the magnitude and direction of its velocity at the highest point? (d) What were the magnitude and direction of its acceleration at the highest point? (e) What was the magnitude of its velocity as it passed a point 64 ft below the starting point?

4–16. A juggler performs in a room whose ceiling is 9 ft above the level of his hands. He throws a ball vertically upward so that it just reaches the ceiling. (a) With what initial velocity does he throw the ball? (b) What time is required for the ball to reach the ceiling?

He throws a second ball upward with the same initial velocity, at the instant that the first ball is at the ceiling. (c) How long after the second ball is thrown do the two balls pass each other? (d) When the balls pass each other, how far are they above the juggler's hands?

4–17. An object is thrown vertically upward. It has a speed of 32 ft/sec when it has reached one-half its maximum height. (a) How high does it rise? (b) What is its velocity and acceleration 1 sec after it is thrown? (c) 3 sec after? (d) What is the average velocity during the first half-sec?

4–18. A student determined to test the law of gravity for himself walks off a skyscraper 900 ft high, stopwatch in hand, and starts his free fall (zero initial velocity). Five seconds later, Superman arrives at the scene and dives off the roof to save the student. (a) What must Superman's initial velocity be in order that he catch the student just before the ground is reached? (b) What must be the height of the skyscraper so that even Superman can't save him? (Assume that Superman's acceleration is that of any freely falling body.)

4–19. A ball is thrown vertically upward from the ground and a student gazing out of the window sees it moving upward past him at 16 ft/sec. The window is 32 ft above the ground. (a) How high does the ball go above the ground? (b) How long does it take to go from a height of 32 ft to its highest point? (c) Find its velocity and acceleration $\frac{1}{2}$ sec after it left the ground, and 2 sec after it left the ground.

4–20. A ball is thrown vertically upward from the ground with a velocity of 80 ft/sec. (a) How long will it take to rise to its highest point? (b) How high does the ball rise? (c) How long after projection will the ball have a velocity of 16 ft/sec upward? (d) of 16 ft/sec downward? (e) When is the displacement of the ball zero? (f) When is the magnitude of the ball's velocity equal to half its velocity of projection? (g) When is the magnitude of the ball's displacement equal to half the greatest height to which it rises? (h) What are the magnitude and direction of the acceleration while the ball is moving up-

ward? (i) While moving downward? (j) When at the highest point?

4–21. A ball rolling on an inclined plane moves with a constant acceleration. One ball is released from rest at the top of an inclined plane 18 m long and reaches the bottom 3 sec later. At the same instant that the first ball is released, a second ball is projected upward along the plane from its bottom with a certain initial velocity. The second ball is to travel part way up the plane, stop, and return to the bottom so that it arrives simultaneously with the first ball. (a) Find the acceleration. (b) What must be the initial velocity of the second ball? (c) How far up the plane will it travel?

4–22. The rocket-driven sled Sonic Wind No. 2, used for investigating the physiological effects of large accelerations and decelerations, runs on a straight, level track 3500 ft long. Starting from rest, a speed of 1000 mi/hr can be reached in 1.8 sec. (a) Compute the acceleration, assuming it to be constant. (b) What is the ratio of this acceleration to that of a freely-falling body, g? (c) What is the distance covered? (d) A magazine article states that at the end of a certain run the speed of the sled was decreased from 632 mi/hr to zero in 1.4 sec, and that as the sled decelerated its passenger was subjected to more than 40 times the pull of gravity (that is, the deceleration was greater than $40g$). Are these figures consistent?

4–23. Figure 4–21 is a graph of the acceleration of a body moving on the x-axis. Sketch the graphs of its velocity and coordinate, as functions of time, if $x = v = 0$ when $t = 0$.

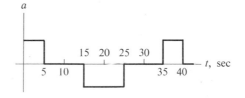

Figure 4–21

4–24. Figure 4–22 is a graph of the coordinate of a body moving on the x-axis. Sketch the graphs of its velocity and acceleration, as functions of the time.

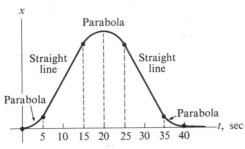

Figure 4–22

4–25. The first stage of a rocket to launch an earth satellite will, if fired vertically upward, attain a speed of 4000 mi/hr at a height of 36 mi above the earth's surface, at which point its fuel supply will be exhausted.   (a) Assuming constant acceleration, find the time to reach a height of 36 mi.   (b) How much higher would the rocket rise if it continued to "coast" vertically upward?

4–26. Suppose the acceleration of gravity were only 3.2 ft/sec^2, instead of 32 ft/sec^2. (a) Estimate the height to which you could jump vertically from a standing start. (b) How high could you throw a baseball? (c) Estimate the maximum height of a window from which you would care to jump to a concrete sidewalk below. (Each story of an average building is about 10 ft high.)   (d) With what speed, in mi/hr, would you strike the sidewalk?   (e) How many seconds would be required?

4–27. After the engine of a moving motorboat is cut off, the boat has an acceleration in the opposite direction to its velocity and directly proportional to the square of its velocity. That is, $dv/dt = -kv^2$, where k is a constant. (a) Show that the magnitude v of the velocity at a time t after the engine is cut off is given by

$$\frac{1}{v} = \frac{1}{v_0} + kt.$$

(b) Show that the distance x traveled in a time t is

$$x = \frac{1}{k} \ln (v_0 kt + 1).$$

(c) Show that the velocity after traveling a distance x is

$$v = v_0 e^{-kx}.$$

As a numerical example, suppose the engine is cut off when the velocity $v_0 = 20$ ft/sec, and that the velocity decreases to 10 ft/sec in a time of 15 sec.   (d) Find the numerical value of the constant k, and the unit in which it is expressed. (e) Find the acceleration at the instant the engine is cut off. (f) Construct graphs of x, v, and a for a time of 20 sec. Let 1 inch = 5 sec horizontally, and 1 inch = 100 ft, 5 ft/sec, and 0.5 ft/sec^2 vertically.

4–28. The equation of motion of a body suspended from a spring and oscillating vertically is $y = A \sin \omega t$, where A and ω are constants. (a) Find the velocity of the body as a function of time. (b) Find its acceleration as a function of time. (c) Find its velocity as a function of its coordinate. (d) Find its acceleration as a function of its coordinate.   (e) What is the maximum distance of the body from the origin? (f) What is its maximum velocity? (g) What is its maximum acceleration? (h) Sketch graphs of y, v, and a as functions of time.

4–29. The acceleration of a body suspended from a spring and oscillating vertically is $a = -Ky$, where K is a constant and y is the coordinate measured from the equilibrium position. Suppose that a body moving in this way is given an initial velocity v_0 at the coordinate y_0. Find the expression for the velocity v of the body as a function of its coordinate y. [*Hint:* Use the expression $a = v\,dv/dy$.]

4–30. Two piers A and B are located on a river, one mile apart.   Two men must make round trips from pier A to pier B and return.   One man is to row a boat at a velocity of 4 mi/hr relative to the water, and the other man is to walk on the shore at a velocity of 4 mi/hr. The velocity of the river is 2 mi/hr in the direction from A to B. How long does it take each man to make the round trip?

4–31. A passenger on a ship traveling due east with a speed of 18 knots observes that the stream of smoke from the ship's funnels makes an angle of 20° with the ship's wake. The wind is blowing from south to north. Assume that the smoke acquires a velocity (with respect to the earth) equal to the velocity of the wind, as soon as it leaves the funnels. Find the velocity of the wind.

4–32. An airplane pilot wishes to fly due north. A wind of 60 mi/hr is blowing toward the west. If the flying speed of the plane (its speed in still air) is 180 mi/hr, in what direction should the pilot head? What is the speed of the plane over the ground? Illustrate with a vector diagram.

4–33. An airplane pilot sets a compass course due west and maintains an air speed of 120 mi/hr. After flying for one-half hour he finds himself over a town which is 75 mi west and 20 mi south of his starting point. (a) Find the wind velocity, in magnitude and direction. (b) If the wind velocity were 60 mi/hr due south, in what direction should the pilot set his course in order to travel due west? Take the same air speed of 120 mi/hr.

4–34. When a train has a speed of 10 mi/hr eastward, raindrops which are falling vertically with respect to the earth make traces on the windows of the train, which are inclined 30° to the vertical. (a) What is the horizontal component of a drop's velocity with respect to the earth? with respect to the train? (b) What is the velocity of the raindrop with respect to the earth? with respect to the train?

4–35. A river flows due north with a velocity of 3 mi/hr. A man rows a boat across the river, his velocity relative to the water being 4 mi/hr due east. (a) What is his velocity relative to the earth? (b) If the river is 1 mi wide, how far north of

his starting point will he reach the opposite bank? (c) How long a time is required to cross the river?

4–36. (a) In what direction should the rowboat in Problem 4–35 be headed in order to reach a point on the opposite bank directly east from the start? (b) What will be the velocity of the boat relative to the earth? (c) How long a time is required to cross the river?

4–37. A motor boat is observed to travel 10 mi/hr relative to the earth in the direction 37° north of east. If the velocity of the boat due to the wind is 2 mi/hr eastward and that due to the current is 4 mi/hr southward, what is the magnitude and direction of the velocity of the boat due to its own power?

4–38. Car B, in Fig. 4–11, is moving to the right relative to car A with a velocity $v_{BA} = 10$ m/sec. Construct a diagram like Fig. 4–15, letting 1 in. along the t-axis represent 10 sec and 1 in. along the x-axis represent 100 m. The origins O_A and O_B are opposite each other at time $t = 0$. (a) What is the value of the angle ϕ? (b) Show the following events in your diagram: E_1, a pistol is fired at the origin O_B at a time $t = 20$ sec; E_2, a point on the x-axis of system B, 100 m to the right of O_B, passes a point on the x-axis of system A, 200 m to the right of O_A. (c) At what value of x_A does event E_1 take place? (d) At what time does event E_2 take place?

4–39. If cars A and B in Fig. 4–11 have velocities with respect to the earth of magnitude $0.6c$ (that is, $v_{AE} = 0.6c$, $v_{BE} = -0.6c$), what is the velocity v_{AB} of A relative to B?

4–40. Figure 4–23 represents a Brehme diagram of a particle moving relative to A and B. The points marked E_1 and E_2 represent two events. (a) Copy the diagram and indicate on your copy Δx_{PA}, Δx_{PB}, $c\Delta t_A$, and $c\Delta t_B$. (b) Prove that

$$v_{PA} = \frac{\Delta x_{PA}}{\Delta t_A} = \frac{c \sin \theta}{\cos (\theta - \alpha)},$$

$$v_{PB} = \frac{\Delta x_{PB}}{\Delta t_B} = \frac{c \sin (\theta - \alpha)}{\cos \theta},$$

$$v_{PA} = \frac{v_{PB} + v_{BA}}{1 + v_{PB}v_{BA}/c^2}.$$

(c) If the particle P is a light signal whose velocity with respect to B is c, calculate its velocity with respect to A.

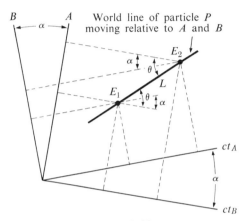

Figure 4–23

4–41. Car B, in Fig. 4–11, is moving to the right relative to car A with a velocity $v_{BA} = 0.6c$. Construct a Brehme diagram like that in Fig. 4–17. Let 1 in. along the x-axis represent 100 m.   (a) What is the value of the angle α?   (b) Show the following events in your diagram: E_1 and E_2, the beginning and end, respectively, of the flash accompanying a pistol shot at the point $x_{1B} = 100$ m at a time $t_{1B} = 10^{-6}$ sec, the duration of the flash being equal to 10^{-7} sec; E_3, a second pistol shot at the point $x_{2B} = 200$ m, fired simultane-

ously with the first, as determined by observer B.   (c) At what time t_{1A} is the first pistol fired?   (d) What is the duration of the flash as measured by observer A? (e) What is the separation of the pistols, as measured by observer A?   (f) According to observer A, were the pistols fired simultaneously? If not, which was fired earlier?

4–42. (a) Complete the derivations of Eqs. (4–34) and (4–35) from Eqs. (4–33). (b) Derive the expressions for x_B and ct_B, in terms of x_A and t_A, from Eqs. (4–33). (c) Show that the expressions for x_B and ct_B can also be obtained from Eqs. (4–34) and (4–35) by interchanging the subscripts A and B, provided the algebraic sign preceding the relative velocity is reversed when v_{BA} is changed to v_{AB}.   (The sign preceding the *square* of the relative velocity is *not* reversed.)

4–43. (a) Show that if a right triangle is constructed as in Fig. 4–24, with base proportional to the rest mass m_0 of a particle and with $\sin \alpha = v/c$, the hypotenuse of the triangle is proportional to the relativistic mass m of the particle. (b) Find the angle α, and the value of v/c, if the mass $m = 2m_0$.   (c) Discuss the limiting cases when $\alpha = 0$ and $\alpha = 90°$.

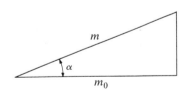

Figure 4–24

CHAPTER 5

Newton's Second Law.
Gravitation

5-1 Introduction

In the preceding chapters we have discussed separately the concepts of force and acceleration. We have made use, in problems in equilibrium, of Newton's first law, which states that when the resultant force on a body is zero, the acceleration of the body is also zero. The next logical step is to ask how a body behaves when the resultant force on it is *not* zero. The answer to this question is contained in Newton's second law, which states that when the resultant force is not zero the body moves with accelerated motion, and that the acceleration, with a given force, depends on a property of the body known as its *mass*.

This part of mechanics, which includes both the study of motion and the forces that bring about the motion, is called *dynamics*. In its broadest sense, dynamics includes nearly the whole of mechanics. Statics treats of special cases in which the acceleration is zero, and kinematics deals with motion only.

It will be assumed in this chapter that all velocities are small compared with the velocity of light, so that relativistic considerations do not arise. We shall also assume that unless otherwise stated all velocities and accelerations are measured relative to an inertial reference system (Section 2-3), and shall consider rectilinear motion only. Motion in a curved path will be discussed in the next chapter.

5-2 Newton's second law. Mass

Figure 5-1(a) is a top view of a small body (a particle) on a level frictionless surface, moving to the right along the x-axis of an inertial reference system. A horizontal force F, measured by a spring balance calibrated as described in Section 1-4, is exerted on the body. We find that the velocity of the body increases as long as the force acts. In other words, the body has an acceleration $a = dv/dt$, toward the right. If the magnitude of the force F is kept constant, the velocity increases at a constant rate. If the force is altered, the rate of change of velocity alters in the same proportion. Doubling the force doubles the rate of change of velocity, halving the force halves the rate of change, etc. If the force is reduced to zero, the rate of change of velocity is zero and the body continues to move with constant velocity.

Before the time of Galileo and Newton, it was generally believed that a force was necessary just to keep a body moving, even on a level frictionless surface or in "outer space." The great contribution of Newton to this part of mechanics was his realization that *no* force is necessary to keep a body moving, once it has been set in motion,

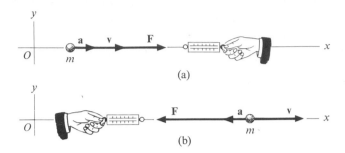

Fig. 5–1. The acceleration $\mathbf{a} = d\mathbf{v}/dt$ is proportional to the force $\mathbf{F}$ and is in the same direction as the force.

and that the effect of a force is not to *maintain* the velocity of body, but to *change* its velocity. The *rate of change* of velocity, for a given body, is directly proportional to the force exerted on it.

In Fig. 5–1(b), the velocity of the body is also toward the right, but the force is toward the left. Under these conditions the body moves more slowly (if the force continues to act, it will ultimately reverse its direction of motion). The acceleration is now toward the *left*, in the same direction as the force $\mathbf{F}$. Hence we conclude not only that the *magnitude* of the acceleration is proportional to that of the force, but that the *direction* of the acceleration is the *same* as that of the force, regardless of the direction of the velocity.

To say that the rate of change of the velocity of a body is directly proportional to the force exerted on it is to say that the ratio of the force to the rate of change of velocity is a constant, regardless of the magnitude of the force. This constant ratio of force to rate of change of velocity is called the *mass m* of the body. Thus

$$m = \frac{F}{dv/dt} = \frac{F}{a},$$

or

$$\mathbf{F} = m\frac{d\mathbf{v}}{dt} = m\mathbf{a}. \tag{5–1}$$

By writing this as a *vector* equation, we automatically include the experimental fact that the direction of the acceleration $\mathbf{a}$ is the same as that of the force $\mathbf{F}$.

The mass of a body can be thought of as the *force per unit of acceleration*. For example, if the acceleration of a certain body is found to be 5 ft/sec^2 when the force is 20 lb, the mass of the body is

$$m = \frac{20\ \mathrm{lb}}{5\ \mathrm{ft/sec^2}} = 4\frac{\mathrm{lb}}{\mathrm{ft/sec^2}},$$

and a force of 4 lb must be exerted on the body for every ft/sec^2 of acceleration.

In *rectilinear* motion, the force $\mathbf{F}$ acting on a body, and its velocity $\mathbf{v}$, always have the same action line, as in Fig. 5–1. If the direction of the force is *not* the same as that of the velocity, the body is deflected sidewise and moves in a curved path. We shall see in the next chapter, however, that Eq. (5–1) applies in this case also, except that the change in velocity $d\mathbf{v}$, or the acceleration $\mathbf{a}$, includes the change in *direction* as well as the change in *magnitude* of the velocity. In every case, then, *the vector force equals the product of the mass and the vector acceleration.*

When two vectors are equal, their rectangular components are equal also. Hence the vector equation (5–1) is equivalent (for forces and accelerations in the xy-plane) to the pair of scalar equations

$$F_x = m\frac{dv_x}{dt} = ma_x, \qquad F_y = m\frac{dv_y}{dt} = ma_y. \qquad (5\text{–}2)$$

This means that each component of the force can be considered to produce its own component of acceleration. It follows that if any number of forces act on a body simultaneously, as is usually the case in problems of practical interest, the forces may be resolved into x- and y-components, the algebraic sums $\sum F_x$ and $\sum F_y$ may be computed, and the components of acceleration are given by

$$\sum F_x = m\frac{dv_x}{dt} = ma_x, \qquad \sum F_y = m\frac{dv_y}{dt} = ma_y.$$

This pair of equations is equivalent to the single vector equation

$$\boxed{\sum \mathbf{F} = m\frac{d\mathbf{v}}{dt} = m\mathbf{a},} \qquad (5\text{–}3)$$

where we write the left-hand side explicitly as $\sum \mathbf{F}$ to emphasize that the acceleration is determined by the *resultant* of *all* of the *external* forces acting *on* the body.

Equation (5–3) is the mathematical statement of Newton's *second law of motion.* If we think of the equation as solved for $\mathbf{a}$ or $d\mathbf{v}/dt$, the law can be stated: *The rate of change of the velocity of a particle, or its acceleration, is equal to the resultant of all external forces exerted on the particle divided by the mass of the particle, and is in the same direction as the resultant force.* The acceleration is to be measured relative to an inertial system.

It is necessary to state the law for a *particle,* because when a resultant force acts on an extended body, the body may be set in rotation and not all particles in it have the same acceleration. We shall discuss this more fully later on, but it may be said at this point that the acceleration of the center of gravity of a body is the same as that of a particle whose mass equals that of the body.

5–3 Systems of units

Nothing was said in the preceding discussion regarding the *units* in which force, mass, and acceleration are to be expressed. It is evident, however, from the equation $\mathbf{F} = m\mathbf{a}$, that these must be such that *unit force imparts unit acceleration to unit mass.*

In the *meter-kilogram-second* (mks) system, the mass of the standard kilogram is the unit of mass, and the unit of acceleration is 1 m/sec^2. The unit force in this system is then *that force which gives a standard kilogram an acceleration of* 1 m/sec^2.

This force is called one newton (1 n). One newton is approximately equal to one-quarter of a pound-force (more precisely, 1 n = 0.22481 lb). Thus in the mks system,

$$F \text{ (newtons)} = m \text{ (kgm)} \times a \text{ (m/sec}^2).$$

The mass unit in the *centimeter-gram-second* (cgs) system is one gram, equal to 1/1000 kgm, and the unit of acceleration is 1 cm/sec². The unit force in this system is then *that force which gives a body whose mass is one gram, an acceleration of* 1 cm/sec². This force is called *one dyne*. Since 1 kgm = 10^3 gm and 1 m/sec² = 10^2 cm/sec², it follows that 1 newton = 10^5 dynes. In the cgs system,

$$F \text{ (dynes)} = m \text{ (gm)} \times a \text{ (cm/sec}^2).$$

In setting up the mks and cgs systems, we first selected units of mass and acceleration, and defined the unit of force in terms of these. In the *British engineering system*, we first select a unit of *force* (1 lb) and a unit of acceleration (1 ft/sec²) and then define the unit of mass as *the mass of a body whose acceleration is* 1 ft/sec² *when the resultant force on the body is* 1 lb. This unit of mass is called *one slug*. (The origin of the name is obscure; it may have arisen from the concept of mass as inertia or *sluggishness*.) Then in the engineering system,

$$F \text{ (pounds)} = m \text{ (slugs)} \times a \text{ (ft/sec}^2).$$

The units of force, mass, and acceleration in the three systems are summarized in Table 5–1.

TABLE 5–1

System of units	Force	Mass	Acceleration
mks	newton (n)	kilogram (kgm)	m/sec²
cgs	dyne	gram (gm)	cm/sec²
engineering	pound (lb)	slug	ft/sec²

EXAMPLE 1.   The acceleration of a certain body is found to be 5 ft/sec² when the resultant force on the body is 20 lb. The mass of the body is

$$m = \frac{F}{a} = \frac{20 \text{ lb}}{5 \text{ ft/sec}^2} = 4 \frac{\text{lb}}{\text{ft/sec}^2} = 4 \text{ slugs.}$$

The unit, 1 slug, is therefore equivalent to 1 lb/(ft/sec²).

EXAMPLE 2.   A constant horizontal force of 2 newtons is applied to a body of mass 4 kgm, resting on a level frictionless surface. The acceleration of the body is

$$a = \frac{F}{m} = \frac{2 \text{ n}}{4 \text{ kgm}} = 0.5 \frac{\text{m}}{\text{sec}^2}.$$

Since the force is constant, the acceleration is constant also. Hence if the initial position and velocity of the body are known, the velocity and position at any later time can be found from the equations of motion with constant acceleration.

EXAMPLE 3. A body of mass 200 gm is given an initial velocity of 40 cm/sec toward the right along a level laboratory table top. The body is observed to slide a distance of 100 cm along the table before coming to rest. What was the magnitude and direction of the friction force f acting on it?

In the absence of further information, let us assume that the friction force is constant. The acceleration is then constant also and from the equations of motion with constant acceleration, we have

$$v^2 = v_0^2 + 2ax, \qquad 0 = (40 \text{ cm/sec})^2 + 2a \times 100 \text{ cm}, \qquad a = -8 \text{ cm/sec}^2.$$

The negative sign means that the acceleration is toward the *left* (although the velocity is toward the right). The friction force on the body is

$$f = ma = 200 \text{ gm} \times (-8 \text{ cm/sec}^2) = -1600 \text{ dynes,}$$

and is toward the left also. (A force of equal magnitude, but directed toward the right, is exerted on the table by the sliding body.)

5–4 Newton's law of universal gravitation

Throughout our study of mechanics we have been continually encountering the force of gravitational attraction between a body and the earth. We now wish to study this phenomenon of gravitation in more detail.

The law of universal gravitation was discovered by Newton, and was published by him in 1686. There seems to be some evidence that Newton was led to deduce the law from speculations concerning the fall of an apple toward the earth, but his first published calculations to justify its correctness had to do with the motion of the moon around the earth.

Newton's law of gravitation may be stated: *Every particle of matter in the universe attracts every other particle with a force which is directly proportional to the product of the masses of the particles and inversely proportional to the square of the distance between them.* Thus

$$F_g = G \frac{mm'}{r^2}, \tag{5–4}$$

where F_g is the gravitational force on either particle, m and m' are their masses, r is the distance between them, and G is a universal constant called the *gravitational constant*, whose numerical value depends on the units in which force, mass, and length are expressed.

The gravitational forces acting on the particles form an action-reaction pair. Although the masses of the particles may be different, forces of *equal* magnitude act on each, and the action line of both forces lies along the line joining the particles.

Newton's law of gravitation refers to the force between two *particles*. How can it be applied to the force between a small body and the *earth*, or between the earth and the moon, since the particles that make up these bodies are at different distances from one another and their forces of attraction are in different directions? Newton delayed publication of his law for eleven years after he became convinced of its validity, because he could not prove mathematically that the force of attraction exerted on or by a homogeneous sphere is the same as if the mass of the sphere were concentrated at its center. (To prove this, he had to invent the methods of calculus.) The proof is not difficult but is too long to give here, and we shall simply state as a fact that *the gravitational force exerted on or by a homogeneous sphere is the same as if the entire mass of the sphere were concentrated in a point at its center.* Thus if the earth were a homogeneous sphere, the force exerted by it on a small body of mass m, at a distance r from its center, would be

$$F_g = G\frac{mm_E}{r^2},$$

where m_E is the mass of the earth. A force of the same magnitude would be exerted *on* the earth by the body.

The magnitude of the gravitational constant G can be found experimentally by measuring the force of gravitational attraction between two bodies of known masses m and m', at a known separation. For bodies of moderate size the force is extremely small, but it can be measured with an instrument which was invented by the Rev. John Michell, although it was first used for this purpose by Sir Henry Cavendish in 1798. The same type of instrument was also used by Coulomb for studying forces of electrical and magnetic attraction and repulsion.

Fig. 5–2.   Principle of the Cavendish balance.

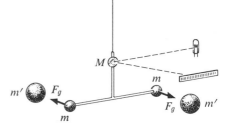

The Cavendish balance consists of a light, rigid T-shaped member (Fig. 5–2) supported by a fine vertical fiber such as a quartz thread or a thin metallic ribbon. Two small spheres of mass m are mounted at the ends of the horizontal portion of the T, and a small mirror M, fastened to the vertical portion, reflects a beam of light onto a scale. To use the balance, two large spheres of mass m' are brought up to the positions shown. The forces of gravitational attraction between the large and small spheres result in a *couple* which twists the system through a small angle, thereby moving the reflected light beam along the scale.

By using an extremely fine fiber, the deflection of the mirror may be made sufficiently large so that the gravitational force can be measured quite accurately. The gravitational constant, measured in this way, is found to be

$$G = 6.670 \times 10^{-11} \text{ newton·m}^2/\text{kgm}^2 = 6.670 \times 10^{-8} \text{ dyne·cm}^2/\text{gm}^2.$$

EXAMPLE 1.   The mass m of one of the small spheres of a Cavendish balance is 1 gm, the mass m' of one of the large spheres is 500 gm, and the center-to-center distance between the spheres is 5 cm. The gravitational force on each sphere is

$$F_g = 6.67 \times 10^{-8} \frac{\text{dyne·cm}^2}{\text{gm}^2} \frac{1 \text{ gm} \times 500 \text{ gm}}{(5 \text{ cm})^2} = 1.33 \times 10^{-6} \text{ dyne,}$$

or about one-millionth of a dyne!

EXAMPLE 2.   Suppose the spheres in Example 1 are placed 5 cm from each other at a point in space far removed from all other bodies. What is the acceleration of each, relative to an inertial system?

The acceleration a of the smaller sphere is

$$a = \frac{F_g}{m} = \frac{1.33 \times 10^{-6} \text{ dyne}}{1 \text{ gm}} = 1.33 \times 10^{-6} \text{ cm/sec}^2.$$

The acceleration a' of the larger sphere is

$$a' = \frac{F_g}{m'} = \frac{1.33 \times 10^{-6} \text{ dyne}}{500 \text{ gm}} = 2.67 \times 10^{-0} \text{ cm/sec}^2.$$

In this case, the accelerations are *not* constant because the gravitational force increases as the spheres approach each other.

5–5 Mass and weight

The *weight* of a body can now be defined more generally than in the preceding chapters as *the resultant gravitational force exerted on the body by all other bodies in the universe.* At or near the surface of the earth, the force of the earth's attraction is so much greater than that of any other body that for practical purposes all other gravitational forces can be neglected and the weight can be considered as arising solely from the gravitational attraction of the earth. Similarly, at the surface of the moon, or of another planet, the weight of a body results almost entirely from the gravitational attraction of the moon or the planet. Thus if the earth were a homogeneous sphere of radius R, the weight w of a small body at or near its surface would be

$$\boxed{w = F_g = G \frac{m m_E}{R^2}.} \qquad (5\text{--}5)$$

There is no general agreement among physicists as to the precise definition of "weight." Some prefer to use this term for a quantity we shall define later and call the "apparent weight" or "relative weight." In the absence of a generally accepted definition we shall continue to use the term as defined above.

Because of inhomogeneities in the composition of the earth, and because the earth is not a perfect sphere but a spheroid flattened at the poles, the weight of a given body varies slightly from point to point of the earth's surface. Also, the weight of a given body decreases inversely with the square of its distance from the earth's center, and at a radial distance of two earth radii, for example, it has decreased to one-quarter of its value at the earth's surface.

The *apparent* weight of a body at the surface of the earth as we shall see later, differs slightly in magnitude and direction from the earth's force of gravitational attraction because of the rotation of the earth about its axis. For the present, we shall ignore the small difference between the apparent weight of a body and the force of the earth's gravitational attraction, and shall assume that the earth is an inertial reference system. Then when a body is allowed to fall freely, the force accelerating it is its weight **w** and the acceleration produced by this force is the acceleration due to gravity, **g**. The general relation

$$\mathbf{F} = m\mathbf{a}$$

therefore becomes, for the special case of a freely falling body,

$$\boxed{\mathbf{w} = m\mathbf{g}.} \tag{5–6}$$

Since

$$w = mg = G\frac{mm_E}{R^2},$$

it follows that

$$g = \frac{Gm_E}{R^2}, \tag{5–7}$$

showing that the acceleration due to gravity is the same for *all* bodies (since m cancelled out) and is very nearly constant (since G and m_E are constants and R varies only slightly from point to point on the earth).

The weight of a body is a force, and must be expressed in terms of the unit of force in the particular system of units one is using. Thus in the mks system the unit of weight is 1 newton, in the cgs system it is 1 dyne, and in the engineering system it is 1 pound. The preceding equation gives the relation between the mass and weight of a body in any consistent set of units.

For example, the weight of a standard kilogram, at a point where $g = 9.80 \text{ m/sec}^2$, is

$$w = mg = 1 \text{ kgm} \times 9.80 \text{ m/sec}^2 = 9.80 \text{ n.}$$

At a second point where $g = 9.78 \text{ m/sec}^2$, the weight is

$$w = 9.78 \text{ n.}$$

Thus, unlike the mass of a body, which is a constant, the weight varies from one point to another.

The weight of a body whose mass is 1 gm, at a point where $g = 980 \text{ cm/sec}^2$, is

$$w = mg = 1 \text{ gm} \times 980 \text{ cm/sec}^2 = 980 \text{ dynes.}$$

The weight of a body whose mass is 1 slug, at a point where $g = 32.0 \text{ ft/sec}^2$, is

$$w = mg = 1 \text{ slug} \times 32.0 \text{ ft/sec}^2 = 32.0 \text{ lb},$$

and the mass of a man who weighs 160 lb at this point is

$$m = \frac{w}{g} = \frac{160 \text{ lb}}{32.0 \text{ ft/sec}^2} = 5 \text{ slugs}.$$

If we insert for the weight w in the equation $w = mg$, the gravitational force F_g as given by Newton's law of gravitation, we obtain, after cancelling the mass m,

$$m_E = \frac{R^2 g}{G},$$

where R is the earth's radius. All of the quantities on the right are known, so the mass of the earth, m_E, can be calculated. Taking $R = 6370 \text{ km} = 6.37 \times 10^6 \text{ m}$, and $g = 9.80 \text{ m/sec}^2$, we find

$$m_E = 5.98 \times 10^{24} \text{ kgm} = 5.98 \times 10^{27} \text{ gm}.$$

The volume of the earth is

$$V = \tfrac{4}{3}\pi R^3 = 1.09 \times 10^{21} \text{ m}^3 = 1.09 \times 10^{27} \text{ cm}^3.$$

The mass of a body divided by its volume is known as its average *density*. (The density of water is $1 \text{ gm/cm}^3 = 1000 \text{ kgm/m}^3$.) The average density of the earth is therefore

$$\frac{m_E}{V} = 5.5 \frac{\text{gm}}{\text{cm}^3} = 5500 \frac{\text{kgm}}{\text{m}^3}.$$

This is considerably larger than the average density of the material near the earth's surface (the density of rock is about $3 \text{ gm/cm}^3 = 3000 \text{ kgm/m}^3$) so the interior of the earth must be of much higher density.

As with many other physical quantities, the mass of a body can be measured in several different ways. One is to use the relation by which the quantity is defined, which in this case is the ratio of the force on the body to its acceleration. A measured force is applied to the body, its acceleration is measured, and the unknown mass is obtained by dividing the force by the acceleration. This method is used exclusively to measure masses of atomic particles.

The second method consists of finding by trial some other body whose mass (a) is equal to that of the given body, and (b) is already known. Consider first a method of determining when two masses are equal. It will be recalled that at the same point on the earth's surface all bodies fall freely with the same acceleration g. Since the weight w of a body equals the product of its mass m and the acceleration g, it follows that if, at the same point, the weights of two bodies are equal, their masses are equal also. The *equal-arm balance* is an instrument by means of which one can determine very precisely when the weights of two bodies are equal, and hence when their masses are equal.

It will be seen from the preceding discussion that the property of matter called *mass* makes itself evident in two very different ways. The force of gravitational attraction between two particles is said to be proportional to the product of their masses, and in this sense mass can be considered as *that property of matter by virtue of which every particle exerts a force of attraction on every other particle.* We may call this property *gravitational mass.* On the other hand, Newton's second law is concerned with an entirely different property of matter, namely, the fact that a force (not necessarily gravitational) must be exerted on a particle in order to accelerate it, i.e., to change its velocity, either in magnitude or direction. This property can be called *inertial mass.* It is not at all obvious that the gravitational mass of a particle should be the same as its inertial mass, but experiment shows that the two are in fact the same or, better, that one is directly proportional to the other. That is, if we have to push twice as hard on body *A* as we do on body *B* to produce a given acceleration, then the force of gravitational attraction between body *A* and some third body *C* is twice as great as the gravitational attraction between body *B* and body *C*, the distance between them being the same. Since the two kinds of mass are proportional, it is customary to consider them equal. Thus when an equal-arm balance is used to compare masses, it is actually *gravitational* mass that is being measured. By convention, we assign the same numerical value to the inertial mass. Therefore the property represented by *m* in Newton's second law can be operationally defined as the result obtained by the prescribed methods of using an equal-arm balance.

5–6 Applications of Newton's second law

We now give a number of applications of Newton's second law to specific problems. In all these examples, and in the problems at the end of the chapter, it will be assumed that the acceleration due to gravity is 9.80 m/sec^2 or 32.0 ft/sec^2, unless otherwise specified.

EXAMPLE 1.   A block whose mass is 10 kgm rests on a horizontal surface. What constant horizontal force **T** is required to give it a velocity of 4 m/sec in 2 sec, starting from rest, if the friction force between the block and the surface is constant and is equal to 5 newtons? Assume that all forces act at the center of the block. (See Fig. 5–3.)

The mass of the block is given. Its *y*-acceleration is zero. Its *x*-acceleration can be found from the data on the velocity acquired in a given time. Since the forces are constant, the *x*-acceleration is constant and from the equations of motion with constant acceleration,

$$a_x = \frac{v - v_0}{t} = \frac{4 \text{ m/sec} - 0}{2 \text{ sec}} = 2 \frac{\text{m}}{\text{sec}^2}.$$

The resultant of the *x*-forces is

$$\Sigma F_x = T - f,$$

and that of the *y*-forces is

$$\Sigma F_y = N - w.$$

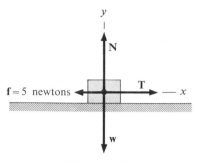

Figure 5–3.

Fig. 5–4. The resultant force is $\mathbf{T} - \mathbf{w}$.

Hence from Newton's second law in component form,

$$T - f = ma_x, \qquad N - w = ma_y = 0.$$

From the second equation, we find that

$$N = w = mg = 10 \text{ kgm} \times 9.80 \text{ m/sec}^2 = 98.0 \text{ n},$$

and from the first,

$$T = f + ma_x = 5 \text{ n} + 10 \text{ kgm} \times 2 \text{ m/sec}^2 = 25 \text{ n}.$$

EXAMPLE 2. An elevator and its load weigh a total of 1600 lb. Find the tension $\mathbf{T}$ in the supporting cable when the elevator, originally moving downward at 20 ft/sec, is brought to rest with constant acceleration in a distance of 50 ft. (See Fig. 5–4.)

The mass of the elevator is

$$m = \frac{w}{g} = \frac{1600 \text{ lb}}{32 \text{ ft/sec}^2} = 50 \text{ slugs}.$$

From the equations of motion with constant acceleration,

$$v^2 = v_0^2 + 2ay, \qquad a - \frac{v^2 - v_0^2}{2y}.$$

The initial velocity v_0 is -20 ft/sec; the velocity v is zero. If we take the origin at the point where the deceleration begins, then $y = -50$ ft. Hence

$$a = \frac{0 - (-20 \text{ ft/sec})^2}{-2 \times 50 \text{ ft}} = 4 \frac{\text{ft}}{\text{sec}^2}.$$

The acceleration is therefore positive (upward). From the free-body diagram (Fig. 5–4) the resultant force is

$$\Sigma F = T - w = T - 1600 \text{ lb}.$$

Since

$$\Sigma F = ma, \qquad T - 1600 \text{ lb} = 50 \text{ slugs} \times 4 \text{ ft/sec}^2 = 200 \text{ lb}, \qquad T = 1800 \text{ lb}.$$

EXAMPLE 3.   What is the acceleration of a block on a frictionless plane inclined at an angle θ with the horizontal?

The only forces acting on the block are its weight $\mathbf{w}$ and the normal force $\mathbf{N}$ exerted by the plane (Fig. 5–5).

Take axes parallel and perpendicular to the surface of the plane and resolve the weight into x- and y-components. Then

$$\sum F_y = N - w \cos \theta, \qquad \sum F_x = w \sin \theta.$$

But we know that $a_y = 0$, so from the equation $\sum F_y = ma_y$ we find that $N = w \cos \theta$. From the equation $\sum F_x = ma_x$, we have

$$w \sin \theta = ma_x,$$

and since $w = mg$,

$$a_x = g \sin \theta.$$

The mass does not appear in the final result, which means that any block, regardless of its mass, will slide on a frictionless inclined plane with an acceleration down the plane of $g \sin \theta$. (Note that the *velocity* is not necessarily down the plane.)

EXAMPLE 4.   Refer to Fig. 2–4 (Chapter 2). Let the mass of the block be 4 kgm and that of the rope be 0.5 kgm. If the force $\mathbf{F}_1$ is 9 newtons, what are the forces $\mathbf{F}'_1$, $\mathbf{F}_2$, and $\mathbf{F}'_2$? The surface on which the block moves is level and frictionless.

We know from Newton's third law that $F_1 = F'_1$ and that $F_2 = F'_2$. Hence $F'_1 = 9$ newtons. The force F_2 could be computed by applying Newton's second law to the block, if its acceleration were known, or the force F'_2 could be computed by applying this law to the rope if its acceleration were known. The acceleration is not given, but it can be found by considering the block and rope together as a single system. The vertical forces on this system need not be considered. Since there is no friction, the resultant *external* force acting *on* the system is the force F_1. (The forces F_2 and F'_2 are *internal* forces when we consider block and rope as a single system, and the force F'_1 does not act on the system, but *on the man*.) Then, from Newton's second law,

$$\sum F = ma,$$
$$9 \text{ n} = (4 \text{ kgm} + 0.5 \text{ kgm}) \times a,$$
$$a = 2 \frac{\text{m}}{\text{sec}^2}.$$

We can now apply Newton's second law to the block.

$$\sum F = ma,$$
$$F_2 = 4 \text{ kgm} \times 2 \frac{\text{m}}{\text{sec}^2} = 8 \text{ n}.$$

Considering the rope alone, the resultant force on it is

$$\sum F = F_1 - F'_2 = 9 \text{ n} - F'_2,$$

and from the second law,

$$9 \text{ n} - F'_2 = 0.5 \text{ kgm} \times 2 \frac{\text{m}}{\text{sec}^2} = 1 \text{ n},$$
$$F'_2 = 8 \text{ n}.$$

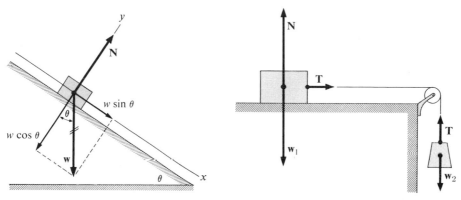

Fig. 5–5. A block on a frictionless inclined plane.   **Figure 5–6.**

In agreement with Newton's third law, which was tacitly used when the forces F_2 and F'_2 were omitted in considering the system as a whole, we find that F_2 and F'_2 are equal in magnitude. Notice, however, that the forces F_1 and F_2 are *not* equal and opposite (the rope is not in equilibrium) and that these forces are *not* an action-reaction pair.

EXAMPLE 5. In Fig. 5–6, a block of weight w_1 (mass $= m_1$) moves on a level frictionless surface, connected by a light flexible cord passing over a small frictionless pulley to a second hanging block of weight w_2 (mass $= m_2$). What is the acceleration of the system, and what is the tension in the cord connecting the two blocks?

The diagram shows the forces acting on each block. The forces exerted on the blocks by the cord can be considered an action-reaction pair, so we have used the same symbol **T** for each. For the block on the surface,

$$\Sigma F_x = T = m_1 a,$$

$$\Sigma F_y = N - w_1 = 0.$$

Since the cord connecting the two blocks is inextensible, the accelerations are the same. Applying Newton's second law to the hanging block, we obtain

$$\Sigma F_y = w_2 - T = m_2 a.$$

Addition of the first and third equations gives

$$w_2 = (m_1 + m_2)a,$$

or

$$a = \frac{w_2}{m_1 + m_2},$$

which says that the acceleration of the *entire system* equals the *resultant external force* (w_2) divided by the *total mass* ($m_1 + m_2$). Since $w_2 = m_2 g$,

$$a = g\,\frac{m_2}{m_1 + m_2}.$$

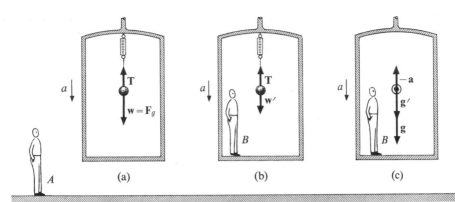

Fig. 5–7. (a) To observer A, the body has a downward acceleration a, and he writes $w - T = ma$. (b) To observer B, the acceleration of the body is zero. He writes $w' = T$. (c) To observer B, the free fall acceleration $g' = g - a$.

Eliminating a from the first and third equations, we get

$$T = w_2 \frac{m_1}{m_1 + m_2},$$

so that T is *only a fraction* of w_2. Although the earth pulls on the *hanging* block with a force w_2, the force exerted on the *sliding* block is only a fraction of w_2. It is not the earth that pulls on the sliding block, but the cord, whose tension *must be less than* w_2 if the hanging block is to accelerate downward.

EXAMPLE 6.   A body of mass m is suspended from a spring balance attached to the roof of an elevator, as shown in Fig. 5–7. What is the reading of the balance if the elevator has an acceleration **a**, relative to the earth? Consider the earth's surface to be an inertial reference system.

The forces on the body are its weight **w** (the gravitational force $\mathbf{F}_g$ exerted on it by the earth) and the upward force **T** exerted on it by the balance. The body is at rest relative to the elevator, and hence has an acceleration **a** relative to the earth. (We take the downward direction as positive.) The resultant force on the body is $w - T$, so from Newton's second law,

$$w - T = ma, \qquad T = w - ma.$$

By Newton's third law, the body pulls down on the balance with a force equal and opposite to **T**, or equal to $w - ma$, so the balance reading equals $w - ma$.

If the same body were suspended in equilibrium from a balance attached to the earth, the balance reading would equal the weight w. To an observer riding in the elevator, the body *appears* to be in equilibrium and hence *appears* to be acted on by a downward force **w'** equal in magnitude to the balance reading, as in Fig. 5–7(b). This *apparent* force **w'** can be called the *apparent weight* of the body. The gravitational force **w** will be called the *true weight*. Then

$$w' = w - ma. \tag{5–8}$$

If the elevator is at rest, or moving vertically (either up or down) with constant velocity, $a = 0$ and the apparent weight equals the true weight. If the acceleration is downward, as in Fig. 5–7, so that a is positive, the apparent weight is less than the true weight; the body appears "lighter." If the acceleration is *upward*, a is negative, the apparent weight is greater than the true weight, and the body appears "heavier." If the elevator falls freely, $a = g$, and since the true weight w also equals mg, the apparent weight is zero and the body *appears* "weightless." It is in this sense that an astronaut orbiting the earth in a space capsule is said to be "weightless." We shall return to this question after considering circular motion in the next chapter.

The problem can be considered from another viewpoint. On the assumption that the earth is an inertial system, the weight of a body is given by

$$\mathbf{w} = m\mathbf{g}, \tag{5-9}$$

where $\mathbf{g}$ is the free-fall acceleration, *relative to the earth*. Suppose the body in Fig. 5–7(c) is released and allowed to fall freely. What is its acceleration $\mathbf{g}'$ *relative to the elevator?*

We showed in Chapter 4 that the velocities of a particle P relative to two systems A and B, which are in motion relative to each other, are related by the equation

$$\mathbf{v}_{PB} = \mathbf{v}_{PA} + \mathbf{v}_{AB} = \mathbf{v}_{PA} - \mathbf{v}_{BA},$$

where $\mathbf{v}_{BA}$ is the velocity of system B relative to system A. Taking the derivative with respect to t, we get

$$\frac{d\mathbf{v}_{PB}}{dt} = \frac{d\mathbf{v}_{PA}}{dt} - \frac{d\mathbf{v}_{BA}}{dt},$$

or

$$\mathbf{a}_{PB} = \mathbf{a}_{PA} - \mathbf{a}_{BA}.$$

(This equation is correct provided that there is no relative rotation of the axes in systems A and B.)

Let system B be the elevator and system A the earth. The $\mathbf{a}_{PB}$ corresponds to the free-fall acceleration $\mathbf{g}'$ relative to the elevator, $\mathbf{a}_{PA}$ to the free-fall acceleration $\mathbf{g}$ relative to the earth, and $\mathbf{a}_{BA}$ to the acceleration $\mathbf{a}$ of the elevator relative to the earth. Hence

$$g' = g - a \tag{5-10}$$

and

$$mg' = mg - ma.$$

But mg equals the true weight w, and $w - ma$ equals the apparent weight w', so

$$w' = mg', \tag{5-11}$$

which has the same *form* as Eq. (5–9). That is, if a body falls freely in the elevator, its observed acceleration $\mathbf{g}'$, *relative to the elevator*, is the same as if it fell freely in an inertial system, under the action of a force $\mathbf{w}'$ equal to its *apparent* weight.

EXAMPLE 7. Figure 5–8(a) represents a simple *accelerometer*. A small body is fastened at one end of a light rod pivoted freely at the point P. When the system has an acceleration a toward the right, the rod makes an angle θ with the vertical. (In a practical instrument, some form of damping must be provided to avoid violent swinging of the rod when the acceleration changes. The rod might hang in a tank of mineral oil.)

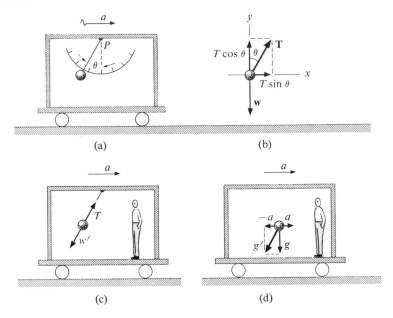

Fig. 5–8. (a) A simple accelerometer. (b) The forces on the body are **w** and **T**. (c) The apparent weight **w'** is equal and opposite to **T**. (d) The free-fall acceleration **g'**, relative to the accelerometer, is given by the equation **g'** = **g** − **a**.

As shown in the free-body diagram, Fig. 5–8(b), two forces are exerted on the body; its weight **w** and the tension **T** in the rod. (We neglect the weight of the rod.) The resultant horizontal force is

$$\sum F_x = T \sin \theta,$$

and the resultant vertical force is

$$\sum F_y = T \cos \theta - w.$$

The x-acceleration is the acceleration a of the system, and the y-acceleration is zero. Hence

$$T \sin \theta = ma, \qquad T \cos \theta = w.$$

When the first equation is divided by the second, and w replaced by mg, we get

$$a = g \tan \theta,$$

and the acceleration a is proportional to the tangent of the angle θ.

Let us consider this problem from the standpoint of an observer riding with the accelerometer, as in Fig. 5–8(c). To him, the body *appears* in equilibrium and hence appears to be acted on by a force **w'**, equal and opposite to **T**, and which he calls the *apparent weight* of the body. To obtain the expression for **w'**, let us write Newton's second law in general vector form. The resultant force on the body is the vector sum of **w** and **T**, and hence

$$\mathbf{w} + \mathbf{T} = m\mathbf{a}, \qquad \mathbf{T} = -\mathbf{w} + m\mathbf{a}.$$

The apparent weight $\mathbf{w}'$ is equal and opposite to $\mathbf{T}$, so $\mathbf{w}' = -\mathbf{T}$ and

$$\mathbf{w}' = \mathbf{w} - m\mathbf{a}. \tag{5–12}$$

This is the general form of Eq. (5–8) for the apparent weight $\mathbf{w}'$ of a body, relative to a system which has an acceleration $\mathbf{a}$ relative to an inertial system. In this example, *the apparent weight differs in both magnitude and direction from the true weight*.

The free-fall acceleration $\mathbf{g}'$ relative to the accelerometer, from Eq. (5–10), is

$$\mathbf{g}' = \mathbf{g} - \mathbf{a},$$

as shown in Fig. 5–8(d). Therefore

$$m\mathbf{g}' = m\mathbf{g} - m\mathbf{a},$$

and again

$$\mathbf{w}' = m\mathbf{g}'.$$

Relative to the accelerometer, the free-fall acceleration $\mathbf{g}'$ is in the direction of the apparent weight $\mathbf{w}'$ and its magnitude is

$$g' = w'/m.$$

Up to this point, applications of Newton's second law have been limited to cases where the resultant force acting on a body was constant, thereby imparting to the body a constant acceleration. Such cases are very important, but make only slight demands on one's mathematical knowledge. When the resultant force is variable, however, the acceleration is not constant and the simple equations of motion with constant acceleration do not apply. We conclude this section with two examples of motion under the action of a variable force.

Example 8. Assume the earth to be a nonrotating, homogeneous sphere. Discuss the motion of a freely falling body (or a body projected vertically upward), taking into account the variation of the gravitational force on the body with its distance from the earth's center. Neglect air resistance.

The gravitational force on the body at a distance r from the earth's center is Gmm_E/r^2, and from Newton's second law its acceleration is

$$g = \frac{w}{m} = -\frac{Gm_E}{r^2},$$

where the positive direction is upward (or better, radially outward).

It was shown in Eq. (4–8) that the acceleration can be expressed as

$$g = v\frac{dv}{dr}.$$

Then

$$v\frac{dv}{dr} = -\frac{Gm_E}{r^2}, \qquad \int_{v_1}^{v_2} v\,dv = -Gm_E\int_{r_1}^{r_2}\frac{dr}{r^2},$$

where v_1 and v_2 are the velocities at the radial distances r_1 and r_2. It follows that

$$v_2^2 - v_1^2 = 2Gm_E\left(\frac{1}{r_2} - \frac{1}{r_1}\right). \tag{5–13}$$

As an illustration, let us find the initial velocity v_1 required to project a body vertically upward so that it rises to a height above the earth's surface equal to the earth's radius R. Then $v_2 = 0$, $r_1 = R$, $r_2 = 2R$, and

$$v_1^2 = \frac{Gm_E}{R} \, . \tag{5–14}$$

Let g_0 represent the acceleration of gravity at the earth's surface, where $r = R$. Then

$$Gm_E = g_0 R^2,$$

and Eq. (5–14) can be written

$$v_1^2 = g_0 R. \tag{5–15}$$

How does this compare with the velocity that would be required if the acceleration had the *constant* value g_0?

EXAMPLE 9.   A resisting force that varies directly with the speed is found frequently in nature. Any small spherical body of radius r, like a raindrop, an oil droplet, or a steel sphere, moving with a small velocity $\mathbf{v}$ through a viscous fluid (liquid or gas) is subjected to a force $\mathbf{R}$, where

$$\mathbf{R} = -6\pi\eta r\mathbf{v},$$

and η is the viscosity. This relation is known as *Stokes' law.* Letting

$$k = 6\pi\eta r,$$

we may write Stokes' law simply as

$$\mathbf{R} = -k\mathbf{v}.$$

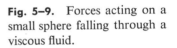

Fig. 5–9. Forces acting on a small sphere falling through a viscous fluid.

A small sphere falling through a viscous fluid is subjected to three vertical forces, as shown in Fig. 5–9: the weight $\mathbf{w}$, the buoyant force $\mathbf{B}$, and the resisting force $\mathbf{R}$.

Let us suppose that the sphere starts from rest and that the positive y-direction is downward. Then

$$\sum F_y = w - B - kv = ma.$$

At first, when $v = 0$, the resisting force is zero and the initial acceleration a_0 is positive:

$$a_0 = \frac{w - B}{m} \, . \tag{5–16}$$

The sphere speeds up and, after a while, when v becomes large enough, the resisting force equals $w - B$ and there is no resultant force acting on the sphere. At this moment the acceleration is zero and the speed undergoes no further increase. The maximum or *terminal speed* v_T may therefore be calculated by setting $a = 0$; thus

$$w - B - kv_T = 0$$

or

$$v_T = \frac{w - B}{k} \, . \tag{5–17}$$

To find the relation between the speed and the time during the interval before the terminal speed is reached, we go back to Newton's second law,

$$m \frac{dv}{dt} = w - B - kv.$$

After rearranging terms and replacing $(w - B)/k$ by v_T, we get

$$\frac{dv}{v - v_T} = - \frac{k}{m} dt.$$

Since $v = 0$ when $t = 0$,

$$\int_0^v \frac{dv}{v - v_T} = - \frac{k}{m} \int_0^t dt,$$

whence

$$\ln \frac{v_T - v}{v_T} = - \frac{k}{m} t,$$

or

$$1 - \frac{v}{v_T} = e^{-(k/m) t},$$

and finally

$$v = v_T(1 - e^{-(k/m) t}). \qquad (5\text{--}18)$$

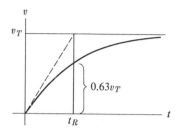

Fig. 5–10. Velocity-time graph for a body falling in a viscous medium.

An important concept related to an exponentially varying quantity is the *relaxation time*, t_R, whose meaning can be seen from Fig. 5–10. Suppose the acceleration remained constant at the initial value a_0, as indicated by the dashed line. The relaxation time can be defined as the time that *would* be required to reach the terminal velocity with this constant acceleration, and evidently

$$t_R = \frac{v_T}{a_0} = \frac{(w - B)/k}{(w - B)/m} = \frac{m}{k}.$$

Equation (5–18) can now be written more simply as

$$v = v_T(1 - e^{-t/t_R}). \qquad (5\text{--}16)$$

At the instant when t equals the relaxation time, $t/t_R = 1$ and

$$v = v_T(1 - e^{-1}) = 0.63 v_T.$$

Thus about 63% of the final velocity is actually acquired in a time equal to the relaxation time.

Problems

(For problem work, use the approximate values of $g = 32 \text{ ft/sec}^2 = 9.80 \text{ m/sec}^2 = 980 \text{ cm/sec}^2$. A force diagram should be constructed for each problem.)

5–1. (a) What is the mass of a body which weighs 1 newton at a point where $g = 9.80 \text{ m/sec}^2$? (b) What is the mass of a body which weighs 1 dyne at a point where $g = 980 \text{ cm/sec}^2$? (c) What is the mass of a standard pound body?

5–2. (a) At what distance from the earth's center would a standard kilogram weigh 1 newton? (b) At what distance would a 1-gm body weigh 1 dyne? (c) At what distance would a 1-slug body weigh 1 pound?

5–3. If action and reaction are always equal in magnitude and opposite in direction, why don't they always cancel each other and leave no net force for accelerating a body?

5–4. The mass of a certain object is 10 gm. (a) What would its mass be if taken to the planet Mars? (b) Is the expression $F = ma$ valid on Mars? (c) Newton's second law is sometimes written in the form $F = wa/g$ instead of $F = ma$. Would this expression be valid on Mars? (d) If a Martian scientist hangs a standard pound body on a spring balance calibrated correctly on the earth, would the spring balance read 1 lb? Explain.

5–5. A constant horizontal force of 10 lb acts on a body on a smooth horizontal plane. The body starts from rest and is observed to move 250 ft in 5 sec. (a) What is the mass of the body? (b) If the force ceases to act at the end of 5 sec, how far will the body move in the next 5 sec?

5–6. A .22 rifle bullet, traveling at 36,000 cm/sec, strikes a block of soft wood, which it penetrates to a depth of 10 cm. The mass of the bullet is 1.8 gm. Assume a constant retarding force. (a) How long a time was required for the bullet to stop? (b) What was the decelerating force, in dynes? in lb?

5–7. An electron (mass $= 9 \times 10^{-28}$ gm) leaves the cathode of a radio tube with zero initial velocity and travels in a straight line to the anode, which is 1 cm away. It reaches the anode with a velocity of 6×10^8 cm/sec. If the accelerating force was constant, compute (a) the accelerating force, in dynes, (b) the time to reach the anode, (c) the acceleration. The gravitational force on the electron may be neglected.

5–8. Give arguments either for or against the statement that "the only reason an apple falls downward to meet the earth instead of the earth falling upward to meet the apple is that the earth, being so much more massive, exerts the greater pull."

5–9. In an experiment using the Cavendish balance to measure the gravitational constant G, it is found that a sphere of mass 800 gm attracts another sphere of mass 4 gm with a force of 13×10^{-6} dyne when the distance between the centers of the spheres is 4 cm. The acceleration of gravity at the earth's surface is 980 cm/sec^2, and the radius of the earth is 6400 km. Compute the mass of the earth from these data.

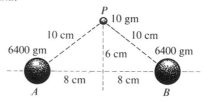

Figure 5–11

5–10. Two spheres, each of mass 6400 gm, are fixed at points A and B (Fig. 5–11). Find the magnitude and direction of the initial acceleration of a sphere of mass 10 gm if released from rest at point P and acted on only by forces of gravitational attraction of the spheres at A and B.

5–11. The mass of the moon is one eighty-first, and its radius one-fourth, that of the earth. What is the acceleration of gravity on the surface of the moon?

5–12. In round numbers, the distance from the earth to the moon is 250,000 mi, the distance from the earth to the sun is 93 million miles, the mass of the earth is 6×10^{27} gm, and the mass of the sun is 2×10^{33} gm. Approximately, what is the ratio of the gravitational pull of the sun on the moon to that of the earth on the moon?

5–13. A 5-kgm block is supported by a cord and pulled upward with an acceleration of 2 m/sec². (a) What is the tension in the cord? (b) After the block has been set in motion the tension in the cord is reduced to 49 n. What sort of motion will the block perform? (c) If the cord is now slackened completely, the block is observed to move up 2 m farther before coming to rest. With what velocity was it traveling?

5–14. A block weighing 10 lb is held up by a string which can be moved up or down. What conclusions can you draw regarding magnitude and direction of the acceleration and velocity of the upper end of the string when the tension in the string is (a) 5 lb, (b) 10 lb, (c) 15 lb?

5–15. A body hangs from a spring balance supported from the roof of an elevator. (a) If the elevator has an upward acceleration of 4 ft/sec² and the balance reads 45 lb, what is the true weight of the body? (b) Under what circumstances will the balance read 35 lb? (c) What will the balance read if the elevator cable breaks?

5–16. A transport plane is to take off from a level landing field with two gliders in tow, one behind the other. Each glider weighs 2400 lb, and the friction force or drag on each may be assumed constant and equal to 400 lb. The tension in the towrope between the transport plane and the first glider is not to exceed 2000 lb. (a) If a velocity of 100 ft/sec is required for the take-off, how long a runway is needed? (b) What is the tension in the towrope between the two gliders while the planes are accelerating for the take-off?

5–17. If the coefficient of friction between tires and road is 0.5, what is the shortest distance in which an automobile can be stopped when traveling at 60 mi/hr?

5–18. An 80-lb packing case is on the floor of a truck. The coefficient of static friction between the case and the truck floor is 0.30, and the coefficient of sliding friction is 0.20. Find the magnitude and direction of the friction force acting on the case (a) when the truck is accelerating at 6 ft/sec², (b) when it is decelerating at 10 ft/sec².

5–19. A balloon is descending with a constant acceleration a, less than the acceleration of gravity g. The weight of the balloon, with its basket and contents, is w. What weight, W, of ballast should be released so that the balloon will begin to be accelerated upward with constant acceleration a? Neglect air resistance.

5–20. A 64-lb block is pushed up a 37° inclined plane by a horizontal force of 100 lb. The coefficient of sliding friction is 0.25. Find (a) the acceleration, (b) the velocity of the block after it has moved a distance of 20 ft along the plane, and (c) the normal force exerted by the plane. Assume that all forces act at the center of the block.

5–21. A block rests on an inclined plane which makes an angle θ with the horizontal. The coefficient of sliding friction is 0.50, and the coefficient of static friction is 0.75. (a) As the angle θ is increased, find the minimum angle at which the block starts to slip. (b) At this angle, find the acceleration once the block has begun to move. (c) How long a time is required for the block to slip 20 ft along the inclined plane?

5–22. (a) What constant horizontal force is required to drag a 16-lb block along a horizontal surface with an acceleration of 4 ft/sec² if the coefficient of sliding friction between block and surface is 0.5? (b) What weight, hanging from a cord attached to the 16-lb block and passing over a small frictionless pulley, will produce this acceleration?

5–23. A block weighing 8 lb resting on a horizontal surface is connected by a cord passing over a light frictionless pulley to a hanging block weighing 8 lb. The coefficient of friction between the block and the horizontal surface is 0.5. Find (a) the tension in the cord, and (b) the acceleration of each block.

5–24. A block having a mass of 2 kgm is projected up a long 30° incline with an initial velocity of 22 m/sec. The coefficient of friction between the block and the plane is 0.3. (a) Find the friction force acting on the block as it moves up the plane. (b) How long does the block move up the plane? (c) How far does the block move up the plane? (d) How long does it take the block to slide down from its position in part (c) to its starting point? (e) With what velocity does it arrive at this point? (f) If the mass of the block had been 5 kgm instead of 2 kgm, would the answers in the preceding parts be changed?

5–25. A 30-lb block on a level frictionless surface is attached by a cord passing over a small frictionless pulley to a hanging block originally at rest 4 ft above the floor. The hanging block strikes the floor in 2 sec. (a) Find the weight of the hanging block. (b) Find the tension in the string while both blocks were in motion.

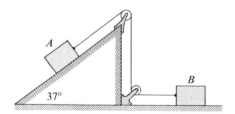

Figure 5–12

5–26. Two blocks, each having mass 20 kgm, rest on frictionless surfaces as shown in Fig. 5–12. Assuming the pulleys to be light and frictionless, compute: (a) the time required for block A to move 1 m down the plane, starting from rest, (b) the tension in the cord connecting the blocks.

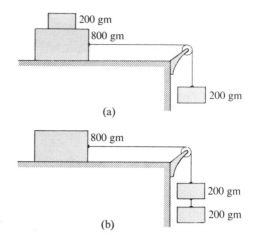

Figure 5–13

5–27. A block of mass 200 gm rests on the top of a block of mass 800 gm. The combination is dragged along a level surface at constant velocity by a hanging block of mass 200 gm as in Fig. 5–13(a). (a) The first 200-gm block is removed from the 800-gm block and attached to the hanging block, as in Fig. 5–13(b). What is now the acceleration of the system? (b) What is the tension in the cord attached to the 800-gm block in part (b) of the figure?

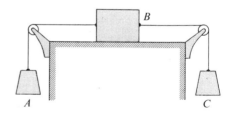

Figure 5–14

5–28. Block A in Fig. 5–14 weighs 3 lb and block B weighs 30 lb. The coefficient of friction between B and the horizontal surface is 0.1. (a) What is the weight of block C if the acceleration of B is 6 ft/sec^2 toward the right? (b) What is the tension in each cord when B has the acceleration stated above?

5–29. Two blocks connected by a cord passing over a small frictionless pulley rest

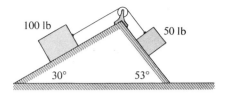

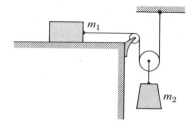

Figure 5–15

Figure 5–17

on frictionless planes as shown in Fig. 5–15.
(a) Which way will the system move?
(b) What is the acceleration of the blocks?
(c) What is the tension in the cord?

Figure 5–16

5–30. Two 100-gm blocks hang at the
ends of a light flexible cord passing over a
small frictionless pulley as in Fig. 5–16. A
40-gm block is placed on the block on the
right, and removed after 2 sec. (a) How far
will each block move in the first second
after the 40-gm block is removed?   (b)
What was the tension in the cord before the
40-gm block was removed?   after it was
removed? (c) What was the tension in the
cord supporting the pulley before the 40-gm
block was removed? Neglect the weight of
the pulley.

5–31. Two 10-lb blocks hang at the ends
of a cord as in Fig. 5–16. What weight
must be added to one of the blocks to cause
it to move down a distance of 4 ft in 2 sec?

5–32. In terms of m_1, m_2, and g, find the
accelerations of both blocks in Fig. 5–17.
Neglect all friction and the masses of the
pulleys.

5–33. The bodies A and B in Fig. 5–18
weigh 40 lb and 24 lb, respectively. They

are initially at rest on the floor and are
connected by a weightless string passing
over a weightless and frictionless pulley.
An upward force **F** is applied to the pulley.
Find the accelerations a_1 of body A and a_2
of body B when F is (a) 24 lb, (b) 40 lb,
(c) 72 lb, (d) 90 lb, (e) 120 lb.

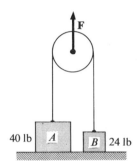

Figure 5–18

5–34. The two blocks in Fig. 5–19 are
connected by a heavy uniform rope which
weighs 8 lb. An upward force of 48 lb is
applied as shown. (a) What is the acceleration of the system? (b) What is the tension
at the top of the 8-lb rope? (c) What is
the tension at the midpoint of the rope?

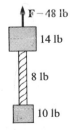

Figure 5–19

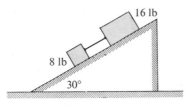

Figure 5–20

5–35. Two blocks, weighing 8 and 16 lb, respectively, are connected by a string and slide down a 30° inclined plane, as in Fig. 5–20. The coefficient of sliding friction between the 8-lb block and the plane is 0.25, and between the 16-lb block and the plane it is 0.50. (a) Calculate the acceleration of each block. (b) Calculate the tension in the string.

5–36. Two bodies weighing 10 lb and 6 lb, respectively, hang 4 ft above the floor from the ends of a cord 12 ft long passing over a frictionless pulley. Both bodies start from rest. Find the maximum height reached by the 6-lb body.

5–37. A man who weighs 160 lb stands on a platform which weighs 80 lb. He pulls a rope which is fastened to the platform and runs over a pulley on the ceiling. With what force does he have to pull in order to give himself and the platform an upward acceleration of 2 ft/sec²?

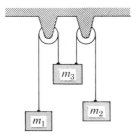

Figure 5–21

5–38. In Fig. 5–21 there is depicted a double Atwood's machine. Calculate the acceleration of the system and the tensions in the strings supporting the bodies of mass m_1 and m_2. Neglect friction and the masses of the pulleys.

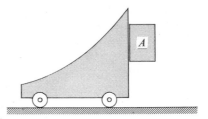

Figure 5–22

5–39. What acceleration must the cart in Fig. 5–22 have in order that the block A will not fall? The coefficient of friction between the block and the cart is μ. How would the behavior of the block be described by an observer on the cart?

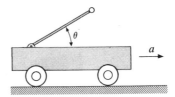

Figure 5–23

5–40. The left end of the weightless rod shown in Fig. 5–23 is hinged to a cart. A heavy particle is attached to the right end. If the cart has an acceleration a to the right, find the angle θ. How would this situation be described by an observer on the cart?

5–41. Which way will the accelerometer in Fig. 5–8 deflect under the following conditions: (a) The cart is moving toward the right and traveling faster. (b) The cart is moving toward the right and traveling more slowly. (c) The cart is moving toward the left and traveling faster. (d) The cart is moving toward the left and traveling more slowly. (e) The cart is at rest on a sloping surface. (f) The cart is given an upward velocity on a frictionless inclined plane. It first moves up, then stops, and then moves down. What is the deflection in each stage of the motion?

5–42. (a) In terms of the acceleration of gravity at the earth's surface, g_0, and the earth's radius R, find the velocity with which a body must be projected vertically upward, in the absence of air resistance, to rise to an infinite distance above the earth's surface. This is called the *escape velocity*. (b) In terms of the same quantities, find the velocity with which a body will strike the earth's surface if it falls from rest toward the earth from an infinitely distant point. (c) Compute both of these velocities in mi/hr. (d) Explain why the velocities are not infinitely large.

5–43. The mass of the motorboat in Problem 4–27 is 100 slugs. Find the force decelerating the boat (a) when its speed is 20 ft/sec, and (b) when its speed is 10 ft/sec. (c) If the boat is being towed at 10 ft/sec, what is the tension in the towline?

5–44. A body of mass $m = 5$ kgm falls from rest in a viscous medium. The body is acted on by a net constant downward force of 20 newtons, and by a viscous retarding force proportional to its speed and equal to $5v$, where v is the speed in m/sec. (a) Find the initial acceleration, a_0. (b) Find the acceleration when the speed is 3 m/sec. (c) Find the speed when the acceleration equals 0.1 a_0. (d) Find the terminal velocity, v_T. (e) Find the relaxation time, t_R. (f) Find the coordinate, velocity, and acceleration 2 sec after the start of the motion. (g) Find the time required to reach a

speed $0.9\,v_T$. (h) Construct a graph of v versus t, for a time of 3 sec.

5–45. A body falls from rest through a medium which exerts a resisting force that varies directly with the square of the velocity $(R = -kv^2)$. (a) Draw a diagram showing the direction of motion and indicate with the aid of vectors all of the forces acting on the body. (b) Apply Newton's second law and infer from the resulting equation the general properties of the motion. (c) Show that the body acquires a terminal velocity and calculate it. (d) Find the relaxation time. (e) Derive the equation for the velocity at any time.

5–46. A particle of mass m, originally at rest, is subjected to a force whose direction is constant but whose magnitude varies with the time according to the relation

$$F = F_0\left[1 - \left(\frac{t - T}{T}\right)^2\right],$$

where F_0 and T are constants. The force acts only for the time interval $2T$. (a) Make a rough graph of F versus t. (b) Prove that the speed v of the particle after a time $2T$ has elapsed is equal to $4F_0T/3m$. (c) Choose numbers for v, T, and m that might be appropriate to a batted baseball, and calculate the force F_0. Judge whether the answer is sensible.

CHAPTER **6**

Motion in a Plane

6–1 Motion in a plane

Thus far we have discussed only motion along a straight line, or *rectilinear motion*. In this chapter we shall consider *plane motion*, that is, motion in a curved path which lies in a fixed plane. Examples of such motion are the flight of a thrown or batted baseball, a projectile shot from a gun, a ball whirled at the end of a cord, the motion of the moon or of a satellite around the earth, and the motion of the planets around the sun.

If the motion is referred to a set of rectangular coordinate axes x and y, the equation of the path expresses y as a function of x, $y = f(x)$. Very often one is interested in the position of the moving body as a function of time. If s is the distance along the path from some fixed point to the position of the body, its position at any time is given by an equation of the form $s = f(t)$. It is usually simpler, however, to deal with the x- and y-coordinates separately and to describe the motion by the two equations

$$x = f_1(t), \qquad y = f_2(t). \tag{6–1}$$

These can be considered as *parametric equations* of the path, expressing the coordinates x and y in terms of the parameter t.

Problems in plane motion can be divided into two classes. In one, the motion of the particle is known and we wish to determine its velocity and acceleration and the resultant force acting on it. An example is that of a ball attached to a cord and whirled in a circle at constant speed. What is the tension in the cord? In the other, the force acting on a particle is known at every point of space and we wish to find the equation of motion of the particle. Examples are the orbit of a planet around the sun, or the path followed by a rocket.

6–2 Average and instantaneous velocity

Consider a particle moving along the curved path in Fig. 6–1(a). Points P and Q represent two positions of the particle. Its displacement as it moves from P to Q is the vector Δs. Just as in the case of rectilinear motion, the average velocity $\bar{v}$ of the particle is defined as the vector displacement Δs divided by the elapsed time Δt:

$$\text{Average velocity } \bar{v} = \Delta s/\Delta t. \tag{6–2}$$

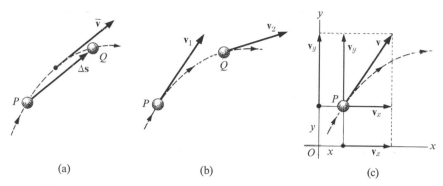

(a)   (b)   (c)

Fig. 6–1. (a) The vector $\bar{\mathbf{v}} = \Delta\mathbf{s}/\Delta t$ represents the average velocity between P and Q. (b) Vectors $\mathbf{v}_1$ and $\mathbf{v}_2$ represent the instantaneous velocities at P and Q. (c) The velocities $\mathbf{v}_x$ and $\mathbf{v}_y$ of the projections of P are the rectangular components of $\mathbf{v}$.

The average velocity would be the same for any path that would take the particle from P to Q in the time interval Δt.

Average velocity is a vector quantity, in the same direction as the vector $\Delta\mathbf{s}$. Because it is associated with the entire displacement $\Delta\mathbf{s}$, the vector $\bar{\mathbf{v}}$ has been constructed in Fig. 6–1(a) at a point midway between P and Q.

The *instantaneous* velocity $\mathbf{v}$ at the point P is defined in magnitude and direction as the limit approached by the average velocity when point Q is taken closer and closer to point P:

$$\text{Instantaneous velocity } \mathbf{v} = \lim_{\Delta t \to 0} \frac{\Delta\mathbf{s}}{\Delta t} = \frac{d\mathbf{s}}{dt}. \tag{6–3}$$

As point Q approaches point P, the direction of the vector $\Delta\mathbf{s}$ approaches that of the tangent to the path at P, so that the instantaneous velocity vector at any point is tangent to the path at that point. The instantaneous velocities at points P and Q are shown in Fig. 6–1(b).

In Fig. 6–1(c), the motion of a particle is referred to a rectangular coordinate system. As the particle moves along its path, its projections onto the x- and y-axes move along these axes in rectilinear motion, with velocities of magnitudes

$$v_x = \frac{dx}{dt}, \qquad v_y = \frac{dy}{dt}.$$

The velocities of the projections, however, are also the rectangular components of the velocity $\mathbf{v}$ of the particle. Thus if the x- and y-coordinates of the particle are known as functions of time, the components v_x and v_y can be found by differentiation and these can then be added vectorially as in Fig. 6–1(c) to obtain the magnitude and direction of the velocity $\mathbf{v}$. The direction of the path is then determined also, since $\mathbf{v}$ is tangent to the path.

Conversely, if the velocities v_x and v_y are known as functions of time, the coordinates x and y can be found by integration.

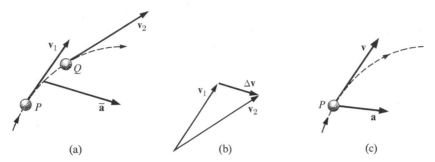

Fig. 6–2. (a) The vector $\bar{\mathbf{a}} = \Delta\mathbf{v}/\Delta t$ represents the average acceleration between P and Q. (b) Construction for obtaining $\Delta\mathbf{v} = \mathbf{v}_2 - \mathbf{v}_1$. (c) Instantaneous velocity $\mathbf{v}$ and instantaneous acceleration $\mathbf{a}$ at point P. Vector $\mathbf{v}$ is tangent to path; vector $\mathbf{a}$ points toward concave side of path.

6–3 Average and instantaneous acceleration

In Fig. 6–2(a), the vectors $\mathbf{v}_1$ and $\mathbf{v}_2$ represent the instantaneous velocities, at points P and Q, of a particle moving in a curved path. The velocity $\mathbf{v}_2$ necessarily differs in *direction* from the velocity $\mathbf{v}_1$. The diagram has been constructed for a case in which it differs in *magnitude* also, although in special cases the magnitude of the velocity may remain constant.

The *average acceleration* $\bar{\mathbf{a}}$ of the particle as it moves from P to Q is defined, just as in the case of rectilinear motion, as the *vector change in velocity*, $\Delta\mathbf{v}$, divided by the time interval Δt:

$$\text{Average acceleration } \bar{\mathbf{a}} = \frac{\Delta\mathbf{v}}{\Delta t}. \qquad (6\text{–}4)$$

Average acceleration is a vector quantity, in the same direction as the vector $\Delta\mathbf{v}$. The vector change in velocity, $\Delta\mathbf{v}$, means the vector difference $\mathbf{v}_2 - \mathbf{v}_1$:

$$\Delta\mathbf{v} = \mathbf{v}_2 - \mathbf{v}_1,$$

or

$$\mathbf{v}_2 = \mathbf{v}_1 + \Delta\mathbf{v}.$$

As explained in Section 1–10, the vector difference $\Delta\mathbf{v}$ can be found by drawing the vectors $\mathbf{v}_1$ and $\mathbf{v}_2$ from a common point, as in Fig. 6–2(b), and constructing the vector from the tip of $\mathbf{v}_1$ to the tip of $\mathbf{v}_2$. Then $\mathbf{v}_2$ is the vector sum of $\mathbf{v}_1$ and $\Delta\mathbf{v}$.

The average acceleration vector, $\bar{\mathbf{a}} = \Delta\mathbf{v}/\Delta t$, is shown in Fig. 6–2(a) at a point midway between P and Q.

The *instantaneous acceleration* $\mathbf{a}$ at point P is defined in magnitude and direction as the limit approached by the average acceleration when point Q approaches point P and $\Delta\mathbf{v}$ and Δt both approach zero:

$$\text{Instantaneous acceleration } \mathbf{a} = \lim_{\Delta t \to 0} \frac{\Delta\mathbf{v}}{\Delta t} = \frac{d\mathbf{v}}{dt}. \qquad (6\text{–}5)$$

The instantaneous acceleration vector at point P is shown in Fig. 6–2(c). Note that it does *not* have the same direction as the velocity vector. Reference to the construction of Fig. 6–2(b) will show that the acceleration vector must always lie on the *concave* side of the curved path.

6–4 Components of acceleration

Figure 6–3(a) again shows the motion of a particle referred to a rectangular coordinate system. The accelerations of the projections of the particle onto the x- and y-axes are

$$a_x = \frac{dv_x}{dt} = \frac{d^2x}{dt^2}, \qquad a_y = \frac{dv_y}{dt} = \frac{d^2y}{dt^2}.$$

These accelerations, however, are also the rectangular components of the acceleration $\mathbf{a}$ of the particle. Thus if the x- and y-coordinates of the particle are known as functions of time, the components a_x and a_y can be found by differentiation and these can then be combined vectorially as in Fig. 6–3(a) to obtain the magnitude and direction of the acceleration $\mathbf{a}$. When this is known, the force on the particle can be found, in magnitude and direction, from Newton's second law,

$$\mathbf{F} = m\frac{d\mathbf{v}}{dt} = m\mathbf{a}.$$

Conversely, if the force $\mathbf{F}$ is known at every point, the acceleration $\mathbf{a}$ and its components $\mathbf{a}_x$ and $\mathbf{a}_y$ can be found from Newton's second law. One integration then gives the velocity components v_x and v_y, and a second integration gives the coordinates x and y.

The acceleration of a particle moving in a curved path can also be resolved into rectangular components $\mathbf{a}_N$ and $\mathbf{a}_T$, in directions *normal* and *tangential* to the path, as shown in Fig. 6–3(b). Unlike the rectangular components referred to a set of

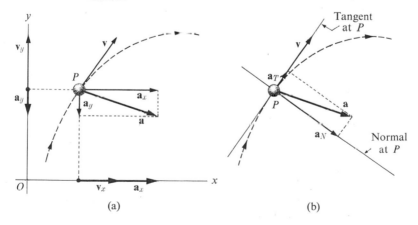

(a)   (b)

Fig. 6–3. In (a) the acceleration $\mathbf{a}$ is resolved into rectangular components $\mathbf{a}_x$ and $\mathbf{a}_y$. In (b) it is resolved into a normal component $\mathbf{a}_N$ and a tangential component $\mathbf{a}_T$.

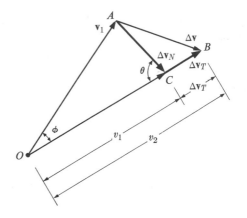

Fig. 6–4. The vector $\Delta\mathbf{v}$ is resolved into normal and tangential components $\Delta\mathbf{v}_N$ and $\Delta\mathbf{v}_T$. The normal component is the change in velocity resulting from the change in *direction* of $\mathbf{v}$; the tangential component is the change resulting from a change in the *magnitude* of $\mathbf{v}$.

fixed axes, the normal and tangential components do not have fixed directions in space. They do, however, have the following physical significance, namely, the component $\mathbf{a}_T$ arises from a change in the *magnitude* of the velocity vector $\mathbf{v}$, while the component $\mathbf{a}_N$ arises from a change in the *direction* of the velocity.

This is illustrated in Fig. 6–4, which corresponds to Fig. 6–2(b). The vector from O to A represents the velocity $\mathbf{v}_1$ of a particle at point P in Fig. 6–2(a), and the vector from O to B represents the velocity $\mathbf{v}_2$ at point Q. The change in velocity, $\Delta\mathbf{v}$, is given by the vector from A to B.

Note that the vectors $\Delta\mathbf{v}$ in Figs. 6–4 and 6–2(b) have the same direction and (apart from the difference in scale of the two diagrams) the same length.

The vector from O to C, in Fig. 6–4, has the same length as $\mathbf{v}_1$. The vector $\Delta\mathbf{v}$ can be resolved into components represented by the vectors from A to C, and from C to B. The length of the vector from C to B equals the difference in *length* between the vectors $\mathbf{v}_2$ and $\mathbf{v}_1$. That is, this vector represents the change in *magnitude* of the velocity, and when divided by Δt gives the component of average acceleration resulting from this change in magnitude.

If the magnitude of the velocity did *not* change between points P and Q, the velocity $\mathbf{v}_2$ at point Q would be represented by the vector from O to C in Fig. 6–4. In this case, however, *there would still be a change in the vector velocity*, represented by the vector from A to C. This change would result from the change in *direction* of the velocity vector, and when divided by Δt would give the component of average acceleration resulting from this change in direction. That is, *motion in a curved path with constant speed is accelerated motion*, because velocity is a vector quantity which can change in magnitude, in direction, or, as in Fig. 6–4, in both.

Now suppose that point Q in Fig. 6–2(a) approaches point P. The vector from O to B in Fig. 6–4 then swings upward toward the vector $\mathbf{v}_1$. The angle ϕ becomes smaller and smaller and the angle θ approaches 90°. The vector from A to C becomes more and more nearly perpendicular to $\mathbf{v}_1$ and the vector from C to B becomes more and more nearly parallel to $\mathbf{v}_1$. In the limit, the vector from A to C becomes normal to $\mathbf{v}_1$ (and hence normal to the path) and the vector from C to B becomes parallel to $\mathbf{v}_1$ (and hence tangent to the path). Thus although the vectors labeled $\Delta\mathbf{v}_N$ and $\Delta\mathbf{v}_T$ in Fig. 6–4 are not normal and parallel to $\mathbf{v}_1$ in this figure, they become so in the limit as point Q approaches point P. The limiting value of $\Delta v_N/\Delta t$ equals the normal component of acceleration a_N, and the limiting value of $\Delta v_T/\Delta t$ equals the tangential component of acceleration a_T.

Is the acceleration resulting from a change in the *direction* of a velocity as "real" as that arising from a change in its *magnitude*? From a purely kinematical viewpoint the answer is of course "Yes," since by definition acceleration equals the vector rate of change of velocity. A more satisfying answer is that a force must be exerted on a body to change its direction of motion, as well as to increase or decrease its speed. In the absence of an external force, a body continues to move not only with constant speed but also *in a straight line*. When a body moves in a *curved* path, a transverse force must be exerted on it to deviate it sidewise, and the ratio of transverse force to normal acceleration is found to equal the ratio of longitudinal force to longitudinal acceleration. That is, if $\mathbf{F}_N$ and $\mathbf{F}_T$ are the normal and tangential components of the force $\mathbf{F}$ on a body moving in a curved path, Newton's second law (with the same value of m) applies to both of these components:

$$F_N = ma_N, \qquad F_T = ma_T.$$

In fact, the usual experimental method of measuring the mass of an individual ion is to project it into a magnetic field. The magnetic field exerts a transverse force on the ion and the mass of the ion is obtained by dividing this force by the measured transverse acceleration.

It follows from the discussion above that if the force on a particle is always normal to the path, then $F_T = 0$, $a_T = 0$, and the particle has no tangential component of acceleration. The *magnitude* of the velocity then remains constant and the only effect of the force is to change the direction of motion, that is, to deviate the particle sidewise.

If the force has no normal component, then $F_N = 0$, $a_N = 0$, and there is no change in the *direction* of the velocity; that is, the particle moves in a straight line.

6–5 Motion of a projectile

Any object that is given an initial velocity and which subsequently follows a path determined by the gravitational force acting on it and by the frictional resistance of the atmosphere is called a *projectile*. Thus the term applies to a missile shot from a gun, a rocket after its fuel is exhausted, a bomb released from an airplane, or a thrown or batted baseball. The motion of a freely falling body discussed in Chapter 4 is a special case of projectile motion. The path followed by a projectile is called its *trajectory*.

The gravitational force on a projectile is directed toward the center of the earth and is inversely proportional to the square of the distance from the earth's center. We shall consider only trajectories which are of sufficiently short range so that the gravitational force can be considered constant in magnitude and direction. The motion will be referred to axes fixed with respect to the earth. Since this is not an inertial system, it is not strictly correct to use Newton's second law to relate the force on the projectile to its acceleration. However, for trajectories of short range the error

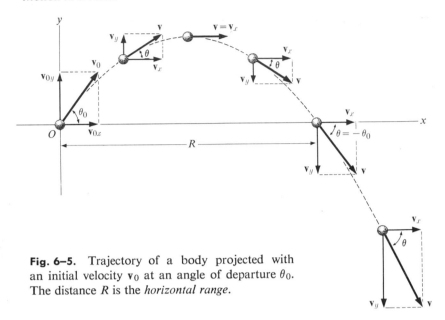

Fig. 6-5. Trajectory of a body projected with an initial velocity v_0 at an angle of departure θ_0. The distance R is the *horizontal range*.

is very small. Finally, all effects of air resistance will be ignored, so that our results apply only to motion in a vacuum on a flat, nonrotating earth.

Since the only force on a projectile in this idealized case is its weight, considered constant in magnitude and direction, the motion is best referred to a set of rectangular coordinate axes. We shall take the x-axis horizontal, the y-axis vertical, and the origin at the point where the projectile starts its free flight, for example at the muzzle of a gun or the point where it leaves the thrower's hand. The x-component of the force on the projectile is then zero and the y-component is the weight of the projectile, $-mg$. Then from Newton's second law,

$$a_x = \frac{F_x}{m} = 0, \qquad a_y = \frac{F_y}{m} = \frac{-mg}{m} = -g.$$

That is, the horizontal component of acceleration is zero and the vertical component is downward and equal to that of a freely falling body. The forward component of velocity does not "support" the projectile in flight. Since zero acceleration means constant velocity, the motion can be described as a combination of *horizontal motion with constant velocity* and *vertical motion with constant acceleration*.

Consider next the velocity of the projectile. In Fig. 6-5, x- and y-axes have been constructed with the origin at the point where the projectile begins its free flight. We shall set $t = 0$ at this point. The velocity at the origin is represented by the vector v_0, called the *initial velocity* or the *muzzle velocity* if the projectile is shot from a gun. The angle θ_0 is the *angle of departure*. The initial velocity has been resolved into a horizontal component v_{0x}, of magnitude $v_0 \cos \theta_0$, and a vertical component v_{0y}, of magnitude $v_0 \sin \theta_0$.

Since the horizontal velocity component is constant, we have at any later time t,

$$v_x = v_{0x} = v_0 \cos \theta_0.$$

The vertical acceleration is $-g$, so the vertical velocity component at time t is

$$v_y = v_{0y} - gt = v_0 \sin \theta_0 - gt.$$

These components can be added vectorially to find the resultant velocity **v**. Its magnitude is

$$v = \sqrt{v_x^2 + v_y^2},$$

and the angle θ it makes with the horizontal is given by

$$\tan \theta = v_y/v_x.$$

The velocity vector **v** is tangent to the trajectory, so its direction is the same as that of the trajectory.

The coordinates of the projectile at any time can now be found from the equations of motion with constant velocity, and with constant acceleration. The x-coordinate is

$$x = v_{0x}t = (v_0 \cos \theta_0)t$$

and the y-coordinate is

$$y = v_{0y}t - \tfrac{1}{2}gt^2 = (v_0 \sin \theta_0)t - \tfrac{1}{2}gt^2.$$

The two preceding equations give the equation of the trajectory in terms of the parameter t. The equation in terms of x and y can be obtained by eliminating t. This gives

$$y = (\tan \theta_0)x - \frac{g}{2v_0^2 \cos^2 \theta_0} x^2. \tag{6-6}$$

The quantities v_0, $\tan \theta_0$, $\cos \theta_0$, and g are constants, so the equation has the form

$$y = ax - bx^2,$$

which will be recognized as the equation of a *parabola*.

EXAMPLE 1.   A ball is projected horizontally with a velocity v_0 of magnitude 8 ft/sec. Find its position and velocity after $\tfrac{1}{4}$ sec (see Fig. 6-6).

In this case, the departure angle is zero. The initial vertical velocity component is therefore zero. The horizontal velocity component equals the initial velocity and is constant. The x- and y-coordinates, when $t = \tfrac{1}{4}$ sec, are

$$x = v_x t = 8 \frac{\text{ft}}{\text{sec}} \times \tfrac{1}{4} \text{ sec} = 2 \text{ ft},$$

$$y = -\tfrac{1}{2}gt^2 = -\tfrac{1}{2} \times 32 \frac{\text{ft}}{\text{sec}^2} \times (\tfrac{1}{4} \text{ sec})^2 = -1 \text{ ft}.$$

The components of velocity are

$$v_x = v_0 = 8 \text{ ft/sec,}$$

$$v_y = -gt = -32 \frac{\text{ft}}{\text{sec}^2} \times \tfrac{1}{4} \text{ sec} = -8 \frac{\text{ft}}{\text{sec}} \cdot$$

The resultant velocity is

$$v = \sqrt{v_x^2 + v_y^2} = 8\sqrt{2} \frac{\text{ft}}{\text{sec}} \cdot$$

The angle θ is

$$\theta = \tan^{-1} \frac{v_y}{v_x} = \tan^{-1} \frac{8 \text{ ft/sec}}{-8 \text{ ft/sec}} = -45°.$$

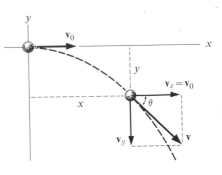

Fig. 6–6. Trajectory of a body projected horizontally.

That is, the velocity is 45° *below* the horizontal.

EXAMPLE 2.   In Fig. 6–5, let $v_0 = 160$ ft/sec, $\theta_0 = 53°$. Then

$$v_{0x} = v_0 \cos \theta_0 = 160 \frac{\text{ft}}{\text{sec}} \times 0.60 = 96 \frac{\text{ft}}{\text{sec}},$$

$$v_{0y} = v_0 \sin \theta_0 = 160 \frac{\text{ft}}{\text{sec}} \times 0.80 = 128 \frac{\text{ft}}{\text{sec}} \cdot$$

(a) Find the position of the projectile, and the magnitude and direction of its velocity, when $t = 2.0$ sec. (This corresponds to the first position of the projectile in Fig. 6–5, after starting its flight.) We have

$$x = 96 \frac{\text{ft}}{\text{sec}} \times 2.0 \text{ sec} = 192 \text{ ft,}$$

$$y = 128 \frac{\text{ft}}{\text{sec}} \times 2.0 \text{ sec} - \tfrac{1}{2} \times 32 \frac{\text{ft}}{\text{sec}^2} \times (2.0 \text{ sec})^2 = 192 \text{ ft,}$$

$$v_x = 96 \frac{\text{ft}}{\text{sec}},$$

$$v_y = 128 \frac{\text{ft}}{\text{sec}} - 32 \frac{\text{ft}}{\text{sec}^2} \times 2.0 \text{ sec} = 64 \frac{\text{ft}}{\text{sec}},$$

$$\theta = \tan^{-1} \frac{64 \text{ ft/sec}}{96 \text{ ft/sec}} = \tan^{-1} 0.667 = 33.5°.$$

(b) Find the time at which the projectile reaches the highest point of its flight, and find the elevation of this point.

At the highest point, the vertical velocity v_y is zero. If t_1 is the time at which this point is reached,

$$v_y = 0 = 128 \frac{\text{ft}}{\text{sec}} - 32 \frac{\text{ft}}{\text{sec}^2} \times t_1,$$

$$t_1 = 4 \text{ sec.}$$

The elevation of the point is

$$y = 128 \frac{ft}{sec} \times 4 \text{ sec} - \tfrac{1}{2} \times 32 \frac{ft}{sec^2} \times (4 \text{ sec})^2 = 256 \text{ ft.}$$

(c) Find the *horizontal range R*, that is, the horizontal distance from the starting point to the point at which the projectile returns to its original elevation and at which, therefore, $y = 0$. Let t_2 be the time at which this point is reached. Then

$$y = 0 = 128 \frac{ft}{sec} \times t_2 - \tfrac{1}{2} \times 32 \frac{ft}{sec^2} \times t_2^2.$$

This quadratic equation has two roots,

$$t_2 = 0 \quad \text{and} \quad t_2 = 8 \text{ sec,}$$

corresponding to the two points at which $y = 0$. Evidently the time desired is the second root, $t_2 = 8$ sec, which is just twice the time to reach the highest point. The time of descent therefore equals the time of rise.

The horizontal range is

$$R = v_x t_2 = 96 \frac{ft}{sec} \times 8 \text{ sec} = 768 \text{ ft.}$$

The vertical velocity at this point is

$$v_y = 128 \frac{ft}{sec} - 32 \frac{ft}{sec^2} \times 8 \text{ sec} = -128 \frac{ft}{sec}.$$

That is, the vertical velocity has the same magnitude as the initial vertical velocity, but the opposite direction. Since v_x is constant, the angle below the horizontal at this point equals the angle of departure.

(d) If unimpeded, the projectile continues to travel beyond its horizontal range. It is left as an exercise to compute the position and velocity at a time 10 sec after the start, corresponding to the last position shown in Fig. 6–5. The results are:

$$x = 960 \text{ ft,} \qquad y = -320 \text{ ft,} \qquad v_x = 96 \text{ ft/sec,} \qquad v_y = -192 \text{ ft/sec.}$$

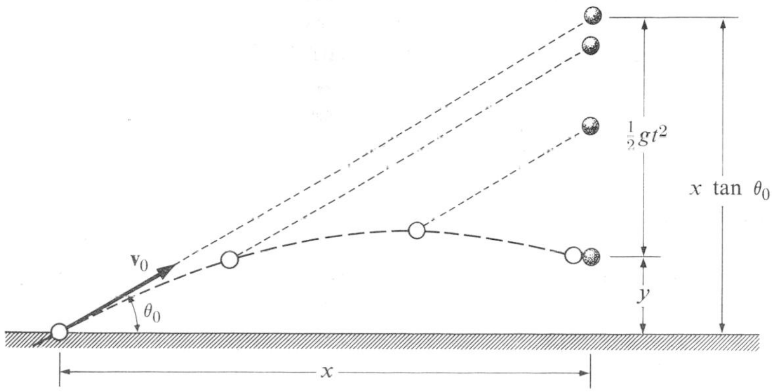

Figure 6–7

EXAMPLE 3.   Figure 6–7 illustrates an interesting experimental demonstration of the properties of projectile motion. A ball (shown by the open circle) is projected directly toward a second ball (the solid circle). The second ball is released from rest at the instant the first is projected, and the balls collide as shown regardless of the values of the initial velocity. To show that this happens, we note that the initial elevation of the second ball is $x \tan \theta_0$, and that in time t it falls a distance $\frac{1}{2}gt^2$. Its elevation at the instant of collision is therefore

$$y = x \tan \theta_0 - \tfrac{1}{2}gt^2,$$

which is the same as the elevation of the first ball as given by Eq. (6–6).

For any given initial velocity, there is one particular angle of departure for which the horizontal range is a maximum. To find this angle, write the general algebraic expression for the horizontal range R as

$$R = v_x t_2 = v_0 \cos \theta_0 \times \frac{2v_0 \sin \theta_0}{g} = \frac{2v_0^2 \sin \theta_0 \cos \theta_0}{g} = \frac{v_0^2 \sin 2\theta_0}{g}. \quad (6\text{–}7)$$

The maximum range is that for which $dR/d\theta_0 = 0$:

$$\frac{dR}{d\theta_0} = \frac{2v_0^2}{g} \cos 2\theta_0 = 0,$$

$$\cos 2\theta_0 = 0,$$

$$2\theta_0 = 90°, \qquad \theta_0 = 45°,$$

and the maximum horizontal range is attained with a departure angle of 45°.

From the standpoint of gunnery, what we usually want to know is what the departure angle should be for a given muzzle velocity v_0 in order to hit a target whose position is known. Let us assume target and gun are at the same elevation. Then, from Eq. (6–7),

$$\theta_0 = \tfrac{1}{2} \sin^{-1} \left(\frac{Rg}{v_0^2} \right).$$

Provided R is less than the maximum range, this equation has two solutions for values of θ_0 between 0° and 90°.

Thus if $R = 800$ ft, $g = 32$ ft/sec^2, and $v_0 = 200$ ft/sec,

$$\theta_0 = \tfrac{1}{2} \sin^{-1} \left[\frac{800 \text{ ft} \times 32 \text{ ft/sec}^2}{(200 \text{ ft/sec})^2} \right]$$

$$= \tfrac{1}{2} \sin^{-1} 0.64.$$

But

$$\sin^{-1} 0.64 = 40° \quad \text{or} \quad 180° - 40° = 140°,$$

so

$$\theta_0 = 20° \quad \text{or} \quad 70°.$$

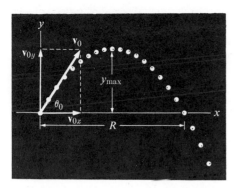

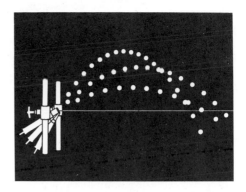

Fig. 6–8. Trajectory of a body projected at an angle with the horizontal.

Fig. 6–9. An angle of departure of 45° gives the maximum horizontal range.

Either of these angles gives the same range. Of course both the time of flight and the maximum height reached are greater for the high-angle trajectory.

Figure 6–8 is a multiflash photograph of the trajectory of a ball, to which have been added x- and y-axes and the initial velocity vector. The horizontal distances between consecutive positions are all equal, showing that the horizontal velocity component is constant. The vertical distances first decrease and then increase, showing that the vertical motion is accelerated.

Figure 6–9 is a composite photograph of the three trajectories of a ball projected from a spring gun with departure angles of 30°, 45°, and 60°. It will be seen that the horizontal ranges are (nearly) the same for the 30° and 60° angles and that both are less than the range when the angle is 45°. (The spring gun does not impart exactly the same initial velocity to the ball as the departure angle is altered.)

If the departure angle is *below* the horizontal, as for instance in the motion of a ball after rolling off a sloping roof or the trajectory of a bomb released from a dive bomber, exactly the same principles apply. The horizontal velocity component remains constant and equal to $v_0 \cos \theta_0$. The vertical motion is the same as that of a body projected *downward* with an initial velocity $v_0 \sin \theta_0$.

6–6 Circular motion

The acceleration of a particle moving in a curved path can be resolved into components normal and tangential to the path. There is a simple relation between the normal component of acceleration, the speed of the particle, and the radius of curvature of the path. We now derive this for the special case of motion in a circle.

Figure 6–10(a) represents a particle moving in a circular path of radius R with center at O. Vectors $\mathbf{v}_1$ and $\mathbf{v}_2$ represent its velocities at points P and Q. The vector change in velocity, $\Delta \mathbf{v}$, is obtained in Fig. 6–10(b), which is the same as Fig. 6–4. Vectors $\Delta \mathbf{v}_N$ and $\Delta \mathbf{v}_T$ are the normal and tangential components of $\Delta \mathbf{v}$.

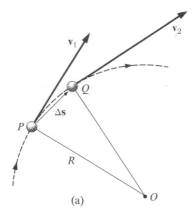

(a)

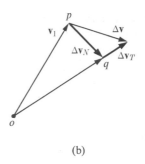

(b)

Fig. 6–10. Construction for finding change in velocity, $\Delta\mathbf{v}$, of particle moving in a circle.

The triangles OPQ and opq in Fig. 6–10(a) and (b) are similar, since both are isosceles triangles and their long sides are mutually perpendicular. Hence

$$\frac{\Delta v_N}{v_1} = \frac{\Delta s}{R}, \quad \text{or} \quad \Delta v_N = \frac{v_1}{R}\Delta s.$$

The magnitude of the average normal acceleration $\bar{a}_N$ is therefore

$$\bar{a}_N = \frac{\Delta v_N}{\Delta t} = \frac{v_1}{R}\frac{\Delta s}{\Delta t}.$$

The instantaneous normal acceleration a_N at point P is the limiting value of this expression, as point Q is taken closer and closer to point P:

$$a_N = \lim_{\Delta t \to 0} \frac{v_1}{R}\frac{\Delta s}{\Delta t} = \frac{v_1}{R}\lim_{\Delta t \to 0}\frac{\Delta s}{\Delta t}.$$

But the limiting value of $\Delta s/\Delta t$ is the speed v_1 at point P, and since P can be any point of the path we can drop the subscript from v_1 and let v represent the speed at any point. Then

$$a_N = \frac{v^2}{R}. \tag{6–8}$$

The magnitude of the instantaneous normal acceleration is therefore equal to the square of the speed divided by the radius. The direction is inward along the radius, toward the center of the circle. Because of this it is called a *central*, a *centripetal*, or a *radial* acceleration. (The term "centripetal" means "seeking a center.")

The unit of radial acceleration is the same as that of an acceleration resulting from a change in the *magnitude* of a velocity. Thus if a particle travels with a speed of

4 ft/sec in a circle of radius 2 ft, its radial acceleration is

$$a = \frac{(4\ \text{ft/sec})^2}{2\ \text{ft}} = 8\ \frac{\text{ft}}{\text{sec}^2}.$$

If the *speed* of the particle changes, it will also have a *tangential* component of acceleration, defined as

$$\mathbf{a}_T = \lim_{\Delta t \to 0} \frac{\Delta \mathbf{v}_T}{\Delta t}.$$

If the speed is constant, there is no tangential component of acceleration and the acceleration is purely normal, resulting from the continuous change in *direction* of the velocity. In general, there will be both tangential and normal components of acceleration.

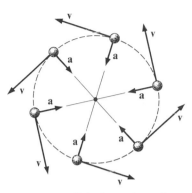

Fig. 6–11. Velocity and acceleration vectors of a particle in uniform circular motion.

Figure 6–11 shows the directions of the velocity and acceleration vectors at a number of points, for a particle revolving in a circle with a velocity of constant magnitude.

A *centrifuge* is a device for whirling an object with a high velocity. The consequent large radial acceleration is equivalent to increasing the value of g, and such processes as sedimentation, which would otherwise take place only slowly, can be greatly accelerated in this way. Very high speed centrifuges, called ultracentrifuges, have been operated at velocities as high as 180,000 rev/min, and small experimental units have been driven as fast as 1,300,000 rev/min.

EXAMPLE.   The moon revolves about the earth in a circle (very nearly) of radius $R = 239,000$ mi or 12.6×10^8 ft, and requires 27.3 days or 23.4×10^5 sec to make a complete revolution.   (a) What is the acceleration of the moon toward the earth?
The velocity of the moon is

$$v = \frac{2\pi R}{T} = \frac{2\pi \times 12.6 \times 10^8\ \text{ft}}{23.4 \times 10^5\ \text{sec}} = 3360\ \frac{\text{ft}}{\text{sec}}.$$

Its radial acceleration is therefore

$$a = \frac{v^2}{R} = \frac{(3360\ \text{ft/sec})^2}{12.6 \times 10^8\ \text{ft}} - 0.00896\ \frac{\text{ft}}{\text{sec}^2}.$$

(b) If the gravitational force exerted on a body by the earth is inversely proportional to the square of the distance from the earth's center, the acceleration produced by this force should vary in the same way.   Therefore, if the acceleration of the moon is caused by the gravitational attraction of the earth, the ratio of the moon's acceleration to that of a falling body at the earth's surface should equal the ratio of the square of the earth's radius (3950 mi or 2.09×10^7 ft) to the square of the radius of the moon's orbit.   Is this true?

The ratio of the two accelerations is

$$\frac{8.96 \times 10^{-3} \text{ ft/sec}^2}{32.2 \text{ ft/sec}^2} = 2.78 \times 10^{-4}.$$

The ratio of the squares of the distances is

$$\frac{(2.09 \times 10^7 \text{ ft})^2}{(12.6 \times 10^8 \text{ ft})^2} = 2.75 \times 10^{-4}.$$

The agreement is very close, although not exact because we have used average values.

It was the calculation above which Newton made to first justify his hypothesis that gravitation was truly *universal* and that the earth's pull extended out indefinitely into space. The numerical values available in Newton's time were not highly precise. While he did not obtain as close an agreement as that above, he states that he found his results to "answer pretty nearly," and he concluded that his hypothesis was verified.

6–7 Centripetal force

Having obtained an expression for the radial acceleration of a particle revolving in a circle, we can now use Newton's second law to find the radial force on the particle. Since the magnitude of the radial acceleration equals v^2/R, and its direction is toward the center, the magnitude of the radial force on a particle of mass m is

$$F = m\frac{v^2}{R}. \tag{6–9}$$

The direction of this force is toward the center also, and it is called a *centripetal force*. (It is unfortunate that it has become common practice to characterize the force by the adjective "centripetal," since this seems to imply that there is some difference in nature between centripetal forces and other forces. This is not the case. Centripetal forces, like other forces, are pushes and pulls exerted by sticks and strings, or arise from the action of gravitational or other causes. The term "centripetal" refers to the *effect* of the force, that is, to the fact that it results in a change in the *direction* of the velocity of the body on which it acts, rather than a change in the *magnitude* of this velocity.)

Anyone who has ever tied an object to a cord and whirled it in a circle will realize the necessity of exerting this inward, centripetal force. If the cord breaks, the direction of the velocity ceases to change (unless other forces are acting) and the object flies off along a tangent to the circle.

EXAMPLE 1.   A small body of mass 200 gm revolves uniformly in a circle on a horizontal frictionless surface, attached by a cord 20 cm long to a pin set in the surface. If the body

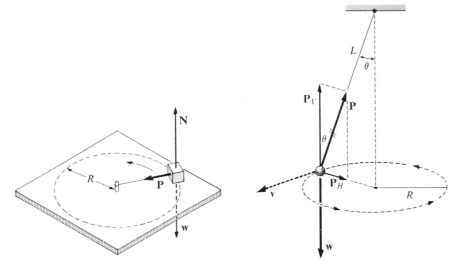

Figure 6–12   Fig. 6–13.   The conical pendulum.

makes two complete revolutions per second, find the force **P** exerted on it by the cord. (See Fig. 6–12.)

The circumference of the circle is

$$2\pi \times 20 \text{ cm} = 40\pi \text{ cm},$$

so the velocity is 80π cm/sec. The magnitude of the centripetal acceleration is

$$a = \frac{v^2}{R} = \frac{(80\pi \text{ cm/sec})^2}{20 \text{ cm}} = 3150 \frac{\text{cm}}{\text{sec}^2}.$$

Since the body has no vertical acceleration, the forces **N** and **w** are equal and opposite and the force **P** is the resultant force. Therefore

$$P = ma = 200 \text{ gm} \times 3150 \frac{\text{cm}}{\text{sec}^2}$$

$$= 6.3 \times 10^5 \text{ dynes}.$$

EXAMPLE 2.   Figure 6–13 represents a small body of mass m revolving in a horizontal circle with velocity **v** of constant magnitude at the end of a cord of length L. As the body swings around its path, the cord sweeps over the surface of a cone. The cord makes an angle θ with the vertical, so the radius of the circle in which the body moves is $R = L \sin\theta$ and the magnitude of the velocity **v** equals $2\pi L \sin\theta/T$, where T is the time for one complete revolution.

The forces exerted on the body when in the position shown are its weight **w** and the tension **P** in the cord. (Note that the force diagram in Fig. 6–13 is exactly like that in Fig. 5–8(b). The only difference is that in this case the acceleration a is the *radial* acceleration, v^2/R.) Let **P** be resolved into a horizontal component $\mathbf{P}_H$ and a vertical component $\mathbf{P}_V$, of magnitudes $P \sin\theta$ and $P \cos\theta$, respectively. The body has no vertical acceleration, so the vertical forces $P \cos \theta$ and w are equal, and the resultant inward, radial, or centripetal force is the horizontal component $P \sin \theta$. Then

$$P \sin \theta = m \frac{v^2}{R}, \qquad P \cos \theta = w.$$

When the first of these equations is divided by the second, and w is replaced by mg, we get

$$\tan \theta = \frac{v^2}{Rg}. \qquad \qquad (6\text{–}10)$$

Making use of the relations $R = L \sin \theta$ and $v = 2\pi L \sin \theta / T$, Eq. (6–10) becomes

$$\cos \theta = \frac{gT^2}{4\pi^2 L}, \qquad \qquad (6\text{–}11)$$

or

$$T = 2\pi \sqrt{L \cos \theta / g}. \qquad \qquad (6\text{–}12)$$

Equation (6–12) indicates how the angle θ depends on the time of revolution T and the length L of the cord. For a given length L, $\cos \theta$ *decreases* as the time is made shorter, and the angle θ *increases*. The angle never becomes 90°, however, since this requires that $T = 0$ or $v = \infty$.

Equation (6–12) is similar in form to the expression for the time of swing of a simple pendulum, which will be derived in Chapter 11. Because of this similarity, the present device is called a *conical pendulum.*

Some readers may wish to add to the forces shown in Fig. 6–13 an outward "centrifugal," force, to "keep the body out there," or to "keep it in equilibrium." ("Centrifugal" means "fleeing a center.") Let us examine this point of view. In the first place, to look for a force to "*keep* the body out there" is an example of faulty observation, because the body doesn't stay there. A moment later it will be at a different position on its circular path. At the instant shown it is moving in the direction of the velocity vector **v**, and unless a resultant force acts on it, it will, according to Newton's first law, continue to move in this direction. If an outward force *were* acting on it, equal and opposite to the inward component of the force P, there would be no resultant inward force to deviate it sidewise from its present direction of motion.

Those who wish to add a force to "keep the body in equilibrium" forget that the term equilibrium refers to a state of rest, or of motion *in a straight line* with constant speed. Here, the body is *not* moving in a straight line, but in a circle. It is *not* in equilibrium, but has an acceleration toward the center of the circle and must be acted on by a resultant or *un*balanced force to produce this acceleration.

EXAMPLE 3.   Figure 6–14(a) represents an automobile or a railway car rounding a curve of radius R, on a level road or track. The forces acting on it are its weight **w**, the normal force **N**, and the centripetal force **P**. The force **P** must be provided by friction, in the case of an automobile, or by a force exerted by the rails against the flanges on the wheels of a railway car.

In order not to have to rely on friction, or to reduce wear on the rails and flanges, the road or the track may be banked as shown in Fig. 6–14(b). The normal force **N** then has a vertical component of magnitude $N \cos \theta$, and a horizontal component of magnitude $N \sin \theta$ toward

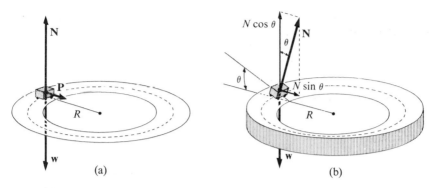

Fig. 6-14. (a) Forces on a vehicle rounding a curve on a level track. (b) Forces when the track is banked.

the center, which provides the centripetal force. The banking angle θ can be computed as follows. If **v** is the velocity and R the radius, then

$$N \sin \theta = \frac{mv^2}{R}.$$

Since there is no vertical acceleration, $N \cos \theta = w$.

Dividing the first equation by the second, and replacing w by mg, we get

$$\tan \theta = \frac{v^2}{Rg}.$$

The tangent of the angle of banking is proportional to the square of the speed and inversely proportional to the radius. For a given radius no one angle is correct for all speeds. Hence in the design of highways and railroads, curves are banked for the average speed of the traffic over them.

The same considerations apply to the correct banking angle of a plane when it makes a turn in level flight.

Note that the banking angle is given by the same expression as that for the angle with the vertical made by the cord of a conical pendulum. In fact, the force diagrams in Figs. 6-13 and 6-14 are identical.

6-8 Motion in a vertical circle

Figure 6-15 represents a small body attached to a cord of length R and whirling in a vertical circle about a fixed point O to which the other end of the cord is attached. The motion, while circular, is not uniform, since the speed increases on the way down and decreases on the way up.

The forces on the body at any point are its weight $\mathbf{w} = m\mathbf{g}$ and the tension **T** in the cord. Let the weight be resolved into a normal component, of magnitude $w \cos \theta$, and a tangential component of magnitude $w \sin \theta$, as in Fig. 6-15. The resultant tangential and normal forces are then $F_T = w \sin \theta$ and $F_N = T - w \cos \theta$. The tangential acceleration, from Newton's second law, is

$$a_T = \frac{F_T}{m} = g \sin \theta,$$

and is the same as that of a body sliding on a frictionless inclined plane of slope angle θ. The radial acceleration, $a_N = v^2/R$, is

$$a_N = \frac{F_N}{m} = \frac{T - w\cos\theta}{m} = \frac{v^2}{R},$$

and the tension in the cord is therefore

$$T = m\left(\frac{v^2}{R} + g\cos\theta\right). \qquad (6\text{–}13)$$

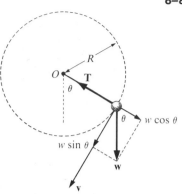

Fig. 6–15. Forces on a body whirling in a vertical circle with center at O.

At the lowest point of the path, $\theta = 0$, $\sin\theta = 0$, $\cos\theta = 1$. Hence at this point $F_T = 0$, $a_T = 0$, and the acceleration is purely radial (upward). The magnitude of the tension, from Eq. (6–13), is

$$T = m\left(\frac{v^2}{R} + g\right).$$

At the highest point, $\theta = 180°$, $\sin\theta = 0$, $\cos\theta = -1$, and the acceleration is again purely radial (downward). The tension is

$$T = m\left(\frac{v^2}{R} - g\right). \qquad (6\text{–}14)$$

With motion of this sort, it is a familiar fact that there is a certain critical speed v_c at the highest point, below which the cord becomes slack. To find this speed, set $T = 0$ in Eq. (6–14):

$$0 = m\left(\frac{v_c^2}{R} - g\right), \qquad v_c = \sqrt{Rg}.$$

The multiflash photographs of Fig. 6–16 illustrate another case of motion in a vertical circle, a small ball "looping-the-loop" on the inside of a vertical circular track. The inward normal force exerted on the ball by the track takes the place of the tension T in Fig. 6–15.

In Fig. 6–16(a), the ball is released from an elevation such that its speed at the top of the track is greater than the critical speed, $\sqrt{Rg}$. In Fig. 6–16(b), the ball starts from a lower elevation and reaches the top of the circle with a speed such that its own weight is slightly larger than the requisite centripetal force. In other words, the track would have to pull *outward* to maintain the circular motion. Since this is impossible, the ball leaves the track and moves for a short distance in a parabola. This parabola soon intersects the circle, however, and the remainder of the trip is completed successfully. In Fig. 6–16(c), the start is made from a still lower elevation, the ball leaves the track sooner, and the parabolic path is clearly evident.

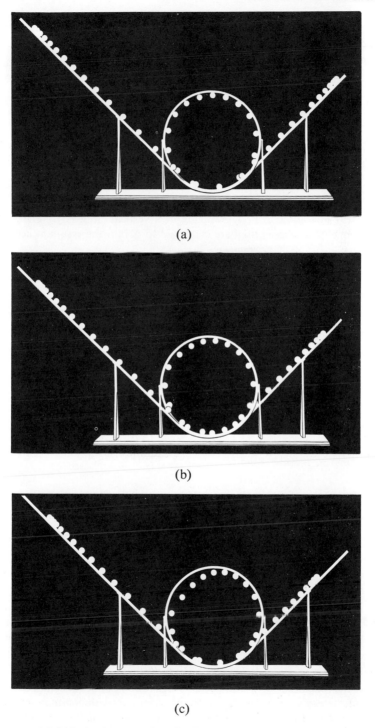

(a)

(b)

(c)

Fig. 6–16. Multiflash photographs of a ball looping-the-loop in a vertical circle.

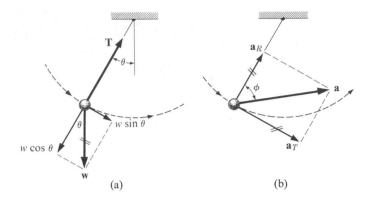

Fig. 6–17. (a) Forces on a body swinging in a vertical circle. (b) The radial and tangential components of acceleration are combined to obtain the resultant acceleration **a**.

EXAMPLE. In Fig. 6–17, a small body of mass $m = 0.10$ kgm swings in a vertical circle at the end of a cord of length $R = 1.0$ m. If its speed $v = 2.0$ m/sec when the cord makes an angle $\theta = 30°$ with the vertical, find (a) the radial and tangential components of its acceleration at this instant, (b) the magnitude and direction of the resultant acceleration, and (c) the tension T in the cord.

(a) The radial component of acceleration is

$$a_R = \frac{v^2}{R} = \frac{(2.0 \text{ m/sec})^2}{1.0 \text{ m}} = 4.0 \frac{\text{m}}{\text{sec}^2}.$$

The tangential component of acceleration is

$$a_T = g \sin \theta = 9.8 \frac{\text{m}}{\text{sec}^2} \times 0.50 = 4.9 \frac{\text{m}}{\text{sec}^2}.$$

(b) The magnitude of the resultant acceleration [see Fig. 6–17(b)] is

$$a = \sqrt{a_R^2 + a_T^2} = 6.3 \frac{\text{m}}{\text{sec}^2}.$$

The angle ϕ is

$$\phi = \tan^{-1} \frac{a_T}{a_R} = 51°.$$

(c) The tension in the cord is

$$T = m \left(\frac{v^2}{R} + g \cos \theta \right) = 1.3 \text{ n}.$$

Note that the magnitude of the tangential acceleration is not constant but is proportional to the sine of the angle θ. Hence the equations of motion with constant acceleration *cannot* be used to find the speed at other points of the path. We shall show in the next chapter, however, how the speed at any point can be found from *energy* considerations.

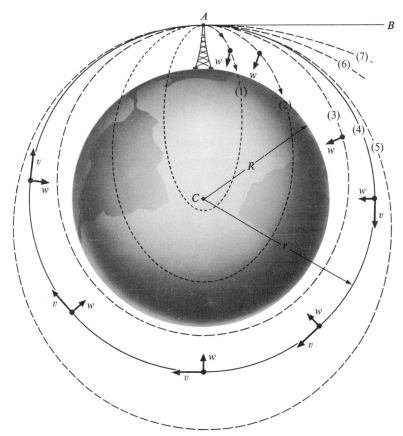

Fig. 6–18.   Trajectories of a body projected from point A in the direction AB with different initial velocities.

6–9 Motion of a satellite

In discussing the trajectory of a projectile in Section 6–5, we assumed that the gravitational force on the projectile (its weight **w**) had the same direction and magnitude at all points of the trajectory. Under these conditions the trajectory is a parabola.

In reality, the gravitational force is directed toward the center of the earth and is inversely proportional to the square of the distance from the earth's center, so that it is not constant in either magnitude or direction. It can be shown that under an inverse square force directed toward a fixed point the trajectory will be a *conic section* (ellipse, circle, parabola, or hyperbola).

Suppose that a very tall tower could be constructed as in Fig. 6–18, and that a projectile were launched from point A at the top of the tower in the "horizontal" direction AB. If the initial velocity is not too great, the trajectory will be like that numbered (1), which is a portion of an ellipse with the earth's center C at one focus. (If the trajectory is so short that changes in the magnitude and direction of **w** can be neglected, the ellipse *approximates* a parabola.)

The trajectories numbered from (2) to (7) illustrate the effect of increasing the initial velocity. (Any effect of the earth's atmosphere is neglected.) Trajectory (2) is again a portion of an ellipse. Trajectory (3), which just misses the earth, is a *complete* ellipse and the projectile has become an earth satellite. Its velocity when it returns to point A is the same as its initial velocity, and in the absence of retarding forces it will repeat its motion indefinitely. (The earth's rotation will have moved the tower to a different point by the time the satellite returns to point A, but the earth's rotation does not affect the orbit.)

Trajectory (4) is a special case in which the orbit is a circle. Trajectory (5) is again an ellipse, (6) is a parabola, and (7) is a hyperbola. Trajectories (6) and (7) are not closed orbits.

All man-made earth satellites have orbits like (3) or (5), but some are very nearly circles and for simplicity we shall consider circular orbits only. Let us calculate the velocity required for such an orbit, and the time of one revolution. The gravitational force on the satellite is the centripetal force retaining it in its orbit, and is equal to the product of the mass of the satellite and its radial acceleration.

Thus

$$w = F_g = G\frac{mm_E}{r^2} = m\frac{v^2}{r},$$

and from the last two terms,

$$v^2 = \frac{Gm_E}{r}, \qquad v = \sqrt{\frac{Gm_E}{r}}, \tag{6–15}$$

The larger the radius r, the smaller the orbital velocity.

The satellite, like any projectile, is a freely falling body (the only force on it is its weight **w**). Its radial acceleration v^2/r is therefore equal to the free-fall acceleration g *at the orbit*. That is,

$$w = mg = G\frac{mm_E}{r^2},$$

and

$$g = \frac{Gm_E}{r^2}, \qquad \text{or} \qquad \frac{Gm_E}{r} = rg.$$

Hence Eq. (6–15) can also be written as

$$v = \sqrt{rg}.$$

The free-fall acceleration is inversely proportional to the square of the distance from the earth's center. Then if g_R is the free-fall acceleration at the earth's surface, where r equals the earth's radius R,

$$\frac{g}{g_R} = \frac{R^2}{r^2}, \qquad rg = g_R\frac{R^2}{r},$$

and

$$v = R\sqrt{\frac{g_R}{r}}. \tag{6–16}$$

The period T, or the time required for one complete revolution, equals the circumference of the orbit, $2\pi r$, divided by the velocity v:

$$T = \frac{2\pi r}{v} = \frac{2\pi r}{R\sqrt{g_R/r}} = \frac{2\pi}{R\sqrt{g_R}}r^{3/2}, \tag{6–17}$$

and the larger the radius, the longer the period.

EXAMPLE. An earth satellite revolves in a circular orbit at a height of 300 km (about 200 miles) above the earth's surface. (a) What is the velocity of the satellite, assuming the earth's radius to be 6400 km and g_R to be 9.80 m/sec²?

From Eq. (6–16),

$$v = R\sqrt{\frac{g_R}{r}} = 6.40 \times 10^6 \text{ m} \left(\frac{9.80 \text{ m/sec}^2}{6.70 \times 10^6 \text{ m}}\right)^{1/2},$$

$$= 7740 \frac{\text{m}}{\text{sec}} = 25,400 \frac{\text{ft}}{\text{sec}} = 17,300 \frac{\text{mi}}{\text{hr}}.$$

(b) What is the period T?

$$T = \frac{2\pi r}{v} = 90.6 \text{ min} = 1.51 \text{ hr}.$$

(c) What is the radial acceleration of the satellite?

$$a_R = \frac{v^2}{r} = 8.94 \frac{\text{m}}{\text{sec}^2}.$$

This is of course equal to the free-fall acceleration g at a height of 300 km above the earth.

A space vehicle in orbit is a freely falling body, with an acceleration a toward the earth's center equal to the value of **g** at its orbit. As explained in Chapter 5, the free-fall acceleration **g**′ of a body within the vehicle, and relative to it, is

$$\mathbf{g}' = \mathbf{g} - \mathbf{a} = \mathbf{g} - \mathbf{g} = 0,$$

and the apparent weight w' of the body is

$$w' = w - ma = mg - ma - mg' = 0.$$

It is in this sense that an astronaut in the vehicle is said to be "weightless" or in a state of "zero g." The vehicle is like the freely falling elevator discussed in Chapter 5, except that it has a large and constant tangential speed along its orbit.

At a point in space far removed from the earth or any other object, the *true* weight **w** of the vehicle, or of any object within it, is zero and the value of **g** is zero. If the

vehicle, by means of its rocket motors, is given an acceleration **a** relative to an inertial system, the free-fall acceleration **g′** of a body, relative to the vehicle, is

$$\mathbf{g'} = \mathbf{g} - \mathbf{a} = 0 - \mathbf{a} = -\mathbf{a},$$

and the apparent weight **w′** of the body is

$$\mathbf{w'} = \mathbf{w} - m\mathbf{a} = 0 - m\mathbf{a} = -m\mathbf{a}.$$

Hence the free-fall acceleration, and the apparent weight, *relative to an accelerated
reference system*, are the same as if the system were an inertial one, acted on by a
gravitational force $-m\mathbf{a}$. This statement, known as the *principle of equivalence*, plays
a major role in Einstein's general theory of relativity.

6–10 Effect of the earth's rotation on g

Figure 6–19 is a cut-away view of our rotating earth, with three observers each
holding a body of mass m, hanging from a string. Each body is attracted toward
the earth's center with a force $F_g = Gmm_E/R^2$, and which we now designate by w_0.
Let us consider the earth's *center* as the origin of an inertial reference system.

Except at the pole, each body is carried along by the earth's rotation and moves
in a circle with center on the earth's axis. It therefore has a radial acceleration a_R,
equal to v^2/r, toward the axis. The resultant or vector sum of the forces **T** and $\mathbf{w}_0$
must therefore be such as to provide the requisite radial acceleration. That is, in
general vector form,

$$\mathbf{T} + \mathbf{w}_0 = m\mathbf{a}_R.$$

At some arbitrary latitude θ, **T** and $\mathbf{w}_0$ have directions as shown in the diagram,
such that their resultant **F** points toward the point O' and equals ma_R. Thus we see
that except at the pole and the equator, a plumb line does not point toward the
earth's center.

At the pole, where $\mathbf{a}_R = 0$, the force **T** is equal and opposite to the true weight $\mathbf{w}_0$.

At the equator, where the direction of the radial acceleration is toward the earth's
center O, **T** and $\mathbf{w}_0$ have the same action line but the magnitude of $\mathbf{w}_0$ is greater than
that of **T**.

Since each body appears in equilibrium to its respective observer, the *apparent*
weight of each body, which we now represent by **w**, is a force equal and opposite
to **T**, as shown in the inset diagram for the body at latitude θ. That is,

$$\mathbf{w} = -\mathbf{T} = \mathbf{w}_0 - m\mathbf{a}_R.$$

At an intermediate latitude, the apparent weight **w** differs in both magnitude and
direction from the true weight $\mathbf{w}_0$.

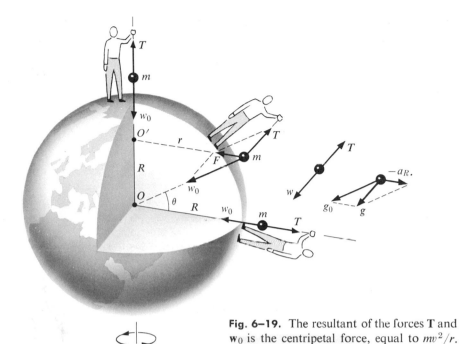

Fig. 6–19. The resultant of the forces **T** and w_0 is the centripetal force, equal to mv^2/r.

At the pole, the apparent and true weights are equal. At the equator,

$$w = w_0 - ma_R,$$

where a_R is the radial acceleration at the equator.

If the bodies are allowed to fall freely, so that the only force on them is their true weight $\mathbf{w}_0$, the acceleration $\mathbf{g}_0$ of each is toward the earth's center and is given by

$$\mathbf{g}_0 = \frac{\mathbf{w}_0}{m}.$$

The acceleration $\mathbf{g}$, relative to a system attached to the earth's surface, and hence having an acceleration $\mathbf{a}_R$ relative to the inertial system with origin at the earth's center, is

$$\mathbf{g} = \mathbf{g}_0 - \mathbf{a}_R,$$

and hence

$$m\mathbf{g} = m\mathbf{g}_0 - m\mathbf{a}_R.$$

But $m\mathbf{g}_0 = \mathbf{w}_0$, and $\mathbf{w}_0 - m\mathbf{a}_R = \mathbf{w}$, so

$$\mathbf{w} = m\mathbf{g}.$$

The acceleration $\mathbf{g}$ is the *observed* free-fall acceleration at any point on the earth's surface, and the *apparent weight* $\mathbf{w}$ is equal to the reading of a spring balance supporting a body at rest relative to the earth's surface.

TABLE 6–1

VARIATIONS OF g WITH LATITUDE AND ELEVATION

Station	North latitude	Elevation, m	g, m/sec^2	g, ft/sec^2
Canal Zone	9°	0	9.78243	32.0944
Jamaica	18°	0	9.78591	32.1059
Bermuda	32°	0	9.79806	32.1548
Denver	40°	1638	9.79609	32.1393
Cambridge	42°	0	9.80398	32.1652
Standard station			9.80665	32.1740
Greenland	70°	0	9.82534	32.2353

Let us calculate the magnitude of the radial acceleration $\mathbf{a}_R$ at the equator. The equatorial velocity v, equal to the earth's circumference divided by the time of one rotation, is

$$v = \frac{2\pi \times 6.4 \times 10^6 \text{ m}}{8.64 \times 10^4 \text{ sec}} = 465 \text{ m/sec,}$$

and hence

$$a_R = \frac{v^2}{R} = 0.034 \frac{\text{m}}{\text{sec}^2} = 3.4 \frac{\text{cm}}{\text{sec}^2}.$$

Thus if the free-fall acceleration g_0 at the equator is 9.880 m/sec^2, the observed acceleration g is 9.766 m/sec^2.

The radial acceleration is a maximum at the equator and decreases to zero at the poles.

Table 6–1 lists the measured free-fall acceleration g at a number of points. A part of the variation results from the fact that the earth is not spherical, that the observation points are at different elevations, or that there are local variations in earth density. It will be seen, however, that the change in the radial acceleration between equator and poles has the right magnitude to account for most of the differences.

Problems

6–1. A ball rolls off the edge of a table top 4 ft above the floor, and strikes the floor at a point 6 ft horizontally from the edge of the table. (a) Find the time of flight. (b) Find the initial velocity. (c) Find the magnitude and direction of the velocity of the ball just before it strikes the floor. Draw a diagram to scale.

6–2. A block slides off a horizontal tabletop 4 ft high with a velocity of 12 ft/sec. Find (a) the horizontal distance from the table at which the block strikes the floor, and (b) the horizontal and vertical components of its velocity when it reaches the floor.

6–3. A level-flight bomber, flying at 300 ft/sec, releases a bomb at an elevation of 6400 ft. (a) How long before the bomb strikes the earth? (b) How far does it travel horizontally? (c) Find the horizontal and vertical components of its velocity when it strikes.

6–4. A block passes a point 10 ft from the edge of a table with a velocity of 12 ft/sec. It slides off the edge of the table, which is 4 ft high, and strikes the floor 4 ft from the edge of the table. What was the coefficient of sliding friction between block and table?

6–5. A golf ball is driven horizontally from an elevated tee with a velocity of 80 ft/sec. It strikes the fairway 2.5 sec later. (a) How far has it fallen vertically? (b) How far has it traveled horizontally? (c) Find the horizontal and vertical components of its velocity, and the magnitude and direction of its resultant velocity, just before it strikes.

6–6. A level-flight bombing plane, flying at an altitude of 1024 ft with a velocity of 240 ft/sec, is overtaking a motor torpedo boat traveling at 80 ft/sec in the same direction as the plane. At what distance astern of the boat should a bomb be released in order to hit the boat?

6–7. A bomber is making a horizontal bombing run on a destroyer from an altitude of 25,600 ft. The magnitude of the velocity of the bomber is 300 mi/hr. (a) How much time is available for the destroyer to change its course after the bombs are released? (b) If the bomber is to be shot down before its bombs can reach the ship, what is the maximum angle that the line of sight from ship to bomber can make with the horizontal? Draw a diagram showing distances approximately to scale.

6–8. A ball is projected with an initial upward velocity component of 80 ft/sec and a horizontal velocity component of 100 ft/sec. (a) Find the position and velocity of the ball after 2 sec; 3 sec; 6 sec. (b) How long a time is required to reach the highest point of the trajectory? (c) How high is this point? (d) How long a time is required for the ball to return to its original level? (e) How far has it traveled horizontally during this time? Show your results in a neat sketch, large enough to show all features clearly.

6–9. A spring gun projects a golf ball at an angle of 45° above the horizontal. The horizontal range is 32 ft. (a) What is the maximum height to which the ball rises? (b) For the same initial speed, what are the two angles of departure for which the range is 20 ft? (c) Sketch all three trajectories to scale, in the same diagram.

6–10. Suppose the departure angle θ_0 in Fig. 6–7 is 15° and the distance $x = 5$ m. Where will the balls collide if the muzzle velocity of the first is (a) 20 m/sec, (b) 5 m/sec? Sketch both trajectories. (c) Will a collision take place if the departure angle is below horizontal?

6–11. If a baseball player can throw a ball a maximum distance of 200 ft over the ground, what is the maximum vertical height to which he can throw it? Assume the ball to have the same initial speed in each case.

6–12. A player kicks a football at an angle of 37° with the horizontal and with an initial velocity of 48 ft/sec. A second player standing at a distance of 100 ft from the first in the direction of the kick starts running to meet the ball at the instant it is kicked. How fast must he run in order to catch the ball before it hits the ground?

6–13. A baseball leaves the bat at a height of 4 ft above the ground, traveling at an angle of 45° with the horizontal, and with a velocity such that the horizontal range would be 400 ft. At a distance of 360 ft from home plate is a fence 30 ft high. Will the ball be a home run?

6–14. (a) What must be the velocity of a projectile fired vertically upward to reach an altitude of 20,000 ft? (b) What velocity is required to reach the same height if the gun makes an angle of 45° with the vertical? (c) Compute the time required to reach the highest point in both trajectories. (d) How many feet would a plane traveling at 300 mi/hr move in this time?

6–15. The angle of elevation of an anti-aircraft gun is 70° and the muzzle velocity is 2700 ft/sec. For what time after firing should the fuse be set if the shell is to explode at an altitude of 5000 ft?

6–16. The Olympic Games record in the high jump is 2.16 m, in the broad jump it is 8.06 m, and in the shot-put it is 18.57 m. Suppose these records were made at a point where $g = 9.82 \text{ m/sec}^2$. Estimate the changes that might be expected at a point where $g = 9.78 \text{ m/sec}^2$. (Treat the changes as differentials.)

6–17. A trench mortar fires a projectile at an angle of 53° above the horizontal with a muzzle velocity of 200 ft/sec. A tank is advancing directly toward the mortar on level ground at a speed of 10 ft/sec. What should be the distance from mortar to tank at the instant the mortar is fired in order to score a hit?

6–18. The projectile of a trench mortar has a muzzle velocity of 300 ft/sec. (a) Find the two angles of elevation to hit a target at the same level as the mortar and 300 yd distant. (b) Compute the maximum height of each trajectory, and (c) the time

of flight of each. Make a neat sketch of the trajectories, approximately to scale.

6–19. A projectile is fired with an initial speed v_0 at a departure angle θ_0, from the foot of an inclined plane of slope angle α (Fig. 6–20). (a) What is the range R, measured along the plane? (b) Show that the expression for R reduces to that for the horizontal range when $\alpha = 0$.

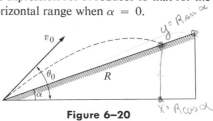

Figure 6–20

6–20. A bomber, diving at an angle of 53° with the vertical, releases a bomb at an altitude of 2400 ft. The bomb is observed to strike the ground 5 sec after its release. (a) What was the velocity of the bomber, in ft/sec? (b) How far did the bomb travel horizontally during its flight? (c) What were the horizontal and vertical components of its velocity just before striking?

6–21. A 15-lb stone is dropped from a cliff in a high wind. The wind exerts a steady horizontal 10-lb force on the stone as it falls. Is the path of the stone a straight line, a parabola, or some more complicated path? Explain.

6–22. A lump of ice slides 20 ft down a smooth sloping roof making an angle of 30° with the horizontal. The edge of the roof is 20 ft above a sidewalk which extends 10 ft out from the side of the building. Will the ice land on the sidewalk or in the street?

6–23. The second stage of a three-stage rocket designed to launch an earth satellite will exhaust its fuel at a height of about 130 mi above the earth's surface, when its speed will be approximately 11,000 mi/hr. The rocket will then "coast" to a height of about 300 mi, at which point its velocity will be horizontal. Assume a flat earth and a constant value of g. (a) Find the direction of the trajectory at the 130-mi high point. (b) Find the horizontal distance traveled while the rocket rises from 130 mi to 300 mi. (c) Find the speed at the 300-mi high point. (d) At a height of 300 mi, the third stage will separate from the second and the latter will fall to the earth. How far will it travel horizontally while falling? (e) How long a time will be required?

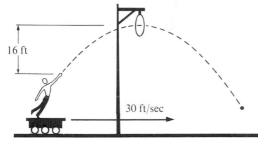

Figure 6–21

✳ 6–24. A man is riding on a flatcar traveling with a constant velocity of 30 ft/sec (Fig. 6–21). He wishes to throw a ball through a stationary hoop 16 ft above the height of his hands in such a manner that the ball will move horizontally as it passes through the hoop. He throws the ball with a velocity of 40 ft/sec with respect to himself. (a) What must be the vertical component of the initial velocity of the ball? (b) How many seconds after he releases the ball will it pass through the hoop? (c) At what horizontal distance in front of the hoop must he release the ball?

6–25. At time $t = 0$ a body is moving east at 10 cm/sec. At time $t = 2$ sec it is moving 25° north of east at 14 cm/sec. Find graphically the magnitude and direction of its change in velocity and the magnitude and direction of its average acceleration.

6–26. An automobile travels around a circular track 5000 ft in circumference at a constant speed of 100 ft/sec. (a) Show in a diagram the velocity vectors of the automobile at the beginning and end of a time interval $\Delta t = 5$ sec. Let 1 cm = 20 ft/sec. (b) Find graphically the change in velocity,

Δv, in this time interval. (c) Find the magnitude of the average acceleration during this interval, $\Delta v/\Delta t$. (d) What is the radial acceleration, v^2/R? (e) If the track is 30 ft wide, what should be the elevation of the outer circumference above the inner circumference, for the speed above?

6–27. The radius of the earth's orbit around the sun (assumed circular) is 93×10^6 miles, and the earth travels around this orbit in 365 days. (a) What is the magnitude of the orbital velocity of the earth, in mi/hr? (b) What is the radial acceleration of the earth toward the sun, in ft/sec²?

6–28. A model of a helicopter rotor has four blades, each 5 ft long, and is rotated in a wind tunnel at 1500 rev/min. (a) What is the linear speed of the blade tip, in ft/sec? (b) What is the radial acceleration of the blade tip, in terms of the acceleration of gravity, g? (c) A pressure measuring device weighing $\frac{1}{4}$ lb is mounted at the blade tip. Find the centripetal force on it, and compare with its weight.

6–29. A stone of mass 1 kgm is attached to one end of a string 1 m long, of breaking strength 500 newtons, and is whirled in a horizontal circle on a frictionless tabletop. The other end of the string is kept fixed. Find the maximum velocity the stone can attain without breaking the string.

6–30. An unbanked circular highway curve on level ground makes a turn of 90°. The highway carries traffic at 60 mi/hr, and the centripetal force on a vehicle is not to exceed $\frac{1}{10}$ of its weight. What is the minimum length of the curve, in miles?

6–31. A coin placed on a 12-inch record will revolve with the record when it is brought up to a speed of 78 rev/min, provided the coin is not more than 2.5 inches from the axis. (a) What is the coefficient of static friction between coin and record? (b) How far from the axis can the coin be placed, without slipping, if the turntable rotates at 45 rev/min?

6–32. (a) At how many revolutions per second must the apparatus of Fig. 6–22

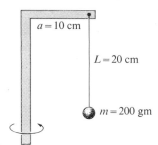

Figure 6–22

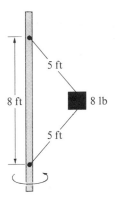

Figure 6–23

rotate about the vertical axis in order that the cord shall make an angle of 45° with the vertical? (b) What is then the tension in the cord? (c) Find the angle θ which the cord makes with the vertical if the system is rotating at 1.5 rev/sec. (Set up the general equation relating the angle θ to the number of revolutions per second, n, the lengths a and L, and the acceleration of gravity, g. Then find by trial the angle θ which satisfies this equation.)

6–33. The "Giant Swing" at a county fair consists of a vertical central shaft with a number of horizontal radial arms attached at its upper end. Each arm supports a seat suspended from a cable 15 ft long, the upper end of the cable being fastened to the arm at a point 12 ft from the central shaft. (a) Find the time of one revolution of the swing if the cable supporting a seat makes an angle of 30° with the vertical. (b) Does the angle depend on the weight of the passenger, for a given rate of revolution?

6–34. The 8-lb block in Fig. 6–23 is attached to a vertical rod by means of two strings. When the system rotates about the axis of the rod the strings are extended as shown in the diagram. (a) How many revolutions per minute must the system make in order that the tension in the upper cord shall be 15 lb? (b) What is then the tension in the lower cord?

6–35. A bead can slide without friction on a circular hoop of radius 10 cm in a vertical plane. The hoop rotates at a constant rate of 2 rev/sec about a vertical diameter, as in Fig. 6–24. (a) Find the

angle θ at which the bead is in vertical equilibrium. (Of course it has a radial acceleration toward the axis.) (b) Is it possible for the bead to "ride" at the same elevation as the center of the hoop? (c) What will happen if the hoop rotates at 1 rev/sec?

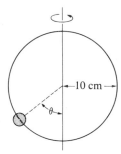

Figure 6–24

6–36. A curve of 600-ft radius on a level road is banked at the correct angle for a velocity of 30 mi/hr. If an automobile rounds this curve at 60 mi/hr, what is the minimum coefficient of friction between tires and road so that the automobile will not skid? Assume all forces to act at the center of gravity.

6–37. An airplane in level flight is said to make a *standard turn* when it makes a complete circular turn in two minutes. (a) What is the banking angle of a standard turn if the speed of the airplane is 400 ft/sec? (b) What is the radius of the circle in which it turns? (c) What is the centripetal force on the airplane, expressed as a fraction (or multiple) of its weight?

6–38. The radius of the circular track in Fig. 6–16 is 40 cm and the mass of the ball is 100 gm. (a) Find the critical velocity at the highest point of the track. (b) If the actual velocity at the highest point of the track is twice the critical velocity, find the force exerted by the ball against the track.

6–39. The pilot of a dive bomber who has been diving at a velocity of 400 mi/hr pulls out of the dive by changing his course to a circle in a vertical plane. (a) What is the minimum radius of the circle in order that the acceleration at the lowest point shall not exceed "$7g$"? (b) How much does a 180-lb pilot apparently weigh at the lowest point of the pullout?

6–40. A cord is tied to a pail of water and the pail is swung in a vertical circle of radius 4 ft. What must be the minimum velocity of the pail at the highest point of the circle if no water is to spill from the pail?

6–41. The radius of a Ferris wheel is 15 ft and it makes one revolution in 10 sec. (a) Find the difference between the apparent weight of a passenger at the highest and lowest points, expressed as a fraction of his weight. (That is, find the difference between the upward force exerted on the passenger by the seat at these two points.) (b) What would the time of one revolution be if his apparent weight at the highest point were zero? (c) What would then be his apparent weight at the lowest point? (d) What would happen, at this rate of revolution, if his seat belt broke at the highest point, and if he did not hang on to his seat?

6–42. A ball is held at rest in position A in Fig. 6–25 by two light cords. The horizontal cord is cut and the ball starts swinging as a pendulum. What is the ratio of the tension in the supporting cord, in position B, to that in position A?

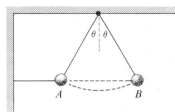

Figure 6–25

6–43. The questions are often asked: "What keeps an earth satellite moving in its orbit?" and "What keeps the satellite up?" (a) What are your answers to these questions? (b) Are your answers applicable to the moon?

6–44. What is the period of revolution of a man-made satellite of mass m which is orbiting the earth in a circular path of radius 8000 km? (Mass of earth = 5.98×10^{24} kgm.)

6–45. Suppose one wishes to establish a space platform or satellite moving in a circle in the earth's equatorial plane and at such a height above the earth's surface that it remains always above the same point. Find the height of the space platform.

6–46. It is desired to launch a satellite 400 miles above the earth in a circular orbit. If suitable rockets are used to reach this elevation, what horizontal orbital velocity must be imparted to the satellite? The radius of the earth is 3950 miles.

$$T = \frac{2\pi R}{v}$$

6–47. An earth satellite rotates in a circular orbit of radius 4400 mi (about 400 mi above the earth's surface) with an orbital speed of 17,000 mi/hr. (a) Find the time of one revolution. (b) Find the acceleration of gravity at the orbit.

6–48. What would be the length of a day if the rate of rotation of the earth were such that $g = 0$ at the equator?

6–49. The weight of a man as determined by a spring balance at the equator is 180 lb. By how many ounces does this differ from the true force of gravitational attraction at the same point?

CHAPTER 7

Work and Energy

7-1 Introduction

The curved line in Fig. 7–1 represents the trajectory, or path, of a particle of mass m moving in the xy-plane and acted on by a *resultant* force **F** which may vary in magnitude and direction from point to point of the path. Let us resolve the force into a component $\mathbf{F}_s$ along the path and a component $\mathbf{F}_n$ normal to the path.

The component $\mathbf{F}_n$, at right angles to the velocity **v**, is a *centripetal* force, and its only effect is to change the *direction* of the velocity. The effect of the component $\mathbf{F}_s$ is to change the *magnitude* of the velocity.

Let s be the distance of the particle from some fixed point O, measured along the path. In general, the magnitude of $\mathbf{F}_s$ will be a function of s. From Newton's second law,

$$F_s = m \frac{dv}{dt}.$$

Since F_s is a function of s, we use the chain rule and write

$$\frac{dv}{dt} = \frac{dv}{ds}\frac{ds}{dt} = v\frac{dv}{ds}.$$

Then

$$F_s = mv\frac{dv}{ds},$$

$$F_s\,ds = mv\,dv.$$

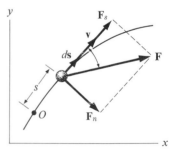

Fig. 7–1. Path of a particle in the xy-plane.

If v_1 is the velocity when $s = s_1$, and v_2 the velocity when $s = s_2$, it follows that

$$\int_{s_1}^{s_2} F_s\,ds = \int_{v_1}^{v_2} mv\,dv. \tag{7–1}$$

The integral on the left is called the *work* W of the force **F**, between the points s_1 and s_2:

$$W = \int_{s_1}^{s_2} F_s(s)\,ds.$$

This integral can be evaluated, of course, only when the component F_s is known as a function of s, or when both F_s and s are known as functions of another variable.

156

The integral on the right, however, can always be evaluated:

$$\int_{v_1}^{v_2} mv\, dv = \tfrac{1}{2}mv_2^2 - \tfrac{1}{2}mv_1^2.$$

One-half the product of the mass of a particle and the square of the magnitude of its velocity is called the *kinetic energy* of the particle, E_k:

$$E_k = \tfrac{1}{2}mv^2.$$

Equation (7–1) can therefore be written

$$W = E_{k2} - E_{k1}. \qquad (7\text{–}2)$$

That is, *the work of the resultant force exerted on a particle equals the change in kinetic energy of the particle.* This statement is known as the *work-energy* principle.

We now discuss these concepts of work and kinetic energy in more detail.

7–2 Work

In everyday life, the word *work* is applied to any form of activity that requires the exertion of muscular or mental effort. In physics, the term is used in a very restricted sense. Work is done only when a force is exerted on a body while the body at the same time moves in such a way that the force has a component along the line of motion of its point of application. If the component of the force is in the *same direction* as the displacement the work is *positive*. If it is *opposite* to the displacement, the work is negative. If the force is at *right angles* to the displacement it has no component in the direction of the displacement and the work is *zero*.

Thus when a body is lifted, the work of the lifting force is positive; when a spring is stretched, the work of the stretching force is positive; when a gas is compressed in a cylinder, again the work of the compressing force is positive. On the other hand, the work of the gravitational force on a body being lifted is negative, since the (downward) gravitational force is opposite to the (upward) displacement. When a body slides on a fixed surface, the work of the frictional force exerted *on the body* is negative, since this force is always opposite to the displacement of the body. No work is done by the frictional force acting *on the fixed surface* because there is no motion of this surface. Also, although it would be considered "hard work" to hold a heavy object stationary at arm's length, no work would be done in the technical sense because there is no motion. Even if one were to walk along a level floor while carrying the object, no work would be done, since the (vertical) supporting force has no component in the direction of the (horizontal) motion. Similarly, the work of the normal force exerted on a body by a surface on which it moves is zero, as is the work of the centripetal force on a body moving in a circle.

In the mks system the unit of work is one *newton·meter* (1 n·m) which is called one *joule* (1 j). The unit of work in the cgs system is 1 *dyne·centimeter* (1 dyne·cm), called one *erg*. Since 1 meter $= 100$ cm and 1 newton $= 10^5$ dynes, it follows that

$$1 \text{ n·m} = 10^7 \text{ dyne·cm}, \quad \text{or} \quad 1 \text{ j} = 10^7 \text{ ergs}.$$

In the engineering system, the unit of work is 1 *foot·pound* (1 ft·lb):

$$1 \text{ j} = 0.7376 \text{ ft·lb}, \quad 1 \text{ ft·lb} = 1.356 \text{ j}.$$

The expression for the work of a force can be written in several ways. If θ is the angle between the force vector $\mathbf{F}$ and the infinitesimal displacement vector $d\mathbf{s}$, the component F_s is equal to $F \cos \theta$, so

$$W = \int_{s_1}^{s_2} F_s \, ds = \int_{s_1}^{s_2} F \cos \theta \, ds.$$

In Chapter 1 we discussed the *addition* and *subtraction* of vectors, and in Chapter 3 the process of *vector multiplication*. The definition of work suggests a fourth process of vector algebra, namely, *scalar multiplication* of two vectors. In computing the work of a force, we multiply the magnitude of the vector $d\mathbf{s}$ by the magnitude of the component of another vector $\mathbf{F}$ in the direction of $d\mathbf{s}$. The product is called the *scalar product* or the *dot product* of the vectors. Thus if $\mathbf{A}$ and $\mathbf{B}$ are any two vectors, their scalar or dot product is defined as a scalar, equal to the product of the magnitudes of the vectors and the cosine of the angle θ between their positive directions:

$$\mathbf{A} \cdot \mathbf{B} = AB \cos \theta.$$

Evidently, $\mathbf{A} \cdot \mathbf{B} = \mathbf{B} \cdot \mathbf{A}$. In this new notation, the work of a force can be written as

$$W = \int_{s_1}^{s_2} \mathbf{F} \cdot d\mathbf{s}.$$

In the special case in which the force $\mathbf{F}$ is constant in magnitude and makes a constant angle with the direction of motion of its point of application, $F \cos \theta$ is constant and may be taken outside the integral sign. If in addition we measure displacements from the starting point of the motion and let $s_1 = 0$ and $s_2 = s$, the work of the force is

$$W = \int_0^s F \cos \theta \, ds = F \cos \theta \int_0^s ds = (F \cos \theta)s.$$

If the force is constant and in the same direction as the motion or opposite to the motion, the angle θ equals zero or $180°$, $\cos \theta = \pm 1$, and

$$W = \pm Fs.$$

That is, in this *very special case only*, we can say, "Work equals force times distance." It is important to remember, however, that the *general* definition of the work of a force is

$$W = \int_{s_1}^{s_2} \mathbf{F} \cdot d\mathbf{s} = \int_{s_1}^{s_2} F \cos \theta \, ds. \tag{7-3}$$

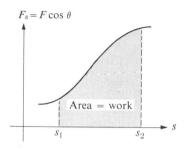

$F_s = F \cos \theta$

Area = work

s_1 s_2 s

Fig. 7–2 Work is equal to the area under the $F \cos \theta$ versus s curve.

In the preceding discussion, the force **F** has represented the *resultant* of *all* external forces on a body. We often wish to consider the works of the separate forces that may act on a body. Each of these may be computed from the general definition of work in Eq. (7–3). Then, since work is a scalar quantity, the total work is the algebraic sum of the individual works. Note, however, that only the *total* work is equal to the change in kinetic energy of the body.

The work of a force can be represented graphically by plotting the component $F \cos \theta$ as a function of s, as in Fig. 7–2. The work in a displacement from s_1 to s_2 is then equal to the *area* under the curve between vertical lines drawn at s_1 and s_2.

EXAMPLE 1. Figure 7–3 shows a box being dragged along a horizontal surface by a constant force **P** making a constant angle θ with the direction of motion. The other forces on the box are its weight **w**, the normal upward force **N** exerted by the surface, and the friction force **f**. What is the work of each force when the box moves a distance s along the surface to the right?

The component of **P** in the direction of motion is $P \cos \theta$. The work of the force **P** is therefore

$$W_P = (P \cos \theta) \cdot s.$$

The forces **w** and **N** are both at right angles to the displacement. Hence

$$W_w = 0, \qquad W_N = 0.$$

The friction force **f** is opposite to the displacement, so the work of the friction force is

$$W_f = -fs.$$

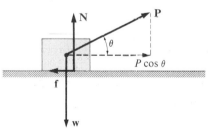

N   P

θ

$P \cos \theta$

f

w

Fig. 7–3. An object on a rough horizontal surface moving to the right under the action of a force **P** inclined at an angle θ.

Since work is a scalar quantity, the total work W of all forces on the body is the algebraic (not the vector) sum of the individual works:

$$\begin{aligned} W &= W_P + W_w + W_N + W_f \\ &= (P \cos \theta) \cdot s + 0 + 0 - f \cdot s \\ &= (P \cos \theta - f)s. \end{aligned}$$

But $(P \cos \theta - f)$ is the *resultant* force on the body. Hence *the total work of all forces is equal to the work of the resultant force.*

Suppose that $w = 100$ lb, $P = 50$ lb, $f = 15$ lb, $\theta = 37°$, and $s = 20$ ft. Then

$$W_P = (P \cos \theta) \cdot s = 50 \times 0.8 \times 20 = 800 \text{ ft·lb,}$$
$$W_f = -fs = -15 \times 20 = -300 \text{ ft·lb,}$$
$$W = W_P + W_f = 500 \text{ ft·lb.}$$

As a check, the total work may be expressed as

$$W = (P \cos \theta - f) \cdot s = (40 \text{ lb} - 15 \text{ lb}) \times 20 \text{ ft} = 500 \text{ ft·lb.}$$

EXAMPLE 2. A small object of weight w hangs from a string of length l, as shown in Fig. 7–4. A *variable* horizontal force **P**, which starts at zero and gradually increases, is used to pull the object very slowly (so that equilibrium exists at all times) until the string makes an angle θ with the vertical. Calculate the work of the force **P**.

Since the object is in equilibrium, the sum of the horizontal forces equals zero, whence

$$P = T \sin \theta.$$

Equating the sum of the vertical forces to zero, we find

$$w = T \cos \theta.$$

Dividing these two equations, we get

$$P = w \tan \theta.$$

The point of application of **P** swings through the arc s. Since $s = l\theta$, $ds = l \, d\theta$ and

$$W = \int \mathbf{P} \cdot d\mathbf{s} = \int P \cos \theta \, ds$$

$$= \int_0^\theta w \tan \theta \cos \theta l \, d\theta = wl \int_0^\theta \sin \theta \, d\theta = wl(1 - \cos \theta). \qquad (7\text{-}4)$$

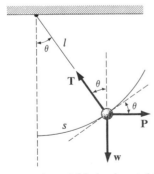

Fig. 7–4. A variable horizontal force **P** acts on a small object while the displacement varies from zero to s.

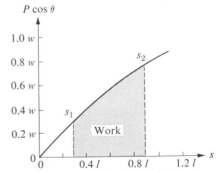

Fig. 7–5. The work of a force **P** when its point of application moves from $s_1 = 0.3l$ to $s_2 = 0.9l$ is the shaded area under the curve of $P \cos \theta$, plotted against s.

A graph of $P \cos \theta$ ($=w \sin \theta$) plotted against s ($=l\theta$) is shown in Fig. 7–5. The work during any displacement is represented by the area under this curve. The shaded area is the work when the point of application of **P** moves from a position where $s_1 = 0.3l$ to a place where $s_2 = 0.9l$.

7–3 Kinetic energy

Kinetic energy, like work, is a scalar quantity. The kinetic energy of a moving body depends only on the *magnitude* of its velocity (or its speed) and not on the direction in which it is moving or on the particular process by which it was set in motion.

It follows from the work-energy principle that the *change* in kinetic energy of a body depends only on the work $W = \int \mathbf{F} \cdot d\mathbf{s}$ and not on the individual values of F and s. That is, the force could have been large and the displacement small, or the reverse might have been true. If the mass m and the speeds v_1 and v_2 are known, the *work* of the resultant force can be found without any knowledge of the force and the displacement.

If the work W is *positive*, the final kinetic energy is greater than the initial kinetic energy and the kinetic energy *increases*. If the work is *negative*, the kinetic energy *decreases*. In the special case in which the work is *zero*, the kinetic energy remains *constant*.

In computing the kinetic energy of a body, consistent units must be used for m and v. In the mks system, m must be in kilograms and v in m/sec. In the cgs system m must be expressed in grams and v in cm/sec. In the engineering system, m must be in slugs and v in ft/sec. The corresponding units of kinetic energy are $1 \text{ kgm·m}^2/\text{sec}^2$, $1 \text{ gm·cm}^2/\text{sec}^2$, and $1 \text{ slug·ft}^2/\text{sec}^2$. However, the unit of kinetic energy in any system is equal to the unit of work in that system, and kinetic energy is customarily expressed in joules, ergs, or foot·pounds. That is,

$$1 \text{ kgm} \frac{\text{m}^2}{\text{sec}^2} = 1 \frac{\text{newton}}{\text{m/sec}^2} \frac{\text{m}^2}{\text{sec}^2} = 1 \text{ newton·m} = 1 \text{ joule.}$$

In the same way,

$$1 \text{ gm} \frac{\text{cm}^2}{\text{sec}^2} = 1 \text{ erg,}$$

$$1 \text{ slug} \frac{\text{ft}^2}{\text{sec}^2} = 1 \text{ ft·lb.}$$

EXAMPLE.   Refer again to the body in Fig. 7–3 and the numerical values given at the end of Example 1. The total work of the external forces was shown to be 500 ft·lb. Hence the kinetic energy of the body increases by 500 ft·lb. To verify this, suppose the initial speed v_1 is 4 ft/sec. The initial kinetic energy is

$$E_{k1} = \frac{1}{2} m v_1^2 = \frac{1}{2} \frac{100}{32} \text{ slugs} \times 16 \frac{\text{ft}^2}{\text{sec}^2} = 25 \text{ ft·lb.}$$

To find the final kinetic energy we must first find the acceleration:

$$a = \frac{F}{m} = \frac{40 \text{ lb} - 15 \text{ lb}}{(100/32) \text{ slugs}} = 8 \frac{\text{ft}}{\text{sec}^2}.$$

Then

$$v_2^2 = v_1^2 + 2as = 16 \frac{\text{ft}^2}{\text{sec}^2} + 2 \times 8 \frac{\text{ft}}{\text{sec}^2} \times 20 \text{ ft} = 336 \frac{\text{ft}^2}{\text{sec}^2},$$

and

$$E_{k2} = \frac{1}{2} \frac{100}{32} \text{ slugs} \times 336 \frac{\text{ft}^2}{\text{sec}^2} = 525 \text{ ft·lb}.$$

The increase in kinetic energy is therefore 500 ft·lb.

7–4 Gravitational potential energy

Suppose a body of mass m (and of weight $\mathbf{w} = m\mathbf{g}$) moves vertically, as in Fig. 7–6(a), from a point where its center of gravity is at a height y_1 above an arbitrarily chosen plane (the *reference level*) to a point at a height y_2. For the present, we shall consider only displacements near the earth's surface, so that variations of gravitational force with distance from the earth's center can be neglected. The downward gravitational force on the body is then constant and equal to $\mathbf{w}$. Let $\mathbf{P}$ represent the resultant of all other forces acting on the body, and let W' be the work of these forces. The direction of the gravitational force $\mathbf{w}$ is opposite to the upward displacement, and the work of this force is

$$W_{\text{grav}} = -w(y_2 - y_1) = -(mgy_2 - mgy_1). \tag{7–5}$$

[The reader should convince himself that the work of the gravitational force is given by $-mg(y_2 - y_1)$ whether the body moves up or down.]

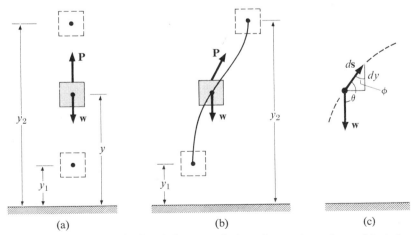

Fig. 7–6. Work of the gravitational force $\mathbf{w}$ during the motion of an object from one point in a gravitational field to another.

Now suppose that the body starts at the same elevation y_1 but is moved up to the elevation y_2 along some arbitrary path, as in Fig. 7-6(b). Part (c) of the figure is an enlarged view of a small portion of the path. The work of the gravitational force is

$$W_{grav} = \int_{s_1}^{s_2} w \cos \theta \, ds.$$

Let ϕ represent the angle between ds and its vertical component dy. Then $dy = ds \cos \phi$, and since $\phi = 180° - \theta$,

$$\cos \phi = -\cos \theta, \qquad \cos \theta \, ds = -dy$$

and

$$W_{grav} = -\int_{y_1}^{y_2} w \, dy = -w(y_2 - y_1) = -(mgy_2 - mgy_1). \qquad (7\text{-}6)$$

The work of the gravitational force therefore depends only on the initial and final elevations and not on the path. If these points are at the *same* elevation the work is zero.

Since the *total* work equals the change in kinetic energy,

$$W' + W_{grav} = E_{k2} - E_{k1}, \qquad W' - (mgy_2 - mgy_1) = (\tfrac{1}{2}mv_2^2 - \tfrac{1}{2}mv_1^2).$$

The quantities $\tfrac{1}{2}mv_2^2$ and $\tfrac{1}{2}mv_1^2$ depend only on the final and initial *speeds;* the quantities mgy_2 and mgy_1 depend only on the final and initial *elevations.* Let us therefore rearrange this equation, transferring the quantities mgy_2 and mgy_1 from the "work" side of the equation to the "energy" side:

$$W' = (\tfrac{1}{2}mv_2^2 - \tfrac{1}{2}mv_1^2) + (mgy_2 - mgy_1). \qquad (7\text{-}7)$$

The left side of Eq. (7-7) contains only the work of the force **P**. The terms on the right depend only on the final and initial states of the body (its speed and elevation) and not specifically on the way in which it moved. The quantity mgy, the product of the weight mg of the body and the height y of its center of gravity above the reference level, is called its *gravitational potential energy*, E_p.

$$E_p \text{ (gravitational)} = mgy. \qquad (7\text{-}8)$$

The first expression in parentheses on the right of Eq. (7-7) is the change in kinetic energy of the body, and the second is the change in its gravitational potential energy. Equation (7-7) can also be written

$$W' = (\tfrac{1}{2}mv_2^2 + mgy_2) - (\tfrac{1}{2}mv_1^2 + mgy_1). \qquad (7\text{-}9)$$

The sum of the kinetic and potential energy of the body is called its *total mechanical energy*. The first expression in parentheses on the right of Eq. (7-9) is the final value of the total mechanical energy, and the second is the initial value. Hence, *the work of all forces acting on the body,* **with the exception of the gravitational force,** *equals the* *change in the total mechanical energy of the body.* If the work W' is positive, the mechanical energy increases. If W' is negative, the energy decreases.

In the special case in which the *only* force on the body is the gravitational force, the work W' is zero. Equation (7–9) can then be written

$$\tfrac{1}{2}mv_2^2 + mgy_2 = \tfrac{1}{2}mv_1^2 + mgy_1.$$

Under these conditions, then, the *total mechanical energy remains constant,* or is *conserved.* This is a special case of the *principle of the conservation of mechanical energy.*

_____

EXAMPLE 1.   A man holds a ball of weight $w = \tfrac{1}{4}$ lb at rest in his hand. He then throws the ball vertically upward. In this process, his hand moves up 2 ft and the ball leaves his hand with an upward velocity of 48 ft/sec. Discuss the motion of the ball from the work-energy standpoint.

First consider the throwing process. Take the reference level at the initial position of the ball. Then $E_{k1} = 0$, $E_{p1} = 0$. Take point 2 at the point where the ball leaves the thrower's hand. Then

$$E_{p2} = mgy_2 = \tfrac{1}{4}\text{ lb} \times 2\text{ ft} = 0.5\text{ ft·lb},$$

$$E_{k2} = \tfrac{1}{2}mv_2^2 = \tfrac{1}{2} \times (\tfrac{1}{4}/32)\text{ slug} \times (48\text{ ft/sec})^2 = 9\text{ ft·lb}.$$

Let P represent the upward force exerted on the ball by the man in the throwing process. The work W' is then the work of this force, and is equal to the sum of the changes in kinetic and potential energy of the ball.

The kinetic energy of the ball increases by 9 ft·lb and its potential energy by 0.5 ft·lb. The work W' of the upward force P is therefore 9.5 ft·lb.

If the force P is constant, the work of this force is given by

$$W' = P(y_2 - y_1),$$

and the force P is then

$$P = \frac{W'}{y_2 - y_1} = \frac{9.5\text{ ft·lb}}{2\text{ ft}} = 4.75\text{ lb}.$$

However, the *work* of the force P is 9.5 ft·lb whether or not the force is constant.

Now consider the flight of the ball after it leaves the thrower's hand. In the absence of air resistance, the only force on the ball is then its weight $\mathbf{w} = m\mathbf{g}$. Hence the total mechanical energy of the ball remains constant. The calculations will be simplified if we take a new reference level at the point where the ball leaves the thrower's hand. Calling this point 1, we have

$$E_{k1} = 9\text{ ft·lb}, \qquad E_{p1} = 0,$$

$$E_k + E_p = 9\text{ ft·lb},$$

and the total mechanical energy at any point of the path equals 9 ft·lb.

Suppose we wish to find the speed of the ball at a height of 20 ft above the reference level. Its potential energy at this elevation is 5 ft·lb. (Why?) Its kinetic energy is therefore 4 ft·lb. To find its speed, we have

$$\tfrac{1}{2}mv^2 = E_k, \qquad v = \pm\sqrt{2E_k/m} = \pm 32\,\frac{\text{ft}}{\text{sec}}.$$

The significance of the $\pm$ sign is that the ball passes this point *twice*, once on the way up and again on the way down. Its *potential* energy at this point is the same whether it is moving up or down. Hence its kinetic energy is the same and its *speed* is the same. The algebraic sign of the speed is $+$ when the ball is moving up and $-$ when it is moving down.

Next, let us find the height of the highest point reached. At this point, $v = 0$ and $E_k = 0$. Therefore $E_p = 9$ ft·lb, and the ball rises to a height of 36 ft above the point where it leaves the thrower's hand.

Finally, suppose we were asked to find the speed at a point 40 ft above the reference level. The potential energy at this point would be 10 ft·lb. But the total energy is only 9 ft·lb, so the ball never reaches a height of 40 ft.

EXAMPLE 2. A body slides down a curved track which is one quadrant of a circle of radius R, as in Fig. 7–7. If it starts from rest and there is no friction, find its speed at the bottom of the track. The motion of this body is exactly the same as that of a body attached to one end of a string of length R, the other end of which is held at point O.

The equations of motion with constant acceleration cannot be used, since the acceleration decreases during the motion. (The slope angle of the track becomes smaller and smaller as the body descends.) However, if there is no friction, the only force on the body in addition to its weight is the normal force N exerted on it by the track. The work of this force is zero, so $W' = 0$ and mechanical energy is conserved. Take point 1 at the starting point and point 2 at the bottom of the track. Take the reference level at point 2. Then $y_1 = R$, $y_2 = 0$, and

$$E_{k2} + E_{p2} = E_{k1} + E_{p1},$$

$$\tfrac{1}{2}mv_2^2 + 0 = 0 + mgR,$$

$$v_2 = \pm\sqrt{2gR}.$$

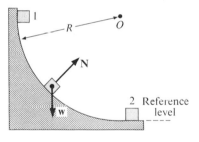

The speed is therefore the same as if the body had fallen *vertically* through a height R. (What is now the significance of the $\pm$ sign?)

As a numerical example, let $R = 1$ m. Then

$$v = \pm\sqrt{2 \times 9.8 \ (\text{m/sec}^2) \times 1 \ \text{m}} = \pm 4.43 \ \frac{\text{m}}{\text{sec}}.$$

Fig. 7–7. An object sliding down a frictionless curved track.

EXAMPLE 3. Suppose a body of mass 0.5 kgm slides down a track of radius $R = 1$ m, like that in Fig. 7–7, but its speed at the bottom is only 3 m/sec. What was the work of the frictional force acting on the body?

In this case, $W' = W_f$, and

$$W_f = (\tfrac{1}{2}mv_2^2 - \tfrac{1}{2}mv_1^2) + (mgy_2 - mgy_1)$$

$$= \left(\frac{1}{2} \times 0.5 \ \text{kgm} \times 9 \ \frac{\text{m}^2}{\text{sec}^2} - 0\right) + \left(0 - 0.5 \ \text{kgm} \times 9.8 \ \frac{\text{m}}{\text{sec}^2} \times 1 \ \text{m}\right)$$

$$= 2.25 \ \text{j} - 4.9 \ \text{j} = -2.65 \ \text{j}.$$

The frictional work was therefore -2.65 j, and the total mechanical energy *decreased* by 2.65 joules. The mechanical energy of a body is *not* conserved when friction forces act on it.

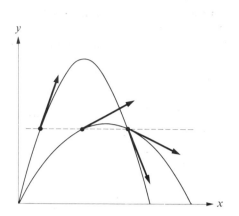

Fig. 7–8. For the same initial speed, the speed is the same at all points at the same elevation.

Fig. 7–9. $\Delta y = l(1 - \cos\theta)$.

EXAMPLE 4.   In the absence of air resistance, the only force on a projectile is its weight, and the mechanical energy of the projectile remains constant. Figure 7–8 shows two trajectories of a projectile with the same initial speed (and hence the same total energy) but with different angles of departure. At all points at the same elevation the potential energy is the same; hence the kinetic energy is the same and the speed is the same.

EXAMPLE 5.   A small object of weight w hangs from a string of length l, as shown in Fig. 7–9. A *variable* horizontal force P, which starts at zero and gradually increases, is used to pull the object very slowly until the string makes an angle θ with the vertical. Calculate the work of the force P.

The sum of the works W' of all the forces other than the gravitational force must equal the change of kinetic energy plus the change of gravitational potential energy. Hence

$$W' = W_P + W_T = \Delta E_k + \Delta E_p.$$

Since T is perpendicular to the path of its point of application, $W_T = 0$; and since the body was pulled very slowly at all times, the change of kinetic energy is also zero. Hence

$$W_P = \Delta E_p = w\Delta y,$$

where Δy is the distance that the object has been raised. From Fig. 7–9, Δy is seen to be $l(1 - \cos\theta)$. Therefore

$$W_P = wl(1 - \cos\theta).$$

The reader is referred to the example at the end of Section 7–2, where this same problem was solved by performing the integration in the equation $W_P = \int P \cos\theta \, ds$. The two answers, of course, are identical, but how much more simply the energy principle leads to the final result!

It has been assumed thus far in this section that the changes in elevation were small enough so that the gravitational force on a body could be considered constant. We now consider the more general case. The force **w** in Fig. 7–6 is the force of gravitational attraction exerted on the body by the earth, and the general expression for the magnitude of this force is

$$G\frac{mm_E}{r^2},$$

where m_E is the mass of the earth and r is the distance from the earth's center. When r increases from r_1 to r_2, the work of the gravitational force is

$$W_{\text{grav}} = -Gmm_E\int_{r_1}^{r_2}\frac{dr}{r^2} = \left(\frac{Gmm_E}{r_2} - \frac{Gmm_E}{r_1}\right).$$

Setting the total work equal to the change in kinetic energy and rearranging terms, we get, instead of Eq. (7–9),

$$W' = \left(\tfrac{1}{2}mv_2^2 - \frac{Gmm_E}{r_2}\right) - \left(\tfrac{1}{2}mv_1^2 - \frac{Gmm_E}{r_1}\right).$$

The quantity $[-G(mm_E/r)]$ is therefore the general expression for the gravitational potential energy of a body attracted by the earth:

$$E_p \text{ (gravitational)} = -G\frac{mm_E}{r}. \qquad (7\text{–}10)$$

The total mechanical energy of the body, the sum of its kinetic energy and potential energy, is

$$E = E_k + E_p = \tfrac{1}{2}mv^2 - G\frac{mm_E}{r}.$$

If the only force on the body is the gravitational force, then $W' = 0$ and the total mechanical energy remains constant, or is conserved.

EXAMPLE. Use the principle of conservation of mechanical energy to find the velocity with which a body must be projected vertically upward, in the absence of air resistance, to rise to a height above the earth's surface equal to the earth's radius, R.

Let v_1 be the initial velocity. Then $r_1 = R$, $r_2 = 2R$, $v_2 = 0$, and

$$\tfrac{1}{2}mv_1^2 - G\frac{mm_E}{R} = 0 - G\frac{mm_E}{2R},$$

or

$$v_1^2 = \frac{Gm_E}{R}.$$

This agrees with the result obtained in Example 8 at the end of Section 5–6.

It may be puzzling at first sight that the general expression for gravitational potential energy should contain a minus sign. The reason for this lies in the choice of a
reference state or reference level in which the potential energy is considered zero.
If we set $E_p = 0$ in Eq. (7–10) and solve for r, we get

$$r = \infty.$$

That is, *the gravitational potential energy of a body is now considered to be zero
when the body is at an infinite distance from the earth*. Since the potential energy
decreases as the body approaches the earth, it must be *negative* at any finite distance
from the earth. The *change* in potential energy of a body as it moves from one point
to another is the same, whatever the choice of reference level, and it is only changes
in potential energy that are significant.

Finally, we show that the general expression for the change in potential energy
reduces to Eq. (7–6) for small changes in elevation near the earth's surface. Thus
the increase in potential energy of a body of mass m, when its distance from the earth's
center increases from r_1 to r_2, is

$$E_{p2} - E_{p1} = -G\frac{mm_E}{r_2} - \left(-G\frac{mm_E}{r_1}\right)$$

$$= Gmm_E\left(\frac{1}{r_1} - \frac{1}{r_2}\right) = Gmm_E\left(\frac{r_2 - r_1}{r_1 r_2}\right).$$

If points 1 and 2 are at elevations y_1 and y_2 above the earth's surface, then

$$r_2 - r_1 = y_2 - y_1.$$

Furthermore, if y_1 and y_2 are both small compared with the earth's radius R, the
product $r_1 r_2$ is very nearly equal to R^2. The preceding equation then reduces to

$$E_{p2} - E_{p1} = \frac{Gmm_E}{R^2}(y_2 - y_1).$$

But

$$\frac{Gm_E}{R^2} = g,$$

where g is the acceleration of gravity at the earth's surface, so

$$E_{p2} - E_{p1} = mg(y_2 - y_1),$$

which is the same as the expression derived earlier when variations in g were neglected.

7–5 Elastic potential energy

Figure 7–10 shows a body of mass m on a level surface. One end of a spring is
attached to the body and the other end of the spring is fixed. Take the origin of
coordinates at the position of the body when the spring is unstretched (Fig. 7–10a).

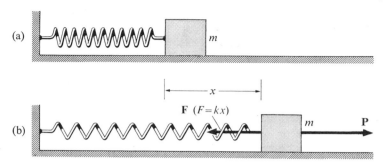

Fig. 7-10. When an applied force **P** produces an extension x of a spring, an elastic restoring force **F** is created within the spring, where $F = kx$.

An outside agent exerts a force **P** of sufficient magnitude to cause the spring to stretch. As soon as the slightest extension takes place, a force **F** is created within the spring which acts in a direction opposite that of increasing x, and therefore opposite that of **P**. The force **F** is called an *elastic force*. If the force **P** is reduced or made zero, the elastic force will restore the spring to its original unstretched condition. It may therefore be referred to as a *restoring force*. The subject of elastic restoring forces was first studied by Robert Hooke, in 1678, who observed that if the extension x of a spring was not so great as to permanently distort the spring, *the elastic force is directly proportional to the extension*, or

$$F = kx, \qquad (7-11)$$

a relation known as *Hooke's law*. The constant of proportionality k is called the *force constant* or the *stiffness coefficient*.

The work of the elastic force W_{el}, during any process in which the spring is extended from a value x_1 to x_2, is

$$W_{\text{el}} = \int \mathbf{F} \cdot d\mathbf{s} = \int_{x_1}^{x_2} F \cos \theta \, dx.$$

Since the direction of F is opposite the direction of dx, $\cos \theta = -1$, whence

$$W_{\text{el}} = -\int_{x_1}^{x_2} kx \, dx,$$

or

$$W_{\text{el}} = -(\tfrac{1}{2}kx_2^2 - \tfrac{1}{2}kx_1^2).$$

Let W' stand for the work of the applied force **P**. Setting the total work equal to the change in kinetic energy of the body, we have

$$W' + W_{\text{el}} = \Delta E_k,$$

$$W' - (\tfrac{1}{2}kx_2^2 - \tfrac{1}{2}kx_1^2) = (\tfrac{1}{2}mv_2^2 - \tfrac{1}{2}mv_1^2).$$

The quantities $\tfrac{1}{2}kx_2^2$ and $\tfrac{1}{2}kx_1^2$ depend only on the initial and final positions of the body and not specifically on the way in which it moved. Let us therefore transfer them from the "work" side of the equation to the "energy" side. Then

$$W' = (\tfrac{1}{2}mv_2^2 - \tfrac{1}{2}mv_1^2) + (\tfrac{1}{2}kx_2^2 - \tfrac{1}{2}kx_1^2). \qquad (7\text{–}12)$$

The quantity $\tfrac{1}{2}kx^2$, one-half the product of the force constant and the square of the coordinate of the body, is called the *elastic potential energy* of the body, E_p. (The symbol E_p is used for any form of potential energy.)

$$E_p \text{ (elastic)} = \tfrac{1}{2}kx^2. \qquad (7\text{–}13)$$

Hence the work W' of the force $\mathbf{P}$ equals the sum of the change in the kinetic energy of the body and the change in its elastic potential energy.

Equation (7–12) can also be written

$$W' = (\tfrac{1}{2}mv_2^2 + \tfrac{1}{2}kx_2^2) - (\tfrac{1}{2}mv_1^2 + \tfrac{1}{2}kx_1^2).$$

The sum of the kinetic and potential energies of the body is its total mechanical energy and *the work of all forces acting on the body,* **with the exception of the elastic force***, equals the change in the total mechanical energy of the body.*

If the work W' is positive, the mechanical energy increases. If W' is negative, it decreases. In the special case in which W' is zero, the mechanical energy remains constant or is *conserved.*

————————————

EXAMPLE 1. Let the force constant k of the spring in Fig. 7–10 be 24 newtons/meter, and let the mass of the body be 4 kgm. The body is initially at rest, and the spring is initially unstretched. Suppose that a constant force $\mathbf{P}$ of 10 newtons is exerted on the body, and that there is no friction. What will be the speed of the body when it has moved 0.5 meter?

The equations of motion with constant acceleration cannot be used, since the resultant force on the body varies as the spring is stretched. However, the speed can be found from energy considerations:

$$W' = \Delta E_k + \Delta E_p,$$

$$10\,\text{n} \times 0.5\,\text{m} = (\tfrac{1}{2} \times 4\,\text{kgm} \times v_2^2 - 0) + \left(\frac{1}{2} \times 24\,\frac{\text{n}}{\text{m}} \times 0.25\,\text{m}^2 - 0\right),$$

$$v_2 = 1\,\frac{\text{m}}{\text{sec}}.$$

EXAMPLE 2. Suppose the force $\mathbf{P}$ ceases to act when the body has moved 0.5 m. How much farther will the body move before coming to rest?

The elastic force is now the only force, and mechanical energy is conserved. The kinetic energy is $\tfrac{1}{2}mv^2 = 2$ joules, and the potential energy is $\tfrac{1}{2}kx^2 = 3$ joules. The total energy is therefore 5 joules (equal to the work of the force $\mathbf{P}$). When the body comes to rest, its kinetic energy is zero and its potential energy is therefore 5 joules. Hence

$$\tfrac{1}{2}kx_{\text{max}}^2 = 5\,\text{j}, \qquad x_{\text{max}} = 0.645\,\text{m}.$$

7–6 Conservative and dissipative forces

When an object is moved from any position above a zero reference level to any other position, the work of the gravitational force is found to be independent of the path and equal to the difference between the final and the initial values of a function called the *gravitational potential energy*. If the gravitational force alone acts on the object, the total mechanical energy (the sum of the kinetic and gravitational potential energies) is constant or conserved, and therefore the gravitational force is called a *conservative force*. Thus, if the object is ascending, the work of the gravitational force is accomplished at the expense of the kinetic energy. If, however, the object is descending, the work of the gravitational force serves to increase the kinetic energy, or, in other words, this work is *completely recovered*. Complete recoverability is an important aspect of the work of a conservative force.

When an object attached to a spring is moved from one value of the spring extension to any other value, the work of the elastic force is also independent of the path and equal to the difference between the final and initial values of a function called the *elastic potential energy*. If the elastic force alone acts on the object, the sum of the kinetic and elastic potential energies is conserved, and therefore the elastic force is also a conservative force. If the object moves so as to increase the extension of the spring, the work of the elastic force is accomplished at the expense of the kinetic energy. If, however, the extension is decreasing, then the work of the elastic force serves to increase the kinetic energy so that this work is completely recovered also.

To summarize, we see that the work of a conservative force has the following properties:

(1) It is independent of the path.

(2) It is equal to the difference between the final and initial values of an energy function.

(3) It is completely recoverable.

Contrast a conservative force with a friction force exerted on a moving object by a fixed surface. The work of the friction force *does depend* on the path; the longer the path, the greater the work. There is *no* function the difference of two values of which equals the work of the friction force. When we slide an object on a rough fixed surface back to its original position, the friction force reverses, and instead of recovering the work done in the first displacement we must again do work on the return trip. In other words, frictional work is *not* completely recoverable. When the friction force acts alone, the total mechanical energy is *not* conserved. The friction force is therefore called a *nonconservative* or *a dissipative* force. *The mechanical energy of a body is conserved only when no dissipative forces act on it.*

We find that when friction forces act on a moving body, another form of energy is involved. The more general principle of conservation of energy includes this other form of energy, along with kinetic and potential energy, and when it is included the *total* energy of any system remains constant. We shall study this general conservation principle more fully in a later chapter.

EXAMPLE. Example 3 in Section 7–4 illustrates the motion of a body acted on by a dissipative, friction force. The initial mechanical energy of the body is its initial potential energy of 4.9 j. Its final mechanical energy is its final kinetic energy of 2.25 j. The frictional work W_f is -2.65 j. A quantity of energy equivalent to 2.65 j is developed as the body slides down the track. The sum of this energy and the final mechanical energy equals the initial mechanical energy, and the total energy of the system is conserved.

7–7 Internal work

Figure 7–11(a) shows a man standing on frictionless roller skates on a level surface, facing a rigid wall. Suppose that he sets himself in motion backward by pushing against the wall. The external forces *on the man* are his weight **w**, the upward forces N_1, N_2 exerted by the ground, and the horizontal force **P** exerted by the wall. (The latter is the reaction to the force with which the man pushes against the wall.) The works of **w** and of **N** are zero because they are perpendicular to the motion. The force **P** is the unbalanced horizontal force which imparts to the system a horizontal acceleration. *The work of* **P**, *however, is zero because there is no motion of its point of application.* We are therefore confronted with a curious situation in which a force is responsible for acceleration, but its work, being zero, is not equal to the increase in kinetic energy of the system!

It is at this point that the concept of *internal work* must be introduced. Although internal forces play no role in accelerating the system, their points of application may move in such a way that work is done. Thus, in this case, an *internal* muscular force is exerted within the man away from the wall. (Think of his lengthening arm as an expanding spring.) Since the point of application of this force moves in the same direction, the work W_i of the internal force is not zero. This is the work responsible for the increase in kinetic energy.

If therefore both external and internal forces act on the particles of a system, the total work W of all forces, external and internal, is the sum of the works W_e and W_i and is equal to the change in the total kinetic energy of the system:

$$W = W_e + W_i = \Delta E_k.$$

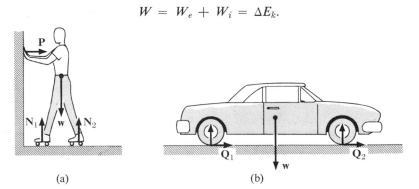

(a)   (b)

Fig. 7–11. (a) External forces acting on a man who is pushing against a wall. The work of these forces is zero. (b) External forces on an automobile. The work of these forces is zero. In both cases, the work of the internal force is responsible for the increase in kinetic energy.

The same principle holds in the case of an accelerated automobile. The portions of the rubber tires that are in contact with the rough roadway push back on the ground and the reactions to these forces, designated by Q_1 and Q_2 in Fig. 7–11(b), are the external horizontal forces acting *on* the automobile responsible for imparting the horizontal acceleration to the system. Since, however, the portions of the tires momentarily in contact with the road are at rest with respect to the road, the works of the forces Q_1 and Q_2 are zero. As a result of the expanding gases in the cylinders of the automobile engine there are many internal forces, some of which do work. Again in this case, it is the work W_i of the internal forces which is equal to the increase in kinetic energy.

7–8 Internal potential energy

If any of the *external* forces on the particles of a system are conservative (gravitational or elastic), the work of these forces can be transferred to the energy side of the work-energy equation and called the change in *external potential energy of the system.* In many instances, the *internal* forces depend only on the distances between *pairs* of particles. The internal work then depends only on the initial and final distances between the particles, and not on the particular way in which they moved. The work of these internal forces can then also be transferred to the energy side of the work-energy equation and called the change in *internal potential energy of the system.* Internal potential energy is a property of the system as a whole and cannot be assigned to any specific particle.

Let W' represent the works of all external and internal forces that have *not* been transferred to the energy side of the work-energy equation and called changes in external and internal potential energy. Let E_p^e and E_p^i represent the external and internal potential energies. The work-energy equation then takes the form

$$W' = \Delta E_k + \Delta E_p^e + \Delta E_p^i, \qquad (7\text{–}14)$$

where the total mechanical energy now includes the kinetic energy of the system and both its external and internal potential energy. If the work W' is zero, the total mechanical energy is conserved.

EXAMPLE 1. Consider a system consisting of two particles in "outer space," very far from all other matter. No external forces act on the system, no external work is done when the bodies move, and the system has no external potential energy. A gravitational force of attraction acts between the bodies, which depends only on the distance between them. We can therefore say that the system has an internal potential energy. Suppose the particles start from rest and accelerate toward each other. The total kinetic energy of the system increases and its internal potential energy decreases. The sum of its kinetic energy and internal potential energy remains constant.

Energy considerations *alone* do not suffice to tell us how much kinetic energy is gained by each body separately. This can be determined, however, from *momentum* considerations, as will be explained in the next chapter.

EXAMPLE 2.   In Section 7–5 we computed the elastic potential energy of a body acted on by a force exerted by a spring. This force was an *external* force acting on the body, and the elastic potential energy $\frac{1}{2}kx^2$ should properly be called the *external* elastic potential energy *of the body*.

Let us now consider the spring itself. The spring is a *system*, composed of an enormous number of molecules which exert internal forces on one another. When the spring is stretched, the distances between its molecules change. The intermolecular forces depend only on the distances between pairs of molecules, so that a stretched spring has an internal elastic potential energy. To calculate this, suppose the spring is slowly stretched from its no-load length by equal and opposite forces applied at its ends. The work of these forces was shown to equal $\frac{1}{2}kx^2$, where x is the elongation of the spring above its no-load length. Let us retain this work on the left side of the work-energy equation so that it becomes the work W' in Eq. (7–14). There is no change in the kinetic energy of the spring and no change in its external potential energy. If we call the internal potential energy zero when $x = 0$, the *change* in internal potential energy in the stretching process equals the final potential energy E_p^i. Then

$$W' = \Delta E_p^i = E_p^i, \qquad E_p^i = \tfrac{1}{2}kx^2.$$

Hence the *internal elastic potential energy of a stretched spring* is equal to $\frac{1}{2}kx^2$. Note that the internal potential energy can be calculated without any detailed information regarding the intermolecular forces.

EXAMPLE 3.   A block of mass m, initially at rest, is dropped from a height h onto a spring whose force constant is k. Find the maximum distance y that the spring will be compressed. See Fig. 7–12.

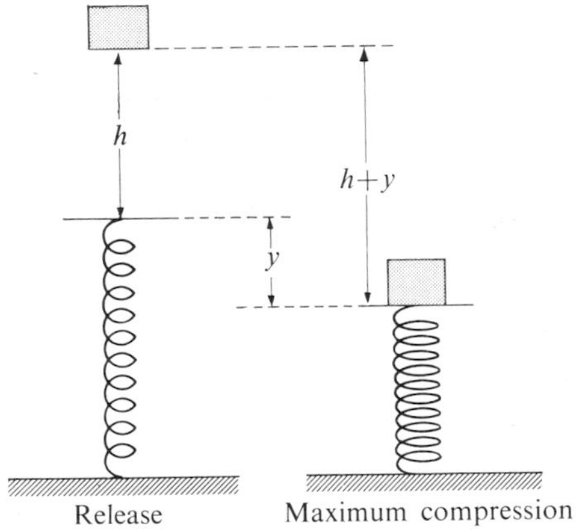

Fig. 7–12.   The total fall of the block is $h + y$.

Release   Maximum compression

This is a process for which the principle of the conservation of mechanical energy holds. At the moment of release, the kinetic energy is zero. At the moment when maximum compression occurs, there is also no kinetic energy. Hence, the loss of gravitational potential energy of the block equals the gain of elastic potential energy of the spring. As shown in Fig. 7–12, the total fall of the block is $h + y$, whence

$$mg(h + y) = \tfrac{1}{2}ky^2, \qquad \text{or} \qquad y^2 - \frac{2mg}{k}y - \frac{2mgh}{k} = 0.$$

Therefore

$$y = \frac{1}{2}\left[\frac{2mg}{k} \pm \sqrt{(2mg/k)^2 + (8mgh/k)}\right].$$

7–9 Power

The time element is not involved in the definition of work. The same amount of work is done in raising a given weight through a given height whether the work is done in one second, or one hour, or one year. In many instances, however, it is necessary to consider the *rate* at which work is done as well as the total amount of work accomplished. The rate at which work is done by a working agent is called the *power* developed by that agent.

If a quantity of work ΔW is done in a time interval Δt, the average power $\overline{P}$ is defined as

$$\text{Average power} = \frac{\text{work done}}{\text{time interval}},$$

$$\overline{P} = \frac{\Delta W}{\Delta t}.$$

The instantaneous power P is the limiting value of this quotient as Δt approaches zero:

$$P = \lim_{\Delta t \to 0} \frac{\Delta W}{\Delta t} = \frac{dW}{dt}. \tag{7–15}$$

The mks unit of power is 1 joule per second, which is called one *watt* (1 w). Since this is a rather small unit, the kilowatt (1 kw $= 10^3$ w) and the megawatt (1 Mw $= 10^6$ w) are commonly used. The cgs power unit is 1 erg per second. No single term is assigned to this unit.

In the engineering system, where work is expressed in foot·pounds and time in seconds, the unit of power is 1 foot·pound per second. Since this unit is inconveniently small, a larger unit called the *horsepower* (hp) is in common use: 1 hp = 550 ft·lb/sec = 33,000 ft·lb/min. That is, a 1-hp motor running at full load is doing 33,000 ft·lb of work every minute it runs.

A common misconception is that there is something inherently *electrical* about a watt or a kilowatt. This is not the case. It is true that electrical power is usually expressed in watts or kilowatts, but the power consumption of an incandescent lamp could equally well be expressed in horsepower, or an automobile engine rated in kilowatts.

From the relations between the newton, pound, meter, and foot, we can show that 1 hp = 746 watts = 0.746 kw, or about $\frac{3}{4}$ of a kilowatt, a useful figure to remember.

Having defined two units of power, the horsepower and the kilowatt, we may use these in turn to define two new units of work, the *horsepower·hour* and the *kilowatt·hour* (kwh).

One horsepower·hour is the work done in one hour by an agent working at the constant rate of one horsepower.

Since such an agent does 33,000 ft·lb of work each minute, the work done in one hour is 60 × 33,000 = 1,980,000 ft·lb.

$$1 \text{ horsepower·hour} = 1.98 \times 10^6 \text{ foot·pounds.}$$

One kilowatt·hour is the work done in one hour by an agent working at the constant rate of one kilowatt.

Since such an agent does 1000 joules of work each second, the work done in one hour is $3600 \times 1000 = 3{,}600{,}000$ joules.

$$1 \text{ kilowatt·hour} = 3.6 \times 10^6 \text{ joules} = 3.6 \text{ Mj}.$$

Note that the horsepower·hour and the kilowatt·hour are units of *work*, not power.

One aspect of work or energy which may be pointed out here is that although it is an abstract physical quantity, it nevertheless has a monetary value. A pound of force or a foot per second of velocity are not things which are bought and sold as such, but a foot·pound or a kilowatt·hour of energy are quantities offered for sale at a definite market rate. In the form of electrical energy, a kilowatt·hour can be purchased at a price varying from a few tenths of a cent to a few cents, depending on the locality and the quantity purchased. In the form of heat, 778 ft·lb (one Btu) costs about a thousandth of a cent.

7–10 Power and velocity

Suppose that a force **F** is exerted on a particle while the particle moves a distance Δs along its path. If $\mathbf{F}_s$ is the magnitude of the component of **F** tangent to the path, then the work of **F** is given by $\Delta W = F_s \, \Delta s$, and the average power is

$$\bar{P} = \frac{\Delta W}{\Delta t} = F_s \frac{\Delta s}{\Delta t} = F_s \bar{v}.$$

The instantaneous power is therefore

$$\boxed{P = F_s v,} \tag{7–16}$$

where v is the instantaneous velocity. Another way of writing Eq. (7–16) is in terms of the scalar product

$$\boxed{P = \mathbf{F} \cdot \mathbf{v}.} \tag{7–17}$$

EXAMPLE. The engine of a jet aircraft develops a thrust of 3000 lb. What horsepower does it develop at a velocity of 600 mi/hr $= 880$ ft/sec?

$$P = F_s v = 3000 \text{ lb} \times 880 \frac{\text{ft}}{\text{sec}} = 2{,}640{,}000 \frac{\text{ft·lb}}{\text{sec}} = \frac{2.64 \times 10^6 \text{ ft·lb/sec}}{550 \text{ (ft·lb/sec)/hp}} = 4800 \text{ hp}.$$

Problems

7-1. The locomotive of a freight train exerts a constant force of 6 tons on the train while drawing it at 50 mi/hr on a level track. How many foot·pounds of work are done in a distance of 1 mi?

7-2. An 80-lb block is pushed a distance of 20 ft along a level floor at constant speed by a force at an angle of 30° below the horizontal. The coefficient of friction between block and floor is 0.25. How many foot·pounds of work are done?

7-3. A horse is towing a canal boat, the towrope making an angle of 10° with the towpath. If the tension in the rope is 100 lb, how many foot·pounds of work are done while moving 100 ft along the towpath?

7-4. A block is pushed 4 ft along a fixed horizontal surface by a horizontal force of 10 lb. The opposing force of friction is 2 lb. (a) How much work is done by the 10-lb force? (b) What is the work of the friction force?

7-5. A body is attracted toward the origin with a force given by $F = -6x^3$, where F is in lb and x in ft. (a) What force is required to hold the body at point a, 1 ft from the origin? (b) At point b, 2 ft from the origin? (c) How much work must be done to move the body from point a to point b?

7-6. The force exerted by a gas in a cylinder on a piston whose area is A is given by $F = pA$, where p is the force per unit area, or *pressure*. The work W in a displacement of the piston from x_1 to x_2 is

$$W = \int_{x_1}^{x_2} F\,dx = \int_{x_1}^{x_2} pA\,dx = \int_{V_1}^{V_2} p\,dV,$$

where dV is the accompanying infinitesimal change of volume of the gas. (a) During an expansion of a gas at constant temperature (isothermal) the pressure depends on the volume according to the relation

$$p = \frac{nRT}{V},$$

where n and R are constants and T is the constant temperature. Calculate the work in expanding isothermally from volume V_1 to volume V_2. (b) During an expansion of a gas at constant entropy (adiabatic) the pressure depends on the volume according to the relation

$$p = \frac{K}{V^\gamma},$$

where K and γ are constants. Calculate the work in expanding adiabatically from V_1 to V_2.

7-7. (a) Compute the kinetic energy of an 1800-lb automobile traveling at 30 mi/hr. (b) How many times as great is the kinetic energy if the velocity is doubled?

7-8. Compute the kinetic energy, in ergs and in joules, of a 2-gm rifle bullet traveling at 500 m/sec.

7-9. An electron strikes the screen of a cathode-ray tube with a velocity of 10^9 cm/sec. Compute its kinetic energy in ergs. The mass of an electron is 9×10^{-28} gm.

7-10. What is the potential energy of a 1600-lb elevator at the top of the Empire State building, 1248 ft above street level? Assume the potential energy at street level to be zero.

7-11. What is the increase in potential energy of a 1-kgm body when lifted from the floor to a table 1 meter high?

7-12. A meter stick whose mass is 300 gm is pivoted at one end as in Fig. 7-13 and displaced through an angle of 60°. What is the increase in its potential energy?

$60°$

Figure 7-13

7-13. The force in pounds required to stretch a certain spring a distance of x ft beyond its unstretched length is given by $F = 10x$. (a) What force will stretch the spring 6 in.? 1 ft? 2 ft? (b) How much work is required to stretch the spring 6 in.? 1 ft? 2 ft?

7-14. The scale of a certain spring balance reads from zero to 400 lb and is 8 in. long. (a) What is the potential energy of the spring when it is stretched 8 in.? 4 in.? (b) When a 50-lb weight hangs from the spring?

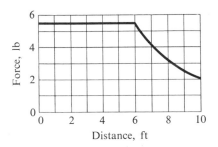

Figure 7–14

7-15. A body moves a distance of 10 ft under the action of a force which has the constant value of 5.5 lb for the first 6 ft and then decreases to a value of 2 lb, as shown by the graph in Fig. 7–14. (a) How much work is done in the first 6 ft of the motion? (b) How much work is done in the last 4 ft?

7-16. A block weighing 16 lb is pushed 20 ft along a horizontal frictionless surface by a horizontal force of 8 lb. The block starts from rest. (a) How much work is done? What becomes of this work? (b) Check your answer by computing the acceleration of the block, its final velocity, and its kinetic energy.

7-17. In the preceding problem, suppose the block had an initial velocity of 10 ft/sec, other quantities remaining the same. (a) How much work is done? (b) Check by computing the final velocity and the increase in kinetic energy.

7-18. A 16-lb block is lifted vertically at a constant velocity of 10 ft/sec through a height of 20 ft. (a) How great a force is required? (b) How much work is done? What becomes of this work?

7-19. A 25-lb block is pushed 100 ft up the sloping surface of a plane inclined at an angle of 37° to the horizontal by a constant force F of 32.5 lb acting parallel to the plane. The coefficient of friction between the block and plane is 0.25. (a) What is the work of the force F? (b) Compute the increase in kinetic energy of the block. (c) Compute the increase in potential energy of the block. (d) Compute the work done against friction. What becomes of this work? (e) What can you say about the sum of (b), (c), and (d)?

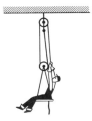

Figure 7–15

7-20. A man weighing 150 lb sits on a platform suspended from a movable pulley and raises himself by a rope passing over a fixed pulley (Fig. 7–15). Assuming no friction losses, find (a) the force he must exert, (b) the increase in his energy when he raises himself 2 ft. Answer part (b) by calculating his increase in potential energy, and also by computing the product of the force on the rope and the length of rope passing through his hands.

7-21. A barrel weighing 250 lb is suspended by a rope 30 ft long. (a) What horizontal force is necessary to hold the barrel sideways 5 ft from the vertical? (b) How much work is done in moving it to this position?

7-22. The system in Fig. 7–16 is released from rest with the 24-lb block 8 ft above the floor. Use the principle of conservation of energy to find the velocity with which the block strikes the floor. Neglect friction and inertia of the pulley.

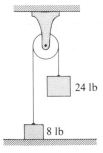

Figure 7–16

7–23. The spring of a spring gun has a force constant of 3 lb per inch. It is compressed 2 inches and a ball weighing 0.02 lb is placed in the barrel against the compressed spring. (a) Compute the maximum velocity with which the ball leaves the gun when released. (b) Determine the maximum velocity if a resisting force of 2.25 lb acts on the ball.

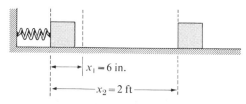

$x_1 = 6$ in.

$x_2 = 2$ ft

Figure 7–17

7–24. A block weighing 2 lb is forced against a horizontal spring of negligible mass, compressing the spring an amount $x_1 = 6$ inches. When released, the block moves on a horizontal table top a distance $x_2 = 2$ ft before coming to rest.   The force constant k is 8 lb/ft (Fig. 7–17). What is the coefficient of friction, μ, between the block and the table?

7–25. A 2-kgm block is dropped from a height of 40 cm onto a spring whose force constant k is 1960 n/m. Find the maximum distance the spring will be compressed.

7–26. A 16-lb projectile is fired from a gun with a muzzle velocity of 800 ft/sec at an angle of departure of 45°. The angle is then increased to 90° and a similar projectile is fired with the same muzzle velocity. (a) Find the maximum heights attained by

the projectiles.   (b) Show that the total energy at the top of the trajectory is the same in the two cases.   (c) Using the energy principle, find the height attained by a similar projectile if fired at an angle of 30°.

Figure 7–18

7–27. A block weighing 2 lb is released from rest at point A on a track which is one quadrant of a circle of radius 4 ft (Fig. 7–18). It slides down the track and reaches point B with a velocity of 12 ft/sec. From point B it slides on a level surface a distance of 9 ft to point C, where it comes to rest. (a) What was the coefficient of sliding friction on the horizontal surface?   (b) How much work was done against friction as the body slid down the circular arc from A to B?

7–28. A small sphere of mass m is fastened to a weightless string of length 2 ft to form a pendulum. The pendulum is swinging so as to make a maximum angle of 60° with the vertical.   (a) What is the velocity of the sphere when it passes through the vertical position?   (b) What is the instantaneous acceleration when the pendulum is at its maximum deflection?

7–29. (a) A ball is tied to a cord and set in rotation in a vertical circle. Prove that the tension in the cord at the lowest point exceeds that at the highest point by six times the weight of the ball. (b) A particle (Fig. 7–19) at the end of a string is origi-

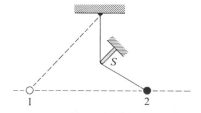

Figure 7–19

nally held in position 1 and then allowed to swing freely until it impinges against the stop S. Prove that position 2 is at the same level as 1 regardless of the position of the stop.

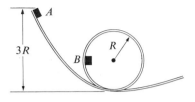

Figure 7–20

7–30. A small body of mass m slides without friction around the loop-the-loop apparatus shown in Fig. 7–20. It starts from rest at point A at a height $3R$ above the bottom of the loop. When it reaches point B at the end of a horizontal diameter of the loop, compute (a) its radial acceleration, and (b) its vertical acceleration.

7–31. A meter stick, pivoted about a horizontal axis through its center, has a body of mass 2 kgm attached to one end and a body of mass 1 kgm attached to the other. The mass of the meter stick can be neglected. The system is released from rest with the stick horizontal. What is the velocity of each body as the stick swings through a vertical position?

7–32. A variable force P is maintained tangent to a frictionless cylindrical surface of radius a, as shown in Fig. 7–21. By slowly varying this force, a block of weight w is moved and the spring to which it is attached is stretched from position 1 to

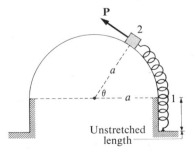

Figure 7–21

position 2. The spring, of force constant k, is unstretched in position 1. Calculate the work of the force P, (a) by integration, (b) by use of the energy principle.

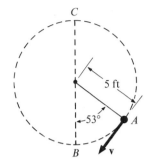

Figure 7–22

7–33. A small 4-lb body is fastened to a weightless string 5 ft long to form a pendulum, as shown in Fig. 7–22. The body is pulled aside until the string makes an angle of 53° with the vertical. (a) With what tangential speed v must the body be started from point A so that it will reach C, the highest point, with a tangential speed of 10 ft/sec? (b) With what speed does it pass through the lowest point B when started from A with the speed v? (c) What is the tension in the cord as the body passes through B? (d) If the body is started from A with the tangential speed v of part (a) in the direction opposite to that shown, with what speed will it then arrive at C?

7–34. The potential energy of a diatomic molecule, as given by Lennard-Jones, is the following function of the distance r between the atoms:

$$E_p(r) = \epsilon_0 \left[\left(\frac{r_0}{r} \right)^{12} - 2 \left(\frac{r_0}{r} \right)^6 \right].$$

Prove that (a) r_0 is the intermolecular separation when the potential energy is a minimum, (b) the minimum potential energy is $-\epsilon_0$, and (c) the intermolecular separation when $E_p(r) = 0$ is equal to $r_0/\sqrt[6]{2}$. (d) Sketch the graph of $E_p(r)$.

7–35. A particle, originally at rest at the origin, is constrained to move along the *x*-axis. Its potential energy is a function of *x*, $E_p(x)$, and its total energy is a constant *E*. Prove that the time *t* to go to a point where the coordinate is *x* is

$$ t = \int_0^x \frac{dx}{\sqrt{(2/m)[E - E_p(x)]}}. $$

7–36. An earth satellite of mass *m* revolves in a circle at a height above the earth equal to twice the earth's radius, 2*R*. In terms of *m*, *R*, the gravitational constant *G*, and the mass of the earth m_E, what are the values of (a) the kinetic energy of the satellite, (b) its gravitational potential energy, and (c) its total mechanical energy?

7–37. A bicycle rider sits still on his seat and pedals so that acceleration takes place. The center of gravity of the system composed of bicycle and rider remains at a constant level. (a) What is the accelerating force? (b) What is the work of the accelerating force? (c) What is responsible for the increase in kinetic energy?

7–38. The hammer of a pile driver weighs 1000 lb and must be lifted a vertical distance of 6 ft in 3 sec. What horsepower engine is required?

7–39. A ski tow is to be operated on a 37° slope 800 ft long. The rope is to move at 8 mi/hr and power must be provided for 80 riders at one time, each weighing, on an average, 150 lb. Estimate the horsepower required to operate the tow.

7–40. (a) If energy costs 5 cents per kwh, how much is one horsepower·hour worth? (b) How many ft·lb can be purchased for one cent?

7–41. Compute the monetary value of the kinetic energy of the projectile of a 14-in. naval gun, at the rate of 2 cents per kwh. The projectile weighs 1400 lb and its muzzle velocity is 2800 ft/sec.

7–42. At 5 cents per kwh, what does it cost to operate a 10-hp motor for 8 hr?

7–43. The engine of an automobile develops 20 hp when the automobile is traveling at 30 mi/hr. (a) What is the resisting force in pounds? (b) If the resisting force

is proportional to the velocity, what horsepower will drive the car at 15 mi/hr? At 60 mi/hr?

7–44. The engine of a motorboat delivers 40 hp to the propeller while the boat is making 20 mi/hr. What would be the tension in the towline if the boat were being towed at the same speed?

7–45. A man whose mass is 70 kgm walks up to the third floor of a building. This is a vertical height of 12 meters above the street level. (a) How many joules of work has he done? (b) By how much has he increased his potential energy? (c) If he climbs the stairs in 20 sec, what was his rate of working, in horsepower?

7–46. A pump is required to lift 200 gallons of water per minute from a well 20 ft deep and eject it with a speed of 30 ft/sec. (a) How much work is done per minute in lifting the water? (b) How much in giving it kinetic energy? (c) What horsepower engine is needed?

7–47. A 4800-lb elevator starts from rest and is pulled upward with a constant acceleration of 10 ft/sec². (a) Find the tension in the supporting cable. (b) What is the velocity of the elevator after it has risen 45 ft? (c) Find the kinetic energy of the elevator 3 sec after it starts. (d) How much is its potential energy increased in the first 3 sec? (e) What horsepower is required when the elevator is traveling 22 ft/sec?

7–48. An automobile weighing 2000 lb has a speed of 100 ft/sec on a horizontal road when the engine is developing 50 hp. What is its speed, with the same horsepower, if the road rises 1 ft in 20 ft? Assume all friction forces to be constant.

7–49. (a) If 20 hp are required to drive a 2400-lb automobile at 30 mi/hr on a level road, what is the retarding force of friction, windage, etc.? (b) What power is necessary to drive the car at 30 mi/hr up a 10% grade, i.e., one rising 10 ft vertically in 100 ft horizontally? (c) What power is necessary to drive the car at 30 mi/hr *down* a 2% grade? (d) Down what grade would the car coast at 30 mi/hr?

CHAPTER 8

Impulse and Momentum

8–1 Impulse and momentum

In the preceding chapter it was shown how the concepts of work and energy are developed from Newton's laws of motion. We shall next see how two similar concepts, those of *impulse* and *momentum*, also arise from these laws.

Let us again consider a particle of mass m moving in the xy-plane, as in Fig. 8–1, and acted on by a resultant force $\mathbf{F}$ that may vary in magnitude and direction. Newton's second law states that at every instant

$$\mathbf{F} = m\frac{d\mathbf{v}}{dt},$$

or

$$\mathbf{F}\,dt = m\,d\mathbf{v}.$$

If $\mathbf{v}_1$ is the velocity when $t = t_1$, and $\mathbf{v}_2$ the velocity when $t = t_2$, it follows that

$$\int_{t_1}^{t_2} \mathbf{F}\,dt = \int_{\mathbf{v}_1}^{\mathbf{v}_2} m\,d\mathbf{v}. \qquad (8\text{–}1)$$

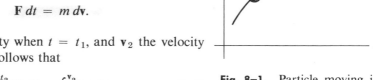

Fig. 8–1. Particle moving in the xy-plane.

The integral on the left is called the *impulse of the force* $\mathbf{F}$ in the time interval $t_2 - t_1$, and is a *vector quantity:*

$$\boxed{\text{Impulse} = \int_{t_1}^{t_2} \mathbf{F}\,dt.}$$

This integral can be evaluated, of course, only when the force is known as a function of the time. The integral on the right, however, always yields the result

$$\int_{\mathbf{v}_1}^{\mathbf{v}_2} m\,d\mathbf{v} = m\mathbf{v}_2 - m\mathbf{v}_1.$$

The product of the mass of a particle and its velocity is called the *linear momentum* of the particle, and is also a *vector* quantity:

$$\boxed{\text{Linear momentum} = m\mathbf{v}.}$$

(We refer to this product as *linear* momentum to distinguish it from a similar quantity called *angular* momentum, which will be discussed later. When there is no opportunity for confusion, we shall speak of the linear momentum simply as the momentum.)

Equation (8–1) is now written as

$$\int_{t_1}^{t_2} \mathbf{F}\, dt = m\mathbf{v}_2 - m\mathbf{v}_1, \tag{8–2}$$

expressing the important fact that: *The* **vector impulse** *of the resultant force on a particle, in any time interval, is equal in magnitude and direction to the* **vector change** *in momentum of the particle.* This is known as the **impulse-momentum** principle.

The impulse-momentum principle finds its chief application in connection with forces of short duration, such as those arising in collisions or explosions. Such forces are called *impulsive forces.*

The unit of impulse, in any system, equals the product of the units of force and time in that system. Thus in the mks system the unit is 1 n·sec, in the cgs system it is 1 dyne·sec, and in the engineering system it is 1 lb·sec.

The unit of momentum in the mks system is 1 kgm·m/sec, in the cgs system it is 1 gm·cm/sec, and in the engineering system it is 1 slug·ft/sec. Since

$$1\, \frac{\text{kgm·m}}{\text{sec}} = 1\, \frac{\text{kgm·m}}{\text{sec}^2}\, \text{sec} = 1\, \text{n·sec},$$

it follows that the unit of momentum in any system equals the unit of impulse in that system.

In contrast to work and energy, which are scalars, impulse and momentum are vector quantities, and therefore Eq. (8–2), like every vector equation, is equivalent (for forces and velocities in the xy-plane) to the two scalar equations

$$\int_{t_1}^{t_2} F_x\, dt = mv_{x2} - mv_{x1},$$
$$\int_{t_1}^{t_2} F_y\, dt = mv_{y2} - mv_{y1}. \tag{8–3}$$

For the special case of a force that is constant in magnitude and direction, we can take $\mathbf{F}$ outside the integral sign in Eq. (8–2), and if we let $t_1 = 0$ and $t_2 = t$, we have

$$\mathbf{F}t = m\mathbf{v}_2 - m\mathbf{v}_1. \tag{8–4}$$

That is, the impulse of a *constant* force equals the product of the force and the time interval during which it acts. The *vector change* in momentum produced by such a force, $(m\mathbf{v}_2 - m\mathbf{v}_1)$, is in the same direction as the force.

If the force and the velocities $\mathbf{v}_1$ and $\mathbf{v}_2$ are in the same direction, Eq. (8–4) reduces to the scalar equation

$$Ft = mv_2 - mv_1.$$

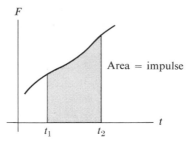

Figure 8–2

The impulse of any force component, or any force whose direction is constant, can be represented graphically by plotting the force vertically and the time horizontally, as in Fig. 8–2. The *area* under the curve, between vertical lines at t_1 and t_2, is equal to the impulse of the force in this time interval.

If the impulse of a force is *positive*, the momentum of the body on which it acts *increases* algebraically. If the impulse is *negative*, the momentum *decreases*. If the impulse is *zero*, there is no change in momentum.

EXAMPLE 1. Consider the changes in momentum produced by the following forces: (a) A body moving on the *x*-axis is acted on for 2 sec by a constant force of 10 n toward the right. (b) The body is acted on for 2 sec by a constant force of 10 n toward the right and then for 2 sec by a constant force of 20 n toward the left. (c) The body is acted on for 2 sec by a constant force of 10 n toward the right and then for 1 sec by a constant force of 20 n toward the left. The three forces are shown graphically in Fig. 8–3.

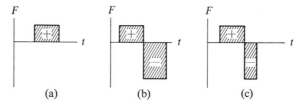

Figure 8–3

(a) The impulse of the force is $+10$ n $\times$ 2 sec $= +20$ n·sec. Hence the momentum of *any* body on which the force acts increases by 20 kgm·m/sec. This change is the same whatever the mass of the body and whatever the magnitude and direction of its initial velocity.

Suppose the mass of the body is 2 kgm and that it is initially at rest. Its *final* momentum then equals its *change* in momentum and its final *velocity* is 10 m/sec toward the right. (The reader should verify by computing the acceleration.)

Had the body been initially moving toward the right at 5 m/sec, its initial momentum would have been 10 kgm·m/sec, its final momentum 30 kgm·m/sec, and its final velocity 15 m/sec toward the right.

Had the body been moving initially toward the *left* at 5 m/sec, its initial momentum would have been -10 kgm·m/sec, its final momentum $+10$ kgm·m/sec, and its final velocity

5 m/sec toward the right. That is, the constant force of 10 n toward the right would first have brought the body to rest and then given it a velocity in the direction opposite to its initial velocity.

(b) The impulse of this force is $(+10 \text{ n} \times 2 \text{ sec} - 20 \text{ n} \times 2 \text{ sec}) = -20 \text{ n·sec}$. The momentum of *any* body on which it acts is decreased by 20 kgm·m/sec. The reader should examine various possibilities, as in the preceding example.

(c) The impulse of this force is $(+10 \text{ n} \times 2 \text{ sec} - 20 \text{ n} \times 1 \text{ sec}) = 0$. Hence the momentum of any body on which it acts is not changed. Of course, the momentum of the body is *increased* during the first two seconds but it is *decreased* by an equal amount in the next second. As an exercise, describe the motion of a body of mass 2 kgm, moving initially to the left at 5 m/sec, and acted on by this force. It will help to construct a graph of velocity versus time.

EXAMPLE 2. A ball of mass 0.4 kgm is thrown against a brick wall. When it strikes the wall it is moving horizontally to the left at 30 m/sec, and it rebounds horizontally to the right at 20 m/sec. Find the impulse of the force exerted on the ball by the wall.

The initial momentum of the ball is $0.4 \text{ kgm} \times -30 \text{ m/sec} = -12 \text{ kgm·m/sec}$. The final momentum is $+8 \text{ kgm·m/sec}$. The *change* in momentum is

$$mv_2 - mv_1 = 8 \text{ kgm·m/sec} - (-12 \text{ kgm·m/sec})$$

$$= 20 \text{ kgm·m/sec}.$$

Hence the impulse of the force exerted on the ball was 20 n·sec. Since the impulse is *positive*, the force is toward the right.

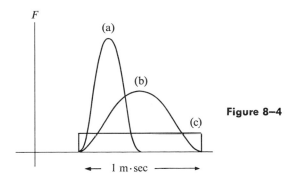

Figure 8–4

Note that the *force* exerted on the ball cannot be found without further information regarding the collision. The general nature of the force-time graph is shown by one of the curves in Fig. 8–4. The force is zero before impact, rises to a maximum, and decreases to zero when the ball leaves the wall. If the ball is relatively rigid, like a baseball, the time of collision is small and the maximum force is large, as in curve (a). If the ball is more yielding, like a tennis ball, the collision time is larger and the maximum force is less, as in curve (b). In any event, the *area* under the force-time graph must equal 20 n·sec.

For an idealized case in which the force is constant and the collision time is 1 msec (10^{-3} sec), as represented by the horizontal straight line, the force is 20,000 n.

Explain why one "eases off" when catching a fast ball.

8-2 Conservation of linear momentum

Whenever there is a force of interaction between two particles, the momentum of each particle is changed as a result of the force exerted on it by the other. (The force may be gravitational, electric, magnetic, or of any other origin.) Furthermore, since by Newton's *third* law the force on one particle is always equal in magnitude and opposite in direction to that on the other, the impulses of the forces are equal in magnitude and opposite in direction. It follows that *the vector change in momentum of either particle*, in any time interval, *is equal in magnitude and opposite in direction to the vector change in momentum of the other.* The *net change in momentum of the* **system** (the two particles together) *is therefore zero.*

The pair of action-reaction forces are *internal* forces of the system and we conclude that *the total momentum of a system of bodies cannot be changed by internal forces between the bodies.* Hence if the *only* forces acting on the particles of a system are *internal* forces (that is, if there are no *external* forces), the total momentum of the system remains constant in magnitude and direction. This is the *principle of* **conservation of linear momentum:** *When* **no resultant external force** *acts on a system, the* **total momentum of the system remains constant in magnitude and direction.**

The principle of conservation of momentum is one of the most fundamental and important principles of mechanics. Note that it is more general than the principle of conservation of mechanical energy; mechanical energy is conserved *only* when the internal forces are *conservative*. The principle of conservation of momentum holds whatever the nature of the internal forces.

EXAMPLE 1.   Figure 8-5 shows a body A of mass m_A moving toward the right on a level frictionless surface with a velocity $\mathbf{v}_{A1}$. It collides with a second body B of mass m_B, moving toward the left with a velocity $\mathbf{v}_{B1}$. Since there is no friction and the resultant vertical force on the system is zero, the only forces on the bodies are the internal action-reaction forces which they exert on each other in the collision process, and the momentum of the system remains constant in magnitude and direction.

Let $\mathbf{v}_{A2}$ and $\mathbf{v}_{B2}$ represent the velocities of A and B after the collision. Then

$$m_A\mathbf{v}_{A1} + m_B\mathbf{v}_{B1} = m_A\mathbf{v}_{A2} + m_B\mathbf{v}_{B2}. \tag{8-5}$$

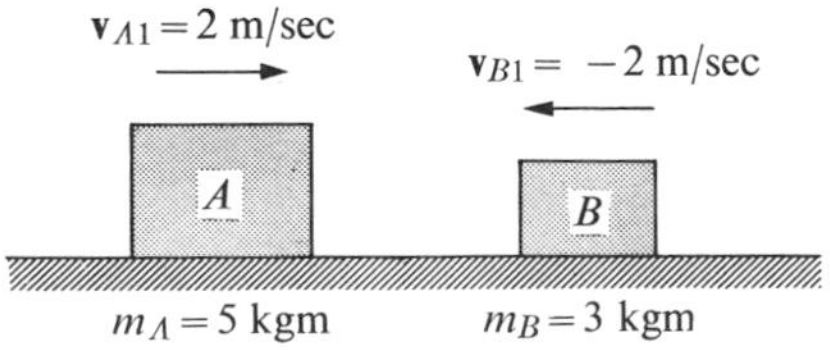

$\mathbf{v}_{A1} = 2 \text{ m/sec}$

$\mathbf{v}_{B1} = -2 \text{ m/sec}$

A B

$m_A = 5 \text{ kgm}$ $m_B = 3 \text{ kgm}$

Figure 8-5

EXAMPLE 2.   In Fig. 8-6, body A of mass m_A is initially moving toward the right with a velocity $\mathbf{v}_{A1}$. It collides with body B, initially at rest, after which the bodies separate and move with velocities $\mathbf{v}_{A2}$ and $\mathbf{v}_{B2}$. No forces act on the system except those in the collision process.

This example illustrates the *vector* nature of momentum, that is, the x- and y-components of momentum are *both* conserved. Let us take the x-axis in the direction of $\mathbf{v}_{A1}$. The initial x-momentum is $m_A v_{A1}$ and the initial y-momentum is zero.

The final x-momentum of the system is

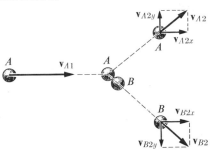

$$m_A v_{A2x} + m_B v_{B2x}$$

and the final y-momentum is

$$m_A v_{A2y} - m_B v_{B2y}.$$

Therefore

$$m_A v_{A2x} + m_B v_{B2x} = m_A v_{A1}, \qquad (8\text{--}6)$$

$$m_A v_{A2y} - m_B v_{B2y} = 0. \qquad (8\text{--}7)$$

Figure 8–6

8–3 Elastic and inelastic collisions

Suppose we are given the masses and initial velocities of two colliding bodies, and we wish to compute their velocities after the collision. If the collision is "head-on," as in Fig. 8–5, Eq. (8–5) provides one equation for the velocities $\mathbf{v}_{A2}$ and $\mathbf{v}_{B2}$. If it is of the type shown in Fig. 8–6, Eqs. (8–6) and (8–7) provide two equations for the four velocity components v_{A2x}, v_{A2y}, v_{B2x}, and v_{B2y}. Hence momentum considerations *alone* do not suffice to completely determine the final velocities; we must have more information about the collision process.

If the forces of interaction between the bodies are *conservative*, the total kinetic energy is the same before and after the collision and the collision is said to be *completely elastic*. Such a collision is closely approximated if one end of an inverted U-shaped steel spring is attached to one of the bodies, as in Fig. 8–7. When the bodies collide the spring is momentarily compressed and some of the original kinetic energy is momentarily converted to elastic potential energy. The spring then expands and when the bodies separate this potential energy is reconverted to kinetic energy.

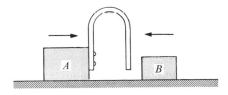

Figure 8–7

At the opposite extreme from a completely elastic collision is one in which the colliding bodies stick together and move as a unit after the collision. Such a collision is called a *completely inelastic* collision, and will result if the bodies in Fig. 8–5 are provided with a coupling mechanism like that between two freight cars, or if the bodies in Fig. 8–7 are locked together at the instant when their velocities become equal and the spring is fully compressed.

8-4 Inelastic collisions

For the special case of a completely inelastic collision between two bodies A and B, we have, from the definition of such a collision,

$$\mathbf{v}_{A2} = \mathbf{v}_{B2} = \mathbf{v}_2.$$

When this is combined with the principle of conservation of momentum, we obtain

$$m_A \mathbf{v}_{A1} + m_B \mathbf{v}_{B1} = (m_A + m_B)\mathbf{v}_2, \tag{8-8}$$

and the final velocity can be computed if the initial velocities, and the masses, are known.

The kinetic energy of the system before collision is $E_{k1} = \frac{1}{2}m_A v_{A1}^2 + \frac{1}{2}m_B v_{B1}^2$. The final kinetic energy is $E_{k2} = \frac{1}{2}(m_A + m_B)v_2^2$.

For the special case in which body B is initially at rest, $v_{B1} = 0$ and the ratio of the final to the initial kinetic energy is

$$\frac{E_{k2}}{E_{k1}} = \frac{(m_A + m_B)v_2^2}{m_A v_{A1}^2}.$$

Inserting the expression for v_2 from Eq. (8-8), we find that this reduces to

$$\frac{E_{k2}}{E_{k1}} = \frac{m_A}{m_A + m_B}.$$

The right side is necessarily less than unity, so *the total kinetic energy decreases in an inelastic collision*.

EXAMPLE 1.   Suppose the collision in Fig. 8-5 is completely inelastic and that the masses and velocities have the values shown. The velocity after the collision is then

$$v_2 = \frac{m_A v_{A1} + m_B v_{B1}}{m_A + m_B} = 0.5 \text{ m/sec.}$$

Since v_2 is positive, the system moves to the right after the collision. The kinetic energy of body A before the collision is

$$\frac{1}{2}m_A v_{A1}^2 = 10 \text{ joules,}$$

and that of body B is

$$\frac{1}{2}m_B v_{B1}^2 = 6 \text{ joules.}$$

The total kinetic energy before collision is therefore 16 joules.

Note that the kinetic energy of body B is positive, although its velocity v_{B1} and its momentum mv_{B1} are both negative.

The kinetic energy after the collision is

$$\frac{1}{2}(m_A + m_B)v_2^2 = 1 \text{ joule.}$$

Hence, far from remaining constant, the final kinetic energy is only 1/16 of the original, and 15/16 is "lost" in the collision. If the bodies couple together like two freight cars, most of this energy is converted to elastic waves which are eventually absorbed.

If there is a spring between the bodies, as in Fig. 8–7, and the bodies are locked together when their velocities become equal, the energy is trapped as potential energy in the compressed spring. If all these forms of energy are taken into account, the *total* energy of the system is conserved although its *kinetic* energy is not. However, *momentum is always conserved* in a collision, whether or not the collision is elastic.

EXAMPLE 2.   The *ballistic pendulum* is a device for measuring the velocity of a bullet. The bullet is allowed to make a completely inelastic collision with a body of much greater mass. The momentum of the system immediately after the collision equals the original momentum of the bullet, but since the velocity is very much smaller it can be determined more easily. Although the ballistic pendulum has now been superseded by other devices, it is still an important laboratory experiment for illustrating the concepts of momentum and energy.

In Fig. 8–8, the pendulum, consisting perhaps of a large wooden block of mass m', hangs vertically by two cords. A bullet of mass m, traveling with a velocity v, strikes the pendulum and remains embedded in it. If the collision time is very small compared with the time of swing of the pendulum, the supporting cords remain practically vertical during this time. Hence no external horizontal forces act on the system during the collision, and the horizontal momentum is conserved. Then if V represents the velocity of bullet and block immediately after the collision,

$$mv = (m + m')V, \qquad v = \frac{m + m'}{m} V.$$

The kinetic energy of the system, immediately after the collision, is $E_k = \frac{1}{2}(m + m')V^2$.

The pendulum now swings to the right and upward until its kinetic energy is converted to gravitational potential energy. (Small frictional effects can be neglected.)   Hence

$$\frac{1}{2}(m + m')V^2 = (m + m')gy,$$
$$V = \sqrt{2gy},$$

and

$$v = \frac{m + m'}{m} \sqrt{2gy}.$$

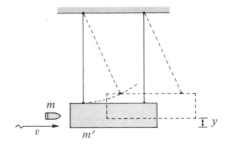

By measuring m, m', and y, the original velocity v of the bullet can be computed.

Fig. 8–8.   The ballistic pendulum.

It is important to remember that kinetic energy is not conserved *in the collision*. The ratio of the kinetic energy of bullet and pendulum, after the collision, to the original kinetic energy of the bullet, is

$$\frac{\frac{1}{2}(m + m')V^2}{\frac{1}{2}mv^2} = \frac{m}{m + m'}.$$

Thus if $m' = 1000$ gm and $m = 1$ gm, only about one-tenth of one percent of the original energy remains as kinetic energy; 99.9% is converted to internal energy.

8-5 Elastic collisions

Consider next a perfectly elastic "head-on" or *central* collision between two bodies A and B. The bodies separate after the collision and have different velocities, v_{A2} and v_{B2}. Since kinetic energy and momentum are *both* conserved, we have:

Conservation of kinetic energy:

$$\tfrac{1}{2}m_A v_{A1}^2 + \tfrac{1}{2}m_B v_{B1}^2 = \tfrac{1}{2}m_A v_{A2}^2 + \tfrac{1}{2}m_B v_{B2}^2.$$

Conservation of momentum:

$$m_A v_{A1} + m_B v_{B1} = m_A v_{A2} + m_B v_{B2}.$$

Hence if the masses and initial velocities are known, we have two independent equations from which the final velocities can be found. Simultaneous solution of these equations gives

$$(v_{B2} - v_{A2}) = -(v_{B1} - v_{A1}), \tag{8-9}$$

$$v_{A2} = \frac{2m_B v_{B1} + v_{A1}(m_A - m_B)}{m_A + m_B}, \tag{8-10}$$

$$v_{B2} = \frac{2m_A v_{A1} - v_{B1}(m_A - m_B)}{m_A + m_B}. \tag{8-11}$$

The difference $(v_{B2} - v_{A2})$ is the velocity of B relative to A after the collision, while $(v_{B1} - v_{A1})$ is its relative velocity before the collision. Thus, from Eq. (8-9), *the relative velocity of two particles in a central, completely elastic collision is unchanged in magnitude but reversed in direction.*

For the special case in which body B is at rest before the collision, $v_{B1} = 0$ and Eqs. (8-10) and (8-11) simplify to

$$v_{A2} = \frac{m_A - m_B}{m_A + m_B} v_{A1}, \qquad v_{B2} = \frac{2m_A}{m_A + m_B} v_{A1}.$$

If the masses of A and B are equal, $v_{A2} = 0$ and $v_{B2} = v_{A1}$. That is, the first body comes to rest and the second moves off with a velocity equal to the original velocity of the first. Both the momentum and kinetic energy of the first are completely transferred to the second.

When the masses are unequal, the kinetic energies after the collision are

$$(E_{k2})_A = \tfrac{1}{2}m_A v_{A2}^2 = \left(\frac{m_A - m_B}{m_A + m_B}\right)^2 (E_{k1})_A,$$

$$(E_{k2})_B = \tfrac{1}{2}m_B v_{B2}^2 = \frac{4m_A m_B}{(m_A + m_B)^2}(E_{k1})_A.$$

It is of interest to derive the expression for the fractional decrease in kinetic energy of body A, that is, the ratio of its decrease in kinetic energy to its original kinetic energy. Since, in an elastic collision, the energy lost by A equals the energy gained by B, this ratio is

$$\frac{(E_{k2})_B}{(E_{k1})_A} = \frac{4m_A m_B}{(m_A + m_B)^2} = 4\,\frac{m_A}{m_B}\,\frac{1}{[1 + (m_A/m_B)]^2}.$$

The fractional decrease in kinetic energy of A is plotted in Fig. 8–9 as a function of the ratio m_A/m_B (note the logarithmic scale). The energy loss approaches zero as m_A/m_B approaches zero (a very small body colliding with a very large one) and also as m_A/m_B approaches infinity (a very large body colliding with a very small one). In the former case, the first body rebounds with practically its original velocity. In the latter, the first body continues to move with very nearly its original velocity. The maximum fractional energy decrease occurs when $m_A = m_B$, and for this ratio of masses the fractional energy loss equals unity, as shown above.

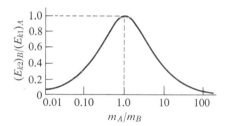

Fig. 8–9. Fractional loss in energy in a head-on elastic collision, plotted as a function of the ratio of the masses of the colliding bodies.

This fact has an important bearing on the problem of slowing down the rapidly moving neutrons resulting from certain nuclear reactions. As neutrons pass through matter, they make occasional elastic collisions with nuclei. In a head-on collision, the greatest loss of kinetic energy results when the mass of the nucleus equals that of the neutron, that is, when the nucleus is that of ordinary hydrogen. The greater the nuclear mass, the less of the neutron's energy is transferred to the nucleus.

EXAMPLE. Suppose the collision illustrated in Fig. 8–5 is completely elastic. What are the velocities of A and B after the collision?

From the principle of conservation of momentum,

$$5\ \text{kgm} \times 2\ \text{m/sec} + 3\ \text{kgm} \times (-2\ \text{m/sec}) = 5\ \text{kgm} \times v_{A2} + 3\ \text{kgm} \times v_{B2},$$

$$5v_{A2} + 3v_{B2} = 4\ \text{m/sec}.$$

Since the collision is completely elastic,

$$v_{B2} - v_{A2} = -(v_{B1} - v_{A1}) = 4\ \text{m/sec}.$$

When these equations are solved simultaneously, we get

$$v_{A2} = -1\ \text{m/sec}, \qquad v_{B2} = 3\ \text{m/sec}.$$

Both bodies therefore reverse their directions of motion, A traveling to the left at 1 m/sec and B to the right at 3 m/sec.

The total kinetic energy after the collision is

$$\tfrac{1}{2} \cdot 5 \text{ kgm} \cdot \left(-1 \frac{m}{\text{sec}}\right)^2 + \tfrac{1}{2} \cdot 3 \text{ kgm} \cdot \left(3 \frac{m}{\text{sec}}\right)^2 = 16 \text{ joules},$$

which equals the total kinetic energy before the collision.

8–6 Recoil

Figure 8–10 shows two blocks A and B, between which there is a compressed spring. When the system is released from rest, the spring exerts equal and opposite forces on the blocks until it has expanded to its natural unstressed length. It then drops to the surface, while the blocks continue to move. The original momentum of the system is zero, and if frictional forces can be neglected, the resultant external force on the system is zero. The momentum of the system therefore remains constant and equal to zero. Then if v_A and v_B are the velocities acquired by A and B, we have

$$m_A v_A + m_B v_B = 0, \qquad \frac{v_A}{v_B} = - \frac{m_B}{m_A}.$$

The velocities are of opposite sign and their magnitudes are inversely proportional to the corresponding masses.

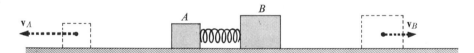

Fig. 8–10.   Conservation of momentum in recoil.

The original kinetic energy of the system is also zero. The final kinetic energy is

$$E_k = \tfrac{1}{2} m_A v_A^2 + \tfrac{1}{2} m_B v_B^2.$$

The source of this energy is the original elastic potential energy of the system. The ratio of kinetic energies is

$$\frac{\tfrac{1}{2} m_A v_A^2}{\tfrac{1}{2} m_B v_B^2} = \frac{m_A}{m_B}\left(\frac{v_A}{v_B}\right)^2 = \frac{m_B}{m_A}.$$

Thus, although the momenta are equal in magnitude, the kinetic energies are inversely proportional to the corresponding masses, the body of smaller mass receiving the larger share of the original potential energy. The reason is that the change in *momentum* of a body equals the *impulse* of the force acting on it ($\int \mathbf{F}\, dt$), while the change in *kinetic energy* equals the *work* of the force ($\int \mathbf{F}\, d\mathbf{s}$). The forces on the two bodies are equal in magnitude and act for equal times, so they produce equal and opposite changes in momentum. The points of application of the forces, however, do not move through equal distances (except when $m_A = m_B$), since the acceleration,

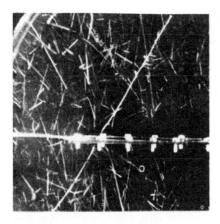

Fig. 8-11. Cloud-chamber photograph of the fission of an atom of uranium. (*From* Bøggild, Brostrøm, and Lauritsen, *Phys. Rev.* **59**, 275, 1941.)

velocity, and displacement of the smaller body are greater than those of the larger. Hence more work is done on the body of smaller mass.

Considerations like those above also apply to the firing of a rifle. The initial momentum of the system is zero. When the rifle is fired, the bullet and the powder gases acquire a forward momentum, and the rifle (together with any system to which it is attached) acquires a rearward momentum of the same magnitude. The ratio of velocities cannot be expressed as simply as in the case discussed above. The bullet travels with a definite velocity, but different portions of the powder gases have different velocities. Because of the relatively large mass of the rifle compared with that of the bullet and powder charge, the velocity and kinetic energy of the rifle are much smaller than those of the bullet and powder gases.

In the processes of radioactive decay and nuclear fission, a nucleus splits into two or more parts which fly off in different directions. Although we do not yet understand the nature of the forces which act in these processes, it has been verified by many experiments that the principle of conservation of momentum applies to them also. The total (vector) momentum of the products equals the original momentum of the system. The source of the kinetic energy of the products is the so-called *binding energy* of the original nucleus, analogous to the chemical energy of the powder charge in a rifle.

Figure 8-11 shows the explosive break-up (fission) of one uranium atom into two fragments of approximately equal mass. The atom was at rest in the thin foil that stretches horizontally in the picture, then it was "triggered off" by a passing neutron, and the two fission products recoiled from each other in opposite directions. While they cannot, of course, be directly observed, the two fragments give themselves away indirectly by the thin streaks of fog or clouds which can be made to condense along their paths.* It is evident that the fragments are slowed down to a stop after a few centimeters in the medium through which they have to plow, but from such data as the length and density of the tracks we can deduce the speeds of separation. From

---

* The equipment for this purpose, a most important tool in contemporary research, is called a *cloud chamber*. It originated in a design devised in 1895 by the British Nobel Prize physicist C. T. R. Wilson.

the law of conservation of momentum, applied to the fission fragments, we can then obtain directly the ratio of their masses, an important aid in the identification of the nuclear reaction.

In this simplified account we are neglecting the contribution to momentum of minor fission products not apparent in this picture, and of the incident neutron. In the "background" can be seen the result of collisions between other incident neutrons and the atmosphere in the cloud chamber.

8-7 Principles of rocket propulsion

A rocket is propelled by the ejection of a portion of its mass to the rear. The forward force on the rocket is the reaction to the backward force on the ejected material, and as more material is ejected the mass of the rocket decreases. The problem is best handled by impulse-momentum considerations. In order not to bring in too many complicating factors, we shall consider a rocket fired vertically upward, and neglect air resistance and variations in $\mathbf{g}$.

Figure 8-12(a) represents the rocket at a time t after take-off, when its mass is m and its upward velocity is $\mathbf{v}$. In part (b), at a time $t + dt$, the velocity of the rocket has increased to $\mathbf{v} + d\mathbf{v}$. Let μ represent the mass ejected per unit time. The mass of the rocket is then $m - \mu \, dt$ and that of the ejected material, represented by the small rectangle, is $\mu \, dt$. Let $\mathbf{v}_r$ represent the velocity of the rocket relative to that of the ejected material. The velocity $\mathbf{v}'$ of the latter is then

$$\mathbf{v}' = \mathbf{v} - \mathbf{v}_r. \qquad (8\text{-}12)$$

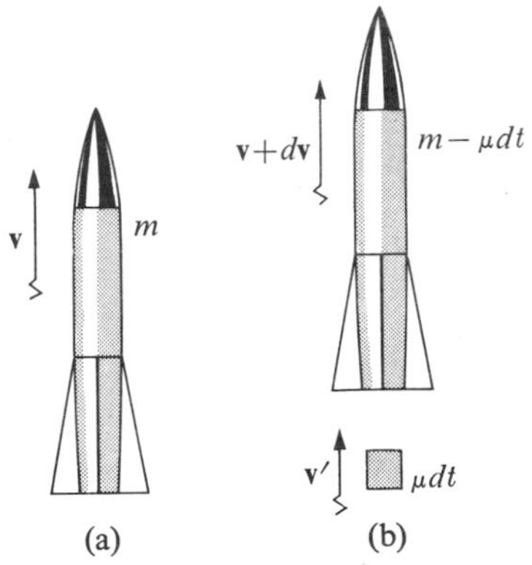

The only external force on the system is its weight $m\mathbf{g}$. The impulse of this force in time dt, taking the upward direction as positive, is $-mg \, dt$, and from the impulse-momentum theorem this equals the change in momentum of the system. The initial momentum is mv. The final momentum of the rocket is $(m - \mu t)(v + dv)$, and that of the ejected material is $v'\mu \, dt$. Then

(a)   (b)

Figure 8-12

$$-mg \, dt = [(m - \mu \, dt)(v + dv) + v'\mu \, dt] - mv.$$

Now expand the right side of this equation, eliminate v' (by Eq. 8-12) and neglect the relatively small quantity $\mu \, dt \, dv$. (The result is therefore valid only so long as m is very large compared with $\mu \, dt$.) This leads to the equation

$$m \, dv = v_r \mu \, dt - mg \, dt.$$

The change in mass of the rocket in time dt is $dm = -\mu \, dt$. Therefore

$$dv = -v_r \frac{dm}{m} - g \, dt,$$

which integrates to

$$v = -v_r \ln m - gt + C.$$

Let m_0 and v_0 be the mass and velocity at time $t = 0$. Then

$$v_0 = -v_r \ln m_0 + C,$$

and

$$v = v_0 - gt + v_r \ln \frac{m_0}{m}. \tag{8–13}$$

The first two terms on the right are the same as those in Eq. (4–18). The third term represents the excess velocity over that of a projectile fired vertically upward with initial velocity v_0. It is evident that in order to attain a high velocity v, the relative velocity v_r and the mass ratio m_0/m must be large.

EXAMPLE. If a single stage rocket, fired vertically from rest at the earth's surface, burns its fuel in a time of 30 seconds, and the relative velocity $v_r = 3000$ m/sec, what must be the mass ratio m_0/m for a final velocity v of 8 km/sec (about equal to the orbital velocity of an earth satellite)?

$$\ln \frac{m_0}{m} = \frac{v + gt}{v_r} = 2.76, \qquad \frac{m_0}{m} = 16.$$

8–8 Relativistic change of mass with velocity

The principles of special relativity were derived in Chapter 4 from the postulate that the measured velocity of a light signal is the same in all reference systems in uniform relative motion. An unexpected consequence is that the mass of a particle depends on its velocity relative to an observer.

To derive the expression for the variation of mass with velocity from the principles of relativity, we make use of a "thought" experiment (in German, a "Gedanken" experiment) devised by Lewis and Tolman and shown in Fig. 8–13. Two experimenters A and B, on flatcars in uniform relative motion, are provided with identical perfectly elastic balls lettered a and b, respectively. They are told to project the balls at right angles to their relative motion and with equal transverse velocities, in such a way that the balls collide at a point midway between the cars, and to catch them after the collision. (A downward gravitational force on the balls can be ignored, or we can imagine the experiment to be carried out by two astronauts, far from all other systems.)

Figure 8–13 shows the paths of the balls as they would appear to an observer for whom the cars had equal and opposite velocities. Each experimenter must anticipate the collision, and throw his ball *before* the cars come abreast. Thus A throws at the time t_{1A} and B at the time t_{1B}. Each ball appears to its thrower to move transversely to his car, but to an outside observer they appear to move along the dotted lines. The collision takes place when the cars are abreast at times t_{2A} and t_{2B}, and the balls are caught at times t_{3A} and t_{3B}.

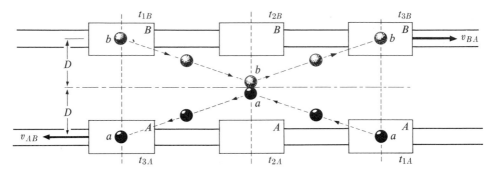

Fig. 8–13. The Lewis-Tolman "thought" experiment for demonstrating that mass depends on relative velocity.

Let us first consider the experiment from the standpoint of Newtonian mechanics. Then the times t_{1A} and t_{1B} are the same, and both can be represented by t_1, as in Fig. 8–14. The collision takes place at time t_2 for both experimenters, and each catches his ball at time t_3. The x-coordinate of each ball remains constant in the system of its thrower, so the world lines of the balls are straight lines perpendicular to the A- and B-axes.

Both experimenters assign the same time interval Δt to the throw-and-catch process, and since each ball travels the same total transverse distance $2D$, they conclude that the transverse velocities are the same for both. From the principle of conservation of momentum, applied to the transverse motion, they conclude that the masses of the balls are equal.

However, we know from the principles of relativistic mechanics that the diagram in Fig. 8–14 is not correct and must be replaced by Fig. 8–15, in which each experimenter has his own time scale. The world line of each ball is still perpendicular to its respective x-axis, but the times are different for the two experimenters.

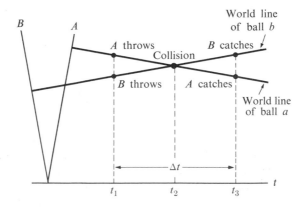

Fig. 8–14. Brehme diagram of the experiment in Fig. 8–13, from the standpoint of Newtonian mechanics.

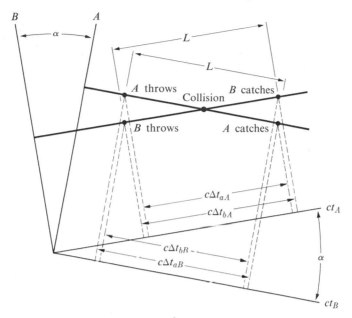

Fig. 8–15. Brehme diagram of the experiment in Fig. 8–13, from the standpoint of relativistic mechanics.

First consider the problem from the standpoint of experimenter A. Reference to Fig. 8–15 shows that on A's time scale, A and B did *not* throw simultaneously. According to A, B threw his ball at an *earlier* time than did A, and caught it at a *later* time. The time interval for the round trip of ball a, according to A, was Δt_{aA}, and the time for the round trip of ball b was Δt_{bA}, larger than Δt_{aA}. Because the transverse *distances* covered by both balls are the same, A concludes that the transverse velocity of ball b was *smaller* than that of his ball. Then since each ball rebounds with the same speed as that with which it was thrown, A is faced with a dilemma: either the principle of conservation of momentum does not apply, or the mass of ball b is *greater* than that of ball a.

But this is not the only dilemma. Consider the experiment from B's viewpoint. Reference to Fig. 8–15 shows that while B, like A, concludes that the two throws were not simultaneous, B thinks that A threw his ball *earlier* than did B, and caught it *later*. Applying the same reasoning as did A, he must also conclude that either momentum is not conserved, or that the mass of ball a is *greater* than the mass of ball b.

The decision taken by A and B (who now represent the community of physicists) is to retain the principle of conservation of momentum, and to recognize that the remaining aspect of the *apparent* dilemma (A thinks ball b has the greater mass, while B thinks ball a has the greater mass) is in fact not a dilemma at all but represents a fundamental law of nature. That is, the mass of a body must not be considered an invariant property of the body, but as one whose value depends on the velocity of the body *relative to the observer*.

To observer A, ball a is at rest (in the x-direction) and ball b is in motion, and ball b appears to have the larger mass. To observer B, ball b is at rest and ball a is in motion, and ball a appears to have the larger mass. There is thus no contradiction between their observations, and both A and B describe the experiment in the same terms (as indeed they must, since there is no fundamental difference between systems A and B).

The relation between the masses of balls a and b, as they appear to each experimenter, is readily derived. Let L represent the length of either world line in Fig. 8–15, between the events "throw" and "catch." Consider first experimenter A. We have

$$c\,\Delta t_{bA} = L, \qquad c\,\Delta t_{aA} = L\cos\alpha, \qquad \frac{\Delta t_{aA}}{\Delta t_{bA}} = \cos\alpha.$$

The transverse velocities assigned to a and b by experimenter A are

$$v_{bA} = \frac{2D}{\Delta t_{bA}}, \qquad v_{aA} = \frac{2D}{\Delta t_{aA}}.$$

Hence

$$\frac{v_{bA}}{v_{aA}} = \frac{\Delta t_{aA}}{\Delta t_{bA}} = \cos\alpha,$$

and if the balls have equal momenta,

$$m_{aA}v_{aA} = m_{bA}v_{bA}, \qquad \frac{m_{bA}}{m_{aA}} = \frac{v_{aA}}{v_{bA}} = \frac{1}{\cos\alpha}.$$

It was shown in Section 4–11 that $\cos\alpha = \sqrt{1 - v_{BA}^2/c^2}$. Hence

$$m_{bA} = \frac{m_{aA}}{\cos\alpha} = \frac{m_{aA}}{\sqrt{1 - v_{BA}^2/c^2}}. \qquad (8\text{–}14)$$

In the same way, experimenter B concludes that

$$m_{aB} = \frac{m_{bB}}{\cos\alpha} = \frac{m_{bB}}{\sqrt{1 - v_{BA}^2/c^2}}. \qquad (8\text{–}15)$$

Either of the preceding equations can be obtained from the other by interchanging the subscripts A and B, and a and b. Note that it makes no difference whether we write v_{AB} or v_{BA}, since the *squares* of the relative velocities are the same.

Equations (8–14) and (8–15) are usually written in a different form. In describing the Lewis-Tolman experiment, it was useful to label the balls a and b to keep track of which was which. But actually the balls are identical, and the real distinction between the terms m_{bA} and m_{aA}, in Eq. (8–14), is that the latter represents the mass of a ball *at rest* relative to system A, while the former represents the mass of an *identical* ball, or even the *same* ball, when it is moving with respect to A. (We might ask A and B to exchange balls and repeat the experiment.) The mass of a body at rest in a given system, called its *rest mass*, is represented by m_0. The mass of the *same body* in motion relative to the system is represented by m. Furthermore, since ball b, in Eq. (8–14), is at rest in system B, its velocity relative to A is equal to v_{BA}. Let us represent by v the velocity of a body relative to the system under consideration.

The usual form of either Eq. (8–14) or (8–15) is then the familiar relation

$$m = \frac{m_0}{\sqrt{1 - v^2/c^2}} \qquad (8\text{--}16)$$

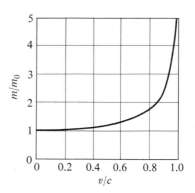

Figure 8–16 is a graph of the ratio m/m_0 plotted as a function of the ratio v/c. For a rifle bullet, v/c is about 3×10^{-6}, and evidently even at this speed the mass equals the rest mass for all practical purposes. On the other hand, an electron accelerated by a potential difference as small as 100,000 volts already has a speed of about $0.6c$, so it

Fig. 8–16. Graph of the ratio m/m_0, plotted as a function of v/c.

is evident that the increase of mass with velocity is of the greatest importance when dealing with atomic and subatomic particles that have been accelerated through millions of volts.

It will be worth while to retrace the steps by which Eq. (8–16) was derived, and which may appear at first to have no relation to the laws of dynamics. The fundamental hypothesis of special relativity is that *the measured velocity of a light signal is the same in all systems in uniform relative motion*. A necessary consequence is that there is *no universal time scale* for all observers, and it follows from this that observers *A* and *B*, in the Lewis-Tolman experiment, assign different transverse velocities to balls *a* and *b*. The principles of dynamics, however, involve the velocities of moving bodies, and if we make the further hypothesis that *the laws of physics* (including the principle of conservation of momentum) *are the same for all observers in uniform relative motion*, then the mass of a body must depend on its relative velocity.

8–9 Mass and energy

It was stated at the beginning of Chapter 5 that the acceleration of a given particle, produced by a given force, is always the same, whatever the velocity of the particle. In other words, the ratio of force to acceleration is a constant m, the mass of the particle:

$$\frac{\mathbf{F}}{d\mathbf{v}/dt} = \text{constant} = m.$$

We now see that the statement above is only an approximation, although a very good approximation, when the velocity of the particle relative to an observer is small compared with the velocity of light, c. The mass is in reality not constant, but increases with increasing velocity.

The relativistic form of the second law, instead of being

$$\mathbf{F} = m\frac{d\mathbf{v}}{dt}, \qquad \text{is} \qquad \mathbf{F} = \frac{d}{dt}(m\mathbf{v}).$$

That is, *the resultant force on a particle equals the rate of change of momentum of the particle*.

If the relative velocity is small, then $m = m_0 = $ constant (very nearly) and

$$\mathbf{F} = m_0 \frac{d\mathbf{v}}{dt}, \qquad (8\text{-}17)$$

so that for small velocities the relativistic equation reduces to the classical form of the second law. In general, however, we have

$$\mathbf{F} = m\frac{d\mathbf{v}}{dt} + \mathbf{v}\frac{dm}{dt}, \qquad (8\text{-}18)$$

and the effect of a force is not only to change the *velocity* v of a particle, but to change its *mass* m as well.

It should be noted, however, that the term v^2 in Eq. (8-16) refers to the square of the relative *speed* of the particle. If the force is at right angles to the velocity, as will be the case when a particle moves in a circle, it produces no change in speed, so that $dm/dt = 0$ and

$$\mathbf{F} = m\frac{d\mathbf{v}}{dt},$$

which has the same *form* as Eq. (8-17), although if the speed of the particle is large the mass m is not equal to the mass m_0.

One of the experimental methods of measuring the masses of electrons and ions is to whirl them in a circular path in a magnetic field such as that of a cyclotron. The force on the particle, its velocity, and the radius of its circular path can all be measured and the mass computed from its definition as the ratio of the force to the radial acceleration. In fact, it is by measurements of this sort that the variation of mass with speed has been verified.

Now consider the motion of a particle acted on by a force in the same direction as the velocity, so that the speed and the mass both increase. We wish to compute the work of the force. If ds is a small displacement along the path, then

$$v = \frac{ds}{dt}, \qquad dt = \frac{ds}{v},$$

and Eq. (8-18) can be written as

$$F\,ds = mv\,dv + v^2\,dm. \qquad (8\text{-}19)$$

Next, we square both sides of Eq. (8-16) and write the result as

$$v^2 = c^2\left(1 - \frac{m_0^2}{m^2}\right).$$

Now take differentials of both sides and multiply by $m/2$:

$$mv\,dv = \frac{m_0 c^2}{m^2}\,dm.$$

When these expressions for v^2 and $mv\,dv$ are inserted in Eq. (8-19), we get the simple relation

$$F\,ds = c^2\,dm.$$

We now *define* the kinetic energy of the particle as the work of the accelerating force:

$$E_k = \int F \, ds = \int_{m_0}^{m} c^2 \, dm = (m - m_0)c^2. \tag{8–20}$$

The kinetic energy therefore equals the increase in mass over the rest mass, multiplied by the square of the velocity of light. The preceding equation is one form of the famous Einstein *mass-energy relation.* It appears very different from the familiar expression $E_k = \frac{1}{2}mv^2$. However, all relativistic equations reduce to those of Newtonian mechanics when v is small compared with c. If this is the case, then v^2/c^2 is very small compared with unity, and

$$\left(1 - \frac{v^2}{c^2}\right)^{-1/2} \approx 1 + \frac{1}{2}\frac{v^2}{c^2},$$

as may be seen by expanding the quantity on the left by the binomial theorem and neglecting the terms in v^4/c^4 and higher powers. Then

$$m = \frac{m_0}{\sqrt{1 - v^2/c^2}} \approx m_0\left(1 + \frac{1}{2}\frac{v^2}{c^2}\right) \quad \text{and} \quad (m - m_0)c^2 \sim \tfrac{1}{2}mv^2.$$

Equation (8–20) can also be written as

$$m = m_0 + \frac{E_k}{c^2}. \tag{8–21}$$

The increase in mass of a particle in relative motion, over its rest mass, equals its kinetic energy divided by c^2. This relation is not restricted to *kinetic* energy, however, but includes *potential* energy as well. Thus the mass of a *system* of particles increases not only when the kinetic energies of the particles increase, but when the internal potential energy of the system increases. The general form of Eq. (8–21) is therefore

$$m = m_0 + \frac{E}{c^2}, \tag{8–22}$$

where E is the total energy, kinetic plus potential, and m_0 is the mass when all of the particles are at rest relative to the observer and are so far apart that their internal potential energy is zero.

For example, the mass of a stretched spring is greater than its mass in an unstretched state by the elastic potential energy E_p divided by c^2. The value of c^2 is so large, however, that the increase in mass is quite undetectable even by the most sensitive mass-measuring instruments. When it comes to the potential energies of nuclei, the situation is different. These energies, associated with the binding forces that hold the nucleons together, are relatively so great that the masses of nuclei can be measurably different from the sums of the masses of their component parts when they are separated from one another.

One frequently reads that in the processes of nuclear fission and nuclear fusion, "mass is converted to energy." Such statements give the impression that the mass of a system *decreases* in a nuclear reaction while at the same time its energy *increases*. This is not the case. Let us consider as an example the fission of a uranium nucleus, pictured in Fig. 8–11.

Before the fission process occurs, the uranium nucleus is at rest, and has a certain rest mass. Immediately after the fission takes place, and before the fission products have made any collisions with the molecules of the surrounding material, the sum of the masses of these products is exactly equal to the original rest mass of the uranium nucleus. The products have a large kinetic energy, but the source of this energy cannot be a decrease in mass of the system because no such decrease has occurred. Rather, we must look for the source of energy in a form of potential energy (binding energy) associated with the original nucleus. The mass-energy relation does not require us to abandon the principles of conservation of mass and conservation of energy. Rather, these two conservation principles remain but become parts of a single principle. Energy and mass are *both* conserved in the process, and there is no conversion of one into the other.

Consider next the collision processes between the fission fragments and the molecules of the surrounding material. Immediately after the fission process, the fragments are traveling at very high speeds and their masses, in accordance with Eq. (8–16), are greater than their rest masses. As they collide with the surrounding molecules their kinetic energies decrease and their masses decrease also. When they have come to rest, their combined rest mass is *less* than that of the original nucleus, and in this sense the mass *has* decreased. But in the process of colliding with the surrounding molecules, the kinetic energies and velocities of these molecules are *increased* and their masses are increased also. The increase in energy of these molecules is just equal to the decrease in energy of the fission fragments, and the increase in mass of the molecules is just equal to the decrease in mass of the fragments. Again, there has been no change in either the total mass or the total energy of the *entire* system. Mass is conserved and energy is conserved also.

It is true, of course, that the mass *of an individual particle* such as an electron or proton can no longer be considered constant. But in any process in which the energy and mass of a particle increase, both the energy and mass of some other particle or particles decrease by exactly the same amounts, and both the total energy and the total mass of the system remain constant.

8–10 Relativistic transformation of accelerations and forces

In relativity, where the mass m of a particle is not a constant but depends on its relative velocity, we must use the relativistic form of Newton's second law given in Eq. (8–18):
$$\mathbf{F} = (d/dt)(m\mathbf{v}) = m(d\mathbf{v}/dt) + \mathbf{v}(dm/dt),$$

or, for a short time interval Δt,

$$\mathbf{F}\,\Delta t = \Delta(m\mathbf{v}) = m\,\Delta\mathbf{v} + \mathbf{v}\,\Delta m. \tag{8–23}$$

The relation between the magnitudes of a force as measured by two observers in relative motion is as important as the relation between the apparent masses of a particle. We consider a particle initially at rest in system B and acted on by a constant force F_B, as measured by observer B. What is the magnitude F_A of this force as measured by observer A in uniform motion in the x-direction relative to B, with a relative velocity v, when the force is (a) at right angles to, and (b) in the same direction as, the relative motion of A and B?

Let us first calculate the ratios of the accelerations of the particle. In the y-direction, transverse to the relative velocity, we have (since the initial *transverse* velocity is zero)

$$\Delta y_A = \tfrac{1}{2}a_{tA}(\Delta t_A)^2, \qquad \Delta y_B = \tfrac{1}{2}a_{tB}(\Delta t_B)^2,$$

where a_{tA} and a_{tB} are the respective transverse accelerations. But transverse *displacements* are the same in both systems, so $\Delta y_A = \Delta y_B$ and

$$a_{tA}/a_{tB} = (\Delta t_B/\Delta t_A)^2.$$

The time intervals Δt_B and Δt_A are measured at the same x-coordinate, so from the expression for time dilation, Eq. (4–37), $\Delta t_B = \Delta t_A \cos \alpha$ and

$$a_{tA}/a_{tB} = \cos^2 \alpha = 1 - v^2/c^2. \tag{8–24}$$

In the longitudinal direction, the initial velocity is zero in system B and

$$\Delta x_B = \tfrac{1}{2}a_{lB}(\Delta t_B)^2,$$

where a_{lB} is the longitudinal acceleration in B's system. In system A, the particle has an initial velocity v and

$$\Delta x_A = v\,\Delta t_A + \tfrac{1}{2}a_{lA}(\Delta t_A)^2,$$
$$\Delta x_A - v\,\Delta t_A = \tfrac{1}{2}a_{lA}(\Delta t_A)^2.$$

Hence

$$\frac{a_{lA}}{a_{lB}} = \left(\frac{\Delta t_B}{\Delta t_A}\right)^2 \frac{\Delta x_A - v\,\Delta t_A}{\Delta x_B}.$$

The term $v\,\Delta t_A$ is the coordinate of B's origin, in system A, at time Δt_A, and the difference $\Delta x_A - v\,\Delta t_A$ is the distance of the particle from B's origin at this time, as measured by A. Hence the expression for length contraction, Eq. (4–36), can be applied to Δx_B and $\Delta x_A - v\,\Delta t_A$:

$$(\Delta x_A - v\,\Delta t_A)/\Delta x_B = \cos \alpha.$$

It follows that

$$a_{lA}/a_{lB} = \cos^3 \alpha = (1 - v^2/c^2)^{3/2}. \tag{8–25}$$

Now return to Eq. (8–23), and consider first the transverse forces. The initial mass of the particle in system B is its rest mass m_0, and the transverse velocity acquired in the short time interval Δt_B is so small that the mass can be considered constant and $\Delta m = 0$. Then Eq. (8–23) becomes

$$F_{tB}\,\Delta t_B = m_0\,\Delta v_{tB}, \qquad F_{tB} = m_0(\Delta v_{tB}/\Delta t_B) = m_0 a_{tB}. \tag{8–26}$$

In A's system, the particle has an initial velocity v and its initial mass is

$$m = m_0/\cos \alpha = m_0 \sec \alpha.$$

This can also be considered constant, and hence

$$F_{tA}\,\Delta t_A = m\,\Delta v_{tA}, \qquad F_{tA} = m a_{tA} = m_0 \sec \alpha\, a_{tA}. \tag{8–27}$$

The ratio of the forces is then

$$F_{tA}/F_{tB} = (m/m_0)(a_{tA}/a_{tB}) = \sec \alpha \cos^2 \alpha = \cos \alpha,$$
$$F_{tA} = F_{tB} \cos \alpha. \tag{8–28}$$

A *transverse* force on a particle in motion relative to an observer therefore appears *smaller* than it does to an observer in whose system the particle is at rest, in contrast to the mass of the particle, which appears *larger* to an observer relative to whom the particle is in motion.

In the longitudinal direction, the mass of the particle in B's system is again its rest mass m_0 and the change in relative velocity is small. Hence

$$F_{lB} \, \Delta t_B = m_0 \, \Delta v_{lB}, \qquad F_{lB} = m_0 a_{lB}.$$

In A's system, however, we must take the increase in mass into account. Since $m = m_0 \sec \alpha$, we have

$$\Delta m = m_0 \sec \alpha \tan \alpha \, \Delta\alpha = m \tan \alpha \, \Delta\alpha.$$

But

$$\sin \alpha = v/c, \qquad \cos \alpha \, \Delta\alpha = \Delta v/c, \qquad \Delta\alpha = \Delta v \sec \alpha/c.$$

Hence

$$v \, \Delta m = m \tan^2 \alpha \, \Delta v$$

and

$$F_{lA} \, \Delta t_A = m \, \Delta v_{lA} + m \tan^2 \alpha \, \Delta v_{lA}$$

$$= m \sec^2 \alpha \, \Delta v_{lA} = m_0 \sec^3 \alpha \, \Delta v_{lA},$$

$$F_{lA} = m \sec^2 \alpha a_{lA} = m_0 \sec^3 \alpha a_{lA}. \tag{8–29}$$

The ratio of the forces is therefore

$$\frac{F_{lA}}{F_{lB}} = \frac{m_0 \sec^3 \alpha}{m_0} \frac{a_{lA}}{a_{lB}} = \sec^3 \alpha \cos^3 \alpha = 1,$$

and to observers A and B the *longitudinal* forces appear *equal*.

8–11 Transverse and longitudinal mass

In Newtonian mechanics, the mass of a particle equals the ratio of the force on the particle to its acceleration. In relativistic mechanics, the terms "transverse mass" and "longitudinal mass" are sometimes applied to the ratio of the transverse force to the transverse acceleration, and to the ratio of longitudinal force to longitudinal acceleration. Thus, from Eq. (8–27), the transverse mass of a particle is

$$m_t = F_{tA}/a_{tA} = m_0 \sec \alpha = m_0(1 - v^2/c^2)^{-1/2},$$

which equals the relativistic mass m. The longitudinal mass, from Eq. (8–29), is

$$m_l = F_{lA}/a_{lA} = m_0 \sec^3 \alpha = m_0(1 - v^2/c^2)^{-3/2}.$$

These concepts are a "dodge" that enable one to write Newton's second law as $F = ma$ even in relativistic mechanics, but they have little physical significance. The fundamental relation is Eq. (8–18), which is better written as

$$\mathbf{F} = (d/dt)(m_0\mathbf{v}/\sqrt{1 - v^2/c^2}),$$

in which form it contains only the *constant* rest mass m_0. Some authors write all their equations in terms of the rest mass only, and represent it by m.

Problems

8–1. (a) What is the momentum of a 10-ton truck whose velocity is 30 mi/hr? At what velocity will a 5-ton truck have (b) the same momentum, (c) the same kinetic energy?

8–2. A baseball weighs $5\frac{1}{2}$ oz. (a) If the velocity of a pitched ball is 80 ft/sec, and after being batted it is 120 ft/sec in the opposite direction, find the change in momentum of the ball and the impulse of the blow. (b) If the ball remains in contact with the bat for 0.002 sec, find the average force of the blow.

8–3. A bullet having a mass of 0.05 kgm, moving with a velocity of 400 m/sec, penetrates a distance of 0.1 m in a wooden block firmly attached to the earth. Assume the decelerating force constant. Compute (a) the deceleration of the bullet, (b) the decelerating force, (c) the time of deceleration, (d) the impulse of the collision. Compare the answer to part (d) with the initial momentum of the bullet.

8–4. A bullet of mass 2 gm emerges from the muzzle of a gun with a velocity of 300 m/sec. The resultant force on the bullet, while it is in the gun barrel, is given by

$$F = 400 - \frac{4 \times 10^5}{3} t,$$

where F is in newtons and t in seconds. (a) Construct a graph of F versus t. (b) Compute the time required for the bullet to travel the length of the barrel.

8–5. A box, initially sliding on the floor of a room, is eventually brought to rest by friction. Is the momentum of the box conserved? If not, does this process contradict the principle of conservation of momentum? What becomes of the original momentum of the box?

8–6. Compare the damage to an automobile (and its occupants) in the following circumstances: (a) The automobile makes a completely inelastic head-on collision with an identical automobile traveling with the same speed in the opposite direction, and

(b) it makes a completely inelastic head-on collision with a vertical rock cliff. (c) Which would be worse (for the occupants of a light car), to collide head-on with a truck traveling in the opposite direction with a momentum of equal magnitude, or to collide head-on with a truck having the same kinetic energy?

8–7. (a) An empty freight car weighing 10 tons rolls at 3 ft/sec along a level track and collides with a loaded car weighing 20 tons, standing at rest with brakes released. If the cars couple together, find their speed after the collision. (b) Find the decrease in kinetic energy as a result of the collision. (c) With what speed should the loaded car be rolling toward the empty car, in order that both shall be brought to rest by the collision?

8–8. When a bullet of mass 20 gm strikes a ballistic pendulum of mass 10 kgm, the center of gravity of the pendulum is observed to rise a vertical distance of 7 cm. The bullet remains embedded in the pendulum. (a) Calculate the original velocity of the bullet. (b) What fraction of the original kinetic energy of the bullet remains as kinetic energy of the system immediately after the collision? (c) What fraction of the original momentum remains as momentum of the system?

8–9. A bullet weighing 0.01 lb is shot through a 2-lb wooden block suspended on a string 5 ft long. The center of gravity of the block is observed to rise a distance of 0.0192 ft. Find the speed of the bullet as it emerges from the block if the initial speed is 1000 ft/sec.

8–10. When a bullet of mass 10 gm strikes a ballistic pendulum of mass 2 kgm, the center of gravity of the pendulum is observed to rise a vertical distance of 10 cm. The bullet remains embedded in the pendulum. Calculate the velocity of the bullet.

8–11. A frame of mass 200 gm, when suspended from a certain coil spring, is found to stretch the spring 10 cm. A lump of putty of mass 200 gm is dropped from

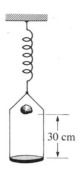

30 cm

Figure 8–17

of mass 1 kgm suspended from a cord 1 m long. The bullet penetrates the pendulum and emerges with a velocity of 100 m/sec. Through what vertical height will the pendulum rise?

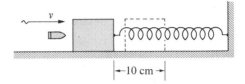

Figure 8–18

rest onto the frame from a height of 30 cm (Fig. 8–17). Find the maximum distance the frame moves downward.

8–12. A bullet of mass 2 gm, traveling in a horizontal direction with a velocity of 500 m/sec, is fired into a wooden block of mass 1 kgm, initially at rest on a level surface. The bullet passes through the block and emerges with its velocity reduced to 100 m/sec. The block slides a distance of 20 cm along the surface from its initial position. (a) What was the coefficient of sliding friction between block and surface? (b) What was the decrease in kinetic energy of the bullet? (c) What was the kinetic energy of the block at the instant after the bullet passed through it?

8–13. A rifle bullet weighing 0.02 lb is fired with a velocity of 2500 ft/sec into a ballistic pendulum weighing 10 lb and suspended from a cord 3 ft long. Compute (a) the vertical height through which the pendulum rises, (b) the initial kinetic energy of the bullet, (c) the kinetic energy of bullet and pendulum after the bullet is embedded in the pendulum.

8–14. A 5-gm bullet is fired horizontally into a 3-kgm wooden block resting on a horizontal surface. The coefficient of sliding friction between block and surface is 0.20. The bullet remains embedded in the block, which is observed to slide 25 cm along the surface. What was the velocity of the bullet?

8–15. A bullet of mass 2 gm, traveling at 500 m/sec, is fired into a ballistic pendulum

8–16. A rifle bullet of mass 10 gm strikes and embeds itself in a block of mass 990 gm which rests on a horizontal frictionless surface and is attached to a coil spring, as shown in Fig. 8–18. The impact compresses the spring 10 cm. Calibration of the spring shows that a force of 100,000 dynes is required to compress the spring 1 cm. (a) Find the maximum potential energy of the spring. (b) Find the velocity of the block just after the impact. (c) What was the initial velocity of the bullet?

8–17. A 4000-lb automobile going eastward on Chestnut Street at 40 mi/hr collides with a truck weighing 4 tons which is going southward across Chestnut Street at 15 mi/hr. If they become coupled on collision, what is the magnitude and direction of their velocity immediately after colliding?

8–18. On a frictionless table, a 3-kgm block moving 4 m/sec to the right collides with an 8-kgm block moving 1.5 m/sec to the left. (a) If the two blocks stick together, what is the final velocity? (b) If the two blocks make a completely elastic head-on collision, what are their final velocities? (c) How much mechanical energy is converted into heat in the collision of part (a)?

8–19. Two blocks of mass 300 gm and 200 gm are moving toward each other along a horizontal frictionless surface with velocities of 50 cm/sec and 100 cm/sec, respectively. (a) If the blocks collide and stick together, find their final velocity. (b)

Find the loss of kinetic energy during the collision. (c) Find the final velocity of each block if the collision is completely elastic.

8–20. (a) Prove that when a moving body makes a perfectly inelastic collision with a second body of equal mass, initially at rest, one-half of the original kinetic energy is "lost." (b) Prove that when a very heavy particle makes a perfectly elastic collision with a very light particle that is at rest, the light one goes off with twice the velocity of the heavy one.

8–21. A 10-gm block slides with a velocity of 20 cm/sec on a smooth level surface and makes a head-on collision with a 30-gm block moving in the opposite direction with a velocity of 10 cm/sec. If the collision is perfectly elastic, find the velocity of each block after the collision.

8–22. A block of mass 200 gm, sliding with a velocity of 12 cm/sec on a smooth, level surface, makes a perfectly elastic head-on collision with a block of mass m gm, initially at rest. After the collision the velocity of the 200-gm block is 4 cm/sec in the same direction as its initial velocity. Find (a) the mass m, and (b) its velocity after the collision.

8–23. A body of mass 600 gm is initially at rest. It is struck by a second body of mass 400 gm initially moving with a velocity of 125 cm/sec toward the right along the x-axis. After the collision the 400-gm body has a velocity of 100 cm/sec at an angle of 37° above the x-axis in the first quadrant. Both bodies move on a horizontal frictionless plane. (a) What is the magnitude and direction of the velocity of the 600-gm body after the collision? (b) What is the loss of kinetic energy during the collision?

8–24. A small steel ball moving with speed v_0 in the positive x-direction makes a perfectly elastic, noncentral collision with an identical ball originally at rest. After impact, the first ball moves with speed v_1 in the first quadrant at an angle θ_1 with the x-axis, and the second with speed v_2 in the fourth quadrant at an angle θ_2 with the

x-axis. (a) Write the equations expressing conservation of linear momentum in the x-direction, and in the y-direction. (b) Square these equations and add them. (c) At this point, introduce the fact that the collision is perfectly elastic. (d) Prove that $\theta_1 + \theta_2 = \pi/2$.

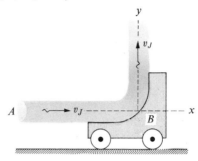

Figure 8–19

8–25. A jet of liquid of cross-sectional area A and density ρ moves with speed v_J in the positive x-direction and impinges against a perfectly smooth blade B which deflects the stream at right angles but does not slow it down, as shown in Fig. 8–19. If the blade is *stationary*, prove that (a) the rate of arrival of mass at the blade is $\Delta m/\Delta t = \rho A v_J$. (b) If the impulse momentum theorem is applied to a small mass Δm, the x-component of the force acting on this mass for the time interval Δt is given by

$$F_x = -\frac{\Delta m}{\Delta t} v_J.$$

(c) The *steady* force exerted *on* the blade in the x-direction is

$$F_x = \rho A v_J^2.$$

If the blade moves to the right with a speed v_B ($v_B < v_J$), derive the equations for (d) the rate of arrival of mass at the moving blade, (e) the force F_x on the blade, and (f) the power delivered to the blade.

8–26. A stone whose mass is 100 gm rests on a horizontal frictionless surface. A bullet of mass 2.5 gm, traveling horizontally at 400 m/sec, strikes the stone and rebounds horizontally at right angles to its original direction with a speed of 300 m/sec. (a) Compute the magnitude and direction of the velocity of the stone after it is struck. (b) Is the collision perfectly elastic?

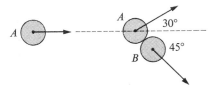

Figure 8–20

8–27. A hockey puck *B* rests on a smooth ice surface and is struck by a second puck *A* which was originally traveling at 80 ft/sec and which is deflected 30° from its original direction (Fig. 8–20). Puck *B* acquires a velocity at 45° with the original velocity of *A*. (a) Compute the speed of each puck after the collision. (b) Is the collision perfectly elastic? If not, what fraction of the original kinetic energy of puck *A* is "lost"?

8–28. Imagine that a ball of mass 200 gm rolls back and forth between opposite sides of a billiard table 1 m wide, with a velocity that remains constant in magnitude but reverses in direction at each collision with the cushions. The magnitude of the velocity is 4 m/sec. (a) What is the change in momentum of the ball at each collision? (b) How many collisions per unit time are made by the ball with one of the cushions? (c) What is the average time rate of change of momentum of the ball as a result of these collisions? (d) What is the average force exerted by the ball on a cushion? (e) Sketch a graph of the force exerted on the ball as a function of time, for a time interval of 5 sec. (*Note:* This problem illustrates how one computes the average force exerted by the molecules of a gas on the walls of the containing vessel.)

8–29. A projectile is fired at an angle of departure of 60° and with a muzzle velocity of 1200 ft/sec. At the highest point of its trajectory the projectile explodes into two fragments of equal mass, one of which

falls vertically. (a) How far from the point of firing does the other fragment strike if the terrain is level? (b) How much energy was released during the explosion?

8–30. A railroad handcar is moving along straight frictionless tracks. In each of the following cases the car initially has a total weight (car and contents) of 500 lb and is traveling with a velocity of 10 ft/sec. Find the final velocity of the car in each of the three cases. (a) A 50-lb weight is thrown sideways out of the car with a velocity of 8 ft/sec relative to the car. (b) A 50-lb weight is thrown backwards out of the car with a velocity of 10 ft/sec relative to the car. (c) A 50-lb weight is thrown into the car with a velocity of 12 ft/sec relative to the ground and opposite in direction to the velocity of the car.

8–31. A bullet weighing 0.02 lb is fired with a muzzle velocity of 2700 ft/sec from a rifle weighing 7.5 lb. (a) Compute the recoil velocity of the rifle, assuming it free to recoil. (b) Find the ratio of the kinetic energy of the bullet to that of the rifle.

8–32. A 75-mm gun fires a projectile weighing 16 lb with a muzzle velocity of 1900 ft/sec. By how many mi/hr is the velocity of a plane mounting such a gun decreased when a projectile is fired directly ahead? The plane weighs 32,000 lb.

8–33. The projectile of a 16-in. seacoast gun weighs 2400 lb, travels a distance of 38 ft in the bore of the gun, and has a muzzle velocity of 2250 ft/sec. The gun weighs 300,000 lb. (a) Compute the initial recoil velocity of the gun, assuming it free to recoil. (b) Find the ratio of the kinetic energy of the projectile to that of the recoiling gun.

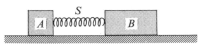

Figure 8–21

8–34. Block *A* in Fig. 8–21 has a mass of 1 kgm and block *B* has a mass of 2 kgm. The blocks are forced together, compressing a spring S between them, and the system is released from rest on a level frictionless surface. The spring is not fastened to either block and drops to the surface after it has expanded. Block B acquires a speed of 0.5 m/sec. How much potential energy was stored in the compressed spring?

8–35. An open-topped freight car weighing 10 tons is coasting without friction along a level track. It is raining very hard, with the rain falling vertically downward. The car is originally empty and moving with a velocity of 2 ft/sec. What is the velocity of the car after it has traveled long enough to collect one ton of rain water?

8–36. A neutron of mass 1.67×10^{-24} gm, moving with a velocity of 2×10^6 cm/sec, makes a head-on collision with a boron nucleus of mass 17.0×10^{-24} gm, originally at rest. (a) If the collision is completely inelastic, what is the final kinetic energy of the system, expressed as a fraction of the original kinetic energy? (b) If the collision is perfectly elastic, what fraction of its original kinetic energy does the neutron transfer to the boron nucleus?

8–37. A nucleus, originally at rest, decays radioactively by emitting an electron of momentum 9.22×10^{-16} gm·cm/sec, and at right angles to the direction of the electron a neutrino with momentum 5.33×10^{-16} gm·cm/sec. (a) In what direction does the residual nucleus recoil? (b) What is its momentum? (c) If the mass of the residual nucleus is 3.90×10^{-22} gm, what is its kinetic energy?

8–38. A 160-lb man standing on ice throws a 6-oz ball horizontally with a speed of 80 ft/sec. (a) With what speed and in what direction will the man begin to move? (b) If the man throws 4 such balls every 3 sec, what is the average force acting on him? [*Hint:* average force equals average rate of change of momentum.]

8–39. Find the average recoil force on a machine gun firing 120 shots per minute. The weight of each bullet is 0.025 lb, and the muzzle velocity is 2700 ft/sec.

8–40. A rifleman, who together with his rifle weighs 160 lb, stands on roller skates and fires 10 shots horizontally from an automatic rifle. Each bullet weighs 0.0257 lb (180 grains) and has a muzzle velocity of 2500 ft/sec. (a) If the rifleman moves back without friction, what is his velocity at the end of the ten shots? (b) If the shots were fired in 10 sec, what was the average force exerted on him? (c) Compare his kinetic energy with that of the 10 bullets.

8–41. A rocket burns 50 gm of fuel per second, ejecting it as a gas with a velocity of 500,000 cm/sec. (a) What force does this gas exert on the rocket? Give the result in dynes and newtons. (b) Would the rocket operate in free space? (c) If it would operate in free space, how would you steer it? Could you brake it?

8–42. This problem illustrates the advantage of using a multistage rather than a single-stage rocket. Suppose that the first stage of a two-stage rocket has a total weight of 12 tons, of which 9 tons is fuel. The total weight of the second stage is 1 ton, of which 0.75 ton is fuel. Assume that the relative velocity v_r of ejected material is constant, and neglect any effect of gravity. (The latter effect is small during the firing period if the rate of fuel consumption is large, as shown by the example in Section 8–7.)

(a) Suppose that the entire fuel supply carried by the two-stage rocket were utilized in a single-stage rocket of the same total weight of 13 tons. What would be the velocity of the rocket, starting from rest, when its fuel was exhausted?

(b) What is the velocity when the fuel of the first stage is exhausted, if the first stage carries the second stage with it to this point? This velocity then becomes the initial velocity of the second stage.

(c) What is the final velocity of the second stage?

(d) The velocity of Sputnik I was about 18,000 mi/hr or 8 km/sec. What value of v_r would be required to give the second stage of the above rocket a velocity of this magnitude?

8–43. Is it possible for a rocket to acquire a velocity greater than the relative velocity of the material ejected?

8–44. (a) Show that the acceleration of a rocket fired vertically upward is given by

$$a = -\frac{v_r}{m}\frac{dm}{dt} - g.$$

(b) Suppose that the rate of ejection of mass by the rocket is constant, that is, the rate of decrease of mass is $dm/dt = -km_0$, where k is a positive constant and m_0 is the initial mass. What is the numerical value of k, and in what units is it expressed, for the rocket in the example at the end of Section 8–7?

(c) Show that the mass at any time t is $m = m_0(1 - kt)$.

(d) Show that the acceleration at any time is $a = v_r k/(1 - kt) - g$.

(e) Find the initial acceleration of the rocket in the example at the end of Section 8–7, in terms of the acceleration of gravity, g.

(f) Find the acceleration 15 sec after the motion starts.

(g) Sketch the acceleration-time graph.

8–45. An atomic bomb containing 20 kgm of plutonium explodes. The rest mass of the products of the explosion is less than the original rest mass by one ten-thousandth of the original rest mass. (a) How much energy is released in the explosion? (b) If the explosion takes place in one microsecond, what is the average power developed by the bomb? (c) How much water could the released energy lift to a height of one mile?

8–46. The rest mass of an electron is $m_0 = 9.1 \times 10^{-31}$ kgm. An electron is traveling with speed $v = 0.6c$, relative to an observer A. (a) Suppose the electron

is given a transverse acceleration of 10^{12} m/sec^2 relative to system B, in which the electron is at rest. What is the transverse acceleration relative to system A? (b) What is the transverse mass of the electron, in systems B and A? (c) What is the transverse force on the electron, in systems B and A? (d) Suppose the electron is given a longitudinal acceleration of 10^{12} m/sec^2, relative to system B. What is its longitudinal acceleration relative to system A? (e) What is the longitudinal mass of the electron, in systems B and A? (f) What is the longitudinal force on the electron, in systems B and A? (g) What force, in system A, would be required to give the electron a transverse acceleration of 10^{12} m/sec^2, relative to system A? (h) What force would be required, in system A, to give the electron a longitudinal acceleration of 10^{12} m/sec^2, relative to system A? (i) What force would be required to give an electron an acceleration of 10^{12} m/sec^2, according to classical Newtonian mechanics?

8–47. Construct a right triangle like that in Fig. 4–24, with base proportional to the product m_0c. (a) Show that the vertical side of the triangle represents the momentum $p = mv$. (b) Construct a second hypotenuse at an angle $\alpha + \Delta\alpha$, and interpret graphically the quantities $\Delta(mv)$, $m\,\Delta v$, and $v\,\Delta m$. (c) Construct a right triangle like that in Fig. 4–24, with base proportional to the rest-mass energy m_0c^2. What does the hypotenuse now represent? (d) Discuss for both triangles the limiting cases in which $\alpha = 0$ and $\alpha = 90°$.

CHAPTER 9

Rotation

9–1 Introduction

The most general type of motion which a body can undergo is a combination of *translation* and *rotation*. Thus far we have considered only the special case of translational motion, along a straight line or along a curve. We next discuss motion of rotation about a fixed axis, that is, motion of rotation without translation. We shall see that many of the equations describing rotation about a fixed axis are exactly analogous to those encountered in rectilinear motion. If the axis is *not* fixed, the problem becomes much more complicated, and we shall not attempt to give a complete discussion of the general case of translation plus rotation.

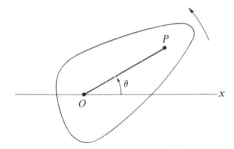

Fig. 9–1. Body rotating about a fixed axis through point *O*.

9–2 Angular velocity

Figure 9–1 represents a rigid body of arbitrary shape rotating about a fixed axis through point *O* and perpendicular to the plane of the diagram. Line *OP* is a line fixed with respect to the body and rotating with it. The position of the entire body is evidently completely specified by the angle θ which the line *OP* makes with some reference line fixed in space, such as *Ox*. The motion of the body is therefore analogous to the rectilinear motion of a particle whose position is completely specified by a single coordinate such as x or y. The equations of motion are greatly simplified if the angle θ is expressed in *radians*.

One radian is the angle subtended at the center of a circle by an arc of length equal to the radius of the circle [Fig. 9–2(a)]. Since the radius is contained 2π times ($2\pi = 6.28\ldots$) in the circumference, there are 2π or $6.28\ldots$ radians in one complete revolution or $360°$.

Hence

$$1 \text{ radian} = \frac{360}{2\pi} = 57.3 \ldots \text{degrees}$$

$$360° = 2\pi \text{ radians} = 6.28 \ldots \text{radians}$$

$$180° = \pi \quad \text{``} \quad = 3.14 \ldots \quad \text{``}$$

$$90° = \pi/2 \quad \text{``} \quad = 1.57 \ldots \quad \text{``}$$

$$60° = \pi/3 \quad \text{``} \quad = 1.05 \ldots \quad \text{``}$$

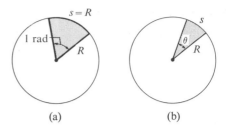

(a)   (b)

Fig. 9–2. An angle θ in radians is defined as the ratio of the arc s to the radius R.

and so on.

In general [Fig. 9–2(b)], if θ represents any arbitrary angle subtended by an arc of length s on the circumference of a circle of radius R, then θ (in radians) is equal to the length of the arc s divided by the radius R.

$$\theta = \frac{s}{R}, \qquad s = R\theta. \tag{9–1}$$

An angle in radians, being defined as the ratio of a length to a length, is a pure number.

In Fig. 9–3, a reference line OP in a rotating body makes an angle θ_1 with the reference line Ox, at a time t_1. At a later time t_2 the angle has increased to θ_2. The *average angular velocity* of the body, $\bar{\omega}$, in the time interval between t_1 and t_2, is defined as the ratio of the *angular displacement* $\theta_2 - \theta_1$, or $\Delta\theta$, to the elapsed time $t_2 - t_1$ or Δt.

$$\bar{\omega} = \frac{\Delta\theta}{\Delta t}.$$

The *instantaneous angular velocity* ω is defined as the limit approached by this ratio as Δt approaches zero.

$$\omega = \lim_{\Delta t \to 0} \frac{\Delta\theta}{\Delta t} = \frac{d\theta}{dt}. \tag{9–2}$$

Since the body is rigid, *all* lines in it rotate through the same angle in the same time, and the angular velocity is characteristic of the body as a whole. If the angle θ is in radians, the unit of angular velocity is 1 *radian per second*. Other units, such as the revolution per minute, are in common use.

Fig. 9–3. Angular displacement $\Delta\theta$ of a rotating body.

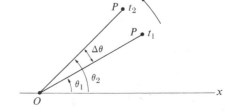

9–3 Angular acceleration

If the angular velocity of a body changes by $\Delta\omega$ in a time interval Δt, it is said to have an angular acceleration. The *average angular acceleration* $\bar{\alpha}$ is defined as

$$\bar{\alpha} = \frac{\Delta\omega}{\Delta t},$$

and the *instantaneous angular acceleration* α is defined as the limit of this ratio when Δt approaches zero:

$$\alpha = \lim_{\Delta t \to 0} \frac{\Delta\omega}{\Delta t} = \frac{d\omega}{dt}. \tag{9–3}$$

The unit of angular acceleration is 1 rad/sec^2.

Since $\omega = d\theta/dt$, the angular acceleration can be written

$$\alpha = \frac{d}{dt}\frac{d\theta}{dt} = \frac{d^2\theta}{dt^2}.$$

Also, by the chain rule,

$$\alpha = \frac{d\omega}{d\theta}\frac{d\theta}{dt} = \omega\frac{d\omega}{d\theta}. \tag{9–4}$$

Angular velocity and angular acceleration are exactly analogous to linear velocity and acceleration.

Many of the equations describing the motion of a rigid body can be written more compactly if we introduce the concepts of *vector angular velocity*, ω, and *vector angular acceleration* α. The vector angular velocity ω is defined as a vector of magnitude ω, pointing in the direction of advance of a right-hand screw which is turned in the direction of rotation of the body. For a rigid body rotating about a fixed axis, the vector ω is parallel to the axis, as shown in Fig. 9–4.

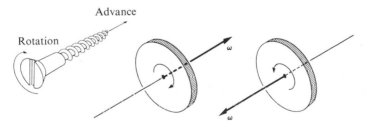

Fig. 9–4. Vector angular velocity ω of a rotating body.

Similarly, the vector angular acceleration α is defined as a vector of magnitude α, having at any instant the direction of the vector change in angular velocity, $d\omega$. For rotation about a fixed axis, where ω is always parallel to the axis, the vector α is parallel to the axis also.

9-4 Rotation with variable angular acceleration

When a rigid body rotates about a fixed axis, the direction of the angular velocity vector remains constant but the magnitude may vary. This variation may be expressed in three ways:

(1) α *is a function of* t:

$$\frac{d\omega}{dt} = \alpha, \qquad d\omega = \alpha\, dt,$$

$$\omega_2 - \omega_1 = \int_{t_1}^{t_2} \alpha\, dt.$$

(2) α *is a function of* ω:

$$\frac{d\omega}{dt} = \alpha, \qquad \frac{d\omega}{\alpha} = dt,$$

$$\int_{\omega_1}^{\omega_2} \frac{d\omega}{\alpha} = t_2 - t_1.$$

(3) α *is a function of* θ:

$$\frac{d\omega}{dt} = \omega\frac{d\omega}{d\theta} = \alpha, \qquad \omega\, d\omega = \alpha\, d\theta,$$

$$\frac{\omega_2^2}{2} - \frac{\omega_1^2}{2} = \int_{\theta_1}^{\theta_2} \alpha\, d\theta.$$

9-5 Rotation with constant angular acceleration

The simplest type of accelerated rotational motion is that in which the angular acceleration is constant. When this is the case, the expressions for the angular velocity and angular coordinate can readily be found by integration. We have

$$d\omega/dt = \alpha = \text{constant},$$

$$\int d\omega = \int \alpha\, dt,$$

$$\omega = \alpha t + C_1.$$

If ω_0 is the angular velocity when $t = 0$, the integration constant $C_1 = \omega_0$ and

$$\boxed{\omega = \omega_0 + \alpha t.} \tag{9-5}$$

Then, since $\omega = d\theta/dt$,

$$\int d\theta = \int \omega_0\, dt + \int \alpha t\, dt,$$

$$\theta = \omega_0 t + \tfrac{1}{2}\alpha t^2 + C_2.$$

In general, the integration constant C_2 is the value of θ when $t = 0$, say θ_0. If $\theta_0 = 0$, then

$$\theta = \omega_0 t + \tfrac{1}{2}\alpha t^2. \tag{9-6}$$

If we write the angular acceleration as

$$\alpha = \omega \frac{d\omega}{d\theta},$$

then

$$\int \alpha\, d\theta = \int \omega\, d\omega + C_3,$$

$$\alpha\theta = \tfrac{1}{2}\omega^2 + C_3.$$

If the angle θ is zero when $t = 0$, and if the initial angular velocity is ω_0, then $C_3 = -\tfrac{1}{2}\omega_0^2$ and

$$\omega^2 = \omega_0^2 + 2\alpha\theta. \tag{9-7}$$

Equations (9–5), (9–6), and (9–7) are exactly analogous to the corresponding equations for linear motion with constant acceleration:

$$v = v_0 + at, \qquad x = v_0 t + \tfrac{1}{2}at^2, \qquad v^2 = v_0^2 + 2ax.$$

EXAMPLE. The angular velocity of a body is 4 rad/sec at time $t = 0$, and its angular acceleration is constant and equal to 2 rad/sec^2. A line OP in the body is horizontal at time $t = 0$. (a) What angle does this line make with the horizontal at time $t = 3$ sec? (b) What is the angular velocity at this time?

(a) $\theta = \omega_0 t + \tfrac{1}{2}\alpha t^2$

$$= 4\,\frac{\text{rad}}{\text{sec}} \times 3\ \text{sec} + \tfrac{1}{2} \times 2\,\frac{\text{rad}}{\text{sec}^2} \times (3\ \text{sec})^2$$

$$= 21\ \text{radians} = 3.34\ \text{revolutions}.$$

(b) $\omega = \omega_0 + \alpha t$

$$= 4\,\frac{\text{rad}}{\text{sec}} + 2\,\frac{\text{rad}}{\text{sec}^2} \times 3\ \text{sec} = 10\,\frac{\text{rad}}{\text{sec}}.$$

Alternatively, from Eq. (9–7),

$$\omega^2 = \omega_0^2 + 2\alpha\theta$$

$$= \left(4\,\frac{\text{rad}}{\text{sec}}\right)^2 + 2 \times 2\,\frac{\text{rad}}{\text{sec}^2} \times 21\ \text{rad} = 100\,\frac{\text{rad}^2}{\text{sec}^2},$$

$$\omega = 10\,\frac{\text{rad}}{\text{sec}}.$$

9–6 Relation between angular and linear velocity and acceleration

In Section 6–2 we discussed the linear velocity and acceleration of a *particle* revolving in a circle. When a *rigid body* rotates about a fixed axis, every point in the body moves in a circle whose center is on the axis and which lies in a plane perpendicular to the axis. There are some useful and simple relations between the *angular* velocity and acceleration of the rotating body and the *linear* velocity and acceleration of points within it.

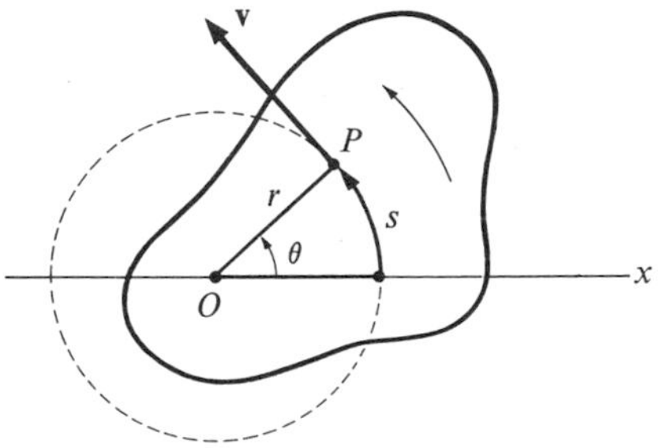

Fig. 9–5. The distance *s* moved through by point *P* equals $r\theta$.

Let *r* be the distance from the axis to some point *P* in the body, so that the point moves in a circle of radius *r*, as in Fig. 9–5. When the radius makes an angle θ with the reference axis, the distance *s* to the point *P*, measured along the circular path, is

$$s = r\theta, \tag{9–8}$$

if θ is in radians.

Differentiating both sides of this equation with respect to *t*, we have, since *r* is constant,

$$\frac{ds}{dt} = r\frac{d\theta}{dt}.$$

But ds/dt is the magnitude of the linear velocity v of point *P*, and $d\theta/dt$ is the angular velocity ω of the rotating body. Hence

$$v = r\omega \tag{9–9}$$

and the magnitude v of the linear velocity equals the product of the angular velocity ω and the distance *r* of the point from the axis.

Differentiating Eq. (9–9) with respect to *t* gives

$$\frac{dv}{dt} = r\frac{d\omega}{dt}.$$

But dv/dt is the magnitude of the tangential component of acceleration a_T of point *P*, and $d\omega/dt$ is the angular acceleration α of the rotating body, so

$$a_T = r\alpha \tag{9–10}$$

and the tangential component of acceleration equals the product of the angular acceleration and the distance from the axis.

The *radial* component of acceleration v^2/r of the point P can also be expressed in terms of the angular velocity:

$$a_R = \frac{v^2}{r} = \omega^2 r = \omega v. \qquad (9\text{--}11)$$

The tangential and radial components of acceleration of any arbitrary point P in a rotating body are shown in Fig. 9–6.

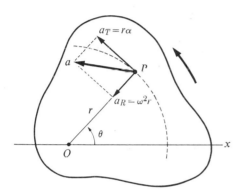

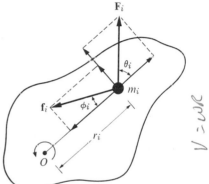

Fig. 9–6. Nonuniform rotation about a fixed axis through point O. The tangential component of acceleration of point P equals $r\alpha$; the radial component equals $\omega^2 r$.

Fig. 9–7. An external force $\mathbf{F}_i$ and an internal force $\mathbf{f}_i$ acting on a particle of mass m_i in a rigid body rotating about a fixed axis.

9–7 Torque and angular acceleration.   Moment of inertia

We are now ready to consider the *dynamics* of rotation about a fixed axis, that is, the relation between the forces on a pivoted body and its angular acceleration.

Figure 9–7 represents a rigid body pivoted about a fixed axis through point O, perpendicular to the plane of the diagram.

The solid circle represents one of the particles of the body, of mass m_i. The particle is acted on by an external force $\mathbf{F}_i$, and by an internal force $\mathbf{f}_i$, the resultant of the forces exerted on it by all of the other particles of the body. It will suffice to consider only the case in which the forces $\mathbf{F}_i$ and $\mathbf{f}_i$ lie in a plane perpendicular to the axis. From Newton's second law,

$$\mathbf{F}_i + \mathbf{f}_i = m_i \mathbf{a}_i.$$

Let us resolve the forces and accelerations into radial and tangential components. Then

$$F_i \cos \theta_i + f_i \cos \phi_i = m_i a_{iR} = m_i r_i \omega^2,$$
$$F_i \sin \theta_i + f_i \sin \phi_i = m_i a_{iT} = m_i r_i \alpha.$$

The first of these equations does not concern us further. When both sides of the second are multiplied by the distance r_i of the particle from the axis, we get

$$F_i r_i \sin \theta_i + f_i r_i \sin \phi_i = m_i r_i^2 \alpha. \tag{9–12}$$

The first term on the left is the moment Γ_i of the external force about the axis, and the second is the moment of the internal force.

Equations corresponding to Eq. (9–12) can be written for every particle of the body. When these equations are added, the moments of the *internal* forces will cancel, since the resultant moment of every internal action-reaction force pair is zero. The sum of the left sides of the equations is then simply the resultant moment Γ of the *external* forces about the axis, or

$$\Gamma = \sum \Gamma_i = \sum F_i r_i \sin \theta_i.$$

Since the body is rigid, all particles have the same angular acceleration α and therefore

$$\Gamma = (m_1 r_1^2 + m_2 r_2^2 + \cdots)\alpha = (\sum m_i r_i^2)\alpha. \tag{9–13}$$

The sum $\sum m_i r_i^2$ is called the *moment of inertia* of the body about the axis through point O, and is represented by I:

$$I = \sum m_i r_i^2. \tag{9–14}$$

Equation (9–13) then becomes

$$\Gamma = I\alpha = I\frac{d\omega}{dt}. \tag{9–15}$$

That is, *when a rigid body is pivoted about a fixed axis, the resultant external torque about the axis equals the product of the moment of inertia of the body about the axis, and the angular acceleration.*

Thus the *angular* acceleration of a rigid body about a fixed axis is given by an equation having exactly the same form as that for the *linear* acceleration of a particle:

$$F = ma = m\frac{dv}{dt}.$$

The resultant torque Γ about the axis corresponds to the resultant force F, the angular acceleration α corresponds to the linear acceleration a, and the moment of inertia I about the axis corresponds to the mass m.

The concept of moment of inertia can be thought of either as the sum of the product of the mass of each particle in a rigid body and the square of its distance from the axis, $I = \sum m_i r_i^2$, or as the ratio of the resultant external torque to the angular acceleration, $I = \Gamma/\alpha$.

TABLE 9-1

ANALOGY BETWEEN TRANSLATIONAL AND ROTATIONAL QUANTITIES

Concept	Translation	Rotation	Comments
Displacement	s	θ	$s = r\theta$
Velocity	$v = ds/dt$	$\omega = d\theta/dt$	$v = r\omega$
Acceleration	$a = dv/dt$	$\alpha = d\omega/dt$	$a_T = r\alpha$
Resultant force, moment	F	Γ	$\Gamma = Fr$
Equilibrium	$F = 0$	$\Gamma = 0$	
Acceleration constant	$\begin{cases} v = v_0 + at \\ s = v_0t + \frac{1}{2}at^2 \\ v^2 = v_0^2 + 2as \end{cases}$	$\omega = \omega_0 + \alpha t$ $\theta = \omega_0 t + \frac{1}{2}\alpha t^2$ $\omega^2 = \omega_0^2 + 2\alpha\theta$	
Mass, moment of inertia	m	I	$I = \sum m_i r_i^2$
Newton's 2nd Law	$F = ma$	$\Gamma = I\alpha$	
Work	$W = \int F\,ds$	$W = \int \Gamma\,d\theta$	
Power	$P = Fv$	$P = \Gamma\omega$	
Potential energy	$E_p = mgy$		
Kinetic energy	$E_k = \frac{1}{2}mv^2$	$E_k = \frac{1}{2}I\omega^2$	
Impulse	$\int F\,dt$	$\int \Gamma\,dt$	
Momentum	mv	$L = I\omega$	

The *vector moment* Γ of a force about an axis is a vector of magnitude Γ, parallel to the axis and pointing in a direction given by the right-hand screw rule. Similarly, the *vector angular velocity* and *acceleration*, for a body rotating about a fixed axis, are also parallel to the axis. Equation (9–15) can therefore be written as a *vector equation:*

$$\mathbf{\Gamma} = I\mathbf{\alpha} = I\frac{d\mathbf{\omega}}{dt}, \tag{9-16}$$

in which form it implies not only the scalar equation, Eq. (9–15), but also that the vectors $\mathbf{\Gamma}$ and $\mathbf{\alpha} = d\mathbf{\omega}/dt$ are in the same direction. Thus in Fig. 9–7 the vectors $\mathbf{\Gamma}$ and $\mathbf{\alpha}$ both point toward the reader.

Equation (9–16) is exactly analogous to the vector equation for the linear motion of a particle:

$$\mathbf{F} = m\mathbf{a} = m\frac{d\mathbf{v}}{dt}.$$

The analogy between translational and rotational quantities is displayed in Table 9–1.

EXAMPLE. A wheel of radius R, mass m_2, and moment of inertia I is mounted on an axle supported in fixed bearings, as in Fig. 9–8. A light flexible cord is wrapped around the rim of the wheel and carries a body of mass m_1. Friction in the bearings can be neglected. Discuss the motion of the system.

We must consider the resultant *force* on the suspended body and the resultant *torque* on the wheel. Let T represent the tension in the cord and P the upward force exerted on the shaft of the wheel by the bearings.

The resultant force on the suspended body is $w_1 - T$, and from Newton's second law for linear motion,

$$w_1 - T = m_1 a.$$

[We have taken the downward direction as positive in order that a positive (counterclockwise) angular displacement of the wheel shall correspond to a positive linear displacement of the suspended body.]

The forces P and w_2 have no moment about the axis of the wheel. The resultant torque on the wheel, about the axis, is TR, and from Newton's second law for rotation

$$TR = I\alpha.$$

Since the linear acceleration of the suspended body equals the tangential acceleration of the rim of the wheel, we have

$$a = R\alpha.$$

Simultaneous solution of these equations gives

$$a = g\,\frac{1}{1 + \left(\dfrac{I}{m_1 R^2}\right)}.$$

If the system starts from rest, the linear speed v of the suspended body, after descending a distance y (the acceleration is constant) is given by

$$v^2 = 2ay = 2\left[g\,\frac{1}{1 + \left(\dfrac{I}{m_1 R^2}\right)}\right]y.$$

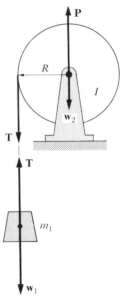

Figure 9–8

9–8 Calculation of moments of inertia

The moment of inertia of a body about an axis can be found *experimentally* by pivoting the body about the axis, applying a measured torque Γ to the body, and measuring the resulting angular acceleration α. The moment of inertia is then given by

$$I = \frac{\Gamma}{\alpha}.$$

A more convenient experimental method is described in Section 11–7.

The moment of inertia can be *calculated* from the defining equation $I = \sum m_i r_i^2$, for any system consisting of discrete point masses.

EXAMPLE. Three small bodies, which can be considered as particles, are connected by light rigid rods, as in Fig. 9–9. What is the moment of inertia of the system (a) about an axis through point A, perpendicular to the plane of the diagram, and (b) about an axis coinciding with the rod BC?

(a) The particle at point A lies on the axis. Its distance *from* the axis is zero and it contributes nothing to the moment of inertia. Therefore

$$I = \sum m_i r_i^2 = 10 \text{ gm} \times (5 \text{ cm})^2 + 20 \text{ gm} \times (4 \text{ cm})^2$$

$$= 570 \text{ gm·cm}^2.$$

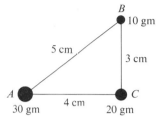

(b) The particles at B and C both lie on the axis. The moment of inertia is

$$I = \sum m_i r_i^2 = 30 \text{ gm} \times (4 \text{ cm})^2$$

$$= 480 \text{ gm·cm}^2.$$

Figure 9–9

This illustrates the important fact that the moment of inertia of a body, unlike its mass, is not a unique property of the body but depends on the axis about which it is computed.

For a body which is not composed of discrete point masses but is a continuous distribution of matter, the summation expressed in the definition of moment of inertia, $I = \sum m_i r_i^2$, must be evaluated by the methods of calculus. The body is imagined to be subdivided into volume elements, each of mass Δm. Let r be the distance from any element to the axis of rotation. If each mass Δm is multiplied by the square of its distance from the axis and all the products $r^2 \Delta m$ summed over the whole body, the moment of inertia is

$$I = \lim_{\Delta m \to 0} \sum r^2 \Delta m = \int r^2 \, dm. \tag{9–17}$$

If dV and dm represent the volume and mass, respectively, of an element, the density ρ is defined by the relation

$$dm = \rho \, dV.$$

Equation (9–17) may therefore be written

$$I = \int r^2 \rho \, dV.$$

If the density of a body is the same at all points, the body is said to be *uniform* or *homogeneous*, in which case

$$I = \rho \int r^2 \, dV.$$

In using this equation any convenient volume element may be chosen, *provided that all points within the element are the same distance r from the axis.*

The evaluation of integrals of this type may present considerable difficulty if the body is irregular, but for bodies of simple shape the integration can be carried out relatively easily. Some examples are given below.

EXAMPLE 1. *Uniform slender rod, axis perpendicular to length.* Figure 9–10 shows a slender uniform rod of mass m and length l. We wish to compute its moment of inertia about an axis through A, at an arbitrary distance h from one end. Select as an element of volume a short section of length dx and cross-sectional area S, at a distance x from point A. Then

$$dm = \rho \, dV = \rho S \, dx = \frac{\rho S l}{l} \, dx = \frac{m}{l} \, dx.$$

Now

$$I_A = \int x^2 \, dm = \frac{m}{l} \int_{-h}^{l-h} x^2 \, dx$$

$$= \frac{m}{l} \frac{x^3}{3} \Big]_{-h}^{l-h} = \tfrac{1}{3}m(l^2 - 3lh + 3h^2).$$

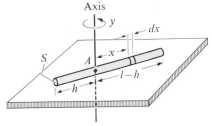

Axis

Figure 9–10

From this general expression, we can find the moment of inertia about an axis through any point on the rod. For example, if the axis is at the left end, $h = 0$ and

$$I = \tfrac{1}{3}ml^2.$$

If the axis is at the right end, $h = l$ and

$$I = \tfrac{1}{3}ml^2,$$

as would be expected. If the axis passes through the center, $h = l/2$ and

$$I = \tfrac{1}{12}ml^2.$$

EXAMPLE 2. *Hollow or solid cylinder, axis of symmetry.* Figure 9–11 shows a hollow cylinder of length l and inner and outer radii R_1 and R_2. We choose as the most convenient volume element the thin cylindrical shell of radius r, thickness dr, and length l. If ρ is the density of the material, that is, the mass per unit volume, then

$$dm = \rho \, dV = \rho(2\pi r \, dr) \times l.$$

The moment of inertia is given by

$$I = \int r^2 \, dm = 2\pi l \int_{R_1}^{R_2} \rho r^3 \, dr.$$

If the body were of nonuniform density, one would have to know ρ as a function of r before the integration could be carried out. For a homogeneous solid, however, ρ is constant, and

$$I = 2\pi l \rho \int_{R_1}^{R_2} r^3 \, dr = \frac{\pi l \rho}{2} (R_2^4 - R_1^4).$$

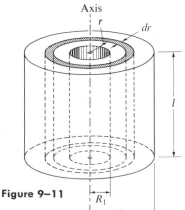

Axis

Figure 9–11

The mass m of the entire cylinder is the product of its density and its volume. The volume is given by

$$\pi l(R_2^2 - R_1^2).$$

Hence

$$m = \pi l\rho(R_2^2 - R_1^2),$$

and the moment of inertia is therefore

$$I = \tfrac{1}{2}m(R_1^2 + R_2^2). \tag{9-18}$$

If the cylinder is solid, $R_1 = 0$, and if we let R represent the outer radius,

$$I = \tfrac{1}{2}mR^2. \tag{9-19}$$

If the cylinder is very thin-walled (like a stovepipe), $R_1 = R_2$ (very nearly) and if R represents this common radius

$$I = mR^2.$$

Note that the moment of inertia of a cylinder, about an axis coinciding with its axis of symmetry, does not depend on thc length l. Two hollow cylinders of the same inner and outer radii, one of wood and one of brass, but having the same mass m, have equal moments of inertia even though the length of the former is much greater. Moment of inertia depends only on the *radial* distribution of mass, not on its distribution along the axis. Thus Eq. (9-18) holds for a very short cylinder like a washer, and Eq. (9-19) for a thin disk.

EXAMPLE 3. *Uniform sphere, axis through center.* Divide the sphere into thin disks, as indicated in Fig. 9-12. The radius r of the disk shown is

$$r = \sqrt{R^2 - x^2}.$$

Its volume is

$$dV = \pi r^2 \, dx = \pi(R^2 - x^2) \, dx$$

and its mass is

$$dm = \rho \, dV.$$

Hence from Eq. (9-19) its moment of inertia is

$$dI = \frac{\pi\rho}{2}(R^2 - x^2)^2 \, dx,$$

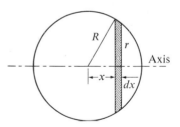

Figure 9-12

and for the whole sphere,

$$I = 2 \times \frac{\pi\rho}{2} \int_0^R (R^2 - x^2)^2 \, dx,$$

since by symmetry the right hemisphere has the same moment of inertia as the left. Carrying out the integration, we get

$$I = \frac{8\pi\rho}{15} R^5.$$

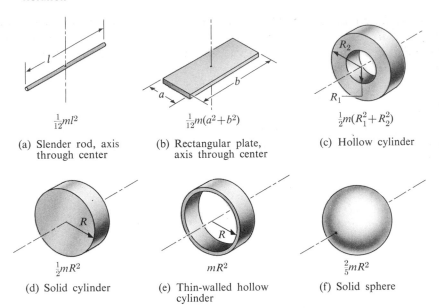

$\frac{1}{12}ml^2$

(a) Slender rod, axis
    through center

$\frac{1}{12}m(a^2+b^2)$

(b) Rectangular plate,
    axis through center

$\frac{1}{2}m(R_1^2+R_2^2)$

(c) Hollow cylinder

$\frac{1}{2}mR^2$

(d) Solid cylinder

mR^2

(e) Thin-walled hollow
    cylinder

$\frac{2}{5}mR^2$

(f) Solid sphere

Fig. 9-13.   Moments of inertia.

The mass m of the sphere is

$$m = \rho V = \frac{4\pi\rho R^3}{3}.$$

Hence

$$I = \tfrac{2}{5}mR^2.$$

The moments of inertia of a few simple but important bodies are shown in Fig. 9-13 for convenience.

Whatever the shape of a body, it is always possible to find a radial distance from any given axis at which the mass of the body could be concentrated without altering the moment of inertia of the body about that axis. This distance is called the *radius of gyration* of the body about the given axis, and is represented by k.

If the mass m of the body actually were concentrated at this distance, the moment of inertia would be that of a particle of mass m at a distance k from an axis, or mk^2. Since this equals the moment of inertia I, then

$$mk^2 = I, \quad k = \sqrt{I/m}. \tag{9-20}$$

EXAMPLE.   What is the radius of gyration of a slender rod of mass m and length l about an axis perpendicular to its length and passing through the center?

The moment of inertia about an axis through the center is $I_0 = \frac{1}{12}ml^2$. Hence

$$k_0 = \sqrt{\frac{\frac{1}{12}ml^2}{m}} = \frac{l}{2\sqrt{3}} = 0.289l.$$

The radius of gyration, like the moment of inertia, depends on the location of the axis.

Note carefully that, in general, the mass of a body can *not* be considered as concentrated at its center of mass for the purpose of computing its moment of inertia. For example, when a rod is pivoted about its center, the distance from the axis to the center of mass is zero, although the radius of gyration is $l/2\sqrt{3}$.

9–9 Kinetic energy, work, and power

When a rigid body rotates about a fixed axis, the velocity v_i of a particle at a perpendicular distance r_i from the axis equals $r_i\omega$, where ω is the angular velocity. The kinetic energy of the particle is then

$$\tfrac{1}{2}m_iv_i^2 = \tfrac{1}{2}m_ir_i^2\omega^2,$$

and the total kinetic energy of the body is

$$E_k = \sum \tfrac{1}{2}m_ir_i^2\omega^2 = \tfrac{1}{2}(\sum m_ir_i^2)\omega^2.$$

But $\sum m_ir_i^2$ equals the moment of inertia I about the axis, so

$$\boxed{E_k = \tfrac{1}{2}I\omega^2.} \qquad\qquad (9–21)$$

Thus the kinetic energy of a rigid body rotating about a fixed axis is given by an expression exactly analogous to that for the kinetic energy of a particle in linear motion, the moment of inertia I corresponding to the mass m and the angular velocity ω corresponding to the linear velocity v. (See Table 9–1.)

EXAMPLE. Let us consider the motion of the system in Fig. 9–8 from the energy standpoint. Looking at the system as a whole, the external forces are the forces **P** and w_2, which do no work, and the force w_1, which is conservative. We can therefore apply the principle of conservation of energy, setting the decrease in potential energy of the body, as it descends a distance y, equal to the sum of the increase in *translational* kinetic energy of the body and the increase in *rotational* kinetic energy of the wheel:

$$m_1gy = \tfrac{1}{2}m_1v^2 + \tfrac{1}{2}I\omega^2.$$

But

$$v = \omega R,$$

and again we find that

$$v^2 = 2\left[g\,\frac{1}{1 + (I/m_1R^2)}\right]y.$$

In Fig. 9–14, an external force **F** is applied at point P of a rigid body rotating about a fixed axis through O, perpendicular to the plane of the diagram. As the body rotates through a small angle $d\theta$, point P moves a distance $ds = r\,d\theta$ and the work done by the force $\mathbf{F}$ is

$$W = \int F_s\,ds = \int F_s r\,d\theta.$$

But $F_s r$ is the moment Γ of the force about the axis, so

$$W = \int_{\theta_1}^{\theta_2} \Gamma\,d\theta. \tag{9-22}$$

If more than one force acts on the body, the total work equals the work of the resultant moment.

From Eq. (9-15),

$$\Gamma = I\alpha = I\omega\,\frac{d\omega}{d\theta}.$$

Hence

$$\Gamma\,d\theta = I\omega\,d\omega,$$

and

$$W = \int_{\theta_1}^{\theta_2} \Gamma\,d\theta = \int_{\omega_1}^{\omega_2} I\omega\,d\omega$$
$$= \tfrac{1}{2}I\omega_2^2 - \tfrac{1}{2}I\omega_1^2. \tag{9-23}$$

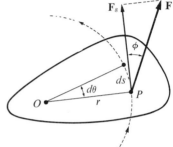

Fig. 9-14. The work done by the force $\mathbf{F}$ in an angular displacement $d\theta$.

That is, *the work of the resultant moment equals the increase in kinetic energy*, in analogy with the work-energy equation for linear motion.

The power developed by the force Γ in Fig. 9-14, if $\mathbf{v}$ is the velocity of its point of application, is

$$P = F_s v = F_s r\omega,$$

and since $F_s r = \Gamma$,

$$\boxed{P = \Gamma\omega,} \tag{9-24}$$

the rotational analogue of $P = F_s v$. The power output of an engine therefore equals the product of torque and angular velocity. The transmission of an automobile engine is often called a "torque converter." An automobile engine can deliver full power only when running at its rated angular velocity and delivering the corresponding torque. When accelerating, or climbing a steep hill, the torque converter permits the engine to run at rated speed, torque, and power, while the same power is transmitted to the drive shaft at a larger torque and a smaller angular velocity.

EXAMPLE. The manufacturers of an automobile state that its engine develops 345 hp and a torque of 475 lb·ft. What is the corresponding angular velocity?

$$\omega = \frac{P}{\Gamma} = \frac{345 \times 550 \text{ ft·lb/sec}}{475 \text{ lb·ft}} = 400\,\frac{\text{rad}}{\text{sec}} \approx 3800\,\frac{\text{rev}}{\text{min}}.$$

9–10 Angular momentum

The equation

$$\Gamma = I\alpha$$

can be written as

$$\Gamma = I\frac{d\omega}{dt} = \frac{d}{dt}(I\omega). \tag{9-25}$$

The product of moment of inertia I and angular velocity ω is the rotational analogue of the product of mass m and linear velocity v. The latter product is the linear momentum, and by analogy we call the product $I\omega$ the *angular momentum L.*

$$\boxed{L = I\omega.} \tag{9-26}$$

(Although in this special case of a rigid body rotating about a fixed axis the angular momentum is equal to $I\omega$, this is not the general definition of this quantity.)

Equation (9–25) can now be written

$$\Gamma = \frac{dL}{dt}, \tag{9-27}$$

or, *the resultant external torque is equal to the rate of change of angular momentum,* just as the resultant external force equals the rate of change of linear momentum.

Multiplying by dt and integrating, we get

$$\int_0^t \Gamma\, dt = L - L_0. \tag{9-28}$$

The integral $\int \Gamma\, dt$ is called the *angular impulse* of the torque and is analogous to the impulse of a force, $\int F\, dt$. The preceding equation is therefore the analogue of the impulse-momentum principle in linear motion. That is, *the resultant angular impulse of the torque on a body is equal to the change in angular momentum of the body.*

Thus far we have considered only problems of rotation about a fixed axis, in which all of the forces were in a plane perpendicular to the axis. When the motion of a body does not take place about a fixed axis it is necessary to make use of the *vector moment of a force*, first introduced in Section 3–2 and Fig. 3–5, but repeated here for convenience.

In Fig. 9–15(a), a force $\mathbf{F}$, lying in the horizontal plane, is applied at the point P. Point O is at a perpendicular distance r from point P, and $\mathbf{r}$ is the vector from O to P. There may or may not be an axis through point O. If there *were* an axis through O, perpendicular to the plane of $\mathbf{r}$ and $\mathbf{F}$, the moment Γ of the force $\mathbf{F}$ about this axis would be

$$\Gamma = rF.$$

We define the *vector moment* of the force $\mathbf{F}$, *about the* **point** O, as a vector Γ whose magnitude equals the moment rF and whose direction is perpendicular to the plane

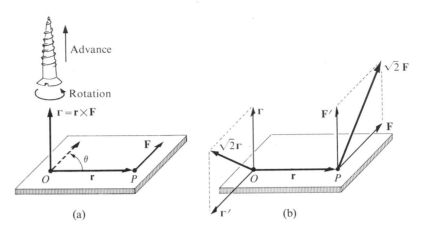

Fig. 9-15. (a) Vector Γ is the vector moment of the force F about the point O: $\Gamma = r \times F$. (b) The resultant vector moment of two forces equals the vector sum of their moments.

of r and F, as shown. The sense of Γ along the axis is specified by the *right-hand screw rule:* Rotate the first vector (r) through the smaller angle (θ) that will bring it into parallelism with the second vector (F), as shown by the broken line in the diagram. The vector Γ then points in the direction of *advance* of a right-hand screw when it is *rotated* through the same angle θ.

The vector moment of F about point O has the same magnitude and direction whatever the direction of an actual axis through O, or even if there is no actual axis through this point. As shown in Section 3-2, the vector moment of F about an axis through O is the *vector product* of r and F, or

$$\Gamma = r \times F,$$

where

$$\Gamma = rF \sin \theta.$$

For the special case in Fig. 9-15, $\theta = 90°$ and $\sin \theta = 1$.

The justification for representing the moment of a force by a vector becomes evident when we ask: How do the moments of two forces add; that is, do they add like numbers or like vectors? Suppose that a second force F', which for simplicity we take equal in magnitude to the first, is also applied at the point P but in a vertically upward direction, as in Fig. 9-15(b). The magnitude of its moment about O also equals rF, and from the right-hand screw rule its direction is perpendicular to that of the first moment vector, as shown.

If the moments of the two forces added *algebraically*, the net moment about O would be $2rF$. But the two forces at P can be combined into a resultant of magnitude $F\sqrt{2}$, and the moment of the resultant about O is $\sqrt{2}\,rF$, which is the result obtained if the moment vectors are added *vectorially*.

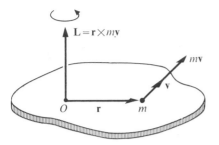

Fig. 9–16. Vector **L** represents the *moment of momentum*, or *angular momentum*, of a particle of mass *m* about point *O*: **L** = **r** × *m***v**.

Figure 9–16 shows a horizontal flat plate rotating about a fixed vertical axis through point *O* with an angular velocity ω. A particle of the plate of mass *m*, at a distance *r* from the axis, has a linear velocity $v = r\omega$ and a linear momentum *mv*. The angular momentum *L* of the particle is defined as the product of the distance *r* and the linear momentum:

$$L = rmv.$$

Since angular momentum is defined in the same way as the moment of a force, it is also called the *moment of momentum*.

The *vector angular momentum* of the particle is defined as the *vector product* of **r** and *m***v**.

$$\mathbf{L} = \mathbf{r} \times m\mathbf{v}.$$

By the right-hand screw rule, the vector **L** points along the axis of rotation, as shown.

The vector angular momentum of any body is the *vector sum* of the angular momenta of the particles composing it. However, since in this case the angular momentum vectors of all particles are in the same direction, the *vector sum* becomes an *arithmetic* sum and the magnitude of the angular momentum of the plate is

$$L = \sum rmv.$$

But $v = r\omega$, and ω has the same value for all particles. Hence

$$L = \left(\sum mr^2\right)\omega = I\omega,$$

and this definition of angular momentum leads to the same expression for *L* as that previously stated.

Now suppose that an external torque Γ is exerted on the plate. In a small time interval Δt the angular momentum of the plate changes by ΔL, where $\Delta L = \Gamma \Delta t$.

Since the *vectors* $\Delta \mathbf{L}$ and $\boldsymbol{\Gamma}$ are both along the axis of rotation, this can be written as a *vector* equation:

$$\boldsymbol{\Delta L} = \boldsymbol{\Gamma} \, \Delta t. \tag{9–29}$$

An analysis of the general case, where **L** and $\boldsymbol{\Gamma}$ may not be in the same direction, shows that the result above is always true. That is, *the **vector change** in angular*

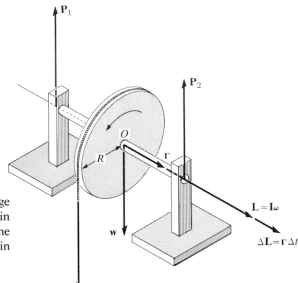

Fig. 9–17. Vector $\Delta \mathbf{L}$ is the change in angular momentum produced in time Δt by the moment $\boldsymbol{\Gamma}$ of the force **F**. Vectors $\Delta \mathbf{L}$ and $\boldsymbol{\Gamma}$ are in the same direction.

momentum of a body, $\Delta \mathbf{L}$, is equal in magnitude and direction to the vector impulse $\boldsymbol{\Gamma}\,\Delta t$ of the resultant external torque on the body.

Let us now apply these vector concepts of torque and angular momentum to a specific example. In Fig. 9–17, a disk is mounted on a shaft through its center, the shaft being supported by fixed bearings. If the disk is rotating as indicated, its angular momentum vector **L** points toward the right, along the axis.

Suppose a cord is wrapped around the rim of the disk and a force **F** is exerted on the cord. The magnitude of the resultant torque on the disk is $\Gamma = FR$, and the torque vector $\boldsymbol{\Gamma}$ also points along the axis. In a time Δt, the torque produces a vector change $\Delta \mathbf{L}$ in the angular momentum, equal to $\boldsymbol{\Gamma}\,\Delta t$ and having the same direction as $\boldsymbol{\Gamma}$. When this change is added vectorially to the original angular momentum **L**, the resultant is a vector of length $L + \Delta L$, in the same direction as **L**. In other words, the *magnitude* of the angular momentum is increased, its *direction* remaining the same. An increase in the magnitude of the angular momentum simply means that the body rotates more rapidly.

The lengthy argument above appears at first to be nothing more than a difficult way of solving an easy problem in rotation about a fixed axis. However, the vector nature of torque and angular momentum are essential to an understanding of the gyroscope, to be discussed in the next section.

If the resultant external torque on a body is zero, then from Eq. (9–29) $\Delta \mathbf{L}$ is zero and *the angular momentum vector remains constant in magnitude and direction* (rotational analogue of Newton's first law). This is the principle of *conservation of angular momentum*, and it ranks with the principles of conservation of linear momentum and conservation of energy as one of the most fundamental relations of mechanics.

A circus acrobat, a diver, or a skater performing a pirouette on the toe of one skate, all take advantage of the principle. Suppose an acrobat has just left a swing,

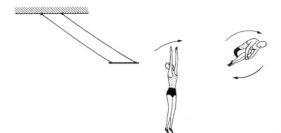

Fig. 9–18.   Conservation of angular
momentum.

as in Fig. 9–18, with arms and legs extended and with a small clockwise angular momentum. When he pulls his arms and legs in, his moment of inertia I becomes much smaller. Since his angular momentum $I\omega$ remains constant and I decreases, his angular velocity ω increases.

EXAMPLE.   A man stands at the center of a turntable, holding his arms extended horizontally with a 10-lb weight in each hand, as shown in Fig. 9–19. He is set rotating about a vertical axis with an angular velocity of one revolution in 2 sec. Find his new angular velocity if he drops his hands to his sides. The moment of inertia of the man may be assumed constant and equal to 4 slug·ft^2. The original distance of the weights from the axis is 3 ft, and their final distance is 6 in.

If friction in the turntable is neglected, no external torques act about a vertical axis and the angular momentum about this axis is constant. That is,

$$I\omega = (I\omega)_0 = I_0\omega_0,$$

where I and ω are the final moment of inertia and angular velocity, and I_0 and ω_0 are the initial values of these quantities.

$$I = I_{\text{man}} + I_{\text{weights}},$$

$$I = 4 + 2(\tfrac{10}{32})(\tfrac{1}{2})^2 = 4.16 \text{ slug·ft}^2,$$

$$I_0 = 4 + 2(\tfrac{10}{32})(3)^2 = 9.63 \text{ slug·ft}^2,$$

$$\omega_0 = \pi \text{ rad/sec},$$

$$\omega = \omega_0 \frac{I_0}{I} = 2.31\pi \text{ rad/sec}.$$

That is, the angular velocity is more than doubled.

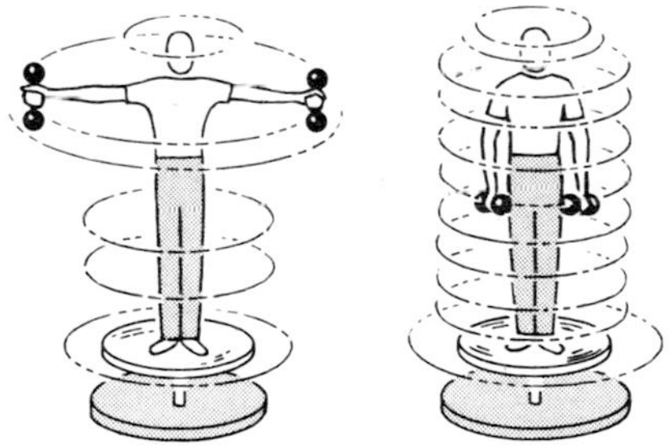

Fig. 9–19.   Conservation of angular momentum about a fixed axis.

9–11 Rotation about a moving axis.   The top and the gyroscope

Figure 9–20 illustrates the usual mounting of a toy gyroscope, more properly called a top, since the fixed point O is not at the center of mass. The top is spinning about its axis of symmetry, and if the axis is initially set in motion in the direction shown, with the proper angular velocity, the system continues to rotate uniformly about the pivot at O, the spin axis remaining horizontal.

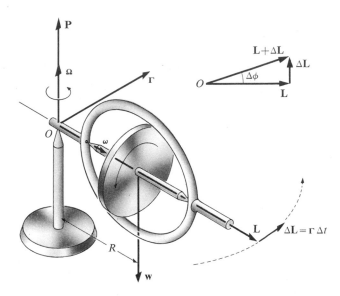

Fig. 9–20. Vector $\Delta\mathbf{L}$ is the change in angular momentum produced in time Δt by the moment $\boldsymbol{\Gamma}$ of the force $\mathbf{w}$. Vectors $\Delta\mathbf{L}$ and $\boldsymbol{\Gamma}$ are in the same direction. (Compare with Fig. 9–17.)

If the axis of the top were fixed in space, its angular momentum would equal the product of its moment of inertia about the axis and its angular velocity about the axis, and would point along the axis. Because the axis itself is rotating, the angular momentum vector no longer lies on the axis. However, if the angular velocity *of* the axis is small compared with the angular velocity *about* the axis, the component of angular momentum arising from the former effect is small, and we shall neglect it. The angular momentum vector $\mathbf{L}$, about the fixed point O, can then be drawn along the axis as shown, and as the top rotates about O its angular momentum vector rotates with it.

The upward force $\mathbf{P}$ at the pivot has no moment about O. The resultant external moment is that due to the weight $\mathbf{w}$ and its magnitude is

$$\Gamma = wR.$$

The direction of $\boldsymbol{\Gamma}$ is perpendicular to the axis, as shown. In a time Δt (compare with the analysis of Fig. 9–17) this torque produces a change $\Delta\mathbf{L}$ in the angular momentum, having the same direction as $\boldsymbol{\Gamma}$ and given by

$$\Delta\mathbf{L} = \boldsymbol{\Gamma}\,\Delta t.$$

The angular momentum $\mathbf{L} + \Delta\mathbf{L}$, after a time Δt, is the vector sum of $\mathbf{L}$ and $\Delta\mathbf{L}$. Since $\Delta\mathbf{L}$ is perpendicular to $\mathbf{L}$, the new angular momentum vector has the same *magnitude* as the old but a different *direction*. The tip of the angular momentum vector moves as shown, and as time goes on it swings around a horizontal circle. But since the angular momentum vector lies along the gyroscope axis, the axis turns also, rotating in a horizontal plane about the point O. This motion of the axis of rotation is called *precession*.

The angle $\Delta\phi$ turned through by the vector **L** in time Δt (see the small inset diagram) is

$$\Delta\phi = \frac{\Delta L}{L}.$$

The *angular velocity of precession*, Ω, is

$$\Omega = \lim_{\Delta t \to 0} \frac{\Delta\phi}{\Delta t} = \frac{1}{L}\frac{dL}{dt}.$$

But

$$\frac{dL}{dt} = \Gamma,$$

so

$$\Omega = \frac{\Gamma}{L}, \qquad \Gamma = \Omega L. \tag{9-30}$$

The angular velocity of precession is therefore inversely proportional to the angular momentum. If this is large, the precessional angular velocity will be small.

The *vector* angular velocity of precession, $\boldsymbol{\Omega}$, by the usual right-hand screw rule, points upward as shown. Equation (9–30) can therefore be written as a vector product:

$$\boldsymbol{\Gamma} = \boldsymbol{\Omega} \times \mathbf{L}.$$

To within the approximation that the magnitude of the angular momentum is equal to $I\omega$, we can write

$$\Gamma = I\omega\Omega. \tag{9-31}$$

It will be noted from Fig. 9–20 that the change in direction of the vector **L** is such as to swing it toward the direction of the torque vector $\boldsymbol{\Gamma}$. This is always the case, and we say that "the angular momentum vector chases the torque vector." In this particular system, the torque vector also turns as the momentum vector turns, so the latter never catches up with the former. In other arrangements, the angular momentum vector eventually becomes aligned with the torque vector and the precessional motion then ceases.

From a purely kinematic point of view, precessional motion of a top is the rotational analogue of uniform circular motion of a particle, as pointed out by Benfield in 1958. The analogy is illustrated in Fig. 9–21, where the diagram and calculation for uniform circular motion are shown on the left and the corresponding diagram and calculation for precessional motion of a top are displayed on the right.

Why doesn't the top in Fig. 9–20 fall? The answer is that the upward force **P** exerted on it by the pivot is just equal in magnitude to its weight **w**, so that the resultant vertical *force* is zero and the vertical acceleration of the center of gravity is zero. In other words, the vertical component of its linear momentum remains zero, since there is no resultant vertical force. The two forces **P** and **w** constitute a *couple* of moment $\Gamma = wR$, so the resultant moment is *not* zero and the angular momentum changes.

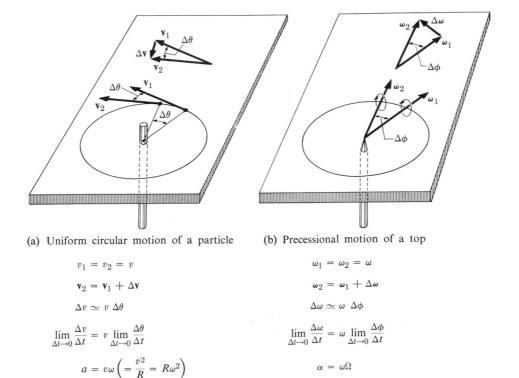

(a) Uniform circular motion of a particle

(b) Precessional motion of a top

$$v_1 = v_2 = v$$

$$\mathbf{v}_2 = \mathbf{v}_1 + \Delta\mathbf{v}$$

$$\Delta v \simeq v\,\Delta\theta$$

$$\lim_{\Delta t \to 0}\frac{\Delta v}{\Delta t} = v\lim_{\Delta t \to 0}\frac{\Delta\theta}{\Delta t}$$

$$a = v\omega\left(= \frac{v^2}{R} = R\omega^2\right)$$

$$F = ma$$

$$F = mv\omega$$

$$\omega_1 = \omega_2 = \omega$$

$$\omega_2 = \omega_1 + \Delta\omega$$

$$\Delta\omega \simeq \omega\,\Delta\phi$$

$$\lim_{\Delta t \to 0}\frac{\Delta\omega}{\Delta t} = \omega\lim_{\Delta t \to 0}\frac{\Delta\phi}{\Delta t}$$

$$\alpha = \omega\Omega$$

$$\Gamma = I\alpha$$

$$\Gamma = I\omega\Omega$$

Fig. 9-21.   Analogy between uniform circular motion of a particle and precessional motion of a top.

If the top were not rotating, it would have no angular momentum **L** to start with. Its angular momentum $\Delta\mathbf{L}$ after a time Δt would be that acquired from the couple acting on it and would be in the same direction as the moment Γ of this couple. In other words, the top would rotate about an axis through O in the direction of the vector Γ. But if the top is originally rotating, the change in its angular momentum produced by the couple adds vectorially to the large angular momentum it already has, and since $\Delta\mathbf{L}$ is horizontal and perpendicular to **L**, the result is a motion of precession with both the angular momentum vector and the axis remaining horizontal.

To understand why the vertical force P should equal w, we must look further into the way in which the precessional motion in Fig. 9-20 originated. If the frame of the top is initially held at rest, say by supporting the projecting portion of the frame opposite O with one's finger, the upward forces exerted by the finger and by the pivot are each equal to $w/2$. If the finger is suddenly removed, the upward force at O, at the first instant, is still $w/2$. The resultant vertical *force* is not zero, and the center of gravity has an initial downward acceleration. At the same time, precessional motion begins, although with a smaller angular velocity than that in the final steady state.

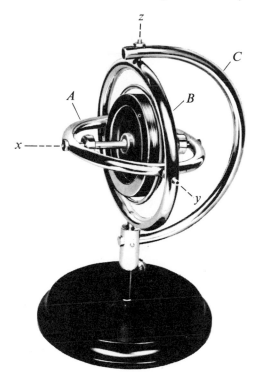

Fig. 9–22.   Photograph of a gimbal-mounted gyro. (Courtesy of Sperry Gyroscope Co.)

The result of this motion is to cause the end of the frame at O to press down on the pivot with a greater force, so that the upward force at O increases and eventually becomes greater than w. When this happens, the center of gravity starts to accelerate upward. The process repeats itself and the motion consists of a precession together with an up-and-down oscillation of the axis, called *nutation*.

To start the top off with pure precession, it is necessary to give the outer end of the axis a push in the direction in which it would normally precess. This causes the end of the frame at O to bear down on the pivot so that the upward force at O increases. When this force equals w, the vertical forces are in equilibrium, the outer end can be released, and the precession continues as in Fig. 9–20.

Figure 9–22 is a photograph of a gyroscope mounted in gimbals. Except when two or more of the gimbal rings lie in the same plane, the outer frame can be turned in any direction in space without exerting a torque on the gyro wheel, except for the small frictional torques in the pivots. If the outer frame is fixed, the center of gravity of the gyro remains fixed whatever the orientation of its axis.

Problems

9–1. An electric motor running at 1800 rev/min has on its shaft three pulleys, of diameters 2, 4, and 6 in. respectively. Find the linear velocity of the surface of each pulley in ft/sec. The pulleys may be connected by a belt to a similar set on a countershaft, the 2 in. to the 6 in., the 4 in. to the 4 in., and the 6 in. to the 2 in. Find the three possible angular velocities of the countershaft in rev/min.

9–2. The angular velocity of a flywheel decreases uniformly from 1000 rev/min to 400 rev/min in 5 sec. Find the angular acceleration and the number of revolutions made by the wheel in the 5-sec interval. How many more seconds are required for the wheel to come to rest?

9–3. A flywheel requires 3 sec to rotate through 234 radians. Its angular velocity at the end of this time is 108 rad/sec. Find its constant angular acceleration.

9–4. A flywheel whose angular acceleration is constant and equal to 2 rad/sec², rotates through an angle of 100 radians in 5 sec. How long had it been in motion at the beginning of the 5–sec interval if it started from rest?

9–5. (a) Distinguish clearly between tangential and radial acceleration. (b) A flywheel rotates with constant angular velocity. Does a point on its rim have a tangential acceleration? a radial acceleration? (c) A flywheel is rotating with constant angular acceleration. Does a point on its rim have a tangential acceleration? a radial acceleration? Are these accelerations constant in magnitude?

9–6. A wheel 30 in. in diameter is rotating about a fixed axis with an initial angular velocity of 2 rev/sec. The acceleration is 3 rev/sec². (a) Compute the angular velocity after 6 sec. (b) Through what angle has the wheel turned in this time interval? (c) What is the tangential velocity of a point on the rim of the wheel at $t = 6$ sec? (d) What is the resultant acceleration of a point on the rim of the wheel at $t = 6$ sec?

9–7. A wheel having a diameter of 1 ft starts from rest and accelerates uniformly to an angular velocity of 900 rev/min in 5 sec. (a) Find the position at the end of 1 sec of a point originally at the top of the wheel. (b) Compute and show in a diagram the magnitude and direction of the acceleration at the end of 1 sec.

9–8. A flywheel of radius 30 cm starts from rest and accelerates with a constant angular acceleration of 0.50 rad/sec². Compute the tangential acceleration, the radial acceleration, and the resultant acceleration, of a point on its rim (a) at the start, (b) after it has turned through 120°, (c) after it has turned through 240°.

9–9. A wheel starts from rest and accelerates uniformly to an angular velocity of 900 rev/min in 20 sec. At the end of 1 sec, (a) find the angle through which the wheel has rotated, and (b) compute and show in a diagram the magnitude and direction of the tangential and radial components of acceleration of a point 6 in. from the axis.

9–10. An automobile engine is idling at 500 rev/min. When the accelerator is depressed, the angular velocity increases to 3000 rev/min in 5 sec. Assume a constant angular acceleration. (a) What are the initial and final angular velocities, expressed in rad/sec? (b) What was the angular acceleration, in rad/sec²? (c) How many revolutions did the engine make during the acceleration period? (d) The flywheel of the engine is 18 in. in diameter. What is the linear speed of a point at its rim when the angular speed is 3000 rev/min? (e) What was the tangential acceleration of the point during the acceleration period? (f) What is the radial acceleration of the point when the angular speed is 3000 rev/min?

9–11. Find the required angular velocity of an ultracentrifuge, in rev/min, in order that the radial acceleration of a point 1 cm from the axis shall equal 300,000 g (i.e., 300,000 times the acceleration due to gravity).

9–12. (a) Prove that when a body starts from rest and rotates about a fixed axis with constant angular acceleration, the radial acceleration of a point in the body is directly proportional to its angular displacement. (b) Through what angle will the body have turned when the resultant acceleration makes an angle of 60° with the radial acceleration?

9–13. A particle moves in the xy-plane according to the law

$$x = R \cos \omega t, \qquad y = R \sin \omega t,$$

where x and y are the coordinates of the body, t is the time, and R and ω are constants. (a) Eliminate t between these equations to find the equation of the curve in which the body moves. (*Hint:* Square each equation.) What is this curve? (b) Differentiate the original equations to find the x- and y-components of the velocity of the particle. Combine these expressions to obtain the magnitude and direction of the resultant velocity. (c) Differentiate again to obtain the magnitude and direction of the resultant acceleration. (This problem illustrates an alternative method of deriving the expressions for the speed and radial acceleration of a particle moving in a circle.)

9–14. Find the moment of inertia of a rod 4 cm in diameter and 2 m long, of mass 8 kgm, (a) about an axis perpendicular to the rod and passing through its center, (b) about an axis perpendicular to the rod and passing through one end, (c) about a longitudinal axis through the center of the rod.

9–15. The four bodies shown in Fig. 9–23 have equal masses m. Body A is a solid cylinder of radius R. Body B is a hollow thin cylinder of radius R. Body C is a solid square with length of side $= 2R$. Body D is the same size as C, but hollow (i.e., made up of four thin walls). The bodies have axes of rotation perpendicular to the page and through the center of gravity of each body. (a) Which body has the smallest moment of inertia? (b) Which body has the largest moment of inertia?

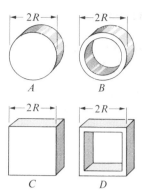

Figure 9–23

9–16. Small blocks, each of mass m, are clamped at the ends and at the center of a light rigid rod of length l. Compute the moment of inertia and the radius of gyration of the system about an axis perpendicular to the rod and passing through a point one-quarter of the length from one end. Neglect the moment of inertia of the rod.

9–17. The radius of the earth is 4000 mi and its mass is 4×10^{23} slugs (approximately). Find (a) its moment of inertia about an axis through its center, and (b) its radius of gyration in miles. Assume the density to be uniform.

9–18. A flywheel consists of a solid disk 1 ft in diameter and 1 in. thick, and two projecting hubs 4 in. in diameter and 3 in. long. If the material of which it is constructed weighs 480 lb/ft³, find (a) its moment of inertia, and (b) its radius of gyration about the axis of rotation.

9–19. The uniform thin rectangular plate in Fig. 9–24 has a length a, a width b, and a mass m. Find its moment of inertia (a) about the axis AA through its center O, (b) about the axis BB at one edge.

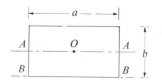

Figure 9–24

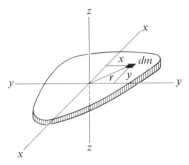

Figure 9–25

9–20. (a) Prove that the moment of inertia of the thin flat plate in Fig. 9–25, about the z-axis, equals the sum of its moments of inertia about the x- and y-axes. (b) Given that the moment of inertia of a disk about an axis through its center and perpendicular to its plane is $mR^2/2$, use the relation above to find its moment of inertia about a diameter. (c) Derive the result of part (b) by direct integration of the defining equation, $I = \int r^2\,dm$. (d) What is the moment of inertia of a disk about an axis tangent to its edge?

9–21. A grindstone 3 ft in diameter, weighing 96 lb, is rotating at 900 rev/min. A tool is pressed normally against the rim with a force of 45 lb, and the grindstone comes to rest in 10 sec. Find the coefficient of friction between the tool and the grindstone. Neglect friction in the bearings.

9–22. A 128-lb grindstone is 3 ft in diameter and has a radius of gyration of $\frac{3}{4}$ ft. A tool is pressed down on the rim with a normal force of 10 lb. The coefficient of sliding friction between the tool and stone is 0.6 and there is a constant friction torque of 3 lb·ft between the axle of the stone and its bearings. (a) How much force must be applied normally at the end of a crank handle 15 in. long to bring the stone from rest to 120 rev/min in 9 sec? (b) After attaining a speed of 120 rev/min, what must the normal force at the end of the handle become to maintain a constant speed of 120 rev/min? (c) How long will it take the grindstone to come from

120 rev/min to rest if it is acted on by the axle friction alone?

9–23. A constant torque of 20 n·m is exerted on a pivoted wheel for 10 sec, during which time the angular velocity of the wheel increases from zero to 100 rev/min. The external torque is then removed and the wheel is brought to rest by friction in its bearings in 100 sec. Compute (a) the moment of inertia of the wheel, (b) the friction torque, and (c) the total number of revolutions made by the wheel.

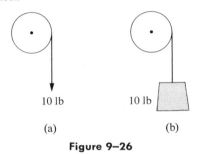

(a)   (b)

Figure 9–26

9–24. A cord is wrapped around the rim of a flywheel 2 ft in radius, and a steady pull of 10 lb is exerted on the cord, as in Fig. 9–26(a). The wheel is mounted in frictionless bearings on a horizontal shaft through its center. The moment of inertia of the wheel is 2 slugs·ft². (a) Compute the angular acceleration of the wheel. (b) Show that the work done in unwinding 20 ft of cord equals the gain in kinetic energy of the wheel. (c) If a 10-lb weight hangs from the cord as in Fig. 9–26(b), compute the angular acceleration of the wheel. Why is this not the same as in part (a)?

9–25. A solid cylinder of mass 15 kgm, 30 cm in diameter, is pivoted about a horizontal axis through its center, and a rope wrapped around the surface of the cylinder carries at its end a block of mass 8 kgm. (a) How far does the block descend in 5 sec, starting from rest? (b) What is the tension in the rope? (c) What is the force exerted on the cylinder by its bearings?

9–26. A bucket of water weighing 64 lb is suspended by a rope wrapped around a windlass in the form of a solid cylinder 1 ft in diameter, also weighing 64 lb. The bucket is released from rest at the top of a well and falls 64 ft to the water. (a) What is the tension in the rope while the bucket is falling? (b) With what velocity does the bucket strike the water? (c) What was the time of fall? Neglect the weight of the rope.

9–27. A 16–lb block rests on a horizontal frictionless surface. A cord attached to the block passes over a pulley, whose diameter is 6 in., to a hanging block which also weighs 16 lb. The system is released from rest, and the blocks are observed to move 16 ft in 2 sec. (a) What was the moment of inertia of the pulley? (b) What was the tension in each part of the cord?

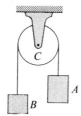

Figure 9–27

9–28. Figure 9–27 represents an Atwood's machine. Find the linear accelerations of blocks A and B, the angular acceleration of the wheel C, and the tension in each side of the cord (a) if the surface of the wheel is frictionless, (b) if there is no slipping between the cord and the surface of the wheel. Let the weights of blocks A and B be 8 lb and 4 lb respectively, the moment of inertia of the wheel about its axis be 0.125 slug·ft^2, and the radius of the wheel be 0.5 ft.

9–29. A flywheel 3 ft in diameter is pivoted on a horizontal axis. A rope is wrapped around the outside of the flywheel and a steady pull of 10 lb is exerted on the rope. It is found that 24 ft of rope are unwound in 4 sec. (a) What was the angular

acceleration of the flywheel? (b) What was its final angular velocity? (c) What was its final kinetic energy? (d) What is its moment of inertia?

9–30. A light rigid rod 100 cm long has a small block of mass 50 gm attached at one end. The other end is pivoted, and the rod rotates in a vertical circle. At a certain instant the rod is 37° above the horizontal, and the tangential speed of the block is 400 cm/sec. (a) What are the horizontal and vertical components of the velocity of the block? (b) What is the moment of inertia of the system? (c) What is the radial acceleration of the block? (d) What is the tension or compression in the rod?

9–31. (a) Compute the torque developed by an airplane engine whose output is 2000 hp at an angular velocity of 2400 rev/min. (b) If a drum 18 in. in diameter were attached to the motor shaft, and the power output of the motor were used to raise a weight hanging from a rope wrapped around the shaft, how large a weight could be lifted? (c) With what velocity would it rise?

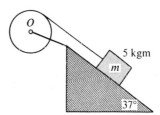

Figure 9–28

9–32. A block of mass $m = 5$ kgm slides down a surface inclined 37° to the horizontal, as shown in Fig. 9–28. The coefficient of sliding friction is 0.25. A string attached to the block is wrapped around a flywheel on a fixed axis at O. The flywheel has a mass $M = 20$ kgm, an outer radius $R = 0.2$ m, and a radius of gyration with respect to the axis $k_0 = 0.1$ m. (a) What is the acceleration of the block down the plane? (b) What is the tension in the string?

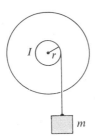

Figure 9–29

9–33. A body of mass m is attached to a light cord wound around the shaft of a wheel, as in Fig. 9–29. The radius of the shaft is r, and the shaft is supported in fixed frictionless bearings. When released from rest, the body descends a distance of 175 cm in 5 sec. Find the moment of inertia of the wheel and shaft, in terms of m and r.

9–34. A disk of mass m and radius R is pivoted about a horizontal axis through its center, and a small body of mass m is attached to the rim of the disk. If the disk is released from rest with the small body at the end of a horizontal radius, find the angular velocity when the small body is at the bottom.

9–35. The flywheel of a gasoline engine is required to give up 380 ft·lb of kinetic energy while its angular velocity decreases from 600 rev/min to 540 rev/min. What moment of inertia is required?

9–36. The flywheel of a punch press has a moment of inertia of 15 slug·ft² and it runs at 300 rev/min. The flywheel supplies all the energy needed in a quick punching operation. (a) Find the speed in rev/min to which the flywheel will be reduced by a sudden punching operation requiring 4500 ft·lb of work. (b) What must be the constant power supply to the flywheel in horsepower to bring it back to its initial speed in 5 sec?

9–37. A magazine article described a passenger bus in Zurich, Switzerland, which derived its motive power from the energy stored in a large flywheel. The wheel was brought up to speed periodically, when the bus stopped at a station, by an electric motor which could then be attached to the electric power lines. The flywheel was a solid cylinder of mass 1000 kgm, diameter 180 cm, and its top speed was 3000 rev/min. (a) At this speed, what is the kinetic energy of the flywheel? (b) If the average power required to operate the bus is 25 hp, how long can it operate between stops?

9–38. A grindstone in the form of a solid cylinder has a radius of 2 ft and weighs 96 lb. (a) What torque will bring it from rest to an angular velocity of 300 rev/min in 10 sec? (b) What is its kinetic energy when rotating at 300 rev/min?

9–39. The flywheel of a motor weighs 640 lb and has a radius of gyration of 4 ft. The motor develops a constant torque of 1280 lb·ft, and the flywheel starts from rest. (a) What is the angular acceleration of the flywheel? (b) What will be its angular velocity after making 4 revolutions? (c) How much work is done by the motor during the first 4 revolutions?

9–40. The flywheel of a stationary engine has a moment of inertia of 20 slugs·ft². (a) What constant torque is required to bring it up to an angular velocity of 900 rev/min in 10 sec, starting from rest? (b) What is its final kinetic energy?

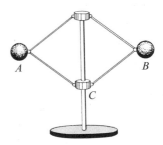

Figure 9–30

9–41. In Fig. 9–30, the steel balls A and B have a mass of 500 gm each, and are rotating about the vertical axis with an angular velocity of 4 rad/sec at a distance of 15 cm from the axis. Collar C is now forced down until the balls are at a distance of 5 cm from the axis. How much work must be done to move the collar down?

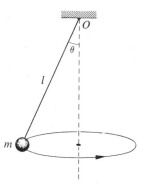

Figure 9–31

9–42. A particle of mass m, attached to a cord of length l, rotates as a conical pendulum, as shown in Fig. 9–31. What is the axial angular momentum of the particle about a fixed vertical axis through point O?

9–43. A man sits on a piano stool holding a pair of dumbbells at a distance of 3 ft from the axis of rotation of the stool. He is given an angular velocity of 2 rad/sec, after which he pulls the dumbbells in until they are but 1 ft distant from the axis. The moment of inertia of the man about the axis of rotation is 3 slugs·ft² and may be considered constant. The dumbbells weigh 16 lb each and may be considered point masses. Neglect friction. (a) What is the initial angular momentum of the system? (b) What is the angular velocity of the system after the dumbbells are pulled in toward the axis? (c) Compute the kinetic energy of the system before and after the dumbbells are pulled in. Account for the difference, if any.

9–44. A block of mass 50 gm is attached to a cord passing through a hole in a horizontal frictionless surface as in Fig. 9–32. The block is originally revolving at a distance of 20 cm from the hole with an angular velocity of 3 rad/sec. The cord is then pulled from below, shortening the radius of the circle in which the block revolves to 10 cm. The block may be considered a

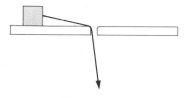

Figure 9–32

point mass. (a) What is the new angular velocity? (b) Find the change in kinetic energy of the block.

9–45. A small block weighing 8 lb is attached to a cord passing through a hole in a horizontal frictionless surface. The block is originally revolving in a circle of radius 2 ft about the hole with a tangential velocity of 12 ft/sec. The cord is then pulled slowly from below, shortening the radius of the circle in which the block revolves. The breaking strength of the cord is 144 lb. What will be the radius of the circle when the cord breaks?

9–46. A block of mass M rests on a turntable which is rotating at constant angular velocity ω. A smooth cord runs from the block through a hole in the center of the table down to a hanging block of mass m. The coefficient of friction between the first block and the turntable is μ. (See Fig. 9–33.) Find the largest and smallest values of the radius r for which the first block will remain at rest relative to the turntable.

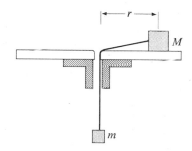

Figure 9–33

9–47. A uniform rod of mass 30 gm and 20 cm long rotates in a horizontal plane about a fixed vertical axis through its center. Two small bodies, each of mass 20 gm, are mounted so that they can slide along the rod. They are initially held by catches at positions 5 cm on each side of the center of the rod, and the system is rotating at 15 rev/min. Without otherwise changing the system, the catches are released and the masses slide outward along the rod and fly off at the ends. (a) What is the angular velocity of the system at the instant when the small masses reach the ends of the rod? (b) What is the angular velocity of the rod after the small masses leave it?

9–48. A turntable rotates about a fixed vertical axis, making one revolution in 10 sec. The moment of inertia of the turn-table about this axis is 720 slugs·ft². A man weighing 160 lb, initially standing at the center of the turntable, runs out along a radius. What is the angular velocity of the turntable when the man is 6 ft from the center?

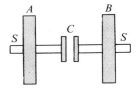

Figure 9–34

9–49. Disks A and B are mounted on a shaft SS and may be connected or discon-nected by a clutch C, as in Fig. 9–34. The moment of inertia of disk A is one-half that of disk B. With the clutch discon-nected, A is brought up to an angular ve-locity ω_0. The accelerating torque is then removed from A and it is coupled to disk B by the clutch. Bearing friction may be neglected. It is found that 3000 ft·lb of heat are developed in the clutch when the con-nection is made. What was the original kinetic energy of disk A?

9–50. A man weighing 160 lb stands at the rim of a turntable of radius 10 ft and moment of inertia 2500 slugs·ft², mounted on a vertical frictionless shaft at its center. The whole system is initially at rest. The man now walks along the outer edge of the

turntable with a velocity of 2 ft/sec, rela-tive to the earth. (a) With what angular velocity and in what direction does the turntable rotate? (b) Through what angle will it have rotated when the man reaches his initial position on the turntable? (c) Through what angle will it have rotated when he reaches his initial position relative to the earth?

9–51. A man weighing 160 lb runs around the edge of a horizontal turntable mounted on a vertical frictionless axis through its center. The velocity of the man, relative to the earth, is 4 ft/sec. The turn-table is rotating in the opposite direction with an angular velocity of 0.2 rad/sec. The radius of the turntable is 8 ft and its moment of inertia about the axis of rota-tion is 320 slugs·ft². Find the final angular velocity of the system if the man comes to rest, relative to the turntable.

9–52. Two flywheels, A and B, are mounted on shafts which can be connected or disengaged by a friction clutch C. (Fig. 9–34.) The moment of inertia of wheel A is 4 slugs·ft². With the clutch disengaged, wheel A is brought up to an angular ve-locity of 600 rev/min. Wheel B is initially at rest. The clutch is now engaged, acceler-ating B and decelerating A until both wheels have the same angular velocity. The final angular velocity of the system is 400 rev/min. (a) What was the moment of inertia of wheel B? (b) How much energy was lost in the process? Neglect all bearing fric-tion.

9–53. The stabilizing gyroscope of a ship weighs 50 tons, its radius of gyration is 5 ft, and it rotates about a vertical axis with an angular velocity of 900 rev/min. (a) How long a time is required to bring it up to speed, starting from rest, with a constant power input of 100 hp? (b) Find the torque needed to cause the axis to precess in a vertical fore-and-aft plane at the rate of 1 degree/sec.

9–54. The mass of the rotor of a toy gyroscope is 150 gm and its moment of inertia about its axis is 1500 gm·cm². The

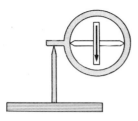

Figure 9–35

mass of the frame is 30 gm. The gyroscope is supported on a single pivot as in Fig. 9–35, with its center of gravity distant 4 cm horizontally from the pivot, and is precessing in a horizontal plane at the rate of one revolution in 6 sec. (a) Find the upward force exerted by the pivot. (b) Find the angular velocity with which the rotor is spinning about its axis, expressed in rev/ min. (c) Copy the diagram, and show by vectors the angular momentum of the rotor and the torque acting on it.

9–55. The moment of inertia of the front wheel of a bicycle is 0.25 slug·ft^2, its radius is 15 in., and the forward speed of the bicycle is 20 ft/sec. With what angular velocity must the front wheel be turned about a vertical axis to counteract the capsizing torque due to a weight of 120 lb, one inch horizontally to the right or left of the line of contact of wheels and ground? (Bicycle riders: compare with experience and see if your answer seems reasonable.)

9–56. The rotor of a small control gyro can be accelerated from rest to an angular velocity of 50,000 rev/min in 0.2 sec. The moment of inertia of the rotor about its spin axis is 385 gm·cm^2. (a) What is the angular acceleration (assumed constant) as the rotor is brought up to speed? (b) What torque is needed to produce this angular acceleration?

Suppose the data above refer to the gyro in Fig. 9–22, and that the rotor is spinning clockwise when viewed from the left along the x-axis. (c) Which way will the spin axis

turn if ring *B* is forced to rotate clockwise, as seen from above, about the z-axis? (d) Suppose that rings *A* and *B* are locked in place. What torque must be exerted about the y-axis to rotate the outer frame about this axis at 1 deg/sec?

9–57. A demonstration gyro wheel is constructed by removing the tire from a bicycle wheel 30 in. in diameter, wrapping lead wire around the rim, and taping it in place. The shaft projects 10 in. at each side of the wheel and a man holds the ends of the shaft in his hands. The weight of the system is 10 lb and its entire mass may be assumed to be located at its rim. The shaft is horizontal and the wheel is spinning about the shaft at 5 rev/sec. Find the magnitude and direction of the force each hand exerts on the shaft under the following conditions: (a) The shaft is at rest. (b) The shaft is rotating in a horizontal plane about its center at 0.04 rev/sec. (c) The shaft is rotating in a horizontal plane about its center at 0.20 rev/sec. (d) At what rate must the shaft rotate in order that it may be supported at one end only?

9–58. A man stands on a turntable free to rotate without friction about a vertical axis. The moment of inertia of man and turntable together about this axis is 1.2 slug·ft^2. The man holds the shaft of the bicycle wheel in Problem 9–57 in one hand, with the shaft vertical. The entire system is initially at rest. (a) The man grasps the rim of the wheel with his free hand and sets the wheel in rotation, in a clockwise direction as viewed from above, with an angular velocity of 5 rev/sec. What is the angular velocity of man and turntable, in magnitude and direction? (b) The man now tips the shaft of the wheel downward until it is horizontal. What is the new angular velocity of man and turntable? (c) What is the kinetic energy of the entire system in part (a)? (d) What is the kinetic energy in part (b)? (e) Explain why the answers to (c) and (d) are not the same.

CHAPTER 10

Elasticity

10–1 Stress

The preceding chapter dealt with the motion of a "rigid" body, a convenient mathematical abstraction, since every real substance yields to some extent under the influence of applied forces. Ultimately, the change in shape or volume of a body when outside forces act on it is determined by the forces between its molecules. Although molecular theory is at present not sufficiently advanced to enable one to calculate the elastic properties of, say, a block of copper starting from the properties of a copper atom, the study of the solid state is an active subject in many research laboratories and our knowledge of it is steadily increasing. In this chapter we shall, however, confine ourselves to quantities that are directly measurable, and not attempt any molecular explanation of the observed behavior.

Figure 10–1(a) shows a bar of uniform cross-sectional area A subjected to equal and opposite pulls $\mathbf{F}$ at its ends. The bar is said to be in *tension*. Consider a section through the bar at right angles to its length, as indicated by the dotted line. Since every portion of the bar is in equilibrium, that portion at the right of the section must be pulling on the portion at the left with a force $\mathbf{F}$, and vice versa. If the section is not too near the ends of the bar, these pulls are uniformly distributed over the cross-sectional area A, as indicated by the short arrows in Fig. 10–1(b). We define the *stress* S at the section as the ratio of the force F to the area A:

$$\text{Stress} = \frac{F}{A}. \qquad (10\text{–}1)$$

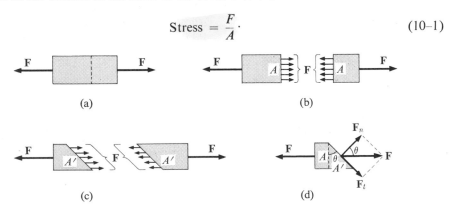

Fig. 10–1. (a) A bar in tension. (b) The stress at a perpendicular section equals F/A. (c) and (d) The stress at an inclined section can be resolved into a *normal stress*, F_n/A', and a *tangential* or *shearing* stress, F_t/A'.

The stress is called a *tensile* stress, meaning that each portion *pulls* on the other, and it is also a *normal* stress because the distributed force is perpendicular to the area. Units of stress are 1 newton/m², 1 dyne/cm², and 1 lb/ft². The hybrid unit 1 lb/in² is also commonly used.

Consider next a section through the bar in some arbitrary direction, as in Fig. 10–1(c). The resultant force exerted on the portion at either side of this section, by the portion at the other, is equal and opposite to the force F at the end of the section. Now, however, the force is distributed over a larger area A' and is not at right angles to the area. If we represent the resultant of the distributed forces by a single vector of magnitude F, as in Fig. 10–1(d), this vector can be resolved into a component F_n normal to the area A', and a component F_t tangent to the area. The *normal* stress is defined, as before, as the ratio of the component F_n to the area A'. The ratio of the component F_t to the area A' is called the *tangential* stress or, more commonly, the *shearing* stress at the section:

$$\text{Normal stress} = \frac{F_n}{A'}, \qquad \text{Tangential (shearing) stress} = \frac{F_t}{A'}. \qquad (10\text{--}2)$$

Stress is not a vector quantity since, unlike a force, we cannot assign to it a specific direction. The *force* acting on the portion of the body on a specified side of a section has a definite direction. Stress is one of a class of physical quantities called *tensors*.

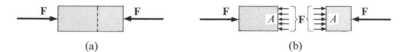

(a)   (b)

Fig. 10–2.   A bar in compression.

A bar subjected to pushes at its ends, as in Fig. 10–2, is said to be in *compression*. The stress on the dotted section, illustrated in part (b), is also a normal stress but is now a *compressive* stress, since each portion pushes on the other. It should be evident that if we take a section in some arbitrary direction it will be subject to both a tangential (shearing) and a normal stress, the latter now being a compression.

As another example of a body under stress, consider the block of square cross section in Fig. 10–3(a), acted on by two equal and opposite couples produced by the

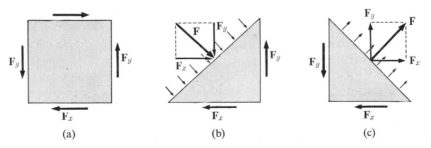

(a)   (b)   (c)

Fig. 10–3.   (a) A body in shear. The stress on one diagonal, part (b), is a pure compression; that on the other, part (c), is a pure tension.

pairs of forces $\mathbf{F}_x$ and $\mathbf{F}_y$ distributed over its surfaces. The block is in equilibrium, and any portion of it is in equilibrium also. Thus the distributed forces over the diagonal face in part (b) must have a resultant $\mathbf{F}$ whose components are equal to $\mathbf{F}_x$ and $\mathbf{F}_y$. The stress at this section is therefore a pure compression, although the stresses at the right face and the bottom are both shearing stresses. Similarly, we see from Fig. 10–3(c) that the other diagonal is in pure tension.

Consider next a fluid under pressure. The term "fluid" means a substance that can flow, hence the term applies to both liquids and gases. If there is a shearing stress at any point in a fluid, the fluid slips sidewise so long as the stress is maintained. Hence in a fluid at rest, the shearing stress is everywhere zero. Figure 10–4 represents a fluid in a cylinder provided with a piston, on which is exerted a downward force. The triangle is a side view of a wedge-shaped portion of the fluid. If for the moment we neglect ·the weight of the fluid, the only forces on this portion are those exerted by the rest of the fluid, and since these forces can have no shearing (or tangential) component, they must be normal to the surfaces of the wedge. Let $\mathbf{F}_x$, $\mathbf{F}_y$, and $\mathbf{F}$ represent the forces against the three faces. Since the fluid is in equilibrium, it follows that

$$F \sin \theta = F_x, \qquad F \cos \theta = F_y.$$

Also,

$$A \sin \theta = A_x, \qquad A \cos \theta = A_y.$$

Dividing the upper equations by the lower, we find

$$\frac{F}{A} = \frac{F_x}{A_x} = \frac{F_y}{A_y}.$$

Hence the force per unit area is the *same*, regardless of the direction of the section, and is always a compression. Any óne of the preceding ratios defines the *hydrostatic pressure p* in the fluid.

$$p = \frac{F}{A}, \qquad F = pA. \tag{10–3}$$

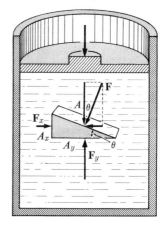

Fig. 10–4. A fluid under hydrostatic pressure. The force on a surface in any direction is normal to the surface.

Units of pressure are 1 newton/m², 1 dyne/cm², or 1 lb/ft². Like other types of stress, pressure is not a vector quantity and no direction can be assigned to it. The *force* against any area within (or bounding) a fluid at rest and under pressure is normal to the area, regardless of the orientation of the area. This is what is meant by the common statement that "the pressure in a fluid is the same in all directions."

The stress within a solid can also be a hydrostatic pressure, provided the stress at all points of the surface of the solid is of this nature. That is, the force per unit area must be the same at *all* points of the surface, and the force must be normal to the surface and directed inward. This is not the case in Fig. 10–2, where forces are applied at the ends of the bar only, but it is automatically the case if a solid is immersed in a fluid under pressure.

10–2 Strain

The term *strain* refers to the relative change in dimensions or shape of a body which is subjected to stress. Associated with each type of stress described in the preceding section is a corresponding type of strain.

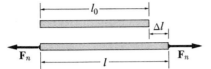

Fig. 10-5. The longitudinal strain is defined as $\Delta l/l_0$.

Figure 10–5 shows a bar whose natural length is l_0 and which elongates to a length l when equal and opposite pulls are exerted at its ends. The elongation, of course, does not occur at the ends only; every element of the bar stretches in the same proportion as does the bar as a whole. The *tensile strain* in the bar is defined as the ratio of the increase in length to the original length:

$$\text{Tensile strain} = \frac{l - l_0}{l_0} = \frac{\Delta l}{l_0}. \qquad (10\text{--}4)$$

The *compressive strain* of a bar in compression is defined in the same way, as the ratio of the decrease in length to the original length.

Figure 10–6(a) illustrates the nature of the deformation when shearing stresses act on the faces of a block, as in Fig. 10–3. The dotted outline *abcd* represents the unstressed block, and the full lines *a'b'c'd'* represent the block under stress. In part (a), the centers of the stressed and unstressed block coincide. In part (b), the edges *ad* and *a'd'* coincide. The lengths of the faces under shear remain very nearly constant, while all dimensions parallel to the diagonal *ac* increase in length, and those parallel to the diagonal *bd* decrease in length. Note that this is to be expected in view of the nature of the corresponding internal stresses (see Fig. 10–3). This type of strain

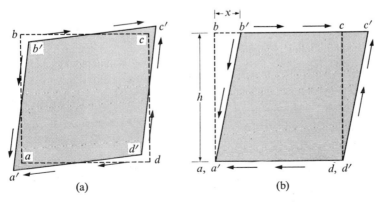

(a)   (b)

Fig.10–6. Change in shape of a block in shear. The shearing strain is defined as x/h.

is called a *shearing strain*, and is defined as the ratio of the displacement x of corner b to the transverse dimension h.

$$\text{Shearing strain} = x/h. \tag{10-5}$$

Like other types of strain, shearing strain is a pure number.

The strain produced by a hydrostatic pressure, called a *volume strain*, is defined as the ratio of the change in volume, ΔV, to the original volume V. It also is a pure number:

$$\text{Volume strain} = \frac{\Delta V}{V}. \tag{10-6}$$

10-3 Elasticity and plasticity

The relation between each of the three kinds of stress and its corresponding strain plays an important role in the branch of physics called the *theory of elasticity*, or its engineering counterpart, *strength of materials*. When any stress is plotted against the appropriate strain, the resulting stress-strain diagram is found to have several different shapes, depending on the kind of material. Two of the most important materials of present-day science and technology are metal and vulcanized rubber.

Even among metals there are wide variations. A typical stress-strain diagram for a ductile metal is shown in Fig. 10-7. The stress is a simple tensile stress and the strain is the percentage elongation. During the first portion of the curve (up to a strain of less than 1%), the stress and strain are proportional until the point a, the *proportional limit*, is reached. The proportional relation between stress and strain in this region is called *Hooke's law*. From a to b stress and strain are not proportional, but nevertheless, if the load is removed at any point between O and b, the curve will be retraced and the material will be restored to its original length. In the region Ob, the material is said to be *elastic* or to exhibit *elastic behavior* and the point b is called the *elastic limit*, or the *yield point*.

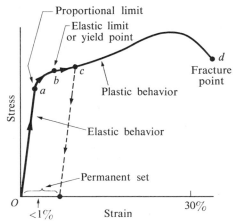

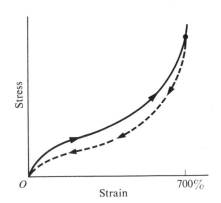

Fig. 10-7. Typical stress-strain diagram for a ductile metal under tension.

Fig. 10-8. Typical stress-strain diagram for vulcanized rubber, showing elastic hysteresis.

If the material is loaded further, the strain increases rapidly, but when the load is removed at some point beyond *b*, say at *c*, the material does not come back to its original length but traverses the dashed line in Fig. 10–7. The length at zero stress is now greater than the original length and the material is said to have a *permanent set*. Further increase of load beyond *c* produces a large increase in strain until a point *d* is reached at which *fracture* takes place. From *b* to *d* the metal is said to undergo *plastic flow* or *plastic deformation*, during which slipping takes place within the metal along the planes of maximum shearing stress. If large plastic deformation takes place between the elastic limit and the fracture point, the metal is said to be *ductile*. If, however, fracture occurs soon after the elastic limit, the metal is said to be *brittle*.

Figure 10–8 shows a stress-strain curve for a typical sample of vulcanized rubber which has been stretched to over seven times its original length. During no portion of this curve is the stress proportional to the strain. The substance however is elastic, in the sense that when the load is removed, the rubber is restored to its original length. On decreasing the load, the stress-strain curve is *not* retraced but follows the dashed curve of Fig. 10–8. The lack of coincidence of the curves for increasing and decreasing stress is known as *elastic hysteresis* (accent on the *third* syllable). An analogous phenomenon observed with magnetic materials is called *magnetic hysteresis*. It can be shown that the area bounded by the two curves, that is, the area of the *hysteresis loop*, is equal to the energy dissipated within the elastic or magnetic material. The large elastic hysteresis of some types of rubber makes these materials very valuable as vibration absorbers. If a block of such material is placed between a piece of vibrating machinery and, let us say, the floor, elastic hysteresis takes place during every cycle of vibration. Mechanical energy is converted to a form known as internal energy which evidences itself by a rise of temperature. As a result, only a small amount of energy of vibration is transmitted to the floor.

10–4 Elastic modulus

The stress required to produce a given strain depends on the nature of the material under stress. The ratio of stress to strain, or the *stress per unit strain*, is called an *elastic modulus* of the material. The larger the elastic modulus, the greater the stress needed for a given strain.

Consider first longitudinal (tensile or compressive) stresses and strains. Experiment shows that up to the proportional limit, a given longitudinal stress produces a strain of the same magnitude whether the stress is a tension or a compression. Hence the ratio of tensile stress to tensile strain, for a given material, equals the ratio of compressive stress to compressive strain. This ratio is called the *stretch modulus* or *Young's modulus* of the material and will be denoted by Y:

$$Y = \frac{\text{tensile stress}}{\text{tensile strain}} = \frac{\text{compressive stress}}{\text{compressive strain}}$$

$$= \frac{F_n/A}{\Delta l/l_0} = \frac{l_0}{A}\frac{F_n}{\Delta l}. \tag{10–7}$$

TABLE 10–1

APPROXIMATE ELASTIC MODULI

Material	Young's modulus, Y		Shear modulus, S		Bulk modulus, B	
	10^{12} dynes cm^2	10^6 lb in^2	10^{12} dynes cm^2	10^6 lb in^2	10^{12} dynes cm^2	10^6 lb in^2
Aluminum	0.70	10	0.24	3.4	0.70	10
Brass	0.91	13	0.36	5.1	0.61	8.5
Copper	1.1	16	0.42	6.0	1.4	20
Glass	0.55	7.8	0.23	3.3	0.37	5.2
Iron	0.91	13	0.70	10	1.0	14
Lead	0.16	2.3	0.056	0.8	0.44	6.2
Nickel	2.1	30	0.77	11	2.6	34
Steel	2.0	29	0.84	12	1.6	23
Tungsten	3.6	51	1.5	21	2.0	29

If the proportional limit is not exceeded, the ratio of stress to strain is constant and Hooke's law is therefore equivalent to the statement that *within the proportional limit, the elastic modulus of a given material is constant*, depending only on the nature of the material.

Since a strain is a pure number, the units of Young's modulus are the same as those of stress, namely, force per unit area. Tabulated values are usually in lb/in^2 or dynes/cm^2. Some typical values are listed in Table 10–1.

If the relation between stress and strain is not linear, an elastic modulus can be defined more generally as the limiting ratio of a small *change* in stress to the *change* in strain produced by it. Thus if the force F_n in Fig. 10–5 is increased by dF_n, and as a result the length of the bar increases by dl, the stretch modulus is defined as

$$Y = \frac{dF_n/A}{dl/l} = \frac{l}{A}\frac{dF_n}{dl}. \qquad (10\text{–}8)$$

This is equivalent to defining the modulus at any point as the *slope* of a curve in a stress-strain diagram. Within the Hooke's law region, the two definitions are equivalent.

The *shear modulus S* of a material, within the Hooke's law region, is defined as the ratio of a shearing stress to the shearing strain it produces:

$$S = \frac{\text{shearing stress}}{\text{shearing strain}} = \frac{F_t/A}{x/h} = \frac{h}{A}\frac{F_t}{x}. \qquad (10\text{–}9)$$

(Refer to Fig. 10–6 for the meaning of x and of h.)

The shear modulus of a material is also expressed as force per unit area. For most materials it is one-half to one-third as great as Young's modulus. The shear modulus is also called the *modulus of rigidity* or the *torsion modulus*.

TABLE 10–2

COMPRESSIBILITIES OF LIQUIDS

Liquid	Compressibility, k		
	$(\text{newtons/m}^2)^{-1}$	$(\text{lb/in}^2)^{-1}$	atm^{-1}
Carbon disulfide	64×10^{-11}	45×10^{-7}	66×10^{-6}
Ethyl alcohol	110	78	115
Glycerine	21	15	22
Mercury	3.7	2.6	3.8
Water	49	34	50

The more general definition of shear modulus is

$$S = \frac{dF_t/A}{dx/h} = \frac{h}{A}\frac{dF_t}{dx},\qquad(10\text{–}10)$$

where dx is the increase in x when the shearing force increases by dF_t.

The shear modulus has a significance for *solid* materials only. A liquid or gas will flow under the influence of a shearing stress and will not *permanently* support such a stress.

The modulus relating a hydrostatic pressure to the volume strain it produces is called the *bulk modulus* and we shall represent it by B. The general definition of bulk modulus is the (negative) ratio of a change in pressure to the change in volume strain produced by it.

$$B = -\frac{dp}{dV/V} = -V\frac{dp}{dV}.\qquad(10\text{–}11)$$

The minus sign is included in the definition of B because an *increase* of pressure always causes a *decrease* in volume. That is, if dp is positive, dV is negative. By including a minus sign in its definition, we make the bulk modulus itself a positive quantity.

The change in volume of a *solid* or *liquid* under pressure is so small that the volume V, in Eq. (10–11) can be considered constant. Provided the pressure is not too great, the ratio dp/dV is constant also and the bulk modulus is constant. We can then replace dp and dV by finite changes in pressure and volume. The volume of a *gas*, however, changes markedly with pressure and the general definition of B must be used for gases.

The reciprocal of the bulk modulus is called the *compressibility k*. From its definition,

$$k = \frac{1}{B} = -\frac{dV/V}{dp} = -\frac{1}{V}\frac{dV}{dp}.\qquad(10\text{–}12)$$

The compressibility of a material thus equals the *fractional decrease in volume*, $-dV/V$, per unit increase dp in pressure.

The units of a bulk modulus are the same as those of pressure, and the units of compressibility are those of a *reciprocal pressure*. Thus the statement that the compressibility of water (see Table 10–2) is 50×10^{-6} atm^{-1} means that the volume decreases by 50 one-millionths of the original volume for each atmosphere increase in pressure. (1 atm $= 14.7$ lb/in^2.)

EXAMPLE 1.   In an experiment to measure Young's modulus, a load of 1000 lb hanging from a steel wire 8 ft long, of cross section 0.025 in^2, was found to stretch the wire 0.010 ft above its no-load length. What were the stress, the strain, and the value of Young's modulus for the steel of which the wire was composed?

$$\text{Stress} = \frac{F_n}{A} = \frac{1000 \text{ lb}}{0.025 \text{ in}^2} = 40,000 \frac{\text{lb}}{\text{in}^2}.$$

$$\text{Strain} = \frac{\Delta l}{l_0} = \frac{0.010 \text{ ft}}{8 \text{ ft}} = 0.00125.$$

$$Y = \frac{\text{stress}}{\text{strain}} = \frac{40,000 \text{ lb/in}^2}{0.00125} = 32 \times 10^6 \frac{\text{lb}}{\text{in}^2}.$$

EXAMPLE 2.   Suppose the object in Fig. 10–6 is a brass plate 2 ft square and $\frac{1}{4}$ in. thick. How large a force F must be exerted on each of its edges if the displacement x in Fig. 10–6(b) is 0.01 in.? The shear modulus of brass is 5×10^6 lb/in^2.
The shearing stress on each edge is

$$\text{Shearing stress} = \frac{F_t}{A} = \frac{F}{24 \times \frac{1}{4} \text{ in}^2} = \frac{F}{6} \text{ in}^{-2}.$$

The shearing strain is

$$\text{Shearing strain} = \frac{x}{h} = \frac{0.01 \text{ in}}{24 \text{ in}} = 4.17 \times 10^{-4}.$$

$$\text{Shear modulus } S = \frac{\text{stress}}{\text{strain}},$$

$$5 \times 10^6 \frac{\text{lb}}{\text{in}^2} = \frac{F/6}{4.17 \times 10^{-4}} \text{ in}^{-2}$$

$$F = 12,500 \text{ lb}.$$

EXAMPLE 3.   The volume of oil contained in a certain hydraulic press is 5 ft^3. Find the decrease in volume of the oil when subjected to a pressure of 2000 lb/in^2. The compressibility of the oil is 20×10^{-6} per atmosphere.
The volume decreases by 20 parts per million for a pressure increase of 1 atm. Since 2000 lb/in^2 $= 136$ atm, the volume decrease is $136 \times 20 = 2720$ parts per million. Since the original volume is 5 ft^3, the actual decrease is

$$\frac{2720}{1,000,000} \times 5 \text{ ft}^3 = 0.0136 \text{ ft}^3 = 23.5 \text{ in}^3.$$

Or, from Eq. (10–12), replacing dV and dp with ΔV and Δp,

$$\Delta V = -kV\Delta p$$
$$= -20 \times 10^{-6}\,\text{atm}^{-1} \times 5\,\text{ft}^3 \times 136\,\text{atm}$$
$$= -0.0136\,\text{ft}^3.$$

10–5 The force constant

The various elastic moduli are quantities which describe the elastic properties of a particular *material* and do not directly indicate how much a given rod, cable, or spring constructed of the material will distort under load. If Eq. (10-7) is solved for F_n, one obtains

$$F_n = \frac{YA}{l_0}\,\Delta l$$

or, if YA/l_0 is replaced by a single constant k, and the elongation Δl is represented

$$F_n = kx. \tag{10–13}$$

In other words, the elongation of a body in tension above its no-load length is directly proportional to the stretching force. Hooke's law was originally stated in this form, rather than in terms of stress and strain.

When a helical wire spring is stretched, the stress in the wire is practically a pure shear. The elongation of the spring as a whole is directly proportional to the stretching force. That is, an equation of the form $F = kx$ still applies, the constant k depending on the shear modulus of the wire, its radius, the radius of the coils, and the number of coils.

The constant k, or the ratio of the force to the elongation, is called the *force constant* or the *stiffness* of the spring, and is expressed in pounds per foot, newtons per meter, or dynes per centimeter. It is equal numerically to the force required to produce unit elongation.

The ratio of the elongation to the force, or the elongation per unit force, is called the *compliance* of the spring. The compliance equals the reciprocal of the force constant and is expressed in feet per pound, meters per newton, or centimeters per dyne. It is numerically equal to the elongation produced by unit force.

Problems

10–1. A steel wire 10 ft long and 0.1 square inch in cross section is found to stretch 0.01 ft under a tension of 2500 lb. What is Young's modulus for this steel?

10–2. The elastic limit of a steel elevator cable is 40,000 lb/in². Find the maximum upward acceleration which can be given a 2-ton elevator when supported by a cable whose cross section is $\frac{1}{2}$ in² if the stress is not to exceed $\frac{1}{4}$ of the elastic limit.

10–3. A copper wire 12 ft long and 0.036 in. in diameter was given the test below. A load of 4.5 lb was originally hung from the wire to keep it taut. The position of the lower end of the wire was read on a scale.

Added load (lb)	Scale reading (in.)
0	3.02
2	3.04
4	3.06
6	3.08
8	3.10
10	3.12
12	3.14
14	3.65

(a) Make a graph of these values, plotting the increase in length horizontally and the added load vertically. (b) Calculate the value of Young's modulus. (c) What was the stress at the proportional limit?

10–4. A steel wire has the following properties:

Length = 10 ft
Cross section = 0.01 in²
Young's modulus = 30,000,000 lb/in²
Shear modulus = 10,000,000 lb/in²
Proportional limit = 60,000 lb/in²
Breaking stress = 120,000 lb/in²
The wire is fastened at its upper end and hangs vertically. (a) How great a load can be supported without exceeding the proportional limit? (b) How much will the wire stretch under this load? (c) What is the maximum load that can be supported?

10–5. (a) What is the maximum load that can be supported by an aluminum wire 0.05 in. in diameter without exceeding the proportional limit of 14,000 lb/in²? (b) If the wire was originally 20 ft long, how much will it elongate under this load?

10–6. A 10-lb weight hangs on a vertical steel wire 2 ft long and 0.001 in² in cross section. Hanging from the bottom of this weight is a similar steel wire which supports a 5-lb weight. Compute (a) the longitudinal strain, and (b) the elongation of each wire.

10–7. A 32-lb weight, fastened to the end of a steel wire of unstretched length 2 ft, is whirled in a vertical circle with an angular velocity of 2 rev/sec at the bottom of the circle. The cross section of the wire is 0.01 in². Calculate the elongation of the wire when the weight is at the lowest point of its path.

10–8. A copper wire 320 inches long and a steel wire 160 in. long, each of cross section 0.1 in², are fastened end-to-end and stretched with a tension of 100 lb. (a) What is the change in length of each wire? (b) What is the elastic potential energy of the system?

10–9. A copper rod of length 3 ft and cross-sectional area 0.5 in² is fastened end-to-end to a steel rod of length L and cross-sectional area 0.2 in². The compound rod is subjected to equal and opposite pulls of magnitude 6000 lb at its ends. (a) Find the length L of the steel rod if the elongations of the two rods are equal. (b) What is the stress in each rod? (c) What is the strain in each rod?

10–10. A rod 105 cm long, whose weight is negligible, is supported at its ends by wires A and B of equal length. The cross section of A is 1 mm², that of B is 2 mm². Young's modulus for wire A is 30×10^6 lb/in² and for B it is 20×10^6 lb/in². At what point along the bar should a weight w be suspended in order to produce (a) equal stresses in A and B, (b) equal strains in A and B? (Fig. 10–9.)

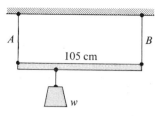

Figure 10–9

10–11. A bar of length L, cross-sectional area A, Young's modulus Y, is subjected to a tension F. Represent the stress in the bar by Q and the strain by P. Derive the expression for the elastic potential energy, per unit volume, of the bar in terms of Q and P.

10–12. The compressibility of sodium is to be measured by observing the displacement of the piston in Fig. 10–4 when a force is applied. The sodium is immersed in an oil which fills the cylinder below the piston. Assume that the piston and walls of the cylinder are perfectly rigid, that there is no friction, and no oil leak. Compute the compressibility of the sodium in terms of the applied force F, the piston displacement x, the piston area A, the initial volume of the oil V_0, the initial volume of the sodium v_0, and the compressibility of the oil k_0.

10–13. Two strips of metal are riveted together at their ends by four rivets, each of diameter 0.25 in. What is the maximum tension that can be exerted by the riveted strip if the shearing stress on the rivets is not to exceed 10,000 lb/in²? Assume each rivet to carry one-quarter of the load.

10–14. Find the weight per cubic foot of occan water at a depth where the pressure is 4700 lb/ft². The weight at the surface is 64 lb/ft³.

10–15. Compute the compressibility of steel, in reciprocal atmospheres, and com-pare with that of water. Which material is the more readily compressed?

10–16. A steel post 6 in. in diameter and 10 ft long is placed vertically and is re-quired to support a load of 20,000 lb. (a) What is the stress in the post? (b) What is the strain in the post? (c) What is the change in length of the post?

10–17. A hollow cylindrical steel column 10 ft high shortens 0.01 in. under a com-pression load of 72,000 lb. If the inner radius of the cylinder is 0.80 of the outer one, what is the outer radius?

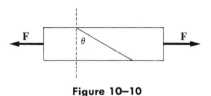

Figure 10–10

10–18. A bar of cross section A is sub-jected to equal and opposite tensile forces F at its ends. Consider a plane through the bar making an angle θ with a plane at right angles to the bar (Fig. 10–10). (a) What is the tensile (normal) stress at this plane, in terms of F, A, θ? (b) What is the shearing (tangential) stress at the plane, in terms of F, A, and θ? (c) For what value of θ is the tensile stress a maximum? (d) For what value of θ is the shearing stress a maximum?

10–19. Suppose the block in Fig. 10–3 is rectangular instead of square, but is in equilibrium under the action of shearing stresses on those outside faces perpendicu-lar to the plane of the diagram. (Note that then $F_x \neq F_y$.) (a) Show that the shearing stress is the same on all outside faces per-pendicular to the plane of the diagram. (b) Show that on all sections perpendicular to the plane of the diagram and making an angle of 45° with an end face, the stress is still a pure tension or compression.

CHAPTER 11

Harmonic Motion

11–1 Introduction

When a body executes a to-and-fro motion about some fixed point, its motion is said to be *oscillatory*. In this chapter we consider a special type of oscillatory motion called *harmonic motion*. Motion of this sort is closely approximated by that of a body suspended from a spring, by a pendulum swinging with a small amplitude, and by the balance wheel of a watch. The vibrations of the strings and air columns of musical instruments either are harmonic or are a superposition of harmonic motions. Modern atomic theory leads us to believe that the molecules of a solid body oscillate with nearly harmonic motion about their fixed lattice positions, although of course their motion cannot be directly observed.

In every form of wave motion, the particles of the medium in which the wave is traveling oscillate with harmonic motion or with a superposition of such motions. This is true even for light waves and radiowaves in empty space, except that instead of material particles the quantities that oscillate are the electric and magnetic intensities associated with the wave. As a final example, the equations describing the behavior of an electrical circuit in which there is an alternating current have the same form as those for the harmonic motion of a material body. It can be seen that a study of harmonic motion will lay the foundation for future work in many different fields of physics.

11–2 Elastic restoring forces

It has been shown in Chapter 10 that when a body is caused to change its shape, the distorting force is proportional to the amount of the change, provided the proportional limit of elasticity is not exceeded. The change may be in the nature of an increase in length, as of a rubber band or a coil spring, or a decrease in length, or a bending as of a flat spring, or a twisting of a rod about its axis, or of many other forms. The term "force" is to be interpreted liberally as the force, or torque, or pressure, or whatever may be producing the distortion. If we restrict the discussion to the case of a push or a pull, where the distortion is simply the displacement of the point of application of the force, the force and displacement are related by Hooke's law,

$$F = kx,$$

where k is a proportionality constant called the *force constant* and x is the displacement from the equilibrium position.

In this equation, F stands for the force which must be exerted *on* an elastic body to produce the displacement x. The force with which the elastic body pulls back on an object to which it is attached is called the *restoring force* and is equal to $-kx$.

11–3 Definitions

To fix our ideas, suppose that a flat strip of steel such as a hacksaw blade is clamped vertically in a vise and a small body is attached to its upper end, as in Fig. 11–1. Assume that the strip is sufficiently long and the displacement sufficiently small so that the motion is essentially along a straight line. The mass of the strip itself is negligible.

Let the top of the strip be pulled to the right a distance A, as in Fig. 11–1, and released. The attached body is then acted on by a restoring force exerted by the steel strip and directed toward the equilibrium position O. It therefore accelerates in the direction of this force, and moves in toward the center with increasing speed. The *rate* of increase (i.e., the acceleration) is not constant, however, since the accelerating force becomes smaller as the body approaches the center.

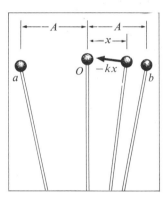

Fig. 11–1.   Motion under an elastic restoring force.

When the body reaches the center the restoring force has decreased to zero, but because of the velocity which has been acquired, the body "overshoots" the equilibrium position and continues to move toward the left. As soon as the equilibrium position is passed the restoring force again comes into play, directed now toward the right. The body therefore decelerates, and at a rate which increases with increasing distance from O. It will therefore be brought to rest at some point to the left of O, and repeat its motion in the opposite direction.

Both experiment and theory show that the motion will be confined to a range $\pm A$ on either side of the equilibrium position, each to-and-fro movement taking place in the same length of time. If there were no loss of energy by friction the motion would continue indefinitely once it had been started. This type of motion, under the influence of an elastic restoring force and in the absence of all friction, is called *simple harmonic motion*, often abbreviated SHM.

Any sort of motion which repeats itself in equal intervals of time is called *periodic*, and if the motion is back and forth over the same path it is also called *oscillatory*.

A *complete vibration* or *oscillation* means one round trip, say from *a* to *b* and back to *a*, or from *O* to *b* to *O* to *a* and back to *O*.

The *periodic time*, or simply the *period* of the motion, represented by *T*, is the time required for one complete vibration.

The *frequency, f*, is the number of complete vibrations per unit time. Evidently the frequency is the reciprocal of the period, or $T = 1/f$.

The *coordinate, x*, at any instant, is the distance away from the equilibrium position or center of the path at that instant.

The *amplitude, A*, is the maximum coordinate. The total range of the motion is therefore $2A$.

11–4 Equations of simple harmonic motion

We now wish to find expressions for the coordinate, velocity, and acceleration of a body moving with simple harmonic motion, just as we found those for a body moving with constant acceleration. It must be emphasized that the equations of motion with *constant* acceleration cannot be applied, since the acceleration is continually changing.

Figure 11–2 represents the vibrating body of Fig. 11–1 at some instant when its coordinate is *x*. The resultant force on it is simply the elastic restoring force, $-kx$, and from Newton's second law,

$$F = -kx = ma = mv \frac{dv}{dx}.$$

From the second and fourth terms, we have

$$mv \frac{dv}{dx} + kx = 0. \qquad (11\text{–}1)$$

Therefore

$$\int mv \, dv + \int kx \, dx = 0,$$

which integrates to

$$\tfrac{1}{2}mv^2 + \tfrac{1}{2}kx^2 = C_1. \qquad (11\text{–}2)$$

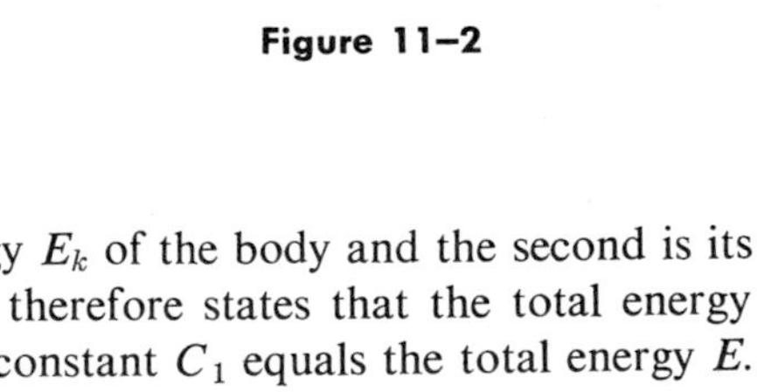

Equilibrium
position

Figure 11–2

The first term on the left is the kinetic energy E_k of the body and the second is its elastic potential energy E_p. Equation (11–2) therefore states that the total energy of the system is constant, and the integration constant C_1 equals the total energy E. (This result is only to be expected, since the system is conservative.)

$$E_k + E_p = E.$$

The significance of this relation can be brought out by the graph shown in Fig. 11–3, in which energy is plotted vertically and the coordinate *x* horizontally. First, the curve representing the potential energy, $E_p = \tfrac{1}{2}kx^2$, is constructed. (This curve is a

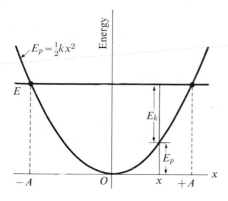

$E_p = \frac{1}{2}kx^2$

Energy

E

E_k

E_p

$-A$ O x $+A$ x

Fig. 11–3. Relation between total energy E, potential energy E_p, and kinetic energy E_k, for a body oscillating with SHM.

parabola.) Next, a horizontal line is drawn at a height equal to the total energy E. We see at once that the motion is restricted to values of x lying between the points at which the horizontal line intersects the parabola, since if x were outside this range the potential energy would exceed the total energy, which is impossible. The motion of the vibrating body is analogous to that of a particle released at a height E on a frictionless track shaped like the potential energy curve, and the motion is said to take place in a "potential energy well."

If a vertical line is constructed at any value of x within the permitted range, the length of the segment between the x-axis and the parabola represents the potential energy E_p at that value of x, and the length of the segment between the parabola and the horizontal line at height E represents the corresponding kinetic energy E_k. At the endpoints, therefore, the energy is all potential and at the midpoint it is all kinetic. The velocity at the midpoint has its maximum (absolute) value v_{max}:

$$\tfrac{1}{2}mv_{max}^2 = E,$$

$$v_{max} = \pm\sqrt{2E/m}, \tag{11–3}$$

the sign of v being positive or negative depending on the direction of motion.

At the ends of the path the coordinate has its maximum (absolute) value x_{max}, equal to the amplitude A:

$$\tfrac{1}{2}kx_{max}^2 = E, \qquad x_{max} = \pm\sqrt{2E/k},$$

$$A = |x_{max}| = \sqrt{2E/k}. \tag{11–4}$$

The velocity v at any coordinate x, from Eq. (11–2), is

$$v = \pm\sqrt{\frac{2E - kx^2}{m}}. \tag{11–5}$$

Making use of Eq. (11–4), this can be written

$$v = \sqrt{k/m}\sqrt{A^2 - x^2}. \tag{11–6}$$

The expression for the coordinate x as a function of time can now be obtained by replacing v with dx/dt, in Eq. (11–6), and integrating. This gives

$$\int \frac{dx}{\sqrt{A^2 - x^2}} = \sqrt{\frac{k}{m}} \int dt,$$

$$\sin^{-1} \frac{x}{A} = \sqrt{\frac{k}{m}}\, t + C_2. \tag{11-7}$$

Let x_0 be the value of x when $t = 0$. The integration constant C_2 is then

$$C_2 = \sin^{-1} \frac{x_0}{A} .$$

That is, C_2 is the *angle* (in radians) whose sine equals x_0/A. Let us represent this angle by θ_0:

$$\sin \theta_0 = \frac{x_0}{A}, \qquad \theta_0 = \sin^{-1} \frac{x_0}{A} . \tag{11-8}$$

Equation (11–7) can now be written

$$\sin^{-1} \frac{x}{A} = \sqrt{\frac{k}{m}}\, t + \theta_0,$$

$$x = A \sin \left(\sqrt{\frac{k}{m}}\, t + \theta_0 \right). \tag{11-9}$$

The coordinate x is therefore a *sinusoidal* function of the time t. The term in parentheses is an *angle*, in radians. It is called the *phase angle*, or simply the *phase* of the motion. The angle θ_0 is the *initial phase angle*, and is also referred to as the *epoch angle*.

The period T is the time required for one complete oscillation. That is, the coordinate x has the same value at the times t and $t + T$. In other words, the phase angle $(\sqrt{k/m}\, t + \theta_0)$ increases by 2π radians in the time T:

$$\sqrt{k/m}\, (t + T) + \theta_0 = (\sqrt{k/m}\, t + \theta_0) + 2\pi,$$

$$\boxed{T = 2\,\pi\, \sqrt{\frac{m}{k}} .} \tag{11-10}$$

The period T therefore depends only on the mass m and the force constant k. It does not depend on the amplitude (or on the total energy). For given values of m and k, the time of one complete oscillation is the same whether the amplitude is large or small. A motion that has this property is said to be *isochronous* (equal time).

The frequency f, or the number of complete oscillations per unit time, is the reciprocal of the period T:

$$f = \frac{1}{T} = \frac{1}{2\pi} \sqrt{\frac{k}{m}} .$$

The *angular frequency* ω is defined as $\omega = 2\pi f$ and is expressed in radians/sec. It follows from the two preceding equations that

$$\omega = \sqrt{k/m},$$

and Eqs. (11–9) and (11–6) can be written more compactly as

$$\boxed{x = A \sin(\omega t + \theta_0),} \qquad (11\text{–}11)$$

$$v = \omega\sqrt{A^2 - x^2}. \qquad (11\text{–}12)$$

Expressions for the velocity and acceleration as functions of time can now be obtained by differentiation:

$$v = \frac{dx}{dt} = \omega A \cos(\omega t + \theta_0), \qquad (11\text{–}13)$$

$$a = \frac{dv}{dt} = -\omega^2 A \sin(\omega t + \theta_0). \qquad (11\text{–}14)$$

Since $A \sin(\omega t + \theta_0) = x$, the expression for the acceleration as a function of x is

$$a = -\omega^2 x. \qquad (11\text{–}15)$$

It follows from Eq. (11–13) that if v_0 is the velocity when $t = 0$, then

$$\cos \theta_0 = \frac{v_0}{\omega A} \cdot \qquad (11\text{–}16)$$

This equation, together with Eq. (11–8), $\sin \theta_0 = x_0/A$, completely determines the initial phase angle θ_0. That is, the angle θ_0 depends both on the initial position x_0 and the initial velocity v_0.

Figure 11–4 shows how the initial phase angle depends on the initial position and initial velocity. It follows from this triangle that

$$A = \sqrt{x_0^2 + (v_0/\omega)^2}, \qquad (11\text{–}17)$$

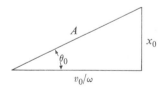

a relation that can also be obtained by setting the initial total energy, $\frac{1}{2}kx_0^2 + \frac{1}{2}mv_0^2$, equal to the potential energy at maximum displacement. The motion is therefore completely determined, for given values of m and k, when the initial position and initial velocity are known.

Fig. 11–4. Relation between the initial phase angle θ_0, initial position x_0, and initial velocity v_0.

The equations of simple harmonic motion may be summarized by comparing them with similar equations for rectilinear motion with constant acceleration (Table 11–1).

Figure 11–5 shows corresponding graphs of the coordinate x, velocity v, and acceleration a of a body oscillating with simple harmonic motion, plotted as functions of

TABLE 11–1

Rectilinear motion with constant acceleration	Simple harmonic motion (in terms of ω and θ_0)
$a = $ constant	$a = -\omega^2 x$
	$a = -\omega^2 A \sin(\omega t + \theta_0)$
$v^2 = v_0^2 + 2a(x - x_0)$	$v = \pm \omega \sqrt{A^2 - x^2}$
$v = v_0 + at$	$v = \omega A \cos(\omega t + \theta_0)$
$x = x_0 + v_0 t + \frac{1}{2}at^2$	$x = A \sin(\omega t + \theta_0)$

$$\omega = 2\pi/T = 2\pi f = \sqrt{k/m}, \qquad A = \sqrt{x_0^2 + (v_0/\omega)^2},$$
$$\sin \theta_0 = x_0/A, \qquad \cos \theta_0 = v_0/\omega A.$$

the time t (or of the angle ωt). The initial coordinate is x_0 and the initial velocity is v_0. The angle θ_0 has been taken as $\pi/4$ rad. Each curve repeats itself in a time interval equal to the period T, during which the angle ωt increases by 2π rad. Note that when the body is at either end of its path, i.e., when the coordinate x has its maximum positive or negative value ($\pm A$), the velocity is zero and the acceleration has its maximum negative or positive value ($\mp a_{max}$). Note also that when the body passes through its equilibrium position ($x = 0$) the velocity has its maximum positive or negative value ($\pm v_{max}$) and the acceleration is zero.

The equations of motion take a simpler form if we set $t = 0$ when the body is at the midpoint, or is at one end of its path. For example, suppose we let $t = 0$ when the body has its maximum positive displacement. Then $x_0 = +A$, $\sin \theta_0 = 1$, $\theta_0 = \pi/2$, and

$$x = A \sin(\omega t + \pi/2) = A \cos \omega t,$$
$$v = -\omega A \sin \omega t, \qquad\qquad\qquad (11\text{–}18)$$
$$a = -\omega^2 A \cos \omega t.$$

This corresponds to moving the origin from the point O, in Fig. 11–5, to the point O'. The graph of x versus t becomes a cosine curve, that of v versus t a negative sine curve, and that of a a negative cosine curve.

If we set $t = 0$ when the body is at the midpoint and moving toward the right, then

$$x_0 = 0, \qquad \sin \theta_0 = 0, \qquad \theta_0 = 0$$

and

$$x = A \sin \omega t,$$
$$v = \omega A \cos \omega t, \qquad\qquad\qquad (11\text{–}19)$$
$$a = -\omega^2 A \sin \omega t.$$

This corresponds to displacing the origin to the point O'' in Fig. 11–5.

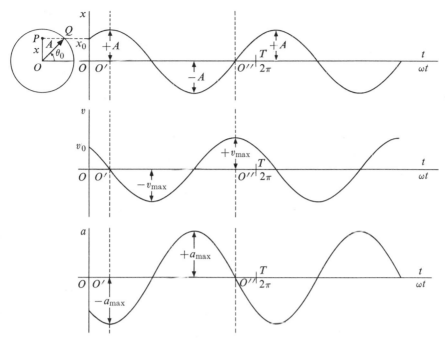

Fig. 11–5. Graphs of coordinate x, velocity v, and acceleration a of a body oscillating with simple harmonic motion.

EXAMPLE. Let the mass of the body in Fig. 11–2 be 25 gm, the force constant k be 400 dynes/cm, and let the motion be started by displacing the body 10 cm to the right of its equilibrium position and imparting to it a velocity toward the right of 40 cm/sec. Compute (a) the period T, (b) the frequency f, (c) the angular frequency ω, (d) the total energy E, (e) the amplitude A, (f) the angle θ_0, (g) the maximum velocity v_{max}, (h) the maximum acceleration a_{max}, (i) the coordinate, velocity, and acceleration at a time $\pi/8$ sec after the start of the motion.

(a) $T = 2\pi \sqrt{\dfrac{m}{k}} = 2\pi \sqrt{\dfrac{25 \text{ gm}}{400 \text{ dynes/cm}}} = \dfrac{\pi}{2} \text{ sec} = 1.57 \text{ sec.}$

(b) $f = \dfrac{1}{T} = \dfrac{2}{\pi} \dfrac{\text{vib}}{\text{sec}} = 0.638 \dfrac{\text{vib}}{\text{sec}}.$

(c) $\omega = 2\pi f = 4 \text{ rad/sec.}$

(d) $E = \frac{1}{2}mv_0^2 + \frac{1}{2}kx_0^2 = 40{,}000 \text{ ergs.}$

(e) $A = \sqrt{2E/k} = 10\sqrt{2} \text{ cm.}$

(f) $\sin \theta_0 = x_0/A = 1/\sqrt{2}, \qquad \theta_0 = \pi/4 \text{ rad.}$

(g) $|v_{max}| = \sqrt{2E/m} = 40\sqrt{2} \text{ cm/sec} = 56.6 \text{ cm/sec.}$

The maximum velocity occurs at the midpoint, where $x = 0$. Hence, from Eq. (11–12),

$$|v_{max}| = \omega A = 40\sqrt{2} \text{ cm/sec.}$$

(h) The maximum acceleration occurs at the ends of the path where the force is a maximum. From Eq. (11–15),

$$|a_{max}| = \omega^2 x_{max} = 160\sqrt{2} \text{ cm/sec}^2.$$

(i) The equations of motion are:

$$x = 10\sqrt{2} \sin\left(4t + \frac{\pi}{4}\right),$$

$$v = 40\sqrt{2} \cos\left(4t + \frac{\pi}{4}\right),$$

$$a = -160\sqrt{2} \sin\left(4t + \frac{\pi}{4}\right).$$

When $t = \pi/8$ sec, the phase angle is

$$\left(4t + \frac{\pi}{4}\right) = \frac{3\pi}{4} \text{ rad,}$$

$$x = 10\sqrt{2} \sin(3\pi/4) = 10 \text{ cm,}$$

$$v = 40\sqrt{2} \cos(3\pi/4) = -40 \text{ cm/sec,}$$

$$a = -160\sqrt{2} \sin(3\pi/4) = -160 \text{ cm/sec}^2.$$

The curves of Fig. 11–5 represent the motion of the body in this example, if the scales of x, v, a, and t are such that

$$A = 10\sqrt{2} \text{ cm,} \qquad v_{max} = 40\sqrt{2} \text{ cm/sec,}$$

$$a_{max} = 160\sqrt{2} \text{ cm/sec}^2, \qquad \text{and} \qquad T = \pi/2 \text{ sec.}$$

The equations of simple harmonic motion can be given a geometrical interpretation as follows. Let the line segment OQ in Fig. 11–6(a), of length equal to the amplitude A, rotate with an angular velocity ω about the fixed point O. The rotating line segment is often referred to as a *rotating vector*, but strictly speaking it is not a vector quantity. That is, while it has a specified direction *in a diagram*, it has no specified direction *in space*. It is better described as a *rotor*. (The German term is "Zeiger," meaning a pointer in the sense of a clock hand or the pointer on a pressure gauge.) Let the rotor OQ make an angle with the horizontal axis, at time $t = 0$, equal to the initial phase angle θ_0. Point P is the projection of point Q onto the vertical axis, and as OQ rotates, point P oscillates along this axis.

We now show that the equations of motion of P are the same as those of a body oscillating with simple harmonic motion of amplitude A, angular frequency ω, and

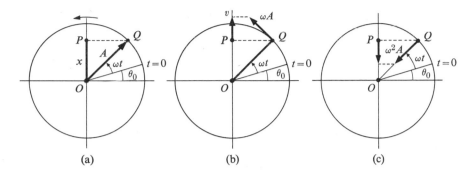

Fig. 11-6. Representation of simple harmonic motion by the projection onto the vertical axis of the tip of the rotor OQ.

initial phase angle θ_0. Let x represent the length of OP. At any time t, the angle between the radius OQ and the horizontal axis equals the phase angle $\omega t + \theta_0$ and

$$x = A \sin (\omega t + \theta_0).$$

The velocity of point Q [see Fig. 11-6(b)] is ωA, and its vertical component, equal to the velocity of P, is

$$v = \omega A \cos (\omega t + \theta_0).$$

The acceleration of Q is its radial acceleration $\omega^2 A$ [see Fig. 11-6(c)] and its vertical component, equal to the acceleration of P, is

$$a = -\omega^2 A \sin (\omega t + \theta_0).$$

The negative sign must be included because the acceleration is negative whenever the sine of the phase angle is positive, and vice versa. These equations are, of course, just the general equations of harmonic motion. In the special case corresponding to Eqs. (11–18), the initial phase angle is 90° and the reference point Q is at the top of the circle when $t = 0$. If the reference point is at the right-hand end of the horizontal diameter when $t = 0$, then $\theta_0 = 0$ and the motion is described by Eqs. (11–19).

11-5 Motion of a body suspended from a coil spring

Figure 11–7(a) shows a coil spring of force constant k and no-load length l. When a body of mass m is attached to the spring as in part (b), it hangs in equilibrium with the spring extended by an amount Δl such that the upward force P exerted by the spring is equal to the weight of the body, mg. But $P = k \, \Delta l$, so

$$k \, \Delta l = mg.$$

Now suppose the body is at a distance x above its equilibrium position, as in part (c). The extension of the spring is now $\Delta l - x$, the upward force it exerts on the body

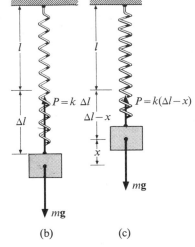

(a)

Fig. 11–7. The restoring force on a body suspended by a spring is proportional to the coordinate measured from the eauilibrium position.

(b)   (c)

is $k(\Delta l - x)$, and the resultant force F on the body is

$$F = k(\Delta l - x) - mg = -kx.$$

The resultant force is therefore proportional to the displacement of the body *from its equilibrium position*, and if set in vertical motion the body oscillates with an angular frequency $\omega = \sqrt{k/m}$.

Except in the idealized case of a spring of zero mass, allowance must be made for the fact that the spring also oscillates. However, we cannot simply add the mass of the spring to that of the suspended body because not all portions of the spring oscillate with the same amplitude; the amplitude at the lower end equals that of the suspended body, while that at the upper end is zero. The correction term can be computed as follows.

Let L represent the length of the spring when the body is in its equilibrium position, and let m_s be the mass of the spring. Let us calculate the kinetic energy of the spring at an instant when the velocity of the lower end is v. Consider an element of the spring of length dy, at a distance y below the fixed upper end. The mass of the element, dm_s, is

$$dm_s = \frac{m_s}{L} dy.$$

All portions of the spring can be assumed to oscillate in phase and the velocity of the element, v_s, is proportional to its distance from the fixed end: $v_s = (y/L)v$.

The kinetic energy of the element is

$$dE_k = \frac{1}{2} \cdot dm_s \cdot v_s^2 = \frac{1}{2} \cdot \frac{m_s}{L} dy \cdot \left(\frac{y}{L} v\right)^2,$$

and the total kinetic energy of the spring is

$$E_k = \frac{1}{2} \cdot \frac{m_s v^2}{L^3} \cdot \int_0^L y^2 \, dy = \frac{1}{2}\left(\frac{1}{3} m_s\right) v^2.$$

This equals the kinetic energy of a body of mass one-third the mass of the spring, moving with the same velocity as that of the suspended body. In other words, the equivalent mass of the *vibrating system* equals that of the suspended body plus one-third the mass of the spring.

EXAMPLE. A body of mass 1 kgm is suspended from a coil spring whose mass is 0.09 kgm and whose force constant is 66 newtons per meter. Find the frequency and amplitude of the ensuing motion if the body is displaced 0.03 m below its equilibrium position and given a downward velocity of 0.4 m/sec. The angular frequency is

$$\omega = \sqrt{\frac{k}{m + m_s/3}} = \sqrt{\frac{66 \text{ n/m}}{1.03 \text{ kgm}}} = 8.00 \frac{\text{rad}}{\text{sec}}.$$

The amplitude is expressed in terms of the initial coordinate and velocity by means of Eq. (11–17). Thus,

$$A = \sqrt{x_0^2 + (v_0/\omega)^2} = \sqrt{(0.03 \text{ m})^2 + (0.4/8 \text{ m})^2} = 0.0582 \text{ m}.$$

11–6 The simple pendulum

A *simple pendulum* (also called a *mathematical pendulum*) is defined as a particle suspended from a fixed point by a weightless, inextensible string. When the pendulum is displaced from the vertical by an angle θ, as in Fig. 11–8, the restoring force is $mg \sin \theta$, and the displacement s from the equilibrium position equals $L\theta$, where L is the length of the string and θ is in radians. The motion is therefore *not* harmonic, since the restoring force is proportional to $\sin \theta$ while the displacement is proportional to θ. However, if the angle θ is small we can approximate $\sin \theta$ by θ, and the restoring force is then

$$F \approx -mg\theta \approx -\left(\frac{mg}{L}\right) s.$$

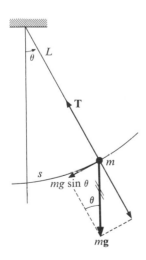

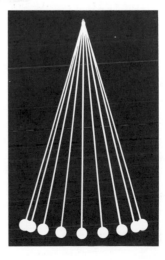

Fig. 11–8. Forces on the bob of a simple pendulum.

Fig. 11–9. A single swing of a simple pendulum.

The effective force constant of the pendulum is therefore $k = mg/L$, and the period is

$$T \approx 2\pi\sqrt{m/k} \approx 2\pi\sqrt{L/g}. \tag{11-20}$$

It can be shown that the exact equation for the period, when the maximum angular displacement is ϕ, is given by the infinite series

$$T = 2\pi\sqrt{\frac{L}{g}}\left(1 + \frac{1^2}{2^2}\sin^2\frac{\phi}{2} + \frac{1^2 \cdot 3^2}{2^2 \cdot 4^2}\sin^4\frac{\phi}{2} + \cdots\right). \tag{11-21}$$

The period can be computed to any desired degree of precision by taking enough terms in the series. When $\phi = 15°$, the true period differs from that given by the approximate equation (11–20) by less than one-half of one percent.

The utility of the pendulum as a timekeeper is based on the fact that the period is practically independent of the amplitude. Thus, as a pendulum clock runs down and the amplitude of the swings becomes slightly smaller, the clock will still keep very nearly correct time.

The simple pendulum is also a precise and convenient method of measuring the acceleration of gravity, g, without actually resorting to free fall, since L and T may readily be measured. More complicated pendulums find considerable application in the field of geophysics. Local deposits of ore or oil, if their density differs from that of their surroundings, affect the local value of g, and precise measurements of this quantity over an area which is being prospected often furnish valuable information regarding the nature of underlying deposits.

Figure 11–9 is a multiflash photograph of a single swing of a simple pendulum.

11-7 Lissajous' figures

The curves known as *Lissajous' figures* are the paths traced out by a particle which is oscillating simultaneously in two mutually perpendicular directions. In general, the amplitude and frequency may be different in the two directions, and the two oscillations may have an arbitrary initial phase difference.

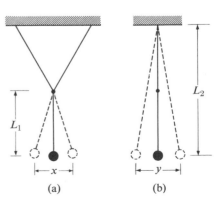

Fig. 11–10. Double pendulum for producing Lissajous' figures.

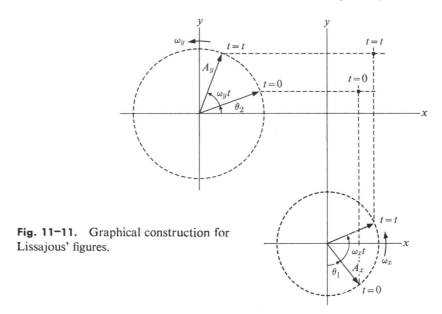

Fig. 11–11. Graphical construction for Lissajous' figures.

The pendulum bob in Fig. 11–10, supported by three cords forming a Y, illustrates one means of producing this type of motion. When vibrating in the x-direction, as in (a), the frequency is that of a simple pendulum of length L_1. In the y-direction the frequency is that of a pendulum of length L_2. If displaced in both the x- and y-directions, and released, the bob executes vibrations of both frequencies simultaneously.

The spot on the screen of a cathode-ray tube, produced by the impact of a rapidly moving stream of electrons, will also move in a Lissajous' figure if sinusoidal alternating voltages are applied simultaneously to the horizontal and vertical deflecting plates.

The general expressions for the x- and y-coordinates of the oscillating particle are

$$x = A_x \sin (\omega_x t + \theta_1), \qquad y = A_y \sin (\omega_y t + \theta_2),$$

where A_x and A_y are the respective amplitudes, ω_x and ω_y the corresponding angular frequencies, and θ_1 and θ_2 the initial phase angles. These are the equations of the path in parametric form.

The equations above are represented graphically by the rotor diagrams of Fig. 11–11. The x-coordinate of the tip of the rotor in the lower diagram gives the x-coordinate of the oscillating particle, and the y-coordinate of the tip of the rotor in the upper diagram gives its y-coordinate. Hence by projecting up, and across, from the tips of these rotors, the position of the particle at any time can be determined. The diagram shows its position at time $t = 0$ and at some arbitrary later time t.

The curves in Fig. 11–12 are a few Lissajous' figures for various frequency ratios and initial phase differences $(\theta_2 - \theta_1)$. The amplitudes A_x and A_y are equal in each case. If the frequencies are commensurable, as in the figures shown, the particle retraces a closed path over and over. If they are not, the path does not close on itself,

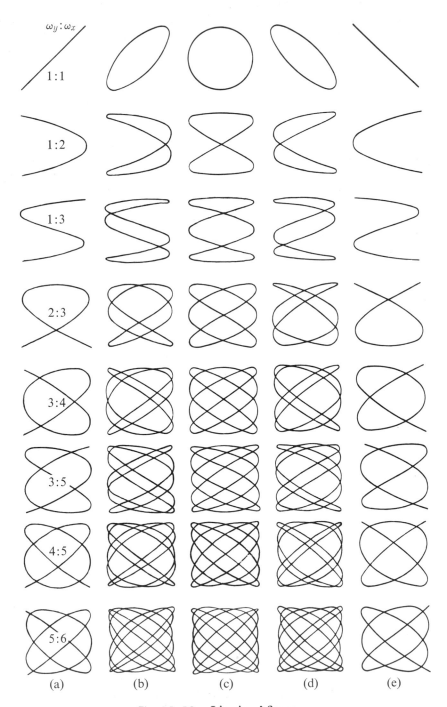

Fig. 11–12.   Lissajous' figures.

and the pattern may be extremely complicated. If the frequencies are very nearly commensurable, the path changes very slowly, and if the motion itself is rapid, as it often is when the figures are formed on an oscilloscope, the impression is that of a closed curve which gradually alters its form. Thus, if the frequencies are very nearly equal ($\omega_x/\omega_y \approx 1$), the path changes slowly from a straight line at 45°, as in Fig. 11–12(a), to an ellipse as in (b), then to a circle as in (c), then to an ellipse as in (d), with its major axis at right angles to that in (b), then to a straight line as in (e), etc.

11-8 Angular harmonic motion

Angular harmonic motion is an exact mathematical analog of linear harmonic motion. Let a body be pivoted about a fixed axis and acted on by a restoring torque Γ proportional to the angular displacement ϕ from some reference position. Then

$$\Gamma = -k'\phi,$$

where the factor k', or the restoring torque per unit of angular displacement, is called the *torque constant*. If frictional torques are negligible, the differential equation of motion is

$$\Gamma = -k'\phi = I\alpha = I\omega \frac{d\omega}{d\phi},$$

or

$$I\omega \frac{d\omega}{d\phi} + k'\phi = 0, \tag{11-22}$$

where I is the moment of inertia about the fixed axis. This equation has exactly the same form as Eq. (11–1): angular displacement ϕ corresponds to linear displacement x, moment of inertia I corresponds to mass m, and the torque constant k' corresponds to the force constant k. By analogy, the equation of motion is

$$\phi = \phi_m \sin (\omega t + \theta_0),$$

where $\omega = \sqrt{k'/I}$, and ϕ_m is the maximum angular displacement or the *angular amplitude*.

The balance wheel of a watch is a common example of a body vibrating with angular harmonic motion. In the ideal case assumed, the motion in isochronous and the watch "keeps time" even though the amplitude decreases as the mainspring unwinds.

11-9 The physical pendulum

In Fig. 11–13, a body of arbitrary shape is pivoted about a fixed axis through O, and the line joining O and the center of gravity is displaced by an angle ϕ from the vertical. Let h represent the distance from the pivot to the center of gravity. The weight mg gives rise to a restoring torque

$$\Gamma = -mgh \sin \phi.$$

When released, the body will oscillate about its equilibrium position but, as in the case of the simple pendulum, the motion is not (angular) harmonic, since the torque Γ is not proportional to ϕ but to $\sin \phi$. However, if ϕ is small, we can approximate sin ϕ by ϕ, and the motion is approximately harmonic. Making this approximation, we get

$$\Gamma \approx -(mgh)\phi,$$

and the effective torque constant, $k' = -\Gamma/\phi$, equals mgh. The angular frequency is

$$\omega \approx \sqrt{k'/I} \approx \sqrt{mgh/I},$$

and the period T is

$$T = \frac{1}{f} = \frac{2\pi}{\omega} \approx 2\pi\sqrt{\frac{I}{mgh}}. \quad (11\text{--}23)$$

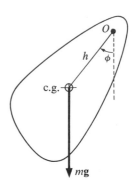

Fig. 11–13. A physical pendulum.

Such a pivoted body is called a *physical pendulum*, as contrasted with the ideal simple pendulum, which is a point mass attached to a weightless cord. Of course, every real pendulum is a physical pendulum.

EXAMPLE. Equation (11–23) may be solved for the moment of inertia I, giving

$$I = \frac{T^2 mgh}{4\pi^2}.$$

The quantities on the right of the equation are all directly measurable. Hence the moment of inertia of a body of any complex shape may be found by suspending the body as a physical pendulum and measuring its period of vibration. The location of the center of gravity can be found by balancing. Since T, m, g, and h are known, I can be computed. For example, Fig. 11–14 illustrates a connecting rod pivoted about a horizontal knife edge. The connecting rod weighs 4 lb and its center of gravity has been found by balancing to be 8 inches below the knife edge. When set into oscillation, it is found to make 100 complete vibrations in 120 sec, so that $T = 120/100 = 1.2$ sec. Therefore

$$I = \frac{(1.2)^2 \text{ sec}^2 \times 4 \text{ lb} \times \frac{2}{3} \text{ ft}}{4\pi^2} = 0.097 \text{ slug·ft}^2.$$

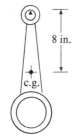

Figure 11–14

11–10 Center of oscillation

It is always possible to find an *equivalent* simple pendulum whose period is equal to that of a given physical pendulum. If L is the length of the equivalent simple pendulum,

$$T = 2\pi\sqrt{\frac{L}{g}} = 2\pi\sqrt{\frac{I}{mgh}}$$

or

$$L = \frac{I}{mh}. \quad (11\text{--}24)$$

Thus, so far as its period of vibration is concerned, the mass of a physical pendulum may be considered to be concentrated at a point whose distance from the pivot is $L = I/mh$. This point is called the *center of oscillation* of the pendulum.

EXAMPLE. A slender uniform rod of length a is pivoted at one end and swings as a physical pendulum. Find the center of oscillation of the pendulum.

The moment of inertia of the rod about an axis through one end is

$$I = \tfrac{1}{3}ma^2.$$

The distance from the pivot to the center of gravity is $h = a/2$. The length of the equivalent simple pendulum is

$$L = \frac{I}{mh} = \frac{\tfrac{1}{3}ma^2}{m(a/2)} = \frac{2}{3}a,$$

and the center of oscillation is at a distance $2a/3$ from the pivot.

Figure 11–15 shows a body pivoted about an axis through O and whose center of oscillation is at point C. The center of oscillation and the point of support have the following interesting property, namely, if the pendulum is pivoted about a new axis through point C its period is unchanged and point O becomes the new center of oscillation. The point of support and the center of oscillation are said to be *conjugate* to each other.

The center of oscillation has another important property. Figure 11–16 shows a baseball bat pivoted at O. If a ball strikes the bat at its center of oscillation, no impulsive force is exerted on the pivot and hence no "sting" is felt if the bat is held at that point. Because of this property, the center of oscillation is called the *center of percussion*.

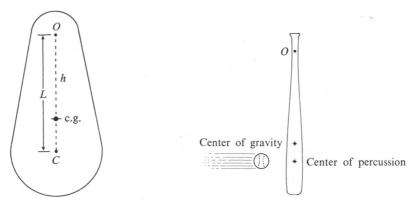

Fig. 11–15. Center of oscillation. The length L equals that of the equivalent simple pendulum.

Fig. 11–16. The center of percussion coincides with the center of oscillation.

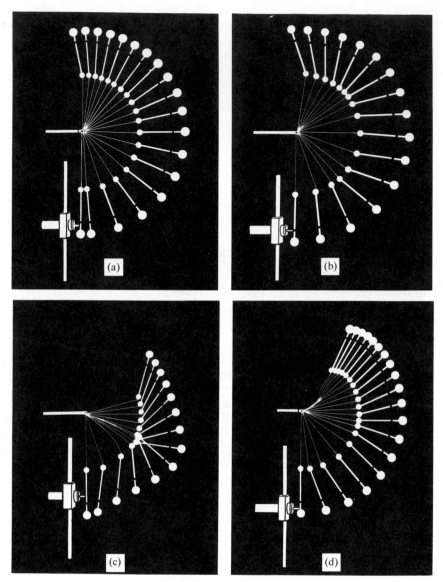

Fig. 11–17. The motion of a body suspended by a cord when the body is struck a horizontal blow.

In Fig. 11–17, a series of multiflash photographs, the *center of gravity* is marked by a black band. In (a), the body is struck at its center of percussion relative to a pivot at the upper end of the cord, and it starts to swing smoothly about this pivot. In (b), the body is struck at its center of gravity. Note that it does not start to rotate about the pivot, but that its initial motion is one of pure translation. That is, the center of percussion does not coincide with the center of gravity. In (c), the body is struck above, and in (d) below its center of percussion.

Problems

11-1. The general equation of simple harmonic motion,

$$y = A \sin (\omega t + \theta_0),$$

can be written in the equivalent form

$$y = B \sin \omega t + C \cos \omega t.$$

(a) Find the expressions for the amplitudes B and C in terms of the amplitude A and the initial phase angle θ_0. (b) Interpret these expressions in terms of a rotating vector diagram.

11-2. A body of mass 0.25 kgm is acted on by an elastic restoring force of force constant $k = 25$ n/m. (a) Construct the graph of elastic potential energy E_p as a function of displacement x, over a range of x from -0.3 m to $+0.3$ m. Let 1 in. = 0.25 joule vertically, and 1 in. = 0.1 m horizontally.

The body is set into oscillation with an initial potential energy of 0.6 joule and an initial kinetic energy of 0.2 joule. Answer the following questions by reference to the graph:

(b) What is the amplitude of oscillation? (c) What is the potential energy when the displacement is one-half the amplitude? (d) At what displacement are the kinetic and potential energies equal? (e) What is the speed of the body at the midpoint of its path? Find (f) the period T, (g) the frequency f, and (h) the angular frequency ω. (i) What is the initial phase angle θ_0 if the amplitude $A = 15$ cm, the initial displacement $x_0 = 7.5$ cm, and the initial velocity v_0 is negative?

11-3. A body is vibrating with simple harmonic motion of amplitude 15 cm and frequency 4 vib/sec. Compute (a) the maximum values of the acceleration and velocity, (b) the acceleration and velocity when the coordinate is 9 cm, (c) the time required to move from the equilibrium position to a point 12 cm distant from it.

11-4. A body of mass 10 gm moves with simple harmonic motion of amplitude

24 cm and period 4 sec. The coordinate is $+24$ cm when $t = 0$. Compute (a) the position of the body when $t = 0.5$ sec, (b) the magnitude and direction of the force acting on the body when $t = 0.5$ sec, (c) the minimum time required for the body to move from its initial position to the point where $x = -12$ cm, (d) the velocity of the body when $x = -12$ cm.

11-5. The motion of the piston of an automobile engine is approximately simple harmonic. (a) If the stroke of an engine (twice the amplitude) is 4 in. and the angular velocity is 3600 rev/min, compute the acceleration of the piston at the end of its stroke. (b) If the piston weighs 1 lb, what resultant force must be exerted on it at this point? (c) What is the velocity of the piston, in mi/hr, at the midpoint of its stroke?

11-6. A body whose weight is 4 lb is suspended from a spring of negligible mass, and is found to stretch the spring 8 in. (a) What is the force constant of the spring? (b) What is the period of oscillation of the body, if pulled down and released? (c) What would be the period of a body weighing 8 lb, hanging from the same spring?

11-7. The scale of a spring balance reading from zero to 32 lb is 6 in. long. A body suspended from the balance is observed to oscillate vertically at 1.5 vib/sec. What is the weight of the body? Neglect the mass of the spring.

11-8. A body weighing 8 lb is attached to a coil spring and oscillates vertically in simple harmonic motion. The amplitude is 2 ft, and at the highest point of the motion the spring has its natural unstretched length. Calculate the elastic potential energy of the spring, the kinetic energy of the body, its gravitational potential energy relative to the lowest point of the motion, and the sum of these three energies, when the body is (a) at its lowest point, (b) at its equilibrium position, and (c) at its highest point.

11–9. A load of 320 lb suspended from a wire whose unstretched length l_0 is 10 ft is found to stretch the wire by 0.12 in. The cross-sectional area of the wire, which can be assumed constant, is 0.016 in². (a) If the load is pulled down a small additional distance and released, find the frequency at which it will vibrate. (b) Compute Young's modulus for the wire.

*11–10. A small block is executing simple harmonic motion in a horizontal plane with an amplitude of 10 cm. At a point 6 cm away from equilibrium the velocity is ±24 cm/sec. (a) What is the period? (b) What is the displacement when the velocity is ±12 cm/sec? (c) If a small object placed on the oscillating block is just on the verge of slipping at the endpoint of the path, what is the coefficient of friction?

11–11. A force of 6 lb stretches a vertical spring 9 in. (a) What weight must be suspended from the spring so that the system will oscillate with a period of $\pi/4$ sec? (b) If the amplitude of the motion is 3 in., where is the body and in what direction is it moving $\pi/12$ sec after it has passed the equilibrium position, moving downward? (c) What force does the spring exert on the body when it is 1.8 in. below the equilibrium position, moving upward?

11–12. A body of mass m is suspended from a coil spring and the time for 100 complete oscillations is measured for the following values of m:

m (gm)	100	200	400	1000
Time of 100 oscil- lations (sec)	23.4	30.6	41.8	64.7

Plot graphs of the measured values of (a) T vs. m, and (b) T^2 vs. m. (c) Are the experimental results in agreement with theory? (d) Is either graph a straight line? (e) Does the straight line pass through the origin? (f) What is the force constant of the spring? (g) What is the mass of the spring?

11–13. A body of mass 100 gm hangs from a long spiral spring. When pulled down 10 cm below its equilibrium position and released, it vibrates with a period of 2 sec. (a) What is its velocity as it passes through the equilibrium position? (b) What is its acceleration when it is 5 cm above the equilibrium position? (c) When it is moving upward, how long a time is required for it to move from a point 5 cm below its equilibrium position to a point 5 cm above it? (d) How much will the spring shorten if the body is removed?

11–14. A body whose mass is 4.9 kgm hangs from a spring and oscillates with a period of 0.5 sec. How much will the spring shorten when the body is removed?

11–15. Four passengers whose combined weight is 600 lb are observed to compress the springs of an automobile by 2 in. when they enter the automobile. If the total load supported by the springs is 1800 lb, find the period of vibration of the loaded automobile.

11–16. (a) A block suspended from a spring vibrates with simple harmonic motion. At an instant when the displacement of the block is equal to one-half the amplitude, what fraction of the total energy of the system is kinetic and what fraction is potential? (b) When the block is in equilibrium, the length of the spring is an amount s greater than in the unstretched state. Prove that $T = 2\pi\sqrt{s/g}$.

11–17. (a) With what additional force must a vertical spring carrying an 8-lb body in equilibrium be stretched so that, when released, it will perform 48 complete oscillations in 32 sec with an amplitude of 3 in.? (b) What force is exerted by the spring on the body when it is at the lowest point, the middle, and the highest point of the path? (c) What is the kinetic energy of the system when the body is 1 in. below the middle of the path? its potential energy?

11–18. A force of 12 lb stretches a certain spring 9 in. A body weighing 8 lb is hung from this spring and allowed to come to rest. It is then pulled down 4 in. and released. (a) What is the period of the motion? (b) What is the magnitude and direction of the acceleration of the body when it is 2 in. above the equilibrium position, moving upward? (c) What is the tension in the spring when the body is 2 in. above the equilibrium position? (d) What is the shortest time required to go from the equilibrium position to the point 2 in. above? (e) If a small object were placed on the oscillating body would it remain or leave? (f) If a small object were placed on the oscillating body and its amplitude doubled, where would the object and the oscillating body begin to separate?

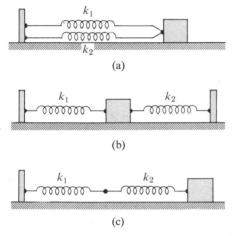

(a)

(b)

(c)

Figure 11–18

11–19. Two springs with different force constants k_1 and k_2 are attached to a block of mass m on a level frictionless surface. Calculate the effective force constant in each of the three cases (a), (b), and (c) depicted in Fig. 11–18. (d) A body of mass m, suspended from a spring with a force constant k, vibrates with a frequency f_1. When the spring is cut in half and the same body is suspended from one of the halves, the frequency is f_2. What is the ratio of f_2/f_1?

11–20. Two springs, each of unstretched length 20 cm but having different force constants k_1 and k_2, are attached to opposite ends of a block of mass m on a level frictionless surface. The outer ends of the springs are now attached to two pins P_1 and P_2, 10 cm from the original positions of the springs. Let $k_1 = 1000$ dynes/cm, $k_2 = 3000$ dynes/cm, $m = 100$ gm. (See Fig. 11–19.) (a) Find the length of each spring when the block is in its new equilibrium position, after the springs have been attached to the pins. (b) Find the period of vibration of the block if it is slightly displaced from its new equilibrium position and released.

11–21. The block in Problem 11–20 and Fig. 11–19 is oscillating with an amplitude of 5 cm. At the instant it passes through its equilibrium position, a lump of putty of mass 100 gm is dropped vertically onto the block and sticks to it. (a) Find the new period and amplitude. (b) Was there a loss of energy and, if so, where did it go? (c) Would the answers be the same if the putty had been dropped on the block when it was at one end of its path?

11–22. A simple pendulum 8 ft long swings with an amplitude of 1 ft. (a) Compute the velocity of the pendulum at its lowest point. (b) Compute its acceleration at the ends of its path.

11–23. Find the length of a simple pendulum whose period is exactly 1 sec at a point where $g = 32.2$ ft/sec^2.

11–24. (a) What is the change dT in the period of a simple pendulum, when the acceleration of gravity changes by dg? (b) What is the fractional change in period, dT/T, in terms of the fractional change dg/g? (c) A pendulum clock which keeps correct time at a point where $g = 980.0$

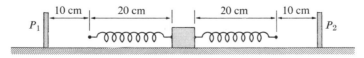

Figure 11–19

cm/sec² is found to lose 10 sec/day at a higher altitude. Use the result of part (b) above to find the value of g at the new location, approximating the differentials dT and dg by the small finite changes in T and g.

(This problem illustrates a useful technique when it is desired to find the new value of a quantity, given a small change in another quantity on which the first depends. It enables one to compute the *change* in the quantity instead of computing the new value directly. To compute the new value of g directly to within 0.1 cm/ sec², computations must be carried out to four significant figures, which is beyond the precision of an ordinary slide rule and requires the use of 4-place logarithms, or longhand multiplication and division. The *change* in g, on the other hand, is readily computed to within 0.1 cm/sec² on a small slide rule.)

11–25. A simple pendulum with a supporting steel wire of cross-sectional area 0.01 cm² is observed to have a period of 2 sec when a 10-kgm lead bob is used. The lead bob is replaced by an aluminum bob of the same dimensions having a mass of 2 kgm, and the period is remeasured. (a) What was the length of the pendulum with the lead bob? (b) By what fraction is the period changed when the aluminum bob is used? Is it an increase or decrease? [*Hint.* Use differentials.]

11–26. The balance wheel of a watch vibrates with an angular amplitude of π radians and with a period of 0.5 sec. (a) Find its maximum angular velocity. (b) Find its angular velocity when its displacement is one-half its amplitude. (c) Find its angular acceleration when its displacement is 45°.

11–27. A monkey wrench is pivoted at one end and allowed to swing as a physical pendulum. The period is 0.9 sec and the pivot is 6 inches from the center of gravity. (a) What is the radius of gyration of the wrench about an axis through the pivot? (b) If the wrench was initially displaced 0.1 radian from its equilibrium position,

what is the angular velocity of the wrench as it passes through the equilibrium position?

11–28. It is shown in textbooks on mechanics that the moment of inertia I of a body about *any* axis through any point is given by

$$I = I_G + mh^2,$$

where I_G is the moment of inertia about a *parallel axis* through the center of gravity, m is the mass, and h is the perpendicular distance between the two parallel axes.

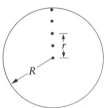

Figure 11–20

A solid disk of radius $R = 12$ cm oscillates as a physical pendulum about an axis perpendicular to the plane of the disk at a distance r from its center. (See Fig. 11–20.) (a) Calculate the period of oscillation (for small amplitudes) for the following values of r: 0, $R/4$, $R/2$, $3R/4$, R. (b) Let T_0 represent the period when $r = R$, and T the period at any other value of r. Construct a graph of the dimensionless ratio T/T_0 as a function of the dimensionless ratio r/R. (Note that the graph then describes the behavior of *any* solid disk, whatever its radius.) (c) Prove by the methods of calculus that the period is a minimum when $r = R/\sqrt{2}$. Does this result agree with your graph?

11–29. It is desired to construct a pendulum of period 10 sec. (a) What is the length of a *simple* pendulum having this period? (b) Suppose the pendulum must be mounted in a case not over 2 ft high. Can you devise a pendulum, having a period of 10 sec, that will satisfy this requirement?

11–30. A meter stick hangs from a horizontal axis at one end and oscillates as a physical pendulum. A body of small dimensions, and of mass equal to that of the meter stick, can be clamped to the stick at a distance h below the axis. Let T represent the period of the system with the body attached, and T_0 the period of the meter stick alone. Find the ratio T/T_0, (a) when $h = 50$ cm, (b) when $h = 100$ cm. (c) Is there any value of h for which $T = T_0$? If so, find it and explain why the period is unchanged when h has this value.

11–31. A meter stick is pivoted at one end. At what distance below the pivot should it be struck in order that it start swinging smoothly about the pivot?

center of percussion

CHAPTER 12

Hydrostatics

12-1 Introduction

The term "hydrostatics" is applied to the study of fluids at rest, and "hydrodynamics" to fluids in motion. The special branch of hydrodynamics relating to the flow of gases and of air in particular is called "aerodynamics."

A fluid is a substance which can flow. Hence the term includes both liquids and gases. Liquids and gases differ markedly in their compressibilities; a gas is easily compressed, while a liquid is practically incompressible. The small volume changes of a liquid under pressure can usually be neglected in this part of the subject.

The density of a homogeneous material is defined as its mass per unit volume. Units of density in the three systems are 1 kgm/m^3, 1 gm/cm^3, and 1 slug/ft^3. We shall represent density by the greek letter ρ (rho).

$$\rho = \frac{m}{V}, \qquad m = \rho V. \tag{12-1}$$

For example, the weight of 1 cubic foot of water is 62.5 lb; its density is $62.5/32.2 = 1.94$ slugs per cubic foot. Typical values of density at room temperature are given in Table 12-1.

TABLE 12-1

DENSITIES

Material	Density, gm/cm^3	Material	Density, gm/cm^3
Aluminum	2.7	Silver	10.5
Brass	8.6	Steel	7.8
Copper	8.9	Mercury	13.6
Gold	19.3	Ethyl alcohol	0.81
Ice	0.92	Benzene	0.90
Iron	7.8	Glycerine	1.26
Lead	11.3	Water	1.00
Platinum	21.4		

The *specific gravity* of a material is the ratio of its density to that of water and is therefore a pure number. "Specific gravity" is an exceedingly poor term, since it has nothing to do with gravity. "Relative density" would describe the concept more precisely.

12–2 Pressure in a fluid

When the concept of hydrostatic pressure was introduced in Section 10–1, the weight of the fluid was neglected and the pressure was assumed the same at all points. It is a familiar fact, however, that atmospheric pressure decreases with increasing altitude and that the pressure in a lake or in the ocean decreases with increasing distance from the bottom. We therefore generalize the definition of pressure and define the pressure *at any point* as the ratio of the normal force dF exerted on a small area dA including the point, to the area dA.

$$p = \frac{dF}{dA}, \quad dF = p\,dA. \tag{12–2}$$

If the pressure is the same at all points of a finite plane surface of area A, these equations reduce to Eq. (10–3),

$$p = \frac{F}{A}, \quad F = pA.$$

Let us find the general relation between the pressure p at any point in a fluid and the elevation of the point, y. If the fluid is in equilibrium, every volume element is in equilibrium. Consider an element in the form of a thin slab, shown in Fig. 12–1, whose thickness is dy and whose faces have an area A. If ρ is the density of the fluid, the mass of the element is $\rho A\,dy$ and its weight dw is $\rho g A\,dy$. The force exerted on the element by the surrounding fluid is everywhere normal to its surface. By symmetry, the resultant horizontal force on its rim is zero. The upward force on its lower

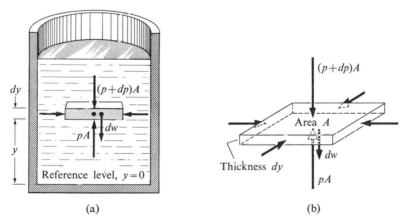

(a)   (b)

Fig. 12–1.   Forces on an element of fluid in equilibrium.

face is pA, and the downward force on its upper face is $(p + dp)A$. Since it is in equilibrium,

$$\Sigma F_y = 0,$$

$$pA - (p + dp)A - \rho gA\, dy = 0,$$

or

$$\boxed{\frac{dp}{dy} = -\rho g.}$$ (12–3)

Since ρ and g are both positive quantities it follows that a positive dy (an increase of elevation) is accompanied by a negative dp (decrease of pressure). If p_1 and p_2 are the pressures at elevations y_1 and y_2 above some reference level, then integration of Eq. (12–3), when ρ and g are constant, gives

$$p_2 - p_1 = -\rho g(y_2 - y_1).$$

Let us apply this equation to a liquid in an open vessel, such as that shown in Fig. 12–2. Take point 1 at any level and let p represent the pressure at this point. Take point 2 at the top where the pressure is atmospheric pressure, p_a. Then

$$p_a - p = -\rho g(y_2 - y_1),$$
$$p = p_a + \rho gh.$$ (12–4)

Notice that the shape of the containing vessel does not affect the pressure, and that the pressure is the same at all points at the same depth. It also follows from Eq. (12–4) that if the pressure p_a is increased in any way, say by inserting a piston on the top surface and pressing down on it, the pressure p at any depth must increase by exactly the same amount. This fact was stated by the French scientist Blaise Pascal (1623–1662) in 1653 and is called "Pascal's law." It is often stated: "*Pressure applied to an enclosed fluid is transmitted undiminished to every portion of the fluid*

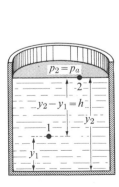

Figure 12–2

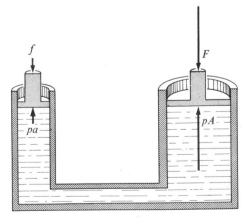

Fig. 12–3. Principle of the hydraulic press.

and the walls of the containing vessel." We can see now that it is not an independent principle but a necessary consequence of the laws of mechanics.

Pascal's law is illustrated by the operation of a hydraulic press, shown in Fig. 12–3. A piston of small cross-sectional area a is used to exert a small force f directly on a liquid such as oil. The pressure $p = f/a$ is transmitted through the connecting pipe to a larger cylinder equipped with a larger piston of area A. Since the pressure is the same in both cylinders,

$$p = \frac{f}{a} = \frac{F}{A} \quad \text{and} \quad F = \frac{A}{a} \times f.$$

It follows that the hydraulic press is a force-multiplying device with a multiplication factor equal to the ratio of the areas of the two pistons. Barber chairs, dentist chairs, car lifts, and hydraulic brakes are all devices that make use of the principle of the hydraulic press.

12–3 The hydrostatic paradox

If a number of vessels of different shapes are interconnected as in Fig. 12–4(a), it will be found that a liquid poured into them will stand at the same level in each. Before the principles of hydrostatics were completely understood, this seemed a very puzzling phenomenon and was called the "hydrostatic paradox." It would appear at first sight, for example, that vessel C should develop a greater pressure at its base than should B, and hence that liquid would be forced from C into B.

Equation (12–4), however, states that the pressure depends only on the depth below the liquid surface and not at all on the shape of the containing vessel. Since the depth of the liquid is the same in each vessel, the pressure at the base of each is the same and hence the system is in equilibrium.

A more detailed explanation may be helpful in understanding the situation. Consider vessel C in Fig. 12–4(b). The forces exerted against the liquid by the walls are shown by arrows, the force being everywhere perpendicular to the walls of the vessel. The inclined forces at the sloping walls may be resolved into horizontal and vertical components. The weight of the liquid in the sections lettered A is supported by the vertical components of these forces. Hence the pressure at the base of the vessel is due only to the weight of the liquid in the cylindrical column B. Any vessel, regardless of its shape, may be treated the same way.

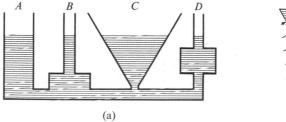
(a)

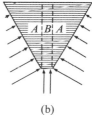
(b)

Fig. 12–4. (a) The hydrostatic paradox. The top of the liquid stands at the same level in each vessel. (b) Forces on the liquid in vessel C.

12–4 Pressure gauges

The simplest type of pressure gauge is the open-tube manometer, illustrated in Fig. 12–5(a). It consists of a U-shaped tube containing a liquid, one end of the tube being at the pressure p which it is desired to measure, while the other end is open to the atmosphere.

The pressure at the bottom of the left column is $p + \rho g y_1$, while that at the bottom of the right column is $p_a + \rho g y_2$, where ρ is the density of the manometric liquid. Since these pressures both refer to the same point, it follows that

$$p + \rho g y_1 = p_a + \rho g y_2,$$

and

$$p - p_a = \rho g(y_2 - y_1) = \rho g h.$$

The pressure p is called the *absolute pressure*, whereas the difference $p - p_a$ between this and the atmospheric pressure is called the *gauge pressure*. It is seen that the gauge pressure is proportional to the difference in height of the liquid columns.

The mercury barometer is a long glass tube that has been filled with mercury and then inverted in a dish of mercury, as shown in Fig. 12–5(b). The space above the mercury column contains only mercury vapor, whose pressure, at room temperature, is so small that it may be neglected. It is easily seen that

$$p_a = \rho g(y_2 - y_1) = \rho g h.$$

Because mercury manometers and barometers are used so frequently in laboratories, it is customary to express atmospheric pressure and other pressures as so many "inches of mercury" or "centimeters of mercury." An "inch of mercury," however, is *not* a real unit of pressure, since pressure is the ratio of force to area.

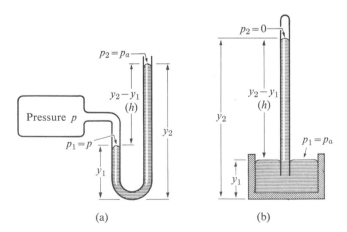

(a)   (b)

Fig. 12–5. (a) The open-tube manometer. (b) The barometer.

EXAMPLE. Compute the atmospheric pressure on a day when the height of the barometer is 76.0 cm.

The height of the mercury column depends on ρ and g as well as on the atmospheric pressure. Hence both the density of mercury and the local acceleration of gravity must be known. The density varies with the temperature, and g with the latitude and elevation above sea level. All accurate barometers are provided with a thermometer and with a table or chart from which corrections for temperature and elevation can be found. If we assume $g = 980$ cm/sec^2 and $\rho = 13.6$ gm/cm^3,

$$p_a = \rho g h = 13.6\,\frac{gm}{cm^3} \times 980\,\frac{cm}{sec^2} \times 76\,cm$$

$$= 1{,}013{,}000\ dynes/cm^2.$$

(About a million dynes per square centimeter.)

In English units,

$$76\ cm = 30\ in. = 2.5\ ft,$$
$$\rho g = 850\ lb/ft^3,$$
$$p_a = 2120\ lb/ft^2 = 14.7\ lb/in^2.$$

A pressure of 1.013×10^6 dynes/cm^2 = 1.013×10^5 newtons/m^2 = 14.7 lb/in^2, is called *one atmosphere*. A pressure of exactly one million dynes per square centimeter is called one *bar*, and a pressure one one-thousandth as great is one *millibar*. Atmospheric pressures are of the order of 1000 millibars, and are now stated in terms of this unit by the United States Weather Bureau.

The Bourdon type pressure gauge is more convenient for most purposes than a liquid manometer. It consists of a flattened brass tube closed at one end and bent into a circular form. The closed end of the tube is connected by a gear and pinion to a pointer which moves over a scale. The open end of the tube is connected to the apparatus, the pressure within which is to be measured. When pressure is exerted within the flattened tube it straightens slightly, just as a bent rubber hose straightens when water is admitted. The resulting motion of the closed end of the tube is transmitted to the pointer.

12–5 Vacuum pumps

Many of the devices of modern life consist of glass or metal tubes from which practically all the air has been exhausted. Among these are, for example, electric light bulbs, radio tubes, cathode-ray oscilloscopes, photoelectric cells, x-ray tubes, and many others. These devices could not have been developed if means had not been available for producing high vacua. It is therefore important to learn how pressures as low as 10^{-8} mm of mercury are obtained. Of all the pumps that have been developed, two are particularly important in physics laboratories: the *rotary oil pump* for pressures as low as 10^{-4} mm of mercury, and the *mercury or oil diffusion pump* for pressures as low as 10^{-8} mm of mercury.

Figure 12–6 depicts schematically a type of rotary oil pump in common use in the United States. The vessel to be exhausted is connected to the tube A, which communicates directly with the space marked B. As an eccentric cylinder C rotates in the direction shown, the point of contact between it and the inner walls of the stationary cylinder moves around in a clockwise direction, thereby trapping some air in the space marked E. The sliding vane D is kept in contact with the rotating cylinder by the pressure of the rod F. When the air in E is compressed enough to increase the pressure slightly above atmospheric, the valve G opens and the air bubbles through the oil and leaves through an opening H in the upper plate. The cylinder is caused to rotate by means of a small electric motor.

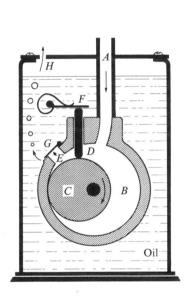

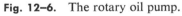

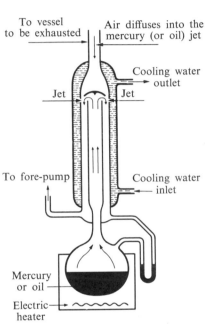

Fig. 12–6.   The rotary oil pump.   **Fig. 12–7.**   The diffusion pump.

To reduce the pressure below about 10^{-3} or 10^{-4} mm of mercury, a diffusion pump is usually employed. In this pump a rapidly moving jet of mercury or of a special oil of extremely low vapor pressure (octoil, butyl phthallate, etc.) sweeps or pushes the air molecules away from the vessel to be exhausted. Air molecules from the vessel keep diffusing into the jet. There are many types and sizes on the market, some of glass and some of metal; some vertical, some horizontal; some with water cooling and some with air cooling; some with one jet and some with multiple jets. A common type is depicted in Fig. 12–7.

A rotary oil pump is used to reduce the pressure within the diffusion pump to the low value necessary to ensure a well-defined jet in which there are fewer air molecules per unit of volume than in the vessel to be exhausted. Otherwise, air molecules might diffuse from the jet to the vessel. The air molecules that diffuse into the jet are eventually removed by the oil pump (called in this case the fore-pump) and the mercury or oil is condensed on the cool walls of the pump and returns to the well at the bottom.

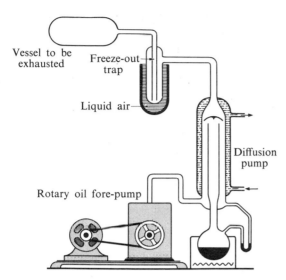

Vessel to be exhausted

Freeze-out trap

Liquid air

Diffusion pump

Rotary oil fore-pump

Fig. 12–8. Typical pumping assembly for the production of a high vacuum.

If a liquid air trap is placed between the diffusion pump and the vessel to be exhausted to condense water vapor and other undesirable vapors, and the walls of the vessel are heated to drive out adsorbed gas (outgassing operation), the pressure in the vessel may be reduced to a value as low as 10^{-8} mm of mercury. A typical pumping assembly is depicted in Fig. 12–8.

12–6 Archimedes' principle

The irregular outline in Fig. 12–9 represents an imaginary surface bounding an arbitrary portion of a fluid at rest. The short arrows represent the forces exerted by the surrounding fluid against small elements of the boundary surface of equal area dA. The force dF against each element is normal to that element and equal to pdA, where p depends only on the vertical depth below the free surface and not on the shape or orientation of the boundary surface.

Since the entire fluid is at rest, the x-component of the resultant of these surface forces is zero. The y-component of the resultant, F_y, must equal the weight of the fluid inside the arbitrary surface, mg, and its line of action must pass through the center of gravity of this fluid.

Now suppose that the fluid inside the surface is removed and replaced by a solid body having exactly the same shape. The pressure at every point will be exactly the same as before, so the force exerted on the body by the surrounding fluid will be unaltered. That is, *the fluid exerts on the body an upward force F_y which is equal to the weight mg of the fluid originally occupying the boundary surface and whose line of action passes through the original center of gravity.*

The submerged body, in general, will *not* be in equilibrium. Its weight may be greater or less than F_y, and if it is not homogeneous, its center of gravity may not lie on the line of F_y. Therefore, in general, it will be acted on by a resultant force through its own center of gravity and by a couple, and will rise or fall and also rotate.

The fact that a body immersed in a fluid should be "buoyed up" with a force equal to the weight of the displaced fluid was deduced by Archimedes (287–212 B.C.) from reasoning along the same lines as above. It is called *Archimedes' principle* and is, of course, a consequence of Newton's laws and the properties of a fluid. The position of the line of action of the upward force, usually omitted from a statement of the principle, is equal in importance to the magnitude of the force.

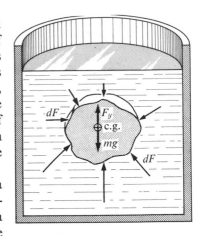

Fig. 12–9. Archimedes' principle. The buoyant force F_y equals the weight of the displaced fluid.

The weight of a dirigible floating in air, or of a submarine floating at some depth below the surface of the water, is just equal to the weight of a volume of air, or water, that is equal to the volume of the dirigible or submarine. That is, the average density of the dirigible equals that of air, and the average density of the submarine equals the density of water.

A body whose average density is less than that of a liquid can float *partially* submerged at the free upper surface of the liquid. However, we not only want a ship to float, but to float upright in stable equilibrium without capsizing. This requires that normally the line of action of the buoyant force should pass through the center of gravity of the ship and also, when the ship heels, the couple set up by its weight and the buoyant force should be in such a direction as to right it.

When making "weighings" with a sensitive analytical balance, correction must be made for the buoyant force of the air if the density of the body being "weighed" is very different from that of the standard "weights," which are usually of brass. For example, suppose a block of wood of density 0.4 gm/cm³ is balanced on an equal-arm balance by brass "weights" of 20 gm, density 8.0 gm/cm³. The apparent weight of each body is the difference between its true weight and the buoyant force of the air. If ρ_w, ρ_b, and ρ_a are the densities of the wood, brass, and air, and V_w and V_b are the volumes of the wood and brass, the apparent weights, which are equal, are

$$\rho_w V_w g - \rho_a V_w g = \rho_b V_b g - \rho_a V_b g.$$

The true mass of the wood is $\rho_w V_w$, and the true mass of the standard is $\rho_b V_b$. Hence,

$$\text{True mass} = \rho_w V_w = \rho_b V_b + \rho_a(V_w - V_b)$$
$$= \text{mass of standard} + \rho_a(V_w - V_b).$$

In the specific example cited

$$V_w = \frac{20}{0.4} = 50 \text{ cm}^3 \text{ (very nearly)},$$

$$V_b = \frac{20}{8} = 2.5 \text{ cm}^3, \qquad \rho_a = 0.0013 \text{ gm/cm}^3.$$

Hence $\rho_a(V_w - V_b) = 0.0013 \times 47.5 = 0.062$ gm.

$$\text{True mass} = 20.062 \text{ gm.}$$

If measurements are being made to one one-thousandth of a gram, it is obvious that the correction of 62 thousandths is of the greatest importance.

EXAMPLE.   A tank containing water is placed on a spring scale, which registers a total weight W. A stone of weight w is hung from a string and lowered into the water without touching the sides or bottom of the tank [Fig. 12–10(a)]. What will be the reading on the spring scale?

First, for the stone alone, the forces are as shown in Fig. 12–10(b), where B is the buoyant force and T is the tension in the string. Since $\sum F_y = 0$,

$$T + B = w.$$

Next, for the tank with the water and stone in it, the forces are as shown in Fig. 12–10(c), where S is the force exerted by the spring scale on the isolated system and, by Newton's third law, is equal in magnitude and opposite in direction to the force exerted on the scale. The condition for equilibrium yields the equation

$$T + S = w + W.$$

Subtracting the first equation from the second, we get

$$S = W + B.$$

That is, the reading of the spring scale has been increased by an amount equal to the buoyant force.

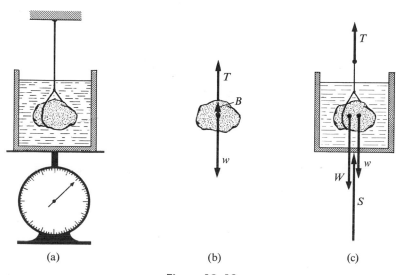

(a)   (b)   (c)

Figure 12–10

12-7 Forces against a dam

Water stands at a depth H behind the vertical upstream face of a dam (Fig. 12–11). It exerts a certain resultant horizontal force on the dam, tending to slide it along its foundation, and a certain moment tending to overturn the dam about the point O. We wish to find the horizontal force and its moment.

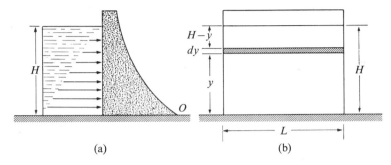

Fig. 12–11.   Forces on a dam.

Figure 12–12(b) is a view of the upstream face of the dam. The pressure at an elevation y is

$$p = \rho g(H - y).$$

(Atmospheric pressure can be omitted, since it also acts upstream against the other face of the dam.) The force against the shaded strip is

$$dF = p \, dA = \rho g(H - y) \times L \, dy.$$

The total force is

$$F = \int dF = \int_0^H \rho g L(H - y) \, dy = \tfrac{1}{2}\rho g L H^2.$$

The moment of the force dF about an axis through O is

$$d\Gamma = y \, dF = \rho g L y (H - y) \, dy.$$

The total torque about O is

$$\Gamma = \int d\Gamma = \int_0^H \rho g L y (H - y) \, dy$$
$$= \tfrac{1}{6}\rho g L H^3.$$

If $\overline{H}$ is the height above O at which the total force F would have to act to produce this torque,

$$F\overline{H} = \tfrac{1}{2}\rho g L H^2 \times \overline{H} = \tfrac{1}{6}\rho g L H^3,$$
$$\overline{H} = \tfrac{1}{3}H.$$

Hence the line of action of the resultant force is at $1/3$ of the depth above O, or at $2/3$ of the depth below the surface.

Problems

12–1. The piston of a hydraulic automobile lift is 12 inches in diameter. What pressure, in lb/in^2, is required to lift a car weighing 2400 lb?

12–2. The expansion tank of a household hot-water heating system is open to the atmosphere and is 30 ft above a pressure gauge attached to the furnace. What is the gauge pressure at the furnace, in lb/in^2?

12–3. Why can't a skin diver obtain an air supply at any desired depth by breathing through a "snorkel," a tube connected to his face mask and having its upper end above the water surface?

12–4. Suppose the door of a room makes an airtight but frictionless fit in its frame. Do you think you could open the door if the air pressure on one side were standard atmospheric pressure and that on the other side differed from standard by one percent?

12–5. The liquid in the open-tube manometer in Fig. 12–5(a) is mercury, and $y_1 = 3$ cm, $y_2 = 8$ cm. Atmospheric pressure is 970 millibars. (a) What is the absolute pressure at the bottom of the U-tube? (b) What is the absolute pressure in the open tube, at a depth of 5 cm below the free surface? (c) What is the absolute pressure of the gas in the tank? (d) What is the gauge pressure of the gas, in "cm of mercury"? (e) What is the gauge pressure in "cm of water"?

Figure 12–12

12–6. (a) A small test tube, partially filled with water, is inverted in a large jar of water and floats as shown in Fig. 12–12.

The lower end of the test tube is open and the top of the large jar is covered by a tightly fitting rubber membrane. When the membrane is pressed down the test tube sinks, and when the membrane is released it rises again. Explain. (A hollow glass figure in human form is often used instead of the test tube, and is called a "Cartesian diver.") (b) A torpedoed ship sinks below the surface of the ocean. If the depth is sufficiently great, is it possible for the ship to remain suspended in equilibrium at some point above the ocean bottom?

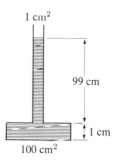

Figure 12–13

12–7. A tube 1 cm^2 in cross section is attached to the top of a vessel 1 cm high and of cross section 100 cm^2. Water is poured into the system, filling it to a depth of 100 cm above the bottom of the vessel, as in Fig. 12–13. (a) What is the force exerted by the water against the bottom of the vessel? (b) What is the weight of the water in the system? (c) Explain why (a) and (b) are not equal.

12–8. A piece of gold-aluminum alloy weighs 10 lb. When suspended from a spring balance and submerged in water, the balance reads 8 lb. What is the weight of gold in the alloy if the specific gravity of gold is 19.3 and the specific gravity of aluminum is 2.5?

12–9. What is the area of the smallest block of ice 1 ft thick that will just support a man weighing 180 lb? The specific gravity of the ice is 0.917, and it is floating in fresh water.

12–10. A cubical block of wood 10 cm on a side floats at the interface between oil and water as in Fig. 12–14, with its lower surface 2 cm below the interface. The density of the oil is 0.6 gm/cm^3. (a) What is the mass of the block? (b) What is the gauge pressure at the lower face of the block?

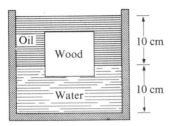

Figure 12–14

12–11. The densities of air, helium, and hydrogen (at standard conditions) are, respectively, 0.00129 gm/cm^3, 0.000178 gm/cm^3, and 0.0000899 gm/cm^3. What is the volume in cubic feet displaced by a hydrogen-filled dirigible which has a total "lift" of 10 tons? What would be the "lift" if helium were used instead of hydrogen?

✳ 12–12. A piece of wood is 2 ft long, 1 ft wide, and 2 inches thick. Its specific gravity is 0.6. What volume of lead must be fastened underneath to sink the wood in calm water so that its top is just even with the water level?

12–13. A cubical block of wood 10 cm on a side and of density 0.5 gm/cm^3 floats in a jar of water. Oil of density 0.8 gm/cm^3 is poured on the water until the top of the oil layer is 4 cm below the top of the block. (a) How deep is the oil layer? (b) What is the gauge pressure at the lower face of the block?

12–14. A cubical block of steel (density = 7.8 gm/cm^3) floats on mercury (density = 13.6 gm/cm^3). (a) What fraction of the block is above the mercury surface? (b) If water is poured on the mercury surface, how deep must the water

layer be so that the water surface just rises to the top of the steel block?

12–15. Block A in Fig. 12–15 hangs by a cord from spring balance D and is submerged in a liquid C contained in beaker B. The weight of the beaker is 2 lb, the weight of the liquid is 3 lb. Balance D reads 5 lb and balance E reads 15 lb. The volume of block A is 0.1 ft^3. (a) What is the weight per unit volume of the liquid? (b) What will each balance read if block A is pulled up out of the liquid?

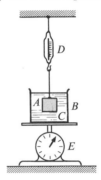

Figure 12–15

✳ 12–16. A hollow sphere of inner radius 9 cm and outer radius 10 cm floats half submerged in a liquid of specific gravity 0.8. (a) Calculate the density of the material of which the sphere is made. (b) What would be the density of a liquid in which the hollow sphere would just float completely submerged?

12–17. Two spherical bodies having the same diameter are released simultaneously from the same height. If the mass of one is ten times that of the other and if the air resistance on each is the *same*, show that the heavier body will arrive at the ground first.

12–18. When a life preserver having a volume of 0.75 ft^3 is immersed in sea water (specific gravity 1.1) it will just support a 160-lb man (specific gravity 1.2) with 2/10 of his volume above water. What is the weight per unit volume of the material composing the life preserver?

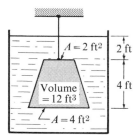

Figure 12–16

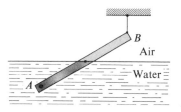

Figure 12–17

12–19. An object in the shape of a truncated cone weighs 1000 lb in vacuum and is suspended by a rope in an open tank of liquid density 2 slugs/ft^3, as in Fig. 12–16. (a) Find the total downward force exerted by the liquid on the top of the object, of area 2 ft^2. (b) Find the total upward force exerted by the liquid on the bottom of the object, of area 4 ft^2. (c) Find the tension in the cord supporting the object.

12–20. A hollow cylindrical can 20 cm in diameter floats in water with 10 cm of its height above the water line when a 10-kgm iron block hangs from its bottom. If the block is now placed inside the can, how much of the cylinder's height will be above the water line? The density of iron is 7.8 gm/cm^3.

12–21. A block of balsa wood placed in one scale pan of an equal-arm balance is found to be exactly balanced by a 100-gm brass "weight" in the other scale pan. Find the true mass of the balsa wood, if its specific gravity is 0.15.

12–22. A 3200-lb cylindrical can buoy floats vertically in salt water (specific gravity = 1.03). The diameter of the buoy is 3 ft. Calculate (a) the additional distance the buoy will sink when a 150-lb man stands on top, (b) the period of the resulting vertical simple harmonic motion when the man dives off.

12–23. A uniform rod AB, 12 ft long, weighing 24 lb, is supported at end B by a flexible cord and weighted at end A with a 12-lb lead weight. The rod floats as shown in Fig. 12–17 with one-half its length sub-

merged. The buoyant force on the lead weight can be neglected. (a) Show in a diagram all the forces acting on the rod. (b) Find the tension in the cord. (c) Find the total volume of the rod.

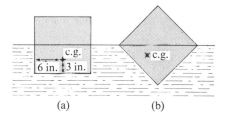

(a)   (b)

Figure 12–18

12–24. A cubical block of wood 1 ft on a side is weighted so that its center of gravity is at the point shown in Fig. 12–18(a), and it floats in water with one-half its volume submerged. Compute the restoring torque when the block is "heeled" at an angle of 45° as in Fig. 12–18(b).

12–25. A hydrometer consists of a spherical bulb and a cylindrical stem of cross section 0.4 cm^2. The total volume of bulb and stem is 13.2 cm^3. When immersed in water the hydrometer floats with 8 cm of the stem above the water surface. In alcohol, 1 cm of the stem is above the surface. Find the density of the alcohol.

12–26. A 12-lb uniform rod 6 ft long, whose specific gravity is 0.50, is hinged at one end 3 ft below a water surface, as in Fig. 12–19. (a) What weight w must be attached to the other end of the rod so that 5 ft of the rod are submerged? (b) Find the magnitude and direction of the force exerted by the hinge on the rod.

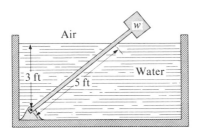

Figure 12–19

12–27. The following is quoted from a letter. How would you reply?

"It is the practice of carpenters hereabouts, when laying out and leveling up the foundations of relatively long buildings, to use a garden hose filled with water, into the ends of the hose being thrust glass tubes 10–12 inches long.

"The theory is that the water, seeking a common level, will be of the same height in both the tubes and thus effect a level. Now the question rises as to what happens if a bubble of air is left in the hose. Our greybeards contend the air will not affect the reading from one end to the other. Others say that it will cause important inaccuracies.

"Can you give a relatively simple answer to this question, together with an explanation? I include a rough sketch (Fig. 12–20) of the situation that caused the dispute."

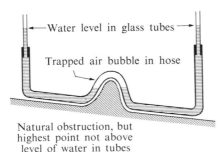

Figure 12–20

12–28. A swimming pool measures 75 × 25 × 8 ft deep. Compute the force exerted by the water against either end and against the bottom.

12–29. The upper edge of a vertical gate in a dam lies along the water surface. The gate is 6 ft wide and is hinged along the bottom edge, which is 10 ft below the water surface. What is the torque about the hinge?

12–30. The upper edge of a gate in a dam runs along the water surface. The gate is 6 ft high and 10 ft wide and is hinged along a horizontal line through its center. Calculate the torque about the hinge.

12–31. The cross section of a certain dam is a rectangle 10 ft wide and 20 ft high. The depth of water behind the dam is 20 ft and the dam is 500 ft long. (a) What is the torque tending to overturn the dam about the bottom edge of the downstream face? (b) If the material of the dam weighs 100 lb/ft^3, show whether or not the restoring torque due to the weight of the dam is greater than the torque due to water pressure.

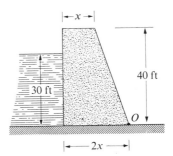

Figure 12–21

12–32. Figure 12–21 is a cross-sectional view of a masonry dam whose length perpendicular to the diagram is 100 ft. The depth of water behind the dam is 30 ft. The masonry of which the dam is constructed weighs 150 lb/ft^3. Water weighs 62.5 lb/ft^3, but for an order-of-magnitude calculation this may be rounded off to 60 lb/ft^3. (a) Find the dimensions x and $2x$, if the weight of the dam is to be 10 times as great as the horizontal force exerted on it by the water. (b) Is the dam then stable with respect to its overturning about the edge through point O? (c) How does the size of the reservoir behind the dam affect the answers above?

12–33. A U-tube of length l (see Fig. 12–22) contains a liquid. What is the difference in height between the liquid columns in the vertical arms (a) if the tube has an acceleration a toward the right, and (b) if the tube is mounted on a horizontal turntable rotating with an angular velocity ω, with one of the vertical arms on the axis of rotation? (c) Explain why the difference in height does not depend on the density of the liquid, or on the cross-sectional area of the tube. Would it be the same if the

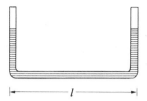

Figure 12–22

vertical tubes did not have equal cross sections? Would it be the same if the horizontal portion were tapered from one end to the other?

CHAPTER 13

Surface Tension

13–1 Surface tension

A liquid flowing slowly from the tip of a medicine dropper emerges, not as a continuous stream, but as a succession of drops. A sewing needle, if placed carefully on a water surface, makes a small depression in the surface and rests there without sinking, even though its density may be as much as ten times that of water. When a clean glass tube of small bore is dipped into water, the water rises in the tube, but if the tube is dipped in mercury, the mercury is depressed. All these phenomena, and many others of a similar nature, are associated with the existence of a *boundary surface* between a liquid and some other substance.

All surface phenomena indicate that the surface of a liquid can be considered to be in a state of stress such that if one considers any line lying in or bounding the surface, the material on either side of the line exerts a pull on the material on the other side. This pull lies in the plane of the surface and is perpendicular to the line. The effect can be demonstrated with the simple apparatus shown in Fig. 13–1. A wire ring a few inches in diameter has attached to it a loop of thread, as shown. When the ring and thread are dipped in a soap solution and removed, a thin film of liquid is formed in which the thread "floats" freely, as shown in part (a). If the film inside the loop of thread is punctured, the thread springs out into a circular shape as in part (b), as if the surfaces of the liquid were pulling radially outward on it, as shown by the arrows. Presumably, the same forces were acting before the film was punctured, but since there was film on *both* sides of the thread the net force exerted by the film on every portion of the thread was zero.

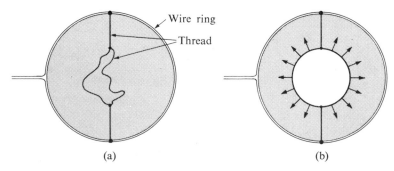

Wire ring

Thread

(a) (b)

Fig. 13–1. A wire ring with a flexible loop of thread, dipped in a soap solution, (a) before and (b) after puncturing the surface films inside the loop.

Another simple apparatus for demonstrating surface effects is shown in Fig. 13–2. A piece of wire is bent into the shape of a U and a second piece of wire is used as a slider. When the apparatus is dipped in a soap solution and removed, the slider (if its weight w_1 is not too great) is quickly pulled up to the top of the U. It may be held in equilibrium by adding a second weight w_2. Surprisingly, the same total force $F = w_1 + w_2$ will hold the slider at rest in *any* position, regardless of the area of the liquid film, provided the film remains at constant temperature. This is very different from the elastic behavior of a sheet of rubber, for which the force would be greater as the sheet was stretched.

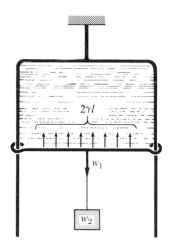

Fig. 13–2. The horizontal slide wire is in equilibrium under the action of the upward surface force $2\gamma l$ and the downward pull $w_1 + w_2$.

Although a soap film like that in Fig. 13–2 is very thin, its thickness is still enormous compared with the size of a molecule. Hence it can be considered as made up chiefly of bulk liquid, bounded by two surface layers a few molecules thick. When the crossbar in Fig. 13–2 is pulled down and the area of the film is increased, molecules formerly in the main body of the liquid move into the surface layers. That is, these layers are not "stretched" as a rubber sheet would be, but more surface is created by molecules moving from the bulk liquid.

Let l be the length of the wire slider. Since the film has two surfaces, the total length along which the surface force acts is $2l$. The *surface tension* in the film, γ, is defined as *the ratio of the surface force to the length* (perpendicular to the force) *along which the force acts.* Hence in this case,

$$\gamma = \frac{F}{2l}. \tag{13–1}$$

The unit of surface tension in the cgs system is 1 dyne/cm.

Another less spectacular way of showing a surface force is embodied in the actual apparatus, shown in Fig. 13–3, that is often used to measure surface tension. A circular wire whose circumference is of length l is lifted out from the body of a liquid. The additional force F needed to balance the surface forces $2\gamma l$ due to the two surface

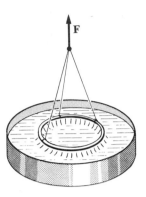

Fig. 13–3. Lifting a circular wire of length l out of a liquid requires an additional force **F** to balance the surface forces $2\gamma l$. This method is commonly used to measure surface tension.

films on each side is measured either by the stretch of a delicate spring or by the twist of a torsion wire. The surface tension is then given by

$$\gamma = \frac{F}{2l}.$$

Other methods of measuring surface tension will be apparent in what is to follow. Some typical values are shown in Table 13–1.

The surface tension of a liquid surface in contact with its own vapor or with air is found to depend only on the nature of the liquid and on the temperature. The values for water in Table 13–1 are typical of the general result that surface tension decreases as the temperature increases. Measurements of the surface tension of an extremely thin layer of oil on the surface of water indicate that, in this case, the surface tension depends on the area of the oil film as well as on the temperature.

TABLE 13–1

EXPERIMENTAL VALUES OF SURFACE TENSION

Liquid in contact with air	t, °C	Surface tension, dynes/cm
Benzene	20	28.9
Carbon tetrachloride	20	26.8
Ethyl alcohol	20	22.3
Glycerine	20	63.1
Mercury	20	465
Olive oil	20	32.0
Soap solution	20	25.0
Water	0	75.6
Water	20	72.8
Water	60	66.2
Water	100	58.9
Oxygen	−193	15.7
Neon	−247	5.15
Helium	−269	0.12

13-2 Surface tension and surface energy

Another useful viewpoint regarding surface effects is the following. Suppose the horizontal wire in Fig. 13–2 is moved down a distance y by applying a downward force $F = w_1 + w_2$. The force F will remain constant provided the temperature of the surface film is kept constant during the motion. The work done is Fy, and the total surface area of the film is increased by $2ly$. The work done per unit area, in increasing the area, is therefore

$$\frac{\text{Work}}{\text{Increase in area}} = \frac{Fy}{2ly} = \frac{F}{2l}. \tag{13–2}$$

But, from Eq. (13–1), this is equal to the surface tension γ, and hence γ can be considered either as the *force per unit length* at right angles to the force, or as the *work per unit area* to increase the area. Using the second definition, the cgs unit of γ would be 1 erg/cm^2, which is equivalent to 1 dyne/cm, since 1 erg $=$ 1 dyne·cm.

However, the work done when the area of a surface film is increased at constant temperature is not equal to the increase in energy of the film, because in order to keep the temperature constant some heat must be supplied to the film. (If heat is not supplied, the temperature of the film decreases. The phenomenon is similar to the drop in temperature when a liquid evaporates.) The increase in surface energy of the film is equal to the sum of the work done and the heat supplied. For further details consult a text on thermodynamics.

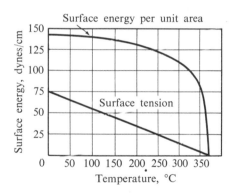

Fig. 13–4. Surface energy and surface tension of water, as functions of temperature.

If we let U represent the energy of a surface film of area A, its surface energy per unit area, U/A, is related to its surface tension by the equation

$$\frac{U}{A} = \gamma - T\frac{d\gamma}{dT},$$

where T is the absolute temperature. Since surface tension always decreases with increasing temperature, $d\gamma/dT$ is negative and the surface energy per unit area is larger than the surface tension. Graphs of surface energy per unit area and of surface tension, as functions of temperature, are given in Fig. 13–4 for water. The temperature of 374°C, where both become zero, is the *critical temperature*.

13–3 Pressure difference across a surface film

A soap bubble consists of two spherical surface films very close together, with liquid between. If we isolate one-half of the bubble and apply the principles of statics to the equilibrium of this half-bubble, we obtain a simple relation between the surface tension and the difference in pressure of the air inside and outside the bubble. Consider first a small element dA of a surface, shown in Fig. 13–5. Suppose the air pressure on the left of this element is p and that on the right is p_a. The force normal to the element is therefore $(p - p_a)\, dA$. The component of this force in the x-direction is

$$(p - p_a)\, dA \cos \theta.$$

But $dA \cos \theta$ is the area projected on a plane perpendicular to the x-axis. The force in the x-direction is therefore the difference of pressure multiplied by the projected area in the x-direction.

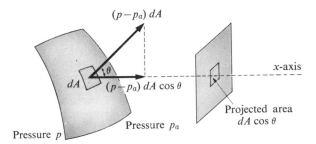

Fig. 13–5.   The force in the x-direction is the difference of pressure multiplied by the *projected* area in the x-direction.

Now consider the half-bubble shown in Fig. 13–6. The other half exerts a force to the left equal to twice the surface tension times the perimeter or

$$F \text{ (to the left)} = 2\gamma \times 2\pi R.$$

The force to the right is equal to the pressure difference $p - p_a$ multiplied by the area obtained by projecting the half-bubble on a plane perpendicular to the direction in question. Since this projected area is πR^2,

$$F \text{ (to the right)} = (p - p_a)\pi R^2.$$

Since the half-bubble is in equilibrium,

$$(p - p_a)\pi R^2 = 4\pi R\gamma,$$

or

$$p - p_a = \frac{4\gamma}{R} \qquad \text{(Soap bubble).} \qquad (13\text{–}3)$$

It follows from this result that if the surface tension remains constant (this means constant temperature), the pressure difference is larger the smaller the value of R. If two bubbles, therefore, are blown at opposite ends of a pipe, the smaller of the two

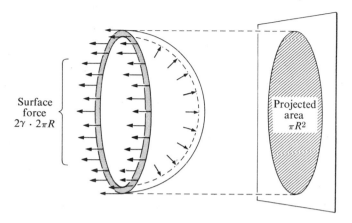

Fig. 13–6. Equilibrium of half a soap bubble. The force exerted by the other half is $2 \cdot \gamma \cdot 2\pi R$, and the net force exerted by the air inside and outside the bubble is the pressure difference times the projected area, or $(p - p_a)\pi R^2$.

will force air into the larger. In other words, the smaller one will get still smaller, and the larger will increase in size.

It may easily be verified that in the case of a liquid drop which has only one surface film, the difference between the pressure of the liquid and that of the outside air is given by

$$p - p_a = 2\gamma/R \qquad \text{(Liquid drop).} \qquad (13\text{--}4)$$

EXAMPLE. Calculate the excess pressure inside a drop of mercury whose temperature is 20°C and whose diameter is 4 mm.

$$p - p_a = \frac{2\gamma}{R} = \frac{2 \times 465 \text{ dynes/cm}}{0.4 \text{ cm}} = 2325 \frac{\text{dynes}}{\text{cm}^2}.$$

Any small portion of any curved surface can be fitted to a surface shaped like a blowout patch, that is, having two different radii of curvature in mutually perpendicular directions. If these radii, known as the *principal radii of curvature*, are called R_1 and R_2, the general expression for the pressure differential is

$$\Delta p = \gamma \left(\frac{1}{R_1} + \frac{1}{R_2} \right). \qquad (13\text{--}5)$$

The radii of curvature of a sphere are equal in any two mutually perpendicular directions and each is equal to the radius of the sphere, R. If $R_1 = R_2 = R$, then from Eq. (13–5) $\Delta p = 2\gamma/R$.

One of the radii of curvature of a cylinder is infinite and the other equals the radius of the cylinder. Hence for a cylinder

$$\Delta p = \frac{\gamma}{R}.$$

13–4 Minimal surfaces

Any surface under tension tends to contract until it occupies the minimum area consistent with the boundaries of the surface and with the difference of pressure on opposite sides of the surface. A small volume of heavy engine oil injected into the center of a mixture of alcohol and water whose density is the same as that of oil will therefore contract until it has the smallest surface area consistent with its volume. The shape of such a surface is spherical.

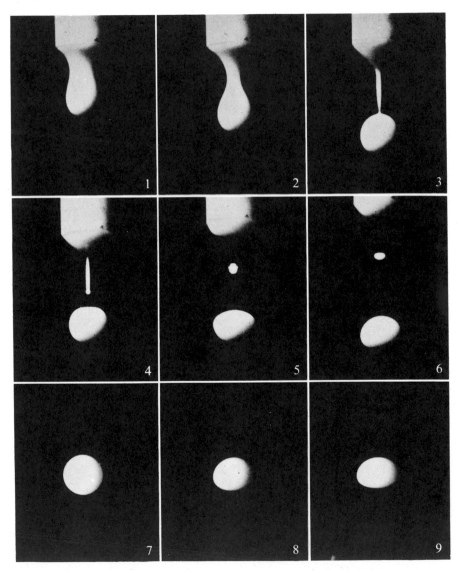

Fig. 13–7. Successive stages in the formation of a drop. (Reproduced from *Flash*, courtesy of Ralph S. Hale & Co.)

A more interesting situation is depicted in Fig. 13–7, which shows a series of high-speed photographs of successive stages in the formation of a drop of milk at the end of a vertical tube. The photographs were taken by Dr. Edgerton of M.I.T. It will be seen that the process, if examined in detail, is exceedingly complex. An interesting feature is the small drop that follows the larger one. Both drops execute a few oscillations after their formation (4, 5, and 6) and eventually assume a spherical shape (7) which would be retained but for the effects of air resistance, as shown in (8) and (9). The drop in (9) has fallen 14 ft.

An approximate relation between the weight of the drop, w, and the radius of the tube from which it falls can be derived by assuming that the limiting size of the drop that can be supported by the tube is reached when the weight of the drop equals the surface tension force around a circle whose diameter equals that of the tube. This leads to the equation

$$w = 2\pi r \gamma.$$

Examination of Fig. 13–7 shows that the assumption that $w = 2\pi r \gamma$ is seriously in error. For one thing, the edge of the drop at the tip of the tube, at the instant the drop breaks away, is rarely vertical, and for another only a part of the drop falls. A very thorough study has been made of the relation between drop weight, radius of tube, and surface tension. When the proper corrections are made to the simple formula this method is one of the most satisfactory means of measuring surface tensions.

Fig. 13–8. A drop of milk splashes on a hard surface. (Reproduced from *Flash*, courtesy of Ralph S. Hale & Co.)

A beautiful photograph of the splash made by a drop of milk falling on a hard surface is reproduced in Fig. 13–8. It also was taken by Dr. Edgerton.

Surface films may be used to solve problems in mathematics whose analytic solution presents great difficulties. If it is required to find the minimal surface (surface of minimum area) bounded by a wire framework bent into an arbitrary shape, the problem may be solved by dipping the wire framework into a soap solution and waiting a few seconds for the film to contract. The results for two frames in the

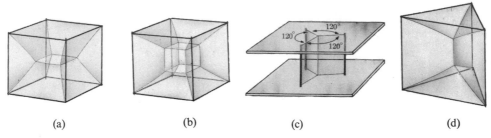

(a)   (b)   (c)   (d)

Fig. 13–9. Solution of mathematical problems involving minimal surfaces by means of surface films. (a) Cubical wire framework dipped once. (b) Cubical wire framework dipped twice to entrap an air bubble in the center. (c) Two plastic plates connected by three wires form three plane surface films at angles of 120° to each other. (d) A wire framework in the form of a prism shows that at most three surface films can intersect in a line and at most four edges can intersect at a point.

form of a cube and one in the form of a prism are shown in Fig. 13–9. These results could hardly have been guessed, and their prediction by purely mathematical methods would have been attended by considerable difficulty. For further details, the reader is referred to a fascinating book called *What is Mathematics* by Courant and Robbins.

13–5 Contact angle

In the preceding sections we have limited the discussion of surface phenomena to surface films lying in the boundary between a liquid and a gas. There are other boundaries, however, in which surface films exist. One is the boundary between a solid wall and a liquid, and another is the boundary between a solid and a vapor. The three boundaries and their accompanying films are shown schematically in Fig. 13–10. The films are only a few molecules thick. Associated with each film is an appropriate surface tension. Thus

$$\gamma_{\mathrm{SL}} = \text{surface tension of the solid-liquid film,}$$
$$\gamma_{\mathrm{SV}} = \text{surface tension of the solid-vapor film,}$$
$$\gamma_{\mathrm{LV}} = \text{surface tension of the liquid-vapor film.}$$

The symbol γ without subscripts, defined and used in the preceding sections, now appears as γ_{LV}.

Fig. 13–10. Surface films exist at the solid-vapor boundary and at the solid-liquid boundary as well as at the liquid-vapor boundary.

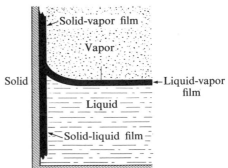

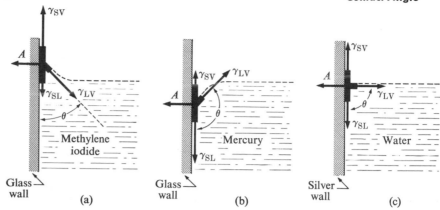

Fig. 13–11. The surface of a liquid near a solid wall is curved if the solid-vapor surface tension γ_{SV} differs from the solid-liquid surface tension γ_{SL}.

The curvature of the surface of a liquid near a solid wall depends upon the difference between γ_{SV} and γ_{SL}. Consider a portion of a glass wall in contact with methylene iodide, as shown in Fig. 13–11(a). At the wall the three films meet. Let us isolate a small portion of all three films at their junction and imagine the films to extend unit distance in a direction perpendicular to the diagram. The isolated portion will be in equilibrium under the action of four forces, three of which are the surface tensions of the three films. The fourth force A is an attraction between the isolated portion and the wall, and is called the *adhesive force*. Applying the conditions for equilibrium, we get

$$\Sigma F_x = \gamma_{LV} \sin \theta - A = 0,$$
$$\Sigma F_y = \gamma_{SV} - \gamma_{SL} - \gamma_{LV} \cos \theta = 0,$$

from which

$$A = \gamma_{LV} \sin \theta, \tag{13–6}$$
$$\gamma_{SV} - \gamma_{SL} = \gamma_{LV} \cos \theta. \tag{13–7}$$

The first equation enables us to calculate the adhesive force from measurements of γ_{LV} and the angle θ, known as the *contact angle*. The second equation shows that the contact angle, which is a measure of the curvature of the liquid-vapor surface adjacent to the wall, depends on the difference between γ_{SV} and γ_{SL}. Thus, in Fig. 13–11(a), γ_{SV} is greater than γ_{SL}, $\cos \theta$ is positive, and θ lies between 0° and 90°. The liquid is said to *wet* the glass.

In Fig. 13–11(b), a glass wall is in contact with mercury. The contact angle θ is about 140°, $\cos \theta$ is negative, and hence γ_{SV} is less than γ_{SL}. When θ lies between 90° and 180°, as it does here, we say that the liquid does *not* wet the glass.

In Fig. 13–11(c) a situation closely approximated by silver in contact with water is shown. In this case, γ_{SV} is very nearly equal to γ_{SL}, $\cos \theta$ is zero, and θ is 90°.

There are a number of liquids whose contact angles are zero when the liquids are in contact with soda-lime glass, lead glass, pyrex, and fused quartz. This is the case for water, alcohol, ether, carbon tetrachloride, xylene, glycerine, and acetic acid. Some liquids, however, such as the first two listed in Table 13–2, have contact angles which depend upon the nature of the wall with which they are in contact.

TABLE 13-2

CONTACT ANGLES

Liquid	Wall	Contact angle
α-Bromonaphthalene $(C_{10}H_7Br)$	Soda-lime glass Lead glass Pyrex Fused quartz	5° 6°45' 20°30' 21°
Methylene iodide (CH_2I_2)	Soda-lime glass Lead glass Pyrex Fused quartz	29° 30° 29° 33°
Water	Paraffin	107°
Mercury	Soda-lime glass	140°

Impurities and adulterants present in or added to a liquid may alter the contact angle considerably. In recent years a number of chemicals have been developed which are very potent as *wetting agents* or *detergents*. These compounds change the contact angle from a large value, greater than 90°, to a value much smaller than 90°. Conversely, waterproofing agents applied to a cloth cause the contact angle of water in contact with the cloth to be larger than 90°.

The effect of a detergent on a drop of water resting on a block of paraffin is shown in Fig. 13-12.

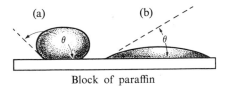

Block of paraffin

Fig. 13-12. Effect of decreasing contact angle by a wetting agent.

13-6 Capillarity

The most familiar surface effect is the elevation of a liquid in an open tube of small cross section. The term *capillarity*, used to describe effects of this sort, originates from the description of such tubes as "capillary" or "hairlike." In the case of a liquid that wets the tube, the contact angle is less than 90° and the liquid rises until an equilibrium height y is reached, as shown in Fig. 13-13(a). The curved liquid surface in the tube is called a *meniscus*.

If the tube radius is r, the liquid makes contact with the tube along a line of length $2\pi r$. When we isolate the cylinder of liquid of height y and radius r, along with its

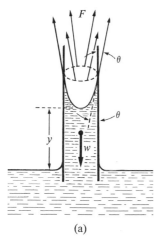

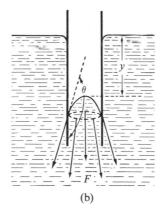

(a)   (b)

Fig. 13–13. Surface tension forces on a liquid in a capillary tube. The liquid rises if $\theta < 90°$ and is depressed if $\theta > 90°$.

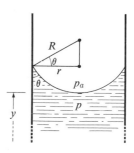

Fig. 13–14. Pressure differential.

liquid-vapor film, the total upward force is

$$F = 2\pi r \gamma_{LV} \cos \theta.$$

The downward force is the weight w of the cylinder, which is equal to the weight-density ρg times the volume $\pi r^2 y$, or

$$w = \rho g \pi r^2 y.$$

Since the cylinder is in equilibrium,

$$\rho g \pi r^2 y = 2\pi r \gamma_{LV} \cos \theta,$$

or

$$y = \frac{2\gamma_{LV} \cos \theta}{\rho g r}. \tag{13–8}$$

The same equation holds for capillary depression, shown in Fig. 13–13(b). Capillarity accounts for the rise of ink in blotting paper, the rise of lighting fluid in the wick of a cigarette lighter, and many other common phenomena.

The expression for the height of rise or fall of a liquid in a capillary tube can also be derived from a consideration of the pressure differential across a surface film. Figure 13–14 shows the top of the liquid column in the tube of Fig. 13–13(a). Let us assume the meniscus to be a portion of a spherical surface. The radius R of the surface is $R = r/\cos \theta$, where r is the tube radius. The pressure differential across the surface, from Eq. (13–4), is $2\gamma_{LV}/R$, so that if the pressure above the surface is atmospheric pressure p_a, the pressure p just below the surface is

$$p = p_a - \frac{2\gamma_{LV} \cos \theta}{r}.$$

The pressure in the liquid column, at the elevation of the flat liquid surface in Fig. 13–13(a), is also atmospheric. The pressure in the column at a height y is then

$$p = p_a - \rho g y.$$

Equating the expressions for p, we get

$$\rho g y = \frac{2\gamma_{LV} \cos \theta}{r},$$

which is the same as Eq. (13–8).

Problems

13–1. Compare the tension of a soap bubble with that of a rubber balloon in the following respects: (a) Has each a surface tension? (b) Does the surface tension depend on area? (c) Is Hooke's law applicable?

13–2. Water can rise to a height y in a certain capillary. Suppose that this tube is immersed in water so that only a length $y/2$ is above the surface. Will you have a fountain or not? Explain.

13–3. A capillary tube is dipped in water with its lower end 10 cm below the water surface. Water rises in the tube to a height of 4 cm above that of the surrounding liquid, and the angle of contact is zero. What gauge pressure is required to blow a hemispherical bubble at the lower end of the tube?

13–4. A glass tube of inside diameter 1 mm is dipped vertically into a container of mercury, with its lower end 1 cm below the mercury surface. (a) What must be the gauge pressure of air in the tube to blow a hemispherical bubble at its lower end? (b) To what height will mercury rise in the tube if the air pressure in the tube is 3×10^4 dynes/cm^2 below atmospheric? The angle of contact between mercury and glass is 140°.

13–5. On a day when the atmospheric pressure is 950 millibars, (a) what would be the height of the mercury column in a barometric tube of inside diameter 2 mm? (b) What would be the height in the absence of any surface tension effects? (c) What is the minimum diameter a barometric tube may have in order that the correction for capillary depression shall be less than 0.01 cm of mercury?

13–6. (a) Derive the expression for the height of capillary rise in the space between two parallel plates dipping in a liquid. (b) Two glass plates, parallel to each other and separated by 0.5 mm, are dipped in water. To what height will the water rise between them? Assume zero angle of contact.

13–7. A tube of circular cross section and outer radius 0.14 cm is closed at one end. This end is weighted and the tube floats vertically in water, heavy end down. The total mass of the tube and weights is 0.20 gm. If the angle of contact is zero, how far below the water surface is the bottom of the tube?

13–8. Find the gauge pressure, in dynes/cm^2, in a soap bubble 5 cm in diameter. The surface tension is 25 dynes/cm.

13–9. Two large glass plates are clamped together along one edge and separated by spacers a few millimeters thick along the opposite edge to form a wedge-shaped air film. These plates are then placed vertically in a dish of colored liquid. Show that the edge of the liquid forms an equilateral hyperbola.

13–10. When mercury is poured onto a flat glass surface which it does not wet, it spreads out into a pool of uniform thickness regardless of the size of the pool. Find the thickness of the pool.

CHAPTER 14

Hydrodynamics and Viscosity

14–1 Introduction

The subject of hydrodynamics deals with the motion of fluids. To begin with, we shall consider only a so-called *ideal fluid*, that is, one which is incompressible and which has no internal friction or viscosity. The assumption of incompressibility is a good approximation when dealing with liquids. A gas can also be treated as in-compressible provided the flow is such that pressure differences are not too great. Internal friction in a fluid gives rise to shearing stresses when two adjacent layers of fluid move relative to each other, or when the fluid flows in a tube or around an obstacle. In many actual flows, the shearing forces can be neglected in comparison with gravitational forces and forces arising from pressure differences.

The path followed by an element of a moving fluid is called a *line of flow*. In general, the velocity of the element changes in both magnitude and direction along its line of flow. If every element passing through a given point follows the same line of flow as that of preceding elements, the flow is said to be *steady* or *stationary*. When any given flow is first started, it passes through a nonsteady state, but in many instances the flow becomes steady after a certain period of time has elapsed. In steady flow, the velocity at every point of space remains constant in time, although the velocity of a particular particle of the fluid may change as it moves from one point to another.

A *streamline* is defined as a curve whose tangent, at any point, is in the direction of the fluid velocity at that point. In steady flow, the streamlines coincide with the lines of flow.

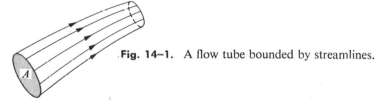

Fig. 14–1. A flow tube bounded by streamlines.

If we construct all of the streamlines passing through the periphery of an element of area, such as the area A in Fig. 14–1, these lines enclose a tube called a *flow tube* or *tube of flow*. From the definition of a streamline, no fluid can cross the side walls of a tube of flow; in steady flow there can be no mixing of the fluids in different flow tubes.

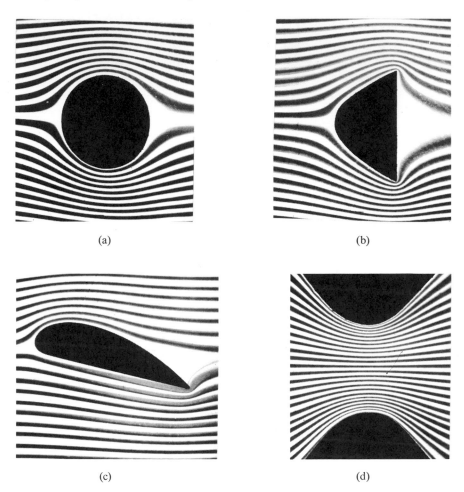

Fig. 14–2. (a), (b), (c): Streamline flow around obstacles of various shapes. (d) Flow in a channel of varying cross-sectional area.

The simplest type of fluid flow is a *homogeneous* flow, in which all flow tubes are straight and parallel, and the velocity is the same in each. Figure 14–2 illustrates the nature of the flow around a number of obstacles, and in a channel of varying cross section. The photographs were made using an apparatus designed by Pohl, in which alternate streams of clear and colored water flow between two closely spaced glass plates. The obstacles, and the channel walls, are opaque flat plates which fit between the glass plates. It will be noted that each obstacle is completely surrounded by a tube of flow. The tube splits into two portions at a so-called *stagnation point* on the upstream side of the obstacle. These portions rejoin at a second stagnation point on the downstream side. The velocity at the stagnation points is zero. It will also be noted that the cross sections of all flow tubes decrease at a constriction and increase again when the channel widens.

14-2 The equation of continuity

If we consider any fixed, closed surface in a moving fluid then, in general, fluid flows into the volume enclosed by the surface at some points, and flows out at other points. The *equation of continuity* is a mathematical statement of the fact that the *net rate of flow of mass inward* across any closed surface is equal to the rate of increase of the mass within the surface.

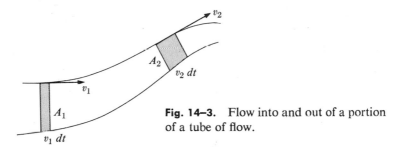

Fig. 14–3. Flow into and out of a portion of a tube of flow.

For an incompressible fluid in steady flow, the equation takes the following form. Figure 14–3 represents a portion of a tube of flow, between two fixed cross sections of areas A_1 and A_2. Let v_1 and v_2 be the speeds at these sections. There is no flow across the side walls of the tube. The volume of fluid that will flow into the tube across A_1 in a time interval dt is that contained in the short cylindrical element of base A_1 and height $v_1\, dt$, or is $A_1 v_1\, dt$. If the density of the fluid is ρ, the mass flowing in is $\rho A_1 v_1\, dt$. Similarly, the mass that will flow out across A_2 in the same time is $\rho A_2 v_2\, dt$. The volume between A_1 and A_2 is constant, and since the flow is steady the mass flowing out equals that flowing in. Hence

$$\rho A_1 v_1\, dt = \rho A_2 v_2\, dt,$$

or

$$A_1 v_1 = A_2 v_2, \tag{14–1}$$

and the product Av is constant along any given tube of flow. It follows that when the cross section of a flow tube decreases, as in the constriction in Fig. 14–2(d), the velocity increases. This can readily be shown by introducing small particles in the fluid and observing their motion.

14-3 Bernoulli's equation

When an incompressible fluid flows along a flow tube of varying cross section its velocity changes, that is, it accelerates or decelerates. It must therefore be acted on by a resultant force, and this means that the pressure must vary *along* the flow tube even though the elevation does not change. For two points at different elevations, the pressure difference depends not only on the difference in level but also on the difference between the velocities at the points. The general expression for the pressure difference can be obtained directly from Newton's second law, but it is simpler to make use of the work-energy theorem. The problem was first solved by Daniel Bernoulli in 1738.

Figure 14–4 represents a portion of a tube of flow. We are to follow a small element of the fluid, indicated by shading, as it moves from one point to another along the tube. Let y_1 be the elevation of the first point above some reference level, v_1 the speed at that point, A_1 the cross-sectional area of the tube, and p_1 the pressure. All these quantities may vary from point to point, and y_2, v_2, A_2, and p_2 are their values at the second point.

Since the fluid is under pressure at all points, inward forces, shown by the heavy arrows, are exerted against both faces of the element. As the element moves from the first point to the second, positive work is done by the force acting on its left face, and negative work by the force acting on its right face. The net work, or the difference between these quantities, equals the change in kinetic energy of the element plus the change in its potential energy.

If A represents the cross-sectional area of the tube at any point and p represents the corresponding pressure, the force against a face of the element at any point is pA. The work of the force acting on the left face of the element, in the motion in the diagram, is

$$\int_a^c F_s \, ds = \int_a^c pA \, ds,$$

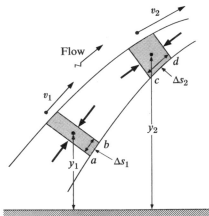

where ds is a short distance measured along the tube of flow. The limits of integration are from a to c, since these are the initial and final positions of the left face. This integral may be written

$$\int_a^c pA \, ds = \int_a^b pA \, ds + \int_b^c pA \, ds.$$

Similarly, the work of the force acting on the right face of the element is

$$\int_b^d pA \, ds = \int_b^c pA \, ds + \int_c^d pA \, ds.$$

Fig. 14–4. The net work done on the shaded element equals the increase in its kinetic and potential energy.

The *net* work is

$$\text{Net work} = \int_a^b pA \, ds + \int_b^c pA \, ds - \int_b^c pA \, ds - \int_c^d pA \, ds$$

$$= \int_a^b pA \, ds - \int_c^d pA \, ds.$$

The distances from a to b and from c to d are sufficiently small so that the pressures and areas may be considered constant along their extent. Then

$$\int_a^b pA \, ds = p_1 A_1 \, \Delta s_1, \qquad \int_c^d pA \, ds = p_2 A_2 \, \Delta s_2.$$

But $A_1 \, \Delta s_1 = A_2 \, \Delta s_2 = V$, where V is the volume of the element. Hence

$$\text{Net work} = (p_1 - p_2)V. \qquad (14\text{–}2)$$

Let ρ be the density of the fluid and m the mass of the element. Then $V = m/\rho$ and Eq. (14–2) becomes

$$\text{Net work} = (p_1 - p_2)\frac{m}{\rho}. \tag{14–3}$$

We now equate the net work to the sum of the changes in potential and kinetic energy of the element:

$$(p_1 - p_2)\frac{m}{\rho} = (mgy_2 - mgy_1) + (\tfrac{1}{2}mv_2^2 - \tfrac{1}{2}mv_1^2).$$

After canceling m and multiplying through by ρ, we obtain

$$p_1 - p_2 = \rho g(y_2 - y_1) + \tfrac{1}{2}\rho(v_2^2 - v_1^2). \tag{14–4}$$

The first term on the right is the pressure difference arising from the weight of the fluid and the difference in elevation between points 1 and 2. The second is the additional pressure difference associated with the change in velocity, or the acceleration of the fluid.

Equation (14–4) can be written

$$p_1 + \rho g y_1 + \tfrac{1}{2}\rho v_1^2 = p_2 + \rho g y_2 + \tfrac{1}{2}\rho v_2^2, \tag{14–5}$$

and since the subscripts 1 and 2 refer to any two points along the tube of flow,

$$\boxed{p + \rho g y + \tfrac{1}{2}\rho v^2 = \text{constant.}} \tag{14–6}$$

This is known as *Bernoulli's equation*. Note carefully that p is the *absolute* (not gauge) pressure, and must be expressed in lb/ft^2, n/m^2, or dynes/cm^2. The density must be expressed in slugs/ft^3, kgm/m^3, or gm/cm^3.

14–4 Applications of Bernoulli's equation

(1) The equations of hydrostatics are special cases of Bernoulli's equation, when the velocity is everywhere zero. Thus when v_1 and v_2 are zero, Eq. (14–4) reduces to

$$p_1 - p_2 = \rho g(y_2 - y_1),$$

which is the same as Eq. (12–4).

(2) *Speed of efflux. Torricelli's theorem.* Figure 14–5 represents a tank of cross-sectional area A_1, filled to a depth h with a liquid of density ρ. The space above the top of the liquid contains air at pressure p, and the liquid flows out of an orifice of area A_2. Let us consider the entire volume of moving fluid as a single tube of flow, and let v_1 and v_2 be the speeds at points 1 and 2. The quantity v_2 is called the *speed of efflux*. The pressure at point 2 is atmospheric, p_a. Applying Bernoulli's equation to points 1 and 2, and taking the bottom of the tank as our reference level, we get

$$p + \tfrac{1}{2}\rho v_1^2 + \rho g h = p_a + \tfrac{1}{2}\rho v_2^2,$$

or

$$v_2^2 = v_1^2 + 2\frac{p - p_a}{\rho} + 2gh. \tag{14–7}$$

From the equation of continuity,

$$v_2 = \frac{A_1}{A_2} v_1. \tag{14–8}$$

Because of the converging of the streamlines as they approach the orifice, the cross section of the stream continues to diminish for a short distance outside the tank. It is the area of smallest cross section, known as the *vena contracta*, which should be used in Eq. (14–8). For a sharp-edged circular opening, the area of the *vena contracta* is about 65% as great as the area of the orifice.

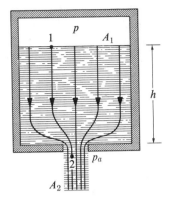

Fig. 14–5. Flow of a liquid out of an orifice.

Now let us consider some special cases. Suppose the tank is open to the atmosphere, so that

$$p = p_a \quad \text{and} \quad p - p_a = 0.$$

Suppose also that $A_1 \gg A_2$. Then v_1^2 is very much less than v_2^2 and can be neglected, and from Eq. (14–7),

$$v_2 = \sqrt{2gh}. \tag{14–9}$$

That is, *the speed of efflux is the same as that acquired by any body in falling freely through a height h.* This is *Torricelli's theorem.* It is not restricted to an opening in the bottom of a vessel, but applies also to a hole in the side walls at a depth h below the surface.

Now suppose again that the ratio of areas is such that v_1^2 is negligible and that the pressure p (in a closed vessel) is so large that the term $2gh$ in Eq. (14–7) can be neglected, compared with $2(p - p_a)/\rho$. The speed of efflux is then

$$v_2 = \sqrt{2(p - p_a)/\rho}. \tag{14–10}$$

The density ρ is that of the fluid escaping from the orifice. If the vessel is partly filled with a liquid, as in Fig. 14–5, ρ is the density of the liquid. On the other hand, if the vessel contains only a gas, ρ is the density of the gas. The efflux speed of a gas may be very great, even for small pressures, since its density is small. However, if the pressure is too great it may no longer be permissible to treat a gas as incompressible, and if the speed is too great the motion may become turbulent (see Section 14–10). Bernoulli's equation can no longer be applied to the motion under these conditions.

A flow of fluid out of an orifice in a vessel gives rise to a *thrust* or *reaction force* on the remainder of the system. The mechanics of the problem are the same as those involved in rocket propulsion. The thrust can be computed as follows, provided conditions are such that Bernoulli's equation is applicable. If A is the area of the orifice, ρ the density of the escaping fluid, and v the speed of efflux, the mass of fluid flowing out in time dt is $\rho A v\, dt$, and its momentum (mass $\times$ velocity) is $\rho A v^2\, dt$. Since we are neglecting the relatively small velocity of the fluid in the container, we can say that the escaping fluid started from rest and acquired the momentum above in time dt. Its *rate of change* of momentum was therefore $\rho A v^2$, and from Newton's second law this equals the force acting on it. By Newton's third law, an equal and opposite reaction force acts on the remainder of the system. Taking the expression for v^2 from Eq. (14–10), the reaction force can be written

$$F = \rho A v^2 = \rho A \frac{2(p - p_a)}{\rho},$$

or

$$F = 2A(p - p_a). \tag{14–11}$$

Thus while the *speed* of efflux is inversely proportional to the density, the *thrust* is independent of the density and depends only on the area of the orifice and the gauge pressure $p - p_a$.

EXAMPLE. Figure 14–6 shows a toy "water rocket." Above the water is air at a pressure $p = 2$ atm. (a) If the rocket is held at rest, what is the speed of efflux out of an opening in the base of the rocket? (b) What is the upward thrust if the area of the opening is 0.5 cm²?

(a) The gauge pressure $p - p_a = 1$ atm $\approx 10^6$ dynes/cm². The efflux speed is therefore

$$v \approx \sqrt{\frac{2 \times 10^6 \text{ dynes/cm}^2}{1 \text{ gm/cm}^3}}$$

$$\approx 1.4 \times 10^3 \frac{\text{cm}}{\text{sec}}.$$

The upward thrust is

$$F \approx 2 \times 0.5 \text{ cm}^2 \times 10^6 \text{ dynes/cm}^2$$

$$\approx 10^6 \text{ dynes}.$$

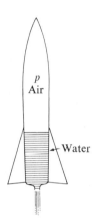

Fig. 14–6. A toy water rocket.

This force is much larger than the weight of the rocket and contents. Note that the reaction force, for the same gauge pressure, would be the same if the rocket initially contained air only. What is the reason for partially filling it with water?

---

(3) The *Venturi tube*, illustrated in Fig. 14–7, consists of a constriction or throat inserted in a pipeline and having properly designed tapers at inlet and outlet to avoid turbulence. Bernoulli's equation, applied to the wide and to the constricted portions of the pipe, becomes

$$p_1 + \tfrac{1}{2}\rho v_1^2 = p_2 + \tfrac{1}{2}\rho v_2^2.$$

From the equation of continuity, the speed v_2 is greater than the speed v_1 and hence the pressure p_2 in the throat is less than the pressure p_1. Thus a net force to the right acts to accelerate the fluid as it enters the throat, and a net force to the left decelerates it as it leaves. The pressures p_1 and p_2 can be measured by attaching

Fig. 14–7. The Venturi tube.

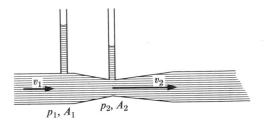

vertical side tubes as shown in the diagram. From a knowledge of these pressures and of the cross-sectional areas A_1 and A_2, the velocities and the mass rate of flow can be computed. When used for this purpose, the device is called a *Venturi meter*.

The reduced pressure at a constriction finds a number of technical applications. Gasoline vapor is drawn into the manifold of an internal combustion engine by the low pressure produced in a Venturi throat to which the carburetor is connected. The aspirator pump is a Venturi throat through which water is forced. Air is drawn into the low-pressure water rushing through the constricted portion.

(4) *Measurement of pressure in a moving fluid.* The so-called *static pressure p* in a fluid flowing in an enclosed channel can be measured with an open-tube manometer, as shown in Fig. 14–8. In (a), one arm of the manometer is connected to an opening in the channel wall. In (b), a *probe* is inserted in the stream. The probe should be small enough so that the flow is not appreciably disturbed and should be shaped so as to avoid turbulence. The difference h_1 in height of the liquid in the arms of the manometer is proportional to the difference between atmospheric pressure p_a and the static pressure p. That is,

$$p_a - p = \rho_m g h_1,$$

$$p = p_a - \rho_m g h_1, \tag{14–12}$$

where ρ_m is the density of the manometric liquid.

The *Pitot tube*, shown in Fig. 14–9, is a probe with an opening at its upstream end. A stagnation point forms at the opening, where the pressure is p_2 and the speed is

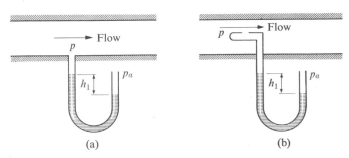

(a)   (b)

Fig. 14–8. Pressure gauges for measuring the static pressure p in a fluid flowing in an enclosed channel.

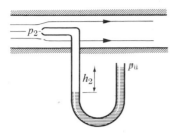

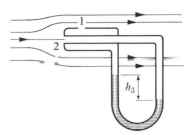

Fig. 14–9.   The Pitot tube.   **Fig. 14–10.**   The Prandtl tube.

zero. Applying Bernoulli's equation to the stagnation point, and to a point at a large distance from the probe where the pressure is p and the speed is v, we get

$$p_2 = p + \tfrac{1}{2}\rho v^2$$

(ρ is the density of the flowing fluid). The pressure p_2 at the stagnation point is therefore the sum of the static pressure p and the quantity $\tfrac{1}{2}\rho v^2$, called the *dynamic pressure*.

The open-tube manometer reads the difference between atmospheric pressure p_a and the pressure p_2.

$$p_a - p_2 = \rho_m g h_2,$$

$$p_2 = p + \tfrac{1}{2}\rho v^2 = p_a - \rho_m g h_2. \tag{14–13}$$

The instrument shown in Fig. 14–10 is known as a *Prandtl tube* (it is also sometimes called a Pitot tube). The pressure at opening 1 is the static pressure p and that at opening 2 is $p + \tfrac{1}{2}\rho v^2$. The manometric height h_3 is proportional to the difference between these, or to the dynamic pressure $\tfrac{1}{2}\rho v^2$. Hence

$$\tfrac{1}{2}\rho v^2 = \rho_m g h_3. \tag{14–14}$$

This instrument is self-contained and its reading does not depend on atmospheric pressure. If held at rest, it can be used to measure the velocity of a stream of fluid flowing past it. If mounted on an aircraft, it indicates the velocity of the aircraft relative to the surrounding air and is known as an *airspeed indicator*.

14–5 Viscosity

Viscosity may be thought of as the internal friction of a fluid. Because of viscosity, a force must be exerted to cause one layer of a fluid to slide past another, or to cause one surface to slide past another if there is a layer of fluid between the surfaces. Both liquids and gases exhibit viscosity, although liquids are much more viscous than gases. In developing the fundamental equations of viscous flow, it will be seen that the problem is very similar to that of the shearing stress and strain in a solid.

Figure 14–11 illustrates one type of apparatus for measuring the viscosity of a liquid. A cylinder is pivoted on nearly frictionless bearings so as to rotate coaxially within a cylindrical vessel. The liquid whose viscosity is to be measured is poured

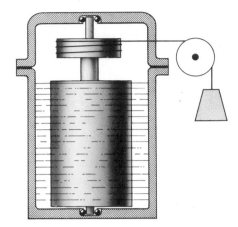

Fig. 14–11. Schematic diagram of one type of viscosimeter.

into the annular space between the cylinders. A torque can be applied to the inner cylinder by the weight-pulley system. When the weight is released, the inner cylinder accelerates momentarily but very quickly comes up to a constant angular velocity and continues to rotate at that velocity so long as the torque acts. It is obvious that this velocity will be smaller with a liquid such as glycerine in the annular space than it will be if the liquid is water or kerosene. From a knowledge of the torque, the dimensions of the apparatus, and the angular velocity, the viscosity of the liquid may be computed.

To reduce the problem to its essential terms, imagine that the cylinders are of nearly the same size, so that the liquid layer between them is thin. A short arc of this layer will then be approximately a straight line. Figure 14–12 shows a portion of the liquid layer between the moving inner wall and the stationary outer wall. The liquid in contact with the moving surface is found to have the same velocity as that surface; the liquid adjacent to the stationary inner wall is at rest. The velocities of intermediate layers of the liquid increase uniformly from one wall to the other, as shown by the arrows.

Flow of this type is called *laminar*. (A lamina is a thin sheet.) The layers of liquid slide over one another much as do the leaves of a book when it is placed flat on a table and a horizontal force applied to the top cover. As a consequence of this motion, a portion of the liquid which at some instant has the shape *abcd*, will a moment later take the shape *abc'd'*, and will become more and more distorted as the motion continues. That is, the liquid is in a state of continually increasing shearing strain.

In order to maintain the motion, it is necessary that a force be continually exerted to the right on the upper, moving plate, and hence indirectly on the upper liquid surface. This force tends to drag the liquid and the lower plate as well to the right. Therefore an equal force must be exerted toward the left on the lower plate to hold it stationary. These forces are lettered F in Fig. 14–12. If A is the area of the liquid over which these forces are applied, the ratio F/A is the shearing stress exerted on the liquid.

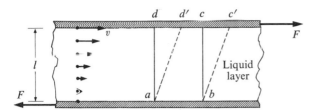

Fig. 14–12. Laminar flow of a viscous fluid.

When a shearing stress is applied to a solid, the effect of the stress is to produce a certain displacement of the solid, such as dd'. The shearing strain is defined as the ratio of this displacement to the transverse dimension l, and within the elastic limit the shearing stress is proportional to the shearing strain. With a fluid, on the other hand, the shearing strain increases without limit so long as the stress is applied, and the stress is found by experiment to depend not on the shearing strain, but on its *rate of change*. The strain in Fig. 14–12, at the instant when the volume of fluid has the shape $abc'd'$, is dd'/ad, or dd'/l. Since l is constant, the rate of change of strain equals $1/l$ times the rate of change of dd'. But the rate of change of dd' is simply the velocity of point d', or the velocity v of the moving wall. Hence

$$\text{Rate of change of shearing strain} = \frac{v}{l}.$$

The *coefficient of viscosity* of the fluid, or simply its *viscosity* η, is defined as the ratio of the shearing stress, F/A, to the rate of change of shearing strain:

$$\eta = \frac{\text{shearing stress}}{\text{rate of change of shearing strain}} = \frac{F/A}{v/l},$$

or,

$$F = \eta A \frac{v}{l}. \tag{14–15}$$

For a liquid which flows readily, like water or kerosene, the shearing stress is relatively small for a given rate of change of shearing strain and the viscosity also is relatively small. For a liquid like molasses or glycerine, a greater shearing stress is necessary for the same rate of change of shearing strain and the viscosity is correspondingly greater. Viscosities of gases are very much less than those of liquids. The viscosities of all fluids are markedly dependent on temperature, increasing for gases and decreasing for liquids as the temperature is increased.

Equation (14–15) was derived for the special case in which the velocity increased at a uniform rate with increasing distance from the lower plate. The general term for the *space* rate of change of velocity, in a direction at right angles to the flow, is the *velocity gradient* in this direction. In this special case it is equal to v/l. In the general case, the velocity gradient is not uniform and its value at any point can be written as dv/dy, where dv is the small difference in velocity between two points separated

TABLE 14–1

TYPICAL VALUES OF VISCOSITY

Temp., °C	Viscosity of castor oil, poise	Viscosity of water, centipoise	Viscosity of air, μpoise
0	53	1.792	171
20	9.86	1.005	181
40	2.31	0.656	190
60	0.80	0.469	200
80	0.30	0.357	209
100	0.17	0.284	218

by a distance dy measured at right angles to the direction of flow. Hence the general form of Eq. (14–15) is

$$F = \eta A \frac{dv}{dy}. \tag{14–16}$$

The unit of viscosity is that of force times distance divided by area times velocity. Thus in the cgs system the unit is 1 dyne·cm/cm^2 × (cm/sec), which reduces to 1 dyne·sec/cm^2. This unit is called 1 *poise*, in honor of the French scientist Poiseuille. Small viscosities are expressed in *centipoises* (1 cp = 10^{-2} poise) or *micropoises* (1 μp = 10^{-6} poise). Some typical values are given in Table 14–1.

14–6 Poiseuille's law

It is evident from the general nature of viscous effects that the velocity of a viscous fluid flowing through a tube will not be the same at all points of a cross section. The outermost layer of fluid clings to the walls of the tube and its velocity is zero. The tube walls exert a backward drag on this layer which in turn drags backward on the next layer beyond it, and so on. Provided the velocity is not too great, the flow is laminar, with a velocity which is a maximum at the center of the tube and which decreases to zero at the walls. The flow is like that of a number of telescoping tubes sliding relative to one another, the central tube advancing most rapidly and the outer tube remaining at rest.

Consider a portion of a tube of inner radius R and of length L, through which a fluid of viscosity η is flowing in laminar flow (Fig. 14–13). A small cylinder of radius r is in equilibrium (moving with constant velocity) under the driving force due to the pressure difference between its ends and the retarding viscous force at its outer surface. The driving force is

$$(p_1 - p_2)\pi r^2.$$

The viscous force, from Eq. (14–16), is

$$-\eta A \frac{dv}{dr} = -\eta \times 2\pi r L \times \frac{dv}{dr},$$

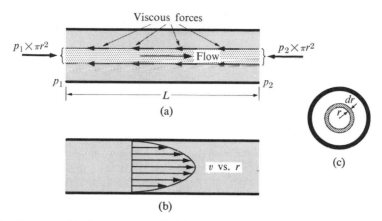

Fig. 14–13. (a) Forces on a cylindrical element of a viscous fluid. (b) Velocity distribution for viscous flow.

where dv/dr is the velocity gradient at a radial distance r from the axis. The negative sign must be introduced because v decreases as r increases. Equating the forces, and integrating, we get

$$-\int_v^0 dv = \frac{p_1 - p_2}{2\eta L}\int_r^R r\, dr,$$

and therefore

$$v = \frac{p_1 - p_2}{4\eta L}(R^2 - r^2), \tag{14–17}$$

which is the equation of a parabola. The curve in Fig. 14–13(b) is a graph of this equation. The lengths of the arrows are proportional to the velocities at their respective positions. The velocity gradient, dv/dr, at any radius, is the slope of this curve measured with respect to a vertical axis. We say that the flow has a *parabolic velocity profile*.

To find the discharge rate Q, or the volume of fluid crossing any section of the tube per unit time, consider the thin-walled element in Fig. 14–13(c). The volume of fluid dV crossing the ends of this element in a time dt is $v\, dA\, dt$, where v is the velocity at the radius r and dA is the shaded area, equal to $2\pi r\, dr$. Taking the expression for v from Eq. (14–17), we get

$$dV = \frac{p_1 - p_2}{4\eta L}(R^2 - r^2)\times 2\pi r\, dr \times dt.$$

The volume flowing across the entire cross section is obtained by integrating over all elements between $r = 0$ and $r = R$. Dividing by dt, for the volume rate of flow Q we get

$$Q = \frac{\pi(p_1 - p_2)}{2\eta L}\int_0^R (R^2 - r^2)r\, dr = \frac{\pi}{8}\frac{R^4}{\eta}\frac{p_1 - p_2}{L}. \tag{14–18}$$

This relation was first derived by Poiseuille (in honor of whom the unit of viscosity is named) and is called *Poiseuille's law*.

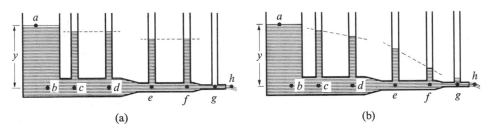

Fig. 14–14. Pressures along a horizontal tube in which is flowing (a) an ideal fluid, (b) a viscous fluid.

The volume rate of flow is inversely proportional to the viscosity, as might be expected. It is proportional to the 4th power of the tube radius, so that if, for example, the radius is halved, the volume rate of flow is reduced by a factor of sixteen. The ratio $(p_1 - p_2)/L$ is the *pressure gradient* along the tube. The flow is directly proportional to the pressure gradient, and we see that for a viscous fluid there is a pressure drop even along a level tube of constant cross section. If the cross section varies from point to point, and if the tube is not horizontal, there will of course be further pressure differences resulting from the acceleration of the fluid or from gravitational effects, these differences being given by Bernoulli's equation.

The difference between the flow of an ideal nonviscous fluid and one having viscosity is illustrated in Fig. 14–14, where fluid is flowing along a horizontal tube of varying cross section. The height of the fluid in the small vertical tubes is proportional to the gauge pressure.

In part (a), the fluid is assumed to have no viscosity. The pressure at b is very nearly the static pressure $\rho g y$, since the velocity is small in the large tank. The pressure at c is less than at b because the fluid must accelerate between these points. The pressures at c and d are equal, however, since the velocity and elevation at these points are the same. There is a further pressure drop between d and e, and between f and g. The pressure at g is atmospheric and the gauge pressure at this point is zero.

Part (b) of the diagram illustrates the effect of viscosity. Again, the pressure at b is nearly the static pressure $\rho g y$. There is a pressure drop from b to c, due now in part to viscous effects, and also a further drop from c to d. The pressure gradient in this part of the tube is represented by the slope of the dashed line. The drop from d to e results in part from acceleration and in part from viscosity. The pressure gradient between e and f is greater than between c and d because of the smaller radius in this portion. Finally, the pressure at g is somewhat above atmospheric, since there is now a pressure gradient between this point and the end of the tube.

14–7 Stokes' law

When an ideal fluid of zero viscosity flows past a sphere, or when a sphere moves through a stationary fluid, the streamlines form a perfectly symmetrical pattern around the sphere, as shown in Fig. 14–2(a). The pressure at any point on the upstream hemispherical surface is exactly the same as that at the corresponding point on the downstream face, and the resultant force on the sphere is zero. If the fluid has viscosity, however, there will be a viscous drag on the sphere. (A viscous drag will, of course, be experienced by a body of any shape, but only for a sphere is the drag readily calculable.)

We shall not attempt to derive the expression for the viscous force directly from the laws of flow of a viscous fluid. The only quantities on which the force can depend are the viscosity η of the fluid, the radius r of the sphere, and its velocity v relative to the fluid. A complete analysis shows that the force F is given by

$$F = 6\pi\eta r v. \tag{14–19}$$

This equation was first deduced by Sir George Stokes in 1845 and is called *Stokes' law*. We have already used it in Section 5–6 (Example 9) to study the motion of a sphere falling in a viscous fluid, although at that point it was only necessary to know that the viscous force on a given sphere in a given fluid is proportional to the relative velocity.

It will be recalled that a sphere falling in a viscous fluid reaches a *terminal velocity* v_T at which the viscous retarding force plus the buoyant force equals the weight of the sphere. Let ρ be the density of the sphere and ρ' the density of the fluid. The weight of the sphere is then $\frac{4}{3}\pi r^3 \rho g$, the buoyant force is $\frac{4}{3}\pi r^3 \rho' g$, and when the terminal velocity is reached

$$\frac{4}{3}\pi r^3 \rho' g + 6\pi\eta r v_T = \frac{4}{3}\pi r^3 \rho g,$$

or

$$v_T = \frac{2}{9}\frac{r^2 g}{\eta}(\rho - \rho'). \tag{14–20}$$

By measuring the terminal velocity of a sphere of known radius and density, the viscosity of the fluid in which it is falling can be found from the equation above. This equation was also used by Millikan to calculate the radius of the tiny submicroscopic, electrically charged oil drops by means of which he determined the charge on an individual electron. In this case, the terminal velocity of the drops was measured as they fell in air of known viscosity.

14–8 Dynamic lift

The upward force on a balloon, equal to the weight of the displaced air, is called a *static lift*. It results from the fact that atmospheric pressure changes with elevation, and as a consequence the pressure at the lower portion of the surface of the balloon is greater than that at the upper surface. The upward force on the wings of a moving aircraft, called a *dynamic lift*, arises from an entirely different cause but its origin can be readily understood from the laws of hydrodynamics for an incompressible fluid.

No force is exerted on a body moving through an ideal fluid when the flow around the body is symmetrical. However, if the flow is altered in such a way that the velocity above the body is increased and that below it is decreased, then according to Bernoulli's equation the static pressure at the upper surface decreases and that at the

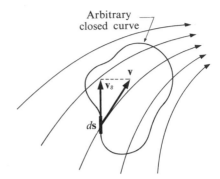

Fig. 14–15. The circulation Γ around an arbitrary closed curve in a moving fluid is $\Gamma = \oint \mathbf{v} \cdot d\mathbf{s}$.

lower surface increases. A resultant upward force then acts on the body, and this force is called a dynamic lift.

An asymmetrical flow around the body will result if a so-called *circulation flow* is superposed on the original symmetrical flow. A circulation flow is one which surrounds the body and whose streamlines are closed curves. It is characterized by a quantity Γ called the *circulation*. Let $d\mathbf{s}$ in Fig. 14–15 be an infinitesimal element of length of an arbitrary closed curve in a moving fluid, and let $\mathbf{v}_s$ be the component of the fluid velocity in the direction of $d\mathbf{s}$. The circulation is defined as the line integral of the product $v_s\, ds$ around the closed curve. It can also be expressed as the line integral of the dot product of the vectors $\mathbf{v}$ and $d\mathbf{s}$:

$$\Gamma = \oint v_s\, ds = \oint \mathbf{v} \cdot d\mathbf{s}. \tag{14–21}$$

As an example, suppose that a fluid is rotating about an axis in such a way that the magnitude of its velocity at every point is inversely proportional to the radius, or

$$v = \frac{k}{r}.$$

Flow of this sort is often observed in the vortex set up when water flows out of an opening in the bottom of a wash basin. Consider a closed curve in the form of a circle of radius r with center on the axis. The velocity component $\mathbf{v}_s$ is then equal to $\mathbf{v}$, and

$$\Gamma = \oint v_s\, ds = \frac{k}{r} \oint ds = \frac{k}{r}\, 2\pi r = 2\pi k.$$

The circulation is therefore the same around a circle of any radius, and it is not difficult to show that it has the same value around *any* closed curve surrounding the axis.

Figure 14–16(a) shows the streamlines around a cylindrical obstacle at rest in a fluid flowing from left to right. Points 1 and 2 are stagnation points. It can be seen on symmetry grounds that the circulation is zero. Figure 14–16(b) shows a circulation flow around the same obstacle. If both flows exist simultaneously, the vector velocity at any point is the vector sum of the velocities of the two flows. At points above the

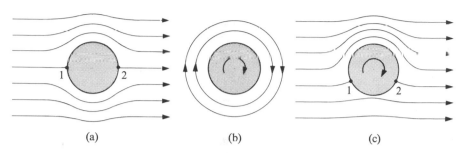

Fig. 14–16. (a) Streamlines around a stationary cylinder in a fluid flowing from left to right. (b) Circulation flow around a rotating cylinder in a fluid at rest. (c) Flow around a rotating cylinder in a moving fluid.

axis of the cylinder the velocities add, and at points below it they subtract. Carrying out the construction at other points, we get the flow diagram shown in Fig. 14–16(c). The stagnation points 1 and 2 are displaced to the lower surface of the cylinder, and the velocity above the cylinder is increased while that below it is decreased. From Bernoulli's equation, the pressure at the upper surface is decreased and that at the lower surface is increased, resulting in a net upward force, or a dynamic lift. The magnitude of the lifting force **F** can be shown to be

$$F = \rho v L \Gamma, \tag{14–22}$$

where ρ is the density of the fluid, v is the velocity in the undisturbed flow at large distances from the cylinder, L is the length of the cylinder, and Γ is the circulation.

A circulatory flow like that of Fig. 14–16(b) can be set up if the cylinder is set in rotation about its axis. As a result of the viscosity of the fluid, a circulatory motion becomes established around the cylinder and if it rotates in a stream of moving fluid we have the flow pattern of Fig. 14–16(c). The transverse force on a rotating cylinder in a stream of moving fluid is known as the *Magnus effect*. The same transverse force results when a rotating cylinder moves through a stationary fluid. Of course, the phenomenon is not restricted to bodies of cylindrical shape. The curved flight of a hooked or sliced golf ball, of a cut tennis or ping-pong ball, or of a pitched baseball results from the same causes.

A circulation can be set up around a nonrotating object in a stream of moving fluid if the object is properly shaped. This is the case with an aircraft wing. The velocity over the upper wing surface is increased and that over the lower surface is decreased, resulting again in a dynamic lift. Here also, the flow can be considered a superposition of a potential flow and a circulatory flow, and the lift is proportional to the circulation Γ of the latter flow. Note that the flow around an aircraft wing does not give rise to a "pull" on the upper surface of the wing. Of course this cannot happen. The air presses against all portions of the wing surface, although the reduction below atmospheric pressure at the upper surface usually exceeds the increase above atmospheric pressure at the lower surface.

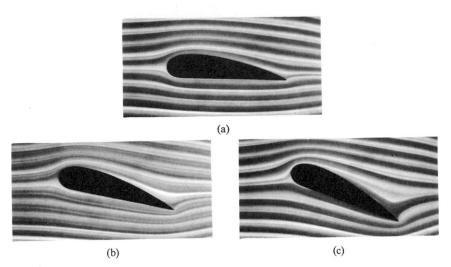

(a)

(b)   (c)

Fig. 14–17. Lines of flow around an airfoil.

Figure 14–17 is a photograph of the lines of flow around an obstacle in the shape of an airfoil, at three different angles of attack.

EXAMPLE. This example illustrates how the dynamic lift on an airplane wing can be found either from a direct application of Bernoulli's equation, or from a consideration of the circulation in the flow around the wing. Let L represent the length of the wing section in Fig. 14–18, perpendicular to the plane of the diagram, and w the width. Assume that the width is constant along the wing, and that it is at rest in a horizontal airstream, as would be the case for a model in a wind tunnel. Let p and v represent the pressure and velocity in the undisturbed flow at a large distance from the wing, p_1 and v_1 the pressure and velocity in the flow tube just above the wing, and p_2 and v_2 the corresponding quantities in the tube just below the wing. Assume for simplicity that p_1 and v_1 have the same values at all points of the upper surface, and that p_2 and v_2 have the same values at all points of the lower surface. The pressure difference between lower and upper surfaces can now be found by applying Bernoulli's equation to a point in the undisturbed flow, and to points above and below the wing:

$$p + \tfrac{1}{2}\rho v^2 = p_1 + \tfrac{1}{2}\rho v_1^2 = p_2 + \tfrac{1}{2}\rho v_2^2,$$

$$p_2 - p_1 = \tfrac{1}{2}\rho(v_1^2 - v_2^2).$$

The dynamic lift F on the wing is the product of the pressure difference $p_2 - p_1$ and the wing area, wL:

$$F = \tfrac{1}{2}wL\rho(v_1^2 - v_2^2).$$

This equation can be written

$$F = L\rho \times w(v_1 - v_2) \times (v_1 + v_2)/2.$$

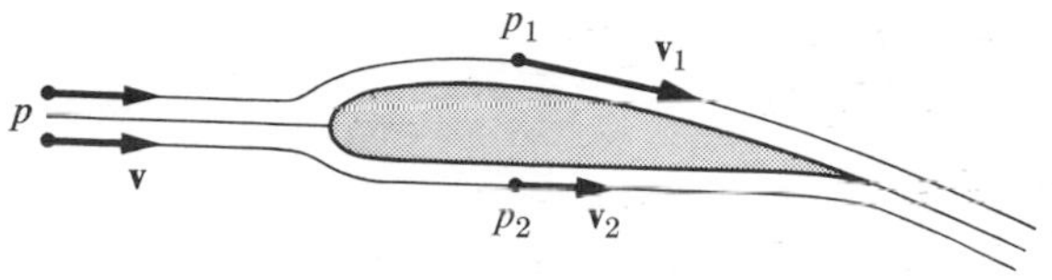

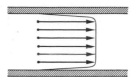

Figure 14–18

Fig. 14–19. Velocity profile in turbulent flow.

But the circulation Γ around a closed path just outside the wing is, very nearly,

$$\Gamma = \oint \mathbf{v} \cdot d\mathbf{s} = v_1 w - v_2 w = w(v_1 - v_2),$$

and the average of the velocities above and below the wing, $(v_1 + v_2)/2$, is very nearly equal to the velocity v in the undisturbed flow. Hence

$$F = L\rho\Gamma v,$$

which is the same as Eq. (14–22).

14–9 Reynolds number

When the velocity of a fluid flowing in a tube exceeds a certain critical value (which depends on the properties of the fluid and the diameter of the tube) the nature of the flow becomes extremely complicated. Within an extremely thin layer adjacent to the tube walls, called the *boundary layer*, the flow is still laminar. The flow velocity in the boundary layer is zero at the tube walls and increases uniformly throughout the layer. The properties of the boundary layer are of the greatest importance in determining the resistance to flow, and the transfer of heat to or from the moving fluid.

Beyond the boundary layer, the motion is highly irregular. Random local circular currents called *vortices* develop within the fluid, with a large increase in the resistance to flow. However, the fluid has at every point an average forward velocity component, and the velocity profile of these components has the shape shown in Fig. 14–19. Flow of this sort is called *turbulent*.

Experiment indicates that a combination of four factors determines whether the flow of a fluid through a tube or pipe is laminar or turbulent. This combination is known as the *Reynolds number*, N_R, and is defined as

$$N_R = \frac{\rho v D}{\eta},$$

where ρ is the density of the fluid, v the average forward velocity, η the viscosity, and D the diameter of the tube. (The average velocity is defined as the uniform velocity over the entire cross section of the tube, which would result in the same volume rate of flow.) The Reynolds number, $\rho v D/\eta$, is a *dimensionless* quantity and has the same numerical value in any consistent system of units. For example, for water at 20°C

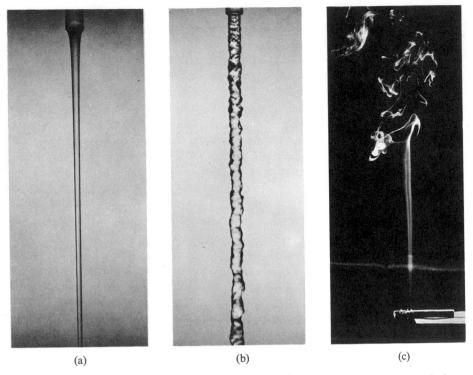

Fig. 14–20. (a) Laminar flow. (b) Turbulent flow. (c) First laminar then turbulent.

flowing in a tube of diameter 1 cm with an average velocity of 10 cm/sec, the Reynolds number is

$$N_R = \frac{\rho v D}{\eta} = \frac{1 \text{ gm/cm}^3 \times 10 \text{ cm/sec} \times 1 \text{ cm}}{0.01 \text{ dyne·sec/cm}^2} = 1000.$$

Had the four quantities been expressed originally in the engineering system of units, the same value of 1000 would have been obtained.

All experiments show that when the Reynolds number is less than about 2000 the flow is laminar, whereas above about 3000 the flow is turbulent. In the transition region between 2000 and 3000 the flow is unstable and may change from one type to the other. Thus for water at 20°C flowing in a tube 1 cm in diameter, the flow is laminar when

$$\frac{\rho v D}{\eta} \lessapprox 2000,$$

or when

$$v \lessapprox \frac{2000 \times 0.01}{1 \times 1} \frac{\text{cm}}{\text{sec}} = 20 \frac{\text{cm}}{\text{sec}}.$$

Above about 30 cm/sec the flow is turbulent. If air at the same temperature were flowing at 30 cm/sec in the same tube, the Reynolds number would be

$$N_R = \frac{0.0013 \times 30 \times 1}{181 \times 10^{-6}} = 216.$$

Since this is much less than 3000, the flow would be laminar and would not become turbulent unless the velocity were as great as 420 cm/sec.

The distinction between laminar and turbulent flow is shown most effectively in the photographs of Fig. 14–20. In (b) the fluid is water and in (c) air and smoke particles.

The Reynolds number of a system forms the basis for the study of the behavior of real systems through the use of small scale models. A common example is the wind tunnel, in which one measures the aerodynamic forces on a scale model of an aircraft wing. The forces on a full-size wing are then deduced from these measurements.

Two systems are said to be *dynamically similar* if the Reynolds number, $\rho v D/\eta$, is the same for both. The letter D may refer, in general, to any dimension of a system, such as the span or chord of an aircraft wing. Thus the flow of a fluid of given density ρ and viscosity η, about a half-scale model, is dynamically similar to that around the full-size object if the velocity v is twice as great.

Problems

14–1. A circular hole 1 inch in diameter is cut in the side of a large standpipe, 20 ft below the water level in the standpipe. Find (a) the velocity of efflux, and (b) the volume discharged per unit time. Neglect the contraction of the streamlines after emerging from the hole.

14–2. Water stands at a depth H in a large open tank whose side walls are vertical (Fig. 14–21). A hole is made in one of the walls at a depth h below the water surface. (a) At what distance R from the foot of the wall does the emerging stream of water strike the floor? (b) At what height above the bottom of the tank could a second hole be cut so that the stream emerging from it would have the same range?

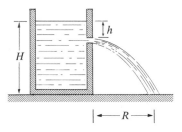

Figure 14–21

14–3. A cylindrical vessel, open at the top, is 20 cm high and 10 cm in diameter. A circular hole whose cross-sectional area is 1 cm² is cut in the center of the bottom of the vessel. Water flows into the vessel from a tube above it at the rate of 140 cm³/ sec. (a) How high will the water in the vessel rise? (b) If the flow into the vessel is stopped after the above height has been reached, how long a time is required for the vessel to empty? Neglect the convergence of the streamlines.

14–4. At a certain point in a pipeline the velocity is 4 ft/sec and the gauge pressure is 2 lb/in² above atmospheric.   Find the gauge pressure at a second point in the line 2 ft lower than the first, if the cross section at the second point is one-half that at the

first.   The liquid in the pipe is sea water weighing 64 lb/ft³.

14–5. Water in an enclosed tank is subjected to a gauge pressure of 4 lb/in² applied by compressed air introduced into the top of the tank. There is a small hole in the side of the tank 16 ft below the level of the water.   Calculate the speed with which water escapes from this hole.

14–6. What gauge pressure is required in the city mains in order that a stream from a fire hose connected to the mains may reach a vertical height of 60 ft?

14–7. A tank of large area is filled with water to a depth of one foot. A hole of 1 in² cross section in the bottom allows water to drain out in a continuous stream. (a) What is the rate at which water flows out of the tank, in ft³/sec? (b) At what distance below the bottom of the tank is the cross-sectional area of the stream equal to one-half the area of the hole?

14–8. A sealed tank containing sea water to a height of 5 ft also contains air above the water at a gauge pressure of 580 lb/ft². Water flows out from a hole at the bottom. The cross-sectional area of the hole is 1.6 in². (a) Calculate the efflux velocity of the water. (b) Calculate the reaction force on the tank exerted by the water in the emergent stream.

14–9. A pipeline 6 inches in diameter, flowing full of water, has a constriction of diameter 3 in. If the velocity in the 6-inch portion is 4 ft/sec, find (a) the velocity in the constriction, and (b) the discharge rate in ft³/sec.

14–10. A horizontal pipe of 6 in² cross section tapers to a cross section of 2 in². If sea water of density 2 slugs/ft³ is flowing with a velocity of 180 ft/min in the large pipe where a pressure gauge reads 10.5 lb/ in², what is the gauge pressure in the adjoining part of the small pipe? The barometer reads 30 inches of mercury.

14–11. At a certain point in a pipeline the velocity is 2 ft/sec and the gauge pressure is 35 lb/in². Find the gauge pressure at a second point in the line 50 ft lower than the first, if the cross section at the second point is one-half that at the first. The liquid in the pipe is water.

14–12. Water stands at a depth of 4 ft in an enclosed tank whose side walls are vertical. The space above the water surface contains air at a gauge pressure of 120 lb/in². The tank rests on a platform 8 ft above the floor. A hole of cross-sectional area 0.5 in² is made in one of the side walls just above the bottom of the tank. (a) Where does the stream of water from the hole strike the floor? (b) What is the vertical force exerted on the floor by the stream? (c) What is the horizontal force exerted on the tank? Assume the water level and the pressure in the tank to remain constant, and neglect any effect of viscosity.

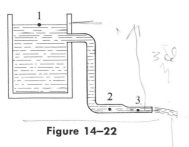

Figure 14–22

14–13. Water flows steadily from a reservoir, as in Fig. 14–22. The elevation of point 1 is 40 ft; of points 2 and 3 it is 4 ft. The cross section at point 2 is 0.5 ft² and at point 3 it is 0.25 ft². The area of the reservoir is very large compared with the cross sections of the pipe. (a) Compute the gauge pressure at point 2. (b) Compute the discharge rate in ft³/sec.

14–14. Sea water of density 2 slugs/ft³ flows steadily in a pipeline of constant cross section leading out of an elevated tank. At a point 4.5 ft below the water level in the tank the gauge pressure in the flowing stream is 1 lb/in². (a) What is the velocity of the water at this point? (b) If the pipe rises to a point 9 ft above the level of the water in the tank, what are the velocity and the pressure at the latter point?

14–15. Sea water weighing 64 lb/ft³ flows through a horizontal pipe of cross-sectional area 1.44 in². At one section the cross-sectional area is 0.72 in². The pressure difference between the two sections is 0.048 lb/in². How many cubic feet of water will flow out of the pipe in one minute?

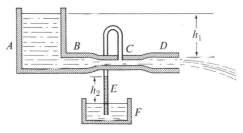

Figure 14–23

14–16. Two very large open tanks, A and F (Fig. 14–23), both contain the same liquid. A horizontal pipe BCD having a constriction at C leads out of the bottom of tank A, and a vertical pipe E opens into the constriction at C and dips into the liquid in tank F. Assume streamline flow and no viscosity. If the cross section at C is one-half that at D, and if D is at a distance h_1 below the level of the liquid in A, to what height h_2 will liquid rise in pipe E? Express your answer in terms of h_1. Neglect changes in atmospheric pressure with elevation.

14–17. At a certain point in a horizontal pipeline the gauge pressure is 6.24 lb/in². At another point the gauge pressure is 4.37 lb/in². If the areas of the pipe at these two points are 3 in² and 1.5 in² respectively, compute the number of cubic feet of water which flow across any cross section of the pipe per minute.

14–18. Water flowing in a horizontal pipe discharges at the rate of 0.12 ft³/sec. At a point in the pipe where the cross section is 0.01 ft², the absolute pressure is 18 lb/in². What must be the cross section of a constriction in the pipe such that the pressure there is reduced to 15 lb/in²?

14–19. The pressure difference between the main pipeline and the throat of a Venturi meter is 15 lb/in². The areas of the pipe and the constriction are 1 ft² and 0.5 ft². How many cubic feet per second are flowing through the pipe? The liquid in the pipe is water.

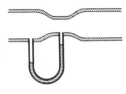

Figure 14–24

14–20. The section of pipe shown in Fig. 14–24 has a cross section of 0.04 ft² at the wider portions and 0.01 ft² at the constriction. One cubic foot of water is discharged from the pipe in 5 sec. (a) Find the velocities at the wide and the narrow portions. (b) Find the pressure difference between these portions. (c) Find the difference in height between the mercury columns in the U-tube.

14–21. Water is used as the manometric liquid in a Prandtl tube mounted in an aircraft to measure airspeed. If the maximum difference in height between the liquid columns is 10 cm, what is the maximum airspeed that can be measured? The density of air is 1.3×10^{-3} gm/cm³.

14–22. The inner, rotating cylinder of the viscosimeter in Fig. 14–11 is 5 cm in diameter. The inner diameter of the outer, fixed cylinder is 5.4 cm and the diameter of the pulley attached to the inner cylinder is 4 cm. A liquid whose viscosity is 6 poise fills the space between inner and outer cylinders to a depth of 8 cm. A body of mass 30 gm is supported by a thread wrapped around the pulley attached to the inner cylinder and hangs vertically, as shown in Fig. 14–11. Find the speed of descent of the body after it has reached its terminal velocity.

14–23. A viscous liquid flows through a tube with laminar flow, as in Fig. 14–13(b).

Prove that the volume rate of flow is the same as if the velocity were uniform at all points of a cross section and equal to half the velocity at the axis.

14–24. (a) With what terminal velocity will an air bubble 1 mm in diameter rise in a liquid of viscosity 150 cp and density 0.90 gm/cm³? (b) What is the terminal velocity of the same bubble in water?

14–25. (a) With what velocity is a steel ball 1 mm in radius falling in a tank of glycerine at 20°C at an instant when its acceleration is one-half that of a freely falling body? (b) What is the terminal velocity of the ball? The densities of ρ (steel) = 8.52 gm/cm³, ρ (glycerine) = 1.26 gm/cm³, η (glycerine) = 15 poises.

14–26. Assume that air is streaming horizontally past an aircraft wing such that the velocity is 100 ft/sec over the top surface and 80 ft/sec past the bottom surface. If the wing weighs 600 lb and has an area of 40 ft², what is the net force on the wing? The density of air is 0.0013 gm/cm³.

14–27. Modern airplane design calls for a "lift" of about 20 lb/ft² of wing area. Assume that air flows past the wing of an aircraft with streamline flow. If the velocity of flow past the lower wing surface is 300 ft/sec, what is the required velocity over the upper surface to give a "lift" of 20 lb/ft²? The density of air is 0.0013 gm/cm³.

14–28. Water at 20°C flows with a speed of 50 cm/sec through a pipe of diameter 3 mm. (a) What is the Reynolds number? (b) What is the nature of the flow?

14–29. Water at 20°C is pumped through a horizontal smooth pipe 15 cm in diameter and discharges into the air. When the pump maintains an absolute pressure of 1.02 atm at a point 300 m from the discharge end of the pipe, the velocity of flow is 30 cm/sec. (a) What is the nature of the flow? (b) What is the discharge rate in liters/sec?

14–30. The tank at the left of Fig. 14–14(a) has a very large cross section and is open to the atmosphere. The depth $y =$

40 cm. The cross sections of the horizontal tubes leading out of the tank are respectively 1 cm^2, 0.5 cm^2, and 0.2 cm^2. The liquid is ideal, having zero viscosity. (a) What is the volume rate of flow out of the tank? (b) What is the velocity in each portion of the horizontal tube? (c) What are the heights of the liquid in the vertical side tubes?

Suppose that the liquid in Fig. 14–14(b) has a viscosity of 0.5 poise, a density of 0.8 gm/cm^3, and that the depth of liquid in the large tank is such that the volume rate of flow is the same as in part (a) above.

The distance between the side tubes at c and d, and between those at e and f, is 20 cm. The cross sections of the horizontal tubes are the same in both diagrams. (d) What is the difference in level between the tops of the liquid columns in tubes c and d? (e) In tubes e and f? (f) What is the flow velocity on the axis of each part of the horizontal tube?

14–31. (a) Is it reasonable to assume that the flow in the second part of Problem 14–30 is laminar? (b) Would the flow be laminar if the liquid were water?

CHAPTER 15

Temperature-Expansion

15-1 Concept of temperature

To describe the equilibrium states of mechanical systems, as well as to study and predict the motions of rigid bodies and fluids, only three fundamental indefinables were needed: length, mass, and time. All other physical quantities of importance in mechanics could be expressed in terms of these three indefinables. We come, now, however, to a series of phenomena, called *thermal effects* or *heat phenomena*, which involve aspects that are essentially nonmechanical and which require for their description a fourth fundamental indefinable, the *temperature*.

Ever since early childhood we have experienced the sensations of hotness and coldness and described these sensations with the aid of adjectives such as cold, cool, tepid, warm, hot, etc. When we touch an object, we use our *temperature sense* to ascribe *to the object* a property called *temperature*, which determines whether it will feel hot or cold to the touch. The hotter it feels, the higher the temperature. This procedure plays the same role in "qualitative science" that hefting a body does in determining its weight or that kicking an object does in estimating its mass. To determine the mass of an object quantitatively, we must first arrive at the concept of mass by means of *quantitative* operations such as measuring the acceleration imparted to the object by a measured force, and then taking the ratio of F to a. This set of operations is performed without appeal to the sense perceptions associated with flexed muscles, or the discomfort connected with kicking. Similarly, the quantitative determination of temperature requires a set of operations that are independent of our sense perceptions of hotness or coldness, and which involve measurable quantities. How this is done will be explained in the following paragraphs.

There are certain simple systems the state of any one of which may be specified by measuring the value of one physical quantity. Consider for example a liquid such as mercury or alcohol contained in a very thin-walled bulb which communicates with a very narrow tube or capillary, as shown in Fig. 15-1(a). The state of this system is specified by noting the length of the liquid column, starting at an arbitrarily chosen point. The length L is called a *state coordinate*. Another simple system is shown in Fig. 15-1(b) which depicts a thin-walled vessel containing a gas whose volume remains constant and whose state coordinate, the pressure, is read on any convenient pressure gauge. In the next section, use will be made of a coil of fine wire (at constant tension) whose state coordinate is the value of its electrical resistance, and also a junction of two dissimilar metals whose state coordinate is the value of the electromotive force between its ends.

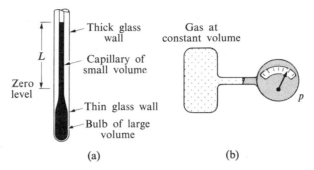

Fig. 15–1. (a) A system whose state is specified by the value of L. (b) A system whose state is given by the value of p.

Let A stand for the liquid-in-capillary system with state coordinate L and let B stand for the gas at constant volume with state coordinate p. If A and B are brought into contact, their state coordinates, in general, are found to change. When A and B are separated, however, the change is slower, and when thick walls of various materials like wood, plaster, felt, asbestos, etc., are used to separate A and B, the values of the respective state coordinates L and p are almost independent of each other. Generalizing from these observations, we postulate the existence of an ideal partition, called an **adiabatic wall,** *which, when used to separate two systems, allows their state coordinates to vary over a large range of values independently.* An adiabatic wall is an idealization that cannot be realized perfectly but may be approximated closely. It is represented as a thick cross-shaded region, as shown in Fig. 15–2(a).

When systems A and B are first put into actual contact or are separated by a thin metallic partition, their state coordinates may or may not change. *A wall which enables a state coordinate of one system to influence that of another is called a* **diathermic wall.** A thin sheet of copper is the most practical diathermic wall. As shown in Fig. 15–2(b), a diathermic wall is depicted as a thin, darkly shaded region. Eventually, a time will be reached when no further change in the coordinates of A and B takes place. *The joint state of both systems that exists when all changes in the coordinates have ceased is called* **thermal equilibrium.**

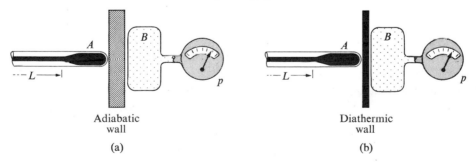

Fig. 15–2. System A, a liquid column, and system B, a gas at constant volume, separated by (a) an adiabatic wall, p and L independent, and (b) a diathermic wall, p and L dependent.

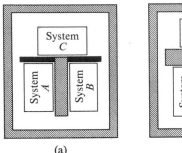
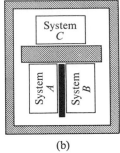

(a)   (b)

Fig. 15–3. The zeroth law of thermodynamics. (a) If A and B are each in thermal equilibrium with C, then (b) A and B are in thermal equilibrium with each other.

Imagine two systems A and B separated from each other by an adiabatic wall but each in contact with a third system C through diathermic walls, the whole assembly being surrounded by an adiabatic wall as shown in Fig. 15–3(a). Experiment shows that the two systems will come to thermal equilibrium with the third and that no further change will occur if the adiabatic wall separating them is then replaced by a diathermic wall [Fig. 15–3(b)]. If, instead of allowing both systems A and B to come to equilibrium with C at the same time, we first have equilibrium between A and C and then equilibrium between B and C (the state of system C being the same in both cases), then, when A and B are brought into communication through a diathermic wall, they will be found to be in thermal equilibrium. We shall use the expression "two systems are in thermal equilibrium" to mean that the two systems are in states such that if the two *were* connected through a diathermic wall, the combined system *would be* in thermal equilibrium.

These experimental facts may then be stated concisely in the following form: *Two systems in thermal equilibrium with a third are in thermal equilibrium with each other.* Following R. H. Fowler, we shall call this postulate *the zeroth law of thermodynamics.* At first thought it might seem that the zeroth law is obvious, but this is not so. An amber rod A that has been rubbed with fur will attract a neutral pith ball C. So will another similarly rubbed amber rod B, but the two amber rods will not attract each other. (Woman A loves man C. Woman B loves man C, but does woman A love woman B?)

When two systems A and B are first put in contact through a diathermic wall, they may or may not be in thermal equilibrium. One is entitled to ask, "What is there about A and B that determines whether or not they are in thermal equilibrium? Experiment shows that the mass, the density, the elastic modulus, the electric charge, the magnetic state, in fact none of the quantities of importance in mechanics, electricity, or magnetism is the determining factor. *We therefore infer the existence of a new property called the* **temperature**. *The temperature of a system is that property which determines whether or not it will be in thermal equilibrium with other systems. When two or more systems are in thermal equilibrium, they are said to have the same temperature.*

The temperature of all systems in thermal equilibrium may be represented by a number. The establishment of a temperature scale is merely the adoption of a set of rules for assigning numbers to temperatures. Once this is done, the condition for thermal equilibrium between two systems is that they have the same temperature. Also, when the temperatures are different, we may be sure that the systems are not in thermal equilibrium.

The preceding operational treatment of the concept of temperature merely expresses the fundamental idea that the temperature of a system is a property which eventually attains the same value as that of other systems when all these systems are put in contact or separated by thin metallic walls within an enclosure of thick asbestos walls. It will be recognized that this concept is identical with the everyday idea of temperature as a measure of the hotness or coldness of a system, since, so far as our senses may be relied upon, the hotness of all objects becomes the same after they have been together long enough. However, it was necessary to express this simple idea in technical language in order to be able to establish a rational set of rules for measuring temperature and also to provide a solid foundation for the study of advanced physics.

15–2 Thermometers

If we want to determine the temperatures of a number of systems, the simplest procedure is to choose *one* of the systems as an indicator of thermal equilibrium between it and the other systems. The system so chosen is called a *thermometer*. The reading of the thermometer is the temperature of all systems in thermal equilibrium with it. The important characteristics of a thermometer are *sensitivity* (an appreciable change in the state coordinate produced by a small change in temperature), *accuracy* in the measurement of the state coordinate, and *reproducibility*. Another often desirable property is *speed* in coming to thermal equilibrium with other systems. The thermometers which satisfy these requirements best will be described in the following paragraphs.

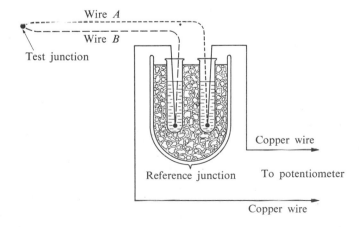

Fig. 15–4. Thermocouple, showing the test junction and the reference junction.

The most useful thermometer in most research and engineering laboratories is the *thermocouple*, which consists of a junction of two different metals or alloys, and which is labeled "test junction" in Fig. 15–4. The test junction is usually embedded in the material whose temperature is to be measured. Since the test junction is small and has a small mass, it can follow temperature changes rapidly and come to equilibrium quickly. The reference junction consists of two junctions: one of A and copper and the other of B and copper. These two junctions are maintained at any desired constant temperature, called the reference temperature. The state coordinate of this thermometer is an electrical quantity called the emf (ee-em-eff, electromotive force) which is measured with an instrument known as a potentiometer. A thermocouple with one junction of pure platinum and the other of 90% platinum and 10% rhodium is often used. Copper and an alloy called constantan are also frequently used.

A *resistance thermometer* consists of a fine wire, often enclosed in a thin-walled silver tube for protection. Copper wires lead from the thermometer unit to a resistance measuring device such as a Wheatstone bridge. Since resistance may be measured with great precision, the resistance thermometer is one of the most precise instruments for the measurement of temperature. In the region of extremely low temperatures a small carbon cylinder or a small piece of germanium crystal is used instead of a coil of platinum wire.

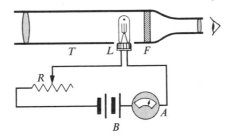

Fig. 15–5.   Principle of the optical pyrometer.

To measure temperatures above the range of thermocouples and resistance thermometers an *optical pyrometer* is used. As shown in Fig. 15–5, it consists essentially of a telescope T, in the tube of which is mounted a filter F of red glass and a small electric lamp bulb L. When the pyrometer is directed toward a furnace, an observer looking through the telescope sees the dark lamp filament against the bright background of the furnace. The lamp filament is connected to a battery B and a rheostat R. By turning the rheostat knob the current in the filament, and hence its brightness, may be gradually increased until the brightness of the filament just matches the brightness of the background. From previous calibration of the instrument at known temperatures, the scale of the ammeter A in the circuit may be marked to read the unknown temperature directly. Since no part of the instrument needs to come into contact with the hot body, the optical pyrometer may be used at temperatures above the melting points of metals.

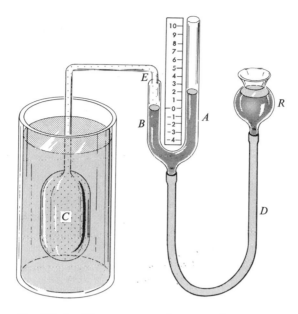

Fig. 15–6. The constant-volume gas thermometer.

Of all the state coordinates or, as they are often called, *thermometric properties*, the pressure of a gas whose volume is maintained constant stands out for its sensitivity, accuracy of measurement, and reproducibility. The constant-volume gas thermometer is illustrated schematically in Fig. 15–6. The materials, construction, and dimensions differ in various laboratories throughout the world and depend on the nature of the gas and the temperature range to be covered.

The gas, usually helium, is contained in bulb *C* and the pressure exerted by it can be measured by the open-tube mercury manometer. As the temperature of the gas increases, the gas expands, forcing the mercury down in tube *B* and up in tube *A*. Tubes *A* and *B* communicate through a rubber tube *D* with a mercury reservoir *R*. By raising *R*, the mercury level in *B* may be brought back to a reference mark *E*. The gas is thus kept at constant volume.

Gas thermometers are used mainly in bureaus of standards and in some university research laboratories. They are usually large, bulky, and slow in coming to thermal equilibrium.

15–3 The establishment of a temperature scale

Any one of the thermometers described in the preceding section may be used to indicate the constancy of a temperature if its state coordinate or thermometric property remains constant. By this means, it has been found that a system composed of a solid and a liquid of the same material maintained at constant pressure will remain in *phase equilibrium* (that is, the liquid and solid exist together without the liquid changing into solid or the solid changing into liquid) only at one definite temperature.

Similarly, a liquid will remain in phase equilibrium with its vapor at only one definite temperature when the pressure is maintained constant.

The temperature at which a solid and liquid of the same material coexist in phase equilibrium *at atmospheric pressure* is called the *normal melting point*, abbreviated NMP. The temperature at which a liquid and its vapor exist in phase equilibrium at atmospheric pressure is called the *normal boiling point*, abbreviated NBP.

Phase equilibrium between a solid and its vapor is sometimes possible at atmospheric pressure. The temperature at which this takes place is the *normal sublimation point*, NSP.

It is possible for all three phases: solid, liquid, and vapor to coexist in equilibrium, but only at one definite pressure and temperature known as the *triple point*, abbreviated TP. The triple-point pressure of water is 4.58 mm of Hg.

The NMP, NBP, NSP, and TP of any material can be chosen as a standard for the purpose of setting up a temperature scale. Any temperature so chosen is called a *fixed point*. Before 1954 there were two standard fixed points, the NBP of water and the equilibrium temperature of pure ice and air-saturated water. Both of these have been given up. *There is only one standard fixed point in modern thermometry and that is the triple point of water* to which is given the arbitrary number

$$273.16°K,$$

read 273.16 degrees kelvin.

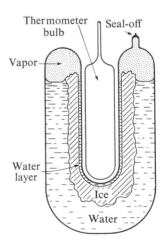

Fig. 15–7. Triple-point cell with a thermometer in the well, which melts a thin layer of ice nearby.

To achieve the triple point, water of the highest purity is distilled into a vessel like that shown schematically in Fig. 15–7. When all air has been removed, the vessel is sealed off. With the aid of a freezing mixture in the inner well, a layer of ice is formed around the well. When the freezing mixture is replaced by a thermometer bulb, a thin layer of ice is melted nearby. So long as the solid, liquid, and vapor phases coexist in equilibrium, the system is at the triple point.

We start our program of setting up a temperature scale by denoting with the letter *X any one* of the thermometric properties mentioned previously:

> the emf of a thermocouple, ε,
> the resistance of a wire, R,
> the pressure of a gas at constant volume, p, etc.

We define the ratio of two temperatures to be the same as the ratio of the two corresponding values of X. Thus, if a thermometer with thermometric property X is put in thermal equilibrium with a system and registers a value X, and is then put in thermal equilibrium with another system and registers a value X_3, the ratio of the temperatures of those two systems is given by

$$\frac{T(X)}{T(X_3)} = \frac{X}{X_3}. \tag{15–1}$$

If now, we let the subscript 3 stand for the standard fixed point, the triple point of water, then $T(X_3) = 273.16°K$. Hence

$$T(X) = 273.16°K \frac{X}{X_3}. \tag{15–2}$$

It is important to understand that the relation represented by Eq. (15–1) is an *arbitrary choice*. The ratio of two temperatures could have been chosen to be the ratio of the squares of the X's, or the logarithm of the ratio of the X's, or the ratio of the negative reciprocals of the X's.

The next step is to see what results are obtained when different thermometers are used to measure the same temperature, following the rules laid down in Eq. (15–2). The results of such a test in which four different thermometers [a copper-nickel thermocouple, a platinum resistance thermometer, and two hydrogen gas thermometers (one at high pressures and one at low pressures)] were used to measure the temperatures of six different fixed points, are listed in Table 15–1. It is clear from Eq. (15–2) that the temperature of the triple point of water must come out to be

TABLE 15–1

COMPARISON OF THERMOMETERS

Fixed point	(Cu-Ni) ε, mv	$T(\varepsilon)$	(Pt) R, ohms	$T(R)$	(H₂, const. V) p, atm	$T(p)$	(H₂, const. V) p, atm	$T(p)$
N₂ (NBP)	−0.10	−9.2	1.96	54.5	1.82	73	0.29	79
O₂ (NBP)	0	0	2.50	69.5	2.13	86	0.33	90
CO₂ (NSP)	+1.52	139	6.65	185	4.80	193	0.72	196
H₂O (TP)	$\varepsilon_3 = 2.98$	273	$R_3 = 9.83$	273	$p_3 = 6.80$	273	$p_3 = 1.00$	273
H₂O (NBP)	5.30	486	13.65	380	9.30	374	1.37	374
Sn (NMP)	9.02	826	18.56	516	12.70	510	1.85	505

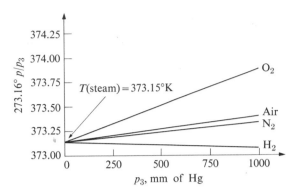

Fig. 15–8. Readings of a constant-volume gas thermometer for the temperature of condensing steam, when different gases are used at various values of p_3.

273.16°K. At any other fixed point, however, the two gas thermometers agree quite well, but differ markedly from the readings of the other two thermometers. Further experiments show that the greatest agreement is found among gas thermometers and that, *regardless of the nature of the gas, all gas thermometers at the same temperature approach the same reading as the pressure of the gas approaches zero.* The results of an experiment of this kind are shown in Fig. 15–8, where four gas thermometers give readings for the NBP of water which approach the same value, 373.15°K, as the pressure approaches zero.

We therefore define the gas temperature T by the equation

$$T = [273.16°K] \lim_{p_3 \to 0} \left(\frac{p}{p_3}\right)_{\text{const. vol.}} . \qquad (15\text{–}3)$$

It should be emphasized that this equation, or the set of rules for measuring temperature which it embodies, does not rest on the assumption that "the pressure of a gas at constant volume is directly proportional to the temperature." Such a statement, before a temperature scale is set up, is meaningless.

Although the temperature scale of Eq. (15–3) is independent of the properties of any one particular gas, it still depends on the properties of gases in general. To measure a low temperature, a gas that does not liquefy at the low temperature must be used. The lowest temperature that can be measured with a gas thermometer is about 1°K, provided low-pressure helium is used. *The temperature $T = 0$ remains as yet undefined.*

The kelvin temperature scale, which is independent of the properties of any particular substance, will be described in Chapter 19. It can be shown that in the temperature region in which a gas thermometer can be used, the gas scale and the kelvin scale are identical. In anticipation of this result, we write °K after a gas temperature. It will also be shown in Chapter 19 how the absolute zero of temperature is defined on the kelvin scale. Until then, the term "absolute zero" will have no meaning. The statement made so often that all molecular activity ceases at the temperature $T = 0$ is entirely erroneous. When it is necessary in statistical mechanics to correlate temperature with molecular activity, it is found that classical statistical mechanics must be modified with the aid of quantum mechanics. When this modification is carried out, the molecules of a substance at absolute zero have a *finite* amount of kinetic energy known as the *zero-point* energy.

15–4 The celsius, rankine, and fahrenheit scales

The celsius* temperature scale (formerly called the centigrade scale in the United States and Great Britain) employs a degree of the same magnitude as that of the kelvin scale, but its zero point is shifted so that *the celsius temperature of the triple point of water is* 0.01 *degree celsius*, abbreviated 0.01°C. Thus, if t denotes the celsius temperature,

$$t = T - 273.15°K. \tag{15–4}$$

The celsius temperature t_S at which steam condenses at 1 atm pressure is

$$t_S = T_S - 273.15°K,$$

and reading T_S from Fig. 15–8,

$$t_S = 373.15° - 273.15° \quad \text{or} \quad t_S = 100.00°C.$$

There are two other scales in common use in engineering and in everyday life in the United States and in Great Britain. The *rankine*† temperature T_R (written °R) is proportional to the kelvin temperature according to the relation

$$T_R = \tfrac{9}{5}T. \tag{15–5}$$

A degree of the same size is used in the *fahrenheit*‡ scale t_F (written °F), but with the zero point shifted according to the relation

$$t_F = T_R - 459.67°R. \tag{15–6}$$

Substituting Eqs. (15–4) and (15–5) into Eq. (15–6), we get

$$t_F = \tfrac{9}{5}t + 32°F, \tag{15–7}$$

from which it follows that the fahrenheit temperature of the ice point ($t = 0°C$) is 32°F and of the steam point ($t = 100°C$) is 212°F. The 100 celsius or kelvin degrees between the ice point and the steam point correspond to 180 fahrenheit or rankine degrees, as shown in Fig. 15–9, where the four scales are compared.

---

* Named after Anders Celsius (1701–1744).
† William John MacQuorn Rankine (1820–1872).
‡ Gabriel Fahrenheit (1686–1736).

The accurate measurement of a boiling point or melting point with the aid of a gas thermometer requires months of painstaking laboratory work and mathematical computation. Fortunately, this has been done for a large number of substances which are obtainable with high purity. Some of these results are shown in Table 15–2. With the aid of these basic fixed points other thermometers may be calibrated.

Suppose the temperature of a beaker of water is raised from 20°C to 30°C, through a temperature interval of 10 celsius degrees. It is desirable to distinguish between such a temperature interval and the actual temperature of 10 degrees above the celsius zero. Hence we shall use the phrase "10 degrees celsius," or "10°C," when referring to an *actual temperature*, and "10 celsius degrees," or "10 C°" to mean a temperature *interval*. Thus there is an interval of 10 celsius degrees between 20 degrees celsius and 30 degrees celsius.

TABLE 15–2

TEMPERATURES OF FIXED POINTS

Basic fixed points	T, °K	t, °C	T_R, °R	t_F, °F
Standard: Triple point of water	**273.16**	**0.01**	**491.688**	**32.018**
NBP of oxygen	90.18	−182.97	162.32	−297.35
Equil. of ice and air-saturated water				
(ice point)	273.15	0.00	491.67	32.00
NBP of water (steam point)	373.15	100.00	671.67	212.00
NMP of zinc	692.66	419.51	1246.78	787.11
NMP of antimony	903.65	630.50	1626.57	1166.90
NMP of silver	1233.95	960.80	2221.11	1761.44
NMP of gold	1336.15	1063.00	2405.07	1945.40

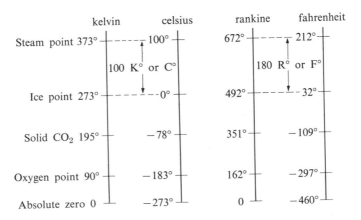

Fig. 15–9. Relations among kelvin, celsius, rankine, and fahrenheit temperature scales. Temperatures have been rounded off to the nearest degree.

15–5 Expansion of solids and liquids

With a few exceptions, the volumes of all bodies increase with increasing temperature if the external pressure on the body remains constant. Suppose that a solid or a
liquid undergoes a change of volume dV when the temperature is changed an amount
dT (or dt, since the kelvin degree and the celsius degree are temperature intervals of
equal magnitude). The *coefficient of volume expansion* β is defined as *the fractional
change in volume dV/V divided by the change of temperature dT*, or

$$\beta = \frac{1}{V}\frac{dV}{dT} = \frac{1}{V}\frac{dV}{dt} \qquad \text{(at constant pressure)}. \qquad (15\text{–}8)$$

The unit of β is 1 *reciprocal degree*, or $1 \ \text{deg}^{-1}$. The numerical value depends, of
course, on the size of the degree. Since the kelvin and celsius degrees are $\frac{9}{5}$ as large
as the rankine and fahrenheit degrees, the fractional volume change per kelvin or
celsius degree is $\frac{9}{5}$ as great as that per rankine or fahrenheit degree.

The coefficient of volume expansion is often calculated from an empirical equation
between the density ρ and the temperature at constant pressure. When this method
is not possible, optical methods involving the interference of light are used.

The coefficient of volume expansion is insensitive to a change of pressure, but
varies markedly with the temperature. Many experiments indicate that β decreases
as the temperature is lowered, approaching zero as the kelvin temperature approaches
zero. It is also a peculiar circumstance that the higher the melting point of a metal,
the lower the coefficient of volume expansion.

Calling $\bar{\beta}$ the average value of β within a moderate temperature interval $\Delta T = \Delta t$,
we may approximate Eq. (15–8) by writing

$$\Delta V = \bar{\beta}V_0 \, \Delta T = \bar{\beta}V_0 \, \Delta t, \qquad (15\text{–}9)$$

where V_0 is the original volume.

Some values of $\bar{\beta}$, in the neighborhood of room temperature, are listed in Table
15–3. Notice that the values for liquids are much larger than those for solids.

If there is a hole in a solid body, the volume of the hole increases when the body
expands, just as if the hole were a solid of the same material as the body. This remains

TABLE 15–3

COEFFICIENT OF VOLUME EXPANSION (APPROXIMATE)

Solids	$\bar{\beta}$, $(\text{C}°)^{-1}$	Liquids	$\bar{\beta}$, $(\text{C}°)^{-1}$
Aluminum	7.2×10^{-5}	Alcohol, ethyl	75×10^{-5}
Brass	6.0	Carbon disulfide	115
Copper	4.2	Glycerine	49
Glass	1.2–2.7	Mercury	18
Steel	3.6		
Invar	0.27		
Quartz (fused)	0.12		

true even if the hole becomes so large that the surrounding body is reduced to a thin shell. Thus the volume enclosed by a thin-walled glass flask or thermometer bulb increases just as would a solid body of glass of the same size.

EXAMPLE. A glass flask of volume 200 cm^3 is just filled with mercury at 20°C. How much mercury will overflow when the temperature of the system is raised to 100°C? The coefficient of volume expansion of the glass is 1.2 × 10^{-5} (C°)$^{-1}$.

The increase in the volume of the flask is

$$\Delta V = 1.2 \times 10^{-5} \times 200 \times (100° - 20°) = 0.192 \text{ cm}^3.$$

The increase in the volume of the mercury is

$$\Delta V = 18 \times 10^{-5} \times 200 \times (100° - 20°) = 2.88 \text{ cm}^3.$$

The volume of mercury overflowing is therefore

$$2.88 - 0.19 = 2.69 \text{ cm}^3.$$

Water, in the temperature range from 0°C to 4°C, *decreases* in volume with increasing temperature, contrary to the behavior of most substances. That is, between 0°C and 4°C the coefficient of expansion of water is *negative*. Above 4°C, water expands when heated. Since the volume of a given mass of water is smaller at 4°C than at any other temperature, the density of water is a maximum at 4°C. This behavior of water is the reason why lakes and ponds freeze first at their upper surface. Figure 15–10 illustrates this anomalous expansion of water in the temperature range from 0°C to 10°C. Table 15–4 covers a wider range of temperatures.

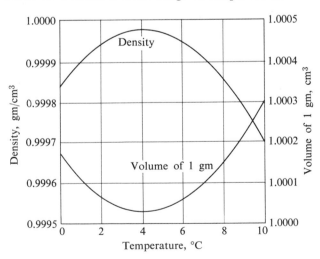

Fig. 15–10. Density of water, and volume of 1 gram, in the temperature range from 0°C to 10°C.

TABLE 15-4

DENSITY AND VOLUME OF WATER

$t°C$	Density (gm/cm^3)	Volume of 1 gram (cm^3)
0	0.9998	1.0002
4	1.0000	1.0000
10	0.9997	1.0003
20	0.9982	1.0018
50	0.9881	1.0121
75	0.9749	1.0258
100	0.9584	1.0434

For a body in the form of a rod or cable, we are often interested only in the change of *length* with temperature, and we define a *coefficient of linear expansion* α. If L is the length,

$$\alpha = \frac{1}{L}\frac{dL}{dT} = \frac{1}{L}\frac{dL}{dt}, \tag{15-10}$$

and, over a moderate temperature change,

$$\Delta L = L_0 \bar{\alpha} \, \Delta T = L_0 \bar{\alpha} \, \Delta t, \tag{15-11}$$

where $\bar{\alpha}$ is the average coefficient within the temperature interval, and L_0 is the original length.

The volume coefficient may be calculated in terms of the linear coefficient as follows. Suppose that a solid body is in the form of a rectangular parallelepiped with dimensions L_1, L_2, and L_3. Then the volume is

$$V = L_1 L_2 L_3,$$

and

$$\frac{dV}{dT} = L_2 L_3 \frac{dL_1}{dT} + L_1 L_3 \frac{dL_2}{dT} + L_1 L_2 \frac{dL_3}{dT}.$$

Dividing by $L_1 L_2 L_3$, we obtain

$$\frac{1}{V}\frac{dV}{dT} = \frac{1}{L_1}\frac{dL_1}{dT} + \frac{1}{L_2}\frac{dL_2}{dT} + \frac{1}{L_3}\frac{dL_3}{dT}.$$

If the solid has the same properties in each of the three directions, each of the three expressions on the right is the coefficient of linear expansion α, and hence

$$\beta = 3\alpha. \tag{15-12}$$

The coefficient of linear expansion is usually measured with the aid of an optical interferometer.

15–6 Thermal stresses

If the ends of a rod are rigidly fixed so as to prevent expansion or contraction and the temperature of the rod is changed, tensile or compressive stresses, called *thermal stresses*, will be set up in the rod. These stresses may become very large, sufficiently so to stress the rod beyond its elastic limit or even beyond its breaking strength. Hence in the design of any structure which is subject to changes in temperature, some provision must, in general, be made for expansion. In a long steam pipe this is accomplished by the insertion of expansion joints or a section of pipe in the form of a U. In bridges, one end may be rigidly fastened to its abutment while the other rests on rollers.

It is a simple matter to compute the thermal stress set up in a rod which is not free to expand or contract. Suppose that a rod at a temperature t has its ends rigidly fastened, and that while they are thus held the temperature is reduced to a lower value, t_0.

The fractional change in length if the rod were free to contract would be

$$\frac{\Delta L}{L_0} = \bar{\alpha}(t - t_0) = \bar{\alpha}\,\Delta t. \tag{15–13}$$

Since the rod is not free to contract, the tension must increase by a sufficient amount to produce the same fractional change in length. But from the definition of Young's modulus,

$$Y = \frac{F/A}{\Delta L/L_0}, \qquad F = AY\frac{\Delta L}{L_0}.$$

Introducing the expression for $\Delta L/L_0$ from Eq. (15–13), we have

$$F = AY\bar{\alpha}\,\Delta t, \tag{15–14}$$

which gives the tension F in the rod. The *stress* in the rod is

$$\frac{F}{A} = Y\bar{\alpha}\,\Delta t. \tag{15–15}$$

Problems

15-1. The limiting value of the ratio of the pressures of a gas at the melting point of lead and at the triple point of water, when the gas is kept at constant volume, is found to be 2.19816. What is the kelvin temperature of the melting point of lead?

15-2. (a) If you feel sick in France and are told you have a fever of 40°C, should you be concerned? (b) What is normal body temperature on the celsius scale? (c) The normal boiling point of liquid oxygen is −182.97°C. What is this temperature on the kelvin and rankine scales? (d) At what temperature do the fahrenheit and celsius scales coincide?

15-3. The pressure p, volume V, number of moles n, and kelvin temperature T of an ideal gas are related by the equation $pV = nRT$. Prove that the coefficient of volume expansion is equal to the reciprocal of the kelvin temperature.

15-4. (a) The relation among the density ρ, the mass m, and the volume V is $\rho = m/V$. Prove that

$$\beta = -\frac{1}{\rho}\frac{\partial \rho}{\partial T}.$$

(b) The density of rock salt between −193°C and −13°C is given by the empirical formula

$$\rho = 2.1680$$

$$\times (1 - 11.2 \times 10^{-5}t - 0.5 \times 10^{-7}t^2).$$

Calculate β at −100°C.

15-5. The total change of volume ΔV of a metal, when the temperature changes from room temperature ($T_r = 300°K$) to the melting point T_m, is still only a small fraction of the original volume, so that

$$\frac{\Delta V}{V} = \int_{T_r}^{T_m} \beta \, dT.$$

Given the data in Table 15-5 (see page 351), calculate the average value of $\Delta V/V$ for these three metals.

15-6. A glass flask whose volume is exactly 1000 cm^3 at 0°C is filled level full of mercury at this temperature. When flask and mercury are heated to 100°C, 15.2 cm^3 of mercury overflow. If the coefficient of volume expansion of mercury is 0.000182 per centigrade degree, compute the coefficient of linear expansion of the glass.

15-7. At a temperature of 20°C, the volume of a certain glass flask, up to a reference mark on the stem of the flask, is exactly 100 cm^3. The flask is filled to this point with a liquid whose cubical coefficient of expansion is 120×10^{-5} per C°, with both flask and liquid at 20°C. The linear coefficient of expansion of the glass is 8×10^{-6} per C°. The cross section of the stem is 1 mm^2 and can be considered constant. How far will the liquid rise or fall in the stem when the temperature is raised to 40°C?

15-8. To ensure a tight fit, the aluminum rivets used in airplane construction are made slightly larger than the rivet holes and cooled by "dry ice" (solid CO_2) before being driven. If the diameter of a hole is 0.2500 inch, what should be the diameter of a rivet at 20°C if its diameter is to equal that of the hole when the rivet is cooled to −78°C, the temperature of dry ice? Assume the expansion coefficient to remain constant at the value given in Table 15-2.

15-9. A metal rod 30.0 cm long expands by 0.075 cm when its temperature is raised from 0°C to 100°C. A rod of a different metal of the same length expands by 0.045 cm for the same rise in temperature. A third rod, also 30.0 cm long, is made up of pieces of each of the above metals placed end-to-end and expands 0.065 cm between 0°C and 100°C. Find the length of each portion of the composite bar.

15-10. A hole 1.000 in. in diameter is bored in a brass plate at a temperature of

20°C. What is the diameter of the hole when the temperature of the plate is increased to 200°C? Assume the expansion coefficient to remain constant.

15–11. Suppose that a steel hoop could be constructed around the earth's equator, just fitting it at a temperature of 20°C. What would be the space between the hoop and the earth if the temperature of the hoop were increased by 1 C°?

15–12. A clock whose pendulum makes one vibration in 2 sec is correct at 25°C. The pendulum shaft is of steel and its mass may be neglected compared with that of the bob. (a) What is the fractional change in length of the shaft when it is cooled to 15°C? (b) How many seconds per day will the clock gain or lose at 15°C? [*Hint.* Use differentials.]

15–13. A clock with a brass pendulum shaft keeps correct time at a certain temperature. (a) How closely must the temperature be controlled if the clock is not to gain or lose more than 1 sec per day? Does the answer depend on the period of the pendulum? (b) Will an increase of temperature cause the clock to gain or lose?

15–14. The length of a bridge is 2000 ft. (a) If it were a continuous span, fixed at one end and free to move at the other, about what would be the range of motion of the free end between a cold winter day ($-20°F$) and a hot summer day ($100°F$)? (b) If both ends were rigidly fixed on the summer day, what would be the stress on the winter day?

15–15. The cross section of a steel rod is 1.5 in². What is the least force that will prevent it from contracting while cooling from 520°C to 20°C?

15–16. A steel wire which is 10 ft long at 20°C is found to increase in length by $\frac{3}{4}$ inch when heated to 520°C. Compute its average coefficient of linear expansion. (b) Find the stress in the wire if it is stretched taut at 520° and cooled to 20° without being allowed to contract.

15–17. A steel rod of length 40 cm and a copper rod of length 36 cm, both of the

same diameter, are placed end-to-end between two rigid supports, with no initial stress in the rods. The temperature of the rods is now raised by 50C°. What is the stress in each rod?

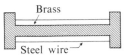

Figure 15–11

15–18. A heavy brass bar has projections at its ends, as in Fig. 15–11. Two fine steel wires fastened between the projections are just taut (zero tension) when the whole system is at 0°C. What is the tensile stress in the steel wires when the temperature of the system is raised to 300°C? Make any simplifying assumptions you think are justified, but state what they are.

15–19. The steel rails of the missile testing track at Tularosa Basin, New Mexico, are welded into 10,000-ft lengths and each length is prestressed by stretching it 3 ft before it is fastened to the concrete base slab. (a) What is the strain in the rails? (b) If the stretch modulus is 30×10^6 lb/in², what is the stress? (c) What stretching force is required if the cross-sectional area of a rail is 50 in²? (d) If the stretched rails are fastened to the base slab at a temperature of 60°F, what is the stress when the temperature decreases to 0°F? (e) At what temperature will the stress change from tension to compression?

15–20. Prove that if a body under hydrostatic pressure is raised in temperature but not allowed to expand, the increase in pressure is

$$\Delta p = B\bar{\beta}\,\Delta t,$$

where the bulk modulus B and the average coefficient of volume expansion $\bar{\beta}$ are both assumed positive and constant.

15–21. (a) A block of metal at a pressure of 1 atm and a temperature of 20°C is kept at constant volume. If the temperature is raised to 32°C, what will be the final pressure? (b) If the block is maintained at constant volume by rigid walls that can withstand a maximum pressure of 1200 atm, what is the highest temperature to which the system may be raised? Assume B and $\bar{\beta}$ to remain practically constant at the values 1.5×10^{12} dynes/cm^2 and $5.0 \times 10^{-5}(C°)^{-1}$, respectively.

15–22. What hydrostatic pressure is necessary to prevent a copper block from expanding when its temperature is increased from 20°C to 30°C?

15–23. Table 15–4 lists the density of water, and the volume of 1 gm, at atmospheric pressure. A steel bomb is filled with water at 10°C and atmospheric pressure, and the system is heated to 75°C. What is then the pressure in the bomb? Assume the bomb to be sufficiently rigid so that its

volume is not affected by the increased pressure.

15–24. A liquid is enclosed in a metal cylinder provided with a piston of the same metal. The system is originally at atmospheric pressure and at a temperature of 80°C. The piston is forced down until the pressure on the liquid is increased by 100 atm, and it is then clamped in this position. Find the new temperature at which the pressure of the liquid is again 1 atmosphere. Assume that the cylinder is sufficiently strong so that its volume is not altered by changes in pressure, but only by changes in temperature. Compressibility of liquid $(k) = 50 \times 10^{-6}$ atm^{-1}. Cubical coefficient of expansion of liquid $(\beta) = 5.3 \times 10^{-4}(C°)^{-1}$. Linear coefficient of expansion of metal $(\alpha) = 10 \times 10^{-6}(C°)^{-1}$.

TABLE 15–5

	T_m, °K	β, $[10^{-6}(K°)^{-1}]$
Copper	1360	$43 + 0.022T$
Palladium	1830	$30 + 0.015T$
Platinum	2050	$24 + 0.0086T$

CHAPTER 16

Heat and Heat Measurements

16–1 Heat, a form of energy

The temperature of a system is a property of the system that determines whether it will or will not be in thermal equilibrium with any other system with which it is put in contact. Suppose that system A, at a higher temperature than system B, is put in contact with B. When thermal equilibrium has been reached, A will be found to have undergone a temperature decrease and B a temperature increase. It was therefore quite natural for the early investigators in this field to assume that A lost something and that this "something" flowed into B. Nowadays, we recognize that there is a flow of energy between two such bodies and the energy *while in transit* is called *heat*.

Heat is the energy transfer between two systems that is connected exclusively with the **temperature difference** *between the systems.*

The process of heat transfer was formerly thought to be a flow of an invisible weightless fluid called *caloric*, which was produced when a substance burned and which could be transmitted by conduction from one body to another. The abandonment of the caloric theory was a part of the general development of physics during the 18th and 19th centuries. Two men who were largely responsible for views we hold today were Count Rumford (1753–1814) (a native of Woburn, Mass.) and Sir James Prescott Joule (1818–1889).

Rumford was engaged in supervising the boring of cannon for the government of Bavaria. To prevent overheating, the bore of the cannon was kept filled with water, and as this boiled away during the boring process the supply had to be continually replenished. It was admitted that caloric had to be supplied to water in order to boil it, and the continual production of caloric was explained by the hypothesis that when matter was more finely subdivided (as in the process of boring) its capacity for retaining caloric grew smaller and the caloric thus released was what caused the water to boil.

Rumford noted, however, that the cooling water continued to boil away even when his boring tools became so dull that they were no longer cutting. That is, even a dull boring tool was apparently an inexhaustible supply of caloric *so long as mechanical work was being done to rotate the tool.*

Now one of the features which justifies our acceptance of many abstract ideas in physics is that they obey a "conservation principle." Here was a process in which *two* quantities failed to be conserved. Mechanical energy was not conserved, since work was continually being expended, and caloric was not conserved, since it was continually being created. Although Rumford did not express his ideas in just this way, he saw the opportunity to eliminate two cases of nonconservation and at the same time to extend the principle of the conservation of energy as it was then understood. He asserted that what had formerly been thought a separate entity, namely caloric, was in reality merely energy in another form. The process was not the continual disappearance of one thing and the appearance of another, but merely the transformation of energy from one form to another. As we would say today, mechanical energy was continually being transformed into heat, the process being one example of the conservation of energy.

Rumford made some measurements of the quantities of work done and of cooling water boiled away, but his experiments were not of great precision. When Joule, in the period from 1843 to 1878, showed that whenever a given quantity of mechanical energy was converted to heat the *same* quantity of heat was always developed, the equivalence of heat and work as two forms of energy was definitely established.

16–2 Units of heat.   The mechanical equivalent of heat

Before the equivalence of work and heat had been established, two units of heat had been defined, the *calorie* and the *British thermal unit* or Btu. The calorie was originally defined as the quantity of heat required to raise the temperature of 1 gram of water through 1 celsius degree, and the Btu as the quantity of heat required to raise the temperature of 1 pound-mass* of water through 1 fahrenheit degree. Although the units are still in use, the definitions above have been abandoned, and for two reasons. One is that since we now feel sure that heat is a form of energy, it is unnecessary to define arbitrary units in which to measure heat and then devote much time and effort to finding the ratio between these units and the joule or the foot·pound. The other reason is that careful measurements showed that the quantity of heat required to raise the temperature of 1 gram of water through 1 celsius degree varied slightly with the location of the degree in the temperature scale, that is, whether it was from 1°C to 2°C, or from 37°C to 38°C. This variation is shown in Table 16–1. By international agreement, the calorie and Btu are now *defined* as specified multiples of the joule. It was found that if 1 calorie was defined as *exactly* 1/860 watt·hour,

TABLE 16–1

HEAT TO RAISE 1 GRAM OF WATER 1 C°

Temperature, °C	0	20	40	60	80	100
Number of calories	1.0087	0.9986	0.9976	0.9993	1.0024	1.0065

---

* In a perfectly consistent engineering system, the unit of heat would be defined as that required to raise the temperature of a *unit mass* (i.e., one slug) of water through 1 fahrenheit degree. To conform to engineering practice, we shall use the *pound-mass* (equal to 1/32.174 slug) as the unit of mass in the section on heat.

the size of this calorie was very nearly the same as the (somewhat vague) original calorie. The Btu is defined in terms of the calorie through the relation

$$1 \text{ cal/gm·C°} = 1 \text{ Btu/lbm·F°}.$$

These definitions lead to the following relations:

$$1 \text{ calorie} = \tfrac{1}{860} \text{ watt·hour} = 4.18605 \text{ joules},$$

$$1 \text{ Btu} = 778.26 \text{ ft·lb} = 251.996 \text{ cal}.$$

The ratios 4.18605 joules/cal and 778.26 ft·lb/Btu are called the *mechanical equivalent of heat*. Their numerical values are now matters of definition, not experiment.

The logical procedure would be to abandon the calorie and Btu, and to express heat, like any other form of energy, in ergs, joules, ft·lb, etc. Many of the current experimental measurements of heat are in fact reported in terms of joules rather than calories, but the calorie and the Btu are so deeply embedded in the literature of science and engineering that many years will elapse before they become obsolete.

16–3 Heat capacity

Suppose that a small quantity of heat dQ is transferred between a system and its surroundings. If the system undergoes a temperature change dt, the *specific heat capacity c of the system is defined as the ratio of the heat dQ to the product of the mass m and temperature difference dt*; thus

$$c = \frac{dQ}{m \, dt}. \tag{16–1}$$

The specific heat capacity of water can be taken to be 1 cal/gm·C° or 1 Btu/lb·F° for most practical purposes.

It is often convenient to use the *gram-mole* as a unit of mass. One gram-mole is a number of grams equal to the molecular weight M. To calculate the number of moles n, we divide the mass in grams by the molecular weight; thus $n = m/M$. Replacing the mass m in Eq. (16–1) by the product nM, we get

$$Mc = \frac{dQ}{n \, dt},$$

a quantity called the *molar heat capacity* and represented by the symbol C. Hence, by definition

$$C = \frac{dQ}{n \, dt} = Mc. \tag{16–2}$$

The molar heat capacity of water is practically 18 cal/mole·C°.

From Eq. (16–1) the total quantity of heat Q that must be supplied to a body of mass m to change its temperature from t_1 to t_2 is

$$Q = m \int_{t_1}^{t_2} c \, dt. \tag{16–3}$$

The specific heat capacities of all materials vary with temperature, and of course c must be expressed as a function of t in order to carry out the integration. Over a temperature range in which c can be considered constant, Eq. (16–3) becomes

$$Q = mc(t_2 - t_1). \tag{16-4}$$

The *mean* specific heat capacity $\bar{c}$ over any range of temperature is defined as the constant value of c which would result in the same heat transfer. Hence, for the temperature range from t_1 to t_2,

$$Q = m\bar{c}(t_2 - t_1) = m\int_{t_1}^{t_2} c\,dt. \tag{16-5}$$

Equations similar to (16–3), (16–4), and (16–5) may be written in terms of n, C, and $\bar{C}$.

The specific or molar heat capacity of a substance is not the only physical property whose experimental determination requires the measurement of a quantity of heat. Heat conductivity, heat of fusion, heat of vaporization, heat of combustion, heat of solution, and heat of reaction are examples of other such properties which are called *thermal properties* of matter. The field of physics and physical chemistry concerned with the measurement of thermal properties is called *calorimetry*, and it is one of the most difficult branches of experimental science.

16–4 The measurement of heat capacity

The simplest method of measuring the mean specific or molar heat capacity of a solid over a temperature interval within the range from 0°C to 100°C involves the use of a *water calorimeter* and a technique known as the *method of mixtures*.

The water calorimeter in its simplest form consists of a thin-walled metal can A (Fig. 16–1) which contains a measured quantity of water and is provided with a cover through which passes thermometer B. Heat losses are reduced by surrounding the can with the heat-insulating jacket C. If the thermometer is read before and after an unknown quantity of heat Q is introduced into the calorimeter, Q may be found from the measured rise in temperature.

The water calorimeter may be used to measure average specific or molar heat capacity as follows. A sample of material is heated in a furnace or steam bath to a known temperature. The water in the calorimeter is thoroughly stirred and its temperature is measured. The sample is then quickly transferred to the calorimeter, the water is again thoroughly stirred, and the new temperature of the water is recorded. If no heat is lost from the calorimeter during the experiment, the heat given up by the sample in cooling must equal the heat gained by the water and the calorimeter can.

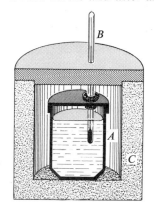

Fig. 16–1. A simple type of water calorimeter.

Let the subscripts s, w, c stand for sample (or specimen), water, and calorimeter, respectively. Let the sample start at the temperature t_s and the water and calorimeter start at t_1. Let the final temperature of the entire system be t_2. Then, assuming all specific heat capacities to be constant,

$$m_s c_s(t_s - t_2) = m_w c_w(t_2 - t_1) + m_c c_c(t_2 - t_1)$$

$$\left\{\begin{matrix} \text{Heat liberated} \\ \text{by the sample} \end{matrix}\right\} = \left\{\begin{matrix} \text{Heat absorbed} \\ \text{by the water} \end{matrix}\right\} + \left\{\begin{matrix} \text{Heat absorbed} \\ \text{by the calorimeter} \end{matrix}\right\}.$$

Actually the calorimeter will gain (or lose) heat from its surroundings during an experiment unless special precautions are taken. One way of minimizing the heat transfer is to start with the calorimeter somewhat cooler than its surroundings and finish with its temperature the same amount higher than the surroundings. Then the heat gained during the first part of the experiment offsets the heat lost in the latter part. It should be emphasized again that the method of mixtures yields only the average specific heat capacity over the rather large temperature range from t_s to t_2. This quantity, although useful to the engineer, is of very little value to the modern physicist who requires many different values of the true specific or molar heat capacity at many different temperatures, all the way from close to absolute zero to the melting point.

The temperature variation of the specific or molar heat capacity provides the closest and most direct approach to the understanding of the energy of the particles constituting matter. The measurement of the heat capacities of chemical compounds, normal metals, metallic alloys, superconducting metals, alloys, compounds, etc., particularly at low temperatures, constitutes one of the liveliest and most interesting topics of modern physics.

Almost all modern calorimetry is electrical. The temperature difference necessary for a flow of heat is provided by maintaining an electric current I in a coil of resistance wire (the heater) usually wound around the material under investigation. Electrical resistance plays the same role as friction in mechanics. As soon as the temperature of the heater coil rises a trifle above that of the sample, heat flows in, and if proper precautions are taken, only a little of this heat is lost to the surroundings. The thermometer is usually a small resistance thermometer or thermocouple embedded in the sample and is chosen for its rapidity and its sensitivity. Readings are taken before the switch in the heater circuit is closed; these are shown on the left of Fig. 16–2. The fact that the temperature rises before energy is supplied to the heater indicates that the surroundings are at a temperature higher than that of the sample. The current is maintained in the heater for a time interval $\Delta\tau$ (τ is the symbol for time) during which no measurements of temperature are made. A short time after the switch in the heater circuit is opened, temperature measurements are resumed, giving rise to the right-hand part of Fig. 16–2, where the positive slope indicates that the surroundings are still higher in temperature than the sample.

If the potential difference across the heater is V, and an electric current I is maintained for a time $\Delta\tau$, then the heat transferred to the sample is $VI\,\Delta\tau$. The molar heat capacity is therefore

$$C = VI\,\Delta\tau/n\,\Delta T, \tag{16–6}$$

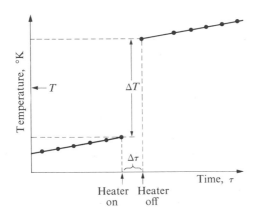

Fig. 16–2. Temperature-time graph of the data taken during a heat capacity measurement.

where C will be expressed in joules/mole·deg when I is expressed in amperes, V in volts, τ in seconds, and ΔT is read from the graph as in Fig. 16–2. The resulting molar heat capacity C is the value at the temperature T which is in the middle of the range ΔT. In careful experiments, ΔT may be as small as $0.01\mathrm{K}°$.

The shape, size, and construction of the calorimeter, heating coils, thermometers, etc., depend on the nature of the material to be studied and the temperature range desired. It is impossible to describe one calorimeter that is sufficient for all purposes. In general, the measurement of any heat capacity is a research problem requiring all the ability of a trained physicist or physical chemist, the facilities of a good shop, and the skill of a good glass blower.

16–5 Experimental values of heat capacities

The amount of heat transferred to or from a system depends on the manner in which the system is controlled or constrained during the transfer, that is, whether the system is kept at *constant pressure* or at *constant volume*. The two corresponding specific or molar heat capacities are denoted by the respective symbols c_P (or C_P) and c_V (or C_V). In the method of mixtures and also in the electrical method of measuring heat capacities, the sample under investigation was maintained at constant pressure. In these and in other practical methods, the quantity measured was c_P or C_P. As a matter of fact, it would be almost impossible to make a precise determination of c_V because there is no effective way of keeping the volume of a system constant and of allowing for the heat transferred to the containing walls.

In the design of practical devices for carrying currents of hot liquids, for heating water, for generating steam, etc., it is sufficient to know, for the materials, merely the *average* specific or molar heat capacity at constant pressure. Measurements made by the method of mixtures are satisfactory for these purposes, and a few such values are listed in Table 16–2. The average values of the specific heat capacity are seen to be less than 1 cal/gm·C° and are smaller, the larger the molecular weight. In the last column, an interesting regularity, first noted in 1819 by two French physicists, Dulong and Petit, appears. The average molar heat capacity at constant pressure for all

TABLE 16–2

MEAN SPECIFIC AND MOLAR HEAT CAPACITIES OF METALS

Metal	(Specific) $\bar{c}_P$, $\dfrac{\text{cal}}{\text{gm·C}°}$	Temperature range, °C	M, $\dfrac{\text{gm}}{\text{mole}}$	(Molar) $\bar{C}_P = M\bar{c}_P$, $\dfrac{\text{cal}}{\text{mole·C}°}$
Beryllium	0.470	20–100	9.01	4.24
Aluminum	0.217	17–100	27.0	5.86
Iron	0.113	18–100	55.9	6.31
Copper	0.093	15–100	63.5	5.90
Silver	0.056	15–100	108	6.05
Mercury	0.033	0–100	201	6.64
Lead	0.031	20–100	207	6.42

metals except the very lightest is approximately the same and equal to about 6 cal/mole·C°. This is known as the *Dulong and Petit law*, and although rough and applying to the average molar heat capacity at constant pressure, $\bar{C}_P$, averaged over a temperature range that is of no particular scientific importance, it contains the germ of a very important idea. We know from chemistry that the number of molecules in one grammole is the same for all substances. It follows that (very nearly) the same amount of heat is required *per molecule* to raise the temperature of each of these metals by a given amount although, for example, the mass of a molecule of lead (At. wt. = 207) is nearly ten times as great as that of a molecule of aluminum (At. wt. = 27). To put it in a different way, the heat required to raise the temperature of a sample of metal depends only on *how many* molecules the sample contains, and not on the mass of an individual molecule. This is the first time in our study of physics that we have met a property of matter so directly related to its molecular structure.

The really important theoretical interpretation of heat capacity measurements can be made only when the theoretician has at his disposal the complete temperature dependence, from the lowest to the highest possible temperatures, of the *molar heat capacity at constant volume*, C_V, because it is this quantity that is directly connected with the energy which, in turn, may be calculated by statistical methods. Fortunately, it is possible to convert experimental values of C_P to values of C_V with the aid of a partly theoretical, partly empirical equation due to Nernst and Lindemann, namely,

$$C_V = C_P\left(1 - 0.0214\,\frac{\text{mole·K}°}{\text{cal}}\,C_P\,\frac{T}{T_m}\right), \tag{16–7}$$

where T_m is the melting temperature. Using this equation in conjunction with measurements of C_P from about 4°K to 1000°K, the curves of Fig. 16–3 were obtained. These curves represent the extremes of behavior. All other metals and nonmetals lie within the boundaries of lead and diamond. Except for certain anomalies that are too complicated to dwell upon, all such curves approach about 6 cal/mole·K° as the

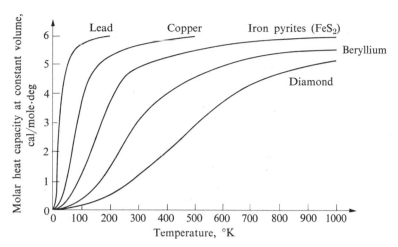

Fig. 16–3. Temperature variation of C_V of solids.

temperature approaches infinity. The Dulong and Petit value, therefore, is approached by all solids, lead arriving at this value at about 200°K (below room temperature) and diamond requiring well over 2000°K.

Each curve in Fig. 16–3 has exactly the same shape: it starts at zero, rises rapidly at first, then bends over and approaches the value 6 cal/mole·K°. It was shown by Debye that the behavior of the molar heat capacity of *nonmetals* over the entire temperature range was accounted for by the *vibrational motion of the molecules occupying regular positions in the crystal lattice.* There are, however, many substances whose temperature variation of heat capacity cannot be explained entirely on the basis of lattice vibrations. The behavior of four "abnormal" types of substance is depicted in Fig. 16–4. There are many more different types of heat capacity curves and all of them indicate some special molecular or atomic or ionic property of the particles that occupy the regular positions within the crystal lattice. The theoretical explanations of heat capacity curves are among the most interesting and complicated theories of modern solid state physics.

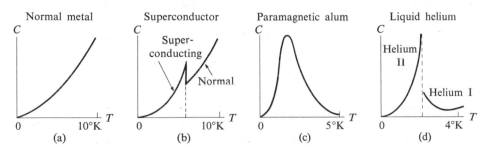

Fig. 16–4. Different ways in which the molar heat capacity varies with the temperature at low temperatures, indicating widely different atomic processes.

16-6 Change of phase

The term *phase* as used here relates to the fact that matter exists either as a solid, liquid, or gas. Thus the chemical substance H_2O exists in the *solid phase* as ice, in the *liquid phase* as water, and in the *gaseous phase* as steam. Provided they do not decompose at high temperatures, all substances can exist in any of the three phases under the proper conditions of temperature and pressure. Transitions from one phase to another are accompanied by the absorption or liberation of heat and usually by a change in volume.

As an illustration, suppose that ice is taken from a refrigerator where its temperature was, say, $-25°C$. Let the ice be crushed quickly, placed in a container, and a thermometer inserted in the mass. Imagine the container to be surrounded by a heating coil which supplies heat to the ice at a uniform rate, and suppose that no other heat reaches the ice. The temperature of the ice would be observed to increase steadily, as shown by the portion of the graph (Fig. 16-5) from a to b, or until the temperature has risen to $0°C$. In this temperature range the specific heat capacity of ice is approximately 0.55 cal/gm·C°. As soon as this temperature is reached, some liquid water will be observed in the container. In other words, the ice begins to melt. The melting process is a *change of phase*, from the solid phase to the liquid phase. The thermometer, however, will show no *increase in temperature*, and even though heat is being supplied at the same rate as before, the temperature will remain at $0°C$ until all the ice is melted (point c, Fig. 16-5). (The ice and water mixture must be kept thoroughly stirred, otherwise the temperature of that part of the water closest to the heater will rise above $0°C$.)

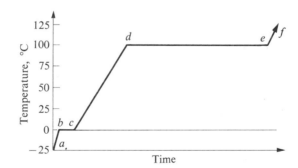

Fig. 16-5.   The temperature remains constant during each change of phase.

As soon as the last of the ice has melted, the temperature begins to rise again at a uniform rate (from c to d, Fig. 16-5) although this rate will be slower than that from a to b because the specific heat of water is greater than that of ice. When a temperature of $100°C$ is reached (point d), bubbles of steam (gaseous water or water vapor) start to escape from the liquid surface, or the water begins to boil. The temperature remains constant at $100°C$ until all the water has boiled away. Another change of phase has therefore taken place, from the liquid phase to the gaseous phase.

TABLE 16–3

HEATS OF FUSION AND VAPORIZATION

Substance	Normal melting point		Heat of fusion, cal/gm	Normal boiling point		Heat of vaporization, cal/gm
	°K	°C		°K	°C	
Helium	3.5	−269.65	1.25	4.216	−268.93	5
Hydrogen	13.84	−259.31	14	20.26	−252.89	108
Nitrogen	63.18	−209.97	6.09	77.34	−195.81	48
Oxygen	54.36	−218.79	3.30	90.18	−182.97	51
Ethyl alcohol	159	−114	24.9	351	78	204
Mercury	234	−39	2.82	630	357	65
Water	273.15	0.00	79.7	373.15	100.00	539
Sulphur	392	119	9.1	717.75	444.60	78
Lead	600.5	327.3	5.86	2023	1750	208
Antimony	903.65	630.50	39.4	1713	1440	134
Silver	1233.95	960.80	21.1	2466	2193	558
Gold	1336.15	1063.00	15.4	2933	2660	377
Copper	1356	1083	32	1460	1187	1211

If all the water vapor had been trapped and not allowed to diffuse away (a very large container would be needed), the heating process could be continued as from e to f. The gas would now be called "superheated steam."

Although water was chosen as an example in the process just described, the same type of curve as in Fig. 16–5 is obtained for many other substances. Some, of course, decompose before reaching a melting or boiling point, and others, such as glass or pitch, do not change state at a definite temperature but become gradually softer as their temperature is raised. Crystalline substances, such as ice, or a metal, melt at a definite temperature. Glass and pitch behave like supercooled liquids of very high viscosity.

The quantity of heat per unit mass that must be supplied to a material at its melting point to convert it completely to a liquid at the same temperature is called the *heat of fusion* of the material. The quantity of heat per unit mass that must be supplied to a material at its boiling point to convert it completely to a gas at the same temperature is called the *heat of vaporization* of the material. Heats of fusion and vaporization are expressed in calories per gram, or Btu per pound. Thus the heat of fusion of ice is about 80 cal/gm or 144 Btu/lb. The heat of vaporization of water (at 100°C) is 539 cal/gm or 970 Btu/lb. Some heats of fusion and vaporization are listed in Table 16–3.

When heat is removed from a gas, its temperature falls and at the same temperature at which it boiled, it returns to the liquid phase, or *condenses*. In so doing it gives up to its surroundings the same quantity of heat which was required to vaporize it. The heat so given up, per unit mass, is called the *heat of condensation* and is equal to the heat of vaporization. Similarly, a liquid returns to the solid phase, or freezes, when cooled to the temperature at which it melted, and gives up heat called *heat of solidification* exactly equal to the heat of fusion. Thus the melting point and the freezing point are at the same temperature, and the boiling point and condensation point are at the same temperature.

Whether a substance, at its melting point, is freezing or melting depends on whether heat is being supplied or removed. That is, if heat is supplied to a beaker containing both ice and water at 0°C, some of the ice will melt; if heat is removed, some of the water will freeze; the temperature in either case remains at 0°C so long as both ice and water are present. If heat is *neither supplied nor removed*, no change at all takes place and the relative amounts of ice and water, and the temperature, all remain constant.

This furnishes, then, another point of view which may be taken regarding the melting point. That is, the melting (or freezing) point of a substance is *that tempera-ture at which both the liquid and solid phases can exist together.* At any higher tempera-ture, the substance can only be a liquid; at any lower temperature, it can only be a solid.

The general term *heat of transformation* is applied both to heats of fusion and heats of vaporization, and both are designated by the letter L. Since L represents the heat absorbed or liberated in the change of phase of unit mass, the heat Q absorbed or liberated in the change of phase of a mass m is

$$Q = mL. \tag{16–8}$$

The household steam-heating system makes use of a boiling-condensing process to transfer heat from the furnace to the radiators. Each pound of water which is turned to steam in the furnace absorbs 970 Btu (the heat of vaporization of water) from the furnace, and gives up 970 Btu when it condenses in the radiators. (This figure is correct if the steam pressure is one atmosphere. It will be slightly smaller at higher pressures.) Thus the steam-heating system does not need to circulate as much water as a hot-water heating system. If water leaves a hot-water furnace at 140°F and returns at 100°F, dropping 40 F°, about 24 lb of water must circulate to carry the same heat as is carried in the form of heat of vaporization by one pound of steam.

Under the proper conditions of temperature and pressure, a substance can change directly from the solid to the gaseous phase without passing through the liquid phase. The transfer from solid to vapor is called *sublimation*, and the solid is said to *sublime.* "Dry ice" (solid carbon dioxide) sublimes at atmospheric pressure. Liquid carbon dioxide cannot exist at a pressure lower than about 73 lb/in^2.

Heat is absorbed in the process of sublimation, and liberated in the reverse process. The quantity of heat per unit mass is called the *heat of sublimation.*

Problems

[*Note:* When no information is given about the temperature variation of specific or molar heat capacity, assume it to be constant and use the average value given in Table 16–2.]

16–1. A combustion experiment is performed by burning a mixture of fuel and oxygen in a constant-volume "bomb" surrounded by a water bath. During the experiment the temperature of the water is observed to rise. Regarding the mixture of fuel and oxygen as the system, (a) has heat been transferred? (b) has work been done?

16–2. A liquid is irregularly stirred in a well-insulated container and thereby undergoes a rise in temperature. Regarding the liquid as the system, (a) has heat been transferred? (b) has work been done?

16–3. An automobile weighing 2000 lb is traveling at 10 ft/sec. How many Btu are transferred in the brake mechanism when it is brought to rest?

16–4. 400 gm of water are contained in a copper vessel of mass 200 gm. The water is heated by a friction device which dissipates mechanical energy, and it is observed that the temperature of the system rises at the rate of 3 C° per minute. Neglect heat losses to the surroundings. What power in watts is dissipated in the water?

16–5. How long could a 2000-hp motor be operated on the heat energy liberated by one cubic mile of ocean water when the temperature of the water is lowered by 1 C° if all this heat were converted to mechanical energy? Why do we not utilize this tremendous reservoir of energy?

16–6. (a) A certain house burns 10 tons of coal in a heating season. The heat of combustion of the coal is 11,000 Btu/lb. If stack losses are 15%, how many Btu were actually used to heat the house? (b) In some localities large tanks of water are heated by solar radiation during the summer and the stored energy is used for heating during the winter. Find the required dimensions of the storage tank, assuming it to be a cube, to store a quantity of energy equal to that computed in part (a). Assume that the water is heated to 120°F in the summer and cooled to 80°F in the winter.

16–7. An artificial satellite, constructed of aluminum, encircles the earth at a speed of 18,000 mi/hr. (a) Find the ratio of its kinetic energy to the energy required to raise its temperature by 600 C°. (The melting point of aluminum is 660°C.) Assume a constant specific heat capacity of 0.20 Btu/lbm·F°. (b) Discuss the bearing of your answer on the problem of the re-entry of a satellite into the earth's atmosphere.

16–8. A calorimeter contains 100 gm of water at 0°C. A 1000-gm copper cylinder and a 1000-gm lead cylinder, both at 100°C, are placed in the calorimeter. Find the final temperature if there is no loss of heat to the surroundings.

16–9. (a) Compare the heat capacities (heat capacity is the heat per unit temperature change) of equal *masses* of water, copper, and lead. (b) Compare the heat capacities of equal *volumes* of water, copper, and lead.

16–10. An aluminum can of mass 500 gm contains 117.5 gm of water at a temperature of 20°C. A 200-gm block of iron at 75°C is dropped into the can. Find the final temperature, assuming no heat loss to the surroundings.

16–11. A casting weighing 100 lb is taken from an annealing furnace where its temperature was 900°F and plunged into a tank containing 800 lb of oil at a temperature of 80°F. The final temperature is 100°F, and the specific heat capacity of the oil is 0.5 Btu/lb·F°. What was the specific heat capacity of the casting? Neglect the heat capacity of the tank itself and any heat losses.

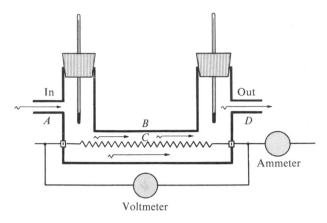

Figure 16–6

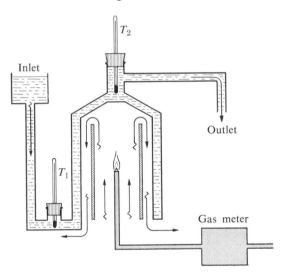

Figure 16–7

16–12. A lead bullet, traveling at 350 m/sec, strikes a target and is brought to rest. What would be the rise in temperature of the bullet if none of the heat developed were lost to the surroundings?

16–13. A copper calorimeter (mass 300 gm) contains 500 gm of water at a temperature of 15°C. A 560-gm block of copper, at a temperature of 100°C, is dropped into the calorimeter and the temperature is observed to increase to 22.5°C. Neglect heat losses to the surroundings. (a) Find the specific heat capacity of copper.

16–14. A 50-gm sample of a material, at a temperature of 100°C, is dropped into a calorimeter containing 200 gm of water initially at 20°C. The calorimeter is of copper and its mass is 100 gm. The final temperature of the calorimeter is 22°C. Compute the specific heat capacity of the sample.

16–15. In Fig. 16–6 an electric heater is shown whose purpose is to provide a continuous supply of hot water. Water is flowing at the rate of 300 gm/min, the inlet thermometer registers 15°C, the voltmeter reads 120 volts and the ammeter 10 amperes. (a) When a steady state is finally reached what is the reading of the outlet thermometer? (b) Why is it unnecessary to take into account the heat capacity (*mc* or *nC*) of the apparatus itself?

16–16. Figure 16–7 shows a sketch of a continuous-flow calorimeter used to measure the heat of combustion of a gaseous fuel. Water is supplied at the rate of 12.5 lb/min and natural gas at 0.020 ft³/min. In the steady state, the inlet and outlet thermometers register 60°F and 76°F, respectively. What is the heat of combustion of natural gas in Btu/ft³? Why should the gas flow be made as small as possible?

16–17. (a) Make a rough sketch of the type of temperature-time graph (such as that in Fig. 16–2) that would result if the surroundings were much cooler than the sample. (b) An electrical resistor is immersed in a liquid and electrical energy is dissipated for 100 sec at a constant rate of 50 watts. The mass of the liquid is 530 gm, and its temperature increases from 17.64°C to 20.77°C. Find the mean specific heat capacity of the liquid in this temperature range.

16–18. (a) Heat is supplied electrically at a constant rate to a cylinder of metal of *n* moles. The kelvin temperature *T* is measured as a function of the time τ and a *T*-τ graph is plotted. In the space around the metal sample is a metal shield whose temperature is controlled with the aid of a separate electric heater. The temperature of the shield is maintained as close as possible to that of the sample at all times while the temperature of the sample is rising. (Why?) Show that the molar heat capacity of the sample is given by

$$C = -\frac{VI}{n(dT/d\tau)}.$$

(b) If the *T*-τ graph has the appearance of Fig. 16–8, draw a rough graph showing the dependence of molar heat capacity on temperature. (c) If the *T*-τ graph has the

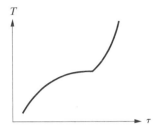

Figure 16–8

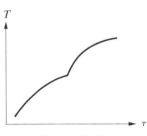

Figure 16–9

appearance of Fig. 16–9, draw a rough graph showing the dependence of molar heat capacity on temperature.

16–19. The molar heat capacity at constant pressure of a substance varies with the temperature according to the empirical equation

$$C_P = 6.50 \frac{\text{cal}}{\text{mole·K°}}$$

$$+ 10^{-3} \frac{\text{cal}}{\text{mole·(K°)}^2} \cdot T.$$

How many calories of heat are necessary to change the temperature of 10 moles from 27°C to 527°C?

16–20. At very low temperatures, the molar heat capacity of rock salt varies with the temperature according to "Debye's T^3 law"; thus

$$C = k\frac{T^3}{\Theta^3},$$

where $k = 464$ cal/mole·K° and $\Theta = 281°K$. (a) How much heat is required to raise the temperature of 2 moles of rock salt from 10°K to 50°K? (b) What is the mean molar heat capacity in this range? (c) What is the true molar heat capacity at 50°K?

16–21. (a) With the aid of the Nernst-Lindemann relation, Eq. (16–7), prove that as T approaches zero, C_P approaches C_V. (b) The true value of C_P of copper at 100°K is 3.88 cal/mole·K° and at 800°K it is 6.70 cal/mole·K°. Calculate the difference $C_P - C_V$ at these two temperatures.

16–22. How much heat is required to convert 1 gm of ice at −10°C to steam at 100°C?

16–23. A beaker of very small mass contains 500 gm of water at a temperature of 80°C. How many grams of ice at a temperature of −20°C must be dropped in the water so that the final temperature of the system will be 50°C?

16–24. An open vessel contains 500 gm of ice at −20°C. The mass of the container can be neglected. Heat is supplied to the vessel at the constant rate of 1000 cal/min for 100 min. Plot a curve showing the elapsed time as abscissa and the temperature as ordinate.

16–25. A copper calorimeter of mass 100 gm contains 150 gm of water and 8 gm of ice in thermal equilibrium at atmospheric pressure. 100 gm of lead at a temperature of 200°C are dropped into the calorimeter. Find the final temperature if no heat is lost to the surroundings.

16–26. 500 gm of ice at −16°C are dropped into a calorimeter containing 1000 gm of water at 20°C. The calorimeter can is of copper and has a mass of 278 gm. Compute the final temperature of the system, assuming no heat losses.

16–27. A tube leads from a flask in which water is boiling under atmospheric pressure to a calorimeter. The mass of the calorimeter is 150 gm, its heat capacity is 15 cal/C° and it contains originally 340 gm of water at 15°C. Steam is allowed to condense in the calorimeter until its temperature increases to 71°C, after which the total mass of calorimeter and contents is found to be 525 gm. Compute the heat of condensation of steam from these data.

16–28. An aluminum canteen whose mass is 500 gm contains 750 gm of water and 100 gm of ice. The canteen is dropped from an aircraft to the ground. After landing, the temperature of the canteen is found to be 25°C. Assuming that no energy is given to the ground in the impact, what was the velocity of the canteen just before it landed?

16–29. A calorimeter contains 500 gm of water and 300 gm of ice, all at a temperature of 0°C. A block of metal of mass 1000 gm is taken from a furnace where its temperature was 240°C and is dropped quickly into the calorimeter. As a result, all the ice is just melted. What would the final temperature of the system have been if the mass of the block had been twice as great? Neglect heat loss from and the heat capacity of the calorimeter.

16–30. An ice cube whose mass is 50 gm is taken from a refrigerator where its temperature was −10°C and is dropped into a glass of water at 0°C. If no heat is gained or lost from outside, how much water will freeze onto the cube?

16–31. A copper calorimeter can ($mc = 30$ cal/deg) contains 50 gm of ice. The system is initially at 0°C. 12 gm of steam at 100°C and 1 atm pressure are run into the calorimeter. What is the final temperature of the calorimeter and its contents?

16–32. A vessel whose walls are thermally insulated contains 2100 gm of water and 200 gm of ice, all at a temperature of 0°C. The outlet of a tube leading from a boiler, in which water is boiling at atmospheric pressure, is inserted in the water. How many grams of steam must condense to raise the temperature of the system to 20°C? Neglect the heat capacity of the container.

16–33. A 2-kgm iron block is taken from a furnace where its temperature was 650°C and placed on a large block of ice at 0°C. Assuming that all the heat given up by the iron is used to melt the ice, how much ice is melted?

16–34. In a household hot-water heating system, water is delivered to the radiators at 140°F and leaves at 100°F. The system is to be replaced by a steam system in which steam at atmospheric pressure condenses in the radiators, the condensed steam leaving the radiators at 180°F. How many pounds of steam will supply the same heat as was supplied by 1 lb of hot water in the first installation?

16–35. A "solar house" has storage facilities for 4 million Btu. Compare the space requirements for this storage on the assumption (a) that the heat is stored in water heated from a minimum temperature of 80°F to a maximum at 120°F, and (b) that the heat is stored in Glauber salt ($Na_2SO_4 \cdot 10H_2O$) heated in the same temperature range.

Properties of Glauber salt:

Specific heat capacity (solid)	0.46 Btu/lb·F°
Specific heat capacity (liquid)	0.68 Btu/lb·F°
Specific gravity	1.6
Melting point	90°F
Heat of fusion	104 Btu/lb

CHAPTER 17

Transfer of Heat

17–1 Conduction

If one end of a metal rod is placed in a flame while the other is held in the hand, that part of the rod one is holding will be felt to become hotter and hotter, although it was not itself in direct contact with the flame. Heat is said to reach the cooler end of the rod by *conduction* along or through the material of the rod.

Conduction of heat can take place in a body only when different parts of the body are at different temperatures, and the direction of heat flow is always from points of higher to points of lower temperature. The phenomenon of heat flow is sometimes made the basis for the definition of temperature equality or inequality. That is, if heat flows from one body to another when the two are in contact, the temperature of the first, by definition, is higher than that of the second. If there is no heat flow, the temperatures are equal.

To fix our ideas, let us consider the following idealized case. A rod of length L and cross-sectional area A is originally at a uniform temperature t_1. At some instant, the right end of the rod is brought into contact with a body which is maintained at the constant temperature t_1, and the left end of the rod is brought into contact with a body kept at a higher temperature t_2. The remainder of the rod is surrounded by a material which is a nonconductor of heat. (This condition cannot be fulfilled exactly, since all materials conduct heat to some extent.) Now, perhaps by means of small thermocouples inserted in holes in the rod, we measure the temperature at a number of points along the rod at times τ_1, τ_2, etc., after the experiment is started. Figure 17–1(a) is a diagram of the experimental setup, and Fig. 17–1(b) shows the graphs of the temperature t vs. distance x along the rod, at times τ_1, τ_2, etc.

Initially, at time $\tau = 0$, the graph is a horizontal straight line at a height t_1. At all later times τ_1, τ_2, etc., the temperature at the left end is t_2 and the temperature decreases from left to right as shown by the corresponding curves. After a sufficiently long time has elapsed the temperature at every point becomes constant (in time) and the rod is said to be in the *steady state*. The steady-state graph is labeled $\tau = \infty$.

We define the *temperature gradient* at any point and at any time as the rate of change of temperature t with distance x along the rod:

$$\text{Temperature gradient} = \frac{dt}{dx}.$$

Graphically, the temperature gradient is represented by the slope of a graph of t vs. x, at any coordinate x and any time τ.

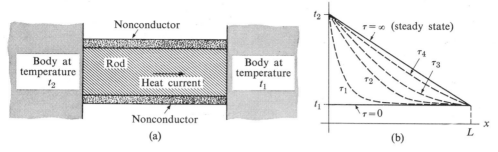

Fig. 17-1. Transient and steady-state temperature distribution along a rod initially at temperature t_1. The transient distributions were computed for $\tau_2 = 5\tau_1$, $\tau_3 = 10\tau_1$, $\tau_4 = 20\tau_1$.

At every instant, both in the transient and in the steady state, there is a flow of heat along the rod from left to right. Let dQ represent the heat flowing across a section of the rod at the coordinate x, during the time interval $d\tau$ between τ and $\tau + d\tau$. The ratio $dQ/d\tau$, the heat flow per unit time, is called the *heat current H*.

$$H = \frac{dQ}{d\tau}.$$

The *thermal conductivity k* of the material of the rod is defined as the (negative of the) heat current per unit area perpendicular to the flow, and per unit temperature gradient.

$$k = -\frac{H}{A(dt/dx)}.$$

The negative sign is introduced in the definition because H is positive (heat flows from left to right) when the temperature gradient, as in Fig. 17-1, is negative. Thus k is a positive quantity. The preceding equation is more commonly written as

$$H = -kA\frac{dt}{dx}. \tag{17-1}$$

The thermal conductivity of most materials is a function of temperature, increasing slightly with increasing temperature, but the variation is small and can often be neglected. Some numerical values of k, at temperatures near room temperature, are given in Table 17-1. In the cgs system the unit of heat current is 1 calorie/sec, that of area is 1 cm^2, and that of temperature gradient is 1 celsius degree/cm. The properties of materials used commercially as heat insulators are expressed in a system in which the unit of heat current is 1 Btu/hr, the unit of area is 1 ft^2, and the unit of temperature gradient is 1 fahrenheit degree per inch.

It is evident from Eq. (17-1) that the larger the thermal conductivity k, the larger the heat current, other factors being equal. A material for which k is large is therefore a good heat conductor, while if k is small the material is a poor conductor or a good

TABLE 17-1

THERMAL CONDUCTIVITIES

	$k, \dfrac{cal}{sec \cdot cm \cdot C°}$
Metals:	
Aluminum	0.49
Brass	0.26
Copper	0.92
Lead	0.083
Mercury	0.020
Silver	0.97
Steel	0.12
Various solids:	
(Representative values)	
Insulating brick	0.00035
Red brick	0.0015
Concrete	0.002
Cork	0.0001
Felt	0.0001
Glass	0.002
Ice	0.004
Rock wool	0.0001
Wood	0.0003–0.0001
Gases:	
Air	0.000057
Argon	0.000039
Helium	0.00034
Hydrogen	0.00033
Oxygen	0.000056

insulator. A "perfect heat conductor" ($k = \infty$) or a "perfect heat insulator" ($k = 0$) does not exist. However, it will be seen from Table 17-1 that the metals as a group have much greater thermal conductivities than the nonmetals, and that those of gases are extremely small.

In the steady state, the heat current in the rod in Fig. 17-1 must be the same at all cross sections. If this were not so, the quantity of heat flowing into an element of the rod between two cross sections would not be the same as that flowing out. Heat would then accumulate in the element and its temperature would change, which contradicts the assumption of a steady state. (In this respect the steady-state flow of heat is like the flow of an incompressible fluid.) It follows that in the steady state the quantity $kA(dt/dx)$ is the same at all cross sections. Then *if A is constant and if k is independent of temperature*, the temperature gradient dt/dx is the same at all cross sections. In other words, the temperature decreases *linearly* along the rod and the steady-state temperature gradient is $(t_2 - t_1)/L$. Hence for a specimen of constant cross section and constant k, in the steady state, the magnitude of the heat current (omitting the negative sign) is

$$H = kA \frac{t_2 - t_1}{L} .$$ (17-2)

Since there are no restrictions on the relative dimensions of the rod in Fig. 17-1, Eq. (17-2) applies also when the length L becomes relatively small and the area A relatively large, as in the case of a sheet or slab of material such as a portion of the wall of a house, a refrigerator, or a furnace. (The dimension L would then ordinarily be described as the "thickness" rather than the "length.")

17-2 Heat flow through a compound wall

Figure 17-2 illustrates a so-called compound wall, constructed of two materials having different thicknesses and different thermal conductivities. The heat current through section 1, in the steady state, is

$$H = \frac{k_1 A(t_2 - t_x)}{L_1}$$ (17-3)

and through section 2 it is

$$H = \frac{k_2 A(t_x - t_1)}{L_2} .$$ (17-4)

In the steady state these currents must be equal. (Why?) Hence

$$\frac{k_1 A(t_2 - t_x)}{L_1} = \frac{k_2 A(t_x - t_1)}{L_2} .$$

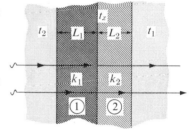

Fig. 17-2. Heat flow through a compound wall.

Solving for t_x and substituting in Eq. (17-3) or (17-4), we find

$$H = \frac{A(t_2 - t_1)}{(L_1/k_1) + (L_2/k_2)} .$$

In general, for any number of sections in series,

$$H = \frac{A(t_2 - t_1)}{\Sigma(L/k)} .$$ (17-5)

Since the heat current is the same in all sections, it follows that the temperature gradient in each material is inversely proportional to its thermal conductivity.

The temperatures t_1 and t_2 in Fig. 17-2 refer to the *outer surfaces* of the respective sections of wall. If the diagram represents the wall of a house, these temperatures are *not* the same as those of the inside and outside air, as measured an inch or so away from the wall. See the example at the end of Section 17-4.

17–3 Radial heat flow in a sphere or cylinder

We next consider two examples of heat flow in which the temperature gradient is not uniform along the direction of flow, even in the steady state. Figure 17–3 represents a steam pipe surrounded by a layer of insulating material, or a sphere surrounded by a spherical shell of insulation. Let t_2 and t_1 be the temperatures of the inner and outer surfaces of the insulation, and a and b be the inner and outer radii. If $t_2 > t_1$, heat flows outward, and in the steady state the heat current H is the same across all surfaces within the insulation, such as that of radius r, shown by a dashed circle. If A is the area of this surface and dt/dr the corresponding temperature gradient,

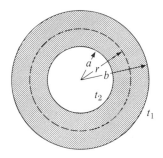

$$H = -kA\frac{dt}{dr} = \text{constant.}$$

Fig. 17–3. Radial heat flow in a cylinder or sphere.

The heat current can be expressed in terms of t_2, t_1, a, and b, by integrating this equation and inserting the appropriate boundary conditions. The calculations for the cylinder and the sphere in parallel have been carried out in Table 17–2.

TABLE 17–2

Cylinder (length L)	Sphere
$A = 2\pi rL$	$A = 4\pi r^2$
$H = -k \cdot 2\pi rL \cdot \dfrac{dt}{dr}$	$H = -k \cdot 4\pi r^2 \dfrac{dt}{dr}$
$H\dfrac{dr}{r} = -2\pi kL\, dt$	$H\dfrac{dr}{r^2} = -4\pi k\, dt$
$H \ln r = -2\pi kLt + C$	$-\dfrac{H}{r} = -4\pi kt + C$
$r = a, \quad t = t_2;$	$r = b, \quad t = t_1$
$H = \dfrac{2\pi k(t_2 - t_1)}{[\ln (b/a)]/L}$	$H = \dfrac{4\pi k(t_2 - t_1)}{(b - a)/ab}$

17–4 Convection

The term *convection* is applied to the transfer of heat from one place to another by the actual motion of material. The hot-air furnace and the hot-water heating system are examples. If the heated material is forced to move by a blower or pump, the process is called *forced* convection; if the material flows because of differences in density, the process is called *natural* or *free* convection. To understand the latter, consider a U-tube as illustrated in Fig. 17–4.

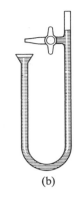

Fig. 17–4.   Convection is brought about by differences in density.

(a)   (b)

In (a), the water is at the same temperature in both arms of the U and hence stands at the same level in each. In (b), the right side of the U has been heated. The water in this side expands and therefore, being of smaller density, a longer column is needed to balance the pressure produced by the cold water in the left column. The stopcock may now be opened and water will flow from the top of the warmer column into the colder column. This increases the pressure at the bottom of the U produced by the cold column, and decreases the pressure at this point due to the hot column. Hence at the bottom of the U, water is forced from the cold to the hot side. If heat is continually applied to the hot side and removed from the cold side, the circulation continues of itself. The net result is a continual transfer of heat from the hot to the cold side of the column. In the common household hot-water heating system, the "cold" side corresponds to the radiators and the "hot" side to the furnace.

The anomalous expansion of water which was mentioned in Chapter 15 has an important effect on the way in which lakes and ponds freeze in winter. Consider a pond at a temperature of, say, 20°C throughout, and suppose the air temperature at its surface falls to $-10°C$. The water at the surface becomes cooled to, say, 19°C. It therefore contracts, becomes more dense than the warmer water below it, and sinks in this less dense water, its place being taken by water at 20°C. The sinking of the cooled water causes a mixing process, which continues until all of the water has been cooled to 4°C. Now, however, when the surface water cools to 3°C, it expands, is less dense than the water below it and hence floats on the surface. Convection and mixing then cease, and the remainder of the water can lose heat only by *conduction*. Since water is an extremely poor heat conductor, cooling takes place very slowly after 4°C is reached, with the result that the pond freezes first at its surface. Then, since the density of ice is even smaller than that of water at 0°C, the ice floats on the water below it, and further freezing can result only from heat flow upward by conduction.

The mathematical theory of heat convection is quite involved. There is no simple equation for convection, as there is for conduction. This arises from the fact that the heat lost or gained by a surface at one temperature in contact with a fluid at another temperature depends on many circumstances, such as (1) whether the surface is flat or curved, (2) whether the surface is horizontal or vertical, (3) whether the fluid in contact with the surface is a gas or a liquid, (4) the density, viscosity, specific heat, and thermal conductivity of the fluid, (5) whether the velocity of the fluid is small enough to give rise to laminar flow or large enough to cause turbulent flow, (6) whether evaporation, condensation, or formation of scale takes place.

The procedure adopted in practical calculations is first to define a *convection coefficient h* by means of the equation

$$H = hA \, \Delta t, \tag{17-6}$$

where H is the heat convection current (the heat gained or lost by convection by a surface per unit of time), A is the area of the surface, and Δt is the temperature difference between the surface and the main body of fluid. The next step is the determination of numerical values of h that are appropriate to a given piece of equipment. Such a determination is accomplished partly by dimensional analysis and partly by an elaborate series of experiments. An enormous amount of research in this field has been done in recent years so that, by now, there are in existence fairly complete tables and graphs from which the physicist or engineer may obtain the convection coefficient appropriate to certain standard types of apparatus.

A case of common occurrence is that of natural convection from a wall or a pipe which is at a constant temperature and is surrounded by air at atmospheric pressure whose temperature differs from that of the wall or pipe by an amount Δt. The convection coefficients applicable in this situation are given in Table 17–3.

TABLE 17–3

COEFFICIENTS OF NATURAL CONVECTION IN AIR AT ATMOSPHERIC PRESSURE

Equipment	Convection coefficient h in $\dfrac{\text{cal}}{\text{sec·cm}^2\text{·C°}}$
Horizontal plate, facing upward	$0.595 \times 10^{-4}(\Delta t)^{1/4}$
Horizontal plate, facing downward	$0.314 \times 10^{-4}(\Delta t)^{1/4}$
Vertical plate	$0.424 \times 10^{-4}(\Delta t)^{1/4}$
Horizontal or vertical pipe $\left(\dfrac{\text{diameter}}{D}\right)$	$1.00 \times 10^{-4}\left(\dfrac{\Delta t}{D}\right)^{1/4}$

EXAMPLE.   The air in a room is at a temperature of 25°C, and the outside air is at -15°C. How much heat is transferred per unit area of a glass windowpane of thermal conductivity 2.5×10^{-3} cgs units and of thickness 2 mm?

To assume that the inner surface of the glass is at 25°C and the outer surface is at -15°C is entirely erroneous, as anyone can verify by touching the inner surface of a glass windowpane on a cold day. One must expect a much smaller temperature difference across the windowpane, so that in the steady state the rates of transfer of heat (1) by convection in the room, (2) by conduction through the glass, and (3) by convection in the outside air, are all equal.

As a first approximation in the solution of this problem, let us assume that the window is at a uniform temperature t. If $t = 5°C$, then the temperature difference between the inside air and the glass is the same as that between the glass and the outside air, or 20 C°. Hence the convection coefficient in both cases is

$$h = 0.424 \times 10^{-4}(20)^{1/4} \frac{\text{cal}}{\text{sec·cm}^2 \text{·C°}} = 0.895 \times 10^{-4} \frac{\text{cal}}{\text{sec·cm}^2 \text{·C°}},$$

and, from Eq. (17–6), the heat transferred per unit area is

$$\frac{H}{A} = 0.895 \times 10^{-4} \times 20 = 17.9 \times 10^{-4} \frac{\text{cal}}{\text{sec·cm}^2}.$$

The glass, however, is not at a uniform temperature; there must be a temperature difference Δt across the glass sufficient to provide heat conduction at the rate of 17.9×10^{-4} cal/sec·cm². Using the conduction equation, Eq. (17–2), we obtain

$$\Delta t = \frac{L}{k} \times \frac{H}{A} = \frac{0.2}{2.5 \times 10^{-3}} \times 17.9 \times 10^{-4} \text{ C°} = 0.14 \text{ C°}.$$

With sufficient accuracy we may therefore say that the inner surface is at 5.07°C and the outer surface is at 4.93°C.

17–5 Radiation

When we hold one end of a metal rod in our hand and insert the other end in a gas flame, heat reaches our hand by *conduction* along the rod. If our hand is held above the flame, heat reaches it by way of the upward-moving *convection* currents of hot gas. When we hold our hand at one side of a hot object our hand still becomes warm, even though conduction through the air is negligible and the hand is not in the path of convection currents. Energy now reaches the hand by *radiation*.

The term *radiation* refers to the continual emission of energy from the surface of all bodies. The energy is called *radiant energy* and is carried by electromagnetic waves. Radiowaves, infrared waves, visible light waves, ultraviolet waves, and x-rays are all electromagnetic waves, differing only in wavelength. All these waves transport radiant energy and their speed, in a vacuum, is the same as the speed of light, 3×10^8 m/sec. When they fall on a body that is not transparent to them they are in part reflected and in part absorbed.

We shall be concerned in this chapter only with the radiant energy emitted by solids and liquids. The radiation from a gas, where the molecules are so far apart that they do not affect one another, obeys very different laws. The radiant energy emitted by a gas like that in a neon sign or a sodium vapor lamp contains waves of (relatively) few frequencies, these frequencies being characteristic of the molecules of the gas. The energy radiated by a solid or liquid, on the other hand, contains waves of *all* frequencies, with relative amplitudes that depend chiefly on the *temperature* of the emitting body rather than on the kind of molecule of which it is composed.

17-6 The complete radiator or blackbody

It is of course impossible to make measurements in the *interior* of a solid or liquid. Thus a thermometer inserted "in a liquid" to measure its temperature is actually *outside* the liquid (although it may be surrounded by the liquid). We believe, however, that the electromagnetic waves in the interior of every solid and liquid body are exactly alike if the bodies are at the same temperature. That is, the interior of a body is uniformly "filled" with waves of all frequencies traveling in all directions, and at a given temperature the amplitude of the waves of any given frequency is the same for every substance.

The radiant energy *emitted* by a solid or liquid, however, is not exactly the same for all substances at the same temperature, even though the waves in the interior are the same for all. The differences depend on the nature of the *surface*.

It is necessary to distinguish carefully between a number of processes taking place at the surface of a body. Radiant energy is continually impinging on the surface, from both inside and outside. That striking the outside comes, of course, from objects surrounding the body, such as the walls of a room or furnace in which it is located. When radiant energy strikes the surface from *either* side, a portion is reflected and the remainder passes through. Consider first radiant energy incident on the outside of the surface of a body and coming from its surroundings. If the surface is smooth and highly polished, like that of a mirror, a large fraction of the incident energy is reflected. The remainder passes through the surface and is absorbed by the molecules of the body. (We shall consider only opaque bodies, that is, those which transmit no energy.) Let r represent the fraction of the incident energy reflected (the *reflectance*) and a the fraction absorbed (the *absorptance*). Since all the energy that is not reflected is absorbed (by an opaque body) it follows that

$$r + a = 1.$$

Thus if $r = 0.90$, then $a = 0.10$ and 90% of the incident energy is reflected and 10% absorbed.

If the outside of a surface reflects a fraction r of the radiant energy striking it, the same fraction r of the radiant energy striking the inside of the surface is reflected, and a fraction $a = 1 - r$ is transmitted. The energy transmitted travels outward from the surface (until it strikes the surface of some other body) and is therefore what we have called the energy *emitted* by the surface. For example, if $r = 0.90$, then $a = 0.10$ and 10% of the radiant energy incident on the surface from the interior is emitted by (or transmitted through) the surface.

Figure 17-5(a) represents the surface above in a schematic manner. The widths of the various bands represent the relative amounts of radiant energy incident on, reflected from, and transmitted through the surface. Figure 17-5(b) shows the same quantities for another body at the same temperature but whose surface reflects only 10% of the energy incident on it. Of the energy incident from the surroundings, 10% is reflected and 90% absorbed. Of that incident from the interior, 90% is emitted. The energy *incident* from the interior is the same in parts (a) and (b), since the temperature is the same in both. The energy emitted from the surface in part (b) is therefore nine times as great as that emitted by the surface in part (a). Hence we can say

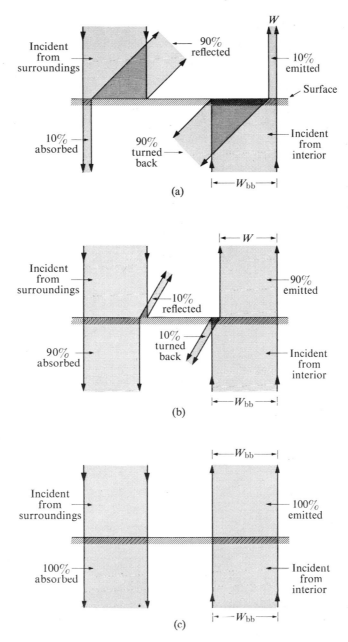

Fig. 17–5. The surface in (a) is a good reflector, hence a poor absorber and a poor emitter. The surface in (b) is a poor reflector, hence a good absorber and a good emitter. The surface in (c) is ideally black; all radiant energy incident from either side is transmitted.

that *a good absorber*, such as surface (b), is also *a good emitter*, while *a poor absorber*, such as surface (a), is *a poor emitter*. This is equivalent to stating that a poor reflector is a good emitter, and a good reflector is a poor emitter. This is the reason for silvering the walls of vacuum ("Thermos") bottles. A vacuum bottle is constructed with double walls of thin glass, the space between the walls being evacuated so that heat flow by conduction and convection are practically eliminated. To reduce the loss by radiation to as low a value as possible, the walls are covered with a coating of silver, which is highly reflecting and hence is a very poor emitter.

The fraction of the incident radiant energy which is reflected by a surface usually depends on the frequency (or wavelength) of the waves carrying the energy. Thus a given surface may be a good reflector and a poor emitter for waves of visible light, but a poor reflector and a good emitter for the longer infrared waves. For simplicity, we have assumed the reflectance *r* to be the same at all wavelengths.

Since a good absorber is a good emitter, the *best emitting surface* will be that which is the *best absorber*. But no surface can absorb more than all of the radiant energy that strikes it. Any surface which *does* absorb all of the incident energy falling on it from outside will be the best possible emitting surface; all of the radiant energy incident from the interior of the body will flow outward through the surface. Such a surface would reflect no incident energy and hence would appear black when viewed by reflected light. It is called an *ideally black surface*, and a body having such a surface is called a *blackbody* or a *complete radiator*. (The term "blackbody" is unfortunate, because although such an object reflects no energy, it does radiate, and if its temperature is sufficiently high it will radiate visible light and appear "red hot" or "white hot.")

The transmission of radiant energy through the surface of a blackbody is shown schematically in Fig. 17–5(c). All the radiant energy incident on the surface from either direction is transmitted.

No material surface absorbs all the radiant energy incident on it. Lampblack reflects about 1%. A blackbody can be very closely approximated, however, by an enclosure with a small opening through which radiant energy may enter or leave (Fig. 17–6). Of the radiant energy entering the opening, a part will be absorbed by the walls and the remainder diffusely reflected. Only a small fraction of the reflected energy escapes through the opening; the remainder strikes the walls, where again only a small fraction is reflected. After repeated reflections practically all of the incoming energy is absorbed. The *opening*, then, behaves like a blackbody, in that all of the energy incident on it is absorbed.

The interior walls of the enclosure in Fig. 17–6 are emitting radiant energy as well as absorbing it, and a part of this energy escapes through the opening. If the walls are not ideally black, they emit less energy than does a blackbody at the same temperature, but their smaller emittance is just compensated by their larger reflectance.

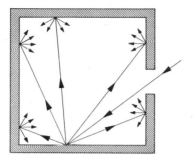

Fig. 17–6. A small opening in the walls of an enclosure is very nearly a complete absorber of radiant energy.

Hence *the energy escaping from the opening is identical with that which would be emitted by a blackbody at the same temperature as the walls of the enclosure.* Blackbody radiation can thus be produced and studied experimentally, even though a completely absorbing *surface* does not exist. The importance of blackbody radiation is that it represents a universal property of all substances; its characteristics depend only on the temperature and not on special properties of particular materials.

The radiant energy emitted by a surface, per unit time and per unit area, is called the *radiant emittance* of the surface and is represented by W. The radiant emittance of a blackbody is represented by W_{bb}. In the mks system, the unit of radiant emittance is

$$1 \text{ joule/sec·m}^2 \quad \text{or} \quad 1 \text{ watt/m}^2.$$

In Fig. 17–5(c), the width of the band representing the energy traveling outward from the surface corresponds to W_{bb}. But this surface is ideally black, so the energy incident on the surface from the interior is equal to W_{bb}. Furthermore, since the energy incident from the interior is the same for *all* bodies at the same temperature, the widths of these bands in parts (a) and (b) of Fig. 17–5 also correspond to W_{bb}.

If a surface absorbs a fraction a of the energy incident on its surface from outside, it emits the same fraction a of the energy incident from within. The radiant emittance W from the surface of *any* body at a given temperature is therefore

$$W = aW_{bb}, \tag{17–7}$$

where W_{bb} is the radiant emittance of a blackbody at the same temperature. The absorptance a is a fraction, lying between 0 (for a perfect reflector) and 1 (for an ideally black surface). It therefore also represents the effectiveness of a surface as a radiator, relative to that of a blackbody. In this sense it can be called the *relative emittance* of a surface, and is represented by e.

$$e - a, \quad W = eW_{bb}, \quad e = W/W_{bb}. \tag{17–8}$$

Since Eq. (17–7) holds for any surface whatever, it follows that W/a, the ratio of the radiant emittance of any surface to its absorptance, is the same for *all* surfaces at the same temperature and is equal to the radiant emittance of a blackbody at that temperature. This fact is known as *Kirchhoff's law*.

17–7 Planck's law

If a beam of radiant energy from a blackbody is dispersed into a spectrum, the reading of a sensitive thermometer or thermocouple placed in the spectrum is an indication of the radiant emittance of the blackbody within the particular range of wavelengths (or frequencies) which the indicating instrument intercepts. As the thermometer is moved along the spectrum its reading passes through a maximum at some one frequency (the particular frequency depends on the temperature of the blackbody) and on each side of the maximum there is a wide range of frequencies throughout which the energy is distributed.

Max Planck, in 1900, developed an empirical equation that satisfactorily represented the observed energy distribution in the spectrum of a blackbody. After unsuccessful attempts to justify his equation by theoretical reasoning based on the laws of classical physics, Planck concluded that these laws did not apply to energy transformations on an atomic scale. Instead, he postulated that a radiating body consisted of an enormous number of elementary oscillators, some vibrating at one frequency and some at another, with all frequencies from zero to infinity being represented. These oscillators were the source of the radiant energy emitted by the body. The energy E of any one oscillator was not permitted to take on any arbitrary value, but was proportional to some integral multiple of the frequency f of the oscillator. That is,

$$E = nhf, \qquad n = 1, 2, 3, \ldots \text{etc.}$$

The proportionality constant h is called *Planck's constant*. Its value, in mks units, is 6.62×10^{-34} joule·sec. This model of a radiating body led to an equation which agreed with the observed energy distribution in blackbody radiation.

Planck's postulate, which marked the beginning of the development of modern quantum theory, was one of the boldest and most imaginative steps ever taken in the history of physics. It is as if a violin string were forbidden to oscillate at any arbitrary amplitude, but was permitted to oscillate only at those amplitudes for which its energy was 1 unit, 2 units, 3 units, etc. Planck called each of his energy units (equal to hf for an oscillator of frequency f) a *quantum* of energy. Planck's original ideas have been somewhat modified, but the basic concept remains as one of the foundation stones of modern physics. The energy of a system on an atomic scale can have only some one of a discrete set of values. The energy can be increased or decreased, but only in stepwise fashion and not continuously.

The derivation of Planck's formula from his hypothesis regarding the energies of the elementary oscillators is too long and involved to

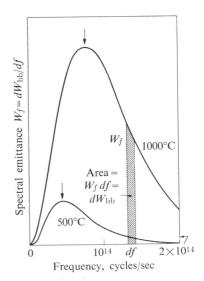

Fig. 17–7. Spectral emittance of a blackbody as a function of frequency, at temperatures of 500°C and 1000°C.

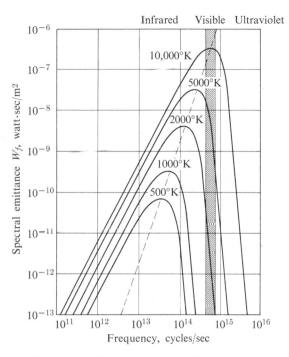

Fig. 17–8. Spectral emittance of a blackbody, as a function of frequency, for various temperatures. Limits of the visible spectrum are indicated by the shaded strip.

be given here. We shall merely give the formula (which can, of course, be found from experiment) without deriving it from theory.

Consider a range of frequencies between f and $f + df$, and let dW_{bb} be the radiant emittance of a blackbody within this frequency range. The radiant emittance *per unit range of frequency*, dW_{bb}/df, is called the *spectral emittance* W_f,

$$W_f = dW_{bb}/df. \qquad (17\text{–}9)$$

The mks unit of spectral emittance is 1 watt/m$^2 \cdot$(cycle/sec) = 1 watt·sec/m^2. Planck's formula for spectral emittance is

$$W_f = \frac{2\pi h}{c^2} \frac{f^3}{e^{hf/kT} - 1}, \qquad (17\text{–}10)$$

where h is Planck's constant, c the speed of light, T the kelvin temperature of the blackbody, k a constant called the *Boltzmann constant* or the gas constant per molecule, equal to 1.38×10^{-23} joule/K°, and e is the base of natural logarithms.

Graphs of W_f are given in Fig. 17–7 for temperatures of 500°C and 1000°C. Figure 17–8 covers a wider range of temperatures and frequencies. Note that it is plotted on a logarithmic scale.

17-8 Wien's displacement law and Stefan's law

Two important laws describing blackbody radiation were deduced from experimental observations before Planck's law was known. They are, however, necessary consequences of Planck's law and can be derived from it.

It will be noted from Fig. 17-7 that the frequency f_m at which the spectral emittance is most intense (marked by a short arrow at the maximum of the curves) is displaced toward higher frequencies (shorter wavelengths) as the temperature is increased from 500°C to 1000°C. The curves in Fig. 17-8 show the same effect. The frequency f_m, at any temperature, can be found by differentiating W_f with respect to f and setting the derivative equal to zero. The result, after inserting numerical values of the constants, is

$$f_m = 5.89 \times 10^{10} T, \tag{17-11}$$

where f is in cycles/sec and T is the kelvin temperature. That is, *the frequency f_m increases linearly with increasing temperature*. This fact is known as *Wien's displacement law*; it was discovered experimentally by Wien before Planck's law was known.

This shift in relative intensities accounts for the change in color of a body emitting visible light as its temperature is raised. At a temperature of 2000°K (see Fig. 17-8) a body emits visible light of appreciable intensity, but the intensity at the red (low-frequency) end of the visible spectrum is much greater than that at the blue (high-frequency) end and the body appears "red hot." At 3000°K, about the temperature of an incandescent lamp filament, the relative amount of blue light has increased, but red still predominates. At 6500°K, about the temperature of the surface of the sun, the distribution is more nearly uniform and the body is "white hot." Above about 10,000°K, blue light is emitted with a greater intensity than red and a body at this temperature appears "blue hot." Some of the hotter stars show this effect.

Stefan's law, which was also first deduced from experimental observations, has to do with the *total* rate of radiation from a blackbody, including *all* frequencies or wavelengths. Consider first the narrow, shaded vertical strip in Fig. 17-7. Its height is W_f, its width is df, and its *area* is $W_f df$. But from the definition of W_f in Eq. (17-9) the product $W_f df$ equals the radiant emittance dW_{bb} of a blackbody in the frequency range between f and $f + df$. The total rate of radiation, W_{bb}, is therefore represented by the total area under a graph of W_f, from $f = 0$ to $f = \infty$, and can be found by integrating $W_f df$ between these limits. Details of the integration will not be given, but the result is

$$W_{bb} = \sigma T^4,$$

where σ is a universal constant equal, in the mks system, to 5.672×10^{-8} watt/ $m^2 \cdot (°K)^4$. The fact that the total rate of radiation increases with the 4th power of the kelvin temperature is called *Stefan's law*.

If a surface is not ideally black, but has an absorptance a and a relative emittance $e = a$ which is the same at all frequencies, its radiant emittance W, as we have shown, is equal to eW_{bb}. Hence a more general form of Stefan's law is

$$W = e\sigma T^4, \tag{17-12}$$

where σ has the value given above for *all* bodies, $e = 1$ for a blackbody, and e is a fraction, less than 1, for other bodies.

Because the total thermal radiation from a body increases with the 4th power of its temperature, it is difficult to thermally insulate a body at high temperature. Even though conduction and convection may be reduced to small values, the energy loss by radiation becomes very large. The only recourse is to make the surface of the body have as low a relative emittance (or as high a reflectance) as possible.

It should be pointed out that infrared waves, whose wavelength is longer than waves of visible light, are often referred to as "heat waves" or "heat rays," as though they were the only waves which transport energy. Of course this is not correct. Electromagnetic waves of *any* wavelength carry energy which may be absorbed by a material body. One joule of visible light, when absorbed by a body, produces exactly the same temperature increase as one joule of infrared "light" or of radiant energy of any other wavelength.

The reason for the usage above can be understood from a reference to Figs. 17–7 and 17–8. Consider first Fig. 17–7. The frequency of visible light is about 5×10^{14} cycles/sec, which lies off the frequency scale to the right. That is, the frequency range covered in this diagram lies wholly in the infrared region. Even at a temperature as high as 1000°C, therefore, at which a body is self-luminous, by far the greater *fraction* of the energy it radiates is carried by infrared waves; the curve approaches very close to the horizontal axis in the visible and ultraviolet regions.

At temperatures above about 10,000°K, as will be seen from Fig. 17–8, the maximum of a graph of W_f vs. f lies in the ultraviolet region, and more energy is carried by ultraviolet waves than by infrared. If radiating bodies at these temperatures were of common occurrence, it would probably have become customary to refer to ultraviolet waves as "heat waves."

17–9 Heat transfer by radiation

The rate at which radiant energy is *emitted* from the surface of a body, per unit of area, is given by Eq. (17–12),

$$W = e\sigma T^4.$$

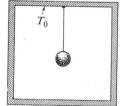

In general, radiant energy is also *incident* on the body's surface. A part of the incident energy is absorbed and the *net* rate of gain or loss of energy, equal to the *difference between the rates of emission and of absorption, is the rate of transfer of heat.* We shall discuss only a simple case, that of a *small* body within an enclosure whose walls are at a uniform temperature.

Fig. 17–9. A small body suspended in an evacuated enclosure with walls at a uniform temperature T_0.

Consider a small body such as that in Fig. 17–9, suspended within a large evacuated enclosure whose walls are at a temperature T_0. Whatever the nature of the surface of the body, it eventually comes to a state of *thermal equilibrium* in which its temperature is the same as that of the walls of the enclosure. Let the area of the body be A, let a represent its absorptance, H the radiant energy incident on its surface, per unit time and per unit area, and W the radiant emittance from its surface. A fraction a

of the incident radiant energy is absorbed, so the rate of *absorption* of energy is AaH. The rate of *emission*, when the state of thermal equilibrium has been reached, is $Ae\sigma T_0^4 = Aa\sigma T_0^4$. But in the equilibrium state there is no net gain or loss of energy, the rate of *emission* equals the rate of *absorption*, and

$$AaH = Aa\sigma T_0^4, \quad \text{or} \quad H = \sigma T_0^4.$$

The rate at which radiant energy is incident on the surface, per unit area, is therefore equal to the rate at which radiant energy is emitted from the surface of a black-body. It depends only on the temperature T_0 and not on the nature of the surface of either the body or the walls of the enclosure.

Now suppose that the body is at a temperature T, different from that of the enclosure. If the body is small, a change in its temperature will have only a negligible influence on the radiant energy in the enclosure. The rate at which energy is *incident* on its surface, per unit area, is the same as before, σT_0^4, and the rate at which energy is *absorbed* is $Aa\sigma T_0^4 = Ae\sigma T_0^4$. The rate at which energy is *emitted* is now $Ae\sigma T^4$, therefore the *net* rate of loss or gain of energy by radiation (or the heat transferred by radiation) is

$$H = dQ/d\tau = Ae\sigma T^4 - Ae\sigma T_0^4 = Ae\sigma(T^4 - T_0^4). \qquad (17\text{–}13)$$

The heat transferred by radiation is proportional to the difference between the 4th powers of the temperatures of the body and of the enclosure, and to the relative emittance e of the surface of the body. It does not depend on the nature of the walls of the enclosure.

17–10 Newton's law of cooling

When the temperature difference between a body and its surroundings is not too large, the combined rate of heat transfer to or from the body by conduction, convection, and radiation is approximately proportional to the temperature difference between the body and its surroundings. The rate of change of temperature of the body is proportional to the rate at which it gains or loses heat, so its rate of change of temperature is approximately proportional to the difference between its temperature and that of its surroundings. This relation was discovered by Newton and is known as *Newton's law of cooling*. It is an approximate empirical relation only and not a fundamental law like Newton's laws of motion. If t is the temperature of a body and t_S that of its surroundings, then

$$\frac{dt}{d\tau} = -k(t - t_S),$$

where τ represents time and k is (approximately) a constant, different for different bodies. The negative sign is included because $dt/d\tau$ is negative if $t > t_S$. The temperature as a function of time can be found by integration. We have

$$\frac{dt}{t - t_S} = -k\,d\tau, \qquad \ln(t - t_S) = -k\tau + C.$$

If t_0 is the temperature of the body when $\tau = 0$, then

$$C = \ln(t_0 - t_S) \quad \text{and} \quad \ln\frac{t - t_S}{t_0 - t_S} = -k\tau$$

or

$$t = t_S + (t_0 - t_S)e^{-k\tau}. \tag{17-14}$$

The temperature therefore changes exponentially with time, and the factor k is the reciprocal of the relaxation time.

Problems

17–1. Suppose that both ends of the rod in Fig. 17–1 are kept at a temperature of 0°C, and that the initial temperature distribution along the rod is given by $t = 100 \sin \pi x/L$, where t is in °C. Let the rod be of copper, of length $L = 10$ cm and of cross section 1 cm². (a) Show the initial temperature distribution in a diagram. (b) What is the final temperature distribution after a very long time has elapsed? (c) Sketch curves which you think would represent the temperature distribution at intermediate times. (d) What is the initial temperature gradient at the ends of the rod? (e) What is the initial heat current from the ends of the rod into the bodies making contact with its ends? (f) What is the initial heat current at the center of the rod? Explain. What is the heat current at this point at any later time? (g) What is the value of $k/\rho C$ for copper, and in what unit is it expressed? (This quantity is called the *diffusivity*.) (h) What is the initial rate of change of temperature at the center of the rod? (i) How long a time would be required for the rod to reach its final temperature, if the temperature continued to decrease at this rate? (This time can be described as the *relaxation time* of the rod.) (j) From the graphs in part (c), would you expect the rate of change of temperature at the midpoint to remain constant, increase, or decrease? (k) What is the initial rate of change of temperature at a point in the rod, 2.5 cm from its left end?

17–2. Suppose that the rod in Fig. 17–1 is of copper, of length 10 cm and of cross-sectional area 1 cm². Let $t_2 = 100$°C and $t_1 = 0$°C. (a) What is the final steady-state temperature gradient along the rod? (b) What is the heat current in the rod, in the final steady state? (c) What is the final steady-state temperature at a point in the rod, 2 cm from its left end?

17–3. A long rod, insulated to prevent heat losses, has one end immersed in boiling water (at atmospheric pressure) and the other end in a water-ice mixture. The rod consists of 100 cm of copper (one end in steam) and a length, L_2, of steel (one end in ice). Both rods are of cross-sectional area 5 cm². The temperature of the copper-iron junction is 60°C, after a steady state has been set up. (a) How many calories per second flow from the steam bath to the ice-water mixture? (b) How long is L_2?

17–4. A rod is initially at a uniform temperature of 0°C throughout. One end is kept at 0°C and the other is brought into contact with a steam bath at 100°C. The surface of the rod is insulated so that heat can flow only lengthwise along the rod. The cross-sectional area of the rod is 2 cm², its length is 100 cm, its thermal conductivity is 0.8 cgs units, its density is 10 gm/cm³, and its specific heat capacity is 0.10 cal/gm·C°. Consider a short cylindrical element of the rod 1 cm in length. (a) If the temperature gradient at one end of this element is 200 C°/cm, how many calories flow across this end per second? (b) If the average temperature of the element is increasing at the rate of 5 C°/sec, what is the temperature gradient at the other end of the element?

17–5. A compound bar 2 m long is constructed of a solid steel core 1 cm in diameter surrounded by a copper casing whose outside diameter is 2 cm. The outer surface of the bar is thermally insulated and one end is maintained at 100°C, the other at 0°C. (a) Find the total heat current in the bar, in the final steady state. (b) What fraction is carried by each material?

17–6. The walls of a furnace are constructed of firebrick 6 in. thick. The thermal conductivity of the brick is such that 3.6 Btu flow in 1 hr through a section of area 1 ft² and thickness 1 in. when the temperature difference between the faces is 1 F°. The temperature of the inner wall is 1000°F and that of the outer wall is 100°F. (a) What thickness of insulating brick whose thermal conductivity is $\frac{1}{3}$ that of the firebrick should be laid outside the latter to reduce the heat loss to 50% of its former value? (b) How many Btu flow in 1 hr through the insulated wall? (c) What is the temperature of the interface between firebrick and insulating brick? Assume that inside and outside temperatures are unaffected by the addition of the insulating brick. (d) Construct graphs of temperature versus distance from inner wall, for the original firebrick wall and for the insulated wall.

17–7. One experimental method of measuring the thermal conductivity of an insulating material is to construct a box of the material and measure the power input to an electric heater, inside the box, which maintains the interior at a measured temperature above the outside surface. Suppose that in such an apparatus a power input of 120 watts is required to keep the interior surface of the box 120 F° above the temperature of the outer surface. The total area of the box is 25 ft^2 and the wall thickness is 1.5 in. Find the thermal conductivity of the material in the commercial system of units.

17–8. A container of wall area 5000 cm^2 and thickness 2 cm is filled with water in which there is a stirrer. The outer surface of the walls is kept at a constant temperature of 0°C. The thermal conductivity of the walls is 0.000478 cgs units, and the effect of edges and corners can be neglected. The power required to run the stirrer at an angular velocity of 1800 rpm is found to be 100 watts. What will be the final steady-state temperature of the water in the container? Assume that the stirrer keeps the entire mass of water at a uniform temperature.

17–9. A boiler with a steel bottom 1.5 cm thick rests on a hot stove. The area of the bottom of the boiler is 1500 cm^2. The water inside the boiler is at 100°C, and 750 gm are evaporated every 5 min. Find the temperature of the lower surface of the boiler, which is in contact with the stove.

17–10. An icebox, having wall area of 2 m^2 and thickness 5 cm, is constructed of insulating material having a thermal conductivity of 10^{-4} cal/sec·cm·C°. The outside temperature is 20°C, and the inside of the box is to be maintained at 5°C by ice. The melted ice leaves the box at a temperature of 15°C. If ice costs one cent per kgm, what will it cost to run the icebox for one hour?

17–11. Heat flows radially outward through a cylindrical insulator of outside radius R_2 surrounding a steam pipe of outside radius R_1. The temperature of the inner surface of the insulator is t_1, that of the outer surface is t_2. (a) At what radial distance from the center of the pipe is the steady-state temperature just halfway between t_1 and t_2? (b) Sketch a graph of t versus r.

17–12. A steam pipe 2 cm in radius is surrounded by a cylindrical jacket of insulating material 2 cm thick. The temperature of the steam pipe is 100°C, and that of the outer surface of the jacket is 20°C. The thermal conductivity of the insulating material is 0.0002 cal/sec·cm·C°. Compute the temperature gradient, dt/dr, at the inner and outer surfaces of the jacket, and sketch the graph of t versus r.

17–13. An electric transformer is in a cylindrical tank 60 cm in diameter and 1 m high, with flat top and bottom. If the tank transfers heat to the air only by natural convection, and the electrical losses are to be dissipated at the rate of 1 kwh, how many degrees will the tank surface rise above room temperature?

17–14. (a) What would be the difference in height between the columns in the U-tube in Fig. 17–4, if the liquid is water and the left arm is one meter high at 4°C while the other is at 75°C? (b) What is the difference between the pressures at the foot of two columns of water each 10 m high, if the temperature of one is 4°C and that of the other is 75°C?

17–15. A flat wall is maintained at a constant temperature of 100°C, and the air on both sides is at atmospheric pressure and at 20°C. How much heat is lost by natural convection from 1 square meter of wall (both sides) in one hour if (a) the wall is vertical and (b) the wall is horizontal?

17–16. A vertical steam pipe of outside diameter 7.5 cm and height 4 m has its outer surface at the constant temperature of 95°C. The surrounding air is at atmospheric pressure and at 20°C. How much heat is delivered to the air by natural convection in one hour?

17–17. The temperature of a blackbody is 3000°K. Compute the ratio of its spectral emittance at a frequency of 3×10^{14} cycles/sec (in the infrared) to its spectral emittance at a frequency of 6×10^{14} cycles/sec (in the visible spectrum).

17–18. At what frequency is the spectral emittance of a blackbody a maximum, if its temperature is (a) 500°K, (b) 5000°K, (c) 500,000°K? (The visible spectrum extends from about 4×10^{14} to about 7.5×10^{14} cycles/sec.)

17–19. What is the radiant emittance of a blackbody at a temperature of (a) 300°K, (b) 3000°K?

17–20. The relative emittance of tungsten is approximately 0.35. A tungsten sphere 1 cm in radius is suspended within a large evacuated enclosure whose walls are at 300°K. What power input is required to maintain the sphere at a temperature of 3000°K, if heat conduction along the supports is neglected?

17–21. A small blackened solid copper sphere of radius 2 cm is placed in an evacuated enclosure whose walls are kept at 100°C. At what rate must energy be supplied to the sphere to keep its temperature constant at 127°C?

17–22. A cylindrical metal can 10 cm high and 5 cm in diameter contains liquid helium at 4°K, at which temperature its heat of vaporization is 5 cal/gm. Completely surrounding the helium can are walls maintained at the temperature of liquid nitrogen, 80°K, the intervening space

being evacuated. How much helium is lost per hour? Assume the emissivity to be 0.2.

17–23. A solid cylindrical copper rod 10 cm long has one end maintained at a temperature of 20.00°K. The other end is blackened and exposed to thermal radiation from a body at 300°K, no energy being lost or gained elsewhere. When equilibrium is reached, what is the temperature of the blackened end? [*Hint:* Since copper is a very good conductor of heat at low temperature ($K = 4$ cal/sec·cm·C°), the temperature of the blackened end is only slightly greater than 20°K.]

17–24. An uninsulated steam pipe of diameter 8 cm and absorptivity 0.8 passes vertically through a room in which the air and all solid surfaces are at the average temperature of 27°C. If the surface temperature of the steam pipe is 97°C, compare the rate of heat loss per meter of pipe by radiation with that by natural convection.

17–25. A small body is suspended in an evacuated enclosure as in Fig. 17–9, so that it can exchange heat with its surroundings only by radiation. The temperature of the walls of the enclosure is T and that of the body is $T + \Delta T$. (a) Show that if ΔT is small compared with T, the rate of change of temperature of the body is given by Newton's law of cooling. [*Hint:* Expand $(T + \Delta T)^4$ by the binomial theorem.] (b) Express the relaxation time in terms of the surface area A of the body, its mass m, its specific heat capacity c, its emissivity e, the temperature T, and any other pertinent factors.

17–26. A thermometer is removed from a beaker of boiling water and dried quickly. Its reading is observed to decrease from 95°C to 80°C in 30 sec. Room temperature is 20°C. If Newton's law of cooling is obeyed, (a) how many more seconds are required for the temperature of the thermometer to decrease to 65°C? (b) After how long a time does the thermometer reach room temperature? (c) Sketch a graph of temperature versus time.

CHAPTER 18

Thermal Properties of Matter

18–1 Equations of state

The volume V occupied by a definite mass m of any substance depends on the pressure p to which the substance is subjected, and on its temperature T. For every pure substance there is a definite relation between these quantities, called the *equation of state* of the substance. In formal mathematical language, the equation can be written

$$f(m, V, p, T) = 0. \tag{18–1}$$

The exact form of the function is usually very complicated. It often suffices to know only how some one of the quantities changes when some other is varied, the rest being kept constant. Thus the compressibility k describes the change in volume when the pressure is changed, for a constant mass at a constant temperature, and the coefficient of volume expansion gives the change in volume when the temperature is changed, for a constant mass at a constant pressure.

The term "state" as used here implies an *equilibrium state*. This means that the temperature and pressure are the same at all points. Hence if heat is added at some point to a system in an equilibrium state, we must wait until the processes of heat transfer within the system have brought about a new uniform temperature before the system is again in an equilibrium state.

18–2 The ideal gas

The simplest equation of state is that of a gas at low pressure. Consider a container whose volume can be varied, such as a cylinder provided with a movable piston. Provision is made for pumping any desired mass of any kind of gas into or out of the cylinder, and the cylinder is provided with a pressure gauge and with a thermometer for determining the kelvin temperature T. Then corresponding values of m, p, V, and T can all be measured. Instead of the mass m, let us express the results in terms of the number of moles, n.

Let us first collect all the measurements made on one particular gas at a given temperature, say T_1. The pressure, volume, and the number of moles present will vary over a wide range. For each individual measurement we compute the quantity pV/nT_1, and construct a graph of the results, plotting pV/nT_1 vertically and p horizontally. The plotted points will all be found to lie on a smooth curve called an *isotherm*, such as the one labeled T_1 in Fig. 18–1. When we collect all the results at some

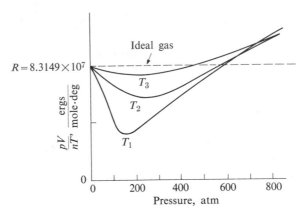

Fig. 18–1. The limiting value of pV/nT is independent of T for all gases. For an ideal gas, pV/nT is constant.

other temperature T_2, the plotted points lie on another isotherm. Similar sets of curves can be constructed for other gases.

We now discover two very remarkable facts: (a) for any one gas, the curves at different temperatures, when extrapolated to zero pressure, all intersect the vertical axis at the same point; and (b) this point of intersection is the same for all gases. In other words, the quantity pV/nT, at low pressures, is *the same for all gases.* This quantity is called the *universal gas constant* and is represented by R. The numerical value of R depends, of course, on the units in which p, V, n, and T are expressed. The adjective "universal" means that in any one system of units R has the same value for *all* gases. In the cgs system, where the unit of p is 1 dyne/cm^2, and the unit of V is 1 cm^3,

$$R = 8.3149 \times 10^7 \frac{(\text{dynes/cm}^2) \times \text{cm}^3}{\text{mole}\cdot°\text{K}} = 8.3149 \times 10^7 \frac{\text{ergs}}{\text{mole}\cdot°\text{K}}$$

$$= 8.3149 \frac{\text{joules}}{\text{mole}\cdot°\text{K}} = 1.99 \frac{\text{cal}}{\text{mole}\cdot°\text{K}}.$$

In chemistry, volumes are commonly expressed in liters, pressures in atmospheres, and temperatures in degrees kelvin. In this system of units,

$$R = 0.08207 \frac{\text{liter}\cdot\text{atm}}{\text{mole}\cdot°\text{K}}.$$

Then for all real gases at sufficiently low pressures,

$$\frac{pV}{nT} = R, \quad \text{or,} \quad pV = nRT.$$

We now define an *ideal gas* as one for which, by definition, the ratio pV/nT is equal to R at *all* pressures. In other words, an ideal gas behaves at *all* pressures in the same way that real gases behave at *low* pressures. The equation of state of an ideal gas is therefore

$$pV = nRT, \tag{18-2}$$

and for an ideal gas the curves in Fig. 18-1 all coalesce into a single horizontal straight line at a height R. Real gases, of course, do not obey this equation except at extremely low pressures. However, the deviations are not very great at moderate pressures, and at temperatures not too near those at which the gas condenses to a liquid. More complicated equations have been developed which describe the behavior of real gases more accurately, but in this chapter we shall assume that Eq. (18-2) is obeyed at all pressures and temperatures.

It follows from the equation above, and the value of the universal gas constant R, that one gram-mole of an ideal gas occupies a volume of 22,400 cm^3 or 22.4 liters at "standard conditions," or at "normal temperature and pressure" (NTP), that is, at a temperature of 0°C = 273°K, and a pressure of 1 atm = 1.01 × 10^6 dynes/cm^2. Thus, from Eq. (18-2),

$$V = \frac{nRT}{p} = \frac{1 \text{ mole} \times 8.31 \times 10^7 \text{ ergs/mole·°K} \times 273°K}{1.01 \times 10^6 \text{ dynes/cm}^2}$$

$$= 22,400 \text{ cm}^3.$$

For a *fixed mass* (or fixed number of moles) of an ideal gas, the product nR is constant and hence pV/T is constant also. Thus if the subscripts 1 and 2 refer to two states of the same mass of a gas, but at different pressures, volumes, and temperatures,

$$\frac{p_1 V_1}{T_1} = \frac{p_2 V_2}{T_2} = \text{constant.} \tag{18-3}$$

If the temperatures T_1 and T_2 are the same, then

$$p_1 V_1 = p_2 V_2 = \text{constant.} \tag{18-4}$$

The fact that the product of the pressure and volume of a fixed mass of gas is very nearly constant at constant temperature was discovered experimentally by Robert Boyle in 1660, and the equation above is called *Boyle's law*. Although exactly true, by definition, for an ideal gas, it is obeyed only approximately by real gases and is not a fundamental law like Newton's laws or the law of conservation of energy.

EXAMPLE 1. The volume of an oxygen tank is 50 liters. As oxygen is withdrawn from the tank, the reading of a pressure gauge drops from 300 lb/in^2 to 100 lb/in^2, and the temperature of the gas remaining in the tank drops from 30°C to 10°C. (a) How many kilograms of oxygen were there in the tank originally? (b) How many kilograms were withdrawn? (c) What volume would be occupied by the oxygen withdrawn from the tank at a pressure of 1 atm and a temperature of 20°C?

(a) Let us express pressures in atmospheres, volumes in liters, and temperatures in deg K. Then $R = 0.082$ lit·atm/mole·deg K. The initial and final gauge pressures are

$$300 \text{ lb/in}^2 = \frac{300}{14.7} = 20.5 \text{ atm}; \qquad 100 \text{ lb/in}^2 = 6.8 \text{ atm}.$$

The corresponding *absolute* pressures are 21.5 atm and 7.8 atm.

Initially,

$$n_1 = \frac{p_1 V}{RT_1} = \frac{21.5 \times 50}{0.082 \times 303} = 43.2 \text{ moles}.$$

The original mass was therefore

$$m_1 = 43.2 \text{ moles} \times \frac{32 \text{ gm}}{\text{mole}} = 1380 \text{ gm} = 1.38 \text{ kgm}.$$

(b) The number of moles remaining in the tank is

$$n_2 = \frac{p_2 V}{RT_2} = \frac{7.8 \times 50}{0.082 \times 283} = 16.7 \text{ moles},$$

$$m_2 = 16.7 \text{ moles} \times \frac{32 \text{ gm}}{\text{mole}} = 536 \text{ gm} = 0.54 \text{ kgm}.$$

The number of kilograms withdrawn is

$$m_1 - m_2 = 1.38 - 0.54 = 0.84 \text{ kgm}.$$

(c) The volume occupied would be

$$V = \frac{nRT}{p} = \frac{16.7 \times 0.082 \times 293}{1} = 403 \text{ liters}.$$

EXAMPLE 2. The *McLeod gauge* (pronounced "McLoud"), illustrated in Fig. 18–2, can be used to measure pressures as low as 5×10^{-6} mm of mercury. In part (a), the entire space above point A is occupied by the gas at the low pressure p which is to be measured. When the mercury container B is raised as in (b), the gas in bulb C, whose volume V might be 500 cm³, is trapped and eventually compressed into a much smaller volume V' above a reference mark on the capillary tube D. Assuming the temperature constant, the pressure p' of the compressed gas is given by applying Boyle's law,

$$p' = \frac{pV}{V'}.$$

The pressure at the upper surface of the mercury in capillary E remains at the value p, so that if h is the difference in elevation between the tops of the mercury columns in E and D,

$$p' = p + \rho g h,$$

where ρ is the density of mercury. Elimination of p' between these equations gives

$$p = \frac{\rho g V'}{V - V'} h \approx \frac{V'}{V} \rho g h,$$

to a good approximation, since $V' \ll V$.

For example, if $p = 4 \times 10^{-4}$ mm of mercury and $V' = 10^{-4} V$, the height $h = 4$ mm. Since ρ, g, V, and V' are constants, the pressure p is directly proportional to h and a uniform pressure scale can be mounted beside tube E. Corrections for capillary depression are eliminated if capillaries D and E have the same diameter.

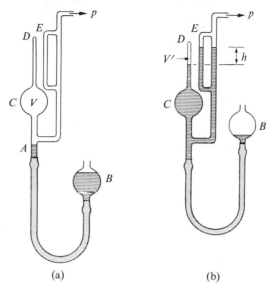

Fig. 18-2. The McLeod gauge.

EXAMPLE 3. In the upper part of the atmosphere (the stratosphere) the temperature varies only slightly with changes in elevation. Find the law of variation of pressure with elevation.

The rate of change of pressure with elevation in a fluid is $dp/dy = -\rho g$.

Let us replace n by m/M in the ideal gas law, where m is the mass and M the molecular weight. Then

$$pV = \frac{m}{M} RT,$$

and the density ρ of an ideal gas is

$$\rho = \frac{m}{V} = \frac{pM}{RT}.$$

Hence

$$\frac{dp}{dy} = -\frac{pMg}{RT}, \qquad \frac{dp}{p} = -\frac{Mg}{RT} dy.$$

If g and T are constant, and if p_1 and p_2 are the pressures at two elevations y_1 and y_2, integration of the preceding equation gives

$$\ln \frac{p_2}{p_1} = -\frac{Mg}{RT} (y_2 - y_1). \tag{18-5}$$

This is known as the *barometric equation*.

18–3 pVT-surface for an ideal gas

Since the equation of state, for a fixed mass of a substance, is a relation among the three variables p, V, and T, it defines a *surface* in a rectangular coordinate system in which p, V, and T are plotted along the three axes. Figure 18–3 shows the pVT-surface of an ideal gas. The full lines on the surface show the relation between p and V when T is constant (Boyle's law), the dashed lines the relation between V and T when p is constant (Gay-Lussac's law), and the dotted lines the relation between p and T when V is constant. When viewed perpendicular to the pV-plane, the surface appears as in Fig. 18–4(a), and Fig. 18–4(b) is its appearance when viewed perpendicular to the pT-plane.

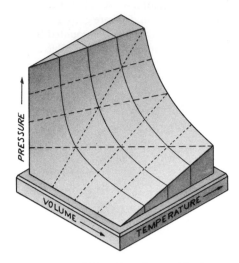

Fig. 18–3. pVT-surface for an ideal gas.

Every possible equilibrium state of the gas corresponds to a point on the surface, and every point of the surface corresponds to a possible equilibrium state. The gas cannot exist in a state that is not on the surface. For example, if the volume and temperature are given, thus locating a point in the base plane of Fig. 18–3, the pressure is then determined by the nature of the gas, and it can have only the value represented by the height of the surface above this point.

In any process in which the gas passes through a succession of equilibrium states, the point representing its state moves along a curve lying in the pVT-surface. Such a process must be carried out very slowly, to give the temperature and pressure time to become uniform at all points of the gas.

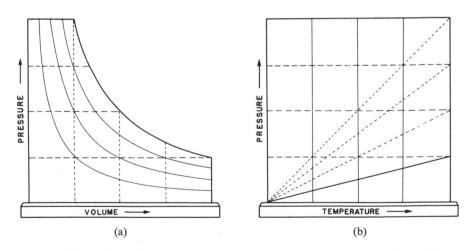

Fig. 18–4.   Projections of ideal gas pVT-surface on (a) the pV-plane, (b) the pT-plane.

18–4 pVT-surface for a real substance

While all real substances approximate ideal gases at sufficiently low pressures, their behavior departs more and more from that of an ideal gas at high pressures and low temperatures. As the temperature is lowered and the pressure increased, all substances change from the *gas phase* to the *liquid phase* or the *solid phase*. For a fixed mass of a substance, however, there is still a definite relation between the pressure, temperature, and total volume. In other words, the substance has an equation of state in any circumstances, and although the general form of the equation is much too complicated to express mathematically, we can represent it graphically by a *pVT*-surface. Figure 18–6 is a schematic diagram (to a greatly distorted scale) of the *pVT*-surface for a substance that expands on melting (the most common case) and Fig. 18–7 is the corresponding diagram for a substance which, like water, contracts on melting. We see that the substance can exist in either the solid, liquid, or gas phase, or in two phases simultaneously, or, along the triple line, in all three phases. (The distinction between the terms "gas" and "vapor" will be explained later. For the present they may be considered synonymous.)

In order that the diagram shall represent the properties of a particular *substance*, but not depend on *how much* of the substance is present, we plot along the volume axis not the actual volume V but the *specific volume* v, the volume per unit mass. Thus for a system of mass m,

$$v = \frac{V}{m}.$$

The actual volume of a unit mass of a substance is numerically equal to its specific volume. The specific volume is the reciprocal of the density ρ,

$$\rho = \frac{m}{V} = \frac{1}{v}.$$

To correlate these diagrams with our familiar experiences regarding the behavior of solids, liquids, and gases, let us start with a substance in the solid phase at point a in Fig. 18 6 or 18–7. Let the substance be contained in a cylinder as in Fig. 18–5, and let a constant force F be exerted on the piston so that the pressure remains constant as the substance expands or contracts. Such a process is called *isobaric*. We now bring the cylinder in contact with some body such as an electric stove, whose temperature can be slowly increased and always kept slightly higher than that of the substance. There will then be a flow of heat into the substance.

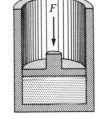

Figure 18–5

At the start of the process, the temperature of the substance rises as heat is added, at a rate determined by the specific heat capacity of the solid, and the volume increases slightly at a rate determined by its coefficient of expansion. When point b is reached in either diagram the substance starts to melt, that is, to change from the solid to the liquid phase. The temperature ceases to rise even though heat is being continuously supplied. The volume increases in Fig. 18–6 and decreases in Fig. 18–7.

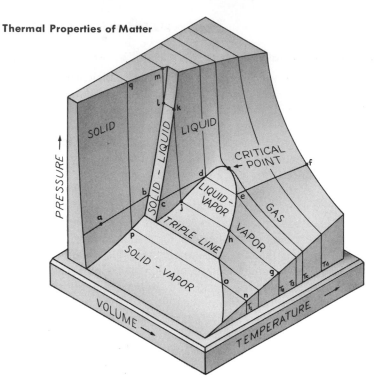

Fig. 18–6. pVT-surface for a substance that expands on melting.

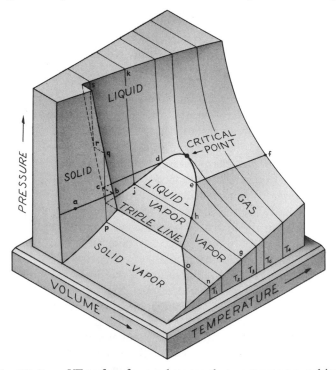

Fig. 18–7. pVT-surface for a substance that contracts on melting.

When point c is reached, the substance is wholly in the liquid phase. The temperature now starts to rise again, at a rate determined by the specific heat capacity of the liquid, and the volume increases at a rate determined by its coefficient of expansion. (For water at atmospheric pressure, there would be a small *decrease* in volume at first.)

When point d is reached, the temperature again ceases to rise, although heat is still supplied, and bubbles of vapor start to form in the cylinder and rise to its upper surface. Since the density of the vapor phase is very much smaller than that of the liquid, the volume increases markedly.

At point e, the substance is wholly in the vapor phase. (The relative volume increase from d to e, except at very high pressures, is enormously greater than the volume change between liquid and solid, so diagrams like Figs. 18–6 and 18–7 are not constructed on a uniform scale.) With further addition of heat the temperature rises again, the rate now being determined by the specific heat capacity of the vapor phase (at constant pressure). The volume also increases much more rapidly than did that of the solid or liquid.

If the cylinder is now brought in contact with a body whose temperature is kept slightly *lower* than that of the substance, heat flows out of the substance and all the changes in the original process take place in reversed order.

As a second illustration to show how the pVT-surface describes the behavior of a substance, suppose we start with a cylinder containing a gas, at a pressure, volume, and temperature corresponding to point g in Fig. 18–6 or 18–7. Let the external pressure be adjusted so that it is always slightly greater than the pressure exerted by the substance, and let the cylinder be kept in contact with a body at a constant temperature. The process is then *isothermal*.

The first effect of the increased external pressure will be to raise the temperature of the gas slightly. There will then be a flow of heat from the gas to the body with which it is in contact, and as the pressure increases the volume decreases along the line gh in a manner not very different from that of an ideal gas. When point h is reached, drops of liquid begin to form in the cylinder, and the volume continues to decrease without further increase of pressure.

At point j, all of the substance has condensed to the liquid phase. With further increase of pressure the volume decreases, but only slightly because of the small compressibility of liquids. For a substance like that in Fig. 18–7, no other change of phase occurs as the pressure is increased to point k and beyond. (Unless other forms of the solid state exist. See Fig. 18–8 and the accompanying discussion.) In Fig. 18–6, however, another break in the curve takes place at point k. Crystals of the solid begin to appear, and the volume again decreases without an increase of external pressure. At point l, in Fig. 18–6, the substance has been completely converted to the solid phase. Further increase of pressure reduces the volume of the solid only slightly and unless the substance can exist in more than one modification of the solid phase, no further changes in phase result.

As one more example, suppose we again start with a gas in the cylinder but at a lower temperature, corresponding to point n in Figs. 18–6 and 18–7. If the pressure is increased isothermally, crystals of the solid begin to appear at point o and the gas changes directly to a solid without passing through the liquid phase. The pressure remains constant along the line *op*, and at point *p* the substance is all in the solid phase. In Fig. 18–6 no further phase change takes place but in Fig. 18–7 the solid starts to melt at point *q* and has completely melted at point *r*.

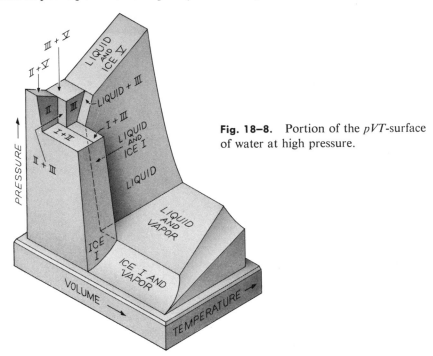

Fig. 18–8. Portion of the *pVT*-surface of water at high pressure.

Bear in mind that in all the processes described above, heat must be removed or added continuously in order to keep the pressure or temperature constant. If at any stage of a process the system is thermally insulated so that there can be no flow of heat in or out, and if the external pressure is kept constant, the system remains in equilibrium. Thus at any point on the surfaces lettered solid-liquid, solid-vapor, or liquid-vapor, *two* phases can coexist in equilibrium, and along the *triple line* all three phases can coexist. A vapor at the pressure and temperature at which it can exist in equilibrium with its liquid is called a *saturated vapor*, and the liquid is called a *saturated liquid*. Thus points *e* and *h* represent saturated vapor, and points *j* and *d*, saturated liquid. (The term "saturated" is poorly chosen. It does not have the same meaning as a "saturated solution" in chemistry. There is no question here of one substance being dissolved in another.)

18–5 Critical point and triple point

A study of Figs. 18–6 and 18–7 will show that the liquid and gas (or vapor) phases can exist together only if the temperature and pressure are less than those at the point lying at the top of the tongue-shaped surface lettered liquid-vapor. This point is called the *critical point*, and the corresponding values of *T*, *p*, and *v* are the *critical temperature*, *pressure*, and *specific volume*. A gas at a temperature above the critical

TABLE 18–1

CRITICAL CONSTANTS

Substance	Critical temp., °K	Critical pressure, atm	Critical volume, cm^3/mole	Critical density, gm/cm^3
Helium (4)	5.3	2.26	57.8	0.0693
Helium (3)	3.34	1.15	72.6	0.0413
Hydrogen (normal)	33.3	12.80	65.0	0.0310
Deuterium (normal)	38.4	16.4		
Nitrogen	126.2	33.5	90.1	0.311
Oxygen	154.8	50.1	78	0.41
Ammonia	405.5	111.3	72.5	0.235
Freon 12	384.7	39.6	218	0.555
Carbon dioxide	304.2	72.9	94.0	0.468
Sulfur dioxide	430.7	77.8	122	0.524
Water	647.4	218.3	56	0.32
Carbon disulfide	552	78	170	0.44

temperature, such as T_4, does not separate into two phases when compressed iso-thermally but its properties change gradually and continuously from those we ordinarily associate with a gas (low density, large compressibility) to those of a liquid (high density, small compressibility). Table 18–1 lists the critical constants for a few substances. The very low critical temperatures of hydrogen and helium make it evident why these gases defied attempts to liquefy them for many years.

The term *vapor* is sometimes used to mean a gas at any temperature below its critical temperature, and sometimes is restricted to mean a gas in equilibrium with the liquid phase, that is, a saturated vapor. The term is really unnecessary; no sudden change takes place in the properties of a substance when the critical isotherm is crossed either on the portion of the surface lettered gas and vapor, or on the portion lettered liquid.

It has been found that some substances can exist in more than one modification of the solid phase. Transitions from one modification to another occur at definite temperatures and pressures, like the phase changes from liquid to solid, etc. Water is one such substance, and at least 8 types of ice have been observed at very high pressures. Figure 18–8 shows a portion of the pVT-surface of water at high pressure. Note that ordinary ice (ice I) is the only form whose specific volume is greater than that of the liquid phase.

Because of the difficulty of drawing three-dimensional diagrams, it is customary to represent the pVT-surface by its projections onto the pT- and pV-planes. Figure 18–9 shows the two projections of Fig. 18–6, and Fig. 18–10 shows those of Fig. 18–7. The reader should follow through on these diagrams the isobaric and isothermal processes indicated in Figs. 18–6 and 18–7.

The curves in Figs. 18–9(a) and 18–10(a) lettered S-L, S-V, and L-V, which are side views of the respective surfaces in 18–9(b) and 18–10(b), are loci of corresponding

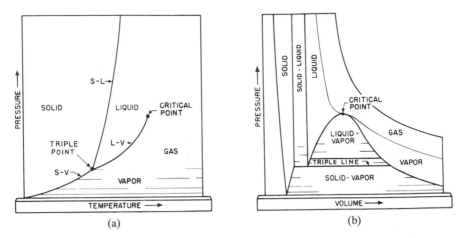

Fig. 18–9. Projections of the surface in Fig. 18–6 on the pT- and pV-planes.

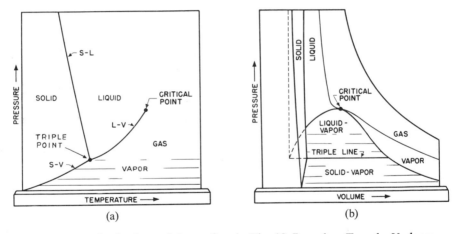

Fig. 18–10. Projections of the surface in Fig. 18–7 on the pT- and pV-planes.

values of pressure and temperature at which the two phases can coexist if a substance is isolated, or at which one phase will transform to the other if heat is supplied or removed. Thus the S-L curve is also a graph of the melting-point temperature or freezing-point temperature of the substance as a function of pressure, the curve S-V is a graph of the *sublimation point* versus *pressure*, and the curve L-V is a graph of the *boiling point* versus *pressure*. The S-V and L-V curves always slope upward to the right. The S-L curve slopes upward to the right for a substance that expands on melting (Fig. 18–9) but upward to the left for a substance like water that contracts on melting (Fig. 18–10). Thus an increase of pressure always increases the temperature of the sublimation point or boiling point, but the temperature of the freezing point may be raised (Fig. 18–9) or lowered (Fig. 18–10) by an increase in pressure.

TABLE 18–2

VAPOR PRESSURE OF WATER

Temperature, °C	Vapor pressure, mm of mercury	Vapor pressure, lb/in^2	Temperature, °F
0	4.58	0.0886	32
5	6.51	0.126	41
10	8.94	0.173	50
15	12.67	0.245	59
20	17.5	0.339	68
40	55.1	1.07	104
60	149	2.89	140
80	355	6.87	176
100	**760**	**14.7**	**212**
120	1490	28.8	248
140	2710	52.4	284
160	4630	89.6	320
180	7510	145	356
200	11650	225	392
220	17390	336	428

The pressure of a vapor in equilibrium with the liquid or solid at any temperature is called the *vapor pressure* of the substance at that temperature. Thus the curves S-V and L-V in Figs. 18–9(a) and 18–10(a) are graphs of vapor pressure versus temperature. The vapor pressure of a substance is a function of *temperature only*, not of volume. That is, in a vessel containing a liquid (or solid) and vapor in equilibrium *at a fixed temperature*, the pressure does not depend on the relative amounts of liquid and vapor present. If the volume is decreased some of the vapor condenses, and vice versa, but if the temperature is kept constant by removing or adding heat the pressure does not change.

The boiling-point temperature of a liquid is the temperature at which its vapor pressure equals the external pressure. Table 18–2 gives the vapor pressure of water as a function of temperature, and we see that the vapor pressure is 1 atm at a temperature of 100°C. If the external pressure is reduced to 17.5 mm of mercury, water will boil at room temperature (20°C), while under a pressure of 90 lb/in^2 (about 6 atm) the boiling point is 160°C.

The point of intersection of the three equilibrium lines in Figs. 18–9(a) and 18–10(a), which is an end view of the triple line in Figs. 18–9(b) and 18–10(b), is called the *triple point*. There is only one pressure and temperature at which all three phases can coexist. Triple-point data for a few substances are given in Table 18–3.

As numerical examples, consider the *pT*-diagrams of water and carbon dioxide, in Fig. 18–11(a) and (b). In (a), a horizontal line at a pressure of 1 atm intersects the freezing-point curve at 0°C and the boiling-point curve at 100°C. The boiling point increases with increasing pressure up to the critical temperature of 374°C. Solid, liquid, and vapor can remain in equilibrium at the triple point, where the vapor pressure is 4.5 mm of mercury and the temperature is 0.01°C.

TABLE 18–3

TRIPLE-POINT DATA

Substance	Temp., °K	Pressure, mm Hg
Helium (4) (λ point)	2.186	38.3
Helium (3)	None	None
Hydrogen (normal)	13.84	52.8
Deuterium (normal)	18.63	128
Neon	24.57	324
Nitrogen	63.18	94
Oxygen	54.36	1.14
Ammonia	195.40	45.57
Carbon dioxide	216.55	3880
Sulfur dioxide	197.68	1.256
Water	273.16	4.58

The freezing point of a substance like water, which expands on solidifying, is *lowered* by an increase in pressure. The reverse is true for substances which contract on solidifying. The change in the freezing-point temperature is much smaller than is that of the boiling point; an increase of one atmosphere lowers the freezing point of water by only about 0.007°C.

The lowering of the freezing point of water (or the melting point of ice) can be demonstrated by passing a loop of fine wire over a block of ice and hanging a weight of a few pounds from each end of the loop. Suppose that the main body of the ice is at 0°C and at atmospheric pressure. The temperature of the small amount of ice directly under the wire decreases until it achieves the melting point appropriate to the pressure under the wire. During this increase of pressure and decrease of temperature, a small amount of melting takes place. The water thus formed is squeezed

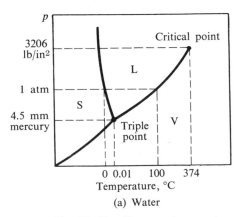

(a) Water

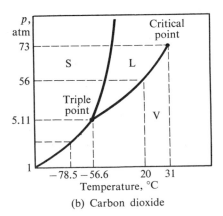

(b) Carbon dioxide

Fig. 18–11. Pressure-temperature diagrams (not to a uniform scale).

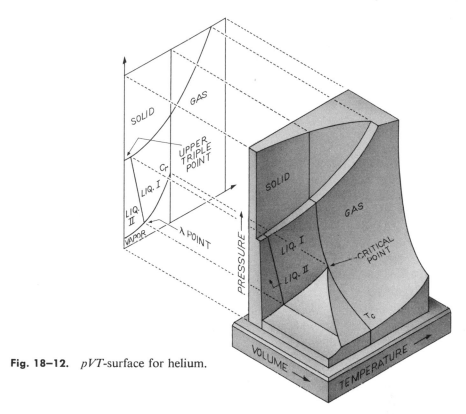

Fig. 18–12.   *pVT*-surface for helium.

out from under the wire and, coming to the top of the wire where the pressure is atmospheric, it refreezes and liberates heat which passes through the wire and serves to melt the next bit of ice below the wire.

The wire thus sinks farther and farther into the block, eventually cutting its way completely through, but leaving a solid block of ice behind it. This phenomenon is known as *regelation* (refreezing). Since heat is conducted from the top to the bottom of the wire while the wire is cutting through the ice, the greater the thermal conductivity of the wire, the faster will the wire cut through the ice. Even a perfectly conducting wire would not cut through the ice very rapidly, however, because of the very low thermal conductivity of the water film which is always present beneath the wire.

For carbon dioxide, the triple-point temperature is $-56.6°C$ and the corresponding pressure is 5.11 atm. Hence at atmospheric pressure CO_2 can exist only as a solid or a vapor. When heat is supplied to solid CO_2, open to the atmosphere, it changes directly to a vapor, without passing through the liquid phase, whence the name "dry ice." Liquid CO_2 can exist only at a pressure greater than 5.11 atm. The steel tanks in which CO_2 is commonly stored contain liquid and vapor (both saturated). The pressure in these tanks is the vapor pressure of CO_2 at the temperature of the tank. If the latter is 20°C the vapor pressure is 56 atm or about 830 lb/in^2.

The *pVT*-surface for ordinary helium (of mass number 4) is shown in Fig. 18–12. Two remarkable properties may be seen. (1) Helium has no triple point at which solid, liquid, and gas coexist in equilibrium. Instead, it has two triple points, the lower one (called the "lambda point") representing the temperature and pressure at which two liquids, I and II, coexist with vapor; and the upper one at which the two liquids coexist with solid. (2) As the temperature is lowered, helium does not solidify, but remains liquid all the way to absolute zero. To get solid helium, the pressure must be raised to a value above 25 atmospheres at which the helium atoms can attract one another and coalesce into a crystal lattice.

18–6 Effect of dissolved substances on freezing and boiling points

The freezing point of a liquid is lowered when some other substance is dissolved in the liquid. A common example is the use of an "antifreeze" to lower the freezing point of the water in the cooling system of an automobile engine.

The freezing point of a saturated solution of common salt in water is about $-20°C$. To understand why a mixture of ice and salt may be used as a freezing mixture, let us make use of the definition of the freezing point as the only temperature at which the liquid and solid phases can exist in equilibrium. When a concentrated salt solution is cooled, it freezes at $-20°C$, and crystals of ice (pure H_2O) separate from the solution. In other words, ice crystals and a salt solution can exist in equilibrium only at $-20°C$, just as ice crystals and pure water can exist together only at $0°C$.

When ice at $0°C$ is mixed with a salt solution at $20°C$, some of the ice melts, abstracting its heat of fusion from the solution until the temperature falls to $0°C$. But ice and salt solution cannot remain in equilibrium at $0°C$, so that the ice continues to melt. Heat is now supplied by both the ice and the solution, and both cool down until the equilibrium temperature of $-20°C$ is reached. If no heat is supplied from outside, the mixture remains unchanged at this temperature. If the mixture is brought into contact with a warmer body, say an ice-cream mixture at $20°C$, heat flows from the ice-cream mixture to the cold salt solution, melting more of the ice but producing no rise in temperature as long as any ice remains. The flow of heat from the ice-cream mixture lowers its temperature to its freezing point (below $0°C$, since it is itself a solution). Further loss of heat to the ice-salt mixture causes the ice cream to freeze.

The boiling point of a liquid is also affected by dissolved substances, but may be either increased or decreased. Thus the boiling point of a water-alcohol solution is *lower* than that of pure water, while the boiling point of a water-salt solution is *higher* than that of pure water.

18–7 Humidity

Atmospheric air is a mixture of gases consisting of about 80% nitrogen, 18% oxygen, and small amounts of carbon dioxide, water vapor, and other gases. The mass of water vapor per unit volume is called the *absolute humidity*. The total pressure exerted by the atmosphere is the sum of the pressures exerted by its component gases. These pressures are called the *partial pressures* of the components. It is found that the partial pressure of each of the component gases of a gas mixture is very nearly the same as would be the actual pressure of that component alone if it occupied the same volume as does the mixture, a fact known as *Dalton's law*. That is, each of the gases of a gas mixture behaves independently of the others. The partial pressure of water vapor in the atmosphere is ordinarily a few millimeters of mercury.

It should be evident that the partial pressure of water vapor at any given air temperature can never exceed the vapor pressure of water at that particular temperature. Thus at 10°C, from Table 18–2, the partial pressure cannot exceed 8.94 mm, or at 15°C it cannot exceed 12.67 mm. If the concentration of water vapor, or the absolute humidity, is such that the partial pressure equals the vapor pressure, the vapor is *saturated*. If the partial pressure is less than the vapor pressure, the vapor is *unsaturated*. The ratio of the partial pressure to the vapor pressure at the same temperature is called the *relative humidity*, and is usually expressed as a percentage.

$$\text{Relative humidity } (\%) = 100 \times \frac{\text{partial pressure of water vapor}}{\text{vapor pressure at same temperature}}.$$

The relative humidity is 100% if the vapor is saturated and zero if no water vapor at all is present.

EXAMPLE. The partial pressure of water vapor in the atmosphere is 10 mm and the temperature is 20°C. Find the relative humidity.

From Table 18–2, the vapor pressure at 20°C is 17.5 mm. Hence,

$$\text{Relative humidity } = 10/17.5 \times 100 = 57\%.$$

Since the water vapor in the atmosphere is saturated when its partial pressure equals the vapor pressure at the air temperature, saturation can be brought about either by increasing the water vapor content or by lowering the temperature. For example, let the partial pressure of water vapor be 10 mm when the air temperature is 20°C, as in the preceding example. Saturation or 100% relative humidity could be attained either by introducing enough more water vapor (keeping the temperature constant) to increase the partial pressure to 17.5 mm, *or by lowering the temperature* to 11.4°C, at which, by interpolation from Table 18–2, the vapor pressure is 10 mm.

If the temperature were to be lowered *below* 11.4°C, the vapor pressure would be less than 10 mm. The partial pressure would then be higher than the vapor pressure and enough vapor would condense to reduce the partial pressure to the vapor pressure at the lower temperature. It is this process which brings about the formation of clouds, fog, and rain. The phenomenon is also of frequent occurrence at night when the earth's surface becomes cooled by radiation. The condensed moisture is called *dew*. If the partial pressure is so low that the temperature must fall below 0°C before saturation exists, the vapor condenses into ice crystals in the form of frost.

The temperature at which the water vapor in a given sample of air becomes saturated is called the *dew point*. Measuring the temperature of the dew point is the most accurate method of determining relative humidity. The usual method is to cool a metal container having a bright, polished surface, and to observe its temperature when the surface becomes clouded with condensed moisture. Suppose the dew point is observed in this way to be 10°C, when the air temperature is 20°C. We then know that the water vapor in the air is saturated at 10°C, hence its partial pressure is 8.94 mm, equal to the vapor pressure at 10°C. The pressure necessary for saturation at 20°C is 17.5 mm. The relative humidity is therefore

$$\frac{8.94}{17.5} \times 100 = 51\%.$$

A simpler but less accurate method of determining relative humidity employs a *wet-* and *dry-bulb thermometer.* Two thermometers are placed side by side, the bulb of one being kept moist by a wick dipping in water. The lower the relative humidity, the more rapid will be the evaporation from the wet bulb, and the lower will be its temperature below that of the dry bulb. The relative humidity corresponding to any pair of wet- and dry-bulb temperatures is read from tables.

18–8 The Wilson cloud chamber and the bubble chamber

The Wilson cloud chamber is an apparatus for securing information about elementary particles such as electrons and α-particles. In principle (Fig. 18–13), it consists of a cylindrical enclosure having glass walls A and a glass top B, and provided with a movable piston C. The enclosed space contains air, water vapor, and sufficient excess water so that the vapor is saturated. (Other liquids such as alcohol are often used in place of water.) When the piston is suddenly pulled down a short distance, the mixture is lowered in temperature below the dew point. If the air is perfectly clean, the cooled vapor does not immediately condense, and it is said to be *super-saturated.* The point representing its state then lies *above* the pVT-surface, but this does not contradict a statement made earlier that all equilibrium states of a substance must lie on its pVT-surface, since the supersaturated state is not an equilibrium state. It is found that any ions which may be present serve as very efficient nuclei upon which the supersaturated vapor condenses to form liquid droplets. Hence if any ions were present just before the expansion, their presence is made evident by the appearance of tiny droplets immediately after the expansion.

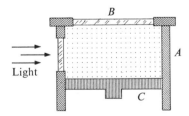

Fig. 18–13.   The Wilson cloud chamber.

Electrons, protons, and α-particles are all capable of traveling several centimeters through air, but as they collide with or pass near the air molecules they may knock off one or more of their electrons and hence leave behind them a trail of ions. Therefore if such a particle passed through the chamber just before the expansion, a trail of droplets appears after the expansion, indicating the path the particle followed. For photographing the tracks, an intense beam of light is projected transversely through the chamber and a camera mounted above it.   Figure 8–11 is a photograph, made with a Wilson cloud chamber, of the paths of the particles resulting from the fission of a uranium nucleus.

The *bubble chamber*, a recently developed apparatus for studying ionizing particles, makes use of a *superheated liquid* instead of a supersaturated vapor.   (A superheated liquid is a liquid at a temperature higher than that of its boiling point at the pressure to which it is subjected.   It also is a nonequilibrium state.)   When ions are produced in a superheated liquid it "boils" in the vicinity of the ion and forms a tiny bubble of vapor.   The track of an ionizing particle through it is thus marked by a line of vapor bubbles rather than of liquid droplets.   The advantage of the bubble chamber is that the molecules of a liquid are much closer together than those of a gas, so that there is a greater chance that a particle passing through the liquid will collide with a molecule and produce an ion.

Problems

(Assume all gases to be ideal.)

18–1. A tank contains 1.5 ft^3 of nitrogen at an absolute pressure of 20 lb/in^2 and a temperature of 40°F. What will be the pressure if the volume is increased to 15 ft^3 and the temperature is raised to 440°F?

18–2. A tank having a capacity of 2 ft^3 is filled with oxygen which has a gauge pressure of 60 lb/in^2 when the temperature is 47°C. At a later time it is found that because of a leak the gauge pressure has dropped to 50 lb/in^2 and the temperature has decreased to 27°C. Find (a) the mass of the oxygen in the tank under the first set of conditions, (b) the amount of oxygen that has leaked out.

18–3. A flask of volume 2 liters, provided with a stopcock, contains oxygen at 300°K and atmospheric pressure. The system is heated to a temperature of 400°K, with the stopcock open to the atmosphere. The stopcock is then closed and the flask cooled to its original temperature. (a) What is the final pressure of the oxygen in the flask? (b) How many grams of oxygen remain in the flask?

18–4. A barrage balloon whose volume is 20,000 ft^3 is to be filled with hydrogen at atmospheric pressure. (a) If the hydrogen is stored in cylinders of volume 2 ft^3 at an absolute pressure of 200 lb/in^2, how many cylinders are required? (b) What is the total weight that can be supported by the balloon, in air at standard conditions? (c) What weight could be supported if the balloon were filled with helium instead of hydrogen?

18–5. Derive from the equation of state of an ideal gas an equation for the density of an ideal gas in terms of pressure, temperature, and appropriate constants.

18–6. At the beginning of the compression stroke, the cylinder of a diesel engine contains 48 in^3 of air at atmospheric pressure and a temperature of 27°C. At the

end of the stroke, the air has been compressed to a volume of 3 in^3 and the gauge pressure has increased to 600 lb/in^2. Compute the temperature.

18–7. A bubble of air rises from the bottom of a lake, where the pressure is 3.03 atm, to the surface, where the pressure is 1 atm. The temperature at the bottom of the lake is 7°C and the temperature at the surface is 27°C. What is the ratio of the size (i.e., the volume) of the bubble as it reaches the surface to the size of the bubble at the bottom?

18–8. A liter of helium under a pressure of 2 atm and at a temperature of 27°C is heated until both pressure and volume are doubled. (a) What is the final temperature? (b) How many grams of helium are there?

18–9. A flask contains 1 gm of oxygen at an absolute pressure of 10 atm and at a temperature of 47°C. At a later time it is found that because of a leak the pressure has dropped to $\frac{5}{8}$ of its original value and the temperature has decreased to 27°C. (a) What is the volume of the flask? (b) How many grams of oxygen leaked out between the two observations?

18–10. The submarine Squalus sank at a point where the depth of water was 240 ft. The temperature at the surface is 27°C and at the bottom it is 7°C. The density of sea water may be taken as 2 slugs/ft^3. (a) If a diving bell in the form of a circular cylinder 8 ft high, open at the bottom and closed at the top, is lowered to this depth, to what height will the water rise within it when it reaches the bottom? (b) At what gauge pressure must compressed air be supplied to the bell while on the bottom to expel all the water from it?

18–11. A bicycle pump is full of air at an absolute pressure of 15 lb/in^2. The length of stroke of the pump is 18 inches. At what part of the stroke does air begin to enter a tire in which the gauge pressure is 40 lb/in^2? Assume the compression to be isothermal.

18–12. A vertical cylindrical tank 1 m high has its top end closed by a tightly fitting frictionless piston of negligible weight. The air inside the cylinder is at an absolute pressure of 1 atm. The piston is depressed by pouring mercury on it slowly. How far will the piston descend before mercury spills over the top of the cylinder? The temperature of the air is maintained constant.

18–13. A barometer is made of a tube 90 cm long and of cross section 1.5 cm². Mercury stands in this tube to a height of 75 cm. The room temperature is 27°C. A small amount of nitrogen is introduced into the evacuated space above the mercury and the column drops to a height of 70 cm. How many grams of nitrogen were introduced?

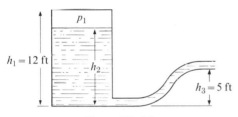

Figure 18–14

18–14. A large tank of water has a hose connected to it, as shown in Fig. 18–14. The tank is sealed at the top and has compressed air between the water surface and the top. When the water height h_2 is 10 ft, the gauge pressure p_1 is 15 lb/in². Assume that the air above the water surface expands isothermally and that water weighs 64 lb/ft³. (a) What is the velocity of flow out of the hose when $h_2 = 10$ ft? (b) What is the velocity of flow of the hose when h_2 has decreased to 8 ft? Neglect friction.

18–15. The volume of an ideal gas is 4 liters, the pressure 2 atm, and the temperature is 300°K. The gas first expands at constant pressure to twice its original volume, it is then compressed isothermally to its original volume, and finally cooled at constant volume to its original pressure.

(a) Show the process in a pV-diagram. (b) Compute the temperature during the isothermal compression. (c) Compute the maximum pressure.

18–16. At the beginning of the compression stroke, the cylinder of a diesel engine contains 48 in³ of air at atmospheric pressure and a temperature of 27°C. At the end of the stroke, the air has been compressed to a volume of 3 in³, and the gauge pressure has increased to 600 lb/in². Compute the temperature, (a) in degrees kelvin, (b) degrees celsius, (c) degrees fahrenheit.

18–17. In the lower part of the atmosphere (the troposphere) the temperature is not uniform but decreases with increasing elevation. Show that if the temperature variation is approximated by the linear relation

$$T = T_0 - \alpha y,$$

where T_0 is the temperature at the earth's surface and T is the temperature at a height y, the pressure is given by

$$\ln \frac{p_0}{p} = \frac{Mg}{R\alpha} \ln \frac{T_0}{T_0 - \alpha y}.$$

The coefficient α is called the "lapse rate of temperature." While it varies with atmospheric conditions, an average value is about 0.6 C°/100 meters.

18–18. Construct two graphs for a real substance, one showing pressure as a function of volume, and the other showing pressure as a function of temperature. Show on each graph the region in which the substance exists as (a) a gas or vapor, (b) a liquid, (c) a solid. Show also the triple point and the critical point.

18–19. A small amount of liquid is introduced into a glass tube, all air is removed, and the tube is sealed off. Describe the behavior of the meniscus when the temperature of the system is raised: (a) If the volume of the tube is much greater than the critical volume. (b) If the volume of the tube is much less than the critical volume. (c) If the volume of the tube is only slightly different from the critical volume.

18–20. A piece of ice at 0°C is placed alongside a beaker of water at 0°C in a glass vessel, from which all air has been removed. If the ice, water, and vessel are all maintained at a temperature of 0°C by a suitable thermostat, describe the final equilibrium state inside the vessel.

18–21. A mass m of pure substance is placed in a tube of constant volume V. If there are two phases present, show that (a) the volume occupied by one phase will be

$$V_1 = \frac{m - \rho_2 V_2}{\rho_1 - \rho_2},$$

where ρ_1, V_1, and ρ_2, V_2 are the densities and volumes, respectively, of the two phases; (b) the condition that V_1 will not change as the temperature is increased is given by

$$\frac{V_1}{V_2} = -\frac{d\rho_2/dT}{d\rho_1/dT}.$$

18–22. (a) What is the relative humidity on a day when the temperature is 68°F and the dew point is 41°F? (b) What is the partial pressure of water vapor in the atmosphere? (c) What is the absolute humidity, in gm/m³?

18–23. The temperature in a room is 40°C. A can is gradually cooled by adding cold water. At 10°C the surface of the can clouds over. What is the relative humidity in the room?

18–24. A pan of water is placed in a sealed room of volume 60 m³ and at a temperature of 27°C. (a) What is the absolute humidity in gm/m³ after equilibrium has been reached? (b) If the temperature of the room is then increased 1 C°, how many more grams of water will evaporate?

18–25. (a) What is the dew-point temperature on a day when the air temperature is 20°C and the relative humidity is 60%? (b) What is the absolute humidity, in gm/m³?

18–26. The volume of a closed room, kept at a constant temperature of 20°C, is 60 m³. The relative humidity in the room is 10%. If a pan of water is brought into the room, how many grams will evaporate?

18–27. An air conditioning system is required to increase the relative humidity of 10 ft³ of air per second from 30% to 65%. The air temperature is 68°F. How many pounds of water are needed by the system per hour?

CHAPTER 19

The Laws of Thermodynamics

19–1 Work in thermodynamics

In the study of the equilibrium or the acceleration of a mechanical system, it is necessary to calculate the resultant force F acting *on* the system, because it is this force which when used with Newton's second law provides the means for calculating the acceleration, or when set equal to zero provides one of the conditions of equilibrium. The product of the system's displacement ds and the component of F in the direction of the displacement, F_s, is the *work of the force*. The sign convention of mechanics provides that the work is positive when F_s and ds have the same sign. When this is the case, the energy of the system increases, and the expression "work is done *on* the system" is often used. In the reverse situation, where F_s and ds have opposite sign, the energy of the system decreases, and this is referred to in the words, "work is done *by* the system."

We shall be concerned in this chapter with the principles underlying the subject of *thermodynamics*, a branch of physics that owes its origin to the study of engines whose purpose is to do work. A gasoline engine, for example, is designed to propel an automobile; a steam turbine is often used to turn the rotor of an electric generator. As a result of the study of such devices, all of which have as their goal the performance of work *by* the system, it became the custom many years ago in thermodynamics to refer to such work as positive.

It is a simple matter to bring the mechanical sign convention for work into line with the thermodynamic point of view. All we have to do is to focus our attention on the *resultant force exerted by a system*. If *this* force has the same direction as the displacement, the product of force and displacement is positive and (1) work is done *by* the system, (2) the energy of the system decreases provided there is no other energy transfer.

To summarize:

(a) Calculate the force F exerted *by* the system.

(b) Calculate the displacement ds of the point of application of F.

(c) If F and ds have the same sign, the work is positive.

(d) Positive work is said to be done *by* the system.

(e) When positive work is done, the energy of the system decreases, unless there is some other energy transfer.

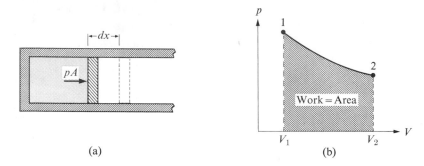

Fig. 19–1. (a) Force exerted *by* a system during a small expansion. (b) Work is the area under the curve on a *pV*-diagram.

19–2 Work in changing the volume

Consider a solid or fluid contained in a cylinder equipped with a movable piston, as shown in Fig. 19–1(a). Suppose that the cylinder has a cross-sectional area A and that the pressure exerted by the system at the piston face is p. The force exerted *by* the system is therefore pA. If the piston moves out an infinitesimal distance dx, the work dW of this force is equal to

$$dW = pA \, dx.$$

But

$$A \, dx = dV,$$

where dV is the change of volume of the system. Therefore

$$dW = p \, dV, \tag{19–1}$$

and in a finite change of volume from V_1 to V_2,

$$W = \int_{V_1}^{V_2} p \, dV. \tag{19–2}$$

This integral may be interpreted graphically as the area under a curve on a *pV*-diagram, as shown in Fig. 19–1(b). If the substance *expands* from 1 to 2 in Fig. 19–1(b), the work and the area are positive. The *compression* from 2 to 1 gives rise to negative work and a negative area.

If the pressure remains constant while the volume changes, then the work is

$$W = p(V_2 - V_1) \qquad \text{(Constant pressure only)}.$$

EXAMPLE. An ideal gas is kept in good thermal contact with a very large body of constant temperature and undergoes an *isothermal expansion* in which its volume changes from V_1 to V_2. How much work is done?

From Eq. (19-2)

$$W = \int_{V_1}^{V_2} p\, dV.$$

For an ideal gas

$$p = \frac{nRT}{V}.$$

Since n, R, and T are constant,

$$W = nRT \int_{V_1}^{V_2} \frac{dV}{V} = nRT \ln \frac{V_2}{V_1}.$$

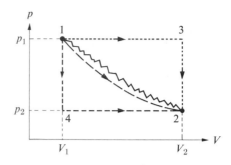

Fig. 19-2. Work depends on the path.

In an expansion, $V_2 > V_1$ and W is positive. At constant T,

$$p_1 V_1 = p_2 V_2, \qquad \text{or} \qquad \frac{V_2}{V_1} = \frac{p_1}{p_2},$$

and the isothermal work may be expressed also in the form

$$W = nRT \ln \frac{p_1}{p_2}.$$

On the pV-diagram in Fig. 19-2 an initial state 1 (characterized by pressure p_1 and volume V_1) and a final state 2 (characterized by pressure p_2 and volume V_2) are represented by the two points 1 and 2. There are many ways in which the system may be taken from 1 to 2. For example, the pressure may be kept constant from 1 to 3 (*isobaric* process) and then the volume kept constant from 3 to 2 (*isochoric* process), in which case the work is equal to the area under the line $1 \rightarrow 3$. Another possibility is the path $1 \rightarrow 4 \rightarrow 2$, in which case the work is the area under the line $4 \rightarrow 2$. The jagged line and the continuous curve from 1 to 2 represent other possibilities, in each of which the work is different. We can see, therefore, that *the work depends not only on the initial and final states but also on the intermediate states, i.e., on the path.*

19-3 Work and heat

As we have seen in Chapter 16, heat is the energy transferred to or from a system by virtue of a temperature difference between the system and its surroundings. Heat is regarded as positive when it enters a system and negative when it leaves. From the point of view of thermodynamics, work and heat are *methods of energy transfer*, that is, methods whereby the energy of a system may be increased or decreased.

The distinction between work and heat may be illustrated simply by the apparatus shown in Fig. 19-3. A cylinder with a diathermic (heat-conducting) base rests upon an adiabatic slab (insulator) which, in turn, rests upon a hot stove. In the cylinder is a liquid and vapor (cooler than the stove) and resting on the piston is some sand whose weight is such that the piston-sand combination is at rest. If some of the sand is removed, the piston will rise. Positive work will be done (by the system) at the expense of the energy of the system, but no heat will be transferred. If the insulating slab separating the cylinder from the stove is removed and *if the piston is held stationary*, then there will be a positive heat transfer (to the system), the energy of the system will increase, but no work will be done. If the clamp anchoring the piston is removed, both methods of energy transfer (work and heat) will occur at the same time.

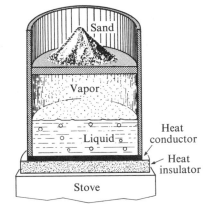

Fig. 19–3. Apparatus for illustrating the two types of energy transfer, work and heat.

But the amount of heat transferred while the piston is rising is different from that when the volume is constant. In other words, not only does the work depend on the path but the *heat also depends on the path.*

It would be just as incorrect to refer to the "heat in a body" as it would be to speak about the "work in a body." For suppose we assigned an arbitrary value to "the heat in a body" in some standard reference state. The "heat in the body" in some other state would then equal the "heat" in the reference state plus the heat added when the body is carried to the second state. But the heat added depends entirely on the path by which we go from one state to the other, and since there are an infinite number of paths which might be followed, there are an infinite number of values which might equally well be assigned to the "heat in the body" in the second state. Since it is not possible to assign any one value to the "heat in the body" we conclude that this concept is meaningless.

19–4 The first law of thermodynamics

The transfer of heat and the performance of work constitute two methods of adding energy to or subtracting energy from a system. They represent energy in transit and are the terms used when energy is moving. Once the transfer of energy is over, the system is said to have undergone a change in *internal energy.*

Suppose a system is caused to change from state 1 to state 2 along a definite path and that the heat absorbed, Q, and the work W are measured. Expressing both Q

and W either in thermal units or in mechanical units, we may then calculate the difference $Q - W$. If now we do the same thing over again for many different paths (between the same states 1 and 2), the important result is obtained that $Q - W$ *is the same for all paths connecting* 1 *and* 2. But Q is the energy that has been added to a system by the transfer of heat and W is equal to the energy that has been extracted from the system by the performance of work. The difference $Q - W$, therefore, must represent the internal energy change of the system. It follows that *the internal energy change of a system is independent of the path*, and is therefore equal to the energy of the system in state 2 minus the energy in state 1, or $U_2 - U_1$.

$$U_2 - U_1 = Q - W.$$

If some arbitrary value is assigned to the internal energy in some standard reference state, its value in any other state is uniquely defined, since $Q - W$ is the same for all processes connecting the states.

The simple algebraic statement of these facts in the form

$$\boxed{Q = U_2 - U_1 + W} \qquad (19\text{–}3)$$

is known as *the first law of thermodynamics*. In applying the law in this form it must be remembered that (1) all quantities must be expressed in the same units, (2) Q is positive when heat goes *into* the system, (3) W is positive when the force exerted *by* the system and the displacement have the same sign.

From the thermodynamic standpoint, it is entirely unnecessary to interpret internal energy in terms of molecular energies. Equation (19–3) is the *definition* of the internal energy of a system or, more precisely, of the *change* in its internal energy in any process. As with other forms of energy, only *differences* in internal energy are defined, and not absolute values.

If a system is carried through a process which eventually returns it to its initial state (a *cyclic* process) then

$$U_2 = U_1 \quad \text{and} \quad Q = W.$$

Thus, although net work W may be done by the system in the process, energy has not been created, since an equal amount of energy must have flowed into the system as heat Q.

An *isolated* system is one which does no external work and into which there is no flow of heat. Then for any process taking place in such a system, $W = Q = 0$ and $U_2 - U_1 = 0$ or $\Delta U = 0$. That is, *the internal energy of an isolated system remains constant*. This is the most general statement of the *principle of conservation of energy*. The internal energy of an *isolated* system cannot be changed by any process (mechanical, electrical, chemical, nuclear, or biological) taking place *within* the system. The energy of a system can be changed only by a flow of heat across its boundary, or by the performance of work. (If either of these takes place, the system is no longer isolated.) The increase in energy of the system is then equal to the energy flowing in as heat, minus the energy flowing out as work.

19–5 Adiabatic process

A process that takes place in such a manner that no heat enters or leaves a system is called an *adiabatic process*. This may be accomplished either by surrounding the system with a thick layer of heat-insulating material (such as cork, asbestos, firebrick, or any light, porous powder) or by performing the process quickly. The flow of heat is a fairly slow process, so that any process performed quickly enough will be practically adiabatic. Applying the first law to an adiabatic process, we get

$$U_2 - U_1 = -W \quad \text{(Adiabatic process)}.$$

Thus the change in the internal energy of a system, in an adiabatic process, is equal in absolute magnitude to the work. If the work W is negative, as when a system is compressed, then $-W$ is positive, U_2 is greater than U_1, and the internal energy of the system increases. If W is positive, as when a system expands, the internal energy of the system decreases. An increase of internal energy is usually accompanied by a rise in temperature and a decrease in internal energy by a temperature drop.

The compression of the mixture of gasoline vapor and air that takes place during the compression stroke of a gasoline engine is an example of an approximately adiabatic process involving a temperature rise. The expansion of the combustion products during the power stroke of the engine is an approximately adiabatic process involving a temperature decrease. Adiabatic processes, therefore, play a very important role in mechanical engineering.

19–6 Isochoric process

If a substance undergoes a process in which the volume remains unchanged, the process is called *isochoric*. The rise of pressure and temperature produced by a flow of heat into a substance contained in a nonexpanding chamber is an example of an isochoric process. If the volume does not change, no work is done and, therefore, from the first law,

$$Q = U_2 - U_1 \quad \text{(Isochoric process)},$$

or all the heat that has been added has served to increase the internal energy. The very sudden increase of temperature and pressure accompanying the explosion of gasoline vapor and air in a gasoline engine may be treated mathematically as though it were an isochoric addition of heat.

19–7 Isothermal process

An isothermal process takes place at constant temperature. For the temperature of a system to remain strictly constant, the changes in the other coordinates must be carried out slowly, and heat must be transferred. In general none of the quantities Q, W, or $U_2 - U_1$ is zero. There are two ideal materials whose *internal energy depends only on the temperature*. These are an *ideal gas* and an *ideal paramagnetic crystal*. When these two substances undergo an isothermal process, the internal energy does not change, and therefore

$$Q = W \quad \text{(Isothermal process)}.$$

19–8 Isobaric process

A process taking place at constant pressure is called an *isobaric process*. When water enters the boiler of a steam engine and is heated to its boiling point, vaporized, and then the steam is superheated, all these processes take place isobarically. Such processes play an important role in mechanical engineering and also in chemistry.

Consider the change of phase of a mass m of liquid to vapor at constant pressure and temperature. If V_L is the volume of liquid and V_V the volume of vapor, the work done in expanding from V_L to V_V at constant pressure p is

$$W = p(V_V - V_L).$$

The heat absorbed by each unit of mass is the heat of vaporization L. Hence

$$Q = mL.$$

From the first law,

$$mL = (U_V - U_L) + p(V_V - V_L). \tag{19–4}$$

EXAMPLE. One gram of water (1 cm³) becomes 1671 cm³ of steam when boiled at a pressure of 1 atm. The heat of vaporization at this pressure is 539 cal/gm. Compute the external work and the increase in internal energy.

$$W = p(V_V - V_L) = 1.013 \times 10^6 \text{ dynes/cm}^2 \,(1671 - 1) \text{ cm}^3$$
$$= 1.695 \times 10^9 \text{ ergs} = 169.5 \text{ joules} = 41 \text{ cal.}$$

From Eq. (19–4),

$$U_V - U_L = mL - W = 539 - 41 = 498 \text{ cal.}$$

Hence the external work, or the external part of the heat of vaporization, equals 41 cal, and the increase in internal energy, or the internal part of the heat of vaporization, is 498 cal.

19–9 Throttling process

A *throttling process* is one in which a fluid, originally at a constant high pressure, seeps through a porous wall or a narrow opening (needle valve or throttling valve) into a region of constant lower pressure, without a transfer of heat taking place. The experiment is sometimes called the *porous plug experiment*. Figure 19–4(a) will help to make the process clear. A fluid is discharged from a pump at a high pressure, then passes through a throttling valve into a pipe which leads directly to the intake or low-pressure side of the pump. Every successive element of fluid undergoes the throttling process in a continuous stream.

Consider any element of fluid enclosed between the piston and throttling valve of Fig. 19–4(b). Suppose this piston to move toward the right and another piston on the other side of the valve to move to the right also at such rates that the pressure on the left remains at a constant high value and that on the right at a constant lower value. After all the fluid has been forced through the valve, the final state is that of Fig. 19–4(c).

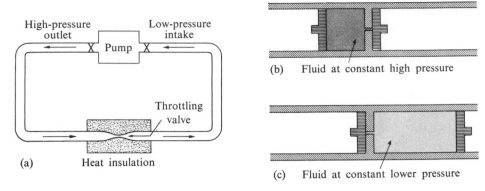

(a)   Heat insulation

(b)   Fluid at constant high pressure

(c)   Fluid at constant lower pressure

Fig. 19–4. Throttling process.

The net work done in this process is the difference between the work done in forcing the right-hand piston out and the work done in forcing the left-hand piston in. Let

$$p_1 = \text{high pressure (on the left)},$$
$$V_1 = \text{volume of fluid at the high pressure},$$
$$p_2 = \text{lower pressure (on the right)},$$
$$V_2 = \text{volume of fluid at the low pressure}.$$

Since the low-pressure fluid changes in volume from zero to V_2 at the constant pressure p_2, the work is

$$p_2(V_2 - 0),$$

and since the high-pressure fluid changes in volume from V_1 to zero at the constant high pressure p_1, the work is

$$p_1(0 - V_1).$$

The net work W is therefore

$$W = p_2V_2 - p_1V_1.$$

Since the process is adiabatic, $Q = 0$, and hence from the first law,

$$0 = U_2 - U_1 + (p_2V_2 - p_1V_1)$$

or

$$U_1 + p_1V_1 = U_2 + p_2V_2. \tag{19–5}$$

This result is of great importance in steam engineering and in refrigeration. The sum $U + pV$, called the *enthalpy*, is tabulated for steam and for many refrigerants. The throttling process plays the main role in the action of a refrigerator, since this is the process that gives rise to the drop in temperature needed for refrigeration. Liquids that are about to evaporate (saturated liquids) always undergo a drop in temperature and partial vaporization as a result of a throttling process. Gases, however, may undergo either a temperature rise or drop, depending on the initial temperature and pressure and on the final pressure.

19–10 Differential form of the first law

Up to this point we have used the first law of thermodynamics only in its finite form,

$$Q = U_2 - U_1 + W.$$

In this form the equation applies to a process in which states 1 and 2 differ in pressure, volume, and temperature by a finite amount. Suppose states 1 and 2 differ only slightly. Then if only a small amount of heat dQ is transferred, and only a small amount of work dW is done, the energy change dU is also very small. In these circumstances, the first law becomes

$$dQ = dU + dW. \qquad (19\text{–}6)$$

If the system is of such a character that the only work possible is by means of expansion or compression, then $dW = p\,dV$, and

$$dQ = dU + p\,dV \qquad (19\text{–}7)$$

is the *differential form of the first law*, applicable to solids, liquids, and gases.

19–11 Internal energy of a gas

Imagine a thermally insulated vessel with rigid walls, divided into two compartments by a partition. Suppose that there is a gas in one compartment and that the other is empty. If the partition is removed, the gas will undergo what is known as a *free expansion* in which no work is done and no heat is transferred. From the first law, since both Q and W are zero, it follows that *the internal energy remains unchanged during a free expansion*. The question as to whether or not the temperature of a gas changes during a free expansion and, if it does, the magnitude of the temperature change, has engaged the attention of physicists for over a hundred years. Starting with Joule in 1843, many attempts have been made to measure the effect of a free expansion, or, as it is often called, the *Joule effect*.

The reason for noting whether there is a temperature change when a gas undergoes a free expansion is to learn the properties on which the internal energy of a gas depends. For if the temperature should change while the internal energy stays the same, one would have to conclude that the internal energy depends on *both* the temperature and the volume, or both the temperature and the pressure, but certainly not on the temperature alone. If, on the other hand, T remains unchanged during a free expansion in which we know U remains unchanged, then the only conclusion that is admissible is that *U is a function of T only*. In the original experiment of Joule, two vessels connected by a short tube and stopcock were immersed in a water bath, as shown in Fig. 19–5. One vessel contained air at high pressure, and the other was evacuated. The temperature of the water was measured before and after the

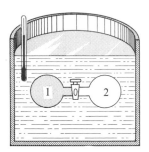

Fig. 19–5. Free expansion of a gas into an evacuated container.

expansion, the idea being to infer the temperature change of the gas from the temperature change of the water. Since the heat capacity of the vessels and the water was approximately one thousand times as large as the heat capacity of the air, Joule was unable to detect any temperature change of the water, although, in the light of our present knowledge, the air must have suffered a temperature change of several degrees.

It is an interesting fact that no one has ever performed an experiment on the free expansion of a gas that was free of objection. Other methods have shown that the internal energy of a *real* gas *does* depend on the pressure or volume as well as on the temperature. The volume or pressure dependence, however, is very much smaller than the temperature dependence. We therefore extend our definition of an *ideal* gas, and say that *the internal energy of an ideal gas depends only on its temperature*.

19–12 Heat capacities of an ideal gas

The temperature of a substance may be raised under a variety of conditions. The volume may be kept constant, or the pressure may be kept constant, or both may be allowed to vary in some definite manner. In each of these cases, the amount of heat per mole necessary to cause unit rise of temperature is different. In other words, a substance has many different molar heat capacities. Only two, however, are of practical use, namely, those at constant volume and at constant pressure. There is a simple and important relation between these two molar heat capacities of an ideal gas.

Figure 19–6 shows two isotherms of an ideal gas at temperatures T and $T + dT$. Since the internal energy of an ideal gas depends only on the temperature, it is constant if the temperature is constant and the isotherms are also curves of *constant internal energy*. The internal energy therefore has a constant value U at all points of the isotherm at temperature T, and a constant value $U + dU$ at all points of the isotherm at $T + dT$. It follows that the *change* in internal energy, dU, is the same in all processes in which the gas is taken from *any* point on one isotherm to *any* point on the other. Thus dU is the same for all the processes ab, ac, ad, and ef, in Fig. 19–6.

Fig. 19–6. The change in internal energy of an ideal gas is the same in all processes between two given temperatures.

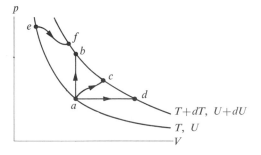

Consider first the process ab, at constant volume. To carry out such a process, the gas at temperature T is enclosed in a rigid container and brought in contact with a body at a slightly higher temperature $T + dT$. There will be a flow of heat dQ into the gas, and by definition of the molar heat capacity at constant volume, C_v,

$$dQ = nC_v \, dT. \tag{19–8}$$

The pressure of the gas increases during this process, but no work is done, since the volume is constant. Hence, from the first law (in differential form),

$$dU = dQ - dW,$$

we have

$$dU = nC_v \, dT. \tag{19–9}$$

But dU is the same for *all* processes between the isotherms in Fig. 19–6, so Eq. (19–9) gives the change in internal energy in all the processes in Fig. 19–6, *even if they are not at constant volume.*

Now consider the process ad in Fig. 19–6, at constant pressure. To carry out such a process the gas might be enclosed in a cylinder with a piston, acted on by a constant external pressure, and brought in contact with a body at a temperature $T + dT$. As heat flows into the gas it expands at constant pressure and does work. By definition of the molar heat capacity at constant pressure, C_p, the heat dQ flowing into the gas is

$$dQ = nC_p \, dT.$$

The work dW is

$$dW = p \, dV.$$

But from the equation of state, since p is constant,

$$pV = nRT, \qquad p \, dV = nR \, dT,$$

so

$$dW = nR \, dT.$$

Then from the first law,

$$dU = dQ - dW,$$

$$nC_v \, dT = nC_p \, dT - nR \, dT,$$

or

$$\boxed{C_p - C_v = R.} \tag{19–10}$$

The molar heat capacity of an ideal gas at constant pressure is therefore greater than that at constant volume by the universal gas constant R. Of course, R must be expressed in the same units as C_p and C_v, usually cal/mole·C°. We have shown in Section 18–2 that in these units $R = 1.99$ cal/mole·C°.

TABLE 19–1

MOLAR HEAT CAPACITIES OF GASES AT LOW PRESSURE

Type of gas	Gas	C_p, cal / mole·C°	C_v, cal / mole·C°	$C_p - C_v$	$\gamma = \dfrac{C_p}{C_v}$
Monatomic	He	4.97	2.98	1.99	1.67
	A	4.97	2.98	1.99	1.67
Diatomic	H_2	6.87	4.88	1.99	1.41
	N_2	6.95	4.96	1.99	1.40
	O_2	7.03	5.04	1.99	1.40
	CO	6.97	4.98	1.99	1.40
Polyatomic	CO_2	8.83	6.80	2.03	1.30
	SO_2	9.65	7.50	2.15	1.29
	H_2S	8.27	6.2	2.1	1.34

Although Eq. (19–10) was derived for an ideal gas, it is very nearly true for real gases at moderate pressures. Measured values of C_p and C_v are given in Table 19–1 for some real gases at low pressures, and the difference is seen to be very nearly 1.99 cal/mole·C°.

In the last column of Table 19–1 are listed the values of the ratio C_p/C_v, denoted by the Greek letter γ (gamma). It is seen that γ is 1.67 for monatomic gases, and is very nearly 1.40 for the so-called permanent diatomic gases. There is no simple regularity for polyatomic gases.

Solids and liquids also expand when heated, if free to do so, and hence perform work. The coefficients of volume expansion of solids and liquids are, however, so much smaller than those of gases that the work is small. The internal energy of a solid or liquid *does* depend on its volume as well as on its temperature, and this must be considered when evaluating the difference between specific heats of solids or liquids. It turns out that here also $C_p > C_v$, but the difference is small and is not expressible as simply as that for a gas. Because of the large stresses set up when solids or liquids are heated and *not* allowed to expand, most heating processes involving them take place at constant pressure, and hence C_p is the quantity usually measured for a solid or liquid.

19–13 Adiabatic process of an ideal gas

Any process in which there is no flow of heat into or out of a system is called *adiabatic*. To perform a truly adiabatic process it would be necessary that the system be surrounded by a perfect heat insulator, or that the surroundings of the system be kept always at the same temperature as the system. However, if a process such as compression or expansion of a gas is carried out very rapidly, it will be nearly adiabatic, since the flow of heat into or out of the system is slow even under favorable conditions. Thus the compression stroke of a gasoline or diesel engine is approximately adiabatic.

Note that external work may be done on or by a system in an adiabatic process, and that the temperature usually changes in such a process.

Let an ideal gas undergo an infinitesimal adiabatic process. Then $dQ = 0$, $dU = nC_v\, dT$, $dW = p\, dV$, and, from the first law,

$$nC_v\, dT = -p\, dV. \tag{19–11}$$

From the equation of state,

$$p\, dV + V\, dp = nR\, dT.$$

Eliminating dT between these equations and making use of the fact that $C_p - C_v = R$, we obtain the relation

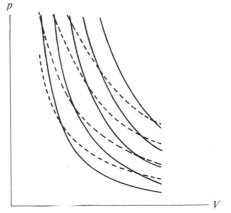

$$\frac{dp}{p} + \frac{C_p}{C_v}\frac{dV}{V} = 0,$$

or, if C_p/C_v is denoted by γ,

$$\frac{dp}{p} + \gamma\frac{dV}{V} = 0.$$

To obtain the relation between p and V in a *finite* adiabatic change we may integrate the preceding equation. This gives

$$\ln p + \gamma \ln V = \ln \text{(constant)}$$

or

$$pV^\gamma = \text{constant}$$

Fig. 19–7. Adiabatic curves (full lines) versus isothermal curves (dashed lines).

If subscripts 1 and 2 refer to any two points of the process,

$$p_1 V_1^\gamma = p_2 V_2^\gamma. \tag{19–12}$$

It is left as a problem to show that by combining Eq. (19–12) with the equation of state one obtains the alternate forms

$$T_1 V_1^{\gamma-1} = T_2 V_2^{\gamma-1}, \tag{19 13}$$

$$T_1 p_1^{(1-\gamma)/\gamma} = T_2 p_2^{(1-\gamma)/\gamma}. \tag{19–14}$$

Values of the specific heat ratio γ are listed in Table 19–1 for some common gases.

An adiabatic expansion or compression of an ideal gas may be represented graphically by a plot of Eq. (19–12), as in Fig. 19–7, in which a number of isothermal curves are shown for comparison. The adiabatic curves, at any point, have a somewhat steeper slope than the isothermal curve passing through the same point. That is, as we follow along an adiabatic from right to left (compression process) the curve continually cuts across isotherms of higher and higher temperatures, in agreement with the fact that the temperature continually increases in an adiabatic compression.

The work done by an ideal gas in an adiabatic expansion is computed as follows. We have, from Eq. (19–11),

$$W = \int_{V_1}^{V_2} p \, dV = \int_{T_1}^{T_2} - nC_v \, dT. \tag{19–15}$$

Hence the work may be found from either integral. Consider first $\int p \, dV$. Since $pV^\gamma = p_1 V_1^\gamma = p_2 V_2^\gamma = $ a constant, K, we may write

$$W = \int_{V_1}^{V_2} p \, dV = K \int_{V_1}^{V_2} \frac{dV}{V^\gamma}$$

$$= \frac{1}{1 - \gamma} (KV_2^{1-\gamma} - KV_1^{1-\gamma}).$$

In the first term let $K = p_2 V_2^\gamma$ and in the second term let $K = p_1 V_1^\gamma$. Then

$$W = \frac{p_2 V_2 - p_1 V_1}{1 - \gamma}. \tag{19–16}$$

This expresses the work in terms of initial and final pressures and volumes. If the initial and final temperatures are known, we may return to Eq. (19–15) and write

$$W = \int_{T_1}^{T_2} - nC_v \, dT = nC_v(T_1 - T_2). \tag{19–17}$$

_____

EXAMPLE. The compression ratio of a diesel engine, V_1/V_2, is about 15. If the cylinder contains air at 15 lb/in^2 (absolute) and 60°F ($= 520$°R) at the start of the compression stroke, compute the pressure and temperature at the end of this stroke. Assume that air behaves like an ideal gas and that the compression is adiabatic. The value of γ for air is 1.40. From Eq. (19–12),

$$p_2 = p_1 \left(\frac{V_1}{V_2}\right)^\gamma$$

or

$$\log p_2 = \log p_1 + \gamma \log \left(\frac{V_1}{V_2}\right) = \log 15 + 1.4 \log 15,$$

$$p_2 = 663 \text{ lb/in}^2.$$

The temperature may now be found either from Eqs. (19–13), (19–14), or by the ideal gas law. Thus, from Eq. (19–13), we have

$$T_2 = T_1 \left(\frac{V_1}{V_2}\right)^{\gamma-1},$$

$$\log T_2 = \log T_1 + (\gamma - 1)\log\left(\frac{V_1}{V_2}\right)$$

$$= \log 520 + (1.4 - 1)\log 15,$$

$$T_2 = 1535°R = 1075°F.$$

Or,

$$T_2 = T_1 \times \frac{p_2 V_2}{p_1 V_1} = 520 \times \frac{663 \times 1}{15 \times 15} = 1535°R.$$

The work done in the compression stroke is found as follows. Let the initial volume be 60 in^3. From Eq. (19–16),

$$W = \frac{p_2 V_2 - p_1 V_1}{1 - \gamma}.$$

The pressures must be expressed in pounds per square *foot* and the volumes in cubic *feet*.

$$W = \frac{(663 \times 144)(4/1728) - (15 \times 144)(60/1728)}{1 - 1.40} = -365 \text{ ft·lb.}$$

19–14 The conversion of heat into work

The dominating feature of an industrial society is its ability to utilize, whether for wise or unwise ends, sources of energy other than the muscles of men or animals. Except for waterpower, where mechanical energy is directly available, most energy supplies are in the form of potential energy of molecular or nuclear aggregations. In chemical or nuclear reactions some of this potential energy is released and converted to random molecular kinetic energy. In other words, the reaction products are at a relatively high temperature. Heat can be withdrawn from them and utilized for heating buildings, for cooking, or for maintaining a furnace at a high temperature in order to carry out other chemical or physical processes. But to operate a machine, or to propel a vehicle or a projectile, mechanical energy is required, and one of the problems of the mechanical engineer is to withdraw heat from a high-temperature source and convert as large a fraction as possible to mechanical energy.

This transformation always requires the services of a *heat engine*, such as a steam engine, gasoline engine, diesel engine, or jet engine. Since it is only heat and work that are of primary concern in a heat engine, we consider for simplicity an engine in which the so-called "working substance" is carried through a *cyclic* process, that is, a sequence of processes in which it eventually returns to its original state. In the condensing type of steam engine used in marine propulsion, the "working substance," in this case pure water, is actually used over and over again. Water is evaporated in the boilers at high pressure and temperature, does work in expanding against a piston or in a turbine, is condensed by cooling water from the ocean, and pumped back into the boilers. The refrigerant in a household refrigerator also undergoes a cyclic process. Internal combustion engines and steam locomotives do not carry a system through a closed cycle, but they can be analyzed in terms of cyclic processes which approximate their actual operations. All these devices absorb heat from a source at a high tempera-ture, perform some mechanical work, and reject heat at a lower temperature. When a system is carried through a cyclic process, its initial and final internal energies are equal, and from the first law, for any number of complete cycles,

$$U_2 - U_1 = 0 = Q - W,$$

$$Q = W.$$

That is, the **net** *heat flowing into the engine in a cyclic process equals the* **net** *work done by the engine.*

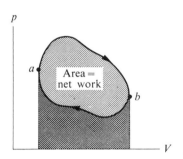

Fig. 19–8. The area enclosed by the curve representing a cyclic process equals the net work.

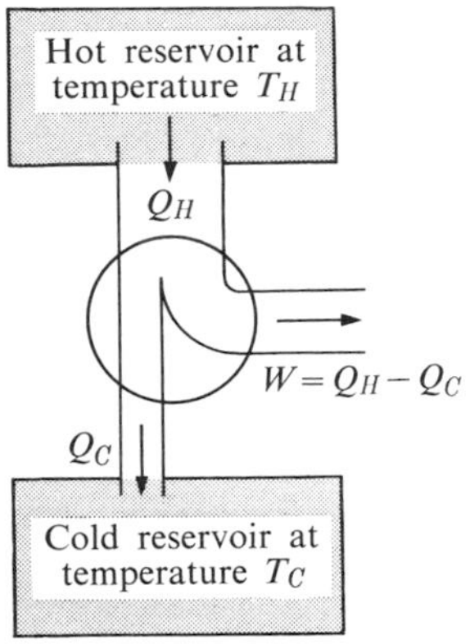

Fig. 19–9. Schematic flow diagram of a heat engine.

The work is represented by the area enclosed by the curve representing the process in the pV-plane. Thus in Fig. 19–8, for example, where the closed curve shows an arbitrary cyclic process, the area under the upper curve from a to b represents positive work done by the system in the expansion from a to b, while the area under the lower curve from b to a represents negative work done by the system in the compression from b to a. Since the average pressure during the compression process is less than that during the expansion, the positive work exceeds the negative work and the area bounded by the closed curve is the net positive work done by the system. If the same process were traversed counterclockwise the net work done by the system would be negative.

In the operation of a heat engine or of a refrigerator there are always two bodies capable of either providing or absorbing large quantities of heat without appreciable changes of temperature. Thus the flames and hot gases surrounding the boilers of a marine steam installation can give up large quantities of heat at a high temperature, and constitute therefore what may be called the *hot reservoir*. Heat transferred between the hot reservoir and the working substance in a heat engine will be represented by the symbol Q_H, where it is understood that a positive value of Q_H means heat entering the working substance. The ocean water used to cool the condenser of the marine installation constitutes the *cold reservoir*. (The words "hot" and "cold" are, of course, relative.) The heat transferred between the working substance and the cold reservoir will be denoted by Q_C. A negative value of Q_C means heat rejected by the working substance.

The energy transformations in a heat engine are conveniently represented schematically by the *flow diagram* of Fig. 19–9. The engine itself is represented by the circle. The heat Q_H supplied to the engine by the hot reservoir is proportional to the cross section of the incoming "pipeline" at the top of the diagram. The cross section of the outgoing pipeline at the bottom is proportional to the heat Q_C which is rejected as heat in the exhaust. The branch line to the right represents that portion of the heat supplied which the engine converts to mechanical work, W.

Consider a heat engine operating in a cycle over and over again and let Q_H and Q_C stand for the heats absorbed and rejected by the working substance *per cycle*. The net heat absorbed is

$$Q = Q_H + Q_C, \tag{19–18}$$

where Q_C is a negative number. The useful output of the engine is the net work W done by the working substance, and from the first law,

$$W = Q = Q_H + Q_C. \tag{19–19}$$

The heat absorbed is usually obtained from the combustion of fuel. The heat rejected ordinarily has no economic value. The *thermal efficiency* of a cycle is defined as the ratio of the useful work to the heat absorbed ("what you get" divided by "what you pay for"):

$$\boxed{\text{Thermal efficiency} = \frac{W}{Q_H} = \frac{Q_H + Q_C}{Q_H}.} \tag{19–20}$$

Because of friction losses, the useful work delivered by an engine is less than the work W, and the over-all efficiency is less than the thermal efficiency.

In terms of the flow diagram in Fig. 19–9, the most efficient engine is the one for which the branch pipeline representing the work obtained is as large as possible, and the exhaust pipeline representing the heat rejected is as small as possible, for a given incoming pipeline or quantity of heat supplied.

We shall now consider, without going into the mechanical details of their construction, the gasoline engine, the diesel engine, and the steam engine.

19–15 The gasoline engine

The common gasoline engine is of the four-cycle type, so called because four processes take place in each cycle. Starting with the piston at the top of its stroke, an explosive mixture of air and gasoline vapor is drawn into the cylinder on the down-stroke, the inlet valve being open and the exhaust valve closed. This is the *intake* stroke. At the end of this stroke the inlet valve closes and the piston rises, performing an approximately adiabatic compression of the air-gasoline mixture. This is the *compression* stroke. At or near the top of this stroke a spark ignites the mixture of air and gasoline vapor, and combustion takes place very rapidly. The pressure and temperature increase at nearly constant volume.

The piston is now forced down, the burned gases expanding approximately adiabatically. This is the *power stroke* or *working stroke*. At the end of the power stroke the exhaust valve opens. The pressure in the cylinder drops rapidly to atmospheric and the rising piston on the *exhaust stroke* forces out most of the remaining gas. The exhaust valve now closes, the inlet valve opens, and the cycle is repeated.

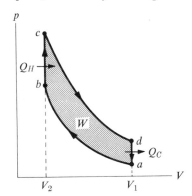

Fig. 19–10. *pV*-diagram of the Otto cycle.

For purposes of computation, the gasoline engine cycle is approximated by the *Otto* cycle illustrated in Fig. 19–10. Starting at point *a*, air at atmospheric pressure is compressed adiabatically in a cylinder to point *b*, heated at constant volume to point *c*, allowed to expand adiabatically to point *d*, and cooled at constant volume to point *a*, after which the cycle is repeated. Line *ab* corresponds to the compression stroke, *bc* to the explosion, *cd* to the working stroke, and *da* to the exhaust of a gasoline engine. V_1 and V_2, in Fig. 19–10, are respectively the maximum and minimum volumes of the air in the cylinder. The ratio V_1/V_2 is called the *compression ratio*, and is about 10 for a modern internal combustion engine.

The work output in Fig. 19–10 is represented by the shaded area enclosed by the figure *abcd*. The heat *input* is the heat supplied at constant volume along the line *bc*. The exhaust heat is removed along *da*. No heat is supplied or removed in the adiabatic processes *ab* and *cd*.

The heat input and the work output can be computed in terms of the compression ratio, assuming air to behave like an ideal gas. The result is

$$\text{Eff}(\%) = 100 \left(1 - \frac{1}{(V_1/V_2)^{\gamma - 1}} \right),$$

where γ is the ratio of the specific heat capacity at constant pressure to the specific heat capacity at constant volume, c_p/c_v. For a compression ratio of 10 and a value of $\gamma = 1.4$, the efficiency is about 60%. It will be seen that the higher the compression ratio, the higher the efficiency. Friction effects, turbulence, loss of heat to cylinder walls, etc., have been neglected. All these effects reduce the efficiency of an actual engine below the figure given above.

19–16 The diesel engine

In the diesel cycle, air is drawn into the cylinder on the intake stroke and compressed adiabatically on the compression stroke to a sufficiently high temperature so that fuel oil injected at the end of this stroke burns in the cylinder without requiring ignition by a spark. The combustion is not as rapid as in the gasoline engine, and the first part of the power stroke proceeds at essentially constant pressure. The remainder of the power stroke is an adiabatic expansion. This is followed by an exhaust stroke which completes the cycle.

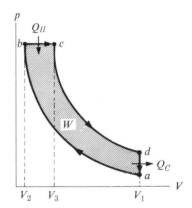

Fig. 19–11. pV-diagram of the diesel cycle.

The idealized air-diesel cycle is shown in Fig. 19–11. Starting at point a, air is compressed adiabatically to point b, heated at constant pressure to point c, expanded adiabatically to point d, and cooled at constant volume to point a.

Since there is no fuel in the cylinder of a diesel engine on the compression stroke, pre-ignition cannot occur and the compression ratio V_1/V_2 may be much higher than that of an internal combustion engine. A value of 15 is typical. The *expansion* ratio V_1/V_3 may be about 5. Using these values, and taking $\gamma = 1.4$, the efficiency of the air-diesel cycle is about 56%.

19–17 The steam engine

The condensing type of steam engine performs the following sequence of operations. Water is converted to steam in the boiler, and the steam thus formed is superheated above the boiler temperature. Superheated steam is admitted to the cylinder, where it expands against a piston; connection is maintained to the boiler for the first part of the working stroke, which thus takes place at constant pressure. The inlet valve is then closed and the steam expands adiabatically for the rest of the working stroke. The adiabatic cooling causes some of the steam to condense. The mixture of water droplets and steam (known as "wet" steam) is forced out of the cylinder on the return stroke and into the condenser, where the remaining steam is condensed into water. This water is forced into the boiler by the feed pump, and the cycle is repeated.

An idealized cycle (called the rankine cycle) which approximates the actual steam cycle is shown in Fig. 19–12. Starting with liquid water at low pressure and temperature (point a), the water is compressed adiabatically to point b at boiler pressure. It is then heated at constant pressure to its boiling point (line bc), converted to steam (line cd), superheated (line de), expanded adiabatically (line ef), and cooled and condensed (along fa) to its initial condition.

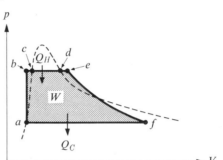

Fig. 19–12.   The rankine cycle.

The efficiency of such a cycle may be computed in the same way as was done in the previous examples, by finding the quantities of heat taken in and rejected along the lines be and fa. Assuming a boiler temperature of 417°F (corresponding to a pressure of 300 lb/in²), a superheat of 63°F above this temperature (480°F), and a condenser temperature of 102°F, the efficiency of a rankine cycle is about 32%. Efficiencies of actual steam engines are, of course, considerably lower.

19–18 The second law of thermodynamics

Although their efficiencies differ from one another, none of the heat engines described above has a thermal efficiency of 100%. That is, none of them absorbs heat and converts it *completely* into work. There is nothing in the *first* law of thermodynamics that precludes this possibility. The first law requires only that the energy output of an engine, in the form of mechanical work, shall equal the difference between the energies absorbed and rejected in the form of heat. An engine which rejected no heat and which converted all the heat absorbed to mechanical work would therefore be perfectly consistent with the first law.

We know now that there is another principle, independent of the first law and not derivable from it, which determines the maximum fraction of the energy absorbed by an engine as heat that can be converted to mechanical work. The basis of this principle lies in the difference between the natures of internal energy and of mechanical energy. The former is the energy of *random* molecular motion, while the latter represents *ordered* molecular motion. Superposed on their random motion, the molecules of a moving body have an ordered motion in the direction of the velocity of the body.

The total molecular kinetic energy associated with the ordered motion is what we call, in mechanics, the kinetic energy of the moving body. The kinetic (and potential) energy associated with the random motion constitutes the internal energy. When the moving body makes an inelastic collision and comes to rest, the *ordered* portion of the molecular kinetic energy becomes converted to *random* motion. Since we cannot control the motions of individual molecules, it is impossible to *completely* reconvert the random motion to ordered motion. We can, however, convert a portion of it and this is what is accomplished by a heat engine.

The science of thermodynamics is concerned only with measurable quantities like heat and work, and the principle known as the *second law of thermodynamics* can be stated entirely apart from any molecular theory. One statement of this law is as follows. *No process is possible whose sole result is the absorption of heat from a reservoir at a single temperature and the conversion of this heat completely into mechanical work.*

If the second law were not true, it would be possible to drive a steamship across the ocean by extracting heat from the ocean, or to run a power plant by extracting heat from the surrounding air. It should be noted again that neither of these "impossibilities" violates the first law of thermodynamics. After all, both the ocean and the surrounding air contain an enormous store of internal energy which, in principle, may be extracted in the form of a flow of heat. The second law, therefore, is not a deduction from the first but stands by itself as a separate law of nature, referring to an aspect of nature different from that contemplated by the first law. The first law denies the possibility of creating or destroying energy; the second denies the possibility of utilizing energy in a particular way.

The fact that work may be dissipated completely into heat, whereas heat may *not* be converted entirely into work, expresses an essential one-sidedness of nature. All natural, spontaneous processes may be studied in the light of the second law, and in all such cases, this peculiar one-sidedness is found. Thus, heat always flows spontaneously from a hotter to a colder body; gases always seep through an opening spontaneously from a region of high pressure to a region of low pressure; gases and liquids left by themselves always tend to mix, not to unmix. Salt dissolves in water but a salt solution does not separate by itself into pure salt and pure water. Rocks weather and crumble; iron rusts; people grow old. These are all examples of *irreversible* processes that take place naturally in only one direction and, by their one-sidedness, express the second law of thermodynamics.

19–19 The refrigerator

A refrigerator may be considered to be a heat engine operated in reverse. That is, a heat engine takes in heat from a hot reservoir, converts a part of the heat into mechanical work output, and rejects the difference as heat to a cold reservoir. A refrigerator, however, takes in heat from a cold reservoir, the compressor supplies mechanical work *input*, and heat is rejected to a hot reservoir. With reference to the ordinary home refrigerator, the food and ice cubes constitute the cold reservoir, work is done by the electric motor, and the hot reservoir is the air in the kitchen.

The flow diagram of a refrigerator is given in Fig. 19–13. In one cycle, heat Q_C enters the refrigerator at low temperature T_C, work W is done on the refrigerator and heat Q_H leaves at a higher temperature T_H. Both W and Q_H are negative quantities. It follows from the first law that

$$-Q_H = Q_C - W,$$

and the heat rejected to the hot reservoir is the sum of the heat taken from the cold reservoir and the heat equivalent of the work done by the motor.

From an economic point of view, the best refrigeration cycle is one that removes the greatest amount of heat Q_C from the refrigerator, for the least expenditure of mechanical work W. We therefore define the *coefficient of performance* (rather than the efficiency) of a refrigerator as the ratio $-Q_C/W$, and since $W = Q_H + Q_C$,

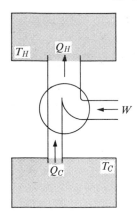

Fig. 19–13. Schematic flow diagram of a refrigerator.

$$\text{Coefficient of performance} = -\frac{Q_C}{Q_H + Q_C}. \qquad (19\text{–}21)$$

The principles of the common refrigeration cycle are illustrated schematically in Fig. 19–14. Compressor A delivers gas (CCl_2F_2, NH_3, etc.) at high temperature and pressure to coils B. Heat is removed from the gas in B by water or air cooling, resulting in condensation of the gas to a liquid, still under high pressure. The liquid passes through the throttling valve or expansion valve C, emerging as a mixture of liquid and vapor at a lower temperature. In coils D, heat is supplied that converts the remaining liquid into vapor which enters compressor A to repeat the cycle. In a domestic refrigerator, coils D are placed in the ice compartment, where they cool the refrigerator directly. In a larger refrigerating plant, these coils are usually immersed in a brine tank and cool the brine, which is then pumped to the refrigerating rooms.

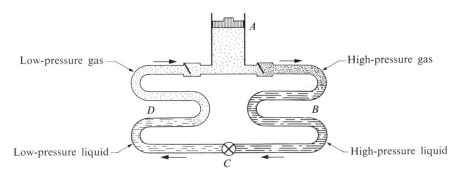

Fig. 19–14. Principle of the mechanical refrigeration cycle.

If no work were needed to operate a refrigerator, the coefficient of performance (heat extracted divided by work done) would be infinite. Coefficients of performance of actual refrigerators vary from about 2 to about 6. Experience shows that work is always needed to transfer heat from a colder to a hotter body. This negative statement leads to another statement of the second law of thermodynamics, namely:

No process is possible whose sole result is the transfer of heat from a cooler to a hotter body.

At first sight, this and the previous statement of the second law appear to be quite unconnected, but it can be shown that they are in all respects equivalent. Any device that would violate one statement would violate the other.

19–20 The Carnot cycle

Although their efficiencies differ from one another, none of the heat engines which have been described has an efficiency of 100%. The question still remains open as to what is the maximum attainable efficiency, given a supply of heat at one temperature and a reservoir at a lower temperature for cooling the exhaust. An idealized engine which can be shown to have the maximum efficiency under these conditions was invented by the French engineer Sadi Carnot in 1824 and is called a *Carnot engine*. The *Carnot cycle*, shown in Fig. 19–15, differs from the Otto and diesel cycles in that it is bounded by two *isothermals* and two *adiabatics*. Thus all the heat input is supplied at a *single* high temperature and all the heat output is rejected at a *single* lower temperature. (Compare with Figs. 19–10 and 19–11, in which the temperature is different at all points of the lines *bc* and *da*.)

This, however, is not the only feature of the Carnot cycle. There are no "one-way" processes in the Carnot cycle, such as explosions or throttling processes. The isothermal and adiabatic processes of the Carnot cycle are idealizations of actual processes. The direction of either process may be reversed by only a slight change in the external pressure; there is no friction, and the working substance is always very close to equilibrium.

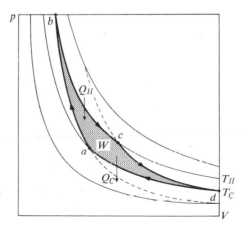

Fig. 19–15. The Carnot cycle.

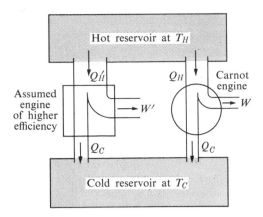

Fig. 19–16.   A Carnot engine and an assumed engine of higher efficiency operating between the same reservoirs and re-jecting the same amount of heat at T_C.

A process that is attended by no equilibrium-disturbing effect (such as an unbalanced force or a finite temperature difference) *and no dissipative effect* (such as friction or electrical resistance) *is said to be reversible.* A reversible process represents the same sort of idealization in thermodynamics that a point mass, a weightless inextensible cord, or a frictionless, moment-of-inertia-less pulley represents in mechanics. It may be approximated but not perfectly achieved.

The isothermal and adiabatic processes of the Carnot cycle may be imagined to proceed in either direction. In the direction shown in Fig. 19–15, heat Q_H goes in, heat Q_C goes out, and work W is done by the engine. If the arrows in the figure are reversed, the cycle becomes a Carnot refrigeration cycle and, *what is most important, the same amount* of heat Q_H which formerly was taken in from the hot reservoir now goes out, and *the same amount* of work W, which formerly was delivered to the outside is now required from the surroundings, and *the same amount* of heat Q_C which formerly was rejected to the cold reservoir is now taken in. These numerical equalities would *not* exist if any ordinary engine cycle were reversed.

Consider two engines represented schematically by their "flow diagrams" in Fig. 19–16 and operating between the same reservoirs. The Carnot engine on the right rejects heat Q_C to the cold reservoir and has an efficiency W/Q_H. The engine on the left operates in an unspecified cycle, rejects the same amount of heat Q_C to the cold reservoir, but is assumed to have an efficiency W'/Q'_H that is *greater* than that of the Carnot engine. It is desired to show that this assumption violates the second law of thermodynamics. The assumption is that $W'/Q'_H > W/Q_H$, or, using the first law,

$$\frac{Q'_H - |Q_C|}{Q'_H} > \frac{Q_H - |Q_C|}{Q_H},$$

whence

$$Q'_H > Q_H, \quad \text{and} \quad W' > W.$$

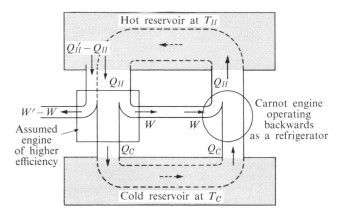

Fig. 19–17. The assumed engine of higher efficiency driving the Carnot engine backward as a refrigerator and violating the second law.

We have shown that a Carnot engine can be operated in reverse as a refrigerator *with no changes* in the magnitudes of Q_H, Q_C, and W. Let us therefore utilize a part of the work output W' of the assumed high-efficiency engine to operate the Carnot engine in reverse as a refrigerator. The pipelines can then be connected as in Fig. 19–17. The heat rejected by the engine on the left provides the heat input to the Carnot refrigerator and the low-temperature reservoir can be dispensed with. The heat rejected by the refrigerator provides a part of the heat input to the engine, the remainder being absorbed from the hot reservoir. A part of the work output of the engine suffices to operate the refrigerator, the remainder being available for useful purposes. The device will operate itself, and its sole result is seen to be the removal of heat from a single reservoir and the performance of an equivalent amount of work. But the second law states that this is impossible, so our original premise was incorrect and the assumed engine cannot have a higher efficiency than the reversible Carnot engine.

Suppose now that we have two Carnot engines, both operating between the same two reservoirs, one of which has a higher efficiency than the other. Let the engine of higher efficiency operate the other in reverse as a refrigerator. Again we have the situation in Fig. 19–17 and the second law would be violated. The conclusion is that *neither* engine can have a higher efficiency than the other, or, *all Carnot engines operating between two given reservoirs have the same efficiency.*

19–21 The kelvin temperature scale

It follows from Carnot's theorem that the efficiency of a Carnot engine operating between reservoirs at two given temperatures *is independent of the nature of the working substance and is a function only of the temperatures.* If we consider a number of Carnot engines using different working substances and absorbing and rejecting heat to the same two reservoirs, the thermal efficiency is the same for all, or

$$\text{Thermal efficiency} = \frac{Q_H + Q_C}{Q_H} = 1 + \frac{Q_C}{Q_H} = \text{constant.}$$

Hence the ratio Q_H/Q_C is a constant for all the engines. Kelvin proposed that the ratio of the temperatures of the reservoirs be *defined* as equal to this constant ratio of the absolute magnitudes of the quantities of heat absorbed and rejected or, since Q_C is a negative quantity, as equal to the negative of the ratio Q_H/Q_C. Thus

$$\frac{T_H}{T_C} = \frac{|Q_H|}{|Q_C|} = -\frac{Q_H}{Q_C}. \tag{19–22}$$

Since the ratio of temperatures does not involve the properties of any particular substance, the kelvin temperature scale is truly *absolute*.

To complete the definition of the kelvin scale we proceed, as in Chapter 15, to assign the arbitrary value of 273.16°K to the temperature of the triple point of water, T_3. For a Carnot engine operating between reservoirs at the temperatures T and T_3, we have

$$\frac{|Q|}{|Q_3|} = \frac{T}{T_3}$$

or

$$\boxed{T = 273.16°K \; \frac{|Q|}{|Q_3|}.} \tag{19–23}$$

Comparing this with the corresponding expression for the ideal gas temperature, namely,

$$273.16°K \; \lim_{p_3 \to 0} \left(\frac{p}{p_3}\right)_{\text{constant volume}},$$

it is seen that, in the kelvin scale, Q plays the role of a "thermometric property." This does not, however, have the objection attached to a coordinate of an arbitrarily chosen thermometer, inasmuch as the behavior of a Carnot engine is independent of the nature of the working substance.

It is a simple matter to show that if an ideal gas is taken around a Carnot cycle, the ratio of the heats absorbed and rejected $|Q_H|/|Q_C|$ is equal to the ratio of the temperatures of the reservoirs *as expressed on the gas scale*, defined in Chapter 15. The proof is somewhat lengthy, and will not be given here. Since, in both scales, the triple point of water is chosen to be 273.16°, it follows that *the kelvin and the ideal gas scales are identical.*

The efficiency of a Carnot engine rejecting heat Q_C to a reservoir at kelvin temperature T_C and absorbing heat Q_H from a source at kelvin temperature T_H is, as usual,

$$\text{Efficiency} = 1 + \frac{Q_C}{Q_H} = 1 - \frac{|Q_C|}{|Q_H|}.$$

But, by definition of the kelvin scale,

$$\frac{|Q_C|}{|Q_H|} = \frac{T_C}{T_H}.$$

Therefore, the efficiency of a Carnot engine is

$$\text{Efficiency (Carnot)} = 1 - \frac{T_C}{T_H}. \tag{19–24}$$

Equation (19–24) points the way to the conditions which a real engine, such as a steam engine, must fulfill to approach as closely as possible the maximum attainable efficiency. These conditions are that the intake temperature T_H must be made as high as possible and the exhaust temperature T_C as low as possible.

The exhaust temperature cannot be lower than the lowest temperature available for cooling the exhaust. This is usually the temperature of the air, or perhaps of river water if this is available at the plant. The only recourse then is to raise the boiler temperature T_H. Since the vapor pressure of all liquids increases rapidly with increasing temperature, a limit is set by the mechanical strength of the boiler. Another possibility is to use, instead of water, some liquid with a lower vapor pressure. Successful experiments in this direction have been made with mercury vapor replacing steam. At a boiler temperature of 200°C, at which the pressure in a steam boiler would be 225 lb/in^2, the pressure in a mercury boiler is only 0.35 lb/in^2.

19–22 Absolute zero

It follows from Eq. (19–23) that the heat transferred isothermally between two given adiabatics decreases as the temperature decreases. Conversely, the smaller the value of Q, the lower the corresponding T. The smallest possible value of Q is zero, and the corresponding T is absolute zero. *Thus, if a system undergoes a reversible isothermal process without transfer of heat, the temperature at which this process takes place is called absolute zero.* In other words, at absolute zero, an isotherm and an adiabatic are identical.

It should be noted that the definition of absolute zero holds for all substances and is therefore independent of the peculiar properties of any one arbitrarily chosen substance. Furthermore, the definition is in terms of purely large-scale concepts. No reference is made to molecules or to molecular energy. Whether absolute zero may be achieved experimentally is a question of some interest and importance. To achieve temperatures below 4.2°K, at which ordinary helium (mass number 4) liquefies, it is necessary to lower the vapor pressure by pumping away the vapor as fast as possible. The lowest temperature that has ever been reached in this way is 0.7°K, and this required larger pumps and larger pumping tubes than are usually employed in low-temperature laboratories. With the aid of the light isotope of helium (mass number 3) which liquefies at 3.2°K, vigorous pumping will yield a temperature of about 0.3°K. Still lower temperatures may be achieved magnetically, but it becomes apparent that the closer one approaches absolute zero, the more difficult it is to go further. It is generally accepted as a law of Nature that, although absolute zero may be approached as close as we please, it is impossible actually to reach the zero of temperature. This is known as the *"unattainability statement of the third law of thermodynamics."*

19-23 Entropy

The first law of thermodynamics is the law of energy, the second law of thermodynamics is the law of entropy, and every process that takes place in Nature, whether it be mechanical, electrical, chemical, or biological, must proceed in conformity with these two laws.

A book of this nature is not the place for a thorough exposition of entropy and the second law of thermodynamics. We shall content ourselves with defining entropy, computing its changes in a few instances, and stating some of its properties.

A re-reading of Section 19-4 will recall to mind that when a system is carried from one state to another it is found by experiment that the difference between the heat added and the work done by the system, $(Q - W)$, has the same value for all paths. The fact that this difference does have the same value makes it possible to introduce the concept of internal energy, the change in internal energy being defined and measured by the quantity $Q - W$.

Entropy, or rather a change in entropy, may be defined in a similar way. Consider two states of a system and a number of *reversible* paths connecting them. (The restriction to reversible paths need not be made with regard to internal energy changes.) Although the heat added to the system is different along different paths, it may be proved that if the heat added at each point of the path is divided by the absolute temperature of the system at the point, and the resulting ratios summed for the entire path, this sum has the same value for all (reversible) paths between the same endpoints. In mathematical symbols,

$$\int_1^2 \frac{dQ}{T} = \begin{array}{l} \text{constant for all reversible} \\ \text{paths between states 1 and 2.} \end{array}$$

It is therefore *possible* (whether it is of any use or not one can only tell later) to introduce a function whose difference between two states, 1 and 2, is defined by the integral above. This function may be assigned any arbitrary value in some standard reference state, and its value in any other state will be a definite quantity. The function is called the *entropy* of the system, and is denoted by S. We then have

$$S_2 - S_1 = \int_1^2 \frac{dQ}{T} \quad \text{(along any reversible path).} \tag{19-25}$$

If the change is infinitesimal, $dS = dQ/T$. The unit of entropy is 1 cal/°K, 1 Btu/°R, 1 joule/°K, etc.

EXAMPLE 1. 1 kgm of ice at 0°C is melted and converted to water at 0°C. Compute its change in entropy.

Since the temperature remains constant at 273°K, T may be taken outside the integral sign. Then

$$S_2 - S_1 = \frac{1}{T} \int dQ = \frac{Q}{T}.$$

But Q is simply the total heat which must be supplied to melt the ice, or 80,000 calories. Hence

$$S_2 - S_1 = \frac{80{,}000}{273} = 293 \text{ cal}/°\text{K},$$

and the increase in entropy of the system is 293 cal/°K. In any *isothermal* reversible process, the entropy change equals the heat added divided by the absolute temperature.

EXAMPLE 2.   1 kgm of water at 0°C is heated to 100°C. Compute its change in entropy.
The temperature is not constant and dQ and T must be expressed in terms of a single variable in order to carry out the integration. This may readily be done, since

$$dQ = mc\, dT.$$

Hence

$$S_2 - S_1 = \int_{273}^{373} mc\, \frac{dT}{T} = mc \ln \frac{373}{273} = 312 \text{ cal}/°\text{K}.$$

EXAMPLE 3.   A gas is allowed to expand adiabatically and reversibly. What is its change in entropy?
In an adiabatic process no heat is allowed to enter or leave the system. Hence $Q = 0$ and there is no change in entropy. It follows that every *reversible* adiabatic process is one of constant entropy, and may be described as *isentropic*.

EXAMPLE 4.   An ideal gas performs a free expansion into an evacuated vessel, as in the Joule experiment illustrated in Fig. 19–5. What is the change in entropy of the gas?
The temperature of the gas is the same in its initial and final states, no work is done, and no heat is absorbed. The process is therefore adiabatic and it might seem from the preceding example that the entropy of the gas remains constant. This is not the case, however, since although the process is adiabatic it is *not* reversible (the gas does not pass through a series of equilibrium states) and $dS = dQ/T$ *for a reversible process only*.
To compute the entropy change in an *irreversible* process, we must devise some *reversible* process that takes the system from the same initial to the same final state. Any reversible process will do, because the entropy change is the same for *all* reversible processes between the same end states. In this example, the simplest reversible process is a reversible, isothermal expansion. The internal energy does not change, but work is done and heat is absorbed. Since $dU = 0$, we have from the first law and the equation of state,

$$dQ = dW = p\, dV = \frac{nRT}{V}\, dV.$$

Hence if the volume increases from V_1 to V_2,

$$S_2 - S_1 = \int \frac{dQ}{T} = nR \int_{V_1}^{V_2} \frac{dV}{V} = nR \ln \frac{V_2}{V_1}.$$

The entropy *increases*, since $V_2 > V_1$, and the increase in entropy is the same as in the original irreversible free expansion.

19-24 The principle of the increase of entropy

One of the features which distinguishes entropy from such concepts as energy, momentum, and angular momentum, is that *there is no principle of conservation of entropy.* In fact, the reverse is true. Entropy *can* be created at will and there is an increase in entropy in every natural process, if all systems taking part in the process are considered.

Consider the process of mixing 1 kgm of water at 100°C with 1 kgm of water at 0°C. Let us arbitrarily call the entropy of water zero when it is in the liquid state at 0°C. This is the reference state adopted in engineering work. Then from Example 2 in the previous section, the entropy of 1 kgm of water at 100°C is 312 cal/°K and the entropy of 1 kgm at 0°C is zero. The entropy of the system, before mixing, is therefore 312 cal/°K.

After the hot and cold water have been mixed, we have 2 kgm of water at a temperature of 50°C or 323°K. From the results of Example 2, we see that the entropy of the system is

$$mc \ln \frac{323}{273} = 2000 \times \ln \frac{323}{273} = 336 \text{ cal}/°K.$$

There has therefore been an increase in entropy of

$$(336 - 312) \text{ cal}/°K = 24 \text{ cal}/°K.$$

Physical mixing of the hot and cold water is, of course, not essential in bringing about the final equilibrium state. We might simply have let heat flow by conduction, or be transferred by radiation, from the hot to the cold water. The same increase in entropy would have resulted.

As a second illustration, consider the free expansion of an ideal gas into an evacuated container, discussed in Example 4 of the preceding section. There also we saw that the entropy of the system increased in the process.

These examples of the mixing of substances at different temperatures, or the flow of heat from a higher to a lower temperature, or the irreversible expansion of a gas, are illustrative of all natural (i.e., irreversible) processes. When all the entropy changes in the process are included, the increases in entropy are always greater than the decreases. In the special case of a reversible process, the increases and decreases are equal. Hence we can formulate the general principle, which is considered a part of the second law of thermodynamics, that *when all systems taking part in a process are included, the entropy either remains constant or increases.* In other words, *no process is possible in which the entropy decreases,* when all systems taking part in the process are included.

EXAMPLE. Use the principle of increase of entropy to show that no engine operating between two given temperatures can have a higher efficiency than a Carnot engine.

We begin by postulating that such an engine exists. If so, its work output can be used to operate a Carnot engine run backward as a refrigerator, as in Fig. 19–17. The sole result of operating the combined system is that a certain amount of heat is removed from the hot reservoir at temperature T_H, and an equivalent amount of mechanical work is done. The only entropy change is that of the hot reservoir, and since heat flows *out* of the reservoir its entropy *decreases*. This contradicts the principle of increase of entropy, so that our postulate was false and no engine can have a higher efficiency than a Carnot engine.

What is the significance of the increase of entropy that accompanies every natural process? The answer, or one answer, is that it represents the extent to which the Universe "runs down" in that process. Consider again the example of the mixing of hot and cold water. We *might* have used the hot and cold water as the high- and low-temperature reservoirs of a heat engine, and in the course of removing heat from the hot water and giving heat to the cold water we could have obtained some mechanical work. But once the hot and cold water have been mixed and have come to a uniform temperature, this opportunity of converting heat to mechanical work is lost and, moreover, it is lost irretrievably. The lukewarm water will never *unmix* itself and separate into a hotter and a colder portion.* Of course, there is no decrease in *energy* when the hot and cold water are mixed, and what has been "lost" in the mixing process is not *energy*, but *opportunity*; the opportunity to convert a portion of the heat flowing out of the hot water to mechanical work. Hence when entropy increases, energy becomes more unavailable, and we say that the Universe has "run down" to that extent. This is the true significance of the term "irreversible."

The tendency of all natural processes such as heat flow, mixing, diffusion, etc., is to bring about a uniformity of temperature, pressure, composition, etc., at all points. One may visualize a distant future in which, as a consequence of these processes, the entire Universe has attained a state of absolute uniformity throughout. When and if such a state is reached, although there would have been no change in the energy of the Universe, all physical, chemical, and presumably biological processes, would have to cease. This goal toward which we appear headed has been described as the "heat death" of the Universe.

---

* The branch of physics called "Statistical Mechanics" would modify this statement to read, "It is highly improbable that the water will separate spontaneously into a hotter and a colder portion, but it is not impossible."

Problems

19–1. A combustion experiment is performed by burning a mixture of fuel and oxygen in a constant-volume "bomb" surrounded by a water bath. During the experiment the temperature of the water is observed to rise. Regarding the mixture of fuel and oxygen as the system: (a) Has heat been transferred? (b) Has work been done? (c) What is the sign of ΔU?

19–2. A liquid is irregularly stirred in a well-insulated container and thereby undergoes a rise in temperature. Regarding the liquid as the system: (a) Has heat been transferred? (b) Has work been done? (c) What is the sign of ΔU?

19–3. A resistor, immersed in running water, carries an electric current. Consider the resistor as the system under consideration. (a) Is there a flow of heat into the resistor? (b) Is there a flow of heat into the water? (c) Is work done? (d) Assuming the state of the resistor to remain unchanged, apply the first law to this process.

19–4. In a certain process, 500 cal of heat are supplied to a system, and at the same time 100 joules of work are done on the system. What is the increase in the internal energy of the system?

19–5. 200 Btu are supplied to a system in a certain process, and at the same time the system expands against a constant external pressure of 100 lb/in^2. The internal energy of the system is the same at the beginning and end of the process. Find the increase in volume of the system.

19–6. An inventor claims to have developed an engine which takes in 100,000 Btu from its fuel supply, rejects 25,000 Btu in the exhaust, and delivers 25 kwh of mechanical work. Do you advise investing money to put this engine on the market?

19–7. A vessel with rigid walls and covered with asbestos is divided into two parts by an insulating partition. One part contains a gas at temperature T and pressure P. The other part contains a gas at temperature T' and pressure P'. The parti-

tion is removed. What conclusion may be drawn by applying the first law of thermodynamics?

19–8. A mixture of hydrogen and oxygen is enclosed in a rigid insulating container and exploded by a spark. The temperature and pressure both increase considerably. Neglecting the small amount of energy provided by the spark itself, what conclusion may be drawn by applying the first law of thermodynamics?

19–9. When water is boiled under a pressure of 2 atm, the heat of vaporization is 946 Btu/lb and the boiling point is 250°F. One lb of steam occupies a volume of 14 ft^3, and 1 lb of water a volume of 0.017 ft^3. (a) Compute the external work, in ft·lb and in Btu, when 1 lb of steam is formed at this temperature. (b) Compute the increase in internal energy, in Btu.

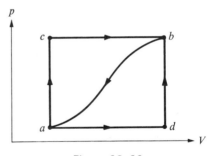

Figure 19–18

19–10. When a system is taken from state a to state b, in Fig. 19–18, along the path acb, 80 Btu of heat flow into the system, and 30 Btu of work are done. (a) How much heat flows into the system along path adb if the work is 10 Btu? (b) When the system is returned from b to a along the curved path, the work is 20 Btu. Does the system absorb or liberate heat and how much? (c) If $U_a = 0$ and $U_d = 40$ Btu, find the heat absorbed in the processes ad and db.

19–11. A steel cylinder of cross-sectional area 0.1 ft^2 contains 0.4 ft^3 of glycerin.

The cylinder is equipped with a tightly fitting piston which supports a load of 6000 lb. The temperature of the system is increased from 60°F to 160°F. Neglect the expansion of the steel cylinder. Find (a) the increase in volume of the glycerin, (b) the mechanical work of the 6000-lb force, (c) the amount of heat added to the glycerin (specific heat of glycerin = 0.58 Btu/lb·F°), (d) the change in internal energy of the glycerin.

19–12. The volume of one mole of an ideal gas is increased isothermally (T = const.) from one to 20 liters at 0°C. The pressure of the gas at any moment is given by the equation $pV = RT$, where $R = 8.31$ joules/mole·K° and T is the kelvin temperature. How many joules of work are done?

19–13. Calculate the work done when a gas expands from volume V_1 to V_2, the relation between pressure and volume being

$$\left(p + \frac{a}{V^2}\right)(V - b) = K,$$

where a, b, and K are constants.

19–14. (a) The change in internal energy, dU, of a system consisting of n moles of a pure substance, in an infinitesimal process at constant volume, is equal to $nC_v\,dT$. Explain why the internal energy change in a process at constant pressure is *not* equal to $nC_p\,dT$. (b) Explain why the change in internal energy of an ideal gas, in *any* infinitesimal process, is given by $nC_v\,dT$.

19–15. A cylinder contains 1 mole of oxygen gas at a temperature of 27°C. The cylinder is provided with a frictionless piston which maintains a constant pressure of 1 atm on the gas. The gas is heated until its temperature increases to 127°C. (a) Draw a diagram representing the process in the pV-plane. (b) How much work is done by the gas in this process? (c) On what is this work done? (d) What is the change in internal energy of the gas? (e) How much heat was supplied to the gas? (f) How much work would have been done if the pressure had been 0.5 atm?

19–16. (a) Compare the quantity of heat required to raise the temperature of 1 gm of hydrogen through 1 C°, at constant pressure, with that required to raise the temperature of 1 gm of water by the same amount. (b) Of the substances listed in Table 19–1, which has the largest specific heat capacity in cal/gm·C°?

19–17. Ten liters of air at atmospheric pressure is compressed isothermally to a volume of 2 liters and is then allowed to expand adiabatically to a volume of 10 liters. Show the process in a pV-diagram.

19–18. An ideal gas is contained in a cylinder closed with a movable piston. The initial pressure is 1 atm and the initial volume is 1 liter. The gas is heated at constant pressure until the volume is doubled, then heated at constant volume until the pressure is doubled, and finally expanded adiabatically until the temperature drops to its initial value. Show the process in a pV-diagram.

19–19. Compressed air at a gauge pressure of 300 lb/in² is used to drive an air engine which exhausts at a gauge pressure of 15 lb/in². What must be the temperature of the compressed air in order that there may be no possibility of frost forming in the exhaust ports of the engine? Assume the expansion to be adiabatic. [*Note:* Frost frequently forms in the exhaust ports of an air-driven engine. This happens when the moist air is cooled below 0°C by the expansion which takes place in the engine.]

19–20. 10 ft³ of air initially at a temperature of 140°F expands at a constant gauge pressure of 20 lb/in² to a volume of 50 ft³, and then expands further adiabatically to a final volume of 80 ft³ and a final gauge pressure of 3 lb/in². Sketch the process in the pV-plane and compute the work done by the air.

19–21. The cylinder of a pump compressing air from atmospheric pressure into a very large tank at 60 lb/in² gauge pressure is 10 inches long. (a) At what position in the stroke will air begin to enter the tank? Assume the compression to be adiabatic. (b) If the air is taken into the pump at 27°C, what is the temperature of the compressed air?

19–22. 2 moles of helium are initially at a temperature of 27°C and occupy a volume of 20 liters. The helium is first expanded at constant pressure until the volume has doubled, and then adiabatically until the temperature returns to its initial value. (a) Draw a diagram of the process in the pV-plane. (b) What is the total heat supplied in the process? (c) What is the total change in internal energy of the helium? (d) What is the total work done by the helium? (e) What is the final volume?

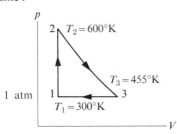

Figure 19–19

19–23. A heat engine carries 0.1 mole of an ideal gas around the cycle shown in the pV-diagram of Fig. 19–19. Process 1–2 is at constant volume, process 2–3 is adiabatic, and process 3–1 is at a constant pressure of 1 atm. The value of γ for this gas is $\frac{5}{3}$. (a) Find the pressure and volume at points 1, 2, and 3. (b) Find the net work done by the gas in the cycle.

19–24. A cylinder contains oxygen at a pressure of 2 atm. The volume is 3 liters and the temperature is 300°K. The oxygen is carried through the following processes:

(1) Heated at constant pressure to 500°K.

(2) Cooled at constant volume to 250°K.

(3) Cooled at constant pressure to 150°K.

(4) Heated at constant volume to 300°K.

(a) Show the four processes above in a pV-diagram, giving the numerical values

of p and V at the end of each process. (b) Calculate the net work done by the oxygen. (c) Find the net heat flowing into the oxygen. (d) What is the efficiency of this device as a heat engine?

19–25. What is the thermal efficiency of an engine which operates by taking an ideal gas through the following cycle? Let $C_v = 3$ cal/mole·C°.

(1) Start with n moles at P_0, V_0, T_0.

(2) Change to $2P_0$, V_0, at constant volume.

(3) Change to $2P_0$, $2V_0$, at constant pressure.

(4) Change to P_0, $2V_0$, at constant volume.

(5) Change to P_0, V_0, at constant pressure.

19–26. A Carnot engine whose low-temperature reservoir is at 280°K has an efficiency of 40%. It is desired to increase this to 50%. (a) By how many degrees must the temperature of the high-temperature reservoir be increased, if the temperature of the low-temperature reservoir remains constant? (b) By how many degrees must the temperature of the low-temperature reservoir be decreased if that of the high-temperature reservoir remains constant?

19–27. A Carnot engine whose high-temperature reservoir is at 400°K takes in 100 cal of heat at this temperature in each cycle, and gives up 80 cal to the low-temperature reservoir. (a) What is the temperature of the latter reservoir? (b) What is the thermal efficiency of the cycle?

19–28. A Carnot refrigerator takes heat from water at 0°C and rejects heat to a room at 27°C. Suppose that 50 kgm of water at 0°C are converted to ice at 0°C. (a) How much heat is rejected to the room? (b) How much energy must be supplied to the refrigerator?

19–29. A Carnot engine is operated between two heat reservoirs at temperatures of 400°K and 300°K. (a) If the engine receives 1200 cal from the reservoir at 400°K in each cycle, how many calories

does it reject to the reservoir at 300°K?
(b) If the engine is operated in reverse, as
a refrigerator, and receives 1200 cal from
the reservoir at 300°K, how many calories
does it deliver to the reservoir at 400°K?
(c) How many calories would be produced
if the mechanical work required to operate
the refrigerator in part (b) were converted
directly to heat?

19–30. Is it possible to cool a closed,
insulated room by operating an electric
refrigerator in the room, leaving the refrigerator door open?

19–31. Consider the entropy of water to
be zero when it is in the liquid phase at
0°C and atmospheric pressure. (a) How
much heat must be supplied to 1 kgm of
water to raise its temperature from 0°C to
100°C? (b) What is the entropy of 1 kgm
of water at 100°C? (c) 1 kgm of water at
0°C is mixed with 1 kgm at 100°C. What
is the final temperature? (d) Find the
entropy of the hot and cold water before
mixing, and the entropy of the system
after mixing. (This is another example of
the increase of entropy in an irreversible
process.)

19–32. (a) Draw a graph of a Carnot
cycle, plotting kelvin temperature vertically
and entropy horizontally (a temperature-
entropy diagram). (b) Show that the area
under any curve in a temperature-entropy
diagram represents the heat absorbed by
the system. (c) Derive from your diagram
the expression for the thermal efficiency of
a Carnot cycle.

CHAPTER 20

Molecular Properties of Matter

20–1 Molecular theory of matter

The fact that matter is compressible suggests that all substances have a granular or spongy structure with spaces into which the granules can penetrate when the external pressure is increased. The ease with which liquids can flow and gases can diffuse points more to a collection of tiny particles than to a spongelike structure. Thousands of physical and chemical facts support the contention that matter in all phases is composed of tiny particles called *molecules*. The molecules of any one substance are identical. They have the same structure, the same mass, and the same mechanical and electrical properties. Many of the large-scale properties of matter which have been discussed heretofore, such as elasticity, surface tension, condensation, vaporization, etc., can be comprehended with deeper understanding of their significance in terms of the molecular theory. For this purpose we may conceive of a molecule as a rigid sphere, like a small billiard ball, capable of moving, of colliding with other molecules or with a wall, and of exerting attractive or repulsive forces on neighboring molecules. In other parts of physics and chemistry it is important to consider the structure of the molecule, but this is not necessary at this point.

One of the outstanding characteristics of a molecule is the force that exists between it and a neighbor. There is, of course, a force of gravitational attraction between every pair of molecules, but it turns out that this is negligible in comparison with the forces we are now considering. The forces that hold the molecules of a liquid (or solid) together are, in part at least, of electrical origin and do not follow a simple inverse square law. When the separation of the molecules is large, as in a gas, the force is extremely small and is an attraction. The attractive force increases as a gas is compressed and its molecules brought closer together. But since tremendous pressures are needed to compress a liquid, i.e., to force its molecules closer together than their normal spacing in the liquid state, we conclude that at separations only slightly less than the dimensions of a molecule the force is one of repulsion and is relatively large. The force must then vary with separation in somewhat the fashion shown in Fig. 20–1. At large separations the force is one of attraction but is extremely small. As the molecules are brought closer together the force of attraction becomes larger, passes through a maximum, and then decreases to zero at a separation r_0. When the distance between the molecules is less than r_0, the force is one of repulsion.

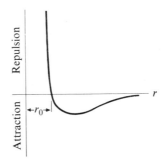

Fig. 20–1. The force between two molecules changes from an attraction, when the separation is large, to a repulsion when the separation is small.

A single pair of molecules could remain in equilibrium at a center-to-center spacing equal to r_0 in Fig. 20–1. If they were separated slightly, the force between them would be attractive and they would be drawn together. If they were forced closer together than the distance r_0, the force would be one of repulsion and they would spring apart. If they were either pulled apart or pushed together, and then released, they would oscillate about their equilibrium separation r_0.

If the only property of a molecule were the force of attraction between it and its neighbors, all matter would eventually coalesce into the liquid or solid phase. The existence of gases points to another property which enables molecules to stay apart. This is accomplished by molecular motion. The more vigorous the motion the less chance there is for condensation into the liquid or solid phase. In solids the molecules execute vibratory motion about more or less fixed centers. The vibratory motion is relatively weak, and the centers remain fixed at regularly spaced positions which comprise a *space lattice*. This gives rise to the extraordinary regularity and symmetry of crystals. A photograph of the individual, very large molecules of *necrosis virus protein* is shown in Fig. 20–2. It was taken with an electron microscope at a magnification of about 80,000. The molecules look like neatly stacked oranges.

In liquids the intermolecular distances are usually only a trifle greater than those of a solid. The molecules execute vibratory motion of greater energy about centers which are free to move but which remain at approximately the same distances from one another. Liquids show a certain regularity of structure only in the immediate neighborhood of a few molecules. This is called *short-range order*, in contrast with the *long-range order* of a solid crystal.

The molecules of a gas have the greatest kinetic energy, so great in fact that they are, on the average, far away from one another, where only very small attractive forces exist. A molecule of a gas therefore moves with linear motion until a collision takes place either with another molecule or with a wall. The molecular definition of an *ideal gas is a gas whose molecules exert no forces of attraction at all.* The mathematical treatment of an assemblage consisting of an enormous number of small, rigid, perfectly elastic spheres executing random linear motions between collisions is called the *kinetic theory of gases*, and was perfected by Clausius, Maxwell, and Boltzmann in the latter part of the nineteenth century. The analysis of an ideal gas given in this chapter is only a simplified version of kinetic theory.

TABLE 20–1

Phase	Attractive forces among molecules	Molecular kinetic energy	Temperature
Solid	Strong	Small	Low
Liquid	Moderate	Moderate	Medium
Gas	Weak	Large	High

A common substance exists in the solid phase at low temperatures. When the temperature is raised beyond a definite value, the liquid phase results, and when the temperature of the liquid is raised further, the substance exists in the gaseous phase; i. e., from a large-scale or *macroscopic* point of view, the transition from solid to liquid to gas is in the direction of increasing temperature. From a *molecular* point of view this transition is in the direction of increasing molecular kinetic energy. Evidently, *there must be some connection between temperature and molecular kinetic energy.*

The preceding paragraphs may be conveniently summarized by means of Table 20–1.

Fig. 20–2. Crystal of necrosis virus protein. The actual size of the entire crystal is about two thousandths of a millimeter. (Courtesy: Ralph Wyckoff. Reprinted with the permission of Educational Services, Inc., from *Physics;* D. C. Heath and Co., Boston, 1960.)

20–2 Avogadro's number

Surprising as it may seem, it was not until 1811 that the suggestion was first made, by Dalton, that the molecules of a given chemical substance are all alike. Before this, even by those who accepted a molecular theory, it had been assumed that the ultimate particles of the same substance varied in size and shape, just as one might find pebbles of different sizes, all made of the same material.

The first reasonably precise determination of the number of molecules in a mole, now called *Avogadro's number* N_0, was made by the French physicist Jean Perrin in the early 1900's. Before describing Perrin's experiment, we first recall an expression previously derived for the variation of atmospheric pressure with elevation. In Example 3 at the end of Section 18–2 we derived from the laws of hydrostatics and the equation of state of an ideal gas an expression for the ratio of the pressures at two different elevations in an ideal gas at a uniform temperature:

$$\ln \frac{p_2}{p_1} = -\frac{Mg}{RT}(y_2 - y_1). \tag{20-1}$$

The molecular "weight" M equals the mass of 1 mole, and can be expressed as the product of Avogadro's number N_0 and the mass m of a single molecule:

$$M = N_0 m. \tag{20-2}$$

Also, the number of moles n in a given sample of a pure substance equals the total number of molecules N divided by Avogadro's number N_0:

$$n = \frac{N}{N_0}.$$

The ideal gas law can therefore be written

$$pV = nRT = \frac{N}{N_0} RT,$$

or

$$\mathbf{n} = \frac{N}{V} = p \frac{N_0}{RT}, \tag{20-3}$$

where $\mathbf{n}$ is the number of molecules per unit volume, N/V. Since N_0 and R are universal constants, it follows that at constant temperature T the number of molecules per unit volume is directly proportional to the pressure. Combining Eqs. (20–2) and (20–3) with Eq. (20–1), we get

$$\ln \frac{\mathbf{n}_2}{\mathbf{n}_1} = -\frac{N_0 mg}{RT}(y_2 - y_1), \tag{20-4}$$

where $\mathbf{n}_2$ and $\mathbf{n}_1$ are the numbers of molecules per unit volume at elevations y_2 and y_1.

We might well ask at this point, if the earth's atmosphere consists of widely separated molecules, not in contact with one another, and with each one attracted by the earth, why in the course of time do the molecules not all settle down to the earth's surface like drops of rain? The explanation is found in the violent random motions of the molecules, which in the absence of any gravitational force would eventually result in their dispersal throughout interstellar space. There are thus two tendencies acting in opposite directions, the gravitational force drawing all molecules toward the earth and their random motions tending to disperse them. The actual distribution represents the compromise between these two tendencies.

It is well known that extremely small particles, called *colloidal* particles, in a liquid of density less than that of the particles, do not all settle to the bottom but remain permanently suspended. These particles are large enough to be observed with a microscope, and the number per unit volume at different heights in the liquid can be counted. Perrin found that the number per unit volume decreased exponentially with height, following the same law as predicted by Eq. (20–4) for the number of molecules per unit volume in the atmosphere. Furthermore, the particles are observed to be in a state of continuous motion called "Brownian motion" after the English botanist Robert Brown, who first observed this effect in 1809 when studying with a microscope small pollen grains suspended in a liquid.

Perrin reasoned that the colloidal particles might be considered as the molecules of a "gas," molecules which were actually large enough to be seen and counted. If a colloidal suspension could be made in which all the particles were exactly alike, and if the mass m of each could be determined, and if Eq. (20–4) really describes the vertical distribution of particles, then Avogadro's number could be found by counting the number of particles per unit volume at two known heights in the suspension. One minor modification must be made in Eq. (20–4) for particles suspended in a fluid, namely, the "effective" value of g is reduced by the buoyant effect of the fluid, but the correction is readily made if the densities of the particles and the fluid are known.

It would occupy too much space to describe the ingenious methods used by Perrin to obtain uniform particles, to count the number per unit volume, and to measure their masses. A most interesting account will be found in Perrin's *Atoms*, translated by Hammick (1916). Suffice it to say that the difficulties were surmounted and that Perrin finally obtained for N_0 a value between 6.5 and 7.2 $\times$ 10^{23} molecules per gram-mole.

The most precise value of N_0 to date, obtained by using x-rays to measure the distance between the layers of molecules in a crystal, is

$$N_0 = 6.02472 \times 10^{23} \text{ molecules/gm-mole.}$$

Once Avogadro's number has been determined, it can be used to compute the mass of a molecule. The mass of one mole of atomic hydrogen is 1.008 gm. Since by definition the number of molecules in one mole is Avogadro's number, it follows that the mass of a single atom of hydrogen is

$$m_\text{H} = \frac{1.008}{6.025 \times 10^{23}} = 1.673 \times 10^{-24} \text{ gm.}$$

The mass of any other molecule can be found by multiplying $1/N_0$ by the numerical value of the molecular weight. Thus, for an oxygen molecule,

$$m_{O_2} = 32 \times 1.660 \times 10^{-24} = 53.12 \times 10^{-24} \text{ gm.}$$

At standard conditions, one mole of an ideal gas occupies 22,400 cm^3. The number of molecules per cubic centimeter in an ideal gas at standard conditions is therefore

$$\frac{6.025 \times 10^{23}}{22,400} = 2.69 \times 10^{19} \text{ molecules/cm}^3.$$

This is known as *Loschmidt's number*, and of course it is the same for *all* gases. The number of molecules per unit volume can also be computed from Eq. (20–3), at any pressure and temperature.

The measurement of Avogadro's number therefore gives us the number of molecules per unit volume in a gas, and the mass of an individual molecule. We next turn to a method for computing the average velocities (or the average kinetic energies) of the molecules of a gas.

20–3 Equation of state of an ideal gas

A molecular theory of matter obviously accomplishes nothing if it simply endows the molecules of a substance with all the properties of that substance. The blue color of copper sulfate is not "explained" by postulating that it consists of molecules, each of which is blue. The fact that a gas is capable of expanding indefinitely is not explained by assuming that it consists of molecules each one of which can expand indefinitely. What one attempts to do is to account for the *complex* properties of matter in bulk as a consequence of *simple* properties ascribed to its molecules. Thus by assuming that a monatomic gas consists of a large number of particles having no properties other than mass and velocity, we can explain the observed equation of state of a gas at low pressure and can show that C_v for the gas should equal 2.99 cal/mole·deg (see Table 19–1). If we add the hypothesis that the "particles" are not simply geometrical points but have a finite size, then the general features of the viscosity, thermal conductivity, and coefficient of diffusion of a gas can be understood, as well as the fact that polyatomic gases have larger values of C_v than monatomic gases. By assuming that there are forces between the particles, the equation of state can be brought into better agreement with that of a real gas and the phenomena of liquefaction and solidification at low temperatures can be explained.

The electrical and magnetic properties of matter, and the emission and absorption of light by matter, call for a molecular model that is itself an aggregate of subatomic particles. Some of these are electrically charged, and the forces between molecules appear to originate in these electric charges. To pursue this development of molecular theory further would take us too far into the whole problem of atomic and nuclear structure. Let us therefore return to the starting point and see what properties of a gas at low pressure can be explained by the simplest possible molecular model, an aggregate of particles having mass and velocity.

We know that a gas in a cylinder like that in Fig. 20–3 exerts a pressure against the piston. The molecular theory interprets the pressure not as a static push but as

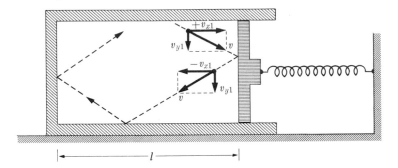

Fig. 20–3.   Collision of a single molecule with a piston.

the average effect of many tiny impulsive blows resulting from the collisions of the molecules with the piston. Thus if the piston is forced to the left by a spring, we would not expect it to remain absolutely at rest but to oscillate slightly about some average position as if it were being bombarded by a helter-skelter rain of shot fired against it. (It is just these random molecular impacts, which do not exactly balance at all instants, that are responsible for the Brownian motion of suspended particles.)

We assume that the gas is composed of a large number of molecules, all having the same mass m and flying about in the cylinder with randomly directed velocities having magnitudes that differ from one molecule to another. Consider first the collision of a single molecule with the piston. Let the mass of the molecule be m, and let the x-component of its velocity be v_{x1}. Figure 20–3 illustrates the collision process. When all the molecules are considered, the *average* y-components of their velocities are not altered by collisions with the piston, since on the average the gas does not gain or lose any vertical motion as a whole. We shall therefore assume that the y-component of the velocity of each molecule is unchanged in the collision. Also, we identify the internal energy of the gas as the sum total of the kinetic energies of its molecules. Since the internal energy remains constant if the gas is isolated, the average kinetic energy of the molecules is constant. We therefore assume also that the kinetic energy of any one molecule is constant in a collision with the walls, that is, the collisions are perfectly elastic. Therefore the magnitude of the velocity v is the same before and after the collision, and since the y-component is unchanged, the *magnitude* of the x-component is unchanged also, although it is reversed in direction.

The average force exerted on the piston by one molecule can now be computed by setting the average force equal to the average rate of change of momentum. Since the x-velocity of the molecule reverses from $+v_{x1}$ to $-v_{x1}$ in each collision, the magnitude of the change in momentum in each collision is $2mv_{x1}$. To find the average force *during the time of one collision* we would divide the change of momentum by this time. However, after having made one collision with the piston, the molecule must travel to the other end of the cylinder and back before colliding again, and during all this time it exerts no force on the piston. To get the correct time average force we must average over the *total* time between collisions. As the molecule travels to the other end of the cylinder and back (see Fig. 20–3), the magnitude of its x-velocity remains constant. If l is the length of the cylinder, the time for the round trip is

$$t = \frac{2l}{v_{x1}}$$

and the average force exerted on the piston by one molecule is

Av. force = Av. rate of change of momentum

$$= \frac{2mv_{x1}}{2l/v_{x1}} = \frac{mv_{x1}^2}{l}.$$

The average pressure p_1 produced by this molecule is the average force divided by the piston area A:

$$p_1 = \frac{mv_{x1}^2}{lA} = \frac{mv_{x1}^2}{V}, \tag{20–5}$$

where $V = lA$ is the total volume of the cylinder.

Now consider other molecules 2, 3, etc., with x-velocities v_{x2}, v_{x3}, etc. The average pressure due to each is given by an expression like Eq. (20–5), and since the pressures add, the total average pressure p is

$$p = p_1 + p_2 + p_3 + \cdots = \frac{m}{V}(v_{x1}^2 + v_{x2}^2 + v_{x3}^2 + \cdots). \tag{20–6}$$

Let N be the total number of molecules. The average value of the square of the x-velocity of all molecules is

$$\overline{v_x^2} = \frac{v_{x1}^2 + v_{x2}^2 + v_{x3}^2 + \cdots}{N}. \tag{20–7}$$

Hence Eq. (20–6) can be written

$$p = \frac{Nm\overline{v_x^2}}{V}. \tag{20–8}$$

The *magnitude* of the resultant velocity v, or the *speed* of any molecule, is given by

$$v^2 = v_x^2 + v_y^2 + v_z^2,$$

and averaging over all molecules,

$$\overline{v^2} = \overline{v_x^2} + \overline{v_y^2} + \overline{v_z^2}.$$

But since the x-, y-, and z-directions are all equivalent,

$$\overline{v_x^2} = \overline{v_y^2} = \overline{v_z^2}.$$

Hence

$$\overline{v^2} = 3\overline{v_x^2},$$

and Eq. (20–8) becomes

$$pV = \tfrac{1}{3}Nm\overline{v^2} = \tfrac{2}{3} \times \tfrac{1}{2}Nm\overline{v^2}. \tag{20–9}$$

But $\frac{1}{2}m\overline{v^2}$ is the average kinetic energy of a single molecule, and the product of this and the total number of molecules N equals the total random kinetic energy, or internal energy U. Hence the product pV equals two-thirds of the internal energy:

$$pV = \tfrac{2}{3}U. \qquad (20\text{--}10)$$

By experiment, at low pressures, the equation of state of a gas is

$$pV = nRT.$$

The theoretical and experimental laws will therefore be in complete agreement if we set

$$U = \tfrac{3}{2}nRT. \qquad (20\text{--}11)$$

The average kinetic energy of a single molecule is then

$$\frac{U}{N} = \tfrac{1}{2}m\overline{v^2} = \frac{3}{2}\frac{nRT}{N}.$$

But the number of moles, n, equals the total number of molecules, N, divided by Avogadro's number N_0, the number of molecules per mole:

$$n = \frac{N}{N_0}, \qquad \frac{n}{N} = \frac{1}{N_0}.$$

Hence

$$\tfrac{1}{2}m\overline{v^2} = \frac{3}{2}\frac{R}{N_0}T.$$

The ratio R/N_0 occurs frequently in molecular theory. It is called the *Boltzmann constant, k*:

$$k = \frac{R}{N_0} = \frac{8.31 \times 10^7 \text{ ergs/mole·deg}}{6.02 \times 10^{23} \text{ molecules/mole}}$$

$$= 1.38 \times 10^{-16} \text{ erg/molecule·deg}.$$

Since R and N_0 are universal constants, the same is true of k. Then

$$\tfrac{1}{2}m\overline{v^2} = \tfrac{3}{2}kT. \qquad (20\text{--}12)$$

The average kinetic energy per molecule, therefore, *depends only on the temperature* and not on the pressure, volume, or species of molecule.

The average value of the square of the speed is

$$\overline{v^2} = \frac{3kT}{m}$$

and the square root of this, or the root-mean-square speed v_{rms} is

$$v_{\text{rms}} = \sqrt{\overline{v^2}} = \sqrt{\frac{3kT}{m}}. \qquad (20\text{--}13)$$

EXAMPLE 1.   What is the average kinetic energy of a molecule of a gas at a temperature of 300°K ?

$$\tfrac{1}{2}m\overline{v^2} = \tfrac{3}{2}kT = \tfrac{3}{2} \times 1.38 \times 10^{-16} \times 300 = 6.20 \times 10^{-14} \text{ erg.}$$

EXAMPLE 2.   What is the total random kinetic energy of the molecules in one mole of a gas at a temperature of 300°K ?

$$U = N_0 \times \tfrac{3}{2}kT = \tfrac{3}{2}RT = \tfrac{3}{2} \times 8.3 \times 10^7 \times 300 = 3750 \times 10^7 \text{ ergs}$$

$$= 3750 \text{ joules} = 900 \text{ calories.}$$

EXAMPLE 3.   What is the root-mean-square speed of a hydrogen molecule at 300°K ?
The mass of a hydrogen molecule (see Section 20–2) is $m_{H_2} = 2 \times 1.66 \times 10^{-24}$ gm $= 3.32 \times 10^{-24}$ gm. Hence

$$v_{\text{rms}} = \sqrt{\frac{3kT}{m}} = \sqrt{\frac{3 \times 1.38 \times 10^{-16} \times 300}{3.32 \times 10^{-24}} \frac{\text{cm}^2}{\text{sec}^2}} = 1.95 \times 10^5 \text{cm/sec.}$$

EXAMPLE 4.   What is the root-mean-square speed of a molecule of mercury vapor at 300°K ?
The *kinetic energy* of a mercury molecule (or atom, since mercury vapor is monatomic) is the same as that of a hydrogen molecule at the same temperature. The mass of a mercury atom is

$$m_{\text{Hg}} = 201 \times 1.66 \times 10^{-24} \text{ gm} = 334 \times 10^{-24} \text{ gm.}$$

Therefore

$$v_{\text{rms}} = \sqrt{\frac{3 \times 1.38 \times 10^{-16} \times 300}{334 \times 10^{-24}} \frac{\text{cm}^2}{\text{sec}^2}} = 0.19 \times 10^5 \text{ m/sec.}$$

EXAMPLE 5.   It was shown in Section 20–2 that the ratio of the numbers of molecules per unit volume at two different elevations is given by

$$\ln \frac{n_2}{n_1} = - \frac{N_0 mg}{RT} (y_2 - y_1),$$

or

$$\frac{n_2}{n_1} = e^{-N_0 mg(y_2 - y_1)/RT}.$$

But

$$\frac{N_0}{R} = \frac{1}{k},$$

and

$$mg(y_2 - y_1)$$

is simply the gravitational potential energy difference between the two elevations, so the exponent of e has the form

$$- \frac{\text{gravitational potential energy}}{kT}.$$

The product kT is a sort of reference amount of molecular energy at any temperature, and the molecular density at any point depends on the ratio of molecular potential energy to the energy kT.

When a gas expands against a moving piston it does work. The source of this work is the random kinetic energy of the gas molecules. Conversely, when work is done in compressing a gas the random kinetic energy of its molecules increases. But if the collisions with the walls are perfectly elastic, as we have assumed, how can a molecule gain or lose energy in a collision with a piston? To understand this, we must consider the collision of a molecule with a moving wall.

When a molecule makes a collision with a *stationary* wall, it exerts a momentary force on the wall but does no work, since the wall does not move. But if the wall is in motion, work *is* done in a collision. Thus if the piston in Fig. 20–3 is moving to the right, work is done on it by the molecules that strike it, and their velocities (and kinetic energies) after colliding are smaller than they were before a collision. The collision is still completely elastic, since the work done on the moving piston is just equal to the decrease in the kinetic energy of the molecule. Similarly, if the piston is moving toward the left, the kinetic energy of a colliding molecule is *increased*, the increase in kinetic energy being equal to the work done on the molecule.

20–4 Molar heat capacity of a gas

When heat flows into a system in a process at constant volume, no work is done and all of the energy inflow goes into an increase in the internal energy U of the system. From the molecular viewpoint, the internal energy of a system is the sum total of the kinetic and potential energies of its molecules. If this sum can be computed as a function of temperature, then from its rate of change with temperature we can derive a theoretical expression for the molar heat capacity.

The simplest system is a monatomic ideal gas, for which the molecular energy is wholly kinetic and is given by Eq. (20–11).

$$\text{Random kinetic energy} = U = \tfrac{3}{2}nRT.$$

If the temperature is increased by dT, the random kinetic energy increases by

$$dU = \tfrac{3}{2}nR\,dT.$$

In a process in which the temperature increases by dT at constant volume, the energy flowing into a system is, by definition of C_v,

$$dQ = nC_v\,dT = dU.$$

Hence

$$C_v = \tfrac{3}{2}R.$$

But we showed in Section 19–12 and Table 19–1 that the experimental values of C_v for monatomic gases are, in fact, almost exactly equal to $\tfrac{3}{2}R$. This agreement is a striking confirmation of the basic correctness of the kinetic model of a gas and did much to establish this theory at a time when many scientists still refused to accept it.

Since $C_p = C_v + R$, it follows that the theoretical ratio of molar heat capacities for a monatomic ideal gas is

$$\frac{C_p}{C_v} = \gamma = \frac{\frac{3}{2}R + R}{\frac{3}{2}R} = \frac{5}{3} = 1.67.$$

This also is in good agreement with the experimental values in Table 19–1.

Polyatomic gases present a more complicated problem. We might expect that a molecule composed of two or more atoms could have an "internal energy" of its own, in the form of vibratory motion of the atoms relative to each other and of rotation of the molecule about its center of mass. Also, since we now feel sure that every atom consists of a positive nucleus and one or more electrons, there may be energy associated with these electric charges.

The *temperature* of a gas depends on the average random *translational* kinetic energy of its molecules. When heat flows into a *monatomic* gas, at constant volume, all of this energy seems to go into an increase in random translational molecular kinetic energy, as evidenced by the agreement between the measured values of C_v and the values computed from the increase in translational kinetic energy. But when heat flows into a *polyatomic* gas, we would expect that a part of the energy would go toward increasing "molecular internal energy." Hence when equal amounts of heat flow into a monatomic and a polyatomic gas containing the same number of molecules, it is to be expected that the temperature rise in the polyatomic gas will be less than in the monatomic, because only a part of the energy is available for increasing *translational* molecular kinetic energy. In other words, to produce *equal* increases of temperature, *more* heat would have to be supplied to the polyatomic gas. This is a qualitative explanation, then, of the larger values of C_v for polyatomic gases listed in Table 19–1.

Before proceeding further with the theory of specific heats of polyatomic gases, we must first discuss the principle of equipartition of energy.

20–5 The principle of equipartition of energy

Suppose that a vessel contains a mixture of gases which do not react chemically with one another. Each species of gas can then be considered independently. For simplicity, let there be just two gases, A and B.

The *partial pressure* of each gas is defined as the pressure it would exert if it alone occupied the entire vessel. Experiment shows that *the total pressure exerted by the mixture is the sum of the partial pressures of its components*, a discovery made by John Dalton (1755–1844) and known as *Dalton's law*. This is only to be expected from the molecular theory of a gas. Each species of molecule acts independently and each can be treated as if the other were not present. Thus if we have N_A molecules of gas A, and N_B molecules of gas B, both in a vessel of volume V, the partial pressures p_A and p_B are, from Eq. (20–9),

$$p_A = \frac{2}{3} \times \frac{N_A}{V} \times \frac{1}{2}m_A\overline{v_A^2}, \qquad p_B = \frac{2}{3} \times \frac{N_B}{V} \times \frac{1}{2}m_B\overline{v_B^2},$$

when m_A and m_B are the molecular masses and $\overline{v_A^2}$ and $\overline{v_B^2}$ their rms speeds.

But since each gas behaves as if it alone occupied the entire vessel,

$$p_A = \frac{n_A RT}{V} = \frac{N_A}{V}\frac{RT}{N_0} = \frac{N_A}{V}kT, \qquad p_B = \frac{n_B RT}{V} = \frac{N_B}{V}\frac{RT}{N_0} = \frac{N_B}{V}kT.$$

Equating the two expressions for p_A and for p_B, we get

$$\tfrac{1}{2}m_A\overline{v_A^2} = \tfrac{3}{2}kT,$$

$$\tfrac{1}{2}m_B\overline{v_B^2} = \tfrac{3}{2}kT.$$

That is, *the average random kinetic energy per molecule is the same for both species.* The same result would hold for a mixture of any number of species. The lighter molecules of a mixture have larger average speeds, so that the average kinetic energy of all species is the same.

The result above is one example of the *principle of equipartition of energy.* All species of molecules in a mixture share equally in the total random kinetic energy.

A second example of the principle can be deduced from symmetry considerations. The translational kinetic energy of a molecule depends on the values of the three rectangular components of its velocity. We say that the molecule has *three translational degrees of freedom.* Since the x-, y-, and z-directions are all equivalent, we expect that on the average the kinetic energies associated with each velocity component are the same. That is, each of these shares equally, on the average, in the translational kinetic energy. Since the total average kinetic energy per molecule is $\tfrac{3}{2}kT$, the average kinetic energy *per translational degree of freedom is* $\tfrac{1}{2}kT$.

A *monatomic* molecule, considered as a geometrical point, can have energy of *translation* only. A rigid diatomic molecule, which we can picture as a dumbbell-like structure, can also have *rotational* kinetic energy. Its axis of rotation can have any direction in space, and its angular velocity vector can be resolved into three rectangular components. Hence the molecule has three rotational degrees of freedom.

How does the average rotational kinetic energy compare with the average translational kinetic energy? The simplest hypothesis is to extend the principle of equipartition and assume that, on the average, an energy $\tfrac{1}{2}kT$ is associated with each rotational degree of freedom.

In general, let f represent the *total* number of degrees of freedom of a molecule, of which three are translational. According to our hypothesis, the average total energy of a molecule, u, is

$$u = f \times \tfrac{1}{2}kT,$$

and the total internal energy U of N molecules is

$$U = \frac{f}{2}NkT = \frac{f}{2}nRT.$$

The molar heat capacity at constant volume is then

$$C_v = \frac{1}{n}\frac{dU}{dt} = \frac{f}{2}R,$$

and since $C_p = R + C_v$, the ratio is

$$\gamma = \frac{C_p}{C_v} = \frac{(f/2)R + R}{(f/2)R} = \frac{f + 2}{f}.$$

If $f = 3$, as for a monatomic molecule,

$$C_v = \tfrac{3}{2}R, \qquad \gamma = \tfrac{5}{3} = 1.67,$$

in agreement with the results previously derived.

For a rigid diatomic molecule, we would expect that $f = 6$ (3 translational, 3 rotational). Then

$$C_v = 3R = 5.97 \text{ cal/mole·deg}, \qquad \gamma = \tfrac{8}{6} = 1.33.$$

This is *not* in good agreement with the experimental values for diatomic molecules in Table 19–1. However, if we try $f = 5$, we get

$$C_v = \tfrac{5}{2}R = 4.98 \text{ cal/mole·deg}, \qquad \gamma = \tfrac{7}{5} = 1.40,$$

and the agreement is much better.

But why should the molecule have only two rotational degrees of freedom and not three? Or, if we substitute measured values of C_v and γ in the equations above, and solve for f, why do we not always get *integral* values? What can be the significance of a *fraction* of a degree of freedom? Furthermore, the molar heat capacities of polyatomic gases all vary with the temperature, as if the number of degrees of freedom was not only nonintegral, but changed as the temperature changed.

These questions were puzzling ones for many years. There seemed to be a germ of truth in the equipartition principle, and yet it was certainly not the whole story. Not until the advent of quantum mechanics, in the 1920's, were the questions above answered. It appears now that the basic concept of the sharing of energy among the possible degrees of freedom is correct, but the hypothesis of *equal* shares must be modified. The equipartition principle becomes a limiting case which is approached if the temperature is sufficiently high, but which breaks down at low temperatures. This is one reason for the great interest at the present time in the study of all properties of matter at extremely low temperatures, near absolute zero. It should be stated, however, that quantum ideas have led to what seems to be a complete understanding of the problem, and as a matter of fact molar heat capacities of gases can now be computed from theory more accurately than they can be measured experimentally.

20–6 Distribution of molecular speeds

We would certainly not expect all the molecules in a sample of gas to have the same speed, although the fact that equal masses of a given gas at the same temperature and volume all exert the same pressure shows that the average value of the square of the speed is the same in all. Theory and experiment both lead to the result that not only is the rms speed the same in all such samples, but that the actual speeds are always

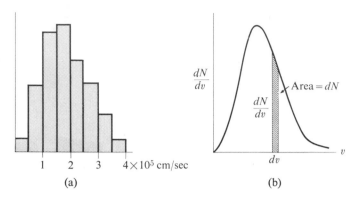

Fig. 20–4. (a) Distribution of molecular velocities. (b) Maxwell-Boltzmann distribution function.

grouped around the average in the same way. Data of this sort are presented mathematically and graphically in the same way as the statistics giving the age distribution of a group of persons, where we do not attempt to state the age of each individual but give instead the number with ages between 0 and 5 years, between 5 and 10 years, and so on.

Figure 20–4(a) is a block diagram or *histogram* of the speed distribution of a very large number of hydrogen molecules at a temperature of 300°K. The *area* of each block represents the number of molecules with speeds in the range covered by that particular block. Thus the area of the third block from the left represents the number with speeds between 1.0×10^5 cm/sec and 1.5×10^5 cm/sec. The total area of all blocks corresponds to the total number of molecules. The range covered in the diagram includes 99.96% of the molecules. The remaining 0.04% have speeds greater than 4×10^5 cm/sec, with smaller and smaller numbers in each range. The rms speed at this temperature is 1.96×10^5 cm/sec.

If the speed range included within each block is made smaller, the blocks become narrower and the variation in height from one to the next becomes less. The total area remains constant, however, since this corresponds to the total number of molecules. In the limit, when each block covers only an infinitesimal range, from a speed v to a speed $v + dv$, the tops of the blocks form the smooth curve shown in Fig. 20–4(b). The number of molecules dN with speeds between v and $v + dv$ is represented by the area of the narrow shaded strip of width dv. The area under the smooth curve equals the total area of the blocks in part (a). The height of the smooth curve, at any value of v, is dN/dv, and its area, base × height, is therefore dN.

The equation giving the height of the smooth curve, or the value of dN/dv as a function of v, was derived, by different methods, by Maxwell and by Boltzmann, and is known as the *Maxwell-Boltzmann distribution function*. The derivation is too long to be given here, but the result is

$$\frac{dN}{dv} = \frac{4N}{\sqrt{\pi}} \left(\frac{m}{2kT} \right)^{3/2} v^2 e^{-(mv^2/2kT)}.$$

Note that the exponent of e can be written

$$-\frac{\frac{1}{2}mv^2}{kT} = -\frac{\text{kinetic energy}}{kT}.$$

It was shown in Section 20–2 that the distribution of molecules in *elevation* is given by an expression in which e is raised to the power

$$-\frac{\text{potential energy}}{kT},$$

and we have another illustration of the way in which the product kT provides a reference level for molecular energies.

20–7 Experimental measurement of molecular speeds

Direct measurements of the distribution of molecular speeds have been made by a number of methods. Figure 20–5 is a diagram of the apparatus used by Zartman and Ko in 1930–1934, a modification of a technique developed by Stern in 1920. Metallic silver is melted and evaporated in the oven O. A beam of silver atoms escapes through a small opening in the oven and passes through the slits S_1 and S_2 into an evacuated region. The cylinder C can be rotated at approximately 6000 rpm about the axis A. If the cylinder is at rest, the molecular beam enters the cylinder through a slit S_3 and strikes a curved glass plate G. The molecules stick to the glass plate, and the number arriving at any portion can be determined by removing the plate and measuring with a recording microphotometer the darkening that has resulted.

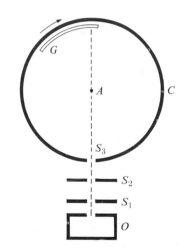

Fig. 20–5. Apparatus used by Zartman and Ko in studying distribution of velocities.

Now suppose the cylinder is rotated. Molecules can enter it only during the short time intervals during which the slit S_3 crosses the molecular beam. If the rotation is clockwise, as indicated, the glass plate moves toward the right while the molecules cross the diameter of the cylinder. They therefore strike the plate at the left of the point of impact when the cylinder is at rest, and the more slowly they travel, the farther to the left is this point of impact. The blackening of the plate is therefore a measure of the "velocity spectrum" of the molecular beam.

A more recent and more precise measurement, making use of the free fall of the molecules in a beam, was performed by Estermann, Simpson, and Stern, in 1947. A simplified diagram of the apparatus is given in Fig. 20–6. A beam of cesium atoms

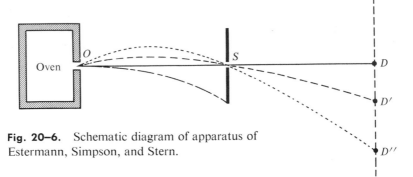

Fig. 20–6. Schematic diagram of apparatus of
Estermann, Simpson, and Stern.

emerges from the oven slit O, passes through the slit S, and impinges on a hot tungsten
wire D. The pressure of the residual gas in the apparatus is of the order of 10^{-8} mm
of mercury. Both the slits and the detecting wire are horizontal. The cesium atoms
striking the tungsten wire become ionized, re-evaporate, and are collected by a negatively charged cylinder surrounding the wire but not shown in the diagram. The ion
current to the collecting cylinder then gives directly the number of cesium atoms
impinging on the wire per second.

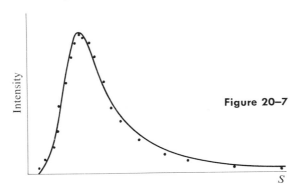

Figure 20–7

In the absence of a gravitational field, only those atoms emerging in a horizontal
direction would pass through the slit S, and they would all strike the collector in the
position D, regardless of their velocities. Actually, the path of each atom is a parabola, and an atom emerging from the slit O in a horizontal direction, as indicated by
the dot and dash line (with the vertical scale greatly exaggerated), would not pass
through the slit S. The dashed line and the dotted line represent the trajectories of
two atoms that can pass through the slit S, the velocity along the dashed trajectory
being greater than that along the dotted. Hence as the detector is moved down from
the position D, those atoms with velocities corresponding to the dashed trajectory
will be collected at D', those with the slower velocity corresponding to the dotted
trajectory will be collected at D'', etc. Measurement of the ion current as a function
of the vertical height of the collector then gives the velocity distribution.

Figure 20–7 is a graph of the results. The ordinate is proportional to the collector
current and the abscissa to the vertical distance S of the collector below the position

D in Fig. 20–6. The points are experimental values and the solid line is the theoretical curve computed from the Maxwell velocity distribution. The measured currents at large distances (small velocities) are somewhat smaller than the predicted values, an effect resulting from the collisions of molecules in the beam with one another near the oven slit. The general agreement between theory and experiment is excellent.

20–8 Collision cross section. Mean free path

In deriving the expression for the pressure exerted by a gas, the molecules were treated as geometrical points which could fly freely from one wall of a container to another without colliding with other molecules. One of the objections raised in the early days of the development of the theory was that if molecules acted in this way a small amount of gas released in a large room would spread throughout the room practically instantaneously, whereas we know that when the stopper is removed from a bottle of perfume a considerable time elapses before the odor can be detected even at a point only a few feet away. It was soon realized that this relatively slow *diffusion* of one gas in another resulted from molecular collisions, which cause a molecule to move in an irregular zigzag path.

Actual molecules are of finite size, and for the purposes of this discussion we assume that a molecule is a rigid, perfectly elastic sphere. A collision between two molecules is considered to take place whenever one molecule makes contact with another. Let us refer to one of the colliding molecules as the target molecule, of radius r_t, and to the other as the bullet molecule, of radius r_b. Then a collision occurs whenever the distance between the centers of the molecules becomes equal to the sum of their radii, $r_t + r_b$, as in Fig. 20–8(a).

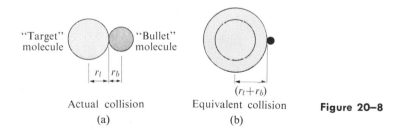

"Target" molecule   "Bullet" molecule

r_t r_b

$(r_t + r_b)$

Actual collision   Equivalent collision   **Figure 20–8**

(a)   (b)

When we are considering collisions of molecules of a given gas with other molecules of the same gas, the radii r_t and r_b are equal and there is no difference between target molecules and bullet molecules. In many instances, however, we wish to consider collisions between different kinds of particles, and so we shall speak of the target molecules as if they differed from the bullet molecules.

Since it is only the center-to-center distance that determines a collision, it does not matter whether the target is large and the bullet is small, or vice versa. We may therefore replace an actual collision with the equivalent collision shown in Fig. 20–8(b), in which the bullet molecule has been considered to shrink to a geometrical point and the target molecule to expand to a sphere of radius $r_t + r_b$.

Now consider a thin layer of gas of dimensions l, l, and Δx. The layer contains (equivalent) target molecules only, and to begin with we assume that these are at rest. We then imagine that a very large number N of bullet molecules are projected toward the face of the layer like a blast of pellets from a shotgun, in such a way that they are distributed over the face. If the thickness of the layer is so small that no target molecule can hide behind another, the layer presents to the bullet molecules the appearance shown in Fig. 20–9, where the shaded circles represent the target molecules and the black dots the bullet molecules.

Most of the bullet molecules will pass through the layer, but some will collide with target molecules. The ratio of the number of collisions, ΔN, to the total number of bullet molecules, N, is equal to the ratio of the area presented by the target molecules to the total area presented by the layer,

$$\frac{\Delta N}{N} = \frac{\text{target area}}{\text{total area}}.$$

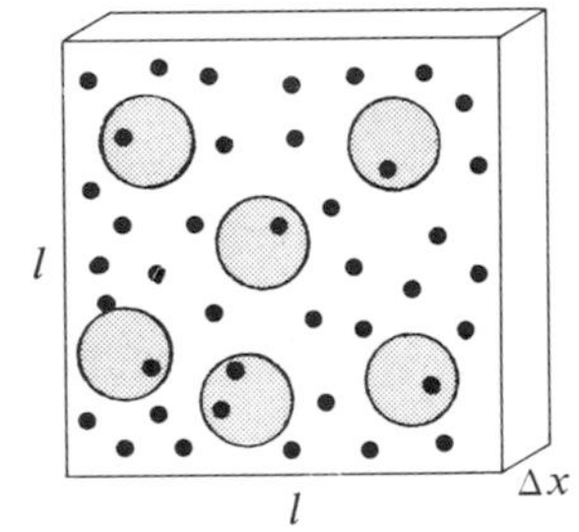

The target area σ of a single (equivalent) molecule is

$$\sigma = \pi(r_t + r_b)^2. \qquad (20\text{–}14)$$

Figure 20–9

This area is called the *microscopic collision cross section* of one (equivalent) molecule. The total target area is the product of this and the number of molecules in the layer. If there are n target molecules per unit volume, this number is $nl^2\,\Delta x$, so the total target area is

$$n\sigma l^2\,\Delta x.$$

The total area of the layer is l^2, so

$$\frac{\Delta N}{N} = \frac{n\sigma l^2\,\Delta x}{l^2} = n\sigma\,\Delta x. \qquad (20\text{–}15)$$

The quantity $n\sigma$ is called the *macroscopic cross section* of the group of (equivalent) molecules. Note that the unit of macroscopic cross section is reciprocal length, not area.

Let us next follow in imagination a single bullet molecule as it makes its way through a gas along the zigzag path shown in Fig. 20–10. We wish to obtain an expression for the average distance traveled between collisions, known as the *mean free path*, L. This can be deduced from the results above by a type of reasoning that is common and useful in problems of this sort.

When molecules are passing through the thin layer of gas in Fig. 20–9, the number removed from the beam by collisions is small compared with the original number, and we can say that N molecules have each traversed a thickness Δx of gas. The total distance traveled by all of the N molecules is then $N\,\Delta x$. We now make the hypothesis that the number of collisions made by a *single* molecule in traversing the same total distance $N\,\Delta x$ is equal to the number of collisions made by N molecules, each traversing a distance Δx. Then from Eq. (20–15), the total number of collisions made by the single molecule in a total path length $N \Delta x$ is

$$\Delta N = N n \sigma \, \Delta x. \tag{20–16}$$

The mean free path of the molecule is equal to the total path length divided by the number of collisions, or

$$L = \frac{\text{total path length}}{\text{total number of collisions}}.$$

From the expressions above for the total path length and the total number of collisions, we have

$$L = \frac{N \, \Delta x}{N n \sigma \, \Delta x}$$

or

$$\boxed{L = \frac{1}{n\sigma}.} \tag{20–17}$$

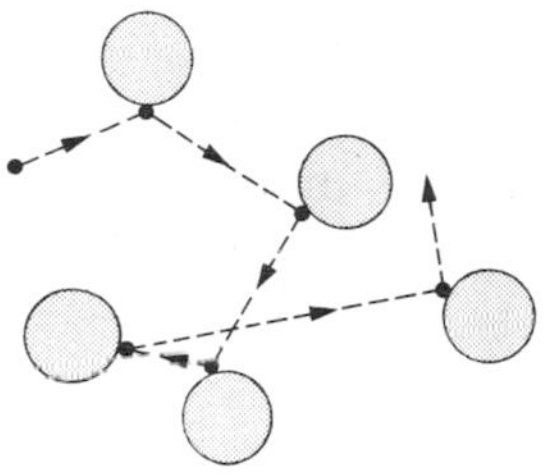

Fig. 20–10. Molecular free paths.

The concept of mean free path may be visualized by thinking of a man shooting a rifle aimlessly into a forest. Most of the bullets will hit trees, but some bullets will travel much farther than others. It is easy to see that the average distance the bullets go will depend inversely on both the denseness of the woods (n) and the size of the trees (σ).

In the above analysis, we assumed that the target molecules were at rest. If, however, we consider a gas in which the molecules have a maxwellian distribution of speeds, it is found that the mean free path of a molecule is

$$\boxed{L = \frac{0.707}{n\sigma}.} \tag{20–18}$$

We shall show in the next section how molecular diameters can be measured. These diameters are about the same for all gases, 2 or 3×10^{-8} cm. It was computed in Section 20–2 that at standard conditions, there are about 3×10^{19} molecules/cm^3 in a gas. For simplicity, suppose that the target radius r_t and the bullet radius r_b are of the same size, say 10^{-8} cm. Then

$$\sigma = \pi (r_t + r_b)^2 = 12.6 \times 10^{-16} \text{ cm}^2,$$

and

$$L = \frac{0.707}{n\sigma} = \frac{0.707}{3 \times 10^{19} \times 12.6 \times 10^{-16}}$$

$$= 1.87 \times 10^{-5} \text{ cm},$$

which is smaller than the wavelength of visible light!

The number of molecules per unit volume, **n**, is directly proportional to the pressure at a given temperature. *The mean free path is therefore inversely proportional to the pressure*, and at a pressure of 10^{-6} atm (a moderately good vacuum) it becomes about 20 cm.

20-9 Viscosity of a gas

At first sight, it appears contradictory that a gas consisting of widely separated molecules making perfectly elastic collisions with one another should exhibit any viscosity or internal friction. Every real gas is viscous, however, and we now show that this property is another necessary consequence of our simple model and that its explanation does not require the assignment of any new properties to the molecules.

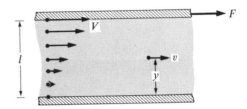

Fig. 20-11. Viscous flow between a stationary lower plate and a moving upper plate.

Figure 20–11 represents a moving upper plate, separated from a stationary lower plate by a layer of gas of thickness *l*, and being pulled to the right with velocity *V* by a force *F*. The molecules of the gas, in addition to their large random speeds, have a forward velocity component which equals *V* at the top plate and decreases uniformly to zero at the bottom plate. The forward velocity *v* at any height *y* above the lower plate can be found by proportion:

$$\frac{v}{y} = \frac{V}{l}, \quad \text{or} \quad v = \frac{y}{l} V.$$

Since the gas is viscous, a shearing force is exerted on the gas below any horizontal plane by the gas above it. The explanation of this force is that momentum is transmitted across any such plane by the molecules crossing it, because those coming from above, where the forward velocity is large, carry more forward momentum than those crossing from below where the velocity is smaller.

Let us make the simple assumption that each molecule crossing a horizontal plane from above makes its last collision before crossing at a height of one mean free path above the plane. Its forward velocity when it crosses is the forward velocity of the gas at the height of this last collision. If *y* is the elevation of some plane in the gas, the forward velocity at a height *L* above this plane is

$$v = \frac{y + L}{l} V$$

and each molecule crossing from above carries across the plane a forward momentum of

$$mv = m \frac{y + L}{l} V.$$

Again for simplicity, let us approximate the random molecular motion by assuming that one-third of the molecules move parallel to each axis with a speed $\bar{v}$ equal to the average random speed. At any instant, one-sixth are moving up and one-sixth down. The number crossing an area A from above in time t is the number moving down and contained in a cylinder of base A and height $\bar{v}t$. If the total number of molecules per unit volume is $\mathbf{n}$, the number crossing from above in time t is

$$\frac{1}{6}\mathbf{n} \times A \times \bar{v}t$$

and the momentum transported across the area from above is

$$\frac{1}{6}\mathbf{n}A\bar{v}tm\frac{y+L}{l}V. \tag{20-19}$$

Similarly, the momentum transported across the area by the molecules moving up from below is

$$\frac{1}{6}\mathbf{n}A\bar{v}tm\frac{y-L}{l}V. \tag{20-20}$$

The increase of momentum of the gas below the area due to this cause is the difference between the two previous expressions, or

$$\frac{1}{3}\frac{\mathbf{n}A\bar{v}tmLV}{l}.$$

The *rate* of increase of momentum, which we set equal to the average force, is

$$F = \frac{1}{3}\left(\frac{\mathbf{n}A\bar{v}mLV}{l}\right) = \frac{1}{3}\mathbf{n}m\bar{v}L\left(\frac{AV}{l}\right).$$

But the defining equation of viscosity is

$$F = \eta A\frac{dv}{dy} = \eta A\frac{V}{l}.$$

Hence

$$\eta = \tfrac{1}{3}\mathbf{n}m\bar{v}L,$$

and when this is combined with Eq. (20–18) for the mean free path L, we obtain

$$\eta = 0.236\frac{m\bar{v}}{\sigma} \tag{20-21}$$

or

$$\sigma = \pi d^2 = 0.236\frac{m\bar{v}}{\eta}. \tag{20-22}$$

Equation (20–22) thus provides a relation from which atomic diameters can be computed, since m, $\bar{v}$, and η can all be computed or measured.

The expression for the viscosity in Eq. (20–21) leads to the unexpected conclusion that *the viscosity of a given gas should depend only on the random velocity $\bar{v}$* (and hence

TABLE 20-2

MOLECULAR DIAMETERS FROM VISCOSITY MEASUREMENTS

Gas	M, $\dfrac{\text{gm}}{\text{mole}}$	η, 0°C $\dfrac{10^{-5}\text{ dyne·sec}}{\text{cm}^2}$	d, 10^{-8} cm
H_2	2.02	8.4	2.35
He	4.00	18.8	1.86
CH_4	16.0	10.3	3.55
NH_3	17.0	9.15	3.83
Ne	20.2	29.9	2.21
N_2	28.0	16.6	3.22
O_2	32.0	19.2	3.09
A	39.9	21.0	3.12
CO_2	44.0	13.8	3.96

only on the temperature) *and not on the number of molecules per unit volume or the density.* However, experiment bears out this prediction very well over wide ranges of density (or pressure). It breaks down at very low pressures, where the mean free path becomes so long that a molecule can travel across a container without making numerous collisions on the way, and at very high pressures, where the molecules are so close together that intermolecular forces become significant.

Diameters of some common gas molecules, calculated from viscosity measurements are listed in Table 20–2.

20–10 The Clausius and van der Waals equations of state

Our derivation of the equation of state of a gas assumed that the molecules were essentially geometrical points which exerted no forces on each other. The effect of the finite size of the molecules was first introduced into the theory by Clausius, and the effect of intermolecular forces by van der Waals.

Clausius reasoned that we should use for the volume available to a single molecule not the actual volume V of the container but a somewhat smaller volume because of the space occupied by the molecules themselves. Let us imagine that at a certain instant all the molecules of a gas except one are "frozen" in position, while the remaining molecule continues to move among the others and collide with them. We assume the molecules to be rigid spheres of diameter d. At the instant of a collision the center-to-center distance of the colliding molecules is the molecular diameter d. The center of the moving molecule is thus excluded from a spherical volume of radius d and this volume is called the *sphere of exclusion.* However, since only the hemisphere facing the moving molecule is effective in excluding the latter, we take one-half of the total volume of the spheres of exclusion of all the other molecules as the effective volume unavailable to any one molecule.

The number of molecules N in n moles of gas is $N = nN_0$, so the unavailable volume is

$$\tfrac{1}{2} \times nN_0 \times \tfrac{4}{3}\pi d^3 = nb,$$

where

$$b = \tfrac{2}{3}N_0\pi d^3$$

is the total unavailable volume per mole. The total volume of one mole of spherical molecules of diameter d is $\tfrac{1}{6}N_0\pi d^3$, and the unavailable volume is 4 times the total molecular volume.

The available volume is $V - nb$, and instead of the ideal gas equation, we have

$$p(V - nb) = nRT. \tag{20–23}$$

This is the *Clausius equation of state*.

Now consider the effect of intermolecular forces. Of course, there is a gravitational force of attraction between any pair of molecules, but gravitational forces are much too small to account for the deviations of real gases from the ideal gas law and the fact that gases condense to liquids (at temperatures below the critical temperature) when sufficiently compressed. All molecules contain electrically charged particles, and even though the molecule as a whole is electrically neutral there do exist between molecules attractive forces of electrical origin, called *van der Waals forces*. At intermolecular distances of a few molecular diameters these forces are much larger than gravitational forces, but they decrease much more rapidly with distance. At very small intermolecular distances, the force changes from one of attraction to one of repulsion.

Let us assume that the attractive forces decrease so rapidly with distance that they are appreciable only between a molecule and its nearest neighbors. Molecules within the body of a gas are, on the average, attracted equally in all directions, but those in the outermost layer experience a net inward force. To reverse the momentum of molecules colliding with it, the inward force that the wall of the container must exert is therefore less than that calculated in Section 20–3, and hence the pressure is less.

The reduction in pressure will be proportional both to the number of molecules per unit volume in the surface layer, *on* which the inward forces act, and to the number per unit volume in the next layer beneath them, *by* which the forces are exerted. The pressure is therefore reduced by an amount proportional to the *square* of N/V, the number of molecules per unit volume. That is, the pressure reduction can be written

$$a'(N/V)^2,$$

where a' is a factor depending on the strength of the attractive forces and which varies from one gas to another. Again replacing N by nN_0, this can be written as

$$an^2/V^2,$$

where

$$a = a'N_0^2.$$

Taking into account the Clausius correction for finite molecular volume, we have instead of the ideal gas equation $p = nRT/V$, the equation

$$p = \frac{nRT}{V - nb} - \frac{an^2}{V^2},$$

or

$$\left(p + \frac{an^2}{V^2}\right)(V - nb) = nRT. \qquad (20\text{--}24)$$

This is the *van der Waals equation of state*. Table 20–3 lists the values of the constants a and b for a few gases. The constant b, which is proportional to the molecular volume, is about the same for all the substances listed. That is, the molecules of these substances do not differ greatly in size. The constant a, however, which is a measure of the intermolecular forces, varies widely from one substance to another and is smallest, as would be expected, for those with low critical temperatures.

TABLE 20–3

Constants a and b in the van der Waals equation.
p in dynes/cm^2, V in cm^3, T in deg K, $R = 8.31 \times 10^7$ ergs/mole·deg K.

Substance	a (dyne·cm^4/mole^2)	b (cm^3/mole)
He	3.44×10^{10}	23.4
H$_2$	24.8	26.6
O$_2$	138	31.8
CO$_2$	366	42.9
H$_2$O	580	31.9

20–11 Crystals

If a stream of ordinary illuminating gas is bubbled through benzine and then ignited, a smoky flame will result. When this flame comes in contact with a cool surface, *soot* (also called lampblack) will be deposited. Soot consists of small pieces of solid carbon. The so-called "lead" in a pencil also contains pieces of solid carbon called *graphite*, and a diamond is another form of solid carbon. The remarkably dissimilar mechanical, thermal, electrical, and optical properties of these three forms of carbon are explained in terms of the arrangement of the carbon atoms. In soot the atoms have no regular arrangement and are said to constitute an *amorphous* solid. Graphite and diamond are both crystals, but the orderly arrangement of atoms is different in the two crystal lattices. The study of the spatial arrangements of atoms (or molecules or ions) in the various types of crystal lattices is a fascinating and complicated part of physics. We shall be concerned in the following pages with only a few of the fundamental ideas needed to understand some of the mechanical and thermal properties of single crystals or solids composed of an aggregate of crystals, that is, *polycrystalline solids*.

Fig. 20–12. Close packing of the sodium ions (black spheres) and chlorine ions (white spheres) in a sodium chloride crystal. (Courtesy of Alan Holden; reprinted with permission of Educational Services, Inc., from *Crystals and Crystal Growing*, Doubleday and Co., New York, 1960.)

The particles comprising a crystal lattice are *closely packed*, as seen in Fig. 20–2 and as suggested by the model in Fig. 20–12, where the sodium and chlorine ions of a sodium chloride crystal are represented as spheres touching one another. Strictly speaking, each ion consists of a nucleus surrounded by electrons in motion, so that the boundary of an ion must be thought of as the average positions of the outermost electrons. It follows that the outer electrons of one particle in a crystal lattice come close to and even at times interpenetrate with the outer electrons of a neighboring particle.

To make crystal structures simpler to comprehend, it is customary to exaggerate the distances between neighboring particles, as shown in Fig. 20–13, where a *face-centered cubic* lattice structure is depicted. Much can be learned by representing other crystal lattices in this way, with the aid of a supply of gum drops and toothpicks.

Suppose that the chemical composition and density of a very small volume element of a substance are measured at many different places. If the composition and density

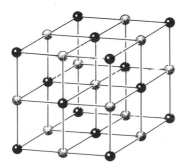

Fig. 20–13. Symbolic representation of a sodium chloride crystal, with exaggerated distances between ions.

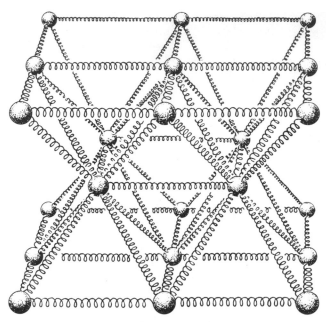

Fig. 20–14. The forces between neighboring particles in a crystal may be visualized by imagining every particle to be connected to its neighbors by springs. In the case of a cubic crystal, all springs are assumed to have the same spring constant. Anisotropy is connected with differing spring constants in different directions.

are the same at all points, the substance is said to be *homogeneous*. If the physical properties determining the transport of heat, electricity, light, etc., are the *same in all directions*, the substance is said to be *isotropic*. Cubic crystals are both homogeneous and isotropic, whereas all other crystals, although homogeneous, are not isotropic, i.e., they are *anisotropic*.

The *anisotropy* (accent on the syllable "ot") of noncubic crystals can be understood when the forces between neighboring particles in a lattice are taken into account. A convenient way of visualizing these forces is shown in Fig. 20–14, where there is depicted a large number of spheres, each connected to its neighbors by springs. The force constants of parallel springs are imagined equal, but the force constant of each spring pointing in one direction may be different from that of each spring pointing in a different direction. If each of the particles represented by black spheres in Fig. 20–14 is imagined to be vibrating about its equilibrium position, a fairly accurate picture of the dynamic character of a crystal lattice will result. The mathematical calculation of the vibration frequencies of such a complex mechanical system was first attempted by Born and Von Karman early in the twentieth century. It is, of course, a very laborious and complicated calculation, but it has been carried out in detail for sodium chloride, potassium chloride, diamond, and silver.

The elastic properties of crystals can be partially understood from a diagram such as that in Fig. 20–14. Young's modulus is simply a measure of the stiffness of the springs in the direction in which the crystal is pulled or pushed. The shear modulus depends on the springs which are stretched and those which are compressed when the crystal is twisted. One of the first tests of the correctness of a lattice structure representing a particular material is to compare a calculated value of an elastic modulus with a measured value.

20–12 Heat capacity of a crystal

In Section 20–3 a gas was assumed to consist of N particles in rapid linear motion so far apart on the average that no force of interaction existed except upon collision with one another or with a wall. Applying simple mechanical principles, it was shown that the product of the pressure p and the volume V is equal to

$$pV = \tfrac{2}{3} \times \tfrac{1}{2}N\overline{mv^2} = \tfrac{2}{3}U,$$

where U is the total energy of the particles, which is entirely translational kinetic energy. In order for this result to agree with the equation of state of an ideal gas,

$$pV = nRT,$$

it is necessary to conclude that the average total energy per particle U/N, under equilibrium conditions, is equal to

$$\frac{U}{N} = \tfrac{3}{2}kT.$$

Since there were three transitional degrees of freedom, $\tfrac{1}{2}kT$ of energy on the average was attributed to each degree of freedom. This was extended also to rotational degrees of freedom, and the rough statement that to every degree of freedom of motion of a molecule there was attributed an average energy, at equilibrium, equal to $\tfrac{1}{2}kT$ was termed the principle of the equipartition of energy.

The methods of calculation just referred to represent a simplified version of the branch of physics called the kinetic theory of gases. There is, however, another way in which the behavior of large numbers of particles may be described and calculated, which, in some respects, is more general and more powerful. This more general method is called *statistical mechanics*. In statistical mechanics it is not necessary to specify whether the particles are molecules of a gas or ions occupying sites in a crystal lattice. The important thing is whether they are almost independent, and if so, whether the weak interaction among the particles is sufficient to enable the particles to exchange energy and finally come to equilibrium. If this is the case, the methods of statistical mechanics enable us to find the equilibrium value of the average energy per particle from a knowledge of the type of energy possessed by each individual particle. If the energy of an individual particle is expressed as the sum of a number of squared terms, like $\tfrac{1}{2}mv_x^2$ or $\tfrac{1}{2}I\omega^2$, or $\tfrac{1}{2}kx^2$, then it can be proved *rigorously* that at equilibrium the average energy per particle *associated with each squared* term is $\tfrac{1}{2}kT$. This is the rigorous statement of the principle of the equipartition of energy.

If we consider an assemblage of N vibrators, each vibrating along the x-axis with very small amplitude almost independently (but not enough to prevent a weak interaction with neighbors), we may consider the energy of each vibrator to consist of two squared terms,

$$\tfrac{1}{2}mv_x^2 + \tfrac{1}{2}kx^2.$$

The principle of equipartition then gives us for the average energy per particle at equilibrium the sum of two terms each equal to $\tfrac{1}{2}kT$, or a total of kT.

Now a crystal composed of N particles each of which interacts strongly with its neighbors vibrates in a very complicated way. In spite of the complications, it may be shown quite generally that the actual situation is *equivalent* to $3N$ oscillators, almost independent of one another, each vibrating with its own frequency. It follows therefore that the total energy at equilibrium is

$$U = 3NkT,$$

or, in terms of the number of moles n and the universal gas constant R,

$$U = 3nRT,$$

and finally

$$C_v = \frac{1}{n}\frac{dU}{dT} = 3R = 5.97\ \frac{\text{cal}}{\text{mole·K}^\circ}.$$

But this is the Dulong and Petit law which a solid *approaches* as T increases but which is in complete disagreement with experiment as T approaches zero. The curves in Fig. 16–3 indicating the temperature dependence of C_v of some solids shown in *every* case that C_v is *not* constant but approaches zero as T approaches zero.

A very careful analysis shows that there is nothing wrong with the methods of statistical mechanics nor with the equivalence between the actual vibrations of a crystal lattice and $3N$ almost independent oscillators. What is wrong is the assumption that a vibrator can assume *any value* of the energy given by $\tfrac{1}{2}mv_x^2 + \tfrac{1}{2}kx^2$. The fundamental idea of the quantum theory, as explained in Section 17–7 in connection with the spectrum of blackbody radiation, is that a vibrator of frequency f may *not* take on *any* value of the energy, but only *discrete energy values* given by whole-number multiples of the product hf:

$$1hf, \quad 2hf, \quad 3hf, \ldots,$$

where h is a constant, called *Planck's constant*. When this postulate is used in conjunction with the classical methods of statistical mechanics, we get as the average energy per particle at equilibrium the value

$$\frac{hf}{e^{hf/kT} - 1}.$$

When T gets very large, the exponent hf/kT gets small and the exponential becomes practically equal to $1 + hf/kT$. The average energy therefore reduces to kT, the classical value, and Dulong and Petit's law is approached as T approaches infinity. As T gets smaller, however, the exponent hf/kT gets larger and the average energy *decreases* and, along with it, the heat capacity of the crystal, in agreement with the experimental curves of Fig. 16–3.

Problems

Molecular Data

N_0 = Avogadro's number = 6.02×10^{23} molecules/mole,
Mass of a hydrogen atom = 1.66×10^{-24} gm,
Mass of a nitrogen molecule = $28 \times 1.66 \times 10^{-24}$ gm,
Mass of an oxygen molecule = $32 \times 1.66 \times 10^{-24}$ gm.

20–1. Consider an ideal gas at 0°C and at 1 atm pressure. Imagine each molecule to be, on the average, at the center of a small cube. (a) What is the length of an edge of this small cube? (b) How does this distance compare with the diameter of a molecule?

20–2. A mole of liquid water occupies a volume of 18 cm³. Imagine each molecule to be, on the average, at the center of a small cube. (a) What is the length of an edge of this small cube? (b) How does this distance compare with the diameter of a molecule?

20–3. What is the length of the side of a cube, in a gas at standard conditions, that contains a number of molecules equal to the population of the United States (about 170 million)?

20–4. (a) What is the average translational kinetic energy of a molecule of oxygen at a temperature of 300°K? (b) What is the average value of the square of its speed? (c) What is the root-mean-square speed? (d) What is the momentum of an oxygen molecule traveling at this speed? (e) Suppose a molecule traveling at this speed bounces back and forth between opposite sides of a cubical vessel 10 cm on a side. What is the average force it exerts on the walls of the container? (f) What is the average force per unit area? (g) How many molecules traveling at this speed are necessary to produce an average pressure of 1 atm? (h) Compare with the number of oxygen molecules actually contained in a vessel of this size, at 300°K and atmospheric pressure.

20–5. The speed of propagation of a sound wave in air at 27°C is about 1100 ft/sec. Compare this with the root-mean-square speed of nitrogen molecules at this temperature.

20–6. What is the total random kinetic energy of the molecules in 1 mole of helium at a temperature of (a) 300°K? (b) 301°K? (c) Compare the difference between these with the change in internal energy of 1 mole of helium when its temperature is increased by 1 K°, as computed from the relation $\Delta U = nC_v \Delta T$. (See Table 19–1.)

20–7. (a) What is the translational kinetic energy of an oxygen molecule at 27°C? (b) If an oxygen molecule has five degrees of freedom, what is its total kinetic energy at this temperature? (c) What is the internal energy of 1 mole of oxygen at this temperature?

20–8. (a) To what pressure must a "vacuum" tube be exhausted in order that the mean free path of the gas molecules within it shall be 20 cm? (b) How many molecules per cm³ remain in the tube at this pressure? Assume a molecular diameter of 3×10^{-8} cm and a temperature of 0°C.

20–9. A flask contains a mixture of mercury vapor, neon, and helium. Compare (a) the average kinetic energies of the three types of atoms, and (b) the root-mean-square speeds.

20–10. The viscosity of oxygen at a temperature of 15°C is 196 micropoise. Compute the effective diameter of an oxygen molecule.

20–11. (a) At what temperature is the rms speed of hydrogen molecules equal to the speed of the first earth satellite (about 18,000 mi/hr)? (b) At what temperature is the rms speed equal to the escape speed from the gravitational field of the earth?

20–12. The oven in Fig. 20–5 contains bismuth at a temperature of 840°K, the drum is 10 cm in diameter and rotates at 6000 rev/min. Find the displacement on the glass plate G, measured from a point directly opposite the slit, of the points of impact of the molecules Bi and Bi_2. Assume that all molecules of each species travel with the rms speed appropriate to that species.

20–13. In the apparatus of Estermann, Simpson, and Stern in Fig. 20–6, the distances OS and SD are each 1 m. (a) Calculate the distance of the detector below the central position D, for cesium atoms having a speed equal to the rms speed in a beam emerging from an oven at a temperature of 460°K. (b) Calculate also the "angle of departure" of the trajectory. The atomic weight of cesium is 133.

20–14. (a) Compute the diameter of a water molecule from the value of the van der Waals constant b in Table 20–3. (b) Compare the total molecular volume of one mole of water with the actual volume occupied by one mole in the liquid phase. (c) Compute the pressure reduction, due to intermolecular forces of attraction, in oxygen at standard conditions. Express your answer as a fraction of the actual pressure.

20–15. Suppose that there is an attractive force between two particles, given by $10^3/r^2$ in arbitrary units, and a repulsive force given by $10^5/r^4$. Construct graphs of the attractive force, the repulsive force, and the resultant force, over a range of values of r from 6 units to 30 units. Compare your result with Fig. 20–1.

CHAPTER 21

Traveling Waves

21-1 Introduction

Waves on the surface of a body of water, produced by the wind or by some other disturbance, are a familiar sight. A source of sound is heard by means of traveling waves in the intervening atmosphere, and the vibrations of the sound source itself constitute a so-called *stationary* wave. Many of the observed properties of light are best explained by a wave theory, and we believe that light waves are of the same fundamental nature as radiowaves, infrared and ultraviolet waves, x-rays, and gamma rays. One of the outstanding developments of 20th century physics has been the discovery that all matter is endowed with wave properties and that a beam of electrons, for example, is reflected by a crystal in much the same way as a beam of x-rays.

The subject of wave motion is closely related to that of harmonic motion. When a wave travels in a material substance, every particle of the substance oscillates about its equilibrium position, so that we must deal with the vibrations of a large number of particles instead of only one.

When the vibrations of the particles are at right angles to the direction of travel of the wave, the wave is called *transverse*. If the particles oscillate in the direction of propagation, the wave is called *longitudinal*. Suppose that one end of a medium is forced to vibrate periodically, the displacement y (either transverse or longitudinal) varying with the time according to the equation of simple harmonic motion:

$$y = \begin{cases} Y \sin \omega t, \\ \quad \text{or} \\ Y \cos \omega t. \end{cases}$$

During half a cycle, a displacement in one direction is propagated through the medium, and during the other half, a displacement in the opposite direction is caused to proceed. The resulting continuous train of disturbances traveling with a speed depending on the properties of the medium is called a *wave*.

To fix our ideas, suppose that one end of a stretched string is forced to vibrate periodically in a transverse direction with simple harmonic motion of amplitude Y, frequency f, and period $\tau = 1/f$. For the present we shall assume the string to be long enough so that any effects at the far end need not be considered. A *continuous train* of transverse sinusoidal waves then advances along the string. The shape of a portion of the string near the end, at intervals of $\frac{1}{8}$ of a period, is shown in Fig. 21-1 for a total time of one period. The string is assumed to have been vibrating for a sufficiently long time so that the shape of the string is sinusoidal for an indefinite

distance from the driven end. It will be
seen from the figure that the wave form
advances steadily toward the right, as indicated by the short arrow pointing to one
particular wave crest, while any one point
on the string (see the black dot) oscillates
about its equilibrium position with simple
harmonic motion. It is important to distinguish between the motion of the *wave
form*, which moves with constant velocity c
along the string, and the motion of *a particle of the string*, which is simple harmonic
and transverse to the string

The distance between two successive
maxima (or between any two successive
points in the same phase) is the *wavelength*
of the wave and is denoted by λ. Since the
wave form, traveling with constant velocity
c, advances a distance of one wavelength
in a time interval of one period, it follows
that $c = \lambda/\tau$, or

$$c = f\lambda. \qquad (21\text{-}1)$$

That is, *the velocity of propagation equals
the product of frequency and wavelength.*

To understand the mechanics of a longitudinal wave, consider a long tube filled
with a fluid and provided with a plunger at
the left end, as shown in Fig. 21-2. The
dots represent particles of the fluid. Suppose the plunger is forced to undergo a
simple harmonic vibration parallel to the
direction of the tube. During a part of each
oscillation, a region whose pressure is
above the equilibrium pressure is formed.
Such a region is called a *condensation* and
is represented by closely spaced dots. Following the production of a condensation,
a region is formed in which the pressure
is lower than the equilibrium value. This
is called a *rarefaction* and is represented by
widely spaced dots. The condensations

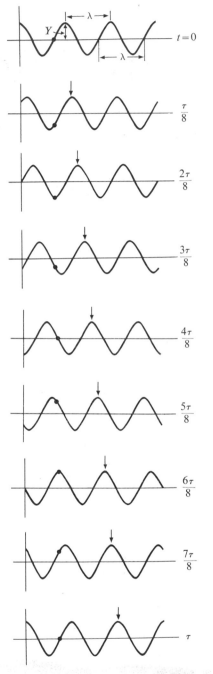

Fig. 21-1. A sinusoidal transverse wave
traveling toward the right, shown at intervals of $\frac{1}{8}$ of a period.

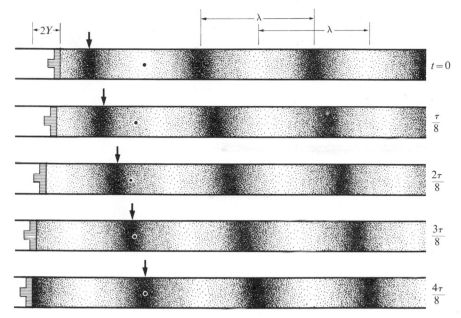

Fig. 21–2. A sinusoidal longitudinal wave traveling toward the right, shown at intervals of $\frac{1}{8}$ of a period.

and rarefactions move to the right with constant velocity c, as indicated by successive positions of the small vertical arrow. The velocity of longitudinal waves in air (sound) at 20°C is 344 m/sec or 1130 ft/sec. The motion of a single particle of the medium, shown by a heavy black dot, is simple harmonic, parallel to the direction of propagation.

The wavelength is the distance between two successive condensations or two successive rarefactions, and the same fundamental equation, $c = f\lambda$, holds in this, as in all types of waves.

21–2 Mathematical representation of a traveling wave

Suppose that a wave of any sort travels from left to right in a medium. Let us compare the motion of any one particle of the medium with that of a second particle to the right of the first. We find that the second particle moves in the same manner as the first, but after a lapse of time that is greater the greater the distance of the second particle from the first. Hence if one end of a stretched string oscillates with simple harmonic motion, all other points oscillate with simple harmonic motion of the same amplitude and frequency. The *phase angle* of the motion, however, is different for different points.

Let the displacement of a particle at the origin ($x = 0$) be given by

$$y = Y \sin \omega t.$$

The displacement of a particle at the right of the origin lags that of the particle at the origin by some angle ϕ. That is,

$$y = Y \sin (\omega t - \phi).$$

The lag angle ϕ is proportional to the distance of the particle from the origin, or to its coordinate x:

$$\phi = kx, \tag{21-2}$$

where k is called the *propagation constant*. Hence for such a particle

$$y = Y \sin (\omega t - kx). \tag{21-3}$$

This equation represents a sine wave traveling to the *right*. If the wave travels to the *left*, particles at the right of the origin *lead* the particle at the origin in phase, and the equation of the wave is

$$y = Y \sin (\omega t + kx). \tag{21-4}$$

A particle at a distance of one wavelength from the origin vibrates in step with that at the origin. Hence it lags (or leads) by an angle $\phi = 2\pi$. By setting $x = \lambda$ and $\phi = 2\pi$ in Eq. (21-2), we get

$$2\pi = k\lambda, \quad k = \frac{2\pi}{\lambda}. \tag{21-5}$$

The propagation constant k is therefore 2π times the reciprocal of the wavelength. Since $\omega = 2\pi f = 2\pi/\tau$, the equation of a traveling wave can also be written as

$$y = Y \sin 2\pi \left(\frac{t}{\tau} \pm \frac{x}{\lambda} \right).$$

At any given *time* t, Eq. (21-3) gives the displacement y of a particle, from its equilibrium position, as a function of the *coordinate* x of the particle. If the wave is a transverse wave in a string, the equation represents the *shape* of the string at that instant, as if we had taken a snapshot of the string. Thus at time $t = 0$,

$$y = Y \sin (-kx) = - Y \sin kx = - Y \sin 2\pi \frac{x}{\lambda}.$$

This curve is plotted in Fig. 21-3.

At any given *coordinate* x, Eq. (21-3) gives the displacement y of the particle at that coordinate, as a function of *time*. Thus at the coordinate $x = 0$,

$$y = Y \sin \omega t = Y \sin 2\pi \frac{t}{\tau}.$$

This curve is plotted in Fig. 21-4.

We see, therefore, that the displacement y of a particle depends both on the coordinate of the particle and on the time. In other words, *y is a function of two* **independ-**

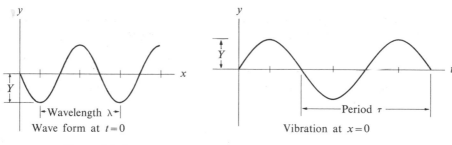

Figure 21–3

Figure 21–4

ent *variables*, x and t. A graph of Eq. (21–3) would be a *surface* if we plotted x and t along rectangular axes in a horizontal plane, and plotted y vertically above this plane.

It is important to distinguish carefully between the *speed of propagation* of the waveform, c, and the *particle speed* v of a particle of the medium in which a wave is traveling. Thus for a transverse traveling sine wave given by

$$y = Y \sin (\omega t + kx).$$

the particle speed v is

$$v = \frac{dy}{dt} = \omega Y \cos (\omega t + kx),$$

which is simply the expression for the velocity of a particle oscillating with simple harmonic motion of amplitude Y and angular frequency ω, with an initial phase angle kx proportional to its x-coordinate.

21–3 Calculation of the speed of a transverse pulse

Suppose that a string is stretched between two fixed supports. If the string is struck a transverse blow at some point, or if a small portion is displaced sidewise and released, disturbances will be observed to travel outward in both directions from the displaced portion. Each of these is called a *transverse pulse*, the direction of motion of the particles of the string being at right angles to the direction of travel, or of *propagation*, of the pulse. Each pulse retains its shape as it travels, and each travels with a constant speed which we shall represent by c.

Consider the string depicted in Fig. 21–5, under a tension S and with linear density (mass per unit length) μ. In Fig. 21–5(a) the string is at rest. At time t = 0, a constant transverse force F is applied at the left end of the string. As a result, this end moves up with a constant transverse speed v. Figure 21–5(b) shows the shape of the string after a time t has elapsed. All points of the string at the left of the point P are moving with speed v, whereas all points at the right of P are still at rest. The boundary between the moving and the stationary portions is traveling to the right with the *speed of propagation c*. The left end of the string has moved up a distance vt and the boundary point P has advanced a distance ct.

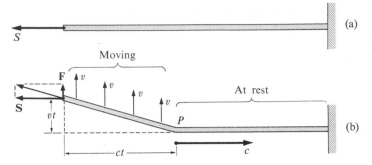

Fig. 21–5. Propagation of a transverse disturbance in a string.

The speed of propagation c can be calculated by setting the transverse impulse (transverse force $\times$ time) equal to the change of transverse momentum of the moving portion (mass $\times$ transverse velocity). The impulse of the transverse force F in time t is Ft. By similar triangles,

$$\frac{F}{S} = \frac{vt}{ct}, \qquad F = S\frac{v}{c}.$$

Hence

$$\text{Transverse impulse} = S\frac{v}{c}t.$$

The mass of the moving portion is the product of the mass per unit length μ and the length ct. Hence

$$\text{Transverse momentum} = \mu ctv.$$

Applying the impulse-momentum theorem, we get

$$S\frac{v}{c}t = \mu ctv,$$

and therefore

$$c = \sqrt{S/\mu}. \qquad \text{(Transverse)} \tag{21–6}$$

Thus it is seen that the velocity of propagation of a transverse pulse in a string depends only on the tension and the mass per unit length.

TABLE 21–1.   UNITS FOR EQ. (21–6)

System of units	S	μ	c
mks	newton	kgm/m	m/sec
cgs	dyne	gm/cm	cm/sec
Engineering	pound	slug/ft	ft/sec

In numerical applications of Eq. (21–6), attention must be paid to the units employed. Appropriate units are shown in Table 21–1.

EXAMPLE 1.   One end of a rubber tube is fastened to a fixed support. The other end passes over a pulley at a distance of 8 m from the fixed end, and carries a load of 2 kgm. The mass of the tube, between the fixed end and the pulley, is 600 gm. What is the speed of a transverse wave in the tube?

The tension in the tube equals the weight of the 2-kgm load, or

$$S = 2 \times 9.8 = 19.6 \text{ newtons.}$$

The mass of the tube, per unit length, is

$$\mu = \frac{m}{L} = \frac{0.60 \text{ kgm}}{8 \text{ m}} = 0.075 \frac{\text{kgm}}{\text{m}}.$$

The speed of propagation is therefore

$$c = \sqrt{\frac{S}{\mu}} = \sqrt{\frac{19.6 \text{ n}}{0.075 \text{ kgm/m}}} = 16 \frac{\text{m}}{\text{sec}}.$$

EXAMPLE 2.   Suppose that a sine wave of amplitude $Y = 10$ cm and wavelength $\lambda = 3$ m travels along the tube from left to right. What is the maximum *transverse* speed of a point of the tube?

The equation of the wave is

$$y = Y \sin (\omega t - kx).$$

The transverse speed is

$$v = \frac{dy}{dt} = \omega Y \cos (\omega t - kx).$$

The maximum transverse speed is

$$v_{\text{max}} = \omega Y = 2\pi f Y = 2\pi \frac{c}{\lambda} Y$$

$$= 2\pi \times \frac{16 \text{ m/sec}}{3 \text{ m}} \times 0.10 \text{ m} = 4.9 \frac{\text{m}}{\text{sec}}.$$

21–4 Calculation of the speed of a longitudinal pulse

Figure 21–6 shows a fluid (liquid or gas) of density ρ in a tube of cross-sectional area A and under a pressure p. In Fig. 21–6(a) the fluid is at rest. At time $t = 0$, the piston at the left end of the tube is set in motion toward the right with a speed v. Figure 21–6(b) shows the fluid after a time t has elapsed. All portions of the fluid at the left of point P are moving with speed v, whereas all portions at the right of P are still at rest. The boundary between the moving and the stationary portions travels to the right with the speed of propagation c. The piston has moved a distance vt and the boundary has advanced a distance ct. As for a transverse disturbance in a string, the speed of propagation can be computed from the impulse-momentum theorem.

The quantity of fluid set in motion in time t is that originally occupying a volume of length ct and of cross-sectional area A. The mass of this fluid is therefore ρctA and the longitudinal momentum it has acquired is

$$\text{Longitudinal momentum} = \rho ctAv.$$

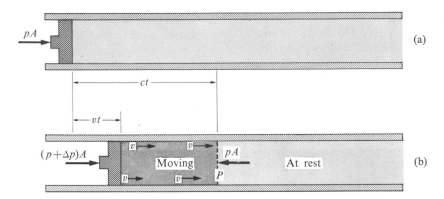

Fig. 21–6. Propagation of a longitudinal disturbance in a fluid confined in a tube.

We next compute the increase of pressure, Δp, in the moving fluid. The original volume of the moving fluid, Act, has been decreased by an amount Avt. From the definition of bulk modulus B (see Chapter 10),

$$B = \frac{\text{change in pressure}}{\text{fractional change in volume}} = \frac{\Delta p}{Avt/Act}.$$

Therefore

$$\Delta p = B\frac{v}{c}.$$

The pressure in the moving fluid is therefore $p + \Delta p$, and the force exerted on it by the piston is $(p + \Delta p)A$. The *net* force on the moving fluid [see Fig. 21–6(b)] is ΔpA, and the longitudinal impulse is

$$\text{Longitudinal impulse} = \Delta pAt = B\frac{v}{c}At.$$

Applying the impulse-momentum theorem, we get

$$B\frac{v}{c}At = \rho ctAv,$$

and therefore

$$\boxed{c = \sqrt{B/\rho}. \quad \text{(Longitudinal)}} \qquad\qquad (21\text{–}7)$$

The speed of propagation of a longitudinal pulse in a fluid therefore depends only on the bulk modulus and density of the medium.

When a solid bar is struck a blow at one end, the situation is somewhat different from that of a fluid confined in a tube of constant cross section, since the bar will expand slightly sidewise when it is compressed longitudinally. It can be shown by the same type of reasoning as that just given that the velocity of a longitudinal pulse in the bar is given by

$$c = \sqrt{Y/\rho}, \quad \text{(Longitudinal)} \tag{21-8}$$

where Y is Young's modulus, defined in Chapter 10.

21-5 Adiabatic character of a longitudinal wave

It is a familiar fact that compression of a fluid causes a rise in its temperature unless heat is withdrawn in some way. Conversely, an expansion is accompanied by a temperature decrease unless heat is added. As a longitudinal wave advances through a fluid, the regions which are compressed at any instant are slightly warmer than those that are expanded. The condition is present, therefore, for the conduction of heat from a condensation to a rarefaction. The quantity of heat conducted per unit time and per unit area depends on the thermal conductivity of the fluid and upon the distance between a condensation and its adjacent rarefaction (half a wavelength). Now for ordinary frequencies, say from 20 vibrations per second to 20,000 vibrations per second, and for even the best known heat conductors, the wavelength is too large and the thermal conductivity too small for an appreciable amount of heat to flow. The compressions and rarefactions are therefore *adiabatic* rather than isothermal.

In the expression for the speed of a longitudinal wave in a fluid, $c = \sqrt{B/\rho}$, the bulk modulus B is defined by the relation

$$B = \frac{\text{change in pressure}}{\text{fractional change in volume}}.$$

The change in volume produced by a given change of pressure depends upon whether the compression (or expansion) is adiabatic or isothermal. There are therefore two bulk moduli, the adiabatic bulk modulus B_{ad} and the isothermal bulk modulus. The expression for the speed of a longitudinal wave should therefore be written

$$c = \sqrt{\frac{B_{ad}}{\rho}}. \tag{21-9}$$

In the case of an ideal gas, the relation between pressure p and volume V during an adiabatic process is given by

$$pV^{\gamma} = \text{constant}, \tag{21-10}$$

where γ is the ratio of the heat capacity at constant pressure to the heat capacity at constant volume.

The definition of the adiabatic bulk modulus is

$$B_{ad} = -\left(\frac{dp}{dV/V}\right)_{ad} = -V\left(\frac{dp}{dV}\right)_{ad}.$$

To calculate the adiabatic bulk modulus B_{ad}, we must evaluate the derivative $(dp/dV)_{ad}$ with the aid of the adiabatic equation. Thus, taking logarithms of both sides of Eq. (21-10), we get

$$\ln p + \gamma \ln V = \ln \text{constant},$$

and, taking the differential of this equation,

$$\frac{dp}{p} + \gamma \frac{dV}{V} = 0, \quad \text{whence} \quad \left(\frac{dp}{dV}\right)_{ad} = -\gamma \frac{p}{V},$$

and

$$B_{ad} = \gamma p. \tag{21-11}$$

Therefore

$$c = \sqrt{\gamma p/\rho}. \quad \text{(Ideal gas)} \tag{21-12}$$

But, for an ideal gas,

$$p/\rho = RT/M,$$

where R is the universal gas constant, M the molecular weight, and T the kelvin temperature. Therefore

$$c = \sqrt{\gamma RT/M}, \quad \text{(Ideal gas)} \tag{21-13}$$

and since for a given gas, γ, R, and M are constants, we see that the velocity of propagation is proportional to the square root of the kelvin temperature.

Let us use Eq. (21-13) to compute the velocity of longitudinal waves in air. The mean molecular weight of air is 28.8, $\gamma = 1.40$, and $R = 8.31 \times 10^7$ ergs/mole·deg. Let $T = 300°$K. Then

$$c = \sqrt{\frac{1.40 \times 8.31 \times 10^7 \dfrac{\text{dyne·cm}}{\text{mole·deg}} \times 300 \text{ deg}}{28.8 \dfrac{\text{gm}}{\text{mole}}}}$$

$$= 34,800 \text{ cm/sec} = 348 \text{ m/sec} = 1140 \text{ ft/sec}.$$

This is in good agreement with the measured velocity at this temperature.

Longitudinal waves in air give rise to the sensation of sound. The ear is sensitive to a range of sound frequencies from about 20 to about 20,000 cycles/sec. From the relation $c = f\lambda$, the corresponding wavelength range is from about 56 ft, corresponding to a 20-cycle note, to about 0.056 ft or 5/8 inch, corresponding to 20,000 cycles/sec.

The molecular nature of a gas has been ignored in the preceding discussion, and a gas has been treated as though it were a continuous medium. Actually, we know that a gas is composed of molecules in random motion, separated by distances which are large compared with their diameters. The vibrations which constitute a wave in a gas are superposed on the random thermal motion. At atmospheric pressure, the mean free path is about 10^{-5} cm, while the displacement amplitude of a faint sound may

Fig. 21-7. Diagram for illustrating longitudinal traveling waves.

be only one ten-thousandth of this amount. An element of gas in which a sound wave is traveling can be compared to a swarm of gnats, where the swarm as a whole can be seen to oscillate slightly while individual insects move about through the swarm, apparently at random.

Since the *shape* of a fluid does not change when a longitudinal wave passes through it, it is not as easy to visualize the relation between particle motion and wave motion as it is for transverse waves in a string. Figure 21–7 may help in correlating these motions. To use this figure, cut a slit about $\frac{1}{16}$ inch wide and $4\frac{1}{4}$ inches long in a 3-inch × 5-inch card, place the card over the figure with the slit at the top of the diagram, and move the card downward with constant velocity. The portions of the sine curves that are visible through the slit correspond to a row of particles along which there is traveling a longitudinal, sinusoidal wave. Notice that each particle executes simple harmonic motion about its equilibrium position, with a phase that increases continuously along the slit, while the regions of maximum condensation and rarefaction move from left to right with constant speed. Moving the card upward produces a wave traveling from right to left.

21–6 Waves in a canal

Probably the most familiar type of wave motion is that observed at the surface of a body of water and produced by the winds or some other disturbance. The oscillations of the water particles in these waves are not confined to the surface, however, but extend with diminishing amplitude to the very bottom. Furthermore, the oscillations have both a longitudinal and a transverse component. For this reason, and also because the motion is governed by the laws of hydrodynamics, a complete derivation of the wave equation calls for mathematical methods beyond the scope of this book. The basic physical approach, however, is perfectly straightforward.

Consider a long canal of rectangular cross section and with frictionless walls, containing a depth h of an ideal incompressible liquid of density ρ and surface tension γ. When a train of waves travels along the canal, each element of the liquid is displaced from its equilibrium position both horizontally and vertically. The restoring force on the element results in part from pressure differences brought about by the variations in depth from point to point, and in part from surface tension effects arising from the curvature of the free surface. The solution of the resulting differential equation of motion must satisfy the boundary conditions that the pressure at the upper surface is constant and equal to atmospheric pressure, and that the vertical displacement at the bottom of the canal is always zero. In addition, the motion of the fluid must satisfy the equation of continuity.

For simple harmonic waves, in which the x- and y-components of displacement are sine or cosine functions of $(x - ct)$, the speed c is given by

$$c^2 = \left(\frac{g\lambda}{2\pi} + \frac{2\pi\gamma}{\rho\lambda} \right) \tanh \frac{2\pi h}{\lambda}, \tag{21–14}$$

where g is the acceleration of gravity and λ is the wavelength.

We immediately recognize one very significant difference between this expression and that for the speed of propagation of transverse waves in a string, or compressional waves in a fluid. Here, the speed depends not only on the properties of the medium *but on the wavelength λ as well.* When this is the case, the medium is said to be *dispersive.* Such a dependence of speed on wavelength occurs in many other types of waves. For example, a prism separates a parallel beam of white light into a spectrum,

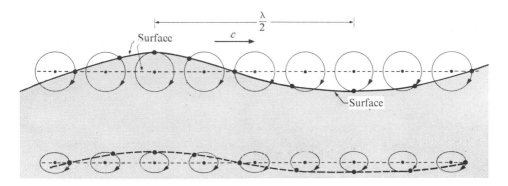

Fig. 21–8. Particle motion and wave shape for waves in a canal.

with different wavelengths emerging in different directions, because glass is a dispersive medium for light waves. In general, the particles of liquid move in ellipses in vertical planes parallel to the length of the canal, the long axis of the ellipse being horizontal. This motion can be considered as the superposition of two simple harmonic oscillations of the same frequency and different amplitudes, one in the horizontal and one in the vertical direction, and with a phase difference of 90°. The wave can therefore be considered as the superposition of a longitudinal and a transverse wave 90° out of phase with each other and having different amplitudes. If the wavelength is as small or smaller than the depth, the two amplitudes are very nearly equal at the surface and the surface particles move in circles. The amplitudes of both components decrease with increasing depth, but the vertical component decreases more rapidly than does the horizontal. At the bottom, the vertical component becomes zero and the oscillation is wholly longitudinal.

Figure 21–8 illustrates the paths of motion of particles in the surface layer and at some depth below the surface. The upper horizontal dotted line represents the free surface of the liquid at rest. The circles are the paths of particles whose equilibrium position is at the center of the circle. When a train of waves travels from left to right, the particles revolve clockwise in these paths. The full line gives the shape of the surface at the instant shown.

The lower dotted line passes through the equilibrium positions of particles at some depth below the surface. Their paths are elliptical, as indicated, and the dashed line is their locus at the instant when the free surface has the shape shown by the full line.

There are certain properties possessed by all waves. Propagation, reflection, refraction, absorption, interference, and diffraction are the most common. These wave phenomena may be demonstrated effectively by means of a "ripple tank" consisting of a horizontal sheet of glass or plastic forming the bottom of a shallow tank, filled with water about one centimeter deep. A strong source of light beneath the tank sends light through the water waves, which cast a shadow on a translucent screen (tracing cloth) above the tank. A convenient source of water waves is provided by

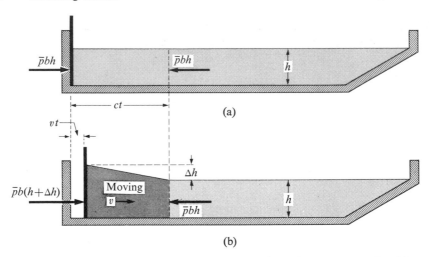

Fig. 21–9. Propagation of an idealized disturbance in shallow water confined in a narrow trough of width b. The average pressure $\bar{p}$ is the pressure at a depth $h/2$.

a smooth sphere about the size of a pencil eraser attached to a rod and dipped periodically into the water. At low frequencies the wavelength λ may be made as large as, say, 10 cm. Then, since the surface tension of water is about 70 dynes/cm and the density of water is 1 gm/cm^3, we have

$$\frac{g\lambda}{2\pi} \approx \frac{980 \times 10}{6} \approx 1600, \qquad \frac{2\pi\gamma}{\rho\lambda} \approx \frac{6 \times 70}{10} \approx 40,$$

and

$$\frac{2\pi h}{\lambda} \approx \frac{6 \times 1}{10} \approx 0.6.$$

Under these conditions, the second term in the parentheses of Eq. (21–14) is negligible compared with the first, and also $\tanh 2\pi h/\lambda$ is very nearly equal to $2\pi h/\lambda$. Then

$$c \approx \sqrt{\frac{g\lambda}{2\pi} \cdot \frac{2\pi h}{\lambda}} \approx \sqrt{gh}. \qquad (21\text{–}15)$$

Thus for long waves the speed depends only on the acceleration due to gravity, g, and the depth h, and is independent of the wavelength (no dispersion). Since, according to Eq. (21–15), the shallower the water, the slower the speed of the waves, it is possible to eliminate reflections from the edges of the ripple tank by beveling the edges of the tank. A wave approaching a "shore" is therefore slowed down to zero speed.

Since Eq. (21–15) holds under particularly simple conditions, it may be derived in a simple manner. Suppose the left end of the liquid in the tank shown in Fig. 21–9(a) is caused to move to the right with speed v. After a time t, the disturbance has traveled a distance ct, where c is the speed of propagation, whereas the left end has moved a distance vt. Since the liquid is incompressible, the surface is slightly raised, say a distance Δh, at the left end and, for the sake of simplicity, is assumed to decline linearly to its normal height h in the distance ct, as shown in Fig. 21–9(b).

If $\bar{p}$ denotes the pressure at a depth $h/2$, then the resultant horizontal force on the moving liquid is

$$\Sigma F_x = \bar{p}b(h + \Delta h) - \bar{p}bh = \bar{p}b\,\Delta h,$$

or since $\bar{p} = \frac{1}{2}h\rho g$,

$$\Sigma F_x = \tfrac{1}{2}h\rho gb\,\Delta h.$$

When both sides of this equation are multiplied by the time, the left-hand member becomes the impulse. Hence,

$$\text{Impulse} = \tfrac{1}{2}h\rho gb\,\Delta h{\cdot}t.$$

The mass of liquid that is set in motion with speed v is the density ρ times the volume, or

$$\text{Mass} = \rho bhct,$$

and the final momentum is

$$\text{Momentum} = \rho bhctv.$$

Equating the impulse to the change of momentum, we get

$$\tfrac{1}{2}h\rho gb\,\Delta ht = \rho bhctv,$$

or

$$\tfrac{1}{2}g\,\Delta h = cv.$$

When the left end was moved a distance vt, a volume of liquid $bhvt$ was displaced. Since the liquid is incompressible, this volume must equal the volume of the triangular prism whose section is the triangle at the top of the moving portion of liquid in Fig. 21–8. Thus

$$bhvt = b\tfrac{1}{2}\,\Delta hct,$$

or

$$v = \frac{c\,\Delta h}{2h}.$$

Substituting this value of v into the previous equation, we get

$$\tfrac{1}{2}g\,\Delta h = \frac{c^2\,\Delta h}{2h},$$

and finally

$$c = \sqrt{gh},$$

in agreement with Eq. (21–15).

Problems

assume 20°C if temperature not specified

21-1. (a) Prove that $c = \omega/k$. (b) A steel wire 6 m long has a mass of 60 gm and is stretched with a tension of 1000 newtons. What is the speed of propagation of a transverse wave in the wire?

21-2. One end of a horizontal string is attached to a prong of an electrically driven tuning fork whose frequency of vibration is 240 vib/sec. The other end passes over a pulley and supports a weight of 6 lb. The linear weight density of the string is 0.0133 lb/ft. (a) What is the speed of a transverse wave in the string? (b) What is the wavelength?

21-3. The equation of a certain traveling transverse wave is

$$y = 2 \sin 2\pi \left(\frac{t}{0.01} - \frac{x}{30} \right),$$

where x and y are in centimeters and t is in seconds. What are (a) the amplitude, (b) the wavelength, (c) the frequency, and (d) the speed of propagation of the wave?

21-4. One end of a rubber tube 50 ft long, weighing 2 lb, is fastened to a fixed support. A cord attached to the other end passes over a pulley and supports a body of weight 20 lb. The tube is struck a transverse blow at one end. Find the time required for the pulse to reach the other end.

21-5. A metal wire has the properties: coefficient of linear expansion = $1.5 \times 10^{-5}(C°)^{-1}$, Young's modulus = 2.0×10^{12} dynes/cm², density = 9.0 gm/cm³. At each end are rigid supports. If the tension is zero at 20°C, what will be the speed of a transverse wave at 8°C?

21-6. A metal wire of density 20 slugs/ft³ with a Young's modulus equal to 15×10^6 lb/in² is stretched between rigid supports. At one temperature the speed of a transverse wave is found to be 657 ft/sec. When the temperature is raised 100 F°, the speed decreases to 536 ft/sec. What is the coefficient of linear expansion?

21-7. A transverse sine wave of amplitude 10 cm and wavelength 200 cm travels from left to right along a long horizontal stretched string with a speed of 100 cm/sec. Take the origin at the left end of the undisturbed string. At time $t = 0$, the left end of the string is at the origin and is moving downward. (a) What is the frequency of the wave? (b) What is the angular frequency? (c) What is the propagation constant? (d) What is the equation of the wave? (e) What is the equation of motion of the left end of the string? (f) What is the equation of motion of a particle 150 cm to the right of the origin? (g) What is the (absolute) maximum transverse velocity of any particle of the string? (h) Find the transverse displacement and the transverse velocity of a particle 150 cm to the right of the origin, at time $t = 3.25$ sec. (i) Make a sketch of the shape of the string, for a length of 400 cm, at time $t = 3.25$ sec.

21-8. What must be the stress (F/A) in a stretched wire of a material whose Young's modulus is Y, in order that the speed of longitudinal waves shall equal 10 times the speed of transverse waves?

21-9. The speed of longitudinal waves in water is approximately 1450 m/sec at 20°C. Compute the adiabatic compressibility $(1/B_{ad})$ of water and compare with the isothermal compressibility in Table 10-2.

21-10. Provided the amplitude is sufficiently great, the human ear can respond to longitudinal waves over a range of frequencies from about 20 vibrations per sec to about 20,000 vibrations per sec. Compute the wavelengths corresponding to these frequencies (a) for waves in air, (b) for waves in water. (See Problem 21-9.)

21-11. At a temperature of 27°C, what is the speed of longitudinal waves in (a) argon, (b) hydrogen? Compare with the speed in air at the same temperature.

21-12. What is the difference between the speeds of longitudinal waves in air at -3°C and at 57°C? *use K°*

21-13. The sound waves from a loudspeaker spread out nearly uniformly in all directions when their wavelength is large compared with the diameter of the speaker. When the wavelength is small compared with the diameter of the speaker, much of the sound energy is concentrated in the forward direction. For a speaker of diameter 10 inches, compute the frequency for which the wavelength of the sound waves, in air, is (a) 10 times the diameter of the speaker, (b) equal to the diameter of the speaker, (c) 1/10 the diameter of the speaker.

21-14. A steel pipe 200 ft long is struck at one end. A person at the other end hears two sounds as a result of two longitudinal waves, one in the pipe and the other in the air. What is the time interval between the two sounds? Take Young's modulus of steel to be 30×10^6 lb/in^2.

21-15. (a) By how many m/sec, at a temperature of 27°C, does the speed of sound in air increase per centigrade degree rise in temperature? [*Hint:* compute dc in terms of dT, and approximate finite changes by differentials.] (b) Is the rate of change of speed with temperature the same at all temperatures?

21-16. Explain why the breakers on a sloping beach are always parallel to the shore line, whatever may be the direction of the waves far from shore.

21-17. A loose coil of flexible rope of length L and mass M rests on a frictionless table. A force S is applied at one end of the rope and more and more rope is pulled from the coil with a constant velocity v. (a) What is the relation between S and v? (b) A transverse pulse is produced while the rope is being pulled from the coil. How does the pulse behave? (c) What is the work of the force S at the moment when the last bit of rope leaves the coil? (d) What is the kinetic energy of the rope? (e) How come?

21-18. The ends of a flexible rope of length L and mass M are joined so as to form a circular loop of radius R. The loop rotates about an axis through its center on a horizontal frictionless surface with a constant linear speed v. (a) Apply Newton's second law to a short piece of rope and calculate the tension S in the rope. (b) Explain the effect of imparting to the rope, while it is spinning, a small rapid radial displacement.

CHAPTER 22

Vibrating Bodies

22-1 Boundary conditions for a string

Let us now consider what will happen when a wave pulse or wave train, advancing along a stretched string, arrives at the end of the string. If fastened to a rigid support, the end must evidently remain at rest. The arriving pulse exerts a force on the support, and the reaction to this force "kicks back" on the string and sets up a *reflected* pulse traveling in the reverse direction. At the opposite extreme from a rigidly fixed end would be one which was perfectly free—a case of no great importance here (it may be realized by a string hanging vertically) but which is of interest since its analogue does occur in other types of waves. At a free end the arriving pulse causes the string to "overshoot" and a reflected wave is also set up. The conditions which must be satisfied at the ends of the string are called *boundary conditions*.

Fig. 22-1. A pulse starts in the upper left corner and is reflected from the fixed end of the string at the right.

The multiflash photograph of Fig. 22-1 shows the reflection of a pulse at a fixed end of a string. (The camera was tipped vertically while the photographs were taken so that successive images lie one under the other. The "string" is a rubber tube and it sags somewhat.) It will be seen that the pulse is reflected with its displacement and its velocity both reversed. When reflection takes place at a free end, the direction of the velocity is reversed but the direction of the displacement is unchanged.

It is helpful to think of the process of reflection in the following way. Imagine the string to be extended indefinitely beyond its actual terminus. The actual pulse can be considered to continue on into the imaginary portion as though the support were not there, while at the same time a "virtual" pulse, which has been traveling in the imaginary portion, moves out into the real string and forms the reflected pulse. The nature of the reflected pulse depends on whether the end is fixed or free. The two cases are shown in Fig. 22–2.

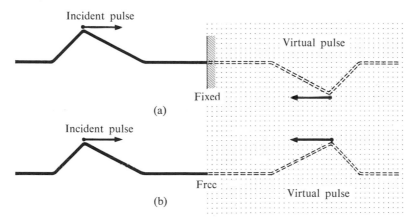

Fig. 22–2.   Description of reflection of a pulse (a) at a fixed end of a string, and (b) at a free end, in terms of an imaginary "virtual" pulse.

The displacement at a point where the actual and virtual pulses cross each other is the algebraic sum of the displacements in the individual pulses. Figures 22–3 and 22–4 show the shape of the end of the string for both types of reflected pulses. It will be seen that Fig. 22–3 corresponds to a free end and Fig. 22–4 to a fixed end. In the latter case, the incident and reflected pulses combine in such a way that the displacement of the end of the string is always zero.

22–2 Stationary waves in a string

When a continuous train of waves arrives at a fixed end of a string, a continuous train of reflected waves appears to originate at the end and travel in the opposite direction. Provided the elastic limit of the string is not exceeded and the displacements are sufficiently small, the actual displacement of any point of the string is the algebraic sum of the displacements of the individual waves, a fact which is called the *principle of superposition*. This principle is extremely important in all types of wave motion and applies not only to waves in a string but to sound waves in air, to light waves, and, in fact, to wave motion of any sort. The general term *interference* is applied to the effect produced by two (or more) sets of wave trains which are simultaneously passing through a given region.

The appearance of the string in these circumstances gives no evidence that two waves are traversing it in opposite directions. If the frequency is sufficiently great so

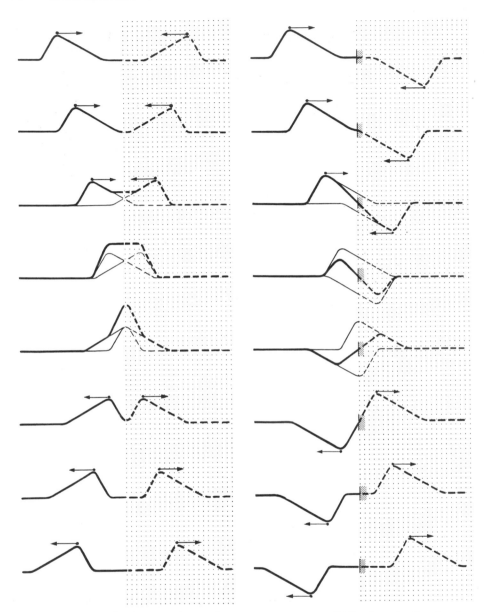

Fig. 22-3. Reflection at a free end.   **Fig. 22-4.** Reflection at a fixed end.

that the eye cannot follow the motion, the string appears subdivided into a number of segments, as in the time exposure photograph of Fig. 22-5(a). A multiflash photograph of the same string, in Fig. 22-5(b), indicates a few of the instantaneous shapes of the string. At any instant (except those when the string is straight) its shape is a sine curve, but whereas in a traveling wave the amplitude remains constant while the wave progresses, here the wave form remains fixed in position (longitudinally) while

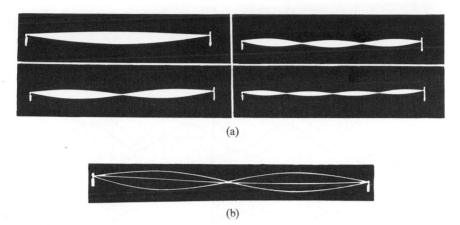

(a)

(b)

Fig. 22–5. (a) Standing waves in a stretched string (time exposure). (b) Multiflash photograph of a standing wave, with nodes at the center and at the ends.

the amplitude fluctuates. Certain points known as the *nodes* remain always at rest. Midway between these points, at the *loops* or *antinodes*, the fluctuations are a maximum. The vibration as a whole is called a *stationary* wave.

To understand the formation of a stationary wave, consider the four separate graphs of wave form at four instants $\frac{1}{10}$ of a period apart, shown in Fig. 22–6. The short dashed curves represent a wave traveling to the right. The long dashed curves represent a wave of the same velocity, same wavelength, and same amplitude traveling to the left. The heavy curves represent the resultant wave form, obtained by applying the principle of superposition, that is, by adding displacements. At those places marked N at the bottom of Fig. 22–6, the resultant displacements are always zero. These are the nodes. Midway between the nodes, the vibrations have the largest amplitude. These are the antinodes. It is evident from the figure that

$$\left.\begin{array}{c} \text{distance between adjacent nodes} \\ \text{or} \\ \text{distance between adjacent antinodes} \end{array}\right\} = \frac{\lambda}{2}.$$

The equation of a stationary wave may be obtained by adding the displacements of two waves of equal amplitude, period, and wavelength, but traveling in opposite directions.

Thus if

$$y_1 = A \sin (\omega t - kx) \quad \text{(positive x-direction)},$$

$$y_2 = -A \sin (\omega t + kx) \quad \text{(negative x-direction)},$$

then

$$y_1 + y_2 = A \left[\sin (\omega t - kx) - \sin (\omega t + kx)\right].$$

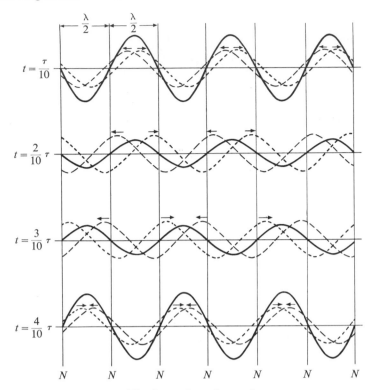

Fig. 22–6. The formation of a stationary wave.

Introducing the expressions for the sine of the sum and difference of two angles and combining terms, we obtain

$$y_1 + y_2 = -[2A \cos \omega t] \sin kx. \qquad (22\text{–}1)$$

The shape of the string at each instant is, therefore, a sine curve whose amplitude (the expression in brackets) varies with time.

22–3 Vibration of a string fixed at both ends

Thus far we have been discussing a long string fixed at one end and have considered the stationary waves set up near that end by interference between the incident and reflected waves. Let us next consider the more usual case, that of a string fixed at both ends. A continuous train of sine or cosine waves is reflected and re-reflected, and since the string is fixed at both ends, both ends must be nodes. Since the nodes are one-half a wavelength apart, the length of the string may be $\lambda/2$, $2\lambda/2$, $3\lambda/2$, or, in general, any integral number of half-wavelengths. Or, to put it differently, if one considers a particular string of length L, stationary waves may be set up in the string by vibrations of a number of different frequencies, namely, those which give rise to waves of wavelengths $2L/1$, $2L/2$, $2L/3$, etc.

From the relation $f = c/\lambda$, and since c is the same for all frequencies, the possible frequencies are

$$\frac{c}{2L}, \quad 2\frac{c}{2L}, \quad 3\frac{c}{2L}, \quad \ldots$$

The lowest frequency, $c/2L$, is called the *fundamental* frequency f_1 and the others are the *overtones*. The frequencies of the latter are, therefore, $2f_1, 3f_1, 4f_1$, and so on. Overtones whose frequencies are integral multiples of the fundamental are said to form a *harmonic series*. The fundamental is the *first harmonic*. The frequency $2f_1$ is the *first overtone* or the *second harmonic*, the frequency $3f_1$ is the *second overtone* or the *third harmonic*, and so on.

We can now see an important difference between a spring-mass system and a vibrating string. The former has but one natural frequency, while the vibrating string has an infinite number of natural frequencies, the fundamental and all of the overtones. If a body suspended from a spring is pulled down and released, only one frequency of vibration will ensue. If a string is initially distorted so that its shape is the same as *any one* of the possible harmonics, it will vibrate, when released, at the frequency of that particular harmonic. But when a piano string is struck, not only the fundamental, but many of the overtones are present in the resulting vibration. The fundamental frequency of the vibrating string is $f_1 = c/2L$, where $c = \sqrt{S/\mu}$. It follows that

$$f_1 = \frac{1}{2L}\sqrt{\frac{S}{\mu}}. \tag{22–2}$$

Stringed instruments afford many examples of the implications of this equation. For example, all such instruments are "tuned" by varying the tension S, an increase of tension increasing the frequency or pitch, and vice versa. The inverse dependence of frequency on length L is illustrated by the long strings of the bass section of the piano or the bass viol compared with the shorter strings of the piano treble or the violin. One reason for winding the bass strings of a piano with wire is to increase the mass per unit length μ, so as to obtain the desired low frequency without resorting to a string which is inconveniently long.

22–4 Demonstration of the harmonic series in a vibrating string

We have seen that a string is capable of vibrating at a number of different frequencies. That it may vibrate with many different frequencies *at the same time* may be demonstrated graphically with the aid of the apparatus depicted in Fig. 22–7. A metal wire is stretched between two metal posts which are in turn connected to a "step-up" transformer. The secondary of the transformer is then connected to those plates of a cathode-ray oscilloscope which impart vertical motion to the electron beam. If the string is made to oscillate in a magnetic field, an alternating current will be set up whose frequency is exactly the same as that of the string. With proper adjustment of the oscilloscope, this alternating current may be caused to give rise to figures on the screen such as those shown.

Suppose that one small magnet is placed over the center of the string [Fig. 22–7(a)] and the string is plucked near the center so that this part of the string vibrates per-

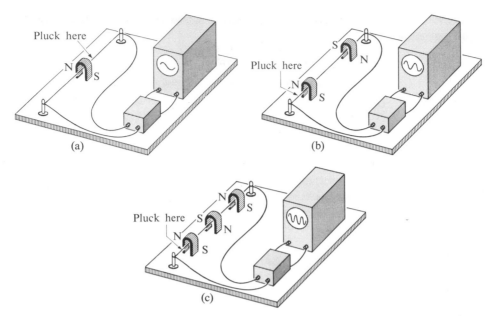

Pluck here

(a)

(b)

Pluck here

(c)

Fig. 22-7. Demonstration of the harmonics present in the vibration of a plucked string.

pendicular to the magnetic lines of force. The figure on the oscilloscope shows the fundamental frequency.

By placing one magnet $\frac{1}{4}$ of the way along the string and another magnet *with its polarity reversed* at the $\frac{3}{4}$ mark [Fig. 22-7(b)], and plucking the string near the $\frac{1}{4}$ point, the second harmonic may be obtained. If one of the magnets is quickly reversed while the string is sounding, so as to set the two magnetic fields in the same direction, the fundamental will occur again, showing that the fundamental and second harmonic exist at the same time.

We now place three magnets on the string at the $\frac{1}{6}, \frac{1}{2}, \frac{5}{6}$ points, with the polarity shown in Fig. 22-7(c). By plucking the string near the $\frac{1}{6}$ point, the third harmonic is obtained. While the string is vibrating, if the middle magnet is reversed so as to make all the magnets point in the same direction, the fundamental will appear. Thus the fundamental and third harmonic exist at the same time.

Proceeding in this manner, we may pick up higher harmonics and demonstrate that a string can vibrate with all of these frequencies at the same time.

22-5 Resonance

In general, whenever a body capable of oscillating is acted on by a periodic series of impulses having a frequency equal to one of the natural frequencies of oscillation of the body, the body is set into vibration with a relatively large amplitude. This phenomenon is called *resonance*, and the body is said to *resonate* with the applied impulses.

A common example of mechanical resonance is provided by pushing a swing. The swing is a pendulum with a single natural frequency depending on its length.

If a series of regularly spaced pushes is given to the swing, with a frequency equal to that of the swing, the motion may be made quite large. If the frequency of the pushes differs from the natural frequency of the swing, or if the pushes occur at irregular intervals, the swing will hardly execute a vibration at all.

Unlike a simple pendulum, which has only one natural frequency, a stretched string (and other systems to be discussed later in this chapter) has a large number of natural frequencies. Suppose that one end of a stretched string is fixed while the other is moved back and forth in a transverse direction. The amplitude at the driven end is fixed by the driving mechanism. Stationary waves will be set up in the string, whatever the value of the frequency f. If the frequency is not equal to one of the natural frequencies of the string, the amplitude at the antinodes will be fairly small. However, if the frequency is equal to *any one* of the natural frequencies, the string is in resonance and the amplitude at the antinodes will be very much larger than that at the driven end. In other words, although the driven end is not a node, it lies much closer to a node than to an antinode when the string is in resonance. In Fig. 22–5(a), the right end of the string was fixed and the left end was forced to oscillate vertically with small amplitude. Stationary waves of relatively large amplitude resulted when the frequency of oscillation of the left end was equal to the fundamental frequency or to any of the first three overtones.

A bridge or, for that matter, any structure, is capable of vibrating with certain natural frequencies. If the regular footsteps of a column of soldiers were to have a frequency equal to one of the natural frequencies of a bridge which the soldiers are crossing, a vibration of dangerously large amplitude might result. Therefore, in crossing a bridge, a column of soldiers is ordered to break step.

Tuning a radio is an example of electrical resonance. By turning a dial, the natural frequency of an alternating current in the receiving circuit is made equal to the frequency of the waves broadcast by the desired station. Optical resonance may also take place between atoms in a gas at low pressure and light waves from a lamp containing the same atoms. Thus light from a sodium lamp may cause the sodium atoms in a glass bulb to glow with characteristic yellow sodium light.

The phenomenon of resonance may be demonstrated with the aid of the longitudinal waves set up in air by a vibrating plate or tuning fork. If two identical tuning forks are placed some distance apart and one is struck, the other will be heard when the first is suddenly damped. Should a small piece of wax or modeling clay be put on one of the forks, the frequency of that fork will be altered enough to destroy the resonance.

22–6 Interference of longitudinal waves

The phenomenon of interference between two longitudinal waves in air may be demonstrated with the aid of the apparatus depicted in Fig. 22–8. A wave emitted by a source S is sent into a metal tube, where it divides into two waves, one following the constant path SAR, the other the path SBR, which may be varied by sliding the tube B to the right. Suppose the frequency of the source is 1100 vibrations per second. Then the wavelength $\lambda = c/f = 1$ ft. If both paths are of equal length, the two waves will arrive at R at the same time and the vibrations set up by both waves will be in phase. The resulting vibration will have an amplitude equal to the sum of the two individual amplitudes and the phenomenon of *reinforcement* may be detected either with the ear at R or with the aid of a microphone, amplifier, and loudspeaker.

Now suppose the tube B is moved out a distance of three inches, thereby making the path SBR 6 inches longer than the path SAR. The right-hand wave will have traveled a distance $\lambda/2$ greater than the left-hand wave and the vibration set up at R by the right-hand wave will therefore be in opposite phase to that set up by the left-hand wave. The consequent interference is shown by the marked reduction in sound at R.

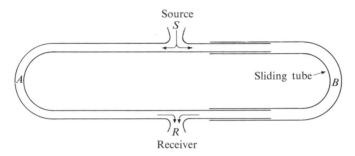

Fig. 22–8. Apparatus for demonstrating interference of longitudinal waves.

If the tube B is now pulled out another 3 inches, so that the *path difference*, SBR minus SAR, is one foot (one wavelength), the two vibrations at R will again reinforce each other. Thus

$$\left\{\begin{matrix}\text{Reinforcement takes place}\\\text{when the path difference}\end{matrix}\right\} = 0,\ \lambda,\ 2\lambda,\ \text{etc.}$$

$$\left\{\begin{matrix}\text{Interference takes place}\\\text{when the path difference}\end{matrix}\right\} = \frac{\lambda}{2},\ \frac{3\lambda}{2},\ \frac{5\lambda}{2},\ \text{etc.}$$

An acoustical interferometer of this sort is of value only in demonstrating the phenomenon of interference. Optical interferometers, however, whose principles of operation are the same, have many practical uses in physical optics.

22–7 Stationary longitudinal waves

Longitudinal waves traveling along a tube of finite length are reflected at the ends of the tube in much the same way that transverse waves in a string are reflected at its ends. Interference between the waves traveling in opposite directions gives rise to stationary waves.

If reflection takes place at a closed end, the displacement of the particles at that end must necessarily be always zero. Hence a closed end is a *node*. If the end of the tube is open, the nature of the reflection is more complex and depends on whether the tube is wide or narrow compared with the wavelength. If the tube is narrow compared with the wavelength, which is the case in most musical instruments, the reflection is such as to make the open end an *antinode*. Therefore the longitudinal waves in a column of fluid are reflected at the closed and open ends of a tube in the same way that transverse waves in a string are reflected at fixed and free ends respectively.

The reflections at the openings where the instrument is blown are found to be such that an antinode is located at or near the opening. The effective length of the air column of a wind instrument is thus less definite than the length of a string fixed at its ends.

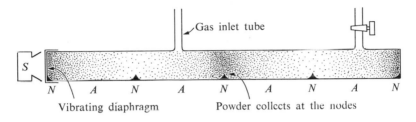

Fig. 22–9. Kundt's tube for determining the velocity of sound in a gas. The dots represent the density of the gas molecules at an instant when the pressure at the displacement nodes is a maximum or a minimum.

Stationary longitudinal waves in a column of gas may be demonstrated conveniently with the aid of the apparatus shown in Fig. 22–9, known as Kundt's tube. A glass tube a few feet long is closed at one end with glass and at the other with a flexible diaphragm. The gas to be studied is admitted to the tube at a known temperature and at atmospheric pressure. A powerful source of longitudinal waves, S, whose frequency may be varied, causes vibration of the flexible diaphragm. A small amount of light powder or cork dust is sprinkled uniformly along the tube.

When a frequency is found at which the air column is in resonance, the amplitude of the stationary waves becomes large enough for the gas particles to sweep the cork dust along the tube, at all points where the gas is in motion. The powder therefore collects at the displacement nodes, where the gas remains at rest. Sometimes a wire,

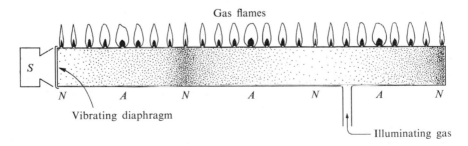

Fig. 22–10. The variations in gas pressure are greatest at the displacement nodes. The dots represent the density of the gas molecules at an instant when the pressure at the displacement nodes is a maximum or a minimum.

Figure 22–11

running along the axis of the tube, is maintained at a dull red heat by an electric current and the nodes show themselves as hot points, compared with the antinodes.

With careful manipulation and with a good variable frequency source, a fair determination of the velocity of the wave may be obtained with Kundt's tube. Since, in a stationary wave, the distance between two adjacent nodes is one-half a wavelength, the wavelength λ is obtained by measuring the distance between alternate clumps of powder. Knowing the frequency f, the velocity c is then

$$c = f\lambda.$$

A constant frequency source may be used if the vibrating element is a piston which may be moved along the tube until resonance is obtained.

At a displacement node, the pressure variations above and below the average are a maximum, whereas at an antinode, there are no pressure variations. This may be understood easily when it is realized that two small masses of gas on opposite sides of a node are vibrating in *opposite phase*. Thus, when they approach each other, the pressure at the node is a maximum, and when they recede from each other, the pressure at the node is a minimum. Two small masses of gas, however, on opposite sides of an antinode vibrate *in phase*, and hence give rise to no pressure variations at the antinode. This may be demonstrated in the case of illuminating gas with the aid of the apparatus shown in Fig. 22–10, where the amplitude of the harmonic variations of gas pressure determines the shape and color of the gas flames.

Figure 22–11 may be helpful in visualizing a longitudinal stationary wave. To use this figure, cut a slit about $\frac{1}{16}$ inch wide and $4\frac{1}{2}$ inches long in a card. Place the card over the diagram with the slit horizontal and move it vertically with constant velocity. The portions of the curves that appear in the slit will correspond to the oscillations of the particles in a longitudinal stationary wave.

22–8 Vibrations of organ pipes

If one end of a pipe is open and a stream of air is directed against an edge, vibrations are set up and the tube resonates at its natural frequencies. As in the case of a plucked string, the fundamental and overtones exist at the same time. In the case of an open pipe, the fundamental frequency f_1 corresponds to an antinode at each end and a node in the middle, as shown at the top of Fig. 22–12. Succeeding diagrams of Fig. 22–12 show two of the overtones, which are seen to be the second and third harmonics. *In an open pipe the fundamental frequency is c/2L and all harmonics are present.*

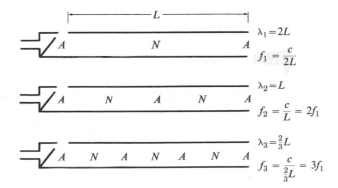

Fig. 22–12.   Modes of vibration of an open organ pipe.

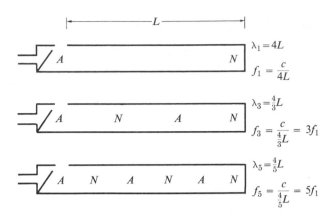

Fig. 22-13.   Modes of vibration of a closed organ pipe.

The properties of a closed pipe are shown in the diagrams of Fig. 22-13. The fundamental frequency is seen to be $c/4L$, which is one-half that of an open pipe of the same length. In the language of music, the pitch of a closed pipe is one octave lower than that of an open pipe of equal length. From the remaining diagrams of Fig. 22-13, it may be seen that the second, fourth, etc., harmonics are missing. Hence, *in a closed pipe, the fundamental frequency is c/4L and only the odd harmonics are present.*

22-9 Vibrations of rods and plates

A rod may be set in longitudinal vibration by clamping it at some point and stroking it with a chamois skin that has been sprinkled with rosin. In Fig. 22-14(a) the rod is clamped in the middle and consequently, when stroked near the end, a stationary wave is set up with a node in the middle and antinodes at each end, exactly the same as the fundamental mode of an open organ pipe. The fundamental frequency of the rod is then $c/2L$, where c is the velocity of a longitudinal wave in the rod. Since the velocity of a longitudinal wave in a solid is much greater than that in air, a rod has a higher fundamental frequency than an open organ pipe of the same length.

By clamping the rod at a point $\frac{1}{4}$ of its length from one end, as shown in Fig. 22-14(b), the second harmonic may be produced.

If a stretched flexible membrane, such as a drumhead, is struck a blow, a two-dimensional pulse travels outward from the struck point and is reflected and re-reflected at

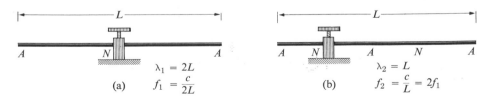

Fig. 22-14.   Modes of vibration of a rod.

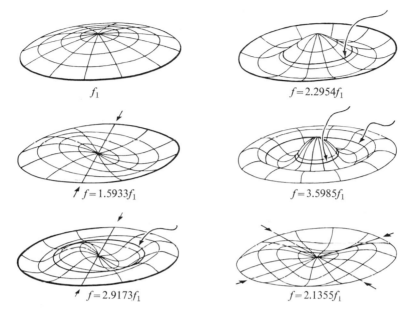

f_1

$f=2.2954f_1$

$f=1.5933f_1$

$f=3.5985f_1$

$f=2.9173f_1$

$f=2.1355f_1$

Fig. 22–15.   Possible modes of vibration of a membrane, showing nodal lines. The frequency of each mode is given in terms of the fundamental frequency, f_1. [Adapted from *Vibration and Sound*, by Philip M. Morse, 2nd edition, McGraw-Hill Book Company, Inc., 1948. By permission of the publishers.]

the boundary of the membrane. If some point of the membrane is forced to vibrate periodically, continuous trains of waves travel along the membrane. Just as with the stretched string, stationary waves can be set up in the membrane and each of these waves has a certain natural frequency. The lowest frequency is the fundamental and the others are overtones. In general, when the membrane is vibrating, a number of overtones are present.

The nodes of a vibrating membrane are lines (nodal lines) rather than points. The boundary of the membrane is evidently one such line. Some of the other possible nodal lines of a circular membrane are indicated by arrows in Fig. 22–15. The natural frequency of each mode is given in terms of the fundamental f_1. It will be noted that the frequencies of the overtones are *not* integral multiples of f_1. That is, they are not harmonics.

The restoring force in a vibrating flexible membrane arises from the tension with which it is stretched. A metal plate, if sufficiently thick, will vibrate in a similar way, the restoring force being produced by bending stresses in the plate. The study of vibrations of membranes and plates is of importance in connection with the design of loudspeaker diaphragms and the diaphragms of telephone receivers and microphones.

Problems

22–1. A steel piano wire 50 cm long, of mass 5 gm, is stretched with a tension of 400 newtons. (a) What is the frequency of its fundamental mode of vibration? (b) What is the number of the highest overtone that could be heard by a person who is capable of hearing frequencies up to 10,000 cycles/sec?

22–2. A steel wire of length $L = 100$ cm and density $\rho = 8$ gm/cm^3 is stretched tightly between two rigid supports. Vibrating in its fundamental mode, the frequency is $f = 200$ cycles per sec. (a) What is the speed of transverse waves on this wire? (b) What is the longitudinal stress in the wire (in dynes/cm^2)? (c) If the maximum acceleration at the midpoint of the wire is 80,000 cm/sec^2, what is the amplitude of vibration at the midpoint?

22–3. A stretched string is observed to vibrate with a frequency of 30 cycles per second in its fundamental mode when the supports are 60 cm apart. The amplitude at the antinode is 3 cm. The string has a mass of 30 gm. (a) What is the speed of propagation of a transverse wave in the string? (b) Compute the tension in the string.

22–4. The fundamental frequency of the A-string on a cello is 220 vib/sec. The vibrating portion of the string is 68 cm long and has a mass of 1.29 gm. With what tension, in pounds, must it be stretched?

22–5. A standing wave of frequency 1100 vibrations per second in a column of methane at 20°C produces nodes that are 20 cm apart. What is the ratio of the heat capacity at constant pressure to that at constant volume?

22–6. An aluminum weight is hung from a steel wire. The fundamental frequency for transverse stationary waves on the wire is 300 cycles/sec. The weight is then immersed in water so that one-half of its volume is submerged. What is the new fundamental frequency?

22–7. Stationary waves are set up in a Kundt's tube by the longitudinal vibration of an iron rod one meter long, clamped at the center. If the frequency of the iron rod is 2480 vibrations per second and the powder heaps within the tube are 6.9 cm apart, (a) what is the speed of the waves in the iron rod, and (b) in the gas?

22–8. The speed of a longitudinal wave in a mixture of helium and neon at 300°K was found to be 758 m/sec. What is the composition of the mixture?

22–9. The atomic weight of iodine is 127. A stationary wave in iodine vapor at 400°K produces nodes that are 6.77 cm apart when the frequency is 1000 vibrations/sec. Is iodine vapor monatomic or diatomic?

22–10. A copper rod 1 m long, clamped at the $\frac{1}{4}$ point, is set in longitudinal vibration and is used to produce stationary waves in a Kundt's tube containing air at 300°K. Heaps of cork dust within the tube are found to be 4.95 cm apart. What is the speed of the longitudinal waves in copper?

22–11. Find the fundamental frequency and the first four overtones of a 6-inch pipe (a) if the pipe is open at both ends, (b) if the pipe is closed at one end. (c) How many overtones may be heard by a person having normal hearing for each of the above cases?

22–12. A long tube contains air at a pressure of 1 atm and temperature 77°C. The tube is open at one end and closed at the other by a movable piston. A tuning fork near the open end is vibrating with a frequency of 500 cycles/sec. Resonance is produced when the piston is at distances 18.0, 55.5, and 93.0 cm from the open end. (a) From these measurements, what is the speed of sound in air at 77°C? (b) From the above result, what is the ratio of the specific heats γ for air?

22–13. An organ pipe A of length 2 ft, closed at one end, is vibrating in the first overtone. Another organ pipe B of length 1.35 ft, open at both ends, is vibrating in its fundamental mode.   Take the speed of sound in air as 1120 ft/sec.   Neglect end corrections. (a) What is the frequency of the tone from A? (b) What is the frequency of the tone from B?

22–14. A plate cut from a quartz crystal is often used to control the frequency of an oscillating electrical circuit. Longitudinal standing waves are set up in the plate with displacement antinodes at opposite faces. The fundamental frequency of vibration is given by the equation

$$f_1 = \frac{2.87 \times 10^5}{s},$$

where f_1 is in cycles/sec and s is the thickness of the plate in cm.   (a) Compute Young's modulus for the quartz plate. (b) Compute the thickness of plate required for a frequency of 1200 kilocycles/sec. (1 kilocycle = 1000 cycles.)   The density of quartz is 2.66 gm/cm^3.

CHAPTER **23**

Acoustical Phenomena

23–1 Pressure variations in a sound wave

We shall limit ourselves in this chapter to the consideration of longitudinal waves only, and in particular to those which, when striking the ear, give rise to the sensation of sound. Such waves, within the frequency range from 20 to 20,000 vibrations per second, are called, for simplicity, *sound waves*.

The reception of a sound wave by the ear gives rise to a vibration of the air particles at the eardrum with a definite frequency and a definite amplitude. This vibration may also be described in terms of the variation of air pressure at the same point. The air pressure rises above atmospheric pressure and then sinks below atmospheric pressure with simple harmonic motion of the same frequency as that of an air particle. The maximum amount by which the pressure differs from atmospheric pressure is called the *pressure amplitude*. It can be proved that the pressure amplitude is proportional to the displacement amplitude.

Measurements of sound waves show that the maximum pressure variations in the loudest sounds which the ear can tolerate are of the order of magnitude of 280 dynes/ cm^2 (above and below atmospheric pressure, which is about 1,000,000 dynes/cm^2). The corresponding maximum displacement for a frequency of 1000 vibrations per second is about a thousandth of a centimeter. The displacement amplitudes, even in the loudest sounds, are therefore extremely small.

The maximum pressure variations in the *faintest* sound of frequency 1000 vibrations per second are only about 2×10^{-4} dyne/cm^2. The corresponding displacement amplitude is about 10^{-9} cm. By way of comparison, the wavelength of yellow light is 6×10^{-5} cm, and the diameter of a molecule is about 10^{-8} cm. It will be appreciated that the ear is an extremely sensitive organ.

23–2 Intensity

From a purely geometrical point of view, that which is propagated by a traveling wave is the *wave form*. From a physical viewpoint, however, something else is propagated by a wave, namely, *energy*. The most outstanding example, of course, is the energy supply of the earth, which reaches us from the sun via electromagnetic waves. The *intensity I* of a traveling wave is defined as *the time average rate at which energy is transported by the wave per unit area* across a surface perpendicular to the direction of propagation. More briefly, the intensity is the average power transported per unit area.

We have seen that the power developed by a force equals the product of force and velocity. Hence the power per unit area in a sound wave equals the product of the excess pressure (force per unit area) and the *particle* velocity. Averaging over one cycle, it can be proved that

$$I = P^2 / 2\rho c , \qquad\qquad (23-1)$$

where P is the pressure amplitude, ρ is the average density of the medium, not necessarily air, and c is the velocity of the sound wave. It will be noted that the *intensity* is proportional to the *square of the amplitude*, a result which is true for any sort of wave motion.

The intensity of a sound wave of pressure amplitude $P = 280$ dynes/cm^2 (roughly, the loudest tolerable sound) is

$$I = \frac{(280 \text{ dynes/cm}^2)^2}{2 \times 1.22 \times 10^{-3} \text{ gm/cm}^3 \times 3.46 \times 10^4 \text{ cm/sec}}$$

$$= 940 \text{ ergs/sec·cm}^2 = 94 \times 10^{-6} \text{ watt/cm}^2.*$$

The pressure amplitude of the faintest sound wave which can be heard is about 0.0003 dyne/cm^2 and the corresponding intensity is about 10^{-16} watt/cm^2.

The total power carried across a surface by a sound wave equals the product of the intensity at the surface and the surface area, if the intensity over the surface is uniform. The average power developed as sound waves by a person speaking in an ordinary conversational tone is about 10^{-5} watt, while a loud shout corresponds to about 3×10^{-2} watt. Since the population of the city of New York is about six million persons, the acoustical power developed if all were to speak at the same time would be about 60 watts, or enough to operate a moderate-sized electric light. On the other hand, the power required to fill a large auditorium with loud sound is considerable. Suppose the intensity over the surface of a hemisphere 20 meters in radius is 10^{-4} watt/cm^2. The area of the surface is about 25×10^6 cm^2. Hence the acoustic power output of a speaker at the center of the sphere would have to be

$$10^{-4} \times 25 \times 10^6 = 2500 \text{ watts,}$$

or 2.5 kilowatts. The electrical power input to the speaker would need to be considerably larger, since the efficiency of such devices is not very high.

23-3 Intensity level and loudness

Because of the large range of intensities over which the car is sensitive, a logarithmic rather than an arithmetic intensity scale is convenient. Accordingly, the *intensity level* β of a sound wave is defined by the equation

$$\beta = 10 \log \frac{I}{I_0} , \qquad\qquad (23-2)$$

---

* The "watt/cm^2" is a hybrid unit, neither cgs nor mks. We shall retain it to conform with general usage in acoustics.

where I_0 is an arbitrary reference intensity which is taken as 10^{-16} watt/cm^2, corresponding roughly to the faintest sound which can be heard. Intensity levels are expressed in *decibels*, abbreviated db.*

If the intensity of a sound wave equals I_0 or 10^{-16} watt/cm^2, its intensity level is zero. The maximum intensity which the ear can tolerate, about 10^{-4} watt/cm^2, corresponds to an intensity level of 120 db. Table 23–1 gives the intensity levels in db of a number of familiar noises. It is taken from a survey made by the New York City Noise Abatement Commission.

TABLE 23–1

NOISE LEVELS DUE TO VARIOUS SOURCES
(Representative values)

Source or description of noise	Noise level, db
Threshold of pain	120
Riveter	95
Elevated train	90
Busy street traffic	70
Ordinary conversation	65
Quiet automobile	50
Quiet radio in home	40
Average whisper	20
Rustle of leaves	10
Threshold of hearing	0

The range of frequencies and intensities to which the ear is sensitive is conveniently represented by a diagram like that of Fig. 23–1, which is a graph of the *auditory area* of a person of good hearing. The lower curve represents the intensity level of the faintest pure tone which can be heard. It will be seen from the diagram that the ear is most sensitive to frequencies between 2000 and 3000 cycles/sec, where the *threshold of hearing*, as it is called, is about -5 db. At intensities above those corresponding to the upper curve, which is called the *threshold of feeling*, the sensation changes from one of hearing to discomfort or even pain. The height of the upper curve is approximately constant at a level of about 120 db for all frequencies. Every pure tone which can be heard may be represented by a point lying somewhere in the area between these two curves.

Only about 1% of the population has a threshold of hearing as low as the bottom curve in Fig. 23–1; 50% of the population can hear pure tones of a frequency

---

* Originally, a scale of intensity levels in *bels* was defined by the relation

$$\text{Intensity level} = \log I/I_0.$$

This unit proved rather large and hence the decibel, one-tenth of a bel, has come into general use. The unit is named in honor of Alexander Graham Bell.

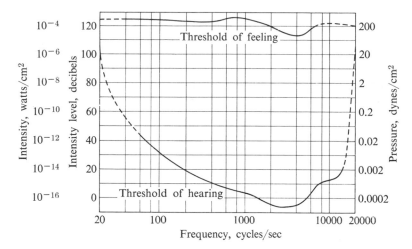

Fig. 23–1. Auditory area between threshold of hearing and threshold of feeling. (Courtesy of Dr. Harvey Fletcher.)

of 2500 cycles/sec when the intensity level is about 8 db, and 90% when the level is 20 db.

For a loud tone of intensity level 80 db, the frequency range of the hearing mechanism is from 20 to 20,000 cycles/sec, but at a level of 20 db it is only from about 200 to about 15,000 cycles/sec. At a frequency of 1000 cycles/sec the range of intensity level is from about 3 db to about 120 db, whereas at 100 cycles/sec it is only from 30 db to 120 db.

The term *loudness* refers to a sensation in the consciousness of a human observer. It is purely subjective, as contrasted with the objective quantity *intensity*, and is not directly measurable with instruments. Loudness increases with intensity but there is no simple linear relationship. Pure tones of the same intensity but different frequencies do not necessarily produce sensations of equal loudness. Thus for a listener whose auditory area is represented in Fig. 23–1, a pure tone of intensity level 30 db and frequency 60 cycles/sec is completely inaudible, while one of the same intensity level but of frequency 1000 cycles/sec is well above the threshold of audibility. For the first tone to appear as loud as the second, its intensity level would have to be raised to about 65 db.

23–4 Quality and pitch

A string that has been plucked or a plate that has been struck, if allowed to vibrate freely, will vibrate with many frequencies at the same time. It is a rare occurrence for a body to vibrate with only one frequency. A carefully made tuning fork struck lightly on a rubber block may vibrate with only one frequency, but in the case of musical instruments, the fundamental and many harmonics are usually present at the same time. The impulses that are sent from the ear to the brain give rise to one

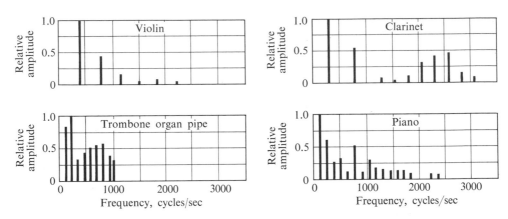

Fig. 23–2. Sound spectra of some musical instruments. (Courtesy of Dr. Harvey Fletcher.)

net effect which is characteristic of the instrument. Suppose, for example, the sound spectrum of a tone consisted of a fundamental of 200 vibrations per second and harmonics 2, 3, 4, and 5, all of different intensity, whereas the sound spectrum of another tone consisted of exactly the same frequencies but with a different intensity distribution. The two tones would sound different; they are said to differ in *quality*

Adjectives used to describe the quality of musical tones are purely subjective in character, such as reedy, golden, round, mellow, tinny, etc. *The quality of a sound is determined by the number of overtones present and their respective intensity*-versus-*time curves.* The sound spectra of various musical instruments are shown in Fig. 23–2.

The term *pitch* refers to the attribute of a sound sensation that enables one to classify a note as "high" or "low." Like loudness, it is a subjective quantity and cannot be measured with instruments. Pitch is related to the objective quantity *frequency*, but there is no one-to-one correspondence. For a pure tone of constant intensity, the pitch becomes higher as the frequency is increased, but the pitch of a pure tone of constant frequency becomes lower as the intensity level is raised.

Many of the notes played on musical instruments are rich in harmonics, some of which may be more prominent than the fundamental. Presented with an array of frequencies constituting a harmonic series, the ear will still assign a characteristic pitch to the combination, this pitch being that associated with the fundamental frequency of the series. So definite is this pitch sensation that it is possible to eliminate the fundamental frequency entirely, by means of filters, without any observable effect upon the pitch! The ear apparently will supply the fundamental, provided the correct harmonics are present. It is this rather surprising property of the ear that enables a small loudspeaker which does not radiate low frequencies well to give nevertheless the impression of good radiation in the low-frequency region. Because the speaker is a fairly efficient radiator for the frequencies of the harmonics, the listener believes he is actually hearing the low frequencies, when instead he is hearing only multiples of these frequencies and his ear is supplying the fundamental. It is possible, by deliberate distortion of the harmonics associated with low musical notes, to make a very small radio set, totally inadequate in the low-frequency range, sound somewhat like a larger, acoustically superior console set. Such synthetic bass is, to the critical ear, inferior to true bass reproduction, where the harmonic content is closer to that of the original sound.

23–5 Spherical waves

In the preceding chapters we have discussed the propagation of plane waves in a fluid contained in a tube of constant cross section. In the absence of frictional effects, a plane wave in the tube remains plane and its amplitude does not change as the wave advances. On the other hand, the waves originating at a vibrating body in the air, or under water, spread out in all directions from the source. We shall consider only the simplest type of source, namely, a sphere whose surface performs radial oscillations as would the surface of a rubber balloon if air were alternately forced into it and withdrawn from it. Such a source is called a *pulsing sphere* and the waves it emits are spherical, concentric with the source. Since the energy transported by the waves spreads out over spheres of radius r and area $4\pi r^2$, the intensity of the waves (energy per unit time per unit area) must vary inversely as the square of the distance from the source. Also, since the intensity varies as the square of the amplitude, according to Eq. (23–1), it follows that the amplitude of the wave varies inversely as the first power of the distance. At sufficiently large distances from the source, however, the waves can be considered plane, with the pressure variations in phase with the particle velocity, so that there is always a flow of energy outward from the source.

At relatively small distances from the source, the situation is more complicated. The pressure is neither exactly in phase with the particle velocity, as in a traveling wave, nor is it exactly 90° out of phase, as in a stationary wave, but the phase difference is somewhere between 0° and 90°. However, the pressure can be resolved into two components, one of which is in phase with the particle velocity while the other is 90° out of phase. The former component gives rise to a flow of energy that is always outward, while the latter is associated with energy surging periodically in and out from the source. Energy which leaves the source permanently is said to be *radiated* by the source, and of course the radiated energy is the same across all surfaces surrounding the source.

The fact that energy is radiated from a sound source means that energy must be supplied to the source to keep it vibrating; therefore the radiation process is analogous to a frictional resistance to the motion of the source. If the source is started vibrating and left to itself, its motion is damped out; we speak of the effect as *radiation damping*. The greater the damping, the more effective is the source as a radiator.

23–6 Radiation from a piston. Diffraction

An actual sound source, such as a loudspeaker diaphragm, can be better approximated by a plane vibrating normally to its surface than by a pulsing sphere. A single surface oscillating in this way radiates from both sides. To simplify the problem, we shall assume that we have an oscillating piston fitting closely in a large wall or

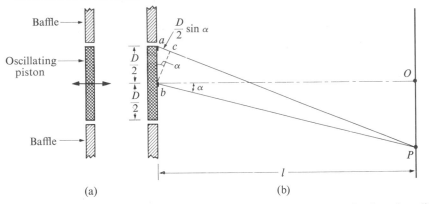

Fig. 23–3. (a) An oscillating piston set in a baffle. (b) Construction for locating diffraction minima in radiation pattern from a long rectangular source.

baffle, as in Fig. 23–3(a). Then only the waves radiated from the right side of the piston need be considered in the space at the right of the baffle.

The distribution of radiated energy in direction depends on the shape of the piston and on its dimensions relative to the wavelength of the emitted waves. The mathematics becomes impossibly complicated for any shapes except circles and rectangles. The simplest case is that of a very long rectangle like a long plank, and Fig. 23–3(b) is an end view of such a piston. Imagine the right face of the piston, of width D, to be subdivided into a large number of very narrow strips parallel to the length of the piston and perpendicular to the plane of the diagram. Each of these strips can be treated as a *line source*, sending out waves having *cylindrical* wave surfaces coaxial with the source. We now apply the principle of superposition to these cylindrical waves.

Point P is a point in space at a distance l large compared with the width D of the source, and with the wavelength λ. Consider the two elementary line sources at a and b, one at the top edge of the piston and the other just below its centerline. With P as a center and Pb as radius, strike the arc shown by the dotted line, intersecting the line Pa at c. The distance ac is then the path difference between the waves reaching P from a and b. Since l is large compared with D, the arc bc is very nearly a straight line and abc is very nearly a right triangle with the angle α equal to the angle between Pb and the normal Ob. The path difference ac is then

$$ac = \frac{D}{2} \sin \alpha. \tag{23–3}$$

If the angle α has such a value that ac equals one-half a wavelength, the waves from a and b will reach P $180°$ out of phase and will very nearly cancel one another. The cancellation will not be complete because (1) the waves have slightly different distances to travel, and the amplitude decreases with distance, and (2) the directions to P are not exactly the same for both sources, and a line source, unlike a spherical source, does not radiate uniformly in all directions. However, both of these effects will be small if l is large compared with D.

Consider next the pair of line sources just below a and b. Except for second-order differences, the same diagram as in Fig. 23–3(b) can be constructed for them and the waves from these sources will also cancel at P. Proceeding in this way over the entire surface of the piston, we see that very nearly complete cancellation results in a direction making an angle α with the normal, provided that

$$ac = \frac{\lambda}{2},$$

or, from Eq. (23–3), that

$$\sin \alpha = \frac{\lambda}{D}. \tag{23–4}$$

As an example, if $D = 12$ inches and $\lambda = 6$ inches (corresponding to a frequency of about 2000 cycles/sec),

$$\sin \alpha = \tfrac{6}{12} = 0.50,$$

$$\alpha = 30°,$$

and no energy is radiated at an angle of $30°$ on either side of the normal.

Other minima will occur in directions for which $\sin \alpha = 2\lambda/D$, $3\lambda/D$, etc. This can be shown by dividing the surface of the piston into quarters, sixths, etc., and pairing off one element against another, as in Fig. 23–3(b).

The relatively simple discussion above, while it gives the angular positions of the *minima*, does not give those of the *maxima* nor does it give the relative intensities in various directions. The complete analysis is too lengthy to give here and we shall only state the results. There is a maximum intensity of radiated energy along the normal to the piston ($\alpha = 0$) and in other directions very nearly halfway between the minima. However, by far the greatest amount of energy is concentrated in the region between the first two minima on either side of the normal, and for most purposes the energy radiated in other directions can be neglected.

The analysis of the radiation pattern from a *circular* piston is carried out in the same way as that for a long rectangle. The piston is subdivided into narrow circular zones instead of long strips, and the effect of the waves from all the zones is summed at a distant point. There is a maximum of intensity along the axis of the piston, as would be expected. The angle α at which the first minimum occurs is given by

$$\sin \alpha = 1.22 \frac{\lambda}{D}, \tag{23–5}$$

where D is now the piston diameter, and about 85% of the radiated energy is concentrated within a cone of this half-angle. If $D = 12$ inches, $\lambda = 6$ inches,

$$\sin \alpha = 1.22 \times \tfrac{6}{12} = 0.61,$$

$$\alpha \approx 37°.$$

Other minima, and maxima of rapidly decreasing intensity, surround the central maximum.

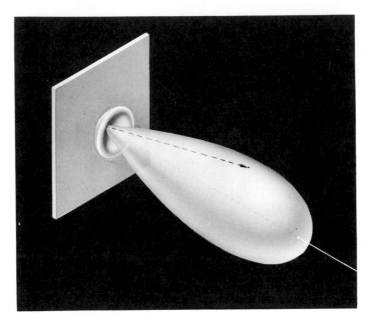

Fig. 23–4. Space diagram of intensity distribution in front of an oscillating circular piston set in a baffle. A vector drawn from the center of the piston to any point on the surface has a length proportional to the sound intensity in that direction, as observed at a large fixed distance from the piston.

Figure 23–4 is a space diagram of the intensity distribution in front of an oscillating circular piston set in a baffle.

This *directivity* of the sound radiated by a piston has a number of important applications. In a motion picture theater, for example, we wish the sound waves radiated by a speaker behind the screen to spread out over a large angle. If a loudspeaker 12 inches in diameter, approximated by a circular piston, is the sound source, then at a frequency of 2000 cycles/sec the directly radiated wave is concentrated mainly in a "beam" of half-angle 37°, centered on the speaker axis. For a frequency of 10,000 cycles/sec, or a wavelength of about 0.1 ft (about the upper frequency limit for such sound systems), the half-angle is

$$\sin \alpha = 1.22 \frac{0.1}{1.0} = 0.122, \qquad \alpha \approx 7°,$$

while at a frequency of 1200 cycles/sec, or a wavelength of about 0.8 ft,

$$\sin \alpha = 1.22 \frac{0.8}{1.0} \approx 1.0, \qquad \alpha \approx 90°.$$

This means that for frequencies of 1200 cycles/sec or less the radiated energy spreads out fairly uniformly, while at 10,000 cycles/sec it is concentrated in a narrow beam, like a searchlight beam.

Since the intelligibility of speech depends largely on the high-frequency components, these are usually channeled into a number of speakers directed toward different parts of the auditorium, while the low frequencies can be handled by a single speaker, since the low-frequency radiation pattern has a much wider angular spread. On the other hand, it is sometimes desirable, as in underwater sound signaling or when leading the cheering section, to produce a beam having only a small angular divergence. To accomplish this, the diameter of the source (approximating it by a circular piston) must be large compared with the wavelength of the radiated sound.

If instead of a vibrating piston set in a wall there is merely an aperture in the wall and a train of plane waves is incident from the left, the waves transmitted through the aperture will propagate beyond it in the same way as waves originating at a piston set in the aperture. If the wavelength is small compared with the dimensions of the aperture, the spreading of the waves is small, while if the wavelength is large the waves spread out in all directions.

When there is an obstacle in the path of a train of waves, the resultant effect at the far side of the obstacle is due to those portions of the advancing wave surface that are *not* obstructed. In very general terms, if the wavelength is relatively small the spreading is small and the obstacle casts a sharp "shadow." The larger the wavelength, the greater the spreading or bending of the waves. Thus one *can* hear around the corner of a wall but the effect is greater for waves of long wavelength (or low frequency) than for waves of short wavelength (or high frequency). The general term for the phenomena described above, in which one is concerned with the resultant effect of a large number of waves from different parts of a source, is *diffraction*.

23–7 Radiating efficiency of a sound source

The directivity of a sound source is not the only factor to be considered in designing such a source. When an oscillating surface is large compared with the wavelength of the waves it emits, most of the sound energy is propagated directly ahead of the source in a fairly well-defined beam of plane waves. The phase relations between pressure and particle velocity in a plane wave are such that energy always travels away from the source. If, on the other hand, the surface is small compared with the wavelength, the phase relations near the source are such that much of the energy in the sound field simply surges alternately away from and back to the source and only a small amount is radiated.

Consider a sound wave having a frequency of 250 cycles/sec and a wavelength of about 4 ft. A loudspeaker 6 inches in diameter (small compared with the wavelength) will radiate waves of this frequency quite uniformly in all directions, but the *power* it can radiate is relatively small unless it is driven with an impossibly large amplitude. A speaker 8 ft in diameter would be a much more efficient radiator at this frequency, but its disadvantages are obvious. A horn, such as a megaphone, the horn of an early phonograph, or the horns often used in loudspeakers, is a device which makes it possible for a source of small dimensions to radiate low frequencies just as efficiently as a much larger source. At the same time, of course, the directivity is increased, which may or may not be desirable.

In very general terms, what a horn does is to control the way in which the waves from a source spread out immediately after leaving the source. Instead of being free to diverge in all directions they are restricted by the walls of the horn. The result is to modify the phase relations in the wave so that a large fraction of the sound energy reaching the mouth of the horn is radiated and only a small fraction is reflected back to the source. Of course, if the horn is itself a musical instrument, like a bugle, trumpet, or French horn, some energy must be reflected at its mouth in order to establish a system of stationary waves in the horn and cause the air column to resonate at the desired frequency.

Because of the necessarily large bulk of a horn with a wide mouth, horns are not widely used in sound reproducing systems in the home. Sufficiently effective radiation of low frequencies can be accomplished with the conventional cone speaker if the amplifier which precedes it has a relatively greater "gain" for low frequencies than for high. Another common practice is to utilize, at low frequencies, the waves radiated from the back of the speaker cone. This is accomplished by mounting the speaker in an enclosure in which there is an opening. If the volume of the enclosure and the area of the opening have the proper values, the enclosure resonates at low frequencies in such a way that waves radiated by the opening are in phase with those from the front of the speaker. The characteristic of the hearing mechanism mentioned in Section 23–4, namely, that the *pitch* associated with a harmonic series is that of the fundamental even if this is absent, also makes the output of a small speaker at least acceptable even if the low frequencies present in the original sound are not reproduced with their original relative intensities.

23–8 Beats

Stationary waves in an air column have been cited as one example of interference. They arise when two wave trains of the same amplitude and frequency are traveling through the same region in opposite directions. We now wish to consider another type of interference, which results when two wave trains of equal amplitude but slightly different frequency travel through the same region. Such a condition exists when two tuning forks of slightly different frequency are sounded simultaneously or when two piano wires struck by the same key are slightly "out of tune."

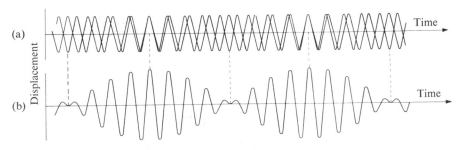

Fig. 23–5. Beats are fluctuations in amplitude produced by two sound waves of slightly different frequency.

Let us consider some one point of space through which the waves are simultaneously passing. The displacements due to the two waves separately are plotted as a function of the time on graph (a) in Fig. 23–5. If the total extent of the time axis represents one second, the graphs correspond to frequencies of 16 vibrations per second and of 18 vibrations per second. Applying the principle of superposition to find the resultant vibration, we get graph (b), where it is seen that the amplitude varies with the time. These variations of amplitude give rise to variations of loudness which are called *beats*. Two strings may be tuned to the same frequency by tightening one of them while sounding both until the beats disappear.

The production of beats may be treated mathematically as follows. The displacements due to the two waves passing simultaneously through some one point of space may be written

$$y_1 = Y \cos 2\pi f_1 t, \qquad y_2 = Y \cos 2\pi f_2 t$$

(the amplitudes are assumed equal).

By the principle of superposition, the resultant displacement is

$$y = y_1 + y_2 = Y (\cos 2\pi f_1 t + \cos 2\pi f_2 t),$$

and, since

$$\cos a + \cos b = 2 \cos \frac{a+b}{2} \cos \frac{a-b}{2},$$

this may be written

$$y = \left[2Y \cos 2\pi \left(\frac{f_1 - f_2}{2} \right) t \right] \cos 2\pi \frac{f_1 + f_2}{2} t. \qquad (23\text{–}6)$$

The resulting vibration can then be considered to be of frequency $(f_1 + f_2)/2$, or the average frequency of the two tones, and of amplitude given by the expression in brackets. The amplitude therefore varies with time at a frequency $(f_1 - f_2)/2$. If f_1 and f_2 are nearly equal, this term is small and the amplitude fluctuates very slowly. When the amplitude is large the sound is loud, and vice versa. A beat, or a maximum of amplitude, will occur when $\cos 2\pi[(f_1 - f_2)/2]t$ equals 1 or -1. Since each of these values occurs once in each cycle, the number of beats per second is twice the frequency $(f_1 - f_2)/2$, or *the number of beats per second equals the difference of the frequencies*.

23–9 The Doppler effect

When a source of sound, or a listener, or both, are in motion relative to the air, the pitch of the sound, as heard by the listener, is in general not the same as when source and listener are at rest. The most common example is the sudden drop in pitch of the sound from an automobile horn as one meets and passes a car proceeding in the opposite direction. This phenomenon is called the *Doppler effect*.

We shall consider only the special case in which the velocities of listener and source, v_L and v_S, lie along the line joining them. Since these velocities may be in the same

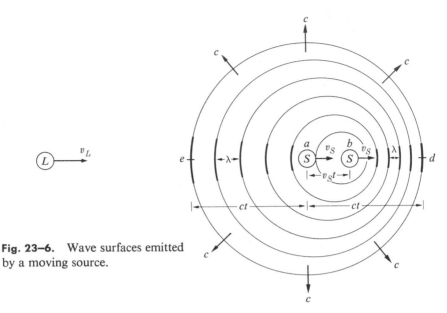

Fig. 23-6.   Wave surfaces emitted by a moving source.

or opposite directions, and the listener may be either ahead of or behind the source, a convention of signs is required. We shall take the positive directions of v_L and v_S as that *from* the position of the listener *to* the position of the source. The velocity of propagation of sound waves, c, will always be considered positive.

In Fig. 23-6, a listener L is at the left of a source S. The positive direction is then from left to right and both v_L and v_S are positive in the diagram. The sound source is at point a at time $t = 0$ and at point b at time t. The outer circle represents the wave surface emitted at time $t = 0$. This surface (in free space) is a sphere with center at a, and is traveling radially outward at all points with speed c. (The fact that the wave originated at a *moving* source does not affect its speed after leaving the source. The wave speed c is a property of the *medium* only; the waves forget about the source as soon as they leave it.) The radius of this sphere (the distance ea or ad) is therefore ct. The distance ab equals $v_S t$, so

$$eb = (c + v_S)t, \qquad bd = (c - v_S)t.$$

In the time interval between $t = 0$ and $t = t$, the number of waves emitted by the source is $f_S t$, where f_S is the frequency of the source. In front of the source these waves are crowded into the distance bd, while behind the source they are spread out over the distance eb. The wavelength in front of the source is therefore

$$\lambda = \frac{(c - v_S)t}{f_S t} = \frac{c - v_S}{f_S},$$

while the wavelength behind the source is

$$\lambda = \frac{(c + v_S)t}{f_S t} = \frac{c + v_S}{f_S}.$$

The waves approaching the moving listener L have a speed of propagation relative to him, given by $c + v_L$. The frequency f_L at which the listener encounters these waves is

$$f_L = \frac{c + v_L}{\lambda} = \frac{c + v_L}{(c + v_S)/f_S},$$

or

$$\frac{f_L}{c + v_L} = \frac{f_S}{c + v_S}, \qquad (23\text{-}7)$$

which expresses the frequency f_L as heard by the listener in terms of the frequency f_S of the source. It is unnecessary to derive equations for other special cases if consistent use is made of the sign convention given above. See the following examples.

If the medium in which the waves are traveling has a velocity v_M parallel to the line joining listener and source, then

$$\frac{f_L}{c + v_L - v_M} = \frac{f_S}{c + v_S - v_M}. \qquad (23\text{-}8)$$

only correct if use sign convention.

EXAMPLES.   Let

$$f_S = 1000 \text{ cycles/sec}, \qquad c = 1000 \text{ ft/sec}.$$

The wavelength of the waves emitted by a stationary source is then

$$c/f_S = 1.00 \text{ ft}.$$

(a) What are the wavelengths ahead of and behind the moving source in Fig. 23–6 if its velocity is 100 ft/sec?

In front of the source,

$$\lambda = \frac{c - v_S}{f_S} = \frac{1000 - 100}{1000} = 0.90 \text{ ft}.$$

Behind the source,

$$\lambda = \frac{c + v_S}{f_S} = \frac{1000 + 100}{1000} = 1.10 \text{ ft}.$$

(b) If the listener L in Fig. 23–6 is at rest and the source is moving away from him at 100 ft/sec, what is the frequency as heard by the listener?

Since

$$v_L = 0 \qquad \text{and} \qquad v_S = 100 \text{ ft/sec},$$

we have

$$f_L = f_S \frac{c}{c + v_S} = 1000 \frac{1000}{1000 + 100} = 909 \text{ cycles/sec}.$$

(c) If the source in Fig. 23–6 is at rest and the listener is moving toward the left at 100 ft/sec, what is the frequency as heard by the listener?

The positive direction (from listener to source) is still from left to right, so

$$v_L = -100 \text{ ft/sec}, \qquad v_S = 0,$$

$$f_L = f_S \frac{c + v_L}{c} = 1000 \frac{1000 - 100}{1000} = 900 \text{ cycles/sec}.$$

Thus while the frequency f_L as heard by the listener is less than the frequency f_S both when the source moves away from the listener and when the listener moves away from the source, the decrease in frequency is not the same for the same speed of recession.

23-10 The relativistic Doppler effect.

The Doppler effect is not confined to sound waves. Light waves are emitted as a result of electronic rearrangements in atoms, and the wavelength of the light from certain stars is found to be slightly longer, and from other stars slightly shorter, than that from the same atoms in a source on the earth. The inference is that the stars have velocity components toward or away from the earth. Even in a gas discharge tube in the laboratory, the atoms are not at rest but are flying about with relatively large velocities. Hence the light from such a source, resulting from a given atomic process, is a mixture of waves with a slight "spread" of wavelengths. Another interesting example is the reflection of radar waves from a moving object such as a plane or an automobile. The wavelength of the reflected waves is decreased if the object is moving toward the source, increased if it is moving away from the source.

The expressions for the Doppler effect for light waves or radar waves differ from the corresponding expressions for sound waves for the following reason. The velocities v_L and v_S, in Eqs. (23-7) and (23-8), are those of a listener and a sound source,

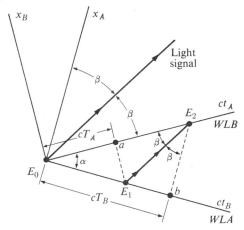

Fig. 23-7. Brehme diagram for computing the relativistic Doppler effect. A light signal sent by A at event E_1, at a time T_A, is received by B at event E_2, at a time T_B.

relative to the medium in which sound waves are traveling, and c is the velocity of sound *relative to the medium.* The principles of special relativity, however, tell us that these relative velocities have no meaning in the case of light waves or radar waves; we cannot invoke an "ether" as the medium relative to which velocities can be specified. The velocity c of a light wave means its velocity relative to an *observer* or to a *source*, and is the same for all observers and all sources, whatever their velocity relative to one another. Similarly, the velocity of an observer can be specified only relative to that of another observer, or relative to that of a source.

Suppose that a source A and an observer B are moving relative to each other with velocity v. If A and B coincide at time $t_A = t_B = 0$, then at later times A is moving away from B. Let A send out a series of regularly spaced light signals, separated by equal time intervals T_A as measured in his frame. We ask, what is the time interval T_B between the reception of the signals by observer B? The problem is readily solved with the help of the Brehme diagram of Fig. 23–7. Since A and B remain at the origins of their respective reference frames, the world line of $A(WLA)$ coincides with the ct_B-axis, and the world line of $B(WLB)$ coincides with the ct_A-axis.

Let one of A's signals be sent out at event E_0, at a time $t_A = 0$. Since A and B coincide at this event, the signal is received by B at time $t_B = 0$.

The next signal is sent by A at event E_1, at a time T_A as measured in A's frame. Hence a perpendicular dropped from E_1 onto the ct_A-axis intersects this axis at a distance cT_A from E_0.

The world line of a light signal traveling from A toward B [see Fig. 4–18(a)] is parallel to the bisector of the angle between the x_A- and ct_A-axes. Hence the signal sent by A at event E_1 is received by B at event E_2. The time T_B of this event, as measured in B's frame, is found by dropping a perpendicular from E_2 to the ct_B-axis, intersecting the axis at point b. The length of segment E_0b then equals cT_B, and we see at once that the time interval T_B between the reception of the signals is *greater* than the interval T_A. The intervals T_A and T_B are the respective *periods* of a regularly spaced set of signals, or of a train of continuous waves.

The ratio of the periods T_A and T_B can be computed as follows. Segment E_0b, equal to cT_B, is the sum of segments E_0E_1 and E_1b. From the triangle E_0E_1a, we see that

$$E_0E_1 = cT_A \sec \alpha.$$

The lengths of segments E_1a and E_1b are equal, since each equals $E_1E_2 \sin \beta$. Hence

$$E_1b = E_1a = cT_A \tan \alpha,$$

and

$$cT_B = E_0E_1 + E_1b = cT_A \sec \alpha + cT_A \tan \alpha,$$

$$T_B = T_A(\sec \alpha + \tan \alpha) = T_A \frac{1 + \sin \alpha}{\cos \alpha}.$$

But from the construction of the Brehme diagram,

$$\sin \alpha = v/c, \cos \alpha = (1 - v^2/c^2)^{1/2},$$

so finally,

$$T_B = T_A \sqrt{\frac{c + v}{c - v}}. \tag{23–9}$$

In terms of frequencies,

$$f_B = f_A \sqrt{\frac{c - v}{c + v}}, \quad \text{or} \quad \frac{f_B}{\sqrt{c - v}} = \frac{f_A}{\sqrt{c + v}}. \tag{23–10}$$

The preceding equations are those of the *relativistic Doppler effect*. Since A corresponds to a sound *source* and B to a *listener*, the frequencies f_B and f_A, in Eq. (23–10), correspond to f_L and f_S in Eq. (23–7). It should be noted carefully, however, that the symbols c and v, in Eq. (23–10), have very different meanings from c, v_L, and v_S, in Eq. (23–7). In the latter equation, these refer to velocities *relative to a medium*. In the former, c is the velocity of light *relative to either A or B*, and v is the *relative velocity of A and B*. The frequency f_A in Eq. (23–10) is that measured by an observer relative to whom the source is at rest, and f_B is the frequency measured by an observer from whom the source is receding with relative velocity v.

If a light source is *approaching* an observer, one merely changes the sign of the velocity v in Eq. (23–10).

Equation (23–10) can be written:

$$f_B = f_A \sqrt{\frac{1 - (v/c)}{1 + (v/c)}}.$$

If $v \ll c$, then to a good approximation,

$$[1 + (v/c)]^{-1} = 1 - (v/c),$$

and hence very nearly,

$$f_B = f_A \left(1 - \frac{v}{c}\right) = f_A \frac{c - v}{c}. \tag{23–11}$$

This equation has the same *form* as that for the frequency f_L heard by a listener when he is receding with a velocity v, relative to the atmosphere, from a source of frequency f_S, at rest relative to the atmosphere. Note, however, that in the case of light waves or radar waves, no distinction can be drawn between the cases of "a moving observer receding from a stationary source," and "a moving source receding from a stationary observer." All we can say is that source and observer are receding from *each other*.

The Doppler effect provides a convenient means of tracking an artificial satellite which is emitting a radio signal of constant frequency f_A. The frequency f_B of the signal that is received on the earth decreases as the satellite is passing, since the velocity component *toward* the observer decreases from position 1 to 2 in Fig. 23–8, and then points *away* from the observer from 2 to 3. If the received signal of frequency f_B is combined with a constant frequency signal generated in the receiver to give rise to *beats*, then the beat frequency may be such as to produce an audible note whose pitch decreases as the satellite passes overhead.

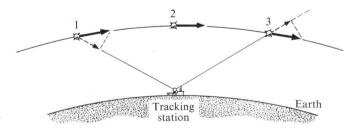

Fig. 23–8. Change of velocity component along the line of sight of a satellite passing a tracking station.

Problems

23–1. (a) If the pressure amplitude in a sound wave is tripled, by how many times is the intensity of the wave increased? (b) By how many times must the pressure amplitude of a sound wave be increased in order to increase the intensity by a factor of 16 times?

23–2. (a) Two sound waves of the same frequency, one in air and one in water, are equal in intensity. What is the ratio of the pressure amplitude of the wave in water to that of the wave in air? If the pressure amplitudes of the waves are equal, (b) what is the ratio of their intensities? (c) What is the difference between their intensity levels? The speed of sound in water may be taken as 1490 m/sec.

23–3. (a) Relative to the arbitrary reference intensity of 10^{-16} watt/cm^2, what is the intensity level in db of a sound wave whose intensity is 10^{-10} watt/cm^2? (b) What is the intensity level of a sound wave in air whose pressure amplitude is 2 dynes/cm^2?

23–4. The intensity due to a number of independent sound sources is the sum of the individual intensities. How many db greater is the intensity level when all five quintuplets cry simultaneously than when a single one cries? How many more crying babies would be required to produce a further increase in the intensity level of the same number of db?

23–5. A window whose area is 1 m^2 opens on a street where the street noises result in an intensity level, at the window, of 60 db. How much "acoustic power" enters the window via the sound waves?

23–6. (a) What are the upper and lower limits of intensity level of a person whose auditory area is represented by the graph of Fig. 23–1? (b) What are the highest and lowest frequencies he can hear when the intensity level is 40 db?

23–7. Two loudspeakers, A and B, radiate sound uniformly in all directions. The output of acoustic power from A is 8 × 10^{-4} watt, and from B it is 13.5 × 10^{-4} watt. Both loudspeakers are vibrating in phase at a frequency of 173 cycles/sec. (a) Determine the difference in phase of the two signals at a point C along the line joining A and B, 3 m from B and 4 m from A. (b) Determine the intensity at C from speaker A if speaker B is turned off, and the intensity at C from speaker B if speaker A is turned off. (c) With both speakers on, what is the intensity and intensity level at C? Take C to be 346 m/sec.

23–8. What should be the diameter of a sound source in the form of a circular piston set in a wall, if the central lobe of the diffraction pattern is to have a half-angle of 45°, for a frequency of 10,000 cycles/sec?

23–9. The sound source of a sonar system operates at a frequency of 50,000 cycles/sec. Approximate the source by a circular disk set in the hull of a destroyer. The velocity of sound in water can be taken as 1450 m/sec. (a) What is the wavelength of the waves emitted by the source? (b) What must be the diameter of the source if the half-angular divergence of the main beam is not to be more than 10°? (c) What is the difference in frequency between the directly radiated waves and the waves reflected from the hull of a submarine traveling directly away from the destroyer at 15 mi/hr?

23–10. Two identical piano wires when stretched with the same tension have a fundamental frequency of 400 vib/sec. By what fractional amount must the tension in one wire be increased in order that 4 beats/sec shall occur when both wires vibrate simultaneously? (Approximate finite changes by differentials.)

23–11. The frequency ratio of a half-tone interval on the diatonic scale is $\frac{16}{15}$. Find the velocity of an automobile passing a listener at rest in still air, if the pitch of the car's horn drops a halftone between the times when the car is coming directly toward him and when it is moving directly away from him.

23–12. (a) Complete the derivation of Eq. (23–8). (b) Refer to Fig. 23–6 and the examples in Section 23–9. Suppose that a wind of velocity 50 ft/sec is blowing in the same direction as that in which the source is moving. Find the wavelengths ahead of and behind the source. (c) Find the frequency heard by a listener at rest when the source is moving away from him.

23–13. A railroad train is traveling at 100 ft/sec in still air. The frequency of the note emitted by the locomotive whistle is 500 cycles/sec. What is the wavelength of the sound waves (a) in front of, and (b) behind the locomotive? What would be the frequency of the sound heard by a stationary listener (c) in front of, (d) behind the locomotive? What frequency would be heard by a passenger on a train traveling at 50 ft/sec and (e) approaching the first, (f) receding from the first? (g) How is each of the preceding answers altered if a wind of velocity 30 ft/sec is blowing in the same direction as that in which the locomotive is traveling?

23–14. A train of plane sound waves of frequency f_0 and wavelength λ_0 travels horizontally toward the right. It strikes and is reflected from a large, rigid, vertical plane surface, perpendicular to the direction of propagation of the wave train and moving toward the left with a velocity v. (a) How many waves strike the surface in a time interval t? (b) At the end of this time interval, how far to the left of the surface is the wave that was reflected at the beginning of the time interval? (c) What is the wavelength of the reflected waves, in terms of λ_0? (d) What is the frequency, in terms of f_0? (e) A listener is at rest at the left of the moving surface. Describe his sound sensation as a result of the combined effect of the incident and reflected wave trains.

23–15. Two whistles, A and B, each have a frequency of 500 cycles/sec. A is stationary and B is moving toward the right (away from A) at a velocity of 200 ft/sec. An observer is between the two whistles, moving toward the right with a velocity of 100 ft/sec. Take the velocity of sound in air as 1100 ft/sec. (a) What is the frequency from A as heard by the observer? (b) What is the frequency from B as heard by the observer? (c) What is the beat frequency heard by the observer?

23–16. A man stands at rest in front of a large smooth wall. Directly in front of him, between him and the wall, he holds a vibrating tuning fork of frequency 400 cycles/sec. He now moves the fork toward the wall with a velocity of 4 ft/sec. How many beats per second will he hear between the sound waves reaching him directly from the fork, and those reaching him after being reflected from the wall?

23–17. A source of sound waves, S, emitting waves of frequency 1000 cycles/sec, is traveling toward the right in still air with a velocity of 100 ft/sec. At the right of the source is a large smooth reflecting surface moving toward the left with a velocity of 400 ft/sec. (a) How far does an emitted wave travel in 0.01 sec? (b) What is the wavelength of the emitted waves in front of (i.e., at the right of) the source? (c) How many waves strike the reflecting surface in 0.01 sec? (d) What is the velocity of the reflected waves? (e) What is the wavelength of the reflected waves?

23–18. Radar waves travel with the velocity of light, $c = 3 \times 10^8$ m/sec. A beam of radar waves of wavelength 10 cm is reflected from an airplane moving toward the wave source. The reflected waves are made to beat with the directly radiated waves, and the beat frequency is observed to be 1000 cycles/sec. What is the velocity of the plane, in mi/hr?

CHAPTER 24

Coulomb's Law

24–1 Electric charges

It was known to the ancient Greeks as far back as 600 B.C. that amber, rubbed with wool, acquired the property of attracting light objects. In describing this property today, we say that the amber is *electrified*, or possesses an *electric charge*, or is *electrically charged*. These terms are derived from the Greek word *elektron*, meaning amber. It is possible to impart an electric charge to any solid material by rubbing it with any other material. Thus, an automobile becomes charged by virtue of its motion through the air; an electric charge is developed on a sheet of paper moving through a printing press; a comb is electrified in passing through dry hair. Actually, intimate contact is all that is needed to give rise to an electric charge. Rubbing merely serves to bring many points of the surfaces into good contact.

In lecture demonstrations hard rubber and fur are commonly used. If, after rubbing with fur, a rubber rod is placed in a dish containing tiny pieces of tissue paper, many of these will at first cling to the rod, but after a few seconds they will fly off. The initial attraction will be explained in Chapter 27; the subsequent repulsion is due to a force that is found to exist whenever two bodies are electrified in the same way. Suppose two small, very light pith balls are suspended near each other by fine silk threads. At first they will be attracted to an electrified rubber rod and will cling to it. A moment later, they will be repelled by the rubber and will also repel each other.

A similar experiment performed with a glass rod that has been rubbed with silk gives rise to the same result; pith balls electrified by contact with such a glass rod are repelled not only by the rod but by each other. On the other hand, when a pith ball that has been in contact with electrified rubber is placed near one that has been in contact with electrified glass, the pith balls *attract* each other. We are therefore led to the conclusion that there are two kinds of electric charge—that possessed by rubber after being rubbed with fur, called a *negative* charge, and that possessed by glass after being rubbed with silk, called a *positive* charge. The experiments on pith balls described above lead to the fundamental results that (1) *like charges repel*, (2) *unlike charges attract.*

These repulsive or attractive forces, of electrical origin, exist in addition to the gravitational force of attraction and, in most situations with which we shall deal, are so much larger than the gravitational force that the latter may be completely neglected.

In addition to the forces of attraction or repulsion, other forces are found to exist between electric charges which depend on their relative motion. It is these forces which are responsible for *magnetic* phenomena. For many years, the apparent force of repulsion or attraction between a pair of bar magnets was explained on the theory that there existed magnetic entities similar to electric charges and called "magnetic poles." It is a familiar fact, however, that magnetic effects are also observed around a wire in which there is a current. But a current is simply a motion of electric charge, and it appears now that all magnetic effects come about as a result of the relative motion of electric charges. Hence magnetism and electricity are not two separate subjects, but are related phenomena arising from the properties of electric charges.

Suppose a rubber rod is rubbed with fur and then touched to a suspended pith ball. Both the rubber and the pith ball are negatively charged. If the fur is now brought near the pith ball, the ball will be attracted, indicating that the fur is positively charged. It follows that when rubber is rubbed with fur, opposite charges appear on the two materials. This is found to happen whenever any substance is rubbed with any other substance. Thus glass becomes positive, while the silk with which the glass was rubbed becomes negative. This suggests strongly that electric charges are not generated or created, but that the process of acquiring an electric charge consists of transferring something from one body to another, so that one body has an excess and the other a deficiency of that something. It was not until the end of the nineteenth century that this "something" was found to consist of very small, light pieces of negative electricity, known today as *electrons*.

24–2 Atomic structure

The word *atom* is derived from the Greek *atomos*, meaning indivisible. It is scarcely necessary to point out that the term is inappropriate. All atoms are more or less complex arrangements of subatomic particles, and there are many methods of splitting off some of these particles, either singly or in groups.

The subatomic particles, the building blocks out of which atoms are constructed, are of three different kinds: the negatively charged *electron*, the positively charged *proton*, and the neutral *neutron*. The negative charge of the electron is of the same magnitude as the positive charge of the proton and no charges of smaller magnitude have ever been observed. The charge of a proton or an electron is the ultimate, natural unit of charge.

The subatomic particles are arranged in the same general way in all atoms. The protons and neutrons always form a closely packed group called the *nucleus*, which has a net positive charge due to the protons. The diameter of the nucleus, if we think of it as a sphere, is of the order of 10^{-12} cm. Outside the nucleus, but at relatively large distances from it, are the electrons, whose number is equal to the number of protons within the nucleus. If the atom is undisturbed, and no electrons are removed from the space around the nucleus, the atom as a whole is electrically neutral. That is, the equal positive and negative charges of the nucleus and the electrons sum to zero, just as equal positive and negative numbers sum to zero. If one or more electrons are removed, the remaining positively charged structure is called a positive *ion*. A negative ion is an atom which has gained one or more extra electrons. The process of losing or gaining electrons is called *ionization*.

In the atomic model proposed by the Danish physicist Niels Bohr in 1913, the electrons were pictured as whirling about the nucleus in circular or elliptical orbits. We now believe this model is not entirely correct, but it is still useful in visualizing the structure of an atom. The diameters of the electronic orbits, which determine the size of an atom as a whole, are of the order of 2 or 3×10^{-8} cm, or about ten thousand times as great as the diameter of the nucleus. A Bohr atom is a solar system in miniature, with electrical forces taking the place of gravitational forces. The positively charged central nucleus corresponds to the sun, while the electrons, moving around the nucleus under the electrical force of its attraction for them, correspond to the planets moving around the sun under the influence of its gravitational attraction.

The masses of a proton and a neutron are nearly equal, and the mass of each is about 1840 times as great as that of an electron. Practically all the mass of an atom, therefore, is concentrated in its nucleus. Since one kilomole of monatomic hydrogen consists of 6.02×10^{26} particles (Avogadro's number) and its mass is 1.008 kgm, the mass of a single hydrogen atom is

$$\frac{1.008 \text{ kgm}}{6.02 \times 10^{26}} = 1.67 \times 10^{-27} \text{ kgm.}$$

The hydrogen atom is the sole exception to the rule that all atoms are constructed of three kinds of subatomic particles. The nucleus of a hydrogen atom is a single proton, outside of which there is a single electron. Hence out of the total mass of the hydrogen atom, 1/1840 part is the mass of the electron and the remainder is the mass of a proton. Then to three significant figures,

$$\text{Mass of electron} = \frac{1.67 \times 10^{-27} \text{ kgm}}{1840} = 9.11 \times 10^{-31} \text{ kgm,}$$

$$\text{Mass of proton} = 1.67 \times 10^{-27} \text{ kgm,}$$

and since the masses of a proton and a neutron are nearly equal,

$$\text{Mass of neutron} = 1.67 \times 10^{-27} \text{ kgm.}$$

The next element beyond hydrogen is helium. Its nucleus consists of two protons and two neutrons, and it has two extranuclear electrons. When these two electrons are absent, the doubly charged helium ion, which is the helium nucleus itself, is often called an *alpha particle*, or α-particle. The next element, lithium, has three protons in its nucleus and has thus a nuclear charge of three units. In the un-ionized state the lithium atom has three extranuclear electrons. Each element has a different number of nuclear protons and therefore a different positive nuclear charge. In the table of elements listed in the back of this book, known as the *periodic table*, each element occupies a box with which is associated a number, called the *atomic number*. *The atomic number represents the number of nuclear protons or, in the undisturbed state, the number of extranuclear electrons.*

Every material body contains a tremendous number of charged particles, positively charged protons in the nuclei of its atoms and negatively charged electrons outside the nuclei. When the total number of protons equals the total number of electrons, the body as a whole is electrically neutral.

Suppose we wish to give a body an *excess* negative charge. This can be accomplished in two different ways. One is to *add* a number of *negative* charges to a neutral body; the other is to *remove* a number of *positive* charges from the body. Similarly, either an *addition* of *positive* charge, or a *removal* of *negative* charge, will result in an excess positive charge. In most instances, it is negative charges (electrons) that are added or removed, and a "positively charged body" is one that has lost some of its normal content of electrons.

The "charge" of a body refers to its *excess* charge only. The excess charge is always a very small fraction of the total positive or negative charge in the body.

24-3 The leaf electroscope and the electrometer

A charged pith ball may be used as a test body to determine whether or not a second body is charged. A more sensitive test is afforded by the *leaf electroscope* (Fig. 24-1). Two strips of thin gold leaf or aluminum foil *A* are fastened at the end of a metal rod *B* which passes through a support *C* of rubber, amber, or sulfur. The surrounding case *D* is provided with windows through which the leaves can be observed and which serve to protect them from air currents. When the knob of the electroscope is touched by a charged body, the leaves acquire charges of the same sign and repel each other, their divergence being a measure of the quantity of charge they have received.

If one terminal of a battery of a few hundred volts potential difference is connected to the knob of an electroscope and the other terminal to the electroscope case, the leaves will diverge just as if they had

Fig. 24-1.   The leaf electroscope.

been charged from a body electrified by contact. There is no difference between the "kinds" of charge given the leaves in the two processes and, in general, there is no distinction between "static electricity" and "current electricity." The term "current" refers to a flow of charge, while "electrostatics" is concerned for the most part with interactions between charges at rest. The charges themselves in either case are those of electrons or protons.

There are available today a number of devices that can be used in place of a leaf electroscope and which have the advantage of much greater sensitivity, so that smaller quantities of charge can be detected. An *electrometer* is an electroscope that has been calibrated so that it indicates not merely the presence of a charge, but its *magnitude* as well.

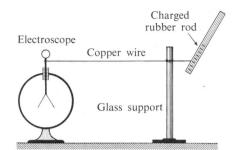

Fig. 24–2. Copper is a conductor of electricity.

24-4 Conductors and insulators

Let one end of a copper wire be attached to the knob of an electroscope, its other end being supported by a glass rod, as in Fig. 24–2. If a charged rubber rod is touched to the far end of the wire, the electroscope leaves will immediately diverge. There has, therefore, been a transfer of charge along or through the wire, and the wire is called a *conductor*. If the experiment is repeated, using a silk thread or rubber band in place of the wire, no such deflection of the electroscope occurs and the thread or rubber is called an *insulator* or *dielectric*. The motion of charge through a material substance will be studied in more detail in Chapter 28, but for our present purposes it is sufficient to state that most substances fall into one or the other of the two classes above. Conductors permit the passage of charge through them, while insulators do not.

Metals in general are good conductors, while nonmetals are insulators. The positive valency of metals and the fact that they form positive ions in solution indicate that the atoms of a metal will part readily with one or more of their outer electrons. Within a metallic conductor such as a copper wire, a few outer electrons become detached from each atom and can move freely throughout the metal in much the same way that the molecules of a gas can move through the spaces between grains of sand in a sand-filled container. In fact, these free electrons are often spoken of as an "electron gas." The positive nuclei and the remainder of the electrons remain fixed in position. Within an insulator, on the other hand, there are none (or at any rate very few) of these free electrons.

The phenomenon of charging by contact is not limited to rubber and fur, or indeed to insulators in general. Any two dissimilar substances exhibit the effect to a greater or lesser extent, but evidently a conductor must be supported on an insulating handle or the charges developed on it will at once leak away.

24-5 Charging by induction

In charging a leaf electroscope by contact with, say, a rubber rod that has been rubbed with fur, some of the extra electrons on the rubber are transferred to the electroscope, leaving the rubber with a smaller negative charge. There is, however, another way to use the rubber rod to charge other bodies, in which the rubber may impart a charge of opposite sign and lose none of its own charge. This process, called *charging by induction*, is illustrated in Fig. 24–3.

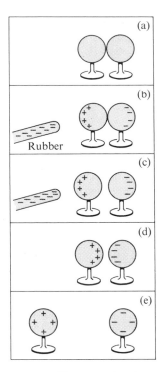

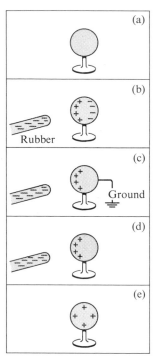

Fig. 24-3. Two metal spheres are oppositely charged by induction.

Fig. 24-4. Charging a single metal sphere by induction.

Part (a) of this figure represents two neutral metal spheres in contact, and both spheres are supported on insulating stands. When a negatively charged rubber rod is brought near one of the spheres but without touching it, as in part (b), the free electrons in the metal spheres are repelled and the entire cloud of electron gas within the spheres drifts slightly away from the rod, toward the right. Since the electrons cannot escape from the spheres, an excess negative charge accumulates at the right surface of the right sphere. This leaves a deficiency of negative charge, or an excess positive charge, at the left surface of the left sphere. These excess charges are called *induced* charges.

It should not be inferred that *all* of the free electrons in the spheres are driven to the surface of the right sphere. As soon as any induced charges develop, they also exert forces on the free electrons within the spheres. This force is toward the left (a repulsion by the negative induced charge and an attraction by the positive induced charge). Within an extremely short time the system reaches an equilibrium state in which, at every point in the interior of the spheres, the force on an electron toward the right, exerted by the charged rod, is just balanced by a force toward the left exerted by the induced charges.

The induced charges will remain on the surfaces of the spheres as long as the rubber rod is held nearby. If the rod is removed, the electron cloud in the spheres moves to the left and the original neutral condition is restored.

Suppose that the spheres are separated slightly, as shown in part (c), while the rubber rod is nearby. If the rod is now removed, as in (d), we are left with two oppositely charged metal spheres. Since these charges attract each other, they remain as close together as possible. Only when the two spheres are separated by a great distance, as in (e), will the two charges be uniformly distributed. It should be noticed that the negatively charged rubber rod has lost none of its charge in the steps from (a) to (e).

The steps from (a) to (e) in Fig. 24–4 should be self-explanatory. In this figure, a single metal sphere (on an insulating stand) is charged by induction. The symbol lettered "ground" in part (c) simply means that the sphere is connected to the earth. The earth thus takes the place of the second sphere in Fig. 24–3. In step (c), electrons are repelled to ground either through a conducting wire, or along the moist skin of a person who touches the sphere with his finger. The earth thus acquires a negative charge equal to the induced positive charge remaining on the sphere.

The processes taking place in Figs. 24–3 and 24–4 could be explained equally well if the mobile charges in the spheres were *positive*, or, in fact, if both positive and negative charges were mobile. Although we believe today that it is actually the negative charges that move in a metallic conductor, it is often convenient to describe a process *as if* it were the positive charges that moved.

24–6 Coulomb's law

The first quantitative investigation of the law of force between charged bodies was carried out by Charles Augustin de Coulomb (1736–1806) in 1784, utilizing for the measurement of forces a torsion balance of the type employed 13 years later by Cavendish in measuring gravitational forces. Coulomb found that the force of attraction or repulsion between two "point charges," that is, charged bodies whose dimensions are small compared with the distance r between them, is inversely proportional to the square of this distance.

The force also depends on the quantity of charge on each body. The net charge of a body might be described by a statement of the excess number of electrons or protons in the body. In practice, however, the charge of a body is expressed in terms of a unit much larger than the charge of an individual electron or proton. We shall use the letter q or Q to represent the charge of a body, postponing for the present the definition of the unit of charge.

In Coulomb's time, no unit of charge had been defined, nor any method of comparing a given charge with a unit. Despite this, Coulomb devised an ingenious method of showing how the force exerted on or by a charged body depended on its charge. He reasoned that if a charged spherical conductor were brought in contact with a second identical conductor, originally *uncharged*, the charge on the first would, by symmetry, be shared equally between the conductors. He thus had a method for obtaining one-half, one-quarter, and so on, of any given charge. The results of his experiments were consistent with the conclusion that the force between two point charges q and q' is proportional to the product of these charges. The complete expression for the force between two point charges is therefore

$$F \propto \frac{qq'}{r^2},$$

or

$$F = k\frac{qq'}{r^2}, \tag{24-1}$$

where k is a proportionality constant whose magnitude depends on the units in which F, q, q', and r are expressed. Equation (24–1) is the mathematical statement of what is known today as *Coulomb's law: The force of attraction or repulsion between two point charges is directly proportional to the product of the charges and inversely proportional to the square of the distance between them.*

The best verification of Coulomb's law lies in the correctness of many conclusions which have been drawn from it, rather than on direct experiments with point charges, which cannot be made with high precision.

The same law of force holds whatever may be the sign of the charges q and q'. If the charges are of like sign the force is a repulsion, if the charges are of opposite sign the force is an attraction. Forces of the same magnitude, but in opposite directions, are exerted on each of the charges.

Note that Coulomb's law has the same form as Newton's law of universal gravitation,

$$F = G\frac{mm'}{r^2}.$$

The electrical constant k corresponds to the gravitational constant G.

If there is matter in the space between the charges, the *net* force acting on each is altered because charges are induced in the molecules of the intervening medium. This effect will be described later on. As a practical matter, the law can be used as it stands for point charges in air, since even at atmospheric pressure the effect of the air is to alter the force from its value in vacuum by only about one part in two thousand.

We shall express length, mass, time, force, etc., in the units of the mks system. In addition, we must introduce one new unit, that of electric charge. This unit is called 1 *coulomb*, and the complete system is referred to as the mksc system.* The electrical constant k, in this system, is

$$k = 8.98742 \times 10^9 \frac{\text{n} \cdot \text{m}^2}{\text{coul}^2} \approx 9 \times 10^9 \frac{\text{n} \cdot \text{m}^2}{\text{coul}^2}.$$

The "natural" unit of charge is the charge carried by an electron or proton. The most precise measurements up to the present time find this charge e to be

$$e = 1.60207 \times 10^{-19} \text{ coul} \approx 1.60 \times 10^{-19} \text{ coul}.$$

---

* It will be shown in a later chapter that the coulomb is defined as the charge flowing past a point of a circuit in 1 sec when there is a current of 1 amp in the circuit. Hence the system is also referred to as the mksa system.

One coulomb therefore represents the aggregate charge carried by about 6×10^{18} electrons. By way of comparison, the population of the earth is estimated to be about 3×10^9 persons, while on the other hand a cube of copper 1 cm on a side contains about 8×10^{22} free electrons.

EXAMPLE 1. An α-particle is a nucleus of doubly ionized helium. It has a mass m of 6.68×10^{-27} kgm and a charge q of $+2e$ or 3.2×10^{-19} coul. Compare the force of electrostatic repulsion between two α-particles with the force of gravitational attraction between them.

The electrostatic force F_e is

$$\vec{F_e} = k\frac{q^2}{r^2},$$

and the gravitational force F_g is

$$F_g = G\frac{m^2}{r^2}.$$

The ratio of the electrostatic to the gravitational force is

$$\frac{F_e}{F_g} = \frac{k}{G}\frac{q^2}{m^2} = 3.1 \times 10^{35}.$$

The gravitational force is evidently negligible compared with the electrostatic force.

EXAMPLE 2. The Bohr model of the hydrogen atom consists of a single electron of charge $-e$ revolving in a circular orbit about a single proton of charge $+e$. The electrostatic force of attraction between electron and proton provides the centripetal force that retains the electron in its orbit. Hence if v is the orbital velocity.

$$k\frac{e^2}{r^2} = m\frac{v^2}{r}.$$

In Bohr's theory, the electron may revolve only in some one of a number of specified orbits. The orbit of smallest radius is that for which the angular momentum L of the electron is $h/2\pi$, where h is a universal constant called *Planck's constant*, equal to 6.625×10^{-34} joule·sec. Then

$$L - mvr = \frac{h}{2\pi}. \tag{24-2}$$

When v is eliminated between the preceding equations, we get

$$r = \frac{h^2}{4\pi^2 k m e^2},$$

and when numerical values are inserted, we find for the radius of the *first Bohr orbit*,

$$r = 5.29 \times 10^{-11} \text{ m} = 0.529 \times 10^{-8} \text{ cm}.$$

Problems

24-1. Two positive point charges, each of magnitude q, are located on the y-axis at points $y = +a$ and $y = -a$. A third positive charge of the same magnitude is located at some point on the x-axis. (a) What is the force exerted on the third charge when it is at the origin? (b) What is the magnitude and direction of the force on the third charge when its coordinate is x? (c) Sketch a graph of the force on the third charge as a function of x, for values of x between $+4a$ and $-4a$. Plot forces to the right upward, forces to the left, downward. (d) For what value of x is the force a maximum?

24-2. A negative point charge of magnitude q is located on the y-axis at the point $y = +a$, and a positive charge of the same magnitude is located at $y = -a$. A third positive charge of the same magnitude is located at some point on the x-axis. (a) What is the magnitude and direction of the force exerted on the third charge when it is at the origin? (b) What is the force on the third charge when its coordinate is x? (c) Sketch a graph of the force on the third charge as a function of x, for values of x between $+4a$ and $-4a$.

24-3. A small ball having a positive charge q_1 hangs by an insulating thread. A second ball with a negative charge $q_2 = -q_1$ is kept at a horizontal distance a to the right of the first. (The distance a is large compared with the diameter of the ball.) (a) Show in a diagram all of the forces on the hanging ball in its final equilibrium position. (b) You are given a third ball having a positive charge $q_3 = 2q_1$. Find at least two points at which this ball can be placed so that the first ball will hang vertically.

24-4. Two small balls, each 10 gm, are attached to silk threads 1 m long and hung from a common point. When the balls are given equal quantities of negative charge, each thread makes an angle of 4° with the vertical. (a) Draw a diagram showing all

of the forces on each ball. (b) Find the magnitude of the charge of each ball.

24-5. A certain metal sphere of volume 1 cm^3 has a mass of 7.5 gm and contains 8.2×10^{22} free electrons. (a) How many electrons must be removed from each of two such spheres so that the electrostatic force of repulsion between them just balances the force of gravitational attraction? Assume the distance between the spheres is great enough so that the charges on them can be treated as point charges. (b) Express the number of electrons removed as a fraction of the total number of free electrons.

24-6. In the Bohr model of atomic hydrogen, an electron of mass 9.11×10^{-31} kgm revolves about a proton in a circular orbit of radius 5.29×10^{-11} m. The proton has a positive charge equal in magnitude to the negative charge on the electron and its mass is 1.67×10^{-27} kgm. (a) What is the radial acceleration of the electron? (b) What is its angular velocity?

24-7. One gram of monatomic hydrogen contains 6.02×10^{23} atoms, each consisting of an electron with charge -1.60×10^{-19} coul and a proton with charge $+1.60 \times 10^{-19}$ coul. (a) Suppose all these electrons could be located at the north pole of the earth and all the protons at the south pole. What would be the total force of attraction exerted on each group of charges by the other, in pounds? The diameter of the earth is 12,800 km. (b) What would be the magnitude and direction of the force exerted by the charges in part (a) on a third positive charge, equal in magnitude to the total charge at one of the poles and located at a point on the equator? Draw a diagram.

24-8. The dimensions of atomic nuclei are of the order of 10^{-13} m. Suppose that two α-particles are separated by this distance. (a) What is the force exerted on each α-particle by the other? (b) What is the acceleration of each? (See the example at the end of Section 24–6 for numerical data.)

24–9. The pair of equal and opposite charges in Problem 24–2 is called an *electric dipole*.   (a) Show that when the x-coordinate of the third charge in Problem 24–2 is large compared with the distance a, the force on it is inversely proportional to the *cube* of its distance from the midpoint of the dipole. (b) Show that if the third charge is located on the y-axis,

at a y-coordinate large compared with the distance a, the force on it is also inversely proportional to the cube of its distance from the midpoint of the dipole.

24–10. Two equal positive point charges are a distance $2a$ apart. Midway between them and normal to the line joining them is a plane. The locus of points where the force on a point charge placed in the plane is a maximum is, by symmetry, a circle. Calculate the radius of this circle.

CHAPTER **25**

The Electric Field. Gauss's Law

25–1 The electric field

Figure 25–1(a) represents two positively charged bodies A and B, between which there is an electrical force of repulsion, **F**. Like the force of gravitational attraction, this force is of the action-at-a-distance type, making itself felt without the presence of any material connection between A and B. No one knows "why" this is possible— it is an experimental fact that charged bodies behave in this way. It is useful, how- ever, to think of each of the charged bodies as modifying the state of affairs in the space around it, so that this state is different in some way from whatever it may be when the charged bodies are not present. Thus, let body B be removed. Point P, Fig. 25–1(b), is the point of space at which B was formerly located. The charged body A is said to produce or set up an *electric field* at the point P, and if the charged body B is now placed at P, one considers that a force is exerted on B by *the field*, rather than by body A directly. Since a force would be experienced by body B at all points of space around body A, the whole of space around A is an electric field.

One can equally well consider that body B sets up a field, and that the force on body A is exerted by the field of B.

The experimental test for the existence of an electric field at any point is simply to place a charged body, which will be called a *test charge*, at the point. If a force (of electrical origin) is exerted on the test charge, then an electric field exists at the point.

An electric field is said to exist at a point if a force of electrical origin is exerted on a charged body placed at the point.

Since force is a vector quantity, the electric field is a vector field whose properties are de- termined when both the magnitude and the

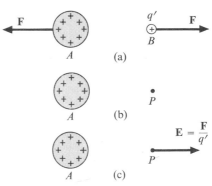

Fig. 25–1. The space around a charged body is an electric field.

direction of an electric force are specified. We define the *electric intensity* **E** at a point as the quotient obtained when the force **F**, acting on a positive test charge, is divided by the quantity of charge q' on the test charge. Thus

$$E = \frac{F}{q'},$$ (25–1)

and the direction of $\mathbf{E}$ is the direction of $\mathbf{F}$. It follows that

$$\mathbf{F} = q'\mathbf{E},$$

so that the force on a negative charge, such as an electron, is opposite to the direction of the electric intensity.

The term electric intensity is sometimes called the *electric field strength* or the *electric field intensity*. In the mksc system, where the unit of force is 1 n and the unit of charge is 1 coul, the unit of electric intensity is 1 *newton per coulomb*. Other units in which electric intensity may be expressed will be defined later.

The electric intensity at point P in Fig. 25-1(b) refers to the intensity set up by the *symmetrical* charge distribution on body A. If we attempt to measure the intensity by placing a charged body B at the point P, the field of B acts on the free charges in A, with the result that the charge distribution on A, when B is at point P, is not symmetrical, but there is an accumulation of positive charge on the left surface of A. (The charge distribution of B is also affected by the field of A.) That is, the introduction of the test charge B at point P alters the very quantity that we wish to measure. However, the smaller the charge of body B, the less the symmetrical charge distribution on A will be disturbed, and the precise definition of the intensity at a point of space is *the limiting value of the force per unit charge on a test charge q' at the point, as the charge q' approaches zero:*

$$\mathbf{E} = \lim_{q' \to 0} \frac{\mathbf{F}}{q'}.$$

If an electric field exists within a *conductor*, a force is exerted on every charge in the conductor. The motion of the free charges brought about by this force is called a *current*. Conversely, if there is no current in a conductor, and hence no motion of its free charges, the electric field in the conductor is zero.

EXAMPLE 1.   When the terminals of a 100-volt battery are connected to two parallel plates 1 cm apart, the electric intensity E in the space between the plates is 10^4 n/coul. Suppose we have a field of this intensity whose direction is vertically upward. Compute the force on an electron in this field and compare with the weight of the electron.

Electron charge $e = 1.60 \times 10^{-19}$ coul,   Electron mass $m = 9.1 \times 10^{-31}$ kgm.

$$F_{elec} = eE = 1.60 \times 10^{-19} \text{ coul} \times 10^4 \frac{\text{n}}{\text{coul}} = 1.60 \times 10^{-15} \text{ n}.$$

$$F_{grav} = mg = 9.1 \times 10^{-31} \text{ kgm} \times 9.8 \frac{\text{n}}{\text{kgm}} = 8.9 \times 10^{-30} \text{ n}.$$

The ratio of the electrical to the gravitational force is therefore

$$\frac{1.60 \times 10^{-15} \text{ n}}{8.9 \times 10^{-30} \text{ n}} = 1.8 \times 10^{14}.$$

It will be seen that the gravitational force is negligible.

EXAMPLE 2. If released from rest, what velocity will the electron of Example 1 acquire while traveling 1 cm? What will then be its kinetic energy? How long a time is required?

The force is constant, so the electron moves with a constant acceleration of

$$a = \frac{F}{m} = \frac{eE}{m} = \frac{1.60 \times 10^{-15}\,\text{n}}{9.1 \times 10^{-31}\,\text{kgm}} = 1.8 \times 10^{15}\,\frac{\text{m}}{\text{sec}^2}.$$

Its velocity after traveling 1 cm, or 10^{-2} m, is

$$v = \sqrt{2ax} = 6.0 \times 10^6\,\frac{\text{m}}{\text{sec}}.$$

Its kinetic energy is

$$\tfrac{1}{2}mv^2 = 1.6 \times 10^{-17}\,\text{joule}.$$

The time is

$$t = \frac{v}{a} = 3.3 \times 10^{-9}\,\text{sec}.$$

EXAMPLE 3. If the electron of Example 1 is projected into the field with a horizontal velocity, find the equation of its trajectory (Fig. 25-2).

The direction of the field is upward in Fig. 25-2, so the force on the electron is downward. The initial velocity is along the positive x-axis. The x-acceleration is zero, the y-acceleration is $-(eE/m)$. Hence, after a time t,

$$x = v_0 t,$$

$$y = -\frac{1}{2}\frac{eE}{m}t^2.$$

Elimination of t gives

$$y = -\frac{eE}{2mv_0^2}x^2,$$

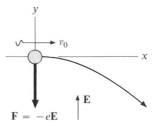

Fig. 25-2. Trajectory of an electron in an electric field.

which is the equation of a parabola. The motion is the same as that of a body projected horizontally in the earth's gravitational field. The deflection of electrons by an electric field is used to control the direction of an electron stream in many electronic devices, such as the cathode-ray oscilloscope.

25-2 Calculation of electric intensity

The preceding section describes an experimental method of measuring the electric intensity at a point. The method consists of placing a small test charge at the point, measuring the force on it, and taking the ratio of the force to the charge. The electric intensity at a point may also be computed from Coulomb's law if the magnitudes and positions of all charges contributing to the field are known. Thus to find the magnitude of the electric intensity at a point of space P, at a distance r from a point charge q, imagine a test charge q' to be placed at P. The force on the test charge, by Coulomb's law, is

$$F = k\frac{qq'}{r^2},$$

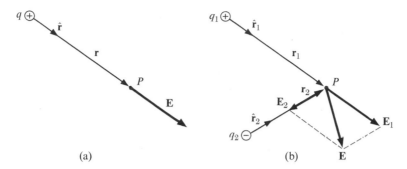

Fig. 25–3.   (a) The electric intensity **E** is in the same direction as the unit vector $\hat{\mathbf{r}}$ when q is positive.   (b) The resultant electric intensity at point P is the vector sum of $\mathbf{E}_1$ and $\mathbf{E}_2$.

and hence the electric intensity at P is

$$E = \frac{F}{q'} = k\frac{q}{r^2}.$$

The direction of the field is away from the charge q if the latter is positive, toward q if it is negative.

The magnitude and direction of **E** can both be expressed by a single *vector* equation. Let **r** be the vector from the charge q to the point P, and $\hat{\mathbf{r}}$ a vector of unit magnitude (or a *unit vector*) in the direction of **r**, as in Fig. 25–3(a).   Then

$$\mathbf{E} = k\frac{q\hat{\mathbf{r}}}{r^2}. \tag{25–2}$$

Since $\hat{\mathbf{r}}$ is of unit magnitude, the *magnitude* of **E** is kq/r^2.   If q is positive, the direction of **E** is the *same* as that of the vector $\hat{\mathbf{r}}$ (away from q) and if q is negative it is opposite to $\hat{\mathbf{r}}$ (toward q).

If a number of point charges q_1, q_2, etc., are at distances r_1, r_2, etc., from a given point P, as in Fig. 25–3(b), each exerts a force on a test charge q' placed at the point, and the resultant force on the test charge is the vector sum of these forces.   The resultant electric intensity is the vector sum of the individual electric intensities, and

$$\mathbf{E} = \mathbf{E}_1 + \mathbf{E}_2 + \cdots = k\sum\frac{q\hat{\mathbf{r}}}{r^2}. \tag{25–3}$$

Because each term to be summed is a vector, the sum is a vector sum.

In practice, electric fields are usually set up by charges distributed over the surfaces of conductors of finite size, rather than by point charges.   The electric intensity is then calculated by imagining the charge on each conductor to be subdivided into small elements Δq.   Not all of the charge in each element will be at the same distance from the point P, but if the elements are small compared with the distance to the point, and r represents the distance from any point within the element to the point P, then approximately

$$\mathbf{E} \approx k\sum\frac{\Delta q\hat{\mathbf{r}}}{r^2}.$$

The finer the subdivision, the better the approximation, and in the limit as $\Delta q \to 0$,

$$\mathbf{E} = k \lim_{\Delta q \to 0} \Sigma \frac{\Delta q \hat{\mathbf{r}}}{r^2}.$$

The limit of the vector sum, however, is the *vector integral*

$$\mathbf{E} = k \int \frac{\hat{\mathbf{r}} \, dq}{r^2}. \tag{25-4}$$

The limits of integration must be assigned so as to include all charges contributing to the field. Like any vector equation, Eq. (25-4) implies three scalar equations, one for each component of the vectors $\mathbf{E}$ and $\hat{\mathbf{r}}$. To evaluate the vector integral, we evaluate each of the three scalar integrals.

EXAMPLE 1. *Point charges.* An electric field is set up by two point charges q_1 and q_2, of the same magnitude but opposite sign, as in Fig. 25-4. What is the electric intensity at points a, b, and c?

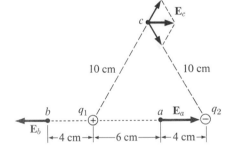

Fig. 25-4. Electric intensity at three points a, b, and c, in the field set up by charges q_1 and q_2.

At every point, the intensity due to the positive charge is directed radially away from that charge, and the intensity due to the negative charge is radially inward toward the charge.

At point a, the intensity due to each charge is directed toward the right. The resultant intensity $\mathbf{E}_a$ is also toward the right and its magnitude is the arithmetic sum of the individual intensities.

At point b, the intensity set up by q_1 is directed toward the left and that set up by q_2 is toward the right. The magnitude of the first is greater than that of the second. The resultant intensity $\mathbf{E}_b$ is toward the left and its magnitude is the difference between the individual intensities.

At point c, the individual intensities have the directions shown and the resultant intensity $\mathbf{E}_c$ is their vector sum. It is left to the reader to verify that if $q_1 = +12 \times 10^{-9}$ coul, $q_2 = -12 \times 10^{-9}$ coul, and the dimensions are as shown in the diagram, then

$$\mathbf{E}_a = 9.75 \times 10^4 \text{ n/coul, toward the right,}$$

$$\mathbf{E}_b = 6.20 \times 10^4 \text{ n/coul, toward the left,}$$

$$\mathbf{E}_c = 1.08 \times 10^4 \text{ n/coul, toward the right.}$$

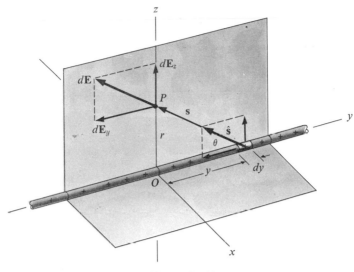

Figure 25-5

EXAMPLE 2. *Long charged wire.* In Fig. 25–5, a fine wire, having a positive charge per unit length λ, lies on the y-axis. We wish to calculate the electric intensity set up by the wire at point P.

Let the wire be subdivided, in imagination, into short elements of length dy. The charge dq on an element is then $\lambda\, dy$. It will be more convenient, in equations to be used later on, to let r represent the perpendicular distance from P to the wire and $\mathbf{s}$ the vector from dq to P. The charge dq sets up at P a field $d\mathbf{E}$ given by

$$d\mathbf{E} = k\,\frac{\hat{s}\, dq}{s^2} = k\,\frac{\hat{s}\lambda\, dy}{s^2},$$

and the resultant intensity $\mathbf{E}$ is

$$\mathbf{E} = k \int \frac{\hat{s}\lambda\, dy}{s^2}.$$

The *unit* vector $\hat{s}$ lies in the yz-plane, so its x-component is zero. The magnitude of its y-component is $\cos\theta$, and that of its z-component is $\sin\theta$. The vector equation above is then equivalent to the three scalar equations

$$E_x = 0,$$

$$E_y = k\lambda \int_{-\infty}^{+\infty} \frac{\cos\theta\, dy}{s^2},$$

$$E_z = k\lambda \int_{-\infty}^{+\infty} \frac{\sin\theta\, dy}{s^2}.$$

The wire is considered to be sufficiently long so that the limits of integration are from $-\infty$ to $+\infty$.

To evaluate the integrals, we must either express $\cos\theta$, $\sin\theta$, and s as functions of y, or express all quantities in terms of the same variable. Simplification results if θ is chosen as the independent variable. It will be seen from the diagram that

$$s = r\csc\theta, \qquad y = r\cot\theta.$$

Hence

$$dy = -r\csc^2\theta\,d\theta$$

and

$$E_y = -k\frac{\lambda}{r}\int_\pi^0 \cos\theta\,d\theta = -k\frac{\lambda}{r}[\sin\theta]_\pi^0 = 0,$$

$$E_z = -k\frac{\lambda}{r}\int_\pi^0 \sin\theta\,d\theta = k\frac{\lambda}{r}[\cos\theta]_\pi^0 = 2k\frac{\lambda}{r}.$$

The y-component of E is zero, as would be expected by symmetry. (For every charge dq at a given positive y, there is an equal charge at the same negative y. The components dE_y set up by these charges are equal and opposite.) The only nonzero component of the field is therefore E_z.

Had the point P been taken on the x-axis (the reader should construct his own diagram) the only nonzero component would have been E_x. It should be evident, therefore, that the electric intensity at *any* point lies in a plane perpendicular to the wire, is directed radially outward, and is of magnitude

$$E = 2k\frac{\lambda}{r}. \tag{25–5}$$

The resultant field is proportional to the charge per unit length λ, and is inversely proportional to the *first* power of the radial distance r from the wire.

EXAMPLE 3. *Infinite plane sheet of charge.* In Fig. 25–6, positive charge is distributed uniformly over the entire xy-plane, with a charge per unit area, or *surface density of charge*, σ. We wish to calculate the electric intensity at the point P.

Let the charge be subdivided into narrow strips parallel to the y-axis and of width dx. Each strip can be considered a *line* charge, and we can use the result of the preceding example.

The area of a portion of a strip of length L is $L\,dx$, and the charge dq on the strip is

$$dq = \sigma L\,dx.$$

The charge per unit length, $d\lambda$, is therefore

$$d\lambda = \frac{dq}{L} = \sigma\,dx.$$

From Eq. (25–5), the strip sets up at point P a field $d\mathrm{E}$, lying in the xz-plane and of magnitude

$$dE = 2k\sigma\frac{dx}{r}.$$

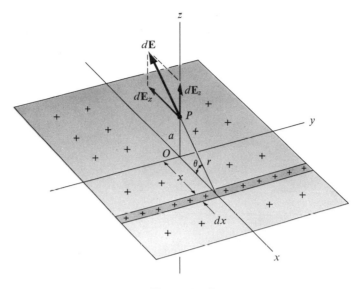

Figure 25–6

The field can be resolved into components dE_x and dE_z. By symmetry, the components dE_x will sum to zero when the entire sheet of charge is considered. (Be sure that you understand why.) The resultant field at P is therefore in the z-direction, perpendicular to the sheet of charge. It will be seen from the diagram that

$$dE_z = dE \sin \theta$$

and hence

$$E = \int dE_z = 2k\sigma \int_{-\infty}^{+\infty} \frac{\sin \theta \, dx}{r} \, .$$

But

$$\sin \theta = \frac{a}{r}, \qquad r^2 = a^2 + x^2,$$

and therefore

$$E = 2k\sigma a \int_{-\infty}^{+\infty} \frac{dx}{a^2 + x^2} = 2k\sigma a \left[\frac{1}{a} \tan^{-1} \frac{x}{a} \right]_{-\infty}^{+\infty},$$

$$E = 2\pi k\sigma. \tag{25–6}$$

Note that the distance a from the plane to the point P does not appear in the final result. This means that the intensity of the field set up by an infinite plane sheet of charge is *independent of the distance from the charge*. In other words, the field is *uniform* and *normal* to the plane of charge.

The same result would have been obtained if point P, in Fig. 25–6, had been taken *below* the xy-plane. That is, a field of the same magnitude but in the opposite sense is set up on the opposite side of the plane.

25–3 Lines of force

The concept of lines of force was introduced by Michael Faraday (1791–1867) as an aid in visualizing electric (and magnetic) fields. A *line of force* (in an electric field) is *an imaginary line drawn in such a way that its direction at any point* (i.e., the direction of its tangent) *is the same as the direction of the field at that point.* (See Fig. 25–7.) Since, in general, the direction of a field varies from point to point, lines of force are usually curves.

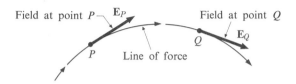

Fig. 25–7. The direction of the electric intensity at any point is tangent to the line of force through that point.

Figure 25–8 shows some of the lines of force around a single positive charge; around two equal charges, one positive and one negative; and around two equal positive charges. The direction of the resultant intensity at every point in each diagram is along the tangent to the line of force passing through the point. Arrowheads on the lines indicate the direction in which the tangent is to be drawn.

No lines of force originate or terminate in the space surrounding a charge. Every line of force in an *electrostatic* field is a continuous line terminated by a positive charge at one end and a negative charge at the other.* While sometimes for convenience we speak of an "isolated" charge and draw its field as in Fig. 25–8(a), this simply means that the charges on which the lines terminate are at large distances from the charge under consideration. For example, if the charged body in Fig. 25–8(a) is a small sphere suspended by a thread from the laboratory ceiling, the negative charges on which its force lines terminate would be found on the walls, floor, or ceiling, or on other objects in the laboratory.

At any one point, the resultant field can have but one direction. Hence only one line of force can pass through each point of the field. In other words, lines of force never intersect.

If a line of force were to be drawn through every point of an electric field, the whole of space and the entire surface of a diagram would be filled with lines, and no individual line could be distinguished. By suitably limiting the number of force lines which one draws to represent a field, the lines can be used to indicate the *magnitude* of a field as well as its *direction*. This is accomplished by spacing the lines in such a way that *the number per unit area crossing a surface at right angles to the direction of the field is at every point proportional to the electric intensity.* In a region where the intensity is large, such as that between the positive and negative charges

---

* We shall see in a later chapter that a *changing magnetic* field sets up an electric field whose lines do not terminate on electric charges, but close on themselves.

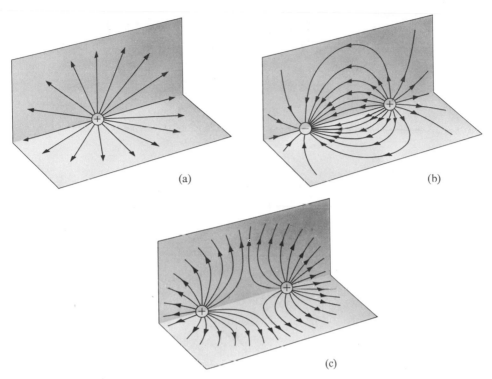

(a)

(b)

(c)

Fig. 25–8. The mapping of an electric field with the aid of lines of force.

of Fig. 25–8(b), the lines of force are closely spaced, whereas in a region where the intensity is small, such as that between the two positive charges of Fig. 25–8(c), the lines are widely separated. In a *uniform* field, like that on opposite sides of the sheet of charge in Fig. 25–6, the lines of force are straight, parallel, and uniformly spaced.

25–4 Gauss's law

Karl Friedrich Gauss (1777–1855) was a German scientist and mathematician who made many contributions to experimental and theoretical physics. The relation known as *Gauss's law* is a statement of an important property of electrostatic fields.

Consider first the field of a single positive point charge q, as in Fig. 25–9(a). The charge is surrounded by a *closed surface* of arbitrary shape. (The surface is to be constructed *in imagination only;* it is *not* the surface of a material body.) The electric intensity $\mathbf{E}$, at every point of the surface, is directed radially outward from the charge q and its magnitude is $E = kq/r^2$.

Over any sufficiently small area dA of the surface, the intensity can be considered to have the same magnitude and direction. The component of $\mathbf{E}$ normal to the surface,

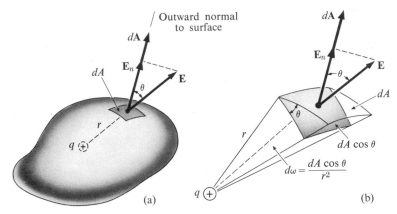

Figure 25–9

E_n, equals $E \cos \theta$, where θ is the angle between **E** and the *outward* normal to the surface, and the product of E_n and the area dA is

$$E_n \, dA = E \cos \theta \, dA = kq \frac{dA \cos \theta}{r^2}.$$

However, we see from Fig. 25–9(b), which is an enlarged view of a portion of Fig. 25–9(a), that the product $dA \cos \theta$ is the projection of the area dA at right angles to r, and that the quotient $dA \cos \theta / r^2$ equals the solid angle* $d\omega$ subtended at the charge q by the area dA.

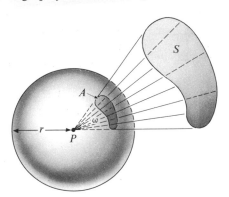

Fig. 25–10. The steradian measure of the solid angle ω is A/r^2.

* The solid angle subtended at a point P by a surface S is defined as follows. Imagine a sphere of arbitrary radius r to be constructed with center at P, as in Fig. 25–10. The lines drawn from P to the perimeter of S form a cone that intercepts an area A on the surface of this sphere. The solid angle ω subtended by S is defined as

$$\omega = \frac{A}{r^2}.$$

The unit solid angle is called one *steradian*. Since the total area of a sphere is $4\pi r^2$, the total solid angle subtended at a point is

$$\omega = \frac{4\pi r^2}{r^2} = 4\pi \text{ steradians}.$$

Hence
$$E_n \, dA = kq \, d\omega. \tag{25-7}$$

We now integrate both sides of Eq. (25–7) over the entire closed surface, as indicated by the symbol $\oint$.
$$\oint E_n \, dA = kq \oint d\omega.$$

Regardless of the shape or size of the closed surface, $\oint d\omega$ is the *total solid angle* surrounding the charge q, and equals 4π steradians. Hence

$$\boxed{\oint E_n \, dA = 4\pi kq.} \tag{25-8}$$

The left side of this equation, formed by multiplying the normal component of **E** at the surface by an element of area of the surface, and summing these products over the entire surface, is called the *surface integral* of **E** over the surface. (It is analogous to the *line integral* of a vector that we encountered earlier in connection with the *work* of a force.) Equation (25–8) states that the surface integral is proportional to the enclosed charge q, regardless of the shape or size of the surface or the location of the charge q within it.

If the point charge in Fig. 25–9 were negative, the field **E** would be directed radially *inward*, the angle θ would be greater than 180°, its cosine would be negative, E_n would be negative, and the surface integral would be negative. But since q would also be negative, the *form* of Eq. (25–8) is correct whatever the sign of the charge q.

If a point charge lies *outside* a closed surface (the reader should construct his own diagram) the field of the charge is *outward* at some points of the surface and *inward* at others. It is not difficult to show that the positive and negative contributions to the surface integral exactly cancel, and the surface integral is zero. But the charge *inside* the closed surface is also zero, so Eq. (25–8) applies whether the charge inside the surface is positive, negative, or zero.

Finally, let a closed surface be constructed in the field of any arbitrary distribution of charges. These can always be subdivided, in imagination, into point charges. We write Eq. (25–8) for each point charge, and sum over all charges. The sum of the integrals becomes the surface integral of the *resultant* field, and the charge q becomes Σq, the *algebraic* sum of all charges *inside* the closed surface. Hence in general,

$$\oint E_n \, dA = 4\pi k \, \Sigma \, q. \tag{25-9}$$

This equation expresses the content of *Gauss's law: The surface integral of the normal component of* **E** *over any closed surface in an electrostatic field, equals $4\pi k$ times the net charge inside the surface.*

The notation can be simplified in two respects. First, we define the *vector area* d**A** as a vector whose magnitude equals dA and whose direction is that of the *outward* normal at dA. The product $E_n \, dA = E \cos \theta \, dA$ can then be written as the *scalar product* or *dot product* of the vectors **E** and d**A**:

$$E_n \, dA = \mathbf{E} \cdot d\mathbf{A}.$$

Second, to avoid having to write the factor 4π in Eq. (25–9), we define a new constant ϵ_0 by the equation

$$\frac{1}{\epsilon_0} = 4\pi k, \qquad \epsilon_0 = \frac{1}{4\pi k} .$$

In the mksc system,

$$\epsilon_0 = \frac{1}{4\pi \times 9 \times 10^9} \frac{\text{coul}^2}{\text{n} \cdot \text{m}^2} = 8.85 \times 10^{-12} \frac{\text{coul}^2}{\text{n} \cdot \text{m}^2} .$$

Many texts write all the equations of electrostatics in terms of ϵ_0. For example, since $k = 1/4\pi\epsilon_0$, Coulomb's law becomes

$$F = \frac{1}{4\pi\epsilon_0} \frac{qq'}{r^2} .$$

Gauss's law can now be written more compactly as

$$\oint \mathbf{E} \cdot d\mathbf{A} = q/\epsilon_0, \qquad q = \epsilon_0 \oint \mathbf{E} \cdot d\mathbf{A}. \tag{25–10}$$

(We omit the summation sign Σ for brevity, but it must be remembered that q stands for the *net* charge *inside* the closed surface.)

One more term may be introduced at this point. The surface integral of $\mathbf{E}$ (or of any vector quantity) over a surface is called the *flux* of $\mathbf{E}$ (or of the vector) over the surface and is represented by Ψ. That is,

$$\Psi \equiv \int \mathbf{E} \cdot d\mathbf{A}.$$

The term flux, which means *flow*, is borrowed from hydrodynamics, where a similar integral gives the net outward flow of fluid across a surface. Gauss's law can then be written

$$q = \epsilon_0 \Psi. \tag{25–11}$$

The flux of $\mathbf{E}$ across a surface, as well as Gauss's law, can be interpreted graphically in terms of lines of force. If the number of lines per unit area at right angles to their direction is proportional to E, the surface integral of $\mathbf{E}$ over a closed surface is proportional to the total number of lines crossing the surface in an outward direction, and the net charge within the surface is proportional to this number. As an example, consider the field of two equal and opposite point charges shown in Fig. 25–11. Surface A encloses the positive charge only, and 18 lines cross it in an outward direction. Surface B encloses the negative charge only and it also is crossed by 18 lines, but in an inward direction. Surface C encloses *both* charges. It is intersected by lines at 16 points, at 8 of which the intersec-

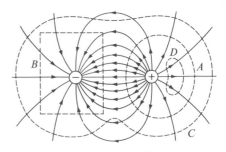

Figure 25–11

tions are outward and at 8 of which they are inward. The *net* number of lines crossing in an outward direction is zero, and the net charge inside the surface is also zero. Surface *D* is intersected at 6 points, at 3 of which the intersections are outward while at the other 3 they are inward. The net number of lines crossing in an outward direction, and the enclosed charge, are both zero.

In evaluating the surface integral of **E** over a closed surface, it is often necessary to divide the surface, in imagination, into a number of portions. The integral over the entire surface is the *sum* of the integrals over each portion. In a number of special cases, the techniques of integral calculus are not necessary to evaluate the surface integral.

1. If **E** is at right angles to a surface of area *A* at all points, and has the same magnitude at all points of the surface, then $E_n = E = $ constant, and

$$\int E_n \, dA = EA.$$

2. If **E** is *parallel* to a surface at all points, $E_n = 0$ and the surface integral is zero.
3. If $\mathbf{E} = 0$ at all points of a surface, the surface integral is zero.

25–5 Applications of Gauss's law

1. *Location of excess charge on a conductor.* It has been explained that the electric intensity **E** is zero at all points within a conductor, when the charges in the conductor are at rest. (If **E** were *not* zero, the charges would move.) Hence if a gaussian surface, such as surface *A*, is constructed within the interior of a charged conductor of arbitrary shape, as in Fig. 25–12(a), $\mathbf{E} = 0$ at all points of this surface. The surface integral of **E** is therefore zero and from Gauss's law the *net* charge *inside* the surface is zero.

If we imagine the surface to shrink to zero like a collapsing balloon, as suggested in the diagram, until it essentially encloses a point, the charge at the point must be zero. Since this process can take place at *any* point in the conductor, there can be no charge at any point within the conductor. It follows that the entire *excess* charge

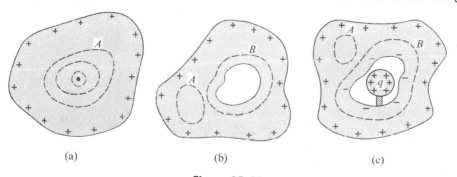

(a)   (b)   (c)

Figure 25–12

on the conductor must be located on the *outer surface* of the conductor, as shown. Gauss's law alone does not enable us to tell precisely how the charge is distributed over the surface. To do this, we must make use of another important property of electrostatic fields that will be developed later.

Now suppose there is a cavity in the conductor, as in Fig. 25–12(b), and there are no charges within the cavity. A gaussian surface, such as *A*, can still be shrunk to zero, so again there is no excess charge at any point within the material of the conductor. Surface *B*, however, cannot shrink to zero and still remain within the material of the conductor. (Students of topology will recognize this situation.) The surface encloses the smallest possible volume when it lies just outside the walls of the cavity. But the surface integral of **E** over surface *B* is still zero and the net charge within it is zero. Since any such charge must lie on the cavity walls, the *net* charge on the wall is zero. This does *not* prove, however, that the entire cavity wall is uncharged; it might be positively charged at some points and negatively charged at others. Again, Gauss's law does not provide a complete answer to the problem, but we shall show later that, in fact, the entire cavity wall is uncharged. Again, the excess charge on the conductor is confined to its *outer* surface.

Suppose next that there is a charge *q* in the cavity but insulated from it, as in Fig. 25–12(c). Application of Gauss's law to surface *B* shows again that the *net* charge inside this surface is zero, so there must be a charge on the cavity wall, equal and opposite in sign to the charge *q*. If the outer conductor were initially *uncharged* before the charge *q* was inserted, and is insulated so that the total charge on it cannot change, there must be a charge on its outer surface, equal and opposite to the charge on the cavity wall and therefore equal to, and of the *same* sign, as the charge *q*. If the outer conductor originally had a charge q', the charge on its outer surface becomes $q + q'$.

It follows that insertion of a charge into a cavity in a hollow conductor results in the appearance of an exactly equal charge on the outer surface of the hollow conductor, whether or not this conductor was originally charged.

Finally, suppose the charged body in the cavity is touched to the cavity wall (or connected to the wall by a conducting wire). The excess charge on the cavity wall then neutralizes the charge *q*, leaving the inner conductor completely uncharged. The charge of magnitude *q* remains on the outer surface of the hollow conductor, so in effect the entire charge *q* has been transferred to the outer surface of the outer conductor.

This process of transferring charge from one conductor to another by *internal* contact was studied by Faraday. For a hollow conductor, he used the metal pail in which the supply of ice for the laboratory was usually kept, and the experiment is still referred to as the "Faraday ice-pail experiment."

Thus if an uncharged metal can is placed on a leaf electroscope, as in Fig. 25–13, and a charged ball on an insulating handle is inserted into the can but without touching it, the electroscope leaves (which in effect form a part of the outer surface of the can) diverge as shown, indicating that they are charged. The charged ball can be moved around inside the can without affecting the separation of the leaves. If the ball is removed from the can, the

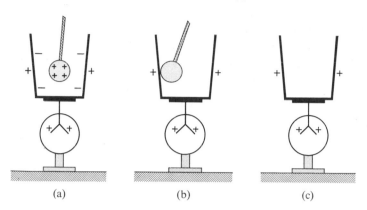

Fig. 25–13. (a) Charged ball within a "Faraday ice pail." (b) Ball touched to inner wall.
(c) Entire charge on ball transferred to pail and electroscope.

leaves collapse. If it is inserted again and touched to the inner surface no change in deflection is observed but the leaves *remain* deflected when the ball is withdrawn and the ball, if tested, is found to have lost *all* of its original charge.

2. *Coulomb's law.* We have considered Coulomb's law as the fundamental equation of electrostatics and have derived Gauss's law from it. An alternative procedure is to consider Gauss's law as a fundamental experimental relation. Coulomb's law can then be derived from Gauss's law, by using this law to obtain the expression for the electric intensity **E** due to a point charge. Note, however, that the general form of Gauss's law does not provide an expression for **E** itself, but only for its *surface integral.* In order to use Gauss's law to compute **E**, it must be possible to replace the surface *integral* by a *product,* of which *E* is one factor. The resulting *algebraic* equation can then be solved for *E.* This procedure is possible, however, only in a small number of instances in which the geometry of the problem is such that *symmetry* considerations enable us to replace the integral with a product.

As an example, we show how Coulomb's law can be derived from Gauss's law. Consider the electric field of a single positive point charge *q*, shown in Fig. 25–14. By *symmetry*, the field is everywhere radial (there is no reason why it should deviate to one side of a radial direction rather than to another) and its magnitude is the same at all points at the same distance *r* from the charge (one point at this distance is like any other). Hence if we select as a gaussian surface a spherical surface of radius *r*, $E_n = E = $ constant at all points of the surface. Then

$$\oint E_n \, dA = EA = 4\pi r^2 E,$$

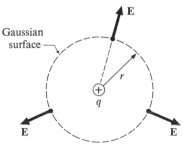

Figure 25–14

and from Gauss's law,

$$4\pi r^2 E = \frac{q}{\epsilon_0} \quad \text{and} \quad E = \frac{1}{4\pi\epsilon_0}\frac{q}{r^2} = k\frac{q}{r^2}.$$

The force on a point charge q' at a distance r from the charge q is then

$$F = q'E = k\frac{qq'}{r^2},$$

which is Coulomb's law.

3. *Field of a charged spherical conductor.* Any excess charge on an isolated spherical conductor is, by symmetry, distributed *uniformly* over its outer surface. The electric intensity at any point can be calculated from Eq. (25–4), but it is much simpler to use Gauss's law. It should be evident that at external points the field has the same symmetry as that of a point charge, so if we construct a gaussian surface of radius r, where r is greater than the radius R of the sphere, and if q is the total charge on the sphere,

$$4\pi r^2 E = q/\epsilon_0,$$

$$E = \frac{1}{4\pi\epsilon_0}\frac{q}{r^2} = k\frac{q}{r^2}.$$

The field *outside* the sphere is therefore the same as though the entire charge were concentrated at a point at its center. Just outside the surface of the sphere, where $r = R$,

$$E = k\frac{q}{R^2},$$

and inside the sphere, if it is solid, $E = 0$.

It is left as a problem to find from Gauss's law the electric intensity in the interspace between a charged sphere and a concentric hollow sphere surrounding it.

There is a simple way of showing that $\mathbf{E} = 0$ at all points inside a *hollow*, charged, spherical conductor. As shown in Fig. 25–15, we construct two narrow cones with their apices at any arbitrary point P. Both cones include the same small solid angle ω, and they intercept areas A_1 and A_2 on the surface of the sphere. The projections of these areas normal to the axes of the cones are, respectively, $A_1 \cos\theta$ and $A_2 \cos\theta$, and hence

$$\omega = \frac{A_1 \cos\theta}{r_1^2} = \frac{A_2 \cos\theta}{r_2^2}$$

or

$$\frac{A_1}{r_1^2} = \frac{A_2}{r_2^2}. \qquad (25\text{–}12)$$

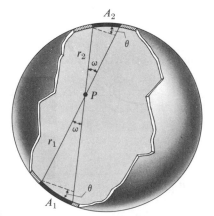

Figure 25–15

Let σ be the charge per unit area (the *surface density* of charge) on the spherical surface, so the charges q_1 and q_2 on A_1 and A_2 are σA_1 and σA_2, and the fields they set up at P are

$$E_1 = k \frac{\sigma A_1}{r_1^2}, \qquad E_2 = k \frac{\sigma A_2}{r_2^2}.$$

When this result is combined with Eq. (25–12), we see that the charges set up equal but opposite fields at P, which cancel each other. (The larger charge on area A_1 is just compensated by its greater distance from P.) The entire charge on the surface can be paired off in this way, with the result that the field at all internal points is zero.

It will be noted that the result above follows only if the electric field obeys an inverse *square* law; if the field were inversely proportional to r^3, or to $r^{2.147}$, the contributions of the elements A_1 and A_2 would not exactly cancel. Very accurate measurements have shown that the internal field of a charged sphere is, in fact, so small that the exponent of r cannot differ from exactly 2 by more than 1 part in 10^7. There seems no reason to doubt that it is exactly 2, and that the exponent 2 expresses a property of the *space* in which we live, as much as it does a special property of electric charges.

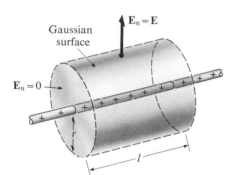

Fig. 25–16. Cylindrical gaussian surface for calculating the electric intensity due to a long charged wire.

4. *Field of a line charge and of a charged cylindrical conductor.* To illustrate the simplification made possible by the use of Gauss's law in problems where considerations of symmetry make it possible to replace the surface integral of $\mathbf{E}$ by a product, we use this law to find the electric intensity set up by a long charged fine wire, a problem that was solved in Section 25–2 by integrating the vector equation

$$\mathbf{E} = k \int \frac{\hat{\mathbf{r}}\, dq}{r^2}.$$

If the wire is very long, and we are not too near either end, then by symmetry the lines of force outside the wire are radial and lie in planes perpendicular to the wire. Also, the intensity has the same magnitude at all points at the same radial distance from the wire. This suggests that we use as a gaussian surface a *cylinder* of arbitrary radius r and arbitrary length l, with its ends perpendicular to the wire, as in Fig. 25–16. If λ is the charge per unit length on the wire, the charge *within* the gaussian surface is λl. Since $\mathbf{E}$ is at right angles to the wire, the component of $\mathbf{E}$ normal to the end faces is zero. At all points of the curved surface, $E_n = E =$ constant, and since the area of this surface is $2\pi rl$, we have

$$\lambda l = \epsilon_0 E \cdot 2\pi rl, \qquad E = \frac{1}{2\pi\epsilon_0} \frac{\lambda}{r} = 2k \frac{\lambda}{r},$$

which agrees with the result obtained in Section 25-2. The calculation is obviously much simpler.

It will be noted that although the *entire* charge on the wire contributes to the field **E**, only that portion of the total charge lying within the gaussian surface is used when we apply Gauss's law. This feature of the law is puzzling at first; it appears as though we had somehow obtained the right answer by ignoring a part of the charge, and that the field of a *short* wire of length *l* would be the same as that of a very long wire. The existence of the entire charge on the wire *is*, however, taken into account when we consider the *symmetry* of the problem. Suppose the wire had been a short one, of length *l*. Then we could *not* conclude by symmetry that the field at one end of the cylinder, say, would equal that at the center, or that the lines of force would everywhere be perpendicular to the wire. So the entire charge on the wire actually is taken into account, but in an indirect way.

It is left as a problem (1) to show that the field outside a long charged cylinder is the same as though the charge on the cylinder were concentrated in a line along its axis, and (2) to calculate the electric intensity in the interspace between a charged cylinder and a coaxial hollow cylinder that surrounds it.

5. *Field of an infinite plane sheet of charge.* To solve this problem, construct the gaussian surface shown by dashed lines in Fig. 25-17, consisting of a cylinder whose ends have an area *A* and whose walls are perpendicular to the sheet of charge. By symmetry, since the sheet is infinite, the electric intensity **E** is the same on both sides of the surface, is uniform, and is directed normally away from the sheet of charge. No lines of force cross the side walls of the cylinder, that is, the component of **E** normal to these walls is zero. At the ends of the cylinder the normal component of **E** is equal to *E*. The surface integral of **E**, calculated over the entire surface of the cylinder, therefore reduces to $2EA$. If σ is the charge per unit area in the plane sheet, the net charge within the gaussian surface is σA. Hence

$$\sigma A = 2\epsilon_0 EA, \qquad E = \frac{\sigma}{2\epsilon_0} = 2\pi k\sigma,$$

which agrees with the result obtained by integration in Eq. (25-6).

Note that the magnitude of the field is independent of the distance from the sheet and does not decrease inversely with the square of the distance. In terms of lines of force, these remain everywhere straight, parallel, and uniformly spaced. This is because the sheet was assumed infinitely large.

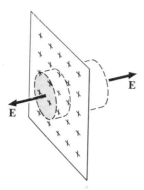

Fig. 25–17. Gaussian surface in the form of a cylinder for finding the field of an infinite plane sheet of charge.

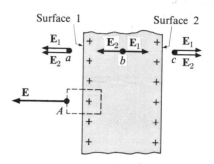

Fig. 25–18. Electric field inside and outside a charged conducting plate.

6. *Field of an infinite charged conducting plate.* When a metal plate is given a net charge, this charge distributes itself over the entire outer surface of the plate, and if the plate is of uniform thickness and is infinitely large (or if we are not too near the edges of a finite plate), the charge per unit area is uniform and is the same on both surfaces. Hence the field of such a charged plate arises from the superposition of the fields of *two* sheets of charge, one on each surface of the plate. By symmetry, the field is perpendicular to the plate, directed away from it if the plate has a positive charge, and is uniform. The magnitude of the electric intensity at any point can be found from Gauss's law or by using the results already derived for a sheet of charge.

Figure 25–18 shows a portion of a large charged conducting plate. Let σ represent the charge per unit area in the sheet of charge on *either* surface. At point a, outside the plate at the left, the component of electric intensity E_1, due to the sheet of charge on the left face of the plate, is directed toward the left and its magnitude is $\sigma/2\epsilon_0$. The component E_2 due to the sheet of charge on the right face of the plate is also toward the left and its magnitude is also $\sigma/2\epsilon_0$. The magnitude of the resultant intensity E is therefore

$$E = E_1 + E_2 = \frac{\sigma}{2\epsilon_0} + \frac{\sigma}{2\epsilon_0} = \frac{\sigma}{\epsilon_0}.$$

At point b, inside the plate, the two components of electric intensity are in opposite directions and their resultant is zero, as it must be in any conductor in which the charges are at rest. At point c the components again add and the magnitude of the resultant is σ/ϵ_0, directed toward the right.

To derive these results from Gauss's law, consider the cylinder shown by dotted lines. Its end faces are of area A and one lies inside and one outside the plate. The field inside the conductor is zero. The field outside, by symmetry, is perpendicular to the plate, so the normal component of E is zero over the walls of the cylinder and is equal to E over the outside end face. Hence, from Gauss's law,

$$EA = \frac{\sigma A}{\epsilon_0}, \qquad E = \frac{\sigma}{\epsilon_0}.$$

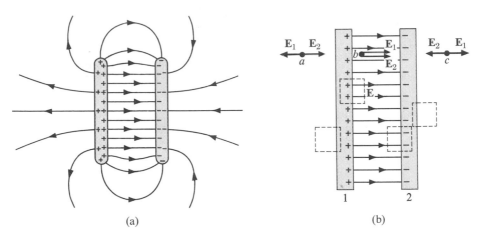

Fig. 25-19.   Electric field between oppositely charged parallel plates.

7. *Field between oppositely charged parallel plates.*   When two plane parallel conducting plates, having the size and spacing shown in Fig. 25-19, are given equal and opposite charges, the field between and around them is approximately as shown in Fig. 25-19(a).   While most of the charge accumulates at the opposing faces of the plates and the field is essentially uniform in the space between them, there is a small quantity of charge on the outer surfaces of the plates and a certain spreading or "fringing" of the field at the edges of the plates.

As the plates are made larger and the distance between them diminished, the fringing becomes relatively less.   Such an arrangement of two oppositely charged plates separated by a distance small compared with their linear dimensions is encountered in many pieces of electrical equipment, notably in capacitors.   In many instances the fringing is entirely negligible, and even if it is not, it is usually neglected for simplicity in computation.   We shall therefore assume that the field between two oppositely charged plates is uniform, as in Fig. 25-19(b), and that the charges are distributed uniformly over the opposing surfaces.

The electric intensity at any point can be considered either as the resultant of that due to two sheets of charge of opposite sign, or it may be found from Gauss's law. Thus at points a and c in Fig. 25-19(b), the components E_1 and E_2 are each of magnitude $\sigma/2\epsilon_0$ but are oppositely directed, so their resultant is zero.   At any point b between the plates the components are in the same direction and their resultant is σ/ϵ_0.   It is left as an exercise to show that the same results follow from applying Gauss's law to the surfaces shown by dotted lines.

8. *Field just outside any charged conductor.*   Figure 25-20 represents a portion of the surface of a charged conductor of irregular shape.   In general, the surface density of charge will vary from point to point of the surface.   Let σ represent the surface density at a small area A.   We shall show in the next chapter that the electric intensity *just outside* the surface of any charged conductor is at right angles to the surface.

Let us construct a gaussian surface in the form of a small cylinder, one of whose end faces, of area A, lies within the conductor, while the other lies just outside.   The

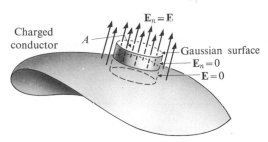

Fig. 25–20. The field just outside a charged conductor is perpendicular to the surface and is equal to σ/ϵ_0.

charge within the gaussian surface is σA. The electric intensity is zero at all points within the conductor. Outside the conductor, the normal component of **E** is zero at the side walls of the cylinder (since **E** is normal to the conductor) while over the end face the normal component is equal to **E**. Hence from Gauss's law,

$$EA = \frac{\sigma A}{\epsilon_0}, \qquad E = \frac{\sigma}{\epsilon_0}. \qquad (25\text{–}13)$$

This agrees with the results already obtained for spherical, cylindrical, and plane surfaces. Just outside the surface of a sphere of radius R, for example, the electric intensity is

$$E - k\frac{q}{R^2} = \frac{1}{4\pi\epsilon_0}\frac{q}{R^2}.$$

But the surface density of charge on the sphere is $q/4\pi R^2$, so $E = \sigma/\epsilon_0$.

The field outside an infinite charged conducting plate was also shown to equal σ/ϵ_0. In this case, the field is the same at *all* distances from the plate, but in general it decreases with increasing distance from the surface.

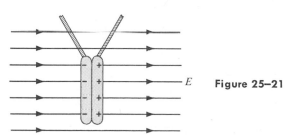

Figure 25–21

An unknown electric field can be "explored" by measuring the magnitude and direction of the force on a test charge at any point. A second method is illustrated in Fig. 25–21. Two small conducting plates of area A, each mounted on an insulating handle, are placed in the field with their faces in contact. Equal and opposite charges are induced on the outer surfaces of the plates as shown and, neglecting edge effects, the magnitude of the field outside the plates is not changed. The surface density of induced charge on each plate is $\sigma = \epsilon_0 E$, and the total charge q on each is

$$q = \sigma A = \epsilon_0 AE. \qquad (25\text{–}14)$$

TABLE 25-1

ELECTRIC FIELDS AROUND SIMPLE CHARGE DISTRIBUTIONS

Charge distribution responsible for the electric field	Arbitrary point in the electric field	Magnitude of the electric intensity at this point
Single point charge q	Distance r from q	$E = k\dfrac{q}{r^2}$
Several point charges, $q_1, q_2, \ldots$	Distance r_1 from q_1, r_2 from $q_2 \ldots$	$E = k\left(\dfrac{q_1}{r_1^2} + \dfrac{q_2}{r_2^2} + \cdots\right)$ (vector sum)
Charge q uniformly distributed on the surface of a conducting sphere of radius R	(a) Outside, $r > R$ (b) Inside, $r < R$	(a) $E = k\dfrac{q}{r^2}$ (b) $E = 0$
Long cylinder of radius R, with charge per unit length λ	(a) Outside, $r > R$ (b) Inside, $r < R$	(a) $E = 2k\dfrac{\lambda}{r}$ (b) $E = 0$
Two oppositely charged conducting plates with charge per unit area σ	Any point between plates	$E = \dfrac{\sigma}{\epsilon_0}$
Any charged conductor	Just outside the surface	$E = \dfrac{\sigma}{\epsilon_0}$

If the plates are now separated while still in the field, the charge on each is "trapped" and can be measured by inserting the plate in a Faraday ice pail connected to an electrometer, as in Fig. 25-13. If the electrometer has been calibrated, and if ϵ_0 is known, the intensity E can be computed from Eq. (25-14). Alternatively, the procedure can be considered as an experimental method for determining the constant ϵ_0, if E has already been measured with a test charge.

Figure 25-21 shows the plates at right angles to the field. If the direction of the field is not known in advance, a number of measurements can be made with the plates in different orientations. The induced charge is a *maximum* when the plates are at right angles to the field, so the experiment provides a method for finding the *direction* of an unknown field, as well as its magnitude.

Problems

25-1. A small object carrying a charge of -5×10^{-9} coul experiences a downward force of 20×10^{-9} n when placed at a certain point in an electric field. (a) What is the electric intensity at the point? (b) What would be the magnitude and direction of the force acting on an electron placed at the point?

25-2. What must be the charge on a particle of mass 2 gm for it to remain stationary in the laboratory when placed in a downward-directed electric field of intensity 500 n/coul?

25-3. A uniform electric field exists in the region between two oppositely charged plane parallel plates. An electron is released from rest at the surface of the negatively charged plate and strikes the surface of the opposite plate, 2 cm distant from the first, in a time interval of 1.5×10^{-8} sec. (a) Find the electric intensity. (b) Find the velocity of the electron when it strikes the second plate.

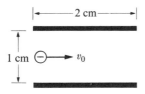

Figure 25-22

25-4. An electron is projected with an initial velocity $v_0 = 10^7$ m/sec into the uniform field between the parallel plates in Fig. 25-22. The direction of the field is vertically downward, and the field is zero except in the space between the plates. The electron enters the field at a point midway between the plates. If the electron just misses the upper plate as it emerges from the field, find the magnitude of the electric intensity.

25-5. An electron is projected into a uniform electric field of intensity 5000 n/coul. The direction of the field is vertically upward. The initial velocity of the electron is 10^7 m/sec, at an angle of $30°$ above the horizontal. (a) Find the maximum distance the electron rises vertically above its initial elevation. (b) After what horizontal distance does the electron return to its original elevation? (c) Sketch the trajectory of the electron.

25-6. In a rectangular coordinate system a charge of 25×10^{-9} coul is placed at the origin of coordinates, and a charge of -25×10^{-9} coul is placed at the point $x = 6$ m, $y = 0$. What is the electric intensity at (a) $x = 3$ m, $y = 0$; (b) $x = 3$ m, $y = 4$ m?

25-7. A charge of 16×10^{-9} coul is fixed at the origin of coordinates, a second charge of unknown magnitude is at $x = 3$ m, $y = 0$, and a third charge of 12×10^{-9} coul is at $x = 6$ m, $y = 0$. What is the magnitude of the unknown charge if the resultant field at $x = 8$ m, $y = 0$ is 20.25 n/coul directed to the right?

25-8. In a rectangular coordinate system, two positive point charges of 10^{-8} coul each are fixed at the points $x = +0.1$ m, $y = 0$, and $x = -0.1$ m, $y = 0$. Find the magnitude and direction of the electric intensity at the following points: (a) the origin; (b) $x = 0.2$ m, $y = 0$; (c) $x = 0.1$ m, $y = 0.15$ m; (d) $x = 0$, $y = 0.1$ m.

25-9. Same as Problem 25-8, except that one of the point charges is positive and the other negative.

25-10. An "electric doublet" or "electric dipole" consists of a pair of electric charges of equal magnitude and opposite sign, as in Fig. 25-23. (a) Prove that the electric intensity set up by the doublet at point a is parallel to the x-axis and is approximately

$$E = k \frac{ql}{r^3} \quad \text{when } r \gg l.$$

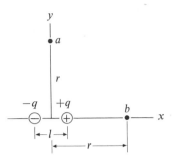

Figure 25-23

(b) Prove that the electric intensity at b is also parallel to the x-axis and is approximately

$$E = k \frac{2ql}{r^3} \quad \text{when } r \gg l.$$

(See Section 26-7 for an alternative method of solving this problem.)

25-11. A small sphere whose mass is 0.1 gm carries a charge of 3×10^{-10} coul and is attached to one end of a silk fiber 5 cm long. The other end of the fiber is attached to a large vertical conducting plate which has a surface charge of 25×10^{-6} coul/m^2. Find the angle which the fiber makes with the vertical.

25-12. How many excess electrons must be added to an isolated spherical conductor 10 cm in diameter to produce a field just outside the surface whose intensity is 1300 n/coul?

25-13. The electric intensity in the region between a pair of oppositely charged plane parallel plates, each 100 cm^2 in area, is 10^4 n/coul. What is the charge on each plate? Neglect edge effects.

25-14. A wire is bent into a ring of radius R and given a charge q. (a) What is the magnitude of the electric intensity at the center of the ring? (b) Derive the expression for the electric intensity at a point on a line perpendicular to the plane of the ring and passing through its center, at a distance r from the center of the ring. What is the direction of the E-vector at points on this line? (c) Sketch a graph of

the magnitude of E as a function of r, from $r = 0$ to $r = 2R$. (d) For what value of r/R is the intensity a maximum?

25-15. The electric intensity E in Fig. 25-24 is everywhere parallel to the x-axis, and has the same magnitude at all points of every plane perpendicular to this axis. Its magnitude in the yz-plane equals 400 n/coul. (a) What is the value of the surface integral of E over surface I in the diagram? (b) What is the value of the surface integral of E over surface II? (c) There is a positive charge of 26.6×10^{-9} coul within the volume. What is the magnitude and direction of E at the face opposite face I?

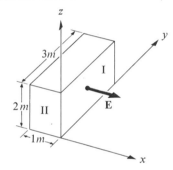

Figure 25-24

25-16. Apply Gauss's law to the dotted gaussian surfaces in Fig. 25-19(b) to calculate the electric intensity between and outside the plates.

25-17. A small conducting sphere of radius r_a, mounted on an insulating handle and having a positive charge q, is inserted through a hole in the walls of a hollow conducting sphere of inner radius r_b and outer radius r_c. The hollow sphere is supported on an insulating stand and is initially uncharged, and the small sphere is placed at the center of the hollow sphere. Neglect any effect of the hole. (a) Show that the electric intensity at a point in the region between the spheres, at a distance r from the center, is equal to

$$E = \frac{kq}{r^2}.$$

(b) What is the intensity at a point outside the hollow sphere? (c) Sketch a graph of the magnitude of **E** as a function of r, from $r = 0$ to $r = 2r_c$. (d) Represent the charge on the small sphere by four $+$ signs. Sketch the lines of force of the system, within a spherical volume of radius $2r_c$. (e) The small sphere is moved to a point near the inner wall of the hollow sphere. Sketch the lines of force.

25–18. (a) If the charge per unit length λ on the wire in Fig. 25–5 is finite, and the wire is infinitely long, the *total* charge on the wire is infinite. Explain why this infinite charge does not give rise to an infinite electric field. (b) Draw a diagram showing an end view of an infinitely long charged wire, and the lines of force in a plane perpendicular to the wire, far from either end. Explain in terms of lines of force why the field decreases with $1/r$, although the field of a point charge decreases with $1/r^2$.

25–19. Prove that the electric field outside an infinitely long cylindrical conductor with a uniform surface charge is the same as if all the charge were on the axis.

25–20. A long coaxial cable consists of an inner cylindrical conductor of radius r_a and an outer coaxial cylinder of inner radius r_b and outer radius r_c. The outer cylinder is mounted on insulating supports. The inner cylinder has a uniform positive charge λ per unit length, and the outer cylinder has an equal negative charge. Calculate the electric intensity (a) at any point between the cylinders, and (b) at

any external point. (c) Sketch a graph of the magnitude of **E** as a function of the distance r from the axis of the cable, from $r = 0$ to $r = 2r_c$.

25–21. Suppose that positive charge is uniformly distributed throughout a spherical volume of radius R, the charge per unit volume being ρ. (a) Use Gauss' law to prove that the electric intensity inside the volume, at a distance r from the center, is

$$E = \frac{\rho r}{3\,\epsilon_0}.$$

(b) What is the electric intensity at a point outside the spherical volume at a distance r from the center? Express your answer in terms of the total charge q within the spherical volume. (c) Compare the answers to (a) and (b) when $r = R$. (d) Sketch a graph of the magnitude of **E** as a function of r, from $r = 0$ to $r = 3R$.

25–22. Suppose that positive charge is uniformly distributed throughout a very long cylindrical volume of radius R, the charge per unit volume being ρ. (a) Derive the expression for the electric intensity inside the volume at a distance r from the axis of the cylinder, in terms of the charge density ρ. (b) What is the electric intensity at a point outside the volume, in terms of the charge per unit length λ in the cylinder? (c) Compare the answers to (a) and (b) when $r = R$. (d) Sketch a graph of the magnitude of **E** as a function of r, from $r = 0$ to $r = 3R$.

CHAPTER 26

Potential

26–1 Line integral of electric intensity

Gauss's law is a statement of one of the fundamental properties of electrostatic fields: the *surface integral* of the electric intensity over a closed surface is proportional to the net charge inside the surface. A second fundamental property, which we now consider, relates to the *line integral* of the electric intensity. As with Gauss's law, we can consider this as an experimental law or can derive it from Coulomb's law. We shall follow the latter procedure.

It will be recalled from the discussion of the work of a force, in Chapter 7, that the line integral of a vector, along any path, is obtained by (1) multiplying the magnitude of the tangential component of the vector, at each point of the path, by the length of a path element, and (2) integrating these products along the path.

Figure 26–1 represents the radial field of a positive point charge q. The full line between points a and b is some arbitrary path between these points. The electric intensity $\mathbf{E}$ at an element of the path of length ds makes an angle θ with the path. The magnitude of its tangential component $\mathbf{E}_s$ is $E \cos \theta$, and the line integral of $\mathbf{E}$ from point a to point b is

$$\int_a^b E_s \, ds = \int_a^b E \cos \theta \, ds = \int_a^b \mathbf{E} \cdot d\mathbf{s}.$$

The magnitude of the electric intensity is

$$E = k \frac{q}{r^2}$$

and it will be seen from the diagram that

$$ds \cos \theta = dr.$$

Hence

$$\int_a^b \mathbf{E} \cdot d\mathbf{s} = kq \int_{r_a}^{r_b} \frac{dr}{r^2} = kq \left(\frac{1}{r_a} - \frac{1}{r_b} \right). \tag{26–1}$$

The line integral therefore depends only on the radial distances r_a and r_b, and not on the *shape* of the path along which the integral is evaluated. Thus the integral along any other path from a to b, such as the dotted path, is equal to that along the original path.

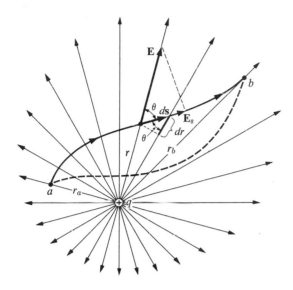

Fig. 26–1. The line integral of **E** from point a to point b is defined as $\int_a^b E_s \, ds$.

If the integral is taken along any path in the *opposite* direction, from b to a, its value is

$$\int_b^a \mathbf{E} \cdot d\mathbf{s} = kq \left(\frac{1}{r_b} - \frac{1}{r_a} \right),$$

which is the *negative* of the integral from a to b.

It follows, then, that the line integral around any *closed* path, such as the full line from a to b and the dotted line from b back to a, is equal to zero. That is,

$$\oint \mathbf{E} \cdot d\mathbf{s} = 0, \qquad (26\text{–}2)$$

where the symbol $\oint$ means that the line integral extends around a closed path. This equation expresses the second fundamental property of an electrostatic field: *the line integral of the electric intensity around any closed path in an electrostatic field is zero.*

The result above was derived for the special case of a single point charge. But any charge distribution can, in imagination, be subdivided into point charges. Since the line integral is zero for the component of **E** due to each point charge, it is zero for the resultant field also.

There are a number of special cases in which the methods of integral calculus are not necessary to evaluate the line integral of **E**.

1. If **E** is *parallel* to a path of length l at all points, and has the same magnitude at all points of the path, then $E_s = E = $ constant, and

$$\int_a^b E_s \, ds = El.$$

2. If **E** is *perpendicular* to a path at all points, $E_s = 0$ and the line integral is zero.
3. If $\mathbf{E} = 0$ at all points of a path, the line integral is zero.

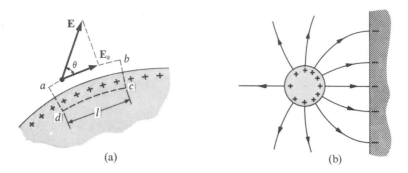

Fig. 26–2. (a) Construction for finding the direction of **E** outside the surface of a conductor. (b) Lines of force always meet charged conducting surfaces at right angles.

This second general property of an electrostatic field can be used to verify a statement that was made in the preceding chapter, namely, that the electric field just outside the surface of any charged conductor is at right angles to the surface, when the charges in the conductor are at rest. Figure 26–2(a) shows a portion of the surface of the conductor. The dotted rectangle *abcd* is a closed path (*not* a closed *surface*). The line integral around the path is the sum of the integrals along the four sides. Assume first that the **E**-vector just outside the surface makes some angle θ, less than 90°, with the surface. The line integral along the side *ab* is then the product of $E\cos\theta$ and the length *l* of this side. We know that $\mathbf{E} = 0$ *inside* the conductor, so the line integral along side *cd* is zero, and sides *bc* and *da* are assumed to be so short that they make no contribution to the line integral. Hence the integral around the entire path is $(E\cos\theta)\cdot l$. But the line integral must equal zero, and this can happen only if $\cos\theta = 0$, or if $\theta = 90°$ (or $-90°$ if the surface has a negative charge). Thus when the charges in a conductor are at rest, *the lines of force just outside the surface of the conductor are normal to the surface;* the lines meet the surface at right angles as in Fig. 26–2(b), whatever the shape of the surface. In general, the lines will change their direction as we move away from the surface, depending on the location of other charges in the vicinity. (If the conductor is carrying a current, the charges within it are not at rest and the lines of force do not intersect it at right angles.)

26–2 Electrical potential energy

The force exerted by an electric field of intensity **E** on a point charge q' is equal to $q'\mathbf{E}$, and the *work* of this force when the charge moves along any path between point *a* and point *b* is

$$W = \int_a^b \mathbf{F}\cdot d\mathbf{s} = q'\int_a^b \mathbf{E}\cdot d\mathbf{s}.$$

It was shown in the preceding section that the latter integral is the same along *all* paths between *a* and *b*, and hence the work of the electrical force is also the same along all paths, or, it is *independent of the path*. The electrical force is therefore a *conservative force* and, as explained in Chapter 7, when a force has this property it is possible to associate a *potential energy* with the force. The work of the force is equal to the negative of the difference in potential energy of the particle between the end point and the starting point. Hence if $(E_p)_a$ and $(E_p)_b$ are the (electrical) potential energies of the charge q' at points a and b,

$$(E_p)_b - (E_p)_a = -W = -q' \int_a^b \mathbf{E} \cdot d\mathbf{s},$$

or

$$(E_p)_a - (E_p)_b = q' \int_a^b \mathbf{E} \cdot d\mathbf{s}. \tag{26–3}$$

26–3 Potential

Instead of dealing directly with the potential energy E_p of a charged particle, it is useful to introduce the more general concept of *potential energy per unit charge*. This quantity is called the *potential;* and *the potential at any point of an electrostatic field is defined as the potential energy per unit charge* at the point. Potential is represented by the letter V:

$$V = \frac{E_p}{q'}, \quad \text{or,} \quad E_p = q'V.$$

Potential energy and charge are both *scalars*, so potential is a scalar quantity. Its basic mksc unit is 1 joule/coulomb. For brevity, a potential of 1 joule/coulomb is called 1 *volt*. The unit is named in honor of the Italian scientist Alessandro Volta (1745–1827). Multiples of the volt are the kilovolt (1 kv $= 10^3$ volts), the megavolt (1 Mv $= 10^6$ volts) and the gigavolt (1 Gv $= 10^9$ volts). Submultiples are the millivolt (1 mv $= 10^{-3}$ volt) and the microvolt (1 μv $= 10^{-6}$ volt).

When both sides of Eq. (26–3) are divided by q', we get

$$\frac{(E_p)_a}{q'} - \frac{(E_p)_b}{q'} = \int_a^b \mathbf{E} \cdot d\mathbf{s}.$$

$c = \frac{?}{V} =$

But $(E_p)_a/q'$ is the potential V_a at point a, and $(E_p)_b/q'$ is the potential V_b at point b. Hence

$$\boxed{V_a - V_b = \int_a^b \mathbf{E} \cdot d\mathbf{s}.} \tag{26–4}$$

The difference $V_a - V_b$ is called the *potential difference* between a and b, and will be abbreviated V_{ab}. The term "potential difference" is often abbreviated to pd, and is spoken of as the "voltage" between a and b. The potential difference between b and a, $V_b - V_a$, is the negative of that between a and b.

$$V_{ab} = V_a - V_b = -(V_b - V_a) = -V_{ba}.$$

Equation (26–4) gives only the *difference* between the potentials at points a and b. A value can be assigned to the potential at a *single* point only when some arbitrary reference point is selected, at which the potential is called zero. It will be recalled that the same problem is encountered in dealing with gravitational potential energy, or in fact with any form of potential energy.

A *voltmeter* is an instrument that measures the potential *difference* between the points to which its terminals are connected. The principle of the common type of moving coil voltmeter will be described later. An *electrometer*, which has been considered thus far as an instrument for measuring quantity of charge, can also be used as a voltmeter. Thus if the knob of a leaf electroscope is connected to a point at one potential and the case to a point at a different potential, the quantity of charge on the leaves is proportional to the potential difference between the points and the instrument can be calibrated to read this potential difference.

26–4 Calculation of potential differences

The potential difference between any two points *a* and *b* in an electrostatic field can be calculated from Eq. (26–4) if we know the electric intensity along *any* line joining the points. We now consider some special cases.

1. *Equipotentials.* In any region in which $\mathbf{E} = 0$ at all points, such as a region very far removed from all charges, or the interior of a conductor in which the charges are at rest, the line integral of $\mathbf{E}$ is zero along any path. The potential difference between any two points is therefore zero or, in other words, all points in the region are at the *same* potential. Thus the interior of a charged conductor is an *equipotential volume*.

If a *surface* is constructed in such a way that it is everywhere at right angles to an electric field, any path lying in the surface is at right angles to the field. The line integral of $\mathbf{E}$ is zero along any such path and the potential *difference* between any two points on the surface is zero. Hence *all points on the surface* are at the *same* potential. The surface is called an *equipotential surface*, or simply an *equipotential*.

The potential distribution in an electric field can be represented graphically by constructing equipotential surfaces, each surface corresponding to a different, constant value of the potential. The lines of force and the equipotential surfaces form a mutually perpendicular network. An equipotential surface can be constructed through every point of a field, but it is customary to show only a few of the equipotentials in a diagram. In general, the lines of force of a field are curves and the equipotentials are curved surfaces. For the special case of a *uniform* field, where the lines of force are straight and parallel, the equipotentials are planes perpendicular to the lines of force.

It has been shown that the lines of force at the surface of a charged conductor are at right angles to the conductor if the charges in it are at rest. Hence the surface of such a conductor is an equipotential.

Figure 26–3 shows the same arrangements of charges as in Fig. 25–8. The lines of force have been drawn dotted and the intersections of some of the equipotentials with the plane of the diagram are shown by full lines.

2. *Point charge or charged spherical conductor.* The electric intensity in the field of a single point charge is

$$E = k \frac{q}{r^2}.$$

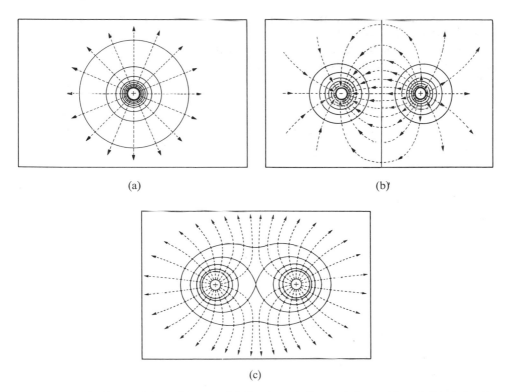

(a)   (b)

(c)

Fig. 26–3. Equipotential surfaces (solid lines) and lines of force (dotted lines) in the neighborhood of point charges.

The same equation gives the intensity in the field of a charged sphere, at points outside the sphere. As explained in Section 26–1, the line integral of $\mathbf{E}$ has the same value along any path from point a, at a radial distance r_a, to point b at a radial distance r_b. The potential difference between the points is

$$V_a - V_b = kq \left(\frac{1}{r_a} - \frac{1}{r_b} \right).$$

(26–5)

In many problems in electrostatics, it is convenient to take the reference level of potential (the point where $V = 0$) at a very large distance (an infinite distance) from all charges. Let us therefore take point b at infinity, so that $r_b = \infty$ and $V_b = 0$. Then, since a can be *any* point in the field of the charge, we can drop the subscript a from r_a and V_a and write for the potential V at a radial distance r, and relative to a point at infinity,

$$V = k\frac{q}{r}.$$

(26–6)

The potential is positive if q is positive, negative if q is negative. Since the potential is constant when r is constant, the equipotential surfaces are spheres and hence are at right angles to the lines of force.

Equation (26–6) applies to the field of a charged spherical conductor only when r is greater than or equal to the radius R of the sphere. The potential *at* the surface is

$$V = k \frac{q}{R},$$ (26–7)

and since the sphere is an equipotential volume, all points within it are at this potential. Hence we can say that Eq. (26–7) gives the potential *of* an isolated charged sphere, relative to a point at infinity.

The electric intensity **E** at the surface has a magnitude

$$E = k \frac{q}{R^2},$$

and when q is eliminated between the preceding equations, we get

$$E = V/R,$$

or

$$V = RE.$$

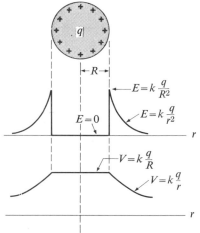

Fig. 26–4. Electric intensity E and potential V at points inside and outside a charged spherical conductor.

Figure 26–4 shows a sphere of radius R having a positive charge q, together with graphs of the electric intensity E and the potential V at points along a line through the center of the sphere.

The maximum potential to which a conductor in air can be raised is limited by the fact that air molecules become ionized, and hence the air becomes a conductor, at an electric intensity of about 3×10^6 n/coul. In general, if E_m represents the upper limit of electric intensity, known as the *dielectric strength*, the maximum potential to which a spherical conductor can be raised is

$$V_m = RE_m.$$

For a sphere 1 cm in radius, in air,

$$V_m = 10^{-2} \text{ m} \times 3 \times 10^6 \text{ n/coul} = 30,000 \text{ volts},$$

and no amount of "charging" could raise the potential of a sphere of this size, in air, higher than about 30,000 volts. It is this fact which necessitates the use of large spherical terminals on high-voltage machines. If we make $R = 2$ meters, then

$$V_m = 2 \text{ m} \times 3 \times 10^6 \text{ n/coul} = 6 \text{ million volts}.$$

At the other extreme is the effect produced by sharp points, a "point" being a surface of very *small* radius of curvature. Since the maximum potential is proportional to the radius, even relatively small potentials applied to sharp points in air will produce sufficiently high fields just outside the point to result in ionization of the surrounding air.

3. *Line charge and charged conducting cylinder.* The field of a line charge, and the field outside a charged conducting cylinder, are both given by

$$E = 2k \frac{\lambda}{r}.$$

The potential difference between any two points a and b at radial distances r_a and r_b is

$$V_a - V_b = 2k\lambda \int_{r_a}^{r_b} \frac{dr}{r} = 2k\lambda \ln \frac{r_b}{r_a}. \qquad (26\text{–}8)$$

If we take point b at infinity and set $V_b = 0$, we find for the potential V_a,

$$V_a = 2k\lambda \ln \frac{\infty}{r_a} = \infty.$$

Hence a reference point at infinity is not suitable for this field. We can, however, set $V = 0$ at some arbitrary radius r_0. Then at any radius r,

$$V = 2k\lambda \ln \frac{r_0}{r}. \qquad (26\text{–}9)$$

Equations (26–8) and (26–9) give the potential in the field of a cylinder only for values of r equal to or greater than the radius R of the cylinder. If r_0 is taken as the cylinder radius R, so that the potential of the cylinder is considered zero, the potential at any external point, relative to that of the cylinder, is

$$V = 2k\lambda \ln \frac{R}{r}. \qquad (26\text{–}10)$$

4. *Parallel plates.* The electric intensity between oppositely charged parallel plates is

$$E = \frac{\sigma}{\epsilon_0} = \text{constant.} \qquad (26\text{–}11)$$

Let us take an x-axis as in Fig. 26–5, perpendicular to the plates and with point a at the origin. Then at any point x,

$$V_a - V_x = \int_0^x E\,dx = Ex,$$

or

$$V_x = V_a - Ex = V_a - \frac{\sigma}{\epsilon_0} x.$$

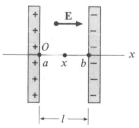

Figure 26–5

The potential therefore decreases *linearly* with x. At point b, where $x = l$ and $V_x = V_b$,

$$V_b = V_a - El,$$

and hence

$$E = \frac{V_a - V_b}{l} = \frac{V_{ab}}{l}.$$ (26-12)

That is, *the electric intensity equals the potential difference between the plates divided by the distance between them.* This is a more useful expression for E than Eq. (26-11) because the potential difference V_{ab} can readily be measured with a voltmeter, while there are no instruments that read surface density of charge directly.

Equation (26-12) also shows that the unit of electric intensity can be expressed as 1 volt/m, as well as 1 n/coul. In practice, the volt/m is most commonly used as the unit of E.

26-5 Potential in terms of charge distribution

If the electric intensity is known at all points of an electrostatic field, the potential difference between two points can be found by evaluating the line integral of $\mathbf{E}$ between the points. This is the method that was followed in the preceding section. However, if the distribution of charges setting up the field is known, the potential can be computed directly. To see how this is done, let us return to the expression for the potential of a single point charge q at a point in the field, relative to a point at infinity:

$$V = k\frac{q}{r}.$$

Since potential is a *scalar*, the potential at any point in the field of a number of point charges is the *algebraic sum* (*not* the vector sum) of the potentials due to the individual charges. Thus if a number of charges $q_1, q_2, \ldots$ are at distances $r_1, r_2, \ldots$ from some point, the potential at the point is

$$V = k\left(\frac{q_1}{r_1} + \frac{q_2}{r_2} + \cdots\right) = k\sum\frac{q}{r}.$$ (26-13)

Distributed charges can be subdivided, in imagination, into point charges dq. The sum in Eq. (26-13) then becomes an integral and

$$V = k\int\frac{dq}{r}.$$ (26-14)

This should be compared with the more complicated *vector* integral for the electric intensity $\mathbf{E}$ due to distributed charges.

EXAMPLE. Figure 26–6 represents the same point charges as in Fig. 25–4. The positive charge q_1 produces a *positive* potential at every point, and the negative charge q_2 produces a *negative* potential. The potential is the *algebraic* (not the vector) sum of these potentials.

If $q_1 = +12 \times 10^{-9}$ coul and $q_2 = -12 \times 10^{-9}$ coul, and the dimensions are as shown in the diagram, it is left to the reader to verify that

$$V_a = -900 \text{ volts}, \quad V_b = +1930 \text{ volts},$$
$$V_c = 0.$$

The potential energy of a charge $q' = +4 \times 10^{-9}$ coul, if placed at point a, is

$$(E_p)_a = q'V_a = -36 \times 10^{-7} \text{ joule}.$$

Its potential energy at point b is

$$(E_p)_b = q'V_b = +77 \times 10^{-7} \text{ joule}.$$

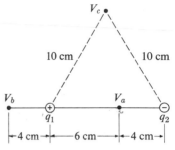

Fig. 26–6. The potential at any point is the algebraic sum of the potentials due to the point charges q_1 and q_2.

At point c, its potential energy is zero, which means that the work of the electrical force on it is zero when it is brought from infinity to point c, along any path. That this is correct can be seen by imagining the path to be the perpendicular bisector of the line joining charges q_1 and q_2. Reference to Fig. 25–4 shows that the electric intensity **E** is *perpendicular* to this path at all points, so the work of the electrical force is zero.

26–6 Potential gradient

If points a and b in Fig. 26–1 are very close together, the potential difference $V_a - V_b$ becomes simply $-dV$, and the line integral of **E** from a to b reduces to $E_s \, ds$. The *differential* form of Eq. (26–4) is therefore

$$-dV = E_s \, ds$$

or

$$E_s = -\frac{dV}{ds}. \qquad (26\text{–}15)$$

The ratio dV/ds, or the rate of change of potential with distance in the direction of ds, is called the *potential gradient*, and E_s is the component of electric intensity in the direction of ds. Hence we have the important relation: *at any point in an electric field, the component of electric intensity in any direction is equal to the negative of the potential gradient in that direction.* In particular, if the direction of ds is the same as that of the electric intensity, the component of **E** in the direction of ds is equal to **E** and *the electric intensity is equal to the negative of the potential gradient in the direction of the field.*

The unit of potential gradient is 1 volt/m and Eq. (26–12) is evidently a special case of Eq. (26–15).

EXAMPLE.   We have shown that the potential at a radial distance r from a point charge q is

$$V = k\frac{q}{r}.$$

By symmetry, the electric intensity is in the radial direction, so

$$E = E_r = -\frac{dV}{dr} = -\frac{d}{dr}\left(k\frac{q}{r}\right) = k\frac{q}{r^2},$$

in agreement with Coulomb's law.

Suppose that a given electric field has been mapped by its network of lines of force and equipotential surfaces, with the (electrical) spacing between the equipotentials equal to some constant difference ΔV such as 1 volt or 100 volts. Let Δs represent the perpendicular distance between two equipotentials. Then Δs is in the direction of the field and it follows that

$$E = -\frac{\Delta V}{\Delta s} \text{ (approximately)} \quad \text{or} \quad \Delta s = -\frac{\Delta V}{E}.$$

That is, the *greater* the electric intensity E, the *smaller* the perpendicular distance Δs between the equipotentials. The equipotentials are therefore crowded close together in a strong field and are more widely separated in a weak field. In a *uniform* field, such as that between two oppositely charged parallel plates, $E_s = E =$ constant along any line perpendicular to the plates. The equipotential planes are therefore uniformly spaced and the potential gradient is constant and equal to the total potential difference between the plates, V_{ab}, divided by their separation l. That is,

$$E = \frac{V_{ab}}{l}.$$

26–7 Field of a dipole

The *potential* in the field of a given charge distribution is usually simpler to calculate than the electric intensity, because the former is a *scalar* while the latter is a *vector*. Equation (26–15) therefore suggests that instead of computing the intensity **E** directly, we first calculate the potential V and then obtain the components of **E** by differentiation. For example, if V has been found as a function of the rectangular coordinates x, y, z, the components E_x, E_y, and E_z are obtained by taking the derivatives of V with respect to x, y, and z.

$$E_x = -\frac{\partial V}{\partial x}, \quad E_y = -\frac{\partial V}{\partial y}, \quad E_z = -\frac{\partial V}{\partial z}. \quad (26\text{–}16)$$

The symbol ∂ means that these are *partial derivatives*. That is, in computing $\partial V/\partial x$, the variables y and z are considered constant.

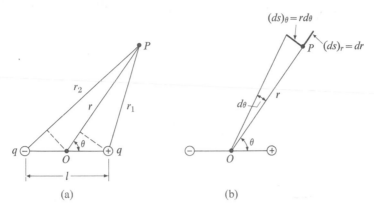

Fig. 26–7. (a) The charges $+q$ and $-q$ form an *electric dipole*. (b) Rectangular elements of length in the direction of increasing r and of increasing θ.

As an illustration, we compute the electric intensity in the field of an *electric doublet* or an *electric dipole*, that is, two point charges of equal magnitude and opposite sign, such as those in part (b) of Fig. 26–3. The dipole is shown in Fig. 26–7(a).

The potential at P is

$$V = k \left(\frac{q}{r_1} - \frac{q}{r_2} \right).$$

Let r represent the distance from the midpoint O of the dipole to a point P, and θ the angle between r and the dipole axis. If r is large compared with the separation l of the charges, the distances r_1 and r_2 are, very nearly,

$$r_1 = r - \frac{l}{2} \cos \theta, \qquad r_2 = r + \frac{l}{2} \cos \theta.$$

Then

$$V = kq \left(\frac{1}{r - (l/2) \cos \theta} - \frac{1}{r + (l/2) \cos \theta} \right)$$

$$= kql \frac{\cos \theta}{r^2 - (l^2/4) \cos^2 \theta}.$$

If $r \gg l$, we can neglect the second term in the denominator. The product of the charge q and the charge separation l is called the *electric moment* or the *dipole moment* and is represented by p. (The dipole moment is analogous to the moment of a couple in mechanics.) The potential can then be written

$$V = kp \frac{\cos \theta}{r^2}.$$

The potential (and hence the field) depends on the polar coordinates r and θ of point P, and on the dipole moment p, but not on the values of q and l separately.

We can now compute the components of **E** in the directions of increasing r and of increasing θ. The change in V when we move along the element $(ds)_r$, *keeping θ constant*, is

$$dV_r = -kp\frac{2\cos\theta}{r^3}\,dr.$$

When we move along the element $(ds)_\theta$, *keeping r constant*, the change in V is

$$dV_\theta = -kp\frac{\sin\theta}{r^2}\,d\theta.$$

The length of the element $(ds)_r$, in the direction of increasing r, is dr, and that of the element $(ds)_\theta$, in the direction of increasing θ, is $r\,d\theta$. [See Fig. 26–7(b).] The corresponding components of **E** are therefore

$$E_r = -\frac{dV_r}{(ds)_r} = k2p\frac{\cos\theta}{r^3}, \tag{26–17}$$

$$E_\theta = -\frac{dV_\theta}{(ds)_\theta} = kp\frac{\sin\theta}{r^3}. \tag{26–18}$$

Thus along any radial line (for which θ is constant) the intensity decreases with the inverse *cube* of the distance r. In the direction of the dipole axis, $\theta = 0$ or $180°$, $\sin\theta = 0$, $\cos\theta = \pm1$. The θ-component is then zero. The only component is the radial component and

$$E = E_r = \pm k\frac{2p}{r^3}. \tag{26–19}$$

The field is *outward* when $\theta = 0$ and $\cos\theta = 1$ and is *inward* when $\theta = 180°$ and $\cos\theta = -1$.

Similarly, in a direction perpendicular to the axis,

$$E = E_\theta = \pm k\frac{p}{r^3}. \tag{26–20}$$

At any arbitrary point, the resultant intensity E is

$$E = \sqrt{E_r^2 + E_\theta^2}$$

and the angle ϕ it makes with the radial direction is given by

$$\tan\phi = \frac{E_\theta}{E_r} = \frac{\sin\theta}{2\cos\theta} = \frac{1}{2}\tan\theta.$$

Figure 26–8 shows the E-vectors at a few points in the dipole field, all at the same radial distance r. Their relative magnitudes are not strictly correct because the analysis above is an approximation, good only when $r \gg l$. Figure 26–8 should be compared with Fig. 26–3(b), which shows the lines of force of the complete dipole field.

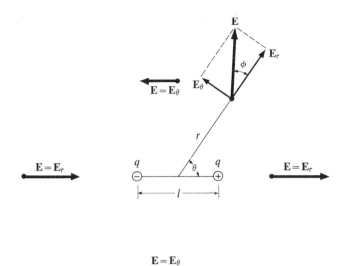

Fig. 26–8. Electric intensity at some points in a dipole field.

Figure 26–9 represents a dipole of moment $p = ql$, in the yz-plane. The dipole is in a uniform *external* field E, parallel to the y-axis, and the axis of the dipole makes an angle α with the field. The charges $+q$ and $-q$ are acted on by equal and opposite forces of magnitude qE. The resultant *force* on the dipole is zero, but the forces on the charges do not have the same line of action and constitute a *couple* of moment

$$\Gamma = (qE)(l \sin \alpha) = (ql)(E \sin \alpha) = pE \sin \alpha.$$

The *vector moment* of the dipole, **p**, is defined as a vector of magnitude p, along the dipole axis and directed from the negative to the positive charge. Hence we can write the equation above in vector form:

$$\Gamma = \mathbf{p} \times \mathbf{E}.$$

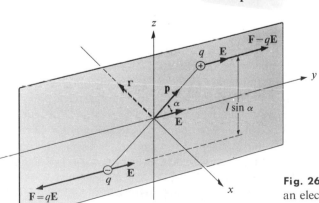

Fig. 26–9. A dipole of moment **p** in an electric field of intensity **E** is acted on by a torque $\Gamma = \mathbf{p} \times \mathbf{E}$.

The torque vector $\boldsymbol{\Gamma}$ points along the negative x-axis, in the direction of the vector product $\mathbf{p} \times \mathbf{E}$.

The effect of the torque $\boldsymbol{\Gamma}$ is to rotate the dipole to a position in which its vector moment $\mathbf{p}$ is parallel to $\mathbf{E}$. In the equilibrium position, the torque is zero.

26–8 The Millikan oil drop experiment

We have now developed the theory of electrostatics to a point where one of the classical physical experiments of all time can be described. In a brilliant series of investigations carried out at the University of Chicago in the period 1909–1913, Robert Andrews Millikan not only demonstrated conclusively the discrete nature of electric charge, but actually measured the charge of an individual electron.

Millikan's apparatus is shown schematically in Fig. 26–10(a). Two accurately parallel horizontal metal plates, A and B, are insulated from each other and separated by a few millimeters. Oil is sprayed in fine droplets from an atomizer above the upper plate and a few of the droplets are allowed to fall through a small hole in this plate. A beam of light is directed horizontally between the plates and a telescope is set up with its axis at right angles to the light beam. The oil drops, illuminated by the light beam, appear like tiny bright stars when viewed through the telescope, falling slowly with a terminal velocity determined by their weight, by the viscous force opposing their motion, and by the buoyant force.

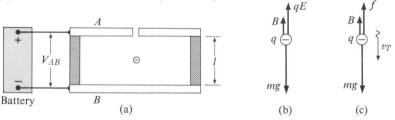

Fig. 26–10. (a) Schematic diagram of Millikan apparatus. (b) Forces on a drop at rest. (c) Forces on a drop falling with its terminal velocity v_T.

It is found that some of the oil droplets are electrically charged, presumably because of frictional effects. Charges can also be given the drops if the air in the apparatus is ionized by x-rays or a bit of radioactive material. Some of the electrons or ions then collide with the drops and stick to them. The drops are usually negatively charged, but occasionally one with a positive charge is found.

The simplest method, in principle, for measuring the charge on a drop is as follows. Suppose a drop has a negative charge and the plates are maintained at a potential difference such that a downward electric field of intensity $E \ (= V_{AB}/l)$ is set up between them. The forces on the drop are then its weight mg, the buoyant force B, and the upward force qE. By adjusting the field E, the sum $B + qE$ can be made just equal to mg, so that the drop remains at rest as indicated in Fig. 26–10(b). Under these circumstances,

$$qE + B = mg \quad \text{or} \quad q = \frac{mg - B}{E}.$$

The mass of the drop equals the product of its density ρ and its volume, and the buoyant force B equals the product of its volume and the weight density $\rho_g g$ of the gas in the apparatus (usually air). Since the volume equals $4\pi r^3/3$, and $E = V_{AB}/l$,

$$ q = \frac{4\pi}{3} \frac{(\rho - \rho_g)r^3 gl}{V_{AB}}. \tag{26-21} $$

All the quantities on the right are readily measurable with the exception of the drop radius r, which is of the order of 10^{-5} cm and is much too small to be measured directly. It can be calculated, however, by cutting off the electric field and measuring the terminal velocity v_T of the drop as it falls through a known distance d defined by reference lines in the ocular of the telescope.

The terminal velocity is that at which the weight mg is just balanced by the sum of the buoyant force B and the viscous force f. The viscous force on a sphere of radius r, moving with a velocity v through a fluid of viscosity η, is given by Stokes' law,*

$$ f = 6\pi\eta rv. $$

If Stokes' law applies, and the drop is falling with its terminal velocity v_T,

$$ mg = B + f, $$

$$ \tfrac{4}{3}\pi r^3 \rho g = \tfrac{4}{3}\pi r^3 \rho_g g + 6\pi\eta r v_T, $$

and

$$ r = 3\sqrt{\eta v_T/2(\rho - \rho_g)g}. $$

When this expression for r is inserted in Eq. (26–21), we have

$$ q = 18\pi \frac{l}{V_{AB}} \sqrt{\frac{\eta^3 v_T^3}{2(\rho - \rho_g)g}}, $$

which expresses the charge q in terms of measurable quantities.

Procedures other than that above are often followed in the laboratory. Thus instead of first balancing the weight of a drop by an electrical force and then timing the drop as it falls in zero field, an arbitrary field larger than that needed for equilibrium is applied, first in one direction and then in the other, and the terminal velocity is measured for both the upward and downward motions. Or, a rapidly alternating field may be superposed on the balancing field so that a charged drop appears to be drawn out into a bright vertical line. The length of this line, for drops of the same radius, is directly proportional to the charge on the drop.

Millikan and his co-workers measured the charges of some thousands of drops, and found that within the limits of their experimental errors every drop had a charge

---

* Stokes' law is a theoretical relation derived for a sphere moving through a *continuous* fluid. For spheres as small as 10^{-5} cm in radius, and for air at atmospheric pressure, the air cannot be considered a continuous fluid and in work of high precision a correction must be made to Stokes' law.

equal to some small, integral multiple of a basic charge e. That is, drops were observed with charges of e, $2e$, $3e$, etc., but never with such values as $0.76e$ or $2.49e$. The evidence is conclusive that electric charge is not something which can be divided indefinitely, but that it exists in nature only in units of magnitude e. When a drop is observed with charge e, we conclude it has acquired one extra electron, if its charge is $2e$, it has two extra electrons, and so on.

26–9 The electron volt. Relativistic variation of mass with velocity

The change in potential energy of a particle having a charge q, when it moves from a point where the potential is V_a to a point where the potential is V_b, is

$$\Delta E_p = qV_{ab}.$$

In particular, if the charge q equals the electronic charge $e = 1.60 \times 10^{-19}$ coul, and the potential difference $V_{ab} = 1$ volt, the change in energy is

$$\Delta E_p = 1.60 \times 10^{-19}\,\text{coul} \times 1\,\text{volt} = 1.60 \times 10^{-19}\,\text{joule}.$$

This quantity of energy is called *one electron volt* (1 ev):

$$1\,\text{electron volt} = 1.60 \times 10^{-19}\,\text{joule}.$$

The electron volt is a convenient energy unit when one is dealing with the motions of electrons and ions in electric fields, because the change in potential energy between two points on the path of a particle having a charge e, when expressed in electron volts, is *numerically* equal to the potential difference between the points, in volts. If the charge is some multiple of e, say Ne, the change in potential energy in electron volts is, numerically, N times the potential difference in volts. For example, if a particle having a charge $2e$ moves between two points for which the potential difference is 1000 volts, the change in its potential energy is

$$\begin{aligned}\Delta E_p = qV_{ab} &= 2 \times 1.6 \times 10^{-19}\,\text{coul} \times 10^3\,\text{volts} \\ &= 3.2 \times 10^{-16}\,\text{joule} \\ &= 2000\,\text{ev}.\end{aligned}$$

Although the electron volt was defined above in terms of *potential* energy, energy of *any* form, such as the kinetic energy of a moving particle, can be expressed in terms of the electron volt. Thus one may speak of a "one million volt electron," meaning an electron having a kinetic energy of one million electron volts.

According to the principles of special relativity, the mass m_0 of a particle at rest relative to an observer is equivalent to a quantity of energy equal to m_0c^2, where c is the speed of light. The rest mass of an electron is 9.108×10^{-31} kgm, and the energy equivalent to this is

$$\begin{aligned}E_0 = m_0c^2 &= 9.108 \times 10^{-31}\,\text{kgm} \times (3 \times 10^8\,\text{m/sec})^2 \\ &= 82 \times 10^{-15}\,\text{joule}.\end{aligned}$$

Since 1 ev $= 1.60 \times 10^{-19}$ joule, this is equivalent to

$$E_0 = 512{,}000 \text{ ev} = 0.512 \text{ Mev.}$$

Suppose that an electron is accelerated from rest through a potential difference of this magnitude, 512,000 volts. It then acquires a *kinetic* energy of 512,000 ev, equal to its rest-mass energy, and its *total* energy, rest-mass energy plus kinetic energy, is twice the rest-mass energy.

$$E = E_0 + E_k = 2m_0 c^2.$$

But its total energy is also equal to mc^2, where m is its "moving" mass, so

$$mc^2 = 2m_0 c^2, \qquad m = 2m_0.$$

That is, the mass of an electron accelerated through a potential difference of 512,000 volts is twice as great as its rest mass.

The mass and velocity are related by the equation

$$m = \frac{m_0}{\sqrt{1 - v^2/c^2}},$$

or,

$$\frac{v}{c} = \sqrt{1 - (m_0/m)^2}.$$

Hence

$$\frac{v}{c} = \sqrt{1 - (\tfrac{1}{2})^2} = 0.866,$$

$$v = 0.866c = 2.6 \times 10^8 \text{ m/sec.}$$

To calculate the velocity from the principles of classical mechanics, we would set the kinetic energy E_k of 512,000 ev or 82.0×10^{-15} joule, equal to $\tfrac{1}{2}m_0 v^2$. Then

$$v = \sqrt{\frac{2E_k}{m_0}} = \sqrt{\frac{2 \times 82 \times 10^{-15} \text{ joule}}{9.108 \times 10^{-31} \text{ kgm}}} = 4.25 \times 10^8 \text{ m/sec,}$$

which is greater than the speed of light! It is evident that relativistic mechanics must be used when dealing with electron energies in this range.

26-10 The cathode-ray oscilloscope

Figure 26–11 is a schematic diagram of the elements of a cathode-ray oscilloscope tube. The interior of the tube is highly evacuated. The *cathode* at the left is raised to a high temperature by the *heater*, and electrons evaporate from its surface. (Before the nature of this process of electron emission was fully understood, these electrons were given the name, "cathode rays.") The *accelerating anode*, which has a small hole at its center, is maintained at a high positive potential V_1 relative to the cathode, so that there is an electric field, directed from right to left, between the anode and cathode. This field is confined to the cathode-anode region and electrons passing

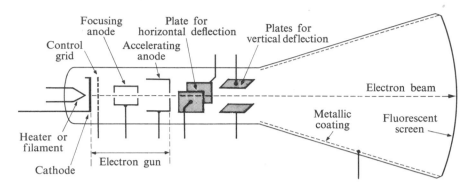

Fig. 26–11.   Basic elements of a cathode-ray tube.

through the hole in the anode travel with a *constant x*-velocity from the anode to the *fluorescent screen*.

The function of the *control grid* is to regulate the number of electrons that reach the anode (and hence the brightness of the spot on the screen). The *focusing anode* ensures that electrons leaving the cathode in slightly different directions all arrive at the same spot on the screen. These two electrodes need not be considered in the following analysis. The complete assembly of cathode, control grid, focusing anode, and accelerating electrode is referred to as an *electron gun*.

The accelerated electrons pass between two pairs of *deflecting plates*. An electric field between the first pair of plates deflects them to the right or left, and a field between the second pair deflects them up or down. In the absence of such fields the electrons travel in a straight line from the hole in the accelerating anode to the *fluorescent screen* and produce a bright spot on the screen where they strike it.

Let us first calculate the velocity imparted to the electrons by the electron gun. The only force on them is the *conservative* electrical force, so we can use the principle of *conservation of energy*. Let subscripts c and a refer to cathode and anode. Then*

$$\tfrac{1}{2}mv_c^2 + eV_c = \tfrac{1}{2}mv_a^2 + eV_a.$$

Although the electrons have a velocity v_c when they evaporate from the cathode, this is very small compared with their final velocity v_a and can be neglected. Therefore

$$v_a = \sqrt{\frac{2e(V_c - V_a)}{m}} = \sqrt{\frac{2eV_1}{m}}, \tag{26–22}$$

where for brevity we have represented the accelerating potential difference V_{ca} by V_1.

The anode is at a *higher* potential than the cathode, so $V_1 = V_{ca}$ is a negative quantity. But the electron charge e is also negative, so the term under the radical is positive.

---

* The potential differences in a typical cathode-ray tube are not so large that relativistic mechanics needs to be used.

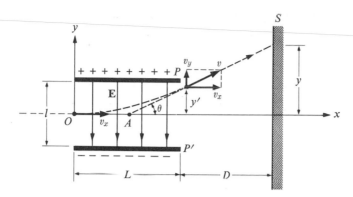

Fig. 26–12. Electrostatic deflection of cathode rays.

As a numerical example, if $V_1 = -2000$ volts,

$$v_a = \sqrt{\frac{2 \times (-1.6 \times 10^{-19} \text{ coul}) \times (-2 \times 10^3 \text{ volts})}{9.11 \times 10^{-31} \text{ kgm}}} = 2.65 \times 10^7 \text{ m/sec.}$$

We can now see one of the advantages of describing electric fields in terms of *potentials*. The kinetic energy of an electron at the anode depends only on the *potential difference* between anode and cathode, and not at all on the fields within the electron gun set up by the screen and focusing anode, or on the shape of the electron trajectory within the gun.

If there is no electric field between the plates for horizontal deflection, the electrons enter the region between the other plates with a velocity equal to v_a and represented by v_x in Fig. 26–12. If there is a potential difference V_2 between these plates, and the upper plate is positive, a downward electric field of intensity $E = V_2/l$ is set up between the plates. A constant upward force eE then acts on the electrons and their upward acceleration is

$$a_y = \frac{eE}{m}. \tag{26–23}$$

The *horizontal* velocity remains constant, so the time required to travel the length L of the plates is

$$t = \frac{L}{v_x}. \tag{26–24}$$

In this time, they acquire an upward velocity given by

$$v_y = a_y t \tag{26–25}$$

and are displaced upward by an amount

$$y' = \tfrac{1}{2} a_y t^2.$$

On emerging from the deflecting field, their velocity v makes an angle θ with the x-axis, where

$$\tan \theta = \frac{v_y}{v_x},$$

and from this point on they travel in a straight line to the screen. It is not difficult to show that this straight line, if projected backward, intersects the x-axis at a point A which is midway between the ends of the plates. Then if y is the vertical coordinate of the point of impact with screen S,

$$\tan \theta = \frac{y}{D + (L/2)} = \frac{v_y}{v_x}.$$

When this is combined with Eqs. (26–23), (26–24), and (26–25), we get finally

$$y = \left[\frac{L}{2l} \left(D + \frac{L}{2} \right) \right] \frac{V_2}{V_1}. \tag{26–26}$$

The term in brackets is a purely geometrical factor. If the accelerating voltage V_1 is held constant, the deflection y is proportional to the deflecting voltage V_2.

If a field is also set up between the horizontal deflecting plates, the beam is deflected in both the x- and y-directions. The coordinates of the luminous spot on the screen are proportional, respectively, to the horizontal and vertical deflecting voltages.

As a numerical illustration, let $L = 2 \text{ cm} = 2 \times 10^{-2} \text{ m}$, $l = 0.5 \text{ cm} = 5 \times 10^{-3} \text{ m}$, and let $v_x = v_a$ have the value computed above of $2.65 \times 10^7 \text{ m/sec}$. If the potential difference V_2 between the deflecting plates is 100 volts, the deflecting field E is

$$E = \frac{V_2}{l} = 2 \times 10^4 \text{ volts/m}.$$

The y-acceleration is

$$a_y = \frac{eE}{m} = 3.52 \times 10^{15} \text{ m/sec}^2.$$

The time to travel the length of the plates is

$$t = \frac{L}{v_x} = 7.55 \times 10^{-10} \text{ sec}.$$

The upward velocity v_y is

$$v_y = a_y t = 2.66 \times 10^6 \text{ m/sec}.$$

The upward displacement y' is

$$y' = \tfrac{1}{2} a_y t^2 = 10^{-3} \text{ m}.$$

The tangent of the angle θ is

$$\tan \theta = \frac{v_y}{v_x} = 0.10.$$

If the distance D to the screen is 20 cm, the displacement y on the screen is

$$y = \left(D + \frac{L}{2} \right) \tan \theta = 2.1 \text{ cm}.$$

26–11 Sharing of charge by conductors

When a charged conductor is brought into electrical contact with one which is uncharged, the original charge is shared between the two. That this should happen is evident from the mutual forces of repulsion between the component parts of the original charge. The question as to precisely how much charge will be transferred has not yet been answered, but we can now see that it must be such as to bring all points of both conductors to the same potential. Thus if a positively charged body makes *external* contact with an uncharged body, the first will lose some of its charge and its potential will decrease, while the second will gain charge and its potential will increase. The flow of charge will cease when both bodies are at the same potential, but there will still remain some charge on the first body.

When a charged body makes contact with the *interior* of a conductor, however, the situation is quite different, as emphasized in Section 25–5. There it was shown that, as a consequence of Gauss's law, an induced charge of opposite sign appears on the inner surface of the hollow conductor, and this charge is independent of the position of the charged body within the cavity. Upon touching the charged body to the wall of the cavity, the first body transfers *all* of its charge to the hollow conductor, in spite of the fact that the latter may have originally been charged.

To study this experiment in more detail, consider the large hollow metal sphere B shown in Fig. 26–13(a) with an original positive charge q_B indicated by positive signs with circles around them and with an inner radius r_B. Let an opening be made in the walls large enough to admit a small metal sphere A of radius r_A and with a positive charge q_A.

When A is at the center of B and the small effect due to the small opening in B is neglected, the positive charge on A and the equal induced negative charge on the interior surface of B are *evenly distributed*, and the electric field between these two

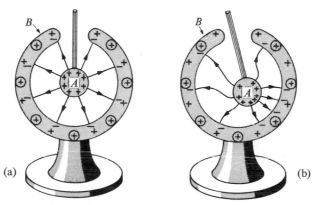

(a)   (b)

Fig. 26–13. Body A, with charge $+q_A$ introduced into a hollow spherical conductor B with an original charge $+q_B$ (indicated by the symbol $\oplus$). (a) When A is at the center, the field around it is symmetrical and the induced negative charge $-q_A$ is distributed evenly on the inner surface of the hollow sphere. (b) When A is off-center, the field around it is asymmetrical and the induced negative charge $-q_A$ is distributed unevenly on the inner surface of the hollow sphere.

charges is symmetrical and radial. By Gauss's law, the field between A and B is due only to the charge on A, and at a distance r from the center of A, is given by

$$E = kq_A \frac{1}{r^2}.$$

The potential difference between A and B is therefore

$$V_A - V_B = kq_A \left(\frac{1}{r_A} - \frac{1}{r_B} \right).$$
(26–27)

This equation expresses two important facts:

(1) $V_A - V_B$ is positive, or A is at a *higher* potential than B.

(2) $V_A - V_B$ depends *only* on q_A, and is thus independent of the original charge residing on B.

If A and B are connected by a conductor, electricity will flow from A to B until $V_A - V_B = 0$, or, from Eq. (26–27), until $q_A = 0$. This leads to the conclusion that *all* of the charge on A is transferred to B, *regardless of the initial value of B's charge and potential.* This is the principle of the Van de Graaff generator, described in the next section.

When body A is off center, as shown in Fig. 26–13(b), the positive charge on A and the equal induced negative charge on the interior wall of B are unevenly distributed. The electric field between A and B is quite asymmetrical and cannot be expressed in simple mathematical form. The difference of potential $V_A - V_B$ is *still positive*, however, but with a value smaller than that which existed when A was at the center, and furthermore, $V_A - V_B$ still depends *only* on q_A, regardless of the original charge and potential of B.

26–12 The Van de Graaff generator

We have already explained that when a charged conductor is inserted in a hollow conductor and makes internal contact with this conductor, all of the charge on the first conductor is transferred to the second, whatever charge the second may already have. Were it not for insulation difficulties, the charge (and hence the potential) of a hollow conductor could be increased without limit by repeating this process. (Of course, as the potential of the conductor is raised, a greater and greater repelling force is exerted on each successive charge brought up to it. Eventually, we might not be strong enough to bring up more charge!)

The generator invented by Robert J. Van de Graaff makes use of the principle above, but instead of inserting charged bodies into a conductor one after another, charge is carried in continuously by a "belt conveyor."

Figure 26–14 is a schematic diagram of a small Van de Graaff generator designed for demonstration purposes. A hollow metal conductor A, approximately spherical, is supported on an insulating tube B mounted on a metal base C which is normally grounded. A nonconducting endless belt D runs over two nonconducting pulleys E and F. Pulley F may be driven by hand or by a small electric motor.

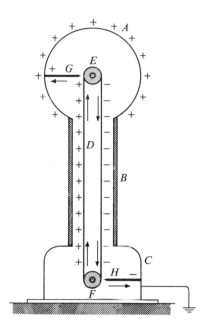

Fig. 26–14. Simple model of a Van de Graaff generator.

Pulleys E and F are covered with different materials, chosen so that when belt D makes contact with F it acquires a positive charge, while on contact with E it acquires a negative charge. Sharp points G and H are connected electrically to the upper conductor A and the base C.

The charges developed on the belt, as it makes contact with the pulleys, stick to it and are carried along by it. The left side of the belt, moving upward, carries a continuous stream of positive charge into the upper conductor. As it passes G, it induces a charge on this conductor which, because of the sharp points, results in a sufficiently high field intensity to ionize the air between the point and the belt. The ionized air provides a conducting path along which the positive charge on the belt can flow to conductor A.

As the belt leaves the pulley E, it becomes negatively charged and the right side of the belt carries negative charge *out* of the upper terminal. Removal of negative charge is equivalent to addition of positive charge, so both sides of the belt act to increase the net positive charge on terminal A. Negative charge is removed from the belt at the sharp point H, and flows to ground.

Problems

26–1. A particle of charge $+3 \times 10^{-9}$ coul is situated in a uniform electric field directed to the left. In moving to the right a distance of 5 cm the work of an applied force is 6×10^{-5} joule and the change in kinetic energy of the particle is $+4.5 \times 10^{-5}$ joule. (a) What is the work of the electrical force? (b) What is the magnitude of the electric intensity?

26–2. A charge of 2.5×10^{-8} coul is placed in an upwardly directed uniform electric field whose intensity is 5×10^4 n/coul. What is the work of the electrical force when the charge is moved (a) 45 cm to the right? (b) 80 cm downward? (c) 260 cm at an angle of 45° upward from the horizontal?

26–3. (a) Show that $1 \, \text{n/coul} = 1 \, \text{volt/m}$. (b) A potential difference of 2000 volts is established between parallel plates in air. If the air becomes electrically conducting when the electric intensity exceeds 3×10^6 n/coul, what is the minimum separation of the plates?

26–4. A small sphere of mass 0.2 gm hangs by a thread between two parallel vertical plates 5 cm apart. The charge on the sphere is 6×10^{-9} coul. What potential difference between the plates will cause the thread to assume an angle of 30° with the vertical?

26–5. The potential at a certain distance from a point charge is 600 volts, and the electric field is 200 n/coul. (a) What is the distance to the point charge? (b) What is the magnitude of the charge?

26–6. Two point charges whose magnitudes are $+20 \times 10^{-9}$ coul and -12×10^{-9} coul are separated by a distance of 5 cm. An electron is released from rest between the two charges, 1 cm from the negative charge, and moves along the line connecting the two charges. What is its velocity when it is 1 cm from the positive charge?

26–7. Two positive point charges, each of magnitude q, are fixed on the y-axis at the points $y = +a$ and $y = -a$. (a) Draw a diagram showing the positions of the charges. (b) What is the potential V_0 at the origin? (c) Show that the potential at any point on the x-axis is

$$V = k \frac{2q}{\sqrt{a^2 + x^2}} \, .$$

(d) Sketch a graph of the potential on the x-axis as a function of x over the range from $x = +4a$ to $x = -4a$. (e) At what value of x is the potential one-half that at the origin?

26–8. Consider the same distribution of charges as in Problem 26–7. (a) Sketch a graph of the potential on the y-axis as a function of y, over the range from $y = +4a$ to $y = -4a$. (b) Discuss the physical meaning of the graph at the points $+a$ and $-a$. (c) At what point or points on the y-axis is the potential equal to that at the origin? (d) At what points on the y-axis is the potential equal to half its value at the origin?

26–9. Consider the same charge distribution as in Problem 26–7. (a) Suppose a positively charged particle of charge q' and mass m is placed precisely at the origin and released from rest. What happens? (b) What will happen if the charge in part (a) is displaced slightly in the direction of the y-axis? (c) What will happen if it is displaced slightly in the direction of the x-axis?

26–10. Again consider the charge distribution in Problem 26–7. Suppose a positively charged particle of charge q' and mass m is displaced slightly from the origin in the direction of the x-axis. (a) What is its velocity at infinity? (b) Sketch a graph of the velocity of the particle as a function of x. (c) If the particle is projected toward the left along the x-axis from a point at a large distance to the right of the origin, with a velocity half that acquired in part (a), at what distance from the origin will it come to rest? (d) If a negatively charged particle were released from rest on the x-axis, at a very large distance to the left of the origin, what would be its velocity as it passed the origin?

26–11. A positive charge $+q$ is located at the point $x = -a$, $y = -a$, and an equal negative charge $-q$ is located at the point $x = +a$, $y = -a$. (a) Draw a diagram showing the positions of the charges. (b) What is the potential at the origin? (c) What is the expression for the potential at a point on the x-axis, as a function of x? (d) Sketch a graph of the potential as a function of x, in the range from $x = +a$ to $x = -4a$. Plot positive potentials upward, negative potentials downward.

26–12. A potential difference of 1600 volts is established between two parallel plates 4 cm apart. An electron is released from the negative plate at the same instant that a proton is released from the positive plate. (a) How far from the positive plate will they pass each other? (b) How do their velocities compare when they strike the opposite plates? (c) How do their energies compare when they strike the opposite plates?

26–13. Consider the same charge distribution as in Problem 26–7. (a) Construct a graph of the potential energy of a positive point charge on the x-axis, as a function of x. (b) Construct a graph of the potential energy of a negative point charge on the axis, as a function of x. (c) What is the potential gradient at the origin, in the direction of the x-axis?

26–14. A vacuum diode consists of a cylindrical cathode of 0.05 cm in radius, mounted coaxially within a cylindrical anode 0.45 cm in radius. The potential of the anode is 300 volts above that of the cathode. An electron leaves the surface of the cathode with zero initial velocity. Find its velocity when it strikes the anode.

26–15. A vacuum triode may be idealized as follows. A plane surface (the cathode) emits electrons with negligible initial velocities. Parallel to the cathode and 3 mm away from it is an open grid of fine wire at a potential of 18 volts above the cathode. A second plane surface (the anode) is 12 mm beyond the grid and is at a potential of 15 volts above the cathode. Assume that the plane of the grid is an equipotential surface, and that the potential gradients between cathode and grid, and between grid and anode, are uniform. Assume also that the structure of the grid is sufficiently open for electrons to pass through it freely. (a) Draw a diagram of potential vs. distance, along a line from cathode to anode. (b) With what velocity will electrons strike the anode?

26–16. A positively charged ring of radius R is placed with its plane perpendicular to the x-axis and with its center at the origin. (a) Construct a graph of the potential V at points on the x-axis, as a function of x. (b) Construct in the same diagram a graph of the magnitude of the electric intensity E. (c) How is the second graph related geometrically to the first?

26–17. The small disks in Fig. 25–21 have an area of 8 cm². They are touched and separated while perpendicular to the field between two large parallel plates 10 cm apart, between which there is a potential difference of 5000 volts. (a) What is the induced charge on each plate? (b) If one of the disks is touched to the inner wall of an isolated hollow sphere of outer radius 20 cm, initially uncharged, what is the potential of the sphere?

26–18. A metal sphere of radius r_a is supported on an insulating stand at the center of a hollow metal sphere of inner radius r_b. There is a charge $+q$ on the inner sphere and a charge $-q$ on the outer. (a) Show that the potential difference between the spheres is

$$V_{ab} = kq \left(\frac{1}{r_a} - \frac{1}{r_b} \right).$$

(b) Show that the electric intensity at any point between the spheres is

$$E = \frac{V_{ab}}{(1/r_a - 1/r_b)} \cdot \frac{1}{r^2}.$$

(See Problem 25–17.)

26–19. A long metal cylinder of radius r_a is supported on an insulating stand on the axis of a long hollow metal cylinder of inner radius r_b. The positive charge per unit length on the inner cylinder is λ and there is an equal negative charge per unit length on the outer cylinder. (a) Show that the potential difference between the cylinders is

$$V_{ab} = 2k\lambda \ln \frac{r_b}{r_a}.$$

(b) Show that the electric intensity at any point between the cylinders is

$$E = \frac{V_{ab}}{\ln (r_b/r_a)} \cdot \frac{1}{r}.$$

(c) What is the potential difference if the outer cylinder has no net charge? (See Problem 25–20.)

26–20. Refer to Problem 25–21. (a) Find the expression for the potential V as a function of r, both inside and outside the sphere, relative to a point at infinity. (b) Sketch graphs of V and E as functions of r from $r = 0$ to $r = 3R$, and compare with Fig. 26–4.

26–21. Refer to Problem 25–22. Find the expressions for the potential V as a function of r, both inside and outside the cylinder. Let $V = 0$ at the surface of the cylinder. (b) Sketch graphs of V and E as functions of r, from $r = 0$ to $r = 3R$, and compare with Fig. 26–4.

26–22. In an apparatus for measuring the electronic charge e by Millikan's method, an electric intensity of 6.34×10^4 volts/m is required to maintain a charged oil drop at rest. If the plates are 1.5 cm apart, what potential difference between them is required?

26–23. An oil droplet of mass 3×10^{-11} gm and of radius 2×10^{-4} cm carries 10 excess electrons. What is its terminal velocity (a) when falling in a region in which there is no electric field? (b) When falling in an electric field whose intensity is 3×10^5 n/coul directed downward? The viscosity of air is 180×10^{-7} n·sec/m². Neglect the buoyant force of the air.

26–24. A charged oil drop, in a Millikan oil-drop apparatus, is observed to fall through a distance of 1 mm in a time of 27.4 sec, in the absence of any external field. The same drop can be held stationary in a field of 2.37×10^4 n/coul. How many excess electrons has the drop acquired? The viscosity of air is 180×10^{-7} n·sec/m². The density of the oil is 824 kgm/m³, and the density of air is 1.29 kgm/m³.

26–25. A charged oil drop falls 4.0 mm in 16.0 sec at constant speed in air in the absence of an electric field. The density of the oil is 0.80 gm/cm³, that of the air is 1.30×10^{-3} gm/cm³, and the coefficient of viscosity of the air is 1.80×10^{-5} n·sec/m². Find (a) the radius of the drop and (b) the mass of the drop. (c) If the drop carries one electronic unit of charge and is in an electric field of 2×10^5 n/coul, what is the ratio of the force of the electric field on the drop to its weight?

26–26. When the oil drop in Problem 26–25 was in a constant electric field of 2×10^5 n/coul, several different times of rise over the distance of 4.0 mm were observed. The measured times were 36.0, 11.2, 17.7, 7.7, and 23.0 sec. Calculate (a) the velocity of fall under gravity, (b) the velocity of rise in each case, and (c) the sum of the velocity in part (a) and each velocity in part (b). (d) Show that the sums in part (c) are integral multiples of some number and interpret this result. (e) Calculate the value of the electronic charge from these data.

26–27. (a) Prove that when a particle of constant mass and charge is accelerated from rest in an electric field, its final velocity is proportional to the square root of the potential difference through which it is accelerated. (b) Find the magnitude of the proportionality constant if the particle is an electron, the velocity is in m/sec, and the potential difference is in volts. (c) What is the final velocity of an electron accelerated through a potential difference of 1136 volts if it has an initial velocity of 10^7 m/sec?

26–28. (a) What is the maximum potential difference through which an electron can be accelerated if its mass is not to exceed its rest mass by more than 1% of the rest mass? (That is, m is not to be larger than $1.01 m_0$.) (b) What is the speed of such an electron, expressed as a fraction of the speed of light, c? (c) Make the same calculations for a proton.

26–29. The Cambridge electron accelerator accelerates electrons through a potential difference of 6.5×10^9 volts, so that their kinetic energy is 6.5×10^9 ev. (a) What is the ratio of the mass m of an electron having this energy, to its rest mass m_0? (b) What is the ratio of its speed v to the speed of light, c? (c) What would the speed be if computed from the principles of classical mechanics?

26–30. An electron in a certain x-ray tube is accelerated from rest through a potential difference of 180,000 volts in going from the cathode to the anode. When it arrives at the anode what is its (a) kinetic energy in ev, (b) its relativistic mass m, (c) its velocity, and (d) the value of e/m? (e) What is the velocity of the electron calculated classically?

26–31. Calculate, relativistically, the amount of work in Mev that must be done (a) to bring an electron from rest to a velocity of $0.4c$, and (b) to increase its velocity from $0.4c$ to $0.8c$. (c) What is the ratio of the kinetic energy of the electron at the velocity of $0.8c$ to that of $0.4c$ when computed from (1) relativistic values and (2) from classical values?

26–32. The electric intensity in the region between the deflecting plates of a certain

cathode-ray oscilloscope is 30,000 n/coul. (a) What is the force on an electron in this region? (b) What is the acceleration of an electron when acted on by this force?

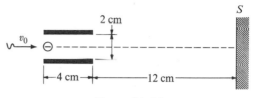

Figure 26–15

26–33. In Fig. 26–15, an electron is projected along the axis midway between the plates of a cathode-ray tube with an initial velocity of 2×10^7 m/sec. The uniform electric field between the plates has an intensity of 20,000 n/coul and is upward. (a) How far below the axis has the electron moved when it reaches the end of the plates? (b) At what angle with the axis is it moving as it leaves the plates? (c) How far below the axis will it strike the fluorescent screen S?

26–34. The maximum charge that can be retained by one of the spherical terminals of a large Van de Graaff generator is about 10^{-3} coul. Assume a positive charge of this magnitude, distributed uniformly over the surface of a sphere in otherwise empty space. (a) Compute the magnitude of the electric intensity at a point outside the sphere, 5 m from its center. (b) If an electron were released at this point, what would be the magnitude and direction of its initial acceleration?

26–35. Suppose the potential difference between the spherical terminal of a Van de Graaff generator and the point at which charges are sprayed onto the upward moving belt is 2 million volts. If the belt delivers negative charge to the sphere at the rate of 2×10^{-3} coul/sec and removes positive charge at the same rate, what horsepower must be expended to drive the belt against electrical forces?

CHAPTER 27

Capacitance.
Properties of Dielectrics

27–1 Capacitors

When a number of charged conductors are in the vicinity of one another, the potential of each is determined not only by its own charge but by the magnitude and sign of the charges on the other conductors and by their shapes, sizes, and locations. For example, the potential of a positively charged sphere is lowered if a second, negatively charged sphere is brought near the first.

An important special case arises in practice when two conductors in the same vicinity are given equal amounts of charge of opposite sign. Such an arrangement of two conductors is called a *capacitor*.

The capacitance C of a capacitor is defined as the ratio of the charge Q on either conductor to the potential difference V_{ab} between the conductors:

$$C = \frac{Q}{V_{ab}}.$$

(27–1)

The net charge on the capacitor as a whole is zero, and "the charge on a capacitor" is understood to mean the charge on *either* conductor, without regard to sign. We see from its definition that the unit of capacitance is 1 *coulomb per volt*. Since 1 volt is equivalent to 1 joule per coulomb, 1 coulomb per volt is equivalent to 1 $(\text{coul})^2$/joule. A capacitance of 1 coulomb per volt is called 1 *farad* (in honor of Michael Faraday). A capacitor is represented by the symbol ———)|(———   .

Capacitors find many applications in electrical circuits. A capacitor is used to eliminate sparking when a circuit containing inductance is suddenly opened. The ignition system of every automobile engine contains a capacitor for this purpose. Capacitors are used for tuning radio circuits and for "smoothing" the rectified current delivered by the power supply. The efficiency of alternating-current power transmission can often be increased by the use of large capacitors.

27–2 The parallel-plate capacitor

The most common type of capacitor consists of two conducting plates parallel to each other and separated by a distance which is small compared with the linear dimensions of the plates (see Fig. 27–1). Practically the entire field of such a capacitor is localized in the region between the plates, as shown. There is a slight "fringing" of the field at its outer boundary, but the fringing becomes relatively less as the plates are brought closer together. If the plates are sufficiently close, the fringing may be neglected, the field between the plates is uniform, and the charges on the plates are uniformly distributed over their opposing surfaces. This arrangement is known as a *parallel-plate capacitor*.

Let us assume first that the plates are in vacuum. It has been shown that the electric intensity between a pair of closely spaced parallel plates in vacuum is

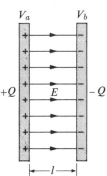

$$E = \frac{1}{\epsilon_0} \sigma = \frac{1}{\epsilon_0} \frac{Q}{A},$$

where A is the area of each plate and Q is the charge on *either* plate. Since the electric intensity or potential gradient between the plates is uniform, the potential difference between the plates is

$$V_{ab} = El = \frac{1}{\epsilon_0} \frac{Ql}{A},$$

Fig. 27–1. Parallel-plate capacitor.

where l is the separation of the plates. Hence the capacitance of a parallel-plate capacitor in vacuum is

$$C = \frac{Q}{V_{ab}} = \epsilon_0 \frac{A}{l}. \qquad (27-2)$$

Since ϵ_0, A, and l are constants for a given capacitor, the capacitance is a constant independent of the charge on the capacitor, and is directly proportional to the area of the plates and inversely proportional to their separation. If mksc units are used, A is to be expressed in square meters and l in meters. The capacitance C will then be in farads.

As an example, let us compute the area of the plates of a one-farad parallel-plate capacitor if the separation of the plates is one millimeter and the plates are in vacuum.

$$C = \epsilon_0 \frac{A}{l},$$

$$A = \frac{Cl}{\epsilon_0} = \frac{1 \text{ farad} \times 10^{-3} \text{ m}}{8.85 \times 10^{-12} \text{ coul}^2/\text{n·m}^2} = 1.13 \times 10^8 \text{ m}^2.$$

This corresponds to a square 10,600 meters, or 34,800 ft, or about $6\frac{1}{2}$ miles on a side!

Since the farad is such a large unit of capacitance, units of more convenient size are the *microfarad* ($1\mu\text{f} = 10^{-6}$ farad), and the *picofarad* (1 pf $= 10^{-12}$ farad). For example, a common radio set contains in its power supply several capacitors whose capacitances are of the order of ten microfarads, while the capacitances of the tuning capacitors are of the order of ten to one hundred picofarads.

Variable capacitors whose capacitance may be varied at will (between limits) are widely used in the tuning circuits of radio receivers. These are usually air capacitors of relatively small capacitance and are constructed of a number of fixed parallel metal plates connected together and constituting one "plate" of the capacitor, while a second set of movable plates also connected together forms the other "plate" (Fig. 27–2). By rotating a shaft on which the movable plates are mounted, the second set may be caused to interleave the first to a greater or lesser extent. The effective area of the capacitor is that of the interleaved portion of the plates only.

A variable capacitor is represented by the symbol

Capacitors consisting of concentric spheres and of coaxial cylinders are sometimes used in standards laboratories, since the corrections for the "fringing" fields can be made more readily and the capacitance can be accurately calculated from the dimensions of the apparatus. Problems involving a spherical and a cylindrical capacitor will be found at the end of the chapter.

Fig. 27–2. Variable air capacitor. (Courtesy of General Radio Company.)

27–3 Capacitors in series and parallel

In Fig. 27–3(a), two capacitors are connected in series between points a and b, maintained at a constant potential difference V_{ab}. The capacitors are both initially uncharged. In this type of connection, both capacitors have the same charge Q.

To understand why this is so, consider the schematic diagrams in Fig. 27–4. Suppose first that only the *upper* plate of capacitor C_1 and the *lower* plate of capacitor C_2 are connected to points a and b, as in part (a). A downward electric field is then set up between the plates. If an uncharged conductor of *any* shape is inserted in this field, as in part (b), a negative charge is induced on its upper surface and an *equal* positive charge on its lower surface. If we insert an uncharged conductor in the form of two flat plates and a connecting wire, as in part (c), the same is true; equal and opposite charges are induced on the plates. If the plates that are inserted have the same size and shape as those in part (a), and if the spacing

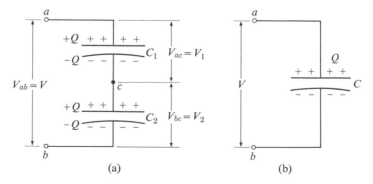

Fig. 27–3. (a) Two capacitors in series, and (b) their equivalent.

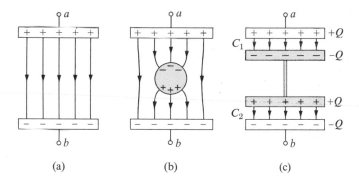

Fig. 27–4. (a) Electric field between the upper plate of C_1 and lower plate of C_2 of Fig. 27–3(a). (b) Induced charges on a spherical conductor. (c) Induced charges on two connected conducting plates.

between the plates is small, practically all of the field is confined to the region between the plates and the *magnitude* of the charge on all plates is the same. But the arrangement in Fig. 27–4(c) is the same as that in Fig. 27–3(a); namely, two capacitors in series between points a and b.

Another point of view is the following. The charges on the opposing surfaces of two closely spaced conducting plates must be equal and opposite, by Gauss's law. Hence the $+$ charge on one plate of capacitor C_1 must equal the $-$ charge on the other plate, and the $+$ charge on one plate of C_2 must equal the $-$ charge on the other plate. But the conductor consisting of the lower plate of C_1, the upper plate of C_2, and the connecting wire was initially uncharged and, since it is insulated from all other conductors, the net charge on it must remain zero. The $-$ charge on the lower plate of C_1 therefore equals the $+$ charge on the upper plate of C_2 and the charges on *all* the plates are of equal magnitude.

Returning now to Fig. 27–3(a), we have

$$V_{ac} \equiv V_1 = \frac{Q}{C_1}, \qquad V_{cb} \equiv V_2 = \frac{Q}{C_2},$$

and

$$V_{ab} \equiv V = V_1 + V_2 = Q\left(\frac{1}{C_1} + \frac{1}{C_2}\right),$$

$$\frac{V}{Q} = \frac{1}{C_1} + \frac{1}{C_2}. \tag{27–3}$$

The *equivalent* capacitance C of the series combination is defined as the capacitance of a *single* capacitor for which the charge Q is the same as for the combination, when the potential difference V is the same. For such a capacitor, shown in Fig. 27–3(b),

$$Q = CV, \qquad \frac{V}{Q} = \frac{1}{C}. \tag{27–4}$$

Hence from Eqs. (27–3) and (27–4)

$$\frac{1}{C} = \frac{1}{C_1} + \frac{1}{C_2}.$$

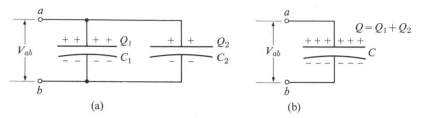

Fig. 27–5. (a) Two capacitors in parallel, and (b) their equivalent.

Similarly, for any number of capacitors in series,

$$\frac{1}{C} = \frac{1}{C_1} + \frac{1}{C_2} + \frac{1}{C_3} + \cdots. \qquad (27\text{-}5)$$

The reciprocal of the equivalent capacitance equals the sum of the reciprocals of the individual capacitances.

In Fig. 27–5(a), two capacitors are connected in *parallel* between points a and b. In this case, the potential difference $V_{ab} \equiv V$ is the same for both, and the charges Q_1 and Q_2 are

$$Q_1 = C_1 V, \qquad Q_2 = C_2 V.$$

The *total* charge Q supplied by the source was

$$Q = Q_1 + Q_2 = V(C_1 + C_2),$$

and

$$\frac{Q}{V} = C_1 + C_2. \qquad (27\text{-}6)$$

The *equivalent* capacitance C of the parallel combination is defined as that of a single capacitor, shown in Fig. 27–5(b), for which the total charge is the same as in part (a). For this capacitor,

$$\frac{Q}{V} = C$$

and hence

$$C = C_1 + C_2.$$

In the same way, for any number of capacitors in parallel

$$C = C_1 + C_2 + C_3 + \cdots. \qquad (27\text{-}7)$$

The equivalent capacitance equals the sum of the individual capacitances.

EXAMPLE.   In Figs. 27–3 and 27–5, let $C_1 = 6\,\mu\text{f}$, $C_2 = 3\,\mu\text{f}$, $V_{ab} = 18$ volts. The equivalent capacitance of the series combination in Fig. 27–3(a) is given by

$$\frac{1}{C} = \frac{1}{6\,\mu\text{f}} + \frac{1}{3\,\mu\text{f}}, \qquad C = 2\,\mu\text{f}.$$

The charge Q is

$$Q = CV = 2\,\mu\text{f} \times 18\text{ volts} = 36\,\mu\text{coul}.$$

The potential differences across the capacitors are

$$V_{ac} \equiv V_1 = \frac{Q}{C_1} = \frac{36\,\mu\text{coul}}{6\,\mu\text{f}} = 6\text{ volts},$$

$$V_{cb} \equiv V_2 = \frac{Q}{C_2} = \frac{36\,\mu\text{coul}}{3\,\mu\text{f}} = 12\text{ volts}.$$

The *larger* potential difference appears across the *smaller* capacitor.

The equivalent capacitance of the parallel combination in Fig. 27–5(a) is

$$C = C_1 + C_2 = 9\,\mu\text{f}.$$

The charges Q_1 and Q_2 are

$$Q_1 = C_1V = 6\,\mu\text{f} \times 18\text{ volts} = 108\,\mu\text{coul},$$

$$Q_2 = C_2V = 3\,\mu\text{f} \times 18\text{ volts} = 54\,\mu\text{coul}.$$

27–4 Energy of a charged capacitor

The process of charging a capacitor consists of transferring charge from the plate at lower potential to the plate at higher potential. The charging process therefore requires the expenditure of energy. Imagine the charging process to be carried out by starting with both plates completely uncharged, and then repeatedly removing small positive charges from one plate and transferring them to the other plate. At a stage of this process when the total quantity of charge has reached an amount q, the potential difference between the plates is v, where

$$q = Cv.$$

The work dW to transfer the next charge dq is

$$dW = v\,dq = \frac{1}{C}q\,dq,$$

and the total work to increase the charge from zero to Q is

$$W = \frac{1}{C}\int_0^Q q\,dq = \frac{1}{2}\frac{Q^2}{C}.$$

With the aid of the relation $Q = CV$, this may also be written as

$$W = \frac{1}{2}\frac{Q^2}{C} = \frac{1}{2}CV^2 = \frac{1}{2}QV. \qquad (27\text{–}8)$$

The work is expressed in joules when Q is in coulombs and V is in volts.

A charged capacitor is the electrical analogue of a stretched spring, whose elastic potential energy equals $\frac{1}{2}kx^2$. The charge Q is analogous to the elongation x, and the *reciprocal* of the capacitance, $1/C$, is analogous to the force constant k.

The energy supplied to a capacitor in the charging process is stored by the capacitor and is released, often in the form of a spark, when the capacitor discharges.

It is often useful to consider the stored energy to be localized in the *electric field* between the capacitor plates. The capacitance of a parallel-plate capacitor in vacuum is

$$C = \epsilon_0 \frac{A}{l}.$$

The electric field fills the space between the plates, of volume equal to Al, and the electric intensity between the plates is

$$E = \frac{V}{l}.$$

The energy per unit volume, or the *energy density*, is

$$\text{Energy density} = \frac{\frac{1}{2}CV^2}{Al}.$$

Making use of the preceding equations, we can express this as

$$\text{Energy density} = \tfrac{1}{2}\epsilon_0 E^2. \tag{27–9}$$

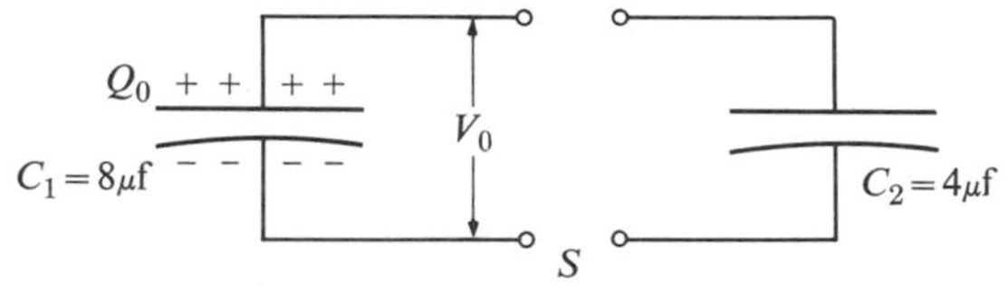

Fig. 27–6. When the switch S is closed, the charged capacitor C_1 is connected to an uncharged capacitor C_2.

EXAMPLE. In Fig. 27–6, let $C_1 = 8\,\mu\text{f}$, $V_0 = 120$ volts. The charge Q_0 is

$$Q_0 = C_1 V_0 = 960\,\mu\text{coul},$$

and the energy of the capacitor is

$$\tfrac{1}{2}Q_0 V_0 = 576 \times 10^{-4} \text{ joule}.$$

When the switch S is closed, the terminals of the charged capacitor are connected to those of a 4-μf capacitor, initially uncharged. The capacitors are then in *parallel* and their equivalent capacitance is

$$C = C_1 + C_2 = 12\,\mu\text{f}.$$

The original charge Q_0 becomes the *total* charge on the equivalent capacitor. The potential difference V (the same for both capacitors) is

$$V = \frac{Q_0}{C} = \frac{960\,\mu\text{coul}}{12\,\mu\text{f}} = 80 \text{ volts}.$$

The charges on the individual capacitors are

$$Q_1 = C_1 V = 640 \, \mu\text{coul},$$

$$Q_2 = C_2 V = 320 \, \mu\text{coul}.$$

The final energy of the system is

$$\tfrac{1}{2} Q_0 V = 384 \times 10^{-4} \, \text{joule}.$$

This is less than the original energy of 576×10^{-4} joule, the difference being converted to energy of some other form. If the resistance of the connecting wires was large, most of the energy was converted to heat. If the resistance was small, most of the energy was radiated in the form of electromagnetic waves.

The process above is exactly analogous to an inelastic collision of a moving with a stationary car. In the electrical case, the charge $Q = CV$ is conserved. In the mechanical case, the momentum $p = mv$ is conserved. The electrical energy $\tfrac{1}{2}CV^2$ is *not* conserved, and the mechanical energy $\tfrac{1}{2}mv^2$ is *not* conserved.

27–5 Effect of a dielectric

Most capacitors have a solid, nonconducting material or *dielectric* between their plates. A common type is the paper and foil capacitor, in which strips of metal foil form the plates and a sheet of paper impregnated with wax is the dielectric. By rolling up such a capacitor, a capacitance of several microfarads can be obtained in a relatively small volume. The "Leyden jar," constructed by cementing metal foil over a portion of the inside and outside surfaces of a glass jar, is essentially a parallel-plate capacitor with the glass forming the dielectric.

Electrolytic capacitors have as their dielectric an extremely thin layer of nonconducting oxide between a metal plate and a conducting solution. Because of the small thickness of the dielectric, electrolytic capacitors of relatively small dimensions may have a capacitance of the order of 100 to 1000 μf.

The function of a solid dielectric between the plates of a capacitor is threefold. First, it solves the mechanical problem of maintaining two large metal sheets at an extremely small separation but without actual contact. Second, since its dielectric strength is larger than that of air, the maximum potential difference which the capacitor can withstand without breakdown is increased. Third, the capacitance of a capacitor of given dimensions is several times larger with a dielectric separating its plates than if the plates were in vacuum. This effect can be demonstrated as follows. Figure 27–7(a) illustrates a parallel-plate capacitor whose plates have been given equal and opposite charges of magnitude Q. The plates are assumed to be in vacuum and the potential difference V_0 between the plates is indicated by an electroscope. If a sheet of dielectric, such as glass, bakelite, or hard rubber, is now inserted between the plates as in Fig. 27–7(b), the potential difference is observed to decrease to a smaller value V. If the dielectric is removed, the potential difference returns to its original value, showing that the original charges on the plates were not affected by insertion of the dielectric.

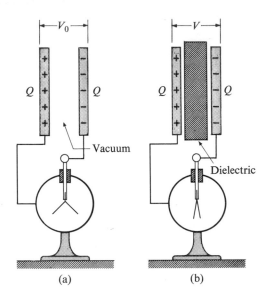

Fig. 27–7. Effect of a dielectric between the plates of a parallel-plate capacitor. (a) With a given charge, the potential difference is V_0. (b) With the same charge, the potential difference V is smaller than V_0.

The observed reduction in potential difference, when a dielectric is inserted between the plates, implies a reduction in the electric intensity, which in turn implies a reduction in the net charge per unit area. Since no charge leaks off the *plates*, such a reduction could be caused only by *induced* charges appearing on the two surfaces of the *dielectric*. That is, the dielectric surface adjacent to the positive plate must have an *induced negative charge*, and that adjacent to the negative plate an *induced positive charge*.

The four parts of Fig. 27–8 illustrate the behavior of a sheet of dielectric when inserted in the field between a pair of oppositely charged plane parallel plates. Part (a) shows the original field. Part (b) is the situation after the dielectric has been inserted

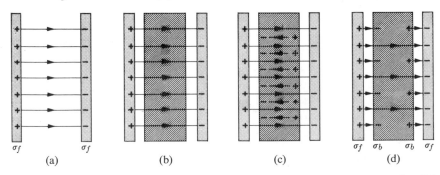

Fig. 27–8. (a) Electric field between two charged plates. (b) Introduction of a dielectric. (c) Induced surface charges and their field. (d) Resultant field when a dielectric is between charged plates.

but before any rearrangement of charges has occurred. Part (c) shows the field set up in the dielectric by its induced surface charges, and part (d) the final resultant field. Some of the lines of force leaving the positive plate penetrate the dielectric; others terminate on the induced charges on the faces of the dielectric. (The sheet of dielectric is assumed to completely fill the region between the plates. Small gaps have been left in the diagram for clarity.)

27-6 Molecular theory of induced charges on a dielectric

When a *conductor* is placed in an electric field, the free charges within it are displaced by the forces exerted on them by the field. In the final steady state, the conductor has an induced charge on its surface, distributed in such a way that the field of this induced charge neutralizes the original field at all internal points and the net electric intensity within the conductor is reduced to zero. A *dielectric*, however, contains no free charges. How, then, is it possible for an induced charge to appear on the surfaces of a dielectric when it is inserted in the electric field between the plates of a charged capacitor?

The molecules of a dielectric may be classified as either *polar* or *nonpolar*. A nonpolar molecule is one in which the "centers of gravity" of the positive nuclei and the electrons normally coincide, while a polar molecule is one in which they do not. Symmetrical molecules like H_2, N_2, and O_2 are nonpolar. In the molecules N_2O and H_2O, on the other hand, both nitrogen atoms or both hydrogen atoms lie on the same side of the oxygen atom, and these molecules are polar.

Under the influence of an electric field, the charges of a nonpolar molecule become displaced, as indicated schematically in Fig. 27-9. The molecules are said to become *polarized* by the field and are called *induced dipoles*. When a nonpolar molecule becomes polarized, restoring forces come into play on the displaced charges, pulling them together much as if they were connected by a spring. Under the influence of a given external field, the charges separate until the restoring force is equal and opposite to the force exerted on the charges by the field. Naturally, the restoring forces vary in magnitude from one kind of molecule to another, with corresponding differences in the displacement produced by a given field.

When a dielectric consists of polar molecules or *permanent dipoles*, these dipoles are oriented at random when no external field is present, as in Fig. 27-10(a). Under the action of an electric field, some degree of orientation takes place. The stronger

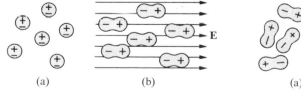

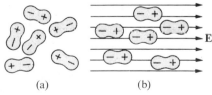

| (a) | (b) | (a) | (b) |

Fig. 27-9. Behavior of nonpolar molecules in the absence and in the presence of an electric field.

Fig. 27-10. Behavior of polar molecules in the absence and in the presence of an electric field.

the field, the greater the number of dipoles pointing in the direction of the field, as shown in Fig. 27–10(b).

Whether the molecules of a dielectric are polar or nonpolar, the net effect of an external field is substantially the same as shown in Fig. 27–11. Within the two extremely thin surface layers indicated by dotted lines there is an excess charge, negative in one layer and positive in the other. It is these layers of charge which give rise to the induced charge on the surfaces of a dielectric. The charges are not free, but each is *bound* to a molecule lying in or near the surface. Within the remainder of the dielectric the net charge per unit volume remains zero.

The charges induced on the surface of a dielectric in an external field afford an explanation of the attraction of an *uncharged* pith ball or bit of paper by a charged rod

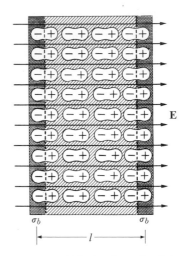

Fig. 27–11.   Polarization of a dielectric in an electric field gives rise to thin layers of bound charges on the surfaces.

of rubber or glass. Figure 27–12 shows an uncharged dielectric sphere B in the radial field of a positive charge A. The induced positive charges on B experience a force toward the right, while the force on the negative charges is toward the left. Since the negative charges are closer to A and therefore in a stronger field than are the positive, the force toward the left exceeds that toward the right, and B, although its net charge is zero, experiences a resultant force toward A. The sign of A's charge does not affect the conclusion, as may readily be seen. Furthermore, the effect is not limited to dielectrics—a conducting sphere would be similarly attracted.

Fig. 27–12.   An uncharged dielectric sphere B in the radial field of a positive charge A.

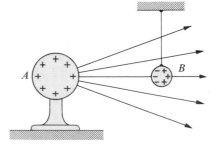

More general arguments based on energy considerations show that a dielectric body in a nonuniform field always experiences a force urging it from a region where the field is weak toward a region where it is stronger, provided the dielectric coefficient of the body (see Section 27–8) is greater than that of the medium in which it is immersed. If the dielectric coefficient is less, the reverse is true.

27-7 Polarization

The extent to which the molecules of a given dielectric become polarized by an electric field is described by a vector quantity called the *polarization* **P**. If **p** is the vector dipole moment of each molecular dipole, and there are n dipoles per unit volume, the polarization is defined as the product $n\mathbf{p}$:

$$\mathbf{P} = n\mathbf{p}. \tag{27-10}$$

Polarization is therefore *dipole moment per unit volume.* For the special case in Fig. 27-11, the polarization vector **P** has the same value at all points of the dielectric. In other cases it may vary from point to point and the quantities n and **p** then refer to a very small volume including the point. The mksc unit of polarization is 1 coul/m^2.

The dipole moment of a dipole is defined as the product of either of the charges making up the dipole, and the charge separation. The polarized sheet in Fig. 27-11 can be considered as a single large dipole, consisting of the induced charges $Q_b = \sigma_b A$, separated by the thickness l of the sheet. The dipole moment of the sheet is then $\sigma_b A l$, and since the volume of the sheet is Al, the dipole moment per unit volume, or the polarization **P**, is

$$P = \frac{\sigma_b A l}{A l} = \sigma_b. \tag{27-11}$$

In this special case, then, *the surface density of bound charge is equal to the polarization.* More generally, the surface density of bound charge at any point of the surface of a polarized body is equal to the *normal component* of **P** at the surface.

27-8 Susceptibility, permittivity, and dielectric coefficient

The polarization **P** in a homogeneous isotropic dielectric is in the same direction as the resultant electric intensity **E** and depends on **E** and on the nature of the dielectric. We define a property of the dielectric called its *susceptibility* χ by the equation

$$\chi = \frac{\mathbf{P}}{\epsilon_0 \mathbf{E}}, \quad \text{or} \quad \mathbf{P} = \chi \epsilon_0 \mathbf{E}. \tag{27-12}$$

The "susceptibility of a vacuum" is zero, since only a material substance can become polarized. Susceptibility is a pure number because the units of **P** and $\epsilon_0 \mathbf{E}$ are both 1 coul/m^2.

For a flat sheet in an electric field at right angles to its faces, the surface density of bound charge equals the polarization, so in this special case

$$\sigma_b = \chi \epsilon_0 E.$$

Let σ_f represent the surface density of charge on the plates in Fig. 27-8(d) (the *free* charge). The field set up by the free charge is $E_f = \sigma_f / \epsilon_0$, and the field set up by the bound charge is $E_b = \sigma_b/\epsilon_0$. Since these are in opposite directions, the resultant intensity E is

$$E = E_f - E_b = E_f - \frac{\sigma_b}{\epsilon_0} = E_f - \chi E,$$

and hence

$$E = \frac{1}{1 + \chi} E_f. \qquad (27\text{–}13)$$

The quantity $\epsilon_0(1 + \chi)$ is also a property of the dielectric called its *permittivity* ϵ:

$$\epsilon = \epsilon_0(1 + \chi). \qquad (27\text{–}14)$$

The mksc unit of permittivity is 1 $\text{coul}^2/\text{n·m}^2$.

Since the susceptibility χ of a vacuum is zero, the "permittivity of a vacuum" equals ϵ_0, and ϵ_0 is often referred to as "the permittivity of a vacuum," or as "the permittivity of free space." The permittivity of a material substance is necessarily larger than that of free space.

In terms of ϵ, Eq. (27–13) becomes

$$E = \frac{\epsilon_0}{\epsilon} E_f = \frac{E_f}{\epsilon/\epsilon_0}.$$

The ratio ϵ/ϵ_0 is called the *relative permittivity* or the *dielectric coefficient* of a dielectric and is represented by K:

$$K = \frac{\epsilon}{\epsilon_0}. \qquad (27\text{–}15)$$

Relative permittivity is a *pure number*, equal to 1 for a vacuum and greater than 1 for a material substance. Some representative values are given in Table 27–1. Finally, then, the resultant intensity E in a sheet of dielectric is related to the intensity E_f set up by the free charges by the equation

$$E = \frac{E_f}{K}. \qquad (27\text{–}16)$$

Although derived from consideration of a special case, the result above is true in general when a homogeneous isotropic dielectric replaces a vacuum at all points where there is an electric field; the intensity E at any point is that set up by free charges on conductors, reduced by a factor of $1/K$.

With a given free charge density σ_f on the plates in Fig. 27–8(d), the field between them in vacuum is $E_0 = E_f = \sigma_f/\epsilon_0$ and the potential difference V_0 is

$$V_0 = E_0 l.$$

With a dielectric between the plates, the field is $E = E_0/K$, and the potential difference V is

$$V = El = \frac{E_0 l}{K} = \frac{V_0}{K}.$$

TABLE 27–1

DIELECTRIC COEFFICIENT K

Material	t, °C	K
Vacuum		1
Glass	25	5–10
Mica	25	3–6
Hevea rubber	27	2.94
Neoprene	24	6.70
Bakelite	27	5.50
	57	7.80
	88	18.2
Plexiglas	27	3.40
Polyethylene	23	2.25
Vinylite	20	3.18
	47	3.60
	76	3.92
	96	6.60
	110	9.9
Teflon	22	2.1
Germanium	20	16
Strontium titanate	20	310
Titanium dioxide (rutile)	20	173($\perp$), 86($\parallel$)
Water	25	78.54
Glycerin	25	42.5
Liquid ammonia	−77.7	25
Benzene	20	2.284
Air (1 atm)	20	1.00059
Air (100 atm)	20	1.0548

Since $K > 1$, we can now understand why the potential difference V, in Fig. 27–7, is *smaller* than V_0. The induced charges on the dielectric *weaken* the field between the plates and reduce the potential difference.

The capacitance of a capacitor in vacuum with a charge Q_f on its plates is

$$C_0 = \frac{Q_f}{V_0}.$$

When a dielectric is inserted between the plates,

$$C = \frac{Q_f}{V} = \frac{Q_f}{V_0/K} = KC_0,$$

and the capacitance is *increased* by a factor K.

For a parallel-plate capacitor in vacuum,

$$C_0 = \frac{\epsilon_0 A}{l},$$

and with a dielectric between the plates

$$C = KC_0 = \frac{K\epsilon_0 A}{l} = \frac{\epsilon A}{l}.$$

The three quantities χ, ϵ, and K are simply different ways of expressing the same basic property of a dielectric, that is, the extent to which it becomes polarized when in an electric field. Any one can be expressed in terms of ϵ_0 and any one of the others, and the three are introduced only for the purpose of simplifying the *form* of a number of useful equations.

_____

EXAMPLE. Suppose the plates in Fig. 27–7 have an area of 2000 cm^2 or 0.20 m^2, and are 1 cm or 10^{-2} m apart. The potential difference between them in vacuum, V_0, is 3000 volts, and it decreases to 1000 volts when a sheet of dielectric 1 cm thick is inserted between the plates. Compute the following: (a) the relative permittivity K of the dielectric, (b) its permittivity ϵ, (c) its susceptibility χ, (d) the electric intensity between the plates in vacuum, (e) the resultant electric intensity in the dielectric, (f) the electric intensity set up by the bound charges, and (g) the ratio of the surface density of bound charge, σ_b, to that of free charge, σ_f.

(a)
$$K = \frac{\epsilon}{\epsilon_0} = \frac{V_0}{V} = \frac{3000 \text{ volts}}{1000 \text{ volts}} = 3$$

(b)
$$\epsilon = K\epsilon_0 = 3\epsilon_0$$

(c)
$$\chi = (\epsilon/\epsilon_0) - 1 = 2$$

(d)
$$E_0 = E_f = \frac{V_0}{l} = 3 \times 10^5 \frac{\text{volts}}{\text{m}}$$

(e)
$$E = \frac{V}{l} = 10^5 \frac{\text{volts}}{\text{m}}$$

(f)
$$E_b = E_f - E = 2 \times 10^5 \frac{\text{volts}}{\text{m}}$$

(g)
$$\sigma_f = \epsilon_0 E_f = \epsilon_0 E_0 = 3 \times 10^5 \; \epsilon_0 \frac{\text{coul}}{\text{m}^2}$$

$$\sigma_b = \epsilon_0 E_b = \chi\epsilon_0 E = 2 \times 10^5 \; \epsilon_0 \frac{\text{coul}}{\text{m}^2}$$

$$\frac{\sigma_b}{\sigma_f} = \frac{2}{3}$$

27–9 Displacement

The *displacement* $\mathbf{D}$ at any point in a polarized dielectric can be defined as the vector sum of the polarization $\mathbf{P}$ and the product $\epsilon_0 \mathbf{E}$:

$$\mathbf{D} = \epsilon_0 \mathbf{E} + \mathbf{P}. \tag{27–17}$$

But $\mathbf{P} = \chi\epsilon_0\mathbf{E}$, so in the dielectric

$$\mathbf{D} = \epsilon_0 \mathbf{E} + \chi\epsilon_0\mathbf{E} = \epsilon_0(1 + \chi)\mathbf{E} = \epsilon\mathbf{E}.$$

In a vacuum, where $P = 0$,

$$\mathbf{D} = \epsilon_0 \mathbf{E}.$$

The concept of displacement simplifies a number of equations in electric field theory, and it has some interesting and useful properties. For example, let us calculate the surface integrals of both $\mathbf{D}$ and $\mathbf{E}$, over the gaussian surface in Fig. 27–13, which consists of a cylinder one of whose ends lies in the metal plate while the other lies in the dielectric. Within the metal plate, both $\mathbf{D}$ and $\mathbf{E}$ are zero. Within the dielectric,

$$E = E_f - E_b = \frac{1}{\epsilon_0}(\sigma_f - \sigma_b),$$

$$D = \epsilon_0 E + P = (\sigma_f - \sigma_b) + \sigma_b = \sigma_f.$$

The surface integral of $\mathbf{E}$ (the flux of $\mathbf{E}$) over the cylinder is

$$\Psi = \oint \mathbf{E} \cdot d\mathbf{A} = EA = \frac{1}{\epsilon_0}(\sigma_f - \sigma_b)A$$

$$= \frac{1}{\epsilon_0}(Q_f - Q_b), \qquad (27\text{–}18)$$

and the surface integral of $\mathbf{D}$ (the flux of displacement) is

$$\Psi_D = \oint \mathbf{D} \cdot d\mathbf{A} = DA = \sigma_f A = Q_f. \qquad (27\text{–}19)$$

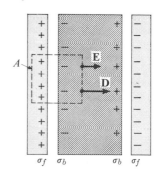

Fig. 27–13. Electric intensity $\mathbf{E}$ and electric displacement $\mathbf{D}$ in a dielectric.

The conclusions from this special case are true in general. The quantity $(Q_f - Q_b)$, in Eq. (27–18), is the *net* charge inside the cylinder, *including the bound charge Q_b as well as the free charge Q_f.* Hence Gauss's law for $\mathbf{E}$ is correct, as previously stated, even when a closed surface cuts through a polarized dielectric and includes both bound and free charges: *The surface integral of $\mathbf{E}$ over a closed surface equals $1/\epsilon_0$ times the net charge inside the surface, including both bound and free charges.*

On the other hand, we see from Eq. (27–19) that the surface integral of the displacement $\mathbf{D}$ over a closed surface is equal to the *free charge only* inside the surface. This statement is *Gauss's law for* $\mathbf{D}$.

EXAMPLE. A conducting sphere of radius R, having a charge Q_f, is immersed in a dielectric liquid of permittivity ϵ. What is the force exerted on a point charge q in the liquid, at a distance r from the center of the sphere?

Construct a spherical gaussian surface of radius r, as in Fig. 27–14. The usual conditions of spherical symmetry apply. The only *free* charge inside the surface is the charge Q_f on the sphere. The surface integral of $\mathbf{D}$ over the gaussian surface is $D \times 4\pi r^2$. Hence

$$D \times 4\pi r^2 = Q_f, \qquad D = \frac{1}{4\pi}\frac{Q_f}{r^2}.$$

The intensity E is

$$E = \frac{D}{\epsilon} = \frac{D}{K\epsilon_0} = \frac{1}{K}\frac{1}{4\pi\epsilon_0}\frac{Q_f}{r^2}.$$

But $(1/4\pi\epsilon_0)(Q_f/r^2)$ is the electric intensity E_f that would be set up in vacuum by the free charges on the sphere, so

$$E = \frac{E_f}{K},$$

in agreement with Eq. (27–16).

The force on the charge q is

$$F = qE = \frac{1}{K}qE_f = \frac{1}{K}\frac{1}{4\pi\epsilon_0}\frac{qQ_f}{r^2},$$

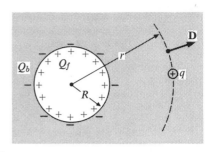

Fig. 27–14.   Point charge q and a charged spherical conductor immersed in a liquid dielectric.

so the effect of the dielectric is to reduce the net force by a factor of $1/K$.

This does not mean, however, that the force between the charge q and the *free* charge Q_f is reduced by the presence of the dielectric; the force between them is still equal to the force qE_f given by Coulomb's law. The reason for the reduction in the force is that the spherical layer of induced bound surface charge in the liquid, just outside the surface of the sphere, sets up an *inward* field, with the result that the *net outward* field is that given by Eq. (27–16). The properties of the displacement **D** enable us to find the field at the charge q, without having to compute first the induced charge Q_b.

One more relation involving the displacement may be mentioned. The capacitance of a parallel-plate capacitor with a dielectric of permittivity ϵ between its plates is

$$C = \epsilon\frac{A}{l}.$$

When the energy per unit volume in the dielectric is calculated by the method used in Section 27–4, we get

$$\text{Energy density} = \frac{1}{2}\epsilon E^2 = \frac{1}{2}DE = \frac{1}{2}\frac{D^2}{\epsilon}. \qquad (27\text{–}20)$$

Problems

27–1. An air capacitor, consisting of two closely spaced parallel plates, has a capacitance of 1000 pf. The charge on each plate is 1 microcoulomb. (a) What is the potential difference between the plates? (b) If the charge is kept constant, what will be the potential difference between the plates if the separation is doubled? (c) How much work is required to double the separation?

27–2. The plates of a parallel-plate capacitor in vacuum have charges $+Q$ and $-Q$ and the distance between the plates is x. The plates are disconnected from the charging voltage and pulled apart a short distance dx. (a) What is the change dC in the capacitance of the capacitor? (b) What is the change dW in its energy? (c) Equate the work $F\,dx$ to the increase in energy dW and find the force of attraction F between the plates. (d) Explain why F is not equal to QE, where E is the electric intensity between the plates.

27–3. The capacitance of a variable radio capacitor can be changed from 50 pf to 950 pf by turning the dial from 0° to 180°. With the dial set at 180° the capacitor is connected to a 400-volt battery. After charging, the capacitor is disconnected from the battery and the dial is turned to 0°. (a) What is the charge on the capacitor? (b) What is the potential difference across the capacitor when the dial reads 0°? (c) What is the energy of the capacitor in this position? (d) How much work is required to turn the dial, if friction is neglected?

27–4. A 20-μf capacitor is charged to a potential difference of 1000 volts. The terminals of the charged capacitor are then connected to those of an uncharged 5-μf capacitor. Compute (a) the original charge of the system, (b) the final potential difference across each capacitor, (c) the final energy of the system, (d) the decrease in energy when the capacitors are connected.

27–5. In Fig. 27–15, each capacitance $C_3 = 3\,\mu$f and each capacitance $C_2 = 2\,\mu$f. (a) Compute the equivalent capacitance of the network between points a and b. (b) Compute the charge on each of the capacitors nearest a and b, when $V_{ab} = 900$ volts. (c) With 900 volts across a and b, compute V_{cd}.

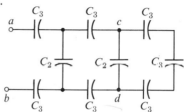

Figure 27–15

27–6. A number of 0.5-μf capacitors are available. The voltage across each is not to exceed 400 volts. A capacitor of capacitance 0.5 μf is required to be connected across a potential difference of 600 volts. (a) Show in a diagram how an equivalent capacitor having the desired properties can be obtained. (b) No dielectric is a perfect insulator, of infinite resistance. Suppose that the dielectric in one of the capacitors in your diagram is a moderately good conductor. What will happen?

27–7. A 1-μf capacitor and a 2-μf capacitor are connected in series across a 1200-volt supply line. (a) Find the charge on each capacitor and the voltage across each. (b) The charged capacitors are disconnected from the line and from each other, and reconnected with terminals of like sign together. Find the final charge on each and the voltage across each.

27–8. A 1-μf capacitor and a 2-μf capacitor are connected in parallel across a 1200-volt supply line. (a) Find the charge on each capacitor and the voltage across each. (b) The charged capacitors are then disconnected from the line and from each other, and reconnected with terminals of unlike sign together. Find the final charge on each and the voltage across each.

27–9. In Fig. 27–5(a), let $C_1 = 6\,\mu f$, $C_2 = 3\,\mu f$, $V_{ab} = 18$ volts. Suppose that the charged capacitors are disconnected from the source and from each other, and reconnected with plates of *opposite* sign connected together. By how much does the energy of the system decrease?

27–10. Three capacitors having capacitances of 8, 8, and $4\,\mu f$ are connected in series across a 12-volt line. (a) What is the charge on the 4-μf capacitor? (b) What is the total energy of all three capacitors? (c) The capacitors are disconnected from the line and reconnected in parallel with the positively charged plates connected together. What is the voltage across the parallel combination? (d) What is the energy of the combination?

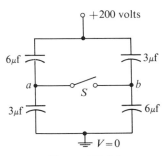

Figure 27–16

27–11. The capacitors in Fig. 27–16 are initially uncharged, and are connected as in the diagram with switch S open. (a) What is the potential difference V_{ab}? (b) What is the potential of point b after switch S is closed? (c) How much charge flowed through the switch when it was closed?

27–12. A parallel-plate capacitor is to be constructed using as a dielectric rubber, having a dielectric coefficient of 3 and a dielectric strength of 2×10^5 volts/cm. The capacitor is to have a capacitance of $0.15\,\mu f$ and must be able to withstand a maximum potential difference of 6000 volts. What is the minimum area the plates of the capacitor may have?

27–13. The paper dielectric, in a paper and foil capacitor, is 0.005 cm thick. Its dielectric coefficient is 2.5 and its dielectric strength is 50×10^6 volts/m. (a) What area of paper, and of tinfoil, is required for a 0.1-μf capacitor? (b) If the electric intensity in the paper is not to exceed one-half the dielectric strength, what is the maximum potential difference that can be applied across the capacitor?

27–14. (a) The permittivity of diamond is 1.46×10^{-10} coul^2/n·m^2. What is the dielectric coefficient of diamond? (b) What is its susceptibility? (c) What is the dielectric coefficient of a metal?

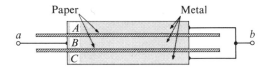

Figure 27–17

27–15. Three square metal plates A, B, and C, each 10 cm on a side and 3 mm thick, are arranged as in Fig. 27–17. The plates are separated by sheets of paper 0.5 mm thick and of dielectric coefficient 5. The outer plates are connected together and connected to point b. The inner plate is connected to point a. (a) Copy the diagram, and show by $+$ and $-$ signs the charge distribution on the plates when point a is maintained at a positive potential relative to point b. (b) What is the capacitance between points a and b?

27–16.–Two parallel plates have equal and opposite charges. When the space between the plates is evacuated, the electric intensity is 2×10^5 volts/m. When the space is filled with dielectric, the electric intensity is 1.2×10^5 volts/m. (a) What is the bound charge density on the surface of the dielectric? (b) What is the susceptibility of the dielectric? (c) What is the permittivity of the dielectric? (d) What is its dielectric coefficient?

27–17. Two oppositely charged conducting plates, having numerically equal quantities of charge per unit area, are separated by a dielectric 5 mm thick, of dielectric coefficient 3. The resultant electric intensity in the dielectric is 10^6 volts/m. Compute: (a) the free charge per unit area on the conducting plates, (b) the bound charge per unit area on the surfaces of the dielectric. (c) The polarization P in the dielectric. (d) The displacement D in the dielectric. (e) The energy density in the dielectric.

27–18. A capacitor consists of two parallel plates of area 25 cm^2 separated by a distance of 0.2 cm. The material between the plates has a dielectric coefficient of 5. The plates of the capacitor are connected to a 300-volt battery. (a) What is the capacitance of the capacitor? (b) What is the charge on either plate? (c) What is the energy in the charged capacitor? (d) What is the polarization in the dielectric? (e) What is the displacement in the dielectric? (f) What is the energy density in the dielectric?

27–19. A spherical capacitor consists of an inner metal sphere of radius r_a supported

on an insulating stand at the center of a hollow metal sphere of inner radius r_b. There is a charge $+Q$ on the inner sphere and a charge $-Q$ on the outer. (a) What is the potential difference V_{ab} between the spheres? (b) Prove that the capacitance is

$$C = \frac{1}{k} \cdot \frac{r_b r_a}{r_b - r_a}.$$

(See Problem 26–18.)

27–20. A coaxial cable consists of an inner solid cylindrical conductor of radius r_a supported by insulating disks on the axis of a conducting tube of inner radius r_b. The two cylinders are oppositely charged with a charge λ per unit length. (a) What is the potential difference between the two cylinders? (b) Prove that the capacitance of a length L of the cable is

$$C = \frac{L}{2k \ln (r_b/r_a)}.$$

Neglect any effect of the supporting disks. (See Problem 26–19.)

CHAPTER 28

Current, Resistance, and Electromotive Force

28–1 Current

When there is a net flow of charge across any area, we say there is a *current* across the area. If an isolated conductor is placed in an electrostatic field, the charges in the conductor rearrange themselves so as to make the interior of the conductor a field-free region throughout which the potential is constant. The motion of the charges in the rearranging process constitutes a *transient* current, of short duration only, and the current ceases when the field in the conductor becomes zero. To maintain a *continuous* current, we must in some way maintain a force on the mobile charges in a conductor. The force may result from an electrostatic field or from other causes that will be described later. For the present, we assume that there is maintained within a conductor an effective electric field **E** such that a charged particle in the conductor is acted on by a force $\mathbf{F} = q\mathbf{E}$. We shall refer to this force as the *driving force* on the particle.

The motion of a free charged particle in a conductor is very different from that of a particle in empty space. After a momentary acceleration, the particle makes an inelastic collision with one of the fixed particles in the conductor, loses whatever velocity it has acquired in the direction of the driving force, and makes a fresh start. Thus on the average it moves in the direction of the driving force with an average velocity called its *drift* velocity. The inelastic collisions with the fixed particles result in a transfer of energy to them which increases their energy of vibration and causes a rise in temperature if the conductor is thermally insulated, or results in a flow of heat from the conductor to its surroundings if it is not.

If we disregard the details of the accelerations and collisions of the particles, their motion is like that of particles moving in a viscous medium, acted on by a driving force **F** and a viscous force **f** opposite to their velocity and which increases with their velocity. In such a case, the particle eventually moves with a constant *terminal velocity* in the same direction as the driving force. The terminal velocity is that at which the viscous retarding force becomes equal to the driving force. We can therefore think of the particles in a conductor as though they were moving in a viscous medium with a drift velocity equal to their terminal velocity. (See Fig. 28–1.) The effective viscous force is so large compared with any realizable driving force that for all practical purposes the terminal velocity can be considered to be attained instantaneously. The paths of the particles, or the *lines of flow*, coincide with the *lines of force* in the conductor.

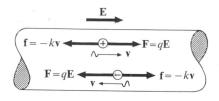

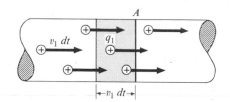

Fig. 28–1. The free charges in a conductor move with a constant drift velocity such that the effective viscous retarding force **f** is equal and opposite to the driving force **F**.

Fig. 28–2. All of the particles, and only those particles, within the shaded cylinder will cross its base in time dt.

The current across an area is defined quantitatively as *the net charge flowing across the area per unit time*. Thus if a net charge dQ flows across an area in a time dt, the current I across the area is

$$I = \frac{dQ}{dt}.$$ (28–1)

Current is a *scalar* quantity.

The mks unit of current, the *ampere*, named in honor of the French scientist André Marie Ampère (1775–1836), will be defined in Section 32–3. Small currents are more conveniently expressed in *milliamperes* (1 ma $= 10^{-3}$ amp) or in *microamperes* (1 μa $= 10^{-6}$ amp).

> Since a current is a flow of charge, the common expression "flow of current" should be avoided, since it means literally "flow of flow of charge."

A *galvanometer* is an instrument that indicates, by the deflection of a pointer or a beam of light reflected from a mirror, the existence of a current through it. If the scale is properly calibrated, the galvanometer becomes an *ammeter* (or a *milliammeter* or *microammeter*). The construction of such instruments will be described later.

The current across an area can be expressed in terms of the drift velocity of the moving charges as follows. Consider a portion of a conductor of cross-sectional area A within which there is an electric field **E** from left to right. The free positively charged particles move in the same direction as the field and the free negatively charged particles move in the opposite direction. A few positive particles are shown in Fig. 28–2. Suppose there are n_1 such particles per unit volume, all moving with a drift velocity v_1. In a time dt each advances a distance $v_1\, dt$. Hence all of the particles within the shaded cylinder of length $v_1\, dt$, and only those particles, will flow across the end of the cylinder in time dt. The volume of the cylinder is $Av_1\, dt$, the number of particles within it is $n_1 Av_1\, dt$, and if each has a charge q_1 the charge dQ_1 flowing across the end of the cylinder in time dt is

$$dQ_1 = n_1 q_1 v_1 A\, dt.$$

The current carried by the positively charged particles is therefore

$$I_1 = \frac{dQ_1}{dt} = n_1 q_1 v_1 A.$$

In the same way, if there are n_2 negative particles per unit volume, each having a charge q_2 and traveling from right to left with velocity v_2, the current carried by them is

$$I_2 = n_2 q_2 v_2 A.$$

Positive particles crossing from left to right *increase* the *positive* charge at the right of the section, while negative particles crossing from right to left *decrease* the *negative* charge at the right of the section. But a *decrease* of *negative* charge is equivalent to an *increase* of *positive* charge, so the motion of *both* kinds of charge has the same effect, namely, to increase the positive charge at the right of the section. The *total* current I at the section is therefore the *sum* of the currents I_1 and I_2:

$$I = A(n_1 q_1 v_1 + n_2 q_2 v_2).$$

In general, if a conductor contains a number of different particles, having different charge densities and moving with different velocities, the current is

$$I = A\Sigma nqv. \qquad (28\text{–}2)$$

The *current per unit of cross-sectional area* is called the *current density J*:

$$J = \frac{I}{A} = \Sigma nqv. \qquad (28\text{–}3)$$

The *vector current density* **J** is defined by the equation

$$\mathbf{J} = \Sigma nq\mathbf{v}. \qquad (28\text{–}4)$$

Current, by definition, is a scalar quantity and thus it is not correct to speak of the "direction of a current." This expression is often used, however, for brevity, meaning thereby the direction of the *vector* current density **J**.

The direction of the vector velocity **v** of a positive charge carrier is the same as that of the electric field **E**, and the direction of the velocity of a negative carrier is opposite to **E**. But since the charge q of such a carrier is negative, each of the vectors $nq\mathbf{v}$ is in the *same* direction as **E**, and hence *the vector current density* **J** *is in the same direction as the field* **E**. Thus even in a metallic conductor, where the charge carriers are negative electrons only and move in the *opposite* direction to **E**, the *vector* current density **J** is in the *same* direction as **E**.

When there is a steady current in a closed circuit, the total charge in every portion of a conductor remains constant. Hence if we consider a portion between two fixed cross sections, the rate of flow of charge *out* of the portion at one end equals the rate of flow of charge *into* the portion at the other end. In other words, the current is the same at any two cross sections and hence is *the same at all cross sections*. Current is not something that squirts out of the positive terminal of a battery and gets all used up by the time it reaches the negative terminal.

Let us estimate the drift velocity of the electrons in a wire carrying a current. Consider a copper conductor of square cross section 1 mm on a side, carrying a constant current of 20 amp. The current density in the wire is

$$J = \frac{I}{A} = 20 \times 10^6 \frac{\text{amp}}{\text{m}^2}.$$

It was stated at the end of Chapter 24 that there are in copper about 10^{29} free electrons per cubic meter. Then, since $J = nqv$ and $q = e = 1.6 \times 10^{-19}$ coul,

$$v = \frac{J}{nq} \approx 10^{-3} \frac{\text{m}}{\text{sec}},$$

or about 1 mm/sec. At this speed, an electron would require 1000 sec or about 15 min to travel the length of a wire 1 meter long. Thus the drift velocity is very small compared with the velocity of propagation of a current pulse along a wire, about 3×10^8 m/sec.

28–2 Resistivity

The current density **J** in a conductor depends on the electric intensity **E**, and on the nature of the conductor. We define a property of a conductor called its *resistivity*, ρ, as *the ratio of the electric intensity to the current density*:

$$\rho = \frac{E}{J}. \tag{28–5}$$

That is, the resistivity is the *electric intensity per unit current density*. The greater the resistivity, the greater the intensity needed to establish a given current density, or the smaller the current density for a given intensity. Representative values are given in Table 28–1. (The unit, ohm·m, will be explained shortly.) A "perfect" conductor would have zero resistivity and a "perfect" insulator an infinite resistivity. Metals and alloys have the lowest resistivities and are the best conductors. The resistivities of insulators exceed those of the metals by a factor of the order of 10^{22}.

Comparison with Table 17–1 shows that *thermal* insulators have thermal resistivities (the reciprocals of their thermal conductivities) that differ from those of good thermal conductors by factors of only about 10^3. By the use of electrical insulators, electric currents can be confined to well-defined paths in good electrical conductors, while it is impossible to confine heat currents to a comparable extent. It is also interesting to note that the metals, as a class, are also the best *thermal* conductors. The free electrons in a metal are largely responsible for both its electrical and its thermal conductivity.

TABLE 28–1

RESISTIVITIES AT ROOM TEMPERATURE

Substance		ρ, ohm·m
CONDUCTORS		
Metals	Silver	1.47×10^{-8}
	Copper	1.72×10^{-8}
	Aluminum	2.63×10^{-8}
	Tungsten	5.51×10^{-8}
Alloys	Manganin	$44 \quad \times 10^{-8}$
	Constantan	$49 \quad \times 10^{-8}$
	Nichrome	$100 \quad \times 10^{-8}$
SEMICONDUCTORS		
Pure	Carbon	3.5×10^{-5}
	Germanium	0.60
	Silicon	2300
INSULATORS		
	Amber	5×10^{14}
	Glass	$10^{10} - 10^{14}$
	Lucite	$> 10^{13}$
	Mica	$10^{11} - 10^{15}$
	Quartz (fused)	75×10^{16}
	Sulfur	10^{15}
	Teflon	$> 10^{13}$
	Wood	$10^{8} - 10^{11}$

The semiconductors form a class intermediate between the metals and the insulators. They are of importance not primarily because of their resistivities, but because of the way in which these are affected by temperature and by small amounts of impurities.

It follows from Eq. (28–5) that $E = \rho J$, and since the vectors **E** and **J** are in the same direction, we can write this as a vector equation,

$$\mathbf{E} = \rho \mathbf{J}. \tag{28–6}$$

It should be noted that Eq. (28–6) does not necessarily imply that the resistivity ρ is a *constant*, or that the current density **J** is *directly* proportional to **E**, or is a *linear* function of **E**. In many conducting materials, however, notably the metals, the resistivity (at a given temperature) *is* a constant independent of **E**, so that if **E** is doubled, for example, the current density is doubled also. The discovery that ρ is a constant for a metallic conductor at constant temperature was made by G. S. Ohm (1789–1854) and is known as *Ohm's law*. A material obeying Ohm's law is called an *ohmic* conductor or a *linear* conductor. If Ohm's law is not obeyed, the con-

TABLE 28–2

TEMPERATURE COEFFICIENTS OF RESISTIVITY

(approximate values near room temperature)

Material	α (°C^{-1})
Aluminum	0.0039
Brass	0.0020
Carbon	−0.0005
Constantan (Cu 60, Ni 40)	+0.000002
Copper (Commercial annealed)	0.00393
Iron	0.0050
Lead	0.0043
Manganin (Cu 84, Mn 12, Ni 4)	0.000000
Mercury	0.00088
Nichrome	0.0004
Silver	0.0038
Tungsten	0.0045

ductor is called *nonlinear*. Thus Ohm's law, like Boyle's law, describes a special property of certain materials and not a general property of all matter.

The resistivity of a material can be expressed in terms of the properties of the model in Fig. 28–1 as follows. Let k represent the effective viscous force per unit velocity, so that $f = -kv$. The driving force $F = qE$, and when v is the terminal velocity,

$$F + f = 0, \qquad qE = kv, \qquad E = kv/q.$$

The current density (if there is only one kind of charge carrier present) is $J = nqv$. Hence

$$\rho = \frac{E}{J} = \frac{kv/q}{nqv} = \frac{k}{nq^2}. \tag{28–7}$$

If k and n are constants, the resistivity is constant and Ohm's law is obeyed.

The resistivity of all metallic conductors increases with increasing temperature, as shown in Fig. 28–3(a). There is no completely satisfactory theory of this effect, but it appears to result from the increasing probability of collisions between the charge carriers and the metallic ions as the thermal vibration of the ions increases with increasing temperature. The effective viscous coefficient k in Eq. (28–7) increases and this increases the resistivity.

Over a temperature range that is not too great, the resistivity of a metal can be represented by the equation

$$\rho_t = \rho_{20}[1 + \alpha(t - 20°)], \tag{28–8}$$

where ρ_{20} is the resistivity at 20°C and ρ_t is the resistivity at a temperature of t°C. The factor α is called the *temperature coefficient of resistivity*. Some representative values are given in Table 28–2.

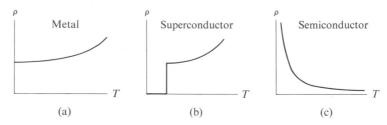

Fig. 28–3. Variation of resistivity with temperature for three conductors: (a) an ordinary metal, (b) a superconducting metal, alloy, or compound, and (c) a semiconductor.

A number of metals have been found to exhibit the property of *superconductivity*. As the temperature is decreased, the resistivity at first decreases regularly, like that of any metal. At the so-called *critical* temperature, of the order of 0.1°K to 10°K, the resistivity suddenly plunges to zero, as shown in Fig. 28–3(b). Once established in a superconducting ring a current will continue of itself, apparently indefinitely, without the presence of any driving field. The principles of classical physics are unable to account for this behavior; it can be understood only on the basis of quantum mechanics.

The resistivity of a semiconductor *decreases* rapidly with increasing temperature, as shown in Fig. 28–3(c). As the temperature increases, the number of charge carriers increases rapidly and the increase in n, in Eq. (28–7), far outweighs any increase in k. Conversely, as the temperature is lowered the resistivity of a semi-conductor becomes so large that it can be classified as an insulator.

A tiny bead of semiconducting material, called a Thermistor, serves as a sensitive thermometer.

28–3 Resistance

The current density **J** at every point within a conductor in which there is an electrostatic field only is given by Eq. (28–6):

$$\mathbf{E}_e = \rho \mathbf{J}.$$

(We use the symbol $\mathbf{E}_e$ to distinguish an electro*static* field from *non*electrostatic fields, which will be discussed later.)

Because there are no instruments that measure $\mathbf{E}_e$ and **J** directly, it is convenient to put this equation in a different form. Let us take the dot product of each side with an element of length $d\mathbf{s}$ of the conductor, in the direction of the current density **J**, and integrate along the conductor from point a to point b. Since **J** and $d\mathbf{s}$ are parallel, the product $\mathbf{J} \cdot d\mathbf{s}$ reduces to $J\,ds$ or $(I/A)\,ds$. Also, we limit the discussion to conductors in which the current I is the same at all cross sections, so that I can be taken outside the integral sign. Then

$$\int_a^b \mathbf{E}_e \cdot d\mathbf{s} = I \int_a^b \frac{\rho}{A}\,ds. \tag{28–9}$$

The integral on the left is simply the potential difference V_{ab} between points a and b. The integral on the right is called the *resistance R* of the conductor, between points a and b:

$$R = \int_a^b \frac{\rho}{A}\, ds. \tag{28–10}$$

Equation (28–9) can now be written as

$$V_{ab} = IR. \tag{28–11}$$

That is, *the potential difference between the terminals of a conductor in which the driving field is purely electrostatic is equal to the product of the current in the conductor and its resistance.* The potential difference and the current can be measured with a voltmeter and an ammeter.

It follows from the preceding equation that the mksc unit of resistance can be expressed as *one volt per ampere*. A resistance of 1 volt per ampere is called *1 ohm*.

The Greek letter omega (Ω) is used to designate a resistance in ohms, and a resistance of 470 ohms is written 470 Ω. Large resistances are expressed in *megohms* (1 megohm = 10^6 ohms) and small resistances in *microhms* (1 microhm = 10^{-6} ohm). In electronic circuitry, the symbol M is often used to mean "millions of ohms" and the symbol K to mean "thousands of ohms." Thus 10M means 10 megohms and 10K, ten thousand ohms.

Resistance units constructed to introduce into a circuit lumped resistances that are large compared with those of leads and contacts are called *resistors*. A resistor is represented by the symbol —⋏⋀⋀⋀—. Portions of a circuit of negligible resistance are shown by straight lines.

An adjustable resistor is called a *rheostat*. A common type consists of a resistor with a sliding contact that can be moved along its length, and is represented by the symbol —⋏⋀⋀—. Connections are made to either end of the resistor and to the sliding contact. The symbol —⋁⋀⋁— is also used for an adjustable resistor.

Every conductor (except a superconductor) has resistance, and is therefore a *resistor* also. In fact, the terms *conductor* and *resistor* may be used interchangeably.

It can be seen from Eq. (28–10) that the unit of resistivity is 1 ohm·meter.

The resistance of a homogeneous conductor of length L and of constant cross-sectional area A is

$$R = \int_0^L \frac{\rho}{A}\, ds = \frac{\rho L}{A}. \tag{28–12}$$

The resistance is directly proportional to the length and inversely proportional to the cross-sectional area.

EXAMPLE. The cross-sectional area of the copper wire used in a household wiring system is approximately 3 mm^2 = 3 × 10^{-6} m^2. The resistance of such a wire 10 m long, at 20°C, is

$$R = \frac{1.72 \times 10^{-8}\ \text{ohm} \cdot \text{m} \times 10\ \text{m}}{3 \times 10^{-6}\ \text{m}^2} = 0.057\ \text{ohm}.$$

If the current I in the wire is 20 amp, the potential difference between its terminals is

$$V_{ab} = IR = 20 \text{ amp} \times 0.057 \text{ ohm} = 1.14 \text{ volts.}$$

The electric intensity or potential gradient in the wire is

$$E_e = \frac{V_{ab}}{L} = 0.114 \frac{\text{v}}{\text{m}} = 0.114 \frac{\text{n}}{\text{coul}} .$$

If the cross section of a conductor varies along its length, the resistance can be calculated by integration, provided the conductor is of relatively simple geometry. See the following example.

EXAMPLE.   The region between two concentric spheres of radii r_a and r_b is filled with a conducting material. The inner sphere is maintained at a potential V_a and the outer sphere at a lower potential V_b, so there is a current radially outward from the inner to the outer sphere, through the material. The cross-sectional area A of the conductor, at any radius r between the spheres, is $A = 4\pi r^2$, and since in this case $ds = dr$, we have

$$R = \frac{\rho}{4\pi} \int_{r_a}^{r_b} \frac{dr}{r^2} = \frac{\rho}{4\pi} \left(\frac{1}{r_a} - \frac{1}{r_b} \right) .$$

The current between the spheres is

$$I = \frac{V_{ab}}{R} ,$$

and the current density J at any spherical surface of radius r is

$$J = \frac{I}{A} = \frac{V_{ab}}{R \times 4\pi r^2} .$$

The corresponding electric intensity E is

$$E = \rho J = \frac{V_{ab}}{(1/r_a) - (1/r_b)} \frac{1}{r^2} .$$

Reference to Problem 26–18 will show that this is equal to the intensity that would be found if the spheres were in vacuum and there were no current between them.

The results of this special case are true in all instances. That is, if any region of space in which an electrostatic field is set up by charged conductors is completely filled by a homogeneous conducting material, and if the potentials of the conductors are not changed, *the lines of force and the equipotential surfaces are the same as they would be in empty space.*

This is often taken advantage of in an experimental study of electric fields. A number of conductors are placed in a shallow tray of conducting liquid, or on a sheet of conducting material, and maintained at different potentials. The potential at any point of the liquid or conducting sheet can then be measured with an ordinary voltmeter. Equipotentials can then be plotted and lines of force (which are now also *lines of flow*) can be constructed at right angles to them. The conductors may be of any arbitrary shape, for which a mathematical solution of the problem would be difficult or impossible.

28–4 Electromotive force

The rectangle in Fig. 28–4 represents schematically a device such as a dry cell, storage battery, or electromagnetic generator. The general term for such a device is a *source*, although the term is not well chosen, since the device is a source neither of electricity nor of energy. We shall see later that, basically, a source functions as an *energy converter*, in which nonelectrical energy is converted to electrical energy or vice versa. Consider first the case in which there is no external conducting path between the terminals *a* and *b*. The source is then said to be on *open circuit*.

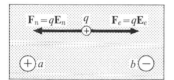

Fig. 28–4. A source on open circuit. The nonelectrostatic force $\mathbf{F}_n$ on a charge q is everywhere equal and opposite to the electrostatic force $\mathbf{F}_e$.

Terminal *a*, marked +, is maintained by the source at a higher potential than terminal *b*, marked −. There is therefore an electro*static* field at all points between and around the terminals, the lines of force of which extend from terminal *a* toward terminal *b*. The source itself is a conductor, however (electrolytic or metallic), and contains free charges (ions or electrons). If the *only* force on the free charges within the source were that exerted by the electrostatic field, the positive charges within the source would move from *a* toward *b*, and negative charges from *b* toward *a*. The excess charges on the terminals would decrease and the potential difference would decrease and eventually become zero. Since this is not observed to happen, we conclude that a *non*electrostatic force, as well as an electrostatic force, must act on the free charges within the source. When the source is on open circuit, the electrostatic and nonelectrostatic forces on a free charge are equal in magnitude and opposite in direction, and the *resultant* force on every charged particle is zero. As indicated in Fig. 28–4, where for simplicity only a positive charge is shown, the electro*static* force $\mathbf{F}_e$, which of itself would drive positive charges from *a* toward *b* (or "from plus toward minus") is balanced by a *non*electrostatic force $\mathbf{F}_n$ which of itself would drive positive charges from *b* toward *a* (or "from minus toward plus").

From another point of view, it was the nonelectrostatic force which originally brought about the excess charges on terminals *a* and *b*. Suppose these are initially uncharged. The nonelectrostatic force is then the only force, and it drives positive charges toward *a* and negative charges toward *b*. These charges then set up an electrostatic field which opposes the motion of the free charges, and the accumulation of charge continues until the electrostatic force builds up to a value equal to the nonelectrostatic force.

Nonelectrostatic forces on the charges in a conductor can arise from a number of causes. In a dry cell or storage battery, the forces are of chemical origin. In the armature of an electromagnetic generator they result from the motion of a conductor

Fig. 28–5. A source on closed circuit. The current is everywhere counterclockwise. The driving force on a charge in the external circuit is purely electrostatic. The net driving force on a charge within the source is the difference between the nonelectrostatic and the electrostatic force.

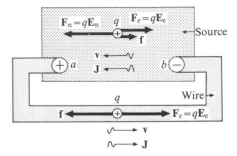

across a magnetic field. A time-varying magnetic field causes a nonelectrostatic force to act on the charges in the windings of a transformer. Differences in temperature produce nonelectrostatic forces in a thermocouple circuit. The charges on the moving belt of a Van de Graaff generator are driven in a direction opposite to that of the electrostatic force by the mechanical force exerted on them by the belt, but the analysis that follows is not directly applicable to this device because the motion of the charges on the belt is not a *conduction* process.

Now suppose that the terminals of a source are connected by a wire, as in Fig. 28–5. The driving force on the free charges in the wire is that due to the electro*static* field set up by the charged terminals a and b of the source. (Actually, the situation is not quite as simple as this. Induced charges accumulate on the surface of the wire until the resultant field in the wire is uniform along its length. The field, however, is purely electrostatic.) This field sets up a current in the wire from a toward b. (The free electrons in the wire drift from b toward a, but for simplicity in the diagram we consider the current to be carried by positive charges.) The charges on the terminals a and b decrease slightly and the electrostatic field both within the wire and within the source decreases also. As a result, the electrostatic force on the free charges within the source becomes smaller than the nonelectrostatic force. These charges are then acted on by a net driving force equal to the difference between the nonelectrostatic and the electrostatic force. Hence positive charges within the source are driven toward the positive terminal, and negative charges toward the negative terminal. The circuit settles down to a steady state in which the resultant of *all* forces on a charge carrier (including the effective viscous force) is everywhere zero, and in which the current is the same at all cross sections.

The current in Fig. 28–5 is counterclockwise at all points of the circuit, both in the source and in the wire. In the wire, the current is from the + toward the − terminal; within the source, it is from the − toward the + terminal. One can say that within the wire positive charges "flow downhill" from the higher potential to the lower potential terminal, while within the source they are "pumped uphill" by the nonelectrostatic force, from the lower to the higher potential terminal. Thus the statement sometimes made that "the direction of a current is always from + to −" is obviously incorrect. Charges cannot flow downhill *everywhere* in a closed circuit; within some portion of the circuit they must be pumped uphill.

In the most general case, the free charges in a conductor are acted on both by an electrostatic force $\mathbf{F}_e$ and by a nonelectrostatic force $\mathbf{F}_n$. Whatever the origin of the nonelectrostatic force, we can say that there exists in the conductor an *effective non-electrostatic field* $\mathbf{E}_n$, equal to the nonelectrostatic force-per-unit charge.* The resultant driving field $\mathbf{E}$ is then the vector sum of $\mathbf{E}_n$ and the electrostatic intensity $\mathbf{E}_e$:

$$\mathbf{E}_e + \mathbf{E}_n = \mathbf{E}.$$

Depending on the nature of a circuit, one or the other of the fields $\mathbf{E}_e$ or $\mathbf{E}_n$ may be zero, and if both are present they may be in the same or opposite directions.

When the resultant intensity $\mathbf{E}$ is replaced by $\rho\mathbf{J}$, we get

$$\mathbf{E}_e + \mathbf{E}_n = \rho\mathbf{J}.$$

As in the preceding section, let us form the dot product of each term with an element of length $d\mathbf{s}$ along the conductor, and integrate from point a to point b:

$$\int_a^b \mathbf{E}_e \cdot d\mathbf{s} + \int_a^b \mathbf{E}_n \cdot d\mathbf{s} = \int_a^b \rho\mathbf{J} \cdot d\mathbf{s}. \qquad (28\text{–}13)$$

The first integral on the left is the potential difference V_{ab}, and the integral on the right is the product IR, where R is the resistance between a and b. The second integral on the left, the line integral of the *non*electrostatic field, is called the *electromotive force* ε between a and b:

$$\varepsilon = \int_a^b \mathbf{E}_n \cdot d\mathbf{s}. \qquad (28\text{–}14)$$

The term "electromotive force" is not well chosen, since the concept to which it refers is not a force but the line integral of a force-per-unit charge. The term "electromotance" is used by some authors, but the concept is usually spoken of simply as the "ee-emm-eff," abbreviated emf.

Although the electro*static* field within a source (and hence the potential difference between its terminals) depends on the current in the source, the *non*electrostatic field (and hence the emf of the source) is in many cases a *constant*, independent of the current, and hence the emf represents a definite property of the source. Unless stated otherwise, we shall assume in what follows that the emf of a source is constant.

The mksc unit of $\mathbf{E}_n$ is the same as that of $\mathbf{E}_e$, so the unit of emf is the same as that of potential, namely, 1 volt. An electromotive force is not the *same thing* as a potential difference, however, since the latter is the line integral of an electro*static* field, and the former is the line integral of a *non*electrostatic field.

Equation (28–13) can now be written as

$$V_{ab} + \varepsilon = IR, \qquad (28\text{–}15)$$

---

* The symbol $\mathbf{E}_n$ has been used previously to represent the component of an electrostatic field normal to a surface, but it should be evident from the context in which sense the symbol is being used.

or

$$V_{ab} = IR - \varepsilon. \tag{28–16}$$

This is the general expression for the potential difference between points a and b of a conductor. It reduces to Eq. (28–11), $V_{ab} = IR$, when the field in the conductor is purely electrostatic and $\varepsilon = 0$.

Instead of integrating the terms in Eq. (28–13) between two points a and b, we can integrate around a complete circuit. Then

$$\oint \mathbf{E}_e \cdot d\mathbf{s} + \oint \mathbf{E}_n \cdot d\mathbf{s} = \oint \rho \mathbf{J} \cdot d\mathbf{s}. \tag{28–17}$$

The first integral is *zero*, because of the *conservative* property of an electrostatic field. In Fig. 28–5, for example, if we start at point a and integrate around the circuit in a counterclockwise direction, the electrostatic field is in the direction of integration from a to b within the conductor and makes a positive contribution to the line integral. Along the path from b back to a, within the source, the electrostatic field is opposite to the direction of integration and its negative contribution to the line integral just cancels the positive contribution within the conductor.

The second integral, however, is not *necessarily* zero, and it is called the emf ε *of the circuit*. Taking Fig. 28–5 again as an example, we find that the *non*electrostatic field is *zero* within the conductor, so this portion of the path contributes nothing to the line integral. Along the path within the source, from b back to a, the line integral of $\mathbf{E}_n$ has a positive value, so the line integral around the complete circuit is positive. In other words, nonelectrostatic fields are *nonconservative*.

In this particular example, the emf *of the circuit* is equal to the emf *of the source*. In more complicated circuits, which may contain a number of sources, the nonelectrostatic fields of some may be the same as the chosen direction of integration and those of others may be opposite to this direction. The emf *of the circuit* is then the *algebraic* sum of the emf's of the sources. In special cases, this algebraic sum may be zero.

We shall see later that when a circuit encloses a time-varying magnetic field, a nonelectrostatic field extends around the entire circuit in the same sense, and the entire circuit may be said to constitute a source.

The integral on the right side of Eq. (28–17) reduces to the product IR, where R is the *total* resistance of the circuit. Hence *for a complete circuit*,

$$\varepsilon = IR \quad \text{or} \quad I = \varepsilon/R, \tag{28–18}$$

a relation called the *circuit equation: the current in a circuit equals the emf of the circuit divided by the total resistance of the circuit.* Note that the circuit equation makes no reference to *potential differences*.

The circuit equation can be considered a special case of Eq. (28–16). If we integrate around a complete circuit, points a and b coincide, the potential difference $V_{ab} = 0$, and the equation reduces to the circuit equation.

In the derivation of Eq. (28–16), it was assumed that the vector quantities $\mathbf{E}_e$, $\mathbf{E}_n$, and $\mathbf{J}$ were all directed from the first point (a) toward the second point (b). If in any specific problem the direction of any of these vectors is from the second point (b) toward the first point (a), the algebraic sign preceding the corresponding quantity in Eq. (28–16), that is, V_{ab}, $\mathcal{E}$, or IR, must be reversed.

Similarly, it was assumed in deriving Eq. (28–18) that the vectors $\mathbf{E}_n$ and $\mathbf{J}$ were in the same sense as the direction of integration around the circuit (clockwise or counterclockwise). If either vector is opposite to the direction of integration, the algebraic sign preceding the corresponding quantity in Eq. (28–18) must be reversed.

28–5 Terminal voltage of a source

Let us use the general expression for the potential difference between two points of a conductor, Eq. (28–16), to compute the potential difference between the terminals of a source, or its *terminal voltage*, under various conditions. Consider first a source on *open circuit*, as in Fig. 28–4. There is then no current in the source, and $I = 0$. Suppose the direction of integration is from terminal a toward terminal b. The direction of $\mathbf{E}_e$ is from a toward b and the direction of $\mathbf{E}_n$ is from b toward a. According to the sign conventions explained at the end of the preceding section, we must reverse the sign preceding $\mathcal{E}$ in Eq. (28–16), which becomes (since $I = 0$)

$$V_{ab} = \mathcal{E}. \tag{28–19}$$

That is, *the open circuit terminal voltage of a source is equal to the emf of the source.* This is simply another way of saying that on open circuit the fields $\mathbf{E}_e$ and $\mathbf{E}_n$ are equal in magnitude at all points of the source and that therefore the line integral of $\mathbf{E}_e$ (the potential difference V_{ab}) is equal to the line integral of $\mathbf{E}_n$ (the emf). The emf of a source can therefore be found by measuring its open-circuit terminal voltage, without any detailed information regarding the nonelectrostatic field $\mathbf{E}_n$ within the source.

Suppose next that the terminals of a source are connected by a conductor, as in Fig. 28–5. The direction of the field $\mathbf{E}_e$ is again from a toward b, and the directions of $\mathbf{E}_n$ and $\mathbf{J}$ are from b toward a. Hence if the direction of integration is from a toward b, we must reverse the signs preceding both $\mathcal{E}$ and I in Eq. (28–16), obtaining

$$V_{ab} = \mathcal{E} - Ir, \tag{28–20}$$

where r is the resistance of the *source*, or its *internal resistance*. (The properties of a source as a circuit element are completely determined by its emf $\mathcal{E}$ and its internal resistance r.) Hence when there is a current in a source, directed from its negative toward its positive terminal, the terminal voltage is *less* than the emf by the product Ir. This is another way of saying that under these conditions the electrostatic field $\mathbf{E}_e$ is less than the nonelectrostatic field $\mathbf{E}_n$, and hence that the terminal voltage (the line integral of $\mathbf{E}_e$) is less than the electromotive force (the line integral of $\mathbf{E}_n$).

Equation (28–19) is evidently simply a special case of Eq. (28–20) when $I = 0$.

The choice of a direction of integration makes no difference. Had we chosen this to be from b toward a, instead of from a toward b, the vectors $\mathbf{E}_n$ and $\mathbf{J}$ would be in the direction of integration and that of $\mathbf{E}_e$ would be in the opposite direction. The sign preceding V_{ab} in Eq. (28–16) would then be reversed, giving

$$-V_{ab} = Ir - \mathcal{E}, \qquad \text{or} \qquad V_{ab} = \mathcal{E} - Ir,$$

which is the same as Eq. (28–20).

Equation (28–20) may be obtained in another way. The total resistance of the circuit in Fig. 28–5 is $R + r$, where R is the resistance of the external conductor. From the circuit equation, Eq. (28–18), the current I is

$$I = \frac{\mathcal{E}}{R + r}.$$

Then

$$IR = \mathcal{E} - Ir.$$

Points a and b can be considered either as the terminals of the source, or of the external conductor. But since there is no emf in the conductor, the potential difference between its terminals is

$$V_{ab} = IR.$$

Elimination of IR between the two preceding equations leads again to Eq. (28–20).

Fig. 28–6. When the terminals of a source are connected by a conductor of zero resistance, the source is said to be short-circuited. The only driving force on the charges in the source is the nonelectrostatic force F_n. There is no driving force on the charges in the conductor.

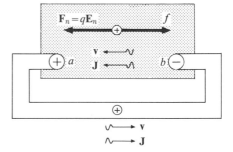

Suppose next that the terminals of a source are connected by a conductor of zero resistance, as in Fig. 28–6. The source is then said to be *short-circuited*. (This is not an advisable procedure to carry out with the storage battery of your car, or with the transmission lines of the local power company.) The only resistance in the circuit is the internal resistance r of the source, and from the circuit equation the current I (the *short-circuit current*) is

$$I = \frac{\mathcal{E}}{r}.$$

The terminal voltage is then

$$V_{ab} = \mathcal{E} - Ir = \mathcal{E} - \frac{\mathcal{E}}{r}r = 0.$$

The terminal voltage therefore drops to zero when a source delivers its short-circuit current. That is, the terminals of the source are at the *same* potential and the electro*static* field of the source is zero. The driving field within the source is the *non*electrostatic field only. There is *no* driving field in the external conductor, but none is required, since by hypothesis this conductor has no resistance. The driving force and the effective viscous retarding force in the conductor are both zero and the free charges simply "coast" through it.

In the cases considered thus far, the terminals of a source have been connected by a *pure resistance*, that is, a resistor in which there is no emf. (This includes the case of the source on open circuit, for which the external resistance is infinite.) Suppose, however, that the external circuit is not a pure resistance but contains one or more sources. These do not affect the *non*electrostatic field in the first source, but their electro*static* fields may add to or subtract from that of the first. Suppose that the resultant electro*static* field in the first source is *greater* than the *non*electrostatic field. The direction of the current in this source is then opposite to that in Fig. 28–6 and (positive) charges in the source are driven in a direction opposite to that of the non-electrostatic field, as indicated in Fig. 28–7. This is the case, for example, in a storage battery when it is being "charged" by the generator, while Fig. 28–6 corresponds to a battery that is operating the headlights and is "discharging." The reversed current in the charging process reverses the chemical reactions that took place when the battery was discharging.

It may be mentioned that the terms "charge" and "discharge," as applied to a storage battery, are misleading. The current into one terminal of a battery is always equal to that out of the other terminal, and the net quantity of charge in the battery (zero) remains constant. What the battery "stores" is not *charge*, but *energy*, in the sense that the internal energy of the battery is increased in the "charging" process, at the expense of an input of electrical energy.

The direction of the field $\mathbf{E}_n$ within the source in Fig. 28–7 is from b toward a, while the directions of $\mathbf{E}_e$ and $\mathbf{J}$ are from a toward b. We therefore reverse the sign

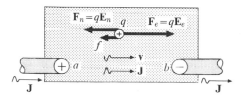

Fig. 28–7. When there are other sources (not shown) in a circuit, the electrostatic field in a given source may be greater than the nonelectrostatic field. Positive charges within the source then move in a direction opposite to the nonelectrostatic field.

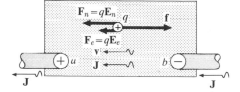

Fig. 28–8. When there are other sources (not shown) in a circuit, the electrostatic field in a given source may be in the same direction as the nonelectrostatic field. The current then exceeds the short-circuit current and terminal a is at a lower potential than terminal b.

of ε in Eq. (28–16), obtaining

$$V_{ab} = \varepsilon + Ir. \qquad (28\text{–}21)$$

The terminal voltage on "charge" is therefore *greater* than the emf, because the field $\mathbf{E}_e$ is greater than the field $\mathbf{E}_n$.

By the proper choice of sources in the external circuit, the electrostatic field in the first source may be *reversed* in direction, relative to that in the preceding examples, so that it is in the *same* direction as the nonelectrostatic field, as shown in Fig. 28–8. This case is not often encountered in practice, but it results in a current in the same direction as the "discharge" current and whose magnitude *exceeds* that of the short-circuit current. The terminal voltage is again given by

$$V_{ab} = \varepsilon - Ir,$$

but the absolute magnitude of the *Ir* product is now greater than ε and the potential difference V_{ab} is *negative*. This means that terminal *b* is at a *higher* potential than terminal *a*; the "negative" terminal of the source becomes its "positive" terminal.

The expressions for the terminal voltage of a source under the various conditions described above can all be represented by the single equation

$$V_{xy} = \varepsilon - Ir, \qquad (28\text{–}22)$$

if we adopt the following sign conventions (which are *not* the same as those used earlier).

1. The letter *x* shall refer to the terminal that is at the higher potential when the source is on open circuit. This is the terminal marked $+$.

2. The letter *y* shall refer to the terminal that is at the lower potential when the source is on open circuit. This is the terminal marked $-$.

3. The emf ε is always considered positive.

4. The current *I* is positive when the current *within the source* is from *y* toward *x*, and is negative when the current is from *x* toward *y*.

5. The internal resistance *r* is always positive.

In the preceding discussion we have represented a source schematically by a rectangle, so as to be able to depict clearly the forces on a charged particle within the source. The conventional symbol for a source is

where the longer line represents the terminal that is at a higher potential when the source is on open circuit. The nonelectrostatic field within the source is therefore directed from the shorter toward the longer terminal. In the examples that follow, we shall modify this symbol by inserting between the vertical lines the symbol representing a resistor, to indicate explicitly the internal resistance of the source. Thus the symbol for a source will be

EXAMPLES. (1) Consider a source whose emf $\mathcal{E}$ is constant and equal to 12 volts, and whose internal resistance r is 2 ohms. (The internal resistance of a commercial 12-volt lead storage battery is only a few thousandths of an ohm.) Figure 28–9 represents the source with a voltmeter V connected between its terminals a and b. A voltmeter reads the potential difference between its terminals. If it is of the conventional type, the voltmeter provides a conducting path between the terminals and so there is a current in the source (and through the voltmeter). We shall assume, however, that the resistance of the voltmeter is so large (essentially infinite) that it draws no appreciable current. The source is then on *open circuit*, corresponding to the source in Fig. 28–4, and the voltmeter reading V_{ab} equals the emf $\mathcal{E}$ of the source, or 12 volts.

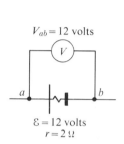

$V_{ab} = 12$ volts

$\mathcal{E} = 12$ volts
$r = 2\,\Omega$

Fig. 28–9. A source on open circuit.

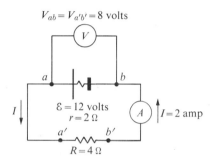

$V_{ab} = V_{a'b'} = 8$ volts

a b

I $\mathcal{E} = 12$ volts
        $r = 2\,\Omega$ A $I = 2$ amp

a' b'
$R = 4\,\Omega$

Fig. 28–10. A source on closed circuit.

(2) In Fig. 28–10, an ammeter A and a resistor of resistance $R = 4\,\Omega$ have been connected to the terminals of the source to form a closed circuit. The total resistance of the circuit is the sum of the resistance R, the internal resistance r, and the resistance of the ammeter. The ammeter resistance, however, can be made very small, and we shall assume it so small (essentially zero) that it can be neglected. The ammeter (whatever its resistance) reads the current I through it. The circuit corresponds to that in Fig. 28–5.

The wires connecting the resistor to the source and the ammeter, shown by straight lines, have zero resistance and hence there is no potential difference between their ends. Thus points a and a' are at the same potential and are electrically equivalent, as are points b and b'. The potential differences V_{ab} and $V_{a'b'}$ are therefore equal. In the future, we shall use the same symbol to represent all points in a circuit that are connected by resistanceless conductors and are at the same potential.

The current I in the resistor (and hence at all points of the circuit) could be found from the relation $I = V_{ab}/R$, if the potential difference V_{ab} were known. However, V_{ab} is the terminal voltage of the source, equal to $\mathcal{E} - Ir$, and since this depends on I it is unknown at the start. We can, however, calculate the current from the circuit equation:

$$I = \frac{\mathcal{E}}{R + r} = \frac{12 \text{ volts}}{4\,\Omega + 2\,\Omega} = 2 \text{ amp.}$$

The potential difference V_{ab} can now be found by considering a and b either as the terminals of the resistor or as those of the source. If we consider them as the terminals of the resistor,

$$V_{a'b'} = IR = 2 \text{ amp} \times 4\,\Omega = 8 \text{ volts.}$$

If we consider them as the terminals of the source,

$$V_{ab} = \mathcal{E} - Ir = 12 \text{ volts} - 2 \text{ amp} \times 2\,\Omega = 8 \text{ volts.}$$

The voltmeter therefore reads 8 volts and the ammeter reads 2 amp.

(3) In Fig. 28–11, the source is short-circuited. The current is

$$I = \frac{\mathcal{E}}{r} = \frac{12 \text{ volts}}{2\,\Omega} = 6 \text{ amp.}$$

The terminal voltage is

$$V_{ab} = \mathcal{E} - Ir = 12 \text{ volts} - 6 \text{ amp} \times 2\,\Omega = 0.$$

The ammeter reads 6 amp and the voltmeter reads zero. The circuit corresponds to Fig. 28–6.

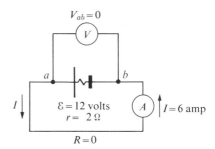

Fig. 28–11. A source on short-circuit.

(4) In Fig. 28–12, a second source of emf $\mathcal{E}_2 = 18$ volts and $r_2 = 2\,\Omega$ has been connected to the first, like terminals of the sources being connected together. Let us represent the emf and resistance of the first source by $\mathcal{E}_1$ and r_1. The emf's of the sources have opposite signs because their nonelectrostatic fields are oppositely directed around the circuit, that of the first source being counterclockwise and that of the second, clockwise. Hence if we take the line integral around the circuit in a clockwise direction,

$$\mathcal{E}_1 = -12 \text{ volts}, \qquad \mathcal{E}_2 = 18 \text{ volts},$$

and the emf $\mathcal{E}$ of the circuit is

$$\mathcal{E} = 18 \text{ volts} - 12 \text{ volts} = 6 \text{ volts}$$

From the circuit equation, the current is

$$I = \frac{\mathcal{E}}{r_1 + r_2} = \frac{6 \text{ volts}}{4\,\Omega} = 1.5 \text{ amp.}$$

Since I has a positive sign, it is in the positive (clockwise) sense and its direction in source 1 is from left to right. This source therefore corresponds to the source in Fig. 28–7, and is being "charged."

Since the direction of the current in the circuit is opposite to that in Figs. 28–10 and 28–11, the connections to the ammeter terminals would have to be reversed if the zero on the meter

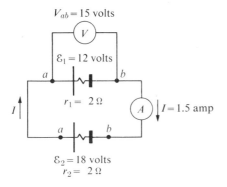

Fig. 28–12. Two sources with like terminals connected together.

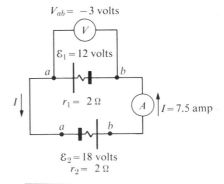

Fig. 28–13. Two sources with unlike terminals connected together.

scale is at its left end, as is the case in most meters. If the meter is of the "zero-center" type, the connections to it need not be reversed, but its deflection will be in the opposite direction to that in Figs. 28–10 and 28–11.

If we consider a and b as the terminals of source 1, Eq. (28–21) applies and

$$V_{ab} = \mathcal{E}_1 + Ir_1 = 12 \text{ volts} + 1.5 \text{ amp} \times 2\Omega = 15 \text{ volts.}$$

If we consider a and b as the terminals of source 2, Eq. (28–20) applies and

$$V_{ab} = \mathcal{E}_2 - Ir_2 = 18 \text{ volts} - 1.5 \text{ amp} \times 2\Omega = 15 \text{ volts.}$$

Either viewpoint must lead to the same answer. The potential difference V_{ab} is *greater* than the emf of source 1, and is *less* than the emf of source 2. The voltmeter reads 15 volts and the ammeter reads 1.5 amp.

(5) In Fig. 28–13, the polarity of source 2 has been reversed and the sources are connected with unlike terminals together. The fields $\mathbf{E}_n$ are now counterclockwise in both sources, and if we consider this as the positive direction the emf $\mathcal{E}$ of the circuit is

$$\mathcal{E} = \mathcal{E}_1 + \mathcal{E}_2 = 30 \text{ volts.}$$

The current is counterclockwise and its magnitude is

$$I = \frac{\mathcal{E}}{r_1 + r_2} = \frac{30 \text{ volts}}{4\Omega} = 7.5 \text{ amp.}$$

The current in source 1 is from right to left, in the same sense as in Fig. 28–11, and it exceeds the short-circuit current of the source (6 amp). Source 1 therefore corresponds to the source in Fig. 28–8.

Considering a and b as the terminals of source 1, the potential difference V_{ab} is

$$V_{ab} = \mathcal{E}_1 - Ir_1 = 12 \text{ volts} - 7.5 \text{ amp} \times 2\Omega = -3 \text{ volts.}$$

Since this is negative, terminal b is at a *higher* potential than terminal a.

Now consider a and b as the terminals of source 2. If we use Eq. (28–16) and the sign conventions at the end of Section 28–4, we must reverse the sign preceding V_{ab}. (Be sure you understand why.) Then

$$-V_{ab} = Ir_2 - \mathcal{E}_2, \quad \text{or} \quad V_{ab} = \mathcal{E}_2 - Ir_2.$$

If we use Eq. (28–22) and its sign conventions, point x becomes point b, point y becomes point a. The direction of the current in source 2 is from y toward x (or from a toward b), so I is positive and

$$V_{xy} = V_{ba} = \mathcal{E}_2 - Ir_2 = 18 \text{ volts} - 7.5 \text{ amp} \times 2\Omega = 3 \text{ volts.}$$

Point b is therefore at a potential 3 volts higher than point a, in agreement with the previous answer.

Unless the voltmeter is of the zero-center type, the connections to its terminals would have to be reversed, relative to the preceding diagrams.

28–6 Current-voltage diagrams

The relation between the current I in a device and the potential difference V_{ab} between its terminals can be represented by a graph, plotting I vertically and V_{ab} horizontally, or vice versa.

The resistivity of a *linear* conductor (one that obeys Ohm's law) is constant at constant temperature, and hence at constant temperature its resistance is constant also. The current-voltage graph for such a conductor is a straight line through the origin, as in Fig. 28–14(a). The resistance R, equal to V_{ab}/I, corresponds to the slope of the line relative to the I-axis, or to the tangent of the angle θ. The greater the resistance, the larger this angle.

A *rectifier* or *diode* is a *nonlinear* circuit element which has a finite resistance when the field within it is in one direction, and has a very high resistance (ideally, an infinite resistance) when the field is in the opposite direction. Figure 28–14(b) is the current-voltage diagram of a diode. The diode acts like a check valve in a circuit, permitting charges to flow in one direction only. The symbol for a diode is

The arrowhead indicates the direction in which the charge is being conducted.

As the voltage across a conductor is increased from zero, the current in it increases, and unless special provisions are made for keeping its temperature constant, its temperature increases also until the rate of heat loss equals the rate of dissipation of energy in the conductor. Hence if the conductor is a metal, such as the tungsten filament of an incandescent lamp, its resistance increases with increasing voltage and its current-voltage graph is nonlinear. If it is a semiconductor, its resistance decreases with increasing temperature.

Figure 28–14(c) is the current-voltage graph of a typical semiconductor, plotted on a logarithmic scale. The temperature of the semiconductor is shown at a few points. Although a linear conductor *at constant temperature*, it is, in effect, nonlinear.

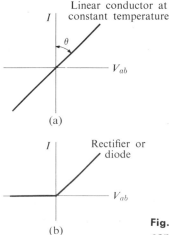

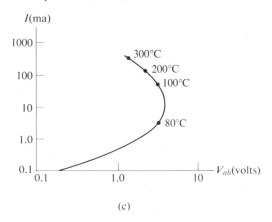

Fig. 28–14. Typical current-voltage curves for (a) a linear conductor, (b) a rectifier, and (c) a semiconductor.

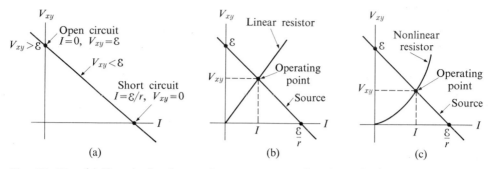

Fig. 28–15. (a) Terminal voltage of a source as a function of current; (b) operating point of a linear resistor; (c) operating point of a nonlinear resistor.

The terminal voltage of a source can be represented as a function of the current I in the source by a graph of Eq. (28–22):

$$V_{xy} = \mathcal{E} - Ir,$$

plotting V_{xy} vertically and I horizontally, as in Fig. 28–15(a). (Note that ordinate and abscissa are interchanged, relative to Fig. 28–14.) If $\mathcal{E}$ and r are constants, Eq. (28–22) represents a straight line. The line intersects the vertical axis (where $I = 0$) at the point where $V_{xy} = \mathcal{E}$, and it intersects the horizontal axis (where $V_{xy} = 0$) at the point where I equals the short-circuit current $\mathcal{E}/r$.

If a circuit contains one source only, as in Fig. 28–10, corresponding values of V_{xy} and I lie on the segment in the first quadrant. If a circuit contains a second source opposing the first and having a larger emf, as in Fig. 28–12, the current is negative, $V_{xy} > \mathcal{E}$, and values of V_{xy} and I correspond to the segment in the second quadrant. If the second source aids the first, as in Fig. 28–13 (and its short-circuit current is greater than that of the first), V_{xy} is negative and corresponds to the segment in the fourth quadrant.

By combining the graph in Fig. 28–15(a) with the voltage-current graph of a second device, one can find graphically the current and terminal voltage when the two are connected. Thus Fig. 28–15(b) shows the voltage-current graphs of a source and a linear resistor. When the resistor is connected across the source, the potential difference V_{xy} must be the same for both, and both carry the same current I. The point of intersection of the graphs is then the operating point of the source, and its coordinates give the terminal voltage and current.

This method is even more useful when a resistor is nonlinear, as in Fig. 28–15(c), and an analytical solution of the problem is difficult or impossible.

28-7 Power and work in electrical circuits

In the preceding sections of this chapter we have focused attention on the electric fields in conductors and sources. We consider next the *work* of the forces on the moving charges in a circuit, or portion of a circuit.

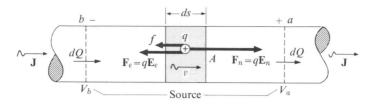

Fig. 28–16.   Forces on a moving charge carrier within a source.

Figure 28–16 represents again a portion of a circuit within which there is a current density **J** from left to right.   A particle of charge q, moving with its drift velocity **v**, is acted on by an electrostatic force $\mathbf{F}_e$, a nonelectrostatic force $\mathbf{F}_n$, and by the effective retarding force **f**.   Since the velocity is constant,

$$F_e + F_n = f.$$

It was shown in Section 7–10 and Eq. (7–17) that the rate at which work is done by a force exerted on a moving particle, or the *power* of the force, is

$$P = \mathbf{F} \cdot \mathbf{v}.$$

The rate at which work is done by each of the forces in Fig. 28–16 is therefore the product of the force and the velocity and hence, for a single particle,

$$(F_e + F_n)v = fv.$$

The forces $\mathbf{F}_e$ and $\mathbf{F}_n$ are equal respectively to $q\mathbf{E}_e$ and $q\mathbf{E}_n$, and the force **f**, from the discussion in Section 28–2, can be expressed as $\mathbf{f} = \rho n q^2 \mathbf{v}$.   Hence

$$qv(E_e + E_n) = \rho n q^2 v^2.$$

The number of charges in the portion of length ds is $nA\,ds$, so for all charges in the portion,

$$nAqv(E_e\,ds + E_n\,ds) = n^2 q^2 v^2 \rho A\,ds.$$

But $nAqv$ equals the current I, so

$$I(E_e\,ds + E_n\,ds) = I^2 \frac{\rho}{A}\,ds,$$

and when both sides are integrated from point a to point b, we get

$$I\int_a^b E_e\,ds + I\int_a^b E_n\,ds = I^2 \int_a^b \frac{\rho}{A}\,ds.$$

The first integral equals the potential difference V_{ab}, the second equals the emf ε between a and b, and the third is the resistance R between a and b.   Hence

$$IV_{ab} + I\varepsilon = I^2 R. \tag{28–23}$$

If the only field between a and b is an electrostatic field $\mathbf{E}_e$, the emf is zero and

$$IV_{ab} = I^2 R. \tag{28-24}$$

If the integral is taken around a complete circuit, so that points a and b coincide, $V_{ab} = 0$ and

$$I\mathcal{E} = I^2 R. \tag{28-25}$$

When each term in the preceding equations is divided by I, we get Eqs. (28–16), (28–11), and (28–18), and the analysis above can be considered an alternate method of deriving these equations.

The products IV_{ab}, $I\mathcal{E}$, and $I^2 R$ are the *rates* at which work is done by the forces $\mathbf{F}_e$, $\mathbf{F}_n$, and $\mathbf{f}$. The quantities of *work* done by each force in a time interval dt are, respectively,

$$IV_{ab}\, dt, \qquad I\mathcal{E}\, dt, \qquad I^2 R\, dt,$$

and since $I\, dt$ equals the charge dQ flowing across any section of the circuit in the time dt, the respective works are

$$V_{ab}dQ, \qquad \mathcal{E}dQ, \qquad IRdQ.$$

The work dW_e of the electrostatic force is

$$dW_e = (V_a - V_b)dQ = V_a dQ - V_b dQ.$$

The products $V_a dQ$ and $V_b dQ$ are respectively the electrical potential energies of the charge dQ as it enters and leaves the portion of the circuit under consideration. Hence the work dW_e equals the *change in electrical potential energy* of the circulating charge. Depending on the relative directions of $\mathbf{J}$ and $\mathbf{E}_e$, the potential energy may increase or decrease. If it *increases*, the circulating charges acquire energy in the source and give up an equal amount to the remainder of the circuit. Any *decrease* in energy comes from energy acquired in other portions of the circuit. Hence dW_e represents an *energy interchange* between the portion of the circuit considered and the remainder of the circuit, and the product IV_{ab} equals the *rate* of this interchange, or the *power* supplied by or delivered to the portion.

The work dW_n of the nonelectrostatic force equals $\mathcal{E}\,dQ$ and hence

$$\mathcal{E} = \frac{dW_n}{dQ}. \tag{28-26}$$

This work can be positive or negative, depending on the relative directions of $\mathbf{J}$ and $\mathbf{E}_n$. That is, work may be done *on* the circulating charge by the system maintaining the field $\mathbf{E}_n$, or work may be done *by* the circulating charge on the system maintaining this field. In either case, there is an energy interchange *between the circulating charge and some other system*, and from this point of view a source can be described as an *energy converter*. If the source is a storage battery, the conversion is between electrical and internal energy. If it is a generator or motor, mechanical energy is converted to electrical, or electrical to mechanical. From Eq. (28–26), the emf ε equals the *energy converted per unit charge flowing across any section of the circuit.*

The product I^2R is the rate at which energy is *dissipated* within the portion of the circuit considered, as a result of the inelastic collisions of the moving charges. If the portion is thermally insulated, so that the process is adiabatic, the temperature increases. If the temperature is kept constant, the process is isothermal and there is a flow of heat out of the portion at a rate equal to I^2R.

If we adopt the convention that in the product IV_{ab} a current is positive when its direction is from a to b and negative when its direction is from b to a, then a positive value of the product represents an electrical power *input* to the portion of the circuit between a and b, and a negative value, a power *output.*

In the product $I\varepsilon$, if I is considered positive when its direction is the same as that of the nonelectrostatic field $\mathbf{E}_n$ associated with the emf ε, a positive value of the product represents energy conversion from nonelectrical to electrical form and a negative value represents energy conversion from electrical to nonelectrical form.

The product I^2R is always positive and always represents a dissipation of electrical energy.

In most instances, however, it is possible to consider only the absolute values of the products IV_{ab} and $I\varepsilon$, and to decide from inspection of a problem whether they represent power inputs or power outputs, or in which direction the conversion of energy is taking place.

In the mksc system, the unit of each of the products IV_{ab}, $I\varepsilon$, and I^2R is 1 joule/sec or 1 watt. Thus the unit of the product IV_{ab} is

$$1 \text{ amp} \times 1 \text{ volt} = 1\,\frac{\text{coul}}{\text{sec}} \times 1\,\frac{\text{joule}}{\text{coul}} = 1\,\frac{\text{joule}}{\text{sec}} = 1 \text{ watt.}$$

Multiples of this unit are the *kilowatt* (1 kw = 10^3 watts) and the *megawatt* (1 Mw = 10^6 watts). Small quantities of power are often expressed in *milliwatts* (1 mw = 10^{-3} watt).

If the unit of power is 1 watt and the unit of time is 1 second, the corresponding unit of energy is

$$1 \text{ watt·second} = 1 \text{ joule.}$$

If the power is expressed in kilowatts and the time in hours, the corresponding energy unit is

$$1 \text{ kilowatt·hour (1 kwh)} = 3.6 \times 10^6 \text{ joules.}$$

It is important to remember that the watt·second (or joule) and the kilowatt·hour are units of *energy*, not power.

EXAMPLES. We shall illustrate the relations developed in this section by applying them to the circuits in Figs. 28–10 through 28–14.

(1) The rate of energy conversion in the source in Fig. 28–10 is

$$I\varepsilon = 2 \text{ amp} \times 12 \text{ volts} = 24 \text{ watts.}$$

The rate of dissipation of energy in the source is

$$I^2r = (2 \text{ amp})^2 \times 2\Omega = 8 \text{ watts.}$$

The power *output* of the source is the difference between these, or 16 watts. The power output is also given by

$$IV_{ab} = 2 \text{ amp} \times 8 \text{ volts} = 16 \text{ watts.}$$

The power input to the resistor is

$$IV_{a'b'} = 2 \text{ amp} \times 8 \text{ volts} = 16 \text{ watts.}$$

This equals the rate of dissipation of energy in the resistor:

$$I^2R = (2 \text{ amp})^2 \times 4\Omega = 16 \text{ watts.}$$

(2) The rate of energy conversion in the source in Fig. 28–11 is

$$I\mathcal{E} = 6 \text{ amp} \times 12 \text{ volts} = 72 \text{ watts.}$$

The rate of dissipation of energy in the source is

$$I^2r = (6 \text{ amp})^2 \times 2\Omega = 72 \text{ watts.}$$

The power *output* of the source (also given by IV_{ab}) equals zero. All of the energy converted is dissipated within the source.

(3) The rate of energy conversion in source 1 in Fig. 28–12 is

$$I\mathcal{E}_1 = 1.5 \text{ amp} \times 12 \text{ volts} = 18 \text{ watts.}$$

Within this source, electrical energy is converted to nonelectrical energy. The rate of dissipation of energy in source 1 is

$$I^2r_1 = (1.5 \text{ amp})^2 \times 2\Omega = 4.5 \text{ watts.}$$

The total power *input* to source 1 is the *sum* of these, or 22.5 watts. The power input is also given by

$$IV_{ab} = 1.5 \text{ amp} \times 15 \text{ volts} = 22.5 \text{ watts.}$$

The same expression gives the power *output* of source 2. The rate of energy conversion in source 2 is

$$I\mathcal{E}_2 = 1.5 \text{ amp} \times 18 \text{ volts} = 27 \text{ watts.}$$

Within this source, nonelectrical energy is converted to electrical energy. The rate of dissipation of energy in source 2 is

$$I^2r_2 = (1.5 \text{ amp})^2 \times 2\Omega = 4.5 \text{ watts.}$$

The *difference* between these equals the power output of 22.5 watts.

(4) In the circuit of Fig. 28–13, nonelectrical energy is converted to electrical energy in *both* sources. The rates of conversion are, respectively,

$$I\mathcal{E}_1 = 7.5 \text{ amp} \times 12 \text{ volts} = 90 \text{ watts,}$$
$$I\mathcal{E}_2 = 7.5 \text{ amp} \times 18 \text{ volts} = 135 \text{ watts.}$$

The rates of energy dissipation within the sources are, respectively,

$$I^2r_1 = (7.5\,\text{amp})^2 \times 2\Omega = 112.5\,\text{watts},$$
$$I^2r_2 = (7.5\,\text{amp})^2 \times 2\Omega = 112.5\,\text{watts}.$$

The sum of these equals the total rate of energy conversion, 225 watts. The power output of source 2 is

$$135\,\text{watts} - 112.5\,\text{watts} = 22.5\,\text{watts}.$$

This equals the power input to source 1 and also equals (in magnitude) the product IV_{ab}. The rate of energy dissipation in source 1, 112.5 watts, equals the sum of the rate of energy conversion in this source, 90 watts, and the power input of 22.5 watts.

28–8 Thermoelectricity

In 1826 Thomas Johann Seebeck (1770–1831) discovered that an emf could be produced by purely thermal means in a circuit composed of two different metals A and B whose junctions are maintained at different temperatures, as shown schematically in Fig. 28–17. The two metals constitute a *thermocouple*, and the emf in the circuit is called a *thermal* emf, or a *Seebeck* emf. When the temperature of the reference junction t_R is kept constant, the Seebeck emf ε_{AB} is found to be a function of the temperature t of the test junction. This fact enables the thermocouple to be used as a thermometer, as described in Section 15–2, and this is its main use today. The advantage of a thermocouple thermometer is that, because its heat capacity is small, the test junction comes quite rapidly to thermal equilibrium with the system whose temperature is to be measured. It therefore follows temperature changes easily.

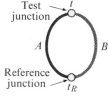

Fig. 28–17. Thermocouple of metals A and B with junctions at t and t_R.

A *thermopile* is an instrument consisting of many fine thermocouples connected in series, so that the total emf is the sum of the separate emf's. In conjunction with a high-sensitivity galvanometer, a thermopile is an extremely sensitive device for detecting and measuring radiant energy. The reference junctions are covered, while the test junctions are blackened and exposed to the radiant energy. Thermopiles are used to measure the radiation from stars and are commonly employed to investigate the distribution of energy in those portions of a spectrum beyond the limits of a photographic plate.

The Seebeck emf arises from the fact that the density of free electrons in a metal differs from one metal to another and, in a given metal, depends on the temperature. When two different metals are connected to form two junctions and the two junctions are maintained at different temperatures, electron diffusion at the junctions takes place at different rates. There is a net motion of the electrons, as though the electrons were driven by a nonelectrostatic field. The line integral of this field around the thermocouple is the Seebeck emf.

If two different materials are joined to form *only one junction*, and if a current is sent through the junction while it is maintained at constant temperature, a heat flow will take place between the junction and its surroundings, called the *Peltier heat*, after its discoverer, Jean C. A. Peltier. Experiment has shown that the Peltier heat transferred at any junction is proportional to the quantity of electricity crossing the junction, and that it reverses its direction of flow when the electric current is reversed. A single junction, therefore, is a source within which electrical energy is converted to heat, or heat is converted to electrical energy. Then the term dW_n in Eq. (28–26) represents the heat absorbed or liberated when a quantity of charge dQ crosses the junction. The Peltier emf of a junction of metals A and B, π_{AB}, is defined as the heat absorbed or liberated per unit quantity of electricity crossing the junction. Thus

$$\pi_{AB} = \frac{\text{Peltier heat}}{\text{charge transferred}}. \tag{28–27}$$

It is found that π_{AB} depends not only on the nature of the two metals, but also on the temperature of the junction, and that it is independent of any other junction that may be present.

In a single wire whose ends are maintained at different temperatures, the free electron density varies from point to point. Each element of a wire of nonuniform temperature is therefore a source, a discovery made by Sir William Thomson (Lord Kelvin). When a current is maintained in a wire of nonuniform temperature, heat is liberated or absorbed at all points of the wire, and this *Thomson heat* is proportional to the quantity of electricity passing the section of wire and to the temperature difference between the ends of the section. If an infinitesimal length of wire A has a temperature difference dt, the amount of heat absorbed or liberated in this length of wire per unit quantity of electricity transferred is called the *Thomson emf*, written $\sigma_A \, dt$. Thus

$$\sigma_A \, dt = \frac{\text{Thomson heat}}{\text{charge transferred}}. \tag{28–28}$$

The total Thomson emf in a wire whose ends are at temperatures t_1 and t_2 is given by

$$\int_{t_1}^{t_2} \sigma_A \, dt.$$

Experiment has shown that the Thomson heat is also reversible, and depends on the nature of the wire and on the average temperature of the portion of the wire under consideration. The coefficient σ_A is sometimes called the "specific heat of electricity."

If we return now to the thermocouple depicted in Fig. 28–17, we see that the Seebeck emf $\mathcal{E}_{AB}$ is the resultant of two Peltier emf's, $(\pi_{AB})_t$ and $(\pi_{AB})_{t_R}$, and two Thomson emf's, $\int_{t_R}^{t} \sigma_A \, dt$ and $\int_{t_R}^{t} \sigma_B \, dt$. The relation among these emf's is the *fundamental thermocouple equation:*

$$\mathcal{E}_{AB} = (\pi_{AB})_t - (\pi_{AB})_{t_R} + \int_{t_R}^{t} (\sigma_A - \sigma_B) \, dt. \tag{28–29}$$

The sign conventions in this equation are:

(1) $\mathcal{E}_{AB}$ is positive when the direction of the thermocouple current is from A to B at the test junction, which is taken to be the *warmer* of the two junctions.

(2) π_{AB} is positive when the current is from A to B and Peltier heat is *absorbed* by the junction.

(3) σ_A is positive when the current is opposite to the direction of the temperature gradient (low to high temperature) and Thomson heat is *absorbed*.

28–9 Applications of the fundamental thermocouple equation

(1) Suppose that three wires A, B, and C are connected in series, as shown in Fig. 28–18, and the three junctions AB, BC, and CA are maintained at the *same* temperature. In this circuit the Seebeck emf $\mathcal{E}_{ABC}$ is zero, and there are no Thomson emf's. Applying the fundamental thermocouple equation, we obtain

$$(\pi_{AB})_t + (\pi_{BC})_t + (\pi_{CA})_t = 0, \tag{28–30}$$

a result which will be found useful in what is to follow.

(2) Now let us consider three wires A, B, and C connected in series, as shown in Fig. 28–19, with the junction AB maintained at the temperature t and the other two junctions BC and CA at the temperature t_R. Applying the fundamental thermocouple equation, we get

$$\mathcal{E}_{ABC} = (\pi_{AB})_t + (\pi_{BC})_{t_R} + (\pi_{CA})_{t_R} + \int_{t_R}^{t} (\sigma_A - \sigma_B)\,dt,$$

since there is no Thomson emf in wire C. Because junctions BC and CA are at the *same* temperature t_R, we may use Eq. (28–30) of the previous example. The result is

$$\mathcal{E}_{ABC} = (\pi_{AB})_t - (\pi_{AB})_{t_R} + \int_{t_R}^{t} (\sigma_A - \sigma_B)\,dt,$$

which is simply the expression for the emf of a thermocouple of wires A and B only, with junctions at t and t_R. Hence

$$\mathcal{E}_{ABC} = \mathcal{E}_{AB}, \tag{28–31}$$

when the ends of C are at the same temperature.

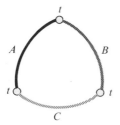

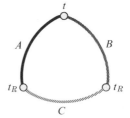

Fig. 28–18. Three wires in series with all junctions at the same temperature. $(\pi_{AB})_t + (\pi_{BC})_t + (\pi_{CA})_t = 0$.

Fig. 28–19. Three wires in series with junction AB at temperature t and junctions BC and CA at temperature t_R. $\mathcal{E}_{ABC} = \mathcal{E}_{AB}$.

In order to connect a thermocouple to a measuring instrument, it is necessary to break the thermocouple circuit at some point and introduce a third metal, thereby creating two new junctions. The preceding equation shows that no disturbing effects are produced, provided both new junctions are maintained at the same temperature. The correct procedure for connecting a thermocouple to a potentiometer* is shown in Fig. 28–20.

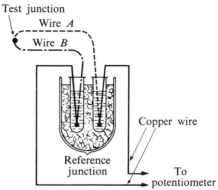

Fig. 28–20. Thermocouple of wires A and B with a reference junction consisting of two junctions with copper.

(3) Consider the two thermocouples depicted in Fig. 28–21, one composed of metals A and C and the other of metals B and C. Applying the fundamental relation of Eq. (28–29) to each thermocouple and subtracting the two equations, we get

$$\mathcal{E}_{AC} - \mathcal{E}_{BC} = (\pi_{AC})_t - (\pi_{BC})_t - (\pi_{AC})_{t_R} + (\pi_{BC})_{t_R} + \int_{t_R}^{t} (\sigma_A - \sigma_B)\, dt.$$

Making use of Eq. (28–30), the preceding result reduces to

$$\mathcal{E}_{AC} - \mathcal{E}_{BC} = (\pi_{AB})_t - (\pi_{AB})_{t_R} + \int_{t_R}^{t} (\sigma_A - \sigma_B)\, dt.$$

But the right side of this equation equals the Seebeck emf of a thermocouple of wires A and B. Hence

$$\mathcal{E}_{AB} = \mathcal{E}_{AC} - \mathcal{E}_{BC}, \tag{28–32}$$

for the same junction temperature.

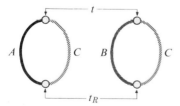

Fig. 28–21. Two separate thermocouples, each with one wire the same, with junctions at the same temperature. $\mathcal{E}_{AB} = \mathcal{E}_{AC} - \mathcal{E}_{BC}$.

* The potentiometer is described in the next chapter. Essentially, it is a voltmeter that draws no current.

TABLE 28–3

CONSTANTS IN THE EQUATION $\mathcal{E}_{ML} = at + \frac{1}{2}bt^2 \ (t_R = 0°C)$

Metal M (L = lead)	$a\left(\dfrac{\mu V}{\deg}\right)$	$b\left(\dfrac{\mu V}{\deg^2}\right)$
Aluminum	−0.47	0.003
Bismuth	−43.7	−0.47
Copper	2.76	0.012
Gold	2.90	0.0093
Iron	16.6	−0.030
Nickel	19.1	−0.030
Platinum	−1.79	−0.035
Silver	2.50	0.012
Steel	10.8	−0.016

The fact that the emf of a thermocouple AB is the difference between the emf's of two thermocouples AC and BC when the junction temperatures are the same enables us to tabulate convenient numbers from which the thermal emf of any thermocouple may be computed. Thus if M is any metal and L is lead, experiment shows that the thermal emf $\mathcal{E}_{ML}$ depends on the temperature t of the test junction, when $t_R = 0°C$, according to the equation

$$\mathcal{E}_{ML} = at + \tfrac{1}{2}bt^2, \tag{28–33}$$

provided t is no more than a few hundred degrees. The constants a and b for various metals M are given in Table 28–3.

EXAMPLE. Find the emf of a copper-iron thermocouple when $t_R = 0°C$.
We write

$$\mathcal{E}_{Cu\ Fe} = \mathcal{E}_{Cu\ Pb} - \mathcal{E}_{Fe\ Pb},$$

and using Eq. (28–33),

$$\mathcal{E}_{Cu\ Fe} = (a_{Cu\ Pb} - a_{Fe\ Pb})t + \tfrac{1}{2}(b_{Cu\ Pb} - b_{Fe\ Pb})t^2.$$

From Table 28–3,

$$\mathcal{E}_{Cu\ Fe} = (2.76 - 16.6)\frac{\mu V}{\deg}t + \tfrac{1}{2}(0.012 + 0.030)\frac{\mu V}{\deg^2}t^2.$$

$$= -13.8\frac{\mu V}{\deg}t + 0.021\frac{\mu V}{\deg^2}t^2.$$

At $t = 100°C$,

$$\mathcal{E}_{Cu\ Fe} = -1.17\ mv,$$

where the minus sign indicates that the direction of the current at the junction is from iron to copper, at 100°C.

The graphs of Fig. 28–22 show the emf of a copper-iron thermocouple as a function of the temperature of the test junction t for three different values of the temperature of the reference junction t_R. It will be seen that at any value of t, the slope $d\mathcal{E}/dt$ is the same for the three curves, and is therefore independent of t_R. It may be shown from thermodynamic reasoning that, in general,

$$\pi_{AB} = T\frac{d\mathcal{E}_{AB}}{dt},$$

where T is the Kelvin temperature. Since $d\mathcal{E}_{AB}/dt$ is independent of t_R, it follows that the Peltier emf depends only on the temperature of the junction under consideration, and not on the temperature of any other junction.

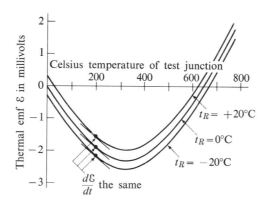

Fig. 28–22. Thermal emf of a copper-iron thermocouple as a function of the temperature of the test junction, for three different values of the temperature of the reference junction.

Problems

28–1. A silver wire 1 mm in diameter carries a charge of 90 coul in 1 hr and 15 min. Silver contains 5.8×10^{28} free electrons per m³. (a) What is the current in the wire? (b) What is the drift velocity of the electrons in the wire?

28–2. When a sufficiently high potential difference is applied between two electrodes in a gas, the gas ionizes, electrons moving toward the positive electrode and positive ions toward the negative electrode. (a) What is the current in a hydrogen discharge tube if in each second 4×10^{18} electrons and 1.5×10^{18} protons move in opposite

directions past a cross section of the tube? (b) What is the direction of the current?

28–3. A vacuum diode can be approximated by a plane cathode and a plane anode, parallel to each other and 5 mm apart. The area of both cathode and anode is 2 cm². In the region between cathode and anode the current is carried solely by electrons. If the electron current is 50 ma, and the electrons strike the anode surface with a velocity of 1.2×10^7 m/sec, find the number of electrons per cubic millimeter in the space just outside the surface of the anode.

28–4. In the Bohr model of the hydrogen atom the electron makes about 6×10^{15} rev/sec around the nucleus. What is the average current at a point on the orbit of the electron?

28–5. The belt of a Van de Graaff generator is one meter wide and travels with a speed of 25 m/sec. (a) Neglecting leakage, at what rate in coul/sec must charge be sprayed on one face of the belt to correspond to a current of 10^{-4} amp into the collecting sphere? (b) Compute the surface charge per unit area on the belt.

28–6. Refer to the first example in Section 28–3. Assume there are 10^{29} free electrons per cubic meter in the wire. Calculate (a) the driving force on an electron, (b) the "viscous" retarding force, (c) the time for an electron to travel the length of the wire.

28–7. It was shown in Example 9 in Section 5–6 that the relaxation time for a particle moving in a viscous fluid (the time for the velocity to increase from zero to within $1/e$th of the terminal velocity) is $t_R = m/k$, where the magnitude of the resisting force $f = kv$. Using the data of Problem 28–6, find the relaxation time for an electron in a copper conductor. Is it reasonable to assume that the electrons acquire their terminal velocities instantaneously when an electric field is set up in copper?

28–8. The current in a wire varies with time according to the relation

$$i = 4 + 2t^2,$$

where i is in amperes and t in seconds. (a) How many coulombs pass a cross section of the wire in the time interval between $t = 5$ sec and $t = 10$ sec? (b) What constant current would transport the same charge in the same time interval?

28–9. The current in a wire varies with time according to the relation

$$i = 20 \sin 377t,$$

where i is in amperes, t in seconds, and

($377t$) in radians. (a) How many coulombs pass a cross section of the wire in the time interval between $t = 0$ and $t = 1/120$ sec? (b) In the interval between $t = 0$ and $t = 1/60$ sec? (c) What constant current would transport the same charge in each of the intervals above?

28–10. A wire 100 m long and 2 mm in diameter has a resistivity of 4.8×10^{-8} ohm·m. (a) What is the resistance of the wire? (b) A second wire of the same material has the same weight as the 100-meter length, but twice its diameter. What is its resistance?

28–11. Refer to the second example in Section 28–3. Let the resistivity of the material between the spherical conductors be 10 ohm·m and let $r_a = 10$ cm, $r_b = 20$ cm. (a) Find the current between the spheres if $V_{ab} = 8$ volts. (b) Find the electric intensity at a radius $r = 15$ cm. (c) Find the current if the radius of the outer sphere is infinite.

28–12. The region between two long concentric cylinders is filled with a conducting material of resistivity ρ. The inner cylinder, of radius r_a, is maintained at a potential V_a and the outer cylinder, of radius r_b, at a lower potential V_b, so there is a current radially outward. Prove that (a) the resistance of length L is equal to

$$\frac{\rho}{2\pi L} \ln \frac{r_b}{r_a},$$

and (b) the electric intensity at a point between the two cylinders is

$$E = \frac{V_{ab}}{\ln (r_b/r_a)} \cdot \frac{1}{r}.$$

[Compare this result with the answer to Problem 26–19(b).] (c) Assume that the cylinders are nonconducting and that one end is at a potential V_1 and the other end at a lower potential V_2. Calculate the resistance to *longitudinal* flow.

28–13. (a) The following measurements of current and potential difference were made on a resistor constructed of Nichrome wire:

I (amp)	V_{ab} (volts)
0.5	2.18
1.0	4.36
2.0	8.72
4.0	17.44

Make a graph of V_{ab} as a function of I. Does the Nichrome obey Ohm's law? What is the resistance of the resistor, in ohms?

(b) The following measurements were made on a Thyrite resistor:

I (amp)	V_{ab} (volts)
0.5	4.76
1.0	5.81
2.0	7.05
4.0	8.56

Make a graph of V_{ab} as a function of I. Does Thyrite have constant resistance? (c) Construct a graph of the resistance R as a function of I.

28–14. (a) Construct a graph of the resistance of the semiconductor in Fig. 28–14(c), as a function of temperature, in the temperature range from 80°C to 300°C. (Plot the resistance on a logarithmic scale.) (b) Estimate the ratio of the number of charge carriers per unit volume at 200°C, to the number at 100°C.

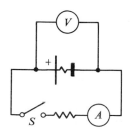

Figure 28–23

28–15. When switch S is open, the voltmeter V, connected across the terminals of the dry cell in Fig. 28–23, reads 1.52 volts. When the switch is closed the voltmeter

reading drops to 1.37 volts and the ammeter A reads 1.5 amp. Find the emf and internal resistance of the cell. Neglect meter corrections.

28–16. The potential difference across the terminals of a battery is 8.5 volts when there is a current of 3 amp in the battery from the negative to the positive terminal. When the current is 2 amp in the reverse direction, the potential difference becomes 11 volts. (a) What is the internal resistance of the battery? (b) What is the emf of the battery?

28–17. (a) What is the potential difference V_{ad} in the circuit of Fig. 28–24? (b) What is the terminal voltage of the 4-volt battery? (c) A battery of emf 17 volts and internal resistance 1 ohm is inserted in the circuit at d, its positive terminal being connected to the positive terminal of the 8-volt battery. What is now the difference of potential between the terminals of the 4-volt battery?

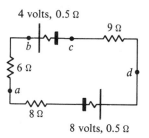

4 volts, 0.5 Ω

9 Ω

b c

6 Ω

d

a

8 Ω

8 volts, 0.5 Ω

Figure 28–24

28–18. A closed circuit consists of a 12-volt battery, a 3.7-ohm resistor, and a switch. The internal resistance of the battery is 0.3 ohm. The switch is opened. What would a high-resistance voltmeter read when placed (a) across the terminals of the battery, (b) across the resistor, (c) across the switch? Repeat (a), (b), and (c) for the case when the switch is closed.

28–19. The internal resistance of a dry cell increases gradually with age, even though the cell is not used. The emf, however, remains fairly constant at about 1.5 volts. Dry cells are often tested for age at the time of purchase by connecting an ammeter directly across the terminals of the cell and reading the current. The resistance of the ammeter is so small that the cell is practically short-circuited. (a) The short-circuit current of a fresh No. 6 dry cell is about 30 amp. Approximately what is the internal resistance? (b) What is the internal resistance if the short-circuit current is only 10 amp? (c) The short-circuit current of a 6-volt storage battery may be as great as 1000 amp. What is its internal resistance?

28–20. The open-circuit terminal voltage of a source is 10 volts and its short-circuit current is 4.0 amp. (a) What will be the current when the source is connected to a linear resistor of resistance 2 ohms? (b) What will be the current in the Thyrite resistor of Problem 28–13(b) when connected across the terminals of this source? (c) What is the terminal voltage at this current?

28–21. A "660-watt" electric heater is designed to operate from 120-volt lines. (a) What is its resistance? (b) What current does it draw? (c) What is the rate of dissipation of energy, in cal/sec? (d) If the line voltage drops to 110 volts, what power does the heater take, in watts? (Assume the resistance constant. Actually, it will change because of the change in temperature.)

28–22. (a) Express the rate of dissipation of energy in a resistor in terms of (1) potential difference and current, (2) resistance and current, (3) potential difference and resistance. (b) Energy is dissipated in a resistor at the rate of 40 watts when the potential difference between its terminals is 60 volts. What is its resistance?

28–23. A storage battery whose emf is 12 volts and whose internal resistance is 0.1 ohm (internal resistances of commercial storage batteries are actually only a few thousandths of an ohm) is to be charged from a 112-volt DC supply. (a) Should the + or the − terminal of the battery be connected to the + side of the line? (b) What will be the charging current if the battery

is connected directly across the line? (c) Compute the resistance of the series resistor required to limit the current to 10 amp. With this resistor in the circuit, compute (d) the potential difference between the terminals of the battery, (e) the power taken from the line, (f) the power dissipated in the series resistor, (g) the *useful* power input to the battery. (h) If electrical energy costs 3 cents per kwh, what is the cost of operating the circuit for 2 hours when the current is 10 amp?

28–24. In the circuit in Fig. 28–25, find (a) the rate of conversion of internal energy to electrical energy within the battery, (b) the rate of dissipation of energy in the battery, (c) the rate of dissipation of energy in the external resistor.

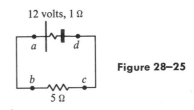

12 volts, 1 Ω

Figure 28–25

28–25. A source whose emf is $\mathcal{E}$ and whose internal resistance is r is connected to an external circuit. (a) Show that the power output of the source is a maximum when the current in the circuit is one-half the short-circuit current of the source. (b) If the external circuit consists of a resistance R, show that the power output is a maximum when $R = r$, and that the maximum power is $\mathcal{E}^2/4r$.

28–26. Using the data of Table 28–3, compute for a copper-nickel thermocouple (a) the thermal emf when $t = 100°C$, (b) $d\mathcal{E}/dt$ at 100°C, (c) the Peltier emf at 100°C. (d) What Peltier heat is transferred at the junction at 100°C if a current of 1 ma is maintained for one hour?

28–27. It is desired to construct a bismuth-silver thermopile that will develop a thermal emf of 1 μv when $t = 0.001°C$, t_R being 0°C. How many separate thermocouples must be connected in series?

CHAPTER 29

Direct-Current Circuits
and Instruments

29–1 Resistors in series and in parallel

Most electrical circuits consist not merely of a single source and a single external resistor, but comprise a number of sources, resistors, or other elements such as capacitors, motors, etc., interconnected in a more or less complicated manner. The general term applied to such a circuit is a *network*. We shall next consider a few of the simpler types of network.

Figure 29–1 illustrates four different ways in which three resistors having resistances R_1, R_2, and R_3 might be connected between points a and b. In part (a), the resistors provide only a single path between the points, and are said to be connected in *series* between these points. Any number of circuit elements such as resistors, cells, motors, etc., are similarly said to be in series with one another between two points if connected as in (a) so as to provide only a single path between the points. The current is the same in each element.

The resistors in Fig. 29–1(b) are said to be in *parallel* between points a and b. Each resistor provides an alternative path between the points, and any number of circuit elements similarly connected are in parallel with one another. The potential difference is the same across each element.

In Fig. 29–1(c), resistors R_2 and R_3 are in parallel with each other, and this combination is in series with the resistor R_1. In Fig. 29–1(d), R_2 and R_3 are in series, and this combination is in parallel with R_1.

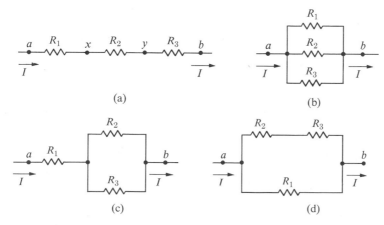

Fig. 29–1. Four different ways of connecting three resistors.

It is always possible to find a single resistor which could replace a combination of resistors in any given circuit and leave unaltered the potential difference between the terminals of the combination and the current in the rest of the circuit. The resistance of this single resistor is called the *equivalent* resistance of the combination. If any one of the networks in Fig. 29–1 were replaced by its equivalent resistance R, we could write

$$V_{ab} = RI \quad \text{or} \quad R = \frac{V_{ab}}{I},$$

where V_{ab} is the potential difference between the terminals of the network and I is the current at the point a or b. Hence the method of computing an equivalent resistance is to assume a potential difference V_{ab} across the actual network, compute the corresponding current I (or vice versa), and take the ratio of one to the other. The simple series and parallel connections of resistors are sufficiently common so that it is worth while to develop formulas for these two special cases.

If the resistors are in series, as in Fig. 29–1(a), the current in each must be the same and equal to the line current I. Hence

$$V_{ax} = IR_1, \qquad V_{xy} = IR_2, \qquad V_{yb} = IR_3,$$

and

$$V_{ab} = V_{ax} + V_{xy} + V_{yb} = I(R_1 + R_2 + R_3),$$

$$\frac{V_{ab}}{I} = R_1 + R_2 + R_3.$$

But V_{ab}/I is, by definition, the equivalent resistance R. Therefore

$$R = R_1 + R_2 + R_3. \tag{29–1}$$

Evidently the equivalent resistance of any number of resistors in series equals the sum of their individual resistances.

If the resistors are in parallel, as in Fig. 29–1(b), the potential difference between the terminals of each must be the same and equal to V_{ab}. If the currents in each are denoted by I_1, I_2, and I_3, respectively,

$$I_1 = \frac{V_{ab}}{R_1}, \qquad I_2 = \frac{V_{ab}}{R_2}, \qquad I_3 = \frac{V_{ab}}{R_3}.$$

Charge is delivered to point a by the line current I, and removed from a by the currents I_1, I_2, and I_3. Since charge is not accumulating at a, it follows that

$$I = I_1 + I_2 + I_3 = V_{ab} \left(\frac{1}{R_1} + \frac{1}{R_2} + \frac{1}{R_3} \right),$$

or

$$\frac{I}{V_{ab}} = \frac{1}{R_1} + \frac{1}{R_2} + \frac{1}{R_3}.$$

But

$$\frac{I}{V_{ab}} = \frac{1}{R},$$

so

$$\frac{1}{R} = \frac{1}{R_1} + \frac{1}{R_2} + \frac{1}{R_3}. \tag{29–2}$$

Evidently, for any number of resistors in parallel, the *reciprocal* of the equivalent resistance equals the *sum of the reciprocals* of their individual resistances.

For the special case of *two* resistors in parallel,

$$\frac{1}{R} = \frac{1}{R_1} + \frac{1}{R_2} = \frac{R_2 + R_1}{R_1 R_2}$$

and

$$R = \frac{R_1 R_2}{R_1 + R_2}.$$

Also, since $V_{ab} = I_1 R_1 = I_2 R_2$,

$$\frac{I_1}{I_2} = \frac{R_2}{R_1}, \tag{29–3}$$

and the currents carried by two resistors in parallel are inversely proportional to their resistances.

The equivalent resistances of the networks in Figs. 29–1(c) and (d) could be found by the same general method, but it is simpler to consider them as combinations of series and parallel arrangements. Thus in (c) the combination of R_2 and R_3 in parallel is first replaced by its equivalent resistance, which then forms a simple series combination with R_1. In (d), the combination of R_2 and R_3 in series forms a simple parallel combination with R_1. Not all networks, however, can be reduced to simple series-parallel combinations, and special methods must be used for handling such networks.

EXAMPLE. Compute the equivalent resistance of the network in Fig. 29–2, and find the current in each resistor.

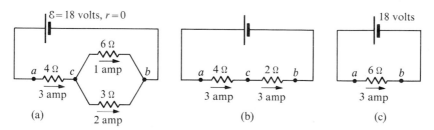

Figure 29–2

Successive stages in the reduction to a single equivalent resistance are shown in parts (b) and (c). The 6-ohm and the 3-ohm resistor in part (a) are equivalent to the single 2-ohm resistor in part (b), and the series combination of this with the 4-ohm resistor results in the single equivalent 6-ohm resistor in part (c).

In the simple series circuit of part (c) the current is 3 amp, and hence the current in the 4-ohm and 2-ohm resistors in part (b) is 3 amp also. The potential difference V_{cb} is therefore 6 volts, and since it must be 6 volts in part (a) as well, the currents in the 6-ohm and 3-ohm resistors in part (a) are 1 amp and 2 amp respectively.

29–2 Kirchhoff's rules

Not all networks can be reduced to simple series-parallel combinations. An example is a resistance network with a cross connection, as in Fig. 29–3(a). A circuit like that in Fig. 29–3(b), which contains sources in parallel paths, is another example. No new *principles* are required to compute the currents in these networks, but there are a number of techniques that enable such problems to be handled systematically. We shall describe only one of these, first developed by Gustav Robert Kirchhoff (1824–1887).

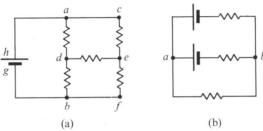

(a)   (b)

Fig. 29–3. Two networks that cannot be reduced to simple series-parallel combinations of resistors.

We first define two terms. A *branch point* in a network is a point where three (or more) conductors are joined. A *loop* (also called a *mesh*) is any closed conducting path. In Fig. 29–3(a), for example, points *a*, *d*, *e*, and *b* are branch points but *c* and *f* are not. In Fig. 29–3(b) there are only two branch points, *a* and *b*.

Possible loops in Fig. 29–3(a) are the closed paths *aceda*, *defbd*, *hadbgh*, and *hadefbgh*.

Kirchhoff's rules consist of the following two statements:

POINT RULE. *The algebraic sum of the currents **toward** any branch point is zero.*

$$\Sigma I = 0. \tag{29–4}$$

LOOP RULE. *The algebraic sum of the emf's in any loop equals the algebraic sum of the IR products in the same loop.*

$$\Sigma \mathcal{E} = \Sigma IR. \tag{29–5}$$

The first rule merely states formally that no charge accumulates at a branch point.

The second rule follows from the expression for the potential difference between any two points of a simple series circuit,

$$V_{ab} = \Sigma IR - \Sigma \mathcal{E}.$$

In a simple series circuit the current I is the same at all points and can be taken outside the summation sign. In a network the current is, in general, different in different resistors, and we must write ΣIR instead of $I\Sigma R$. If one continues completely around a loop, so that the second point coincides with the first, $V_{ab} = 0$ and $\Sigma \mathcal{E} = \Sigma IR$.

As in so many instances, the chief difficulty encountered in applying Kirchhoff's rules is in keeping track of algebraic signs, not in understanding the physical ideas, which are, in fact, very elementary. The first step is to assign a symbol and direction to all unknown currents and emf's, and a symbol to all unknown resistances. These, as well as the known quantities, are represented in a diagram with directions carefully shown. The solution is then carried through on the basis of the assumed directions. If in the numerical solution of the equations a negative value is found for a current or an emf, its correct direction is opposite to that assumed. The correct *numerical* value is obtained in any case. Hence the rules provide a method for ascertaining the *directions* as well as the magnitudes of currents and emf's, and it is not necessary that these directions be known in advance.

The expressions $\sum I$, $\sum IR$, and $\sum \mathcal{E}$ are *algebraic* sums. When applying the point rule, a current is considered *positive* if its direction is *toward* a branch point, negative if away from the point. (Of course, the opposite convention may also be used.) When applying the loop rule, some direction around the loop (i.e., clockwise or counterclockwise) must be chosen as the positive direction. All currents and emf's in this direction are positive; those in the opposite direction are negative. Note that a current which has a positive sign in the point rule may have a negative sign in the term in which it appears in the loop rule. Note also that the direction around the loop which is considered positive is immaterial, the result of choosing the opposite direction being merely to obtain the same equation with signs reversed. There is a temptation to assume that the "correct" direction to consider positive is that of the current in the loop, but in general such a choice is not possible, since the currents in some elements of a loop may be clockwise and in other elements, counterclockwise.

In complicated networks, where a large number of unknown quantities may be involved, it is sometimes puzzling to know how to obtain a sufficient number of *independent* equations to solve for the unknowns. The following rules are helpful:

(1) If there are n branch points in the network, apply the point rule at $n - 1$ of these points. Any points may be chosen. Application of the point rule at the nth point does not lead to an independent equation.

(2) Imagine the network to be separated into a number of simple loops, like the pieces of a jigsaw puzzle. Apply the loop rule to each of these loops.

EXAMPLE. Figure 29–4 is the same as Fig. 29–3(b), prepared for solution by Kirchhoff's rules. Let the magnitudes and directions of the emf's, and the magnitudes of the resistances, be given. We wish to solve for the currents in each branch of the network.

Assign a direction and a letter to each unknown current. The assumed directions are entirely arbitrary. Note that the currents in source 1 and resistor 1 are the same, and require only a single letter, I_1. The same is true for source 2 and resistor 2; the current in both is represented by I_2.

There are only two branch points, a and b. At point b,

$$\sum I = I_1 + I_2 + I_3 = 0.$$

Since there are but two branch points, there is only one independent "point" equation. If the point rule is applied at the other branch point, point a, we get

$$\sum I = -I_1 - I_2 - I_3 = 0,$$

which is the same equation with signs reversed.

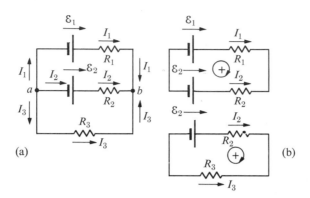

Fig. 29–4. Solution of a network by the application of Kirchhoff's rules. (The internal resistances r_1 and r_2 are not shown.)

In Fig. 29–4(b) the loop is cut up into its "jigsaw" sections. Let us consider the clockwise direction positive in each loop. The loop rule then furnishes the following equations:

$$\mathcal{E}_1 - \mathcal{E}_2 = I_1 r_1 + I_1 R_1 - I_2 R_2 - I_2 r_2,$$

$$\mathcal{E}_2 = I_2 r_2 + I_2 R_2 - I_3 R_3,$$

and we have three independent equations to solve for the three unknown currents.

29–3 Ammeters and voltmeters

The most common type of ammeter or voltmeter is a modified moving-coil galvanometer, in which a pivoted coil of fine wire carrying a current is deflected by the magnetic interaction between this current and the magnetic field of a permanent magnet. For the present, we are interested only in the instrument as a circuit element. The resistance of the coil of a typical instrument is of the order of 10 to 100 ohms, and a current of the order of a few milliamperes will produce full-scale deflection. The deflection is proportional to the current in the coil, but since the coil is a linear conductor the current is proportional to the potential difference between the terminals of the coil, and the deflection is also proportional to this potential difference.

As a numerical example, consider a galvanometer whose coil has a resistance of 20 ohms, and which deflects full scale with a current of 1 ma in its coil. The corresponding potential difference is

$$V_{ab} = IR = 10^{-3} \text{ amp} \times 20 \text{ ohms} = 0.020 \text{ volts} = 20 \text{ mv.}$$

First consider the galvanometer as an ammeter. To measure the current in a circuit, an ammeter must be inserted in *series* in the circuit. If the galvanometer above is inserted in this way, it will measure any current from zero to 1 ma. However, the resistance of the *coil* adds to the total resistance of the circuit, with the result that the current *after* the galvanometer is inserted, although it is correctly indicated by the instrument, may be very much less than it was *before* insertion of the instrument. It

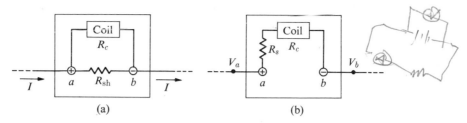

Fig. 29–5. (a) Internal connections of an ammeter.   (b) Internal connections of a voltmeter.

is evidently desirable that the resistance of the instrument should be much smaller than that of the remainder of the circuit, so that when the instrument is inserted it does not change the very thing we wish to measure. An *ideal* ammeter would have *zero* resistance.

Furthermore, the *range* of the galvanometer, if it is used without modification, is limited to a maximum current of 1 ma. The range can be extended, and at the same time the equivalent resistance can be reduced, by connecting a low-resistance R_{sh} in parallel with the moving coil, as in Fig. 29–5(a). The parallel resistor is called a *shunt*. Coil and shunt are mounted inside a case, with binding posts for external connections at *a* and *b*. (In some instruments having interchangeable shunts to cover several different ranges, the shunts are mounted outside the case.)

Suppose we wish to modify the galvanometer above for use as an ammeter with a range of 0–10 amp. That is, the coil is to deflect full scale when the current I in the *circuit* in which the ammeter is inserted equals 10 amp. The *coil* current I_c must then be 1 ma, so the current I_{sh} in the shunt is 9.999 amp. The potential difference V_{ab} is

$$V_{ab} = I_c R_c = I_{sh} R_{sh}.$$

Hence

$$R_{sh} = R_c \frac{I_c}{I_{sh}} = 20 \text{ ohms} \frac{0.001}{9.999} = 0.00200 \text{ ohm},$$

(to three significant figures).

The equivalent resistance R of the instrument is

$$\frac{1}{R} = \frac{1}{R_c} + \frac{1}{R_{sh}},$$

and

$$R = 0.00200 \text{ ohm}$$

(to three significant figures).

Thus we have a low-resistance instrument with the desired range of 0–10 amp. Of course if the current I is *less* than 10 amp, the coil current (and the deflection) is correspondingly less also.

Now consider the construction of a voltmeter. A voltmeter measures the potential difference between two points, and its terminals must be connected to these points. Evidently a moving-coil galvanometer cannot be used to measure the potential difference between, say, two charged spheres. When the galvanometer terminals are connected to the spheres the galvanometer coil provides a conducting path from one sphere to the other. There will be a *momentary* current in the coil, but the charges on the spheres will change until the entire system is at the *same* potential. Only if the resistance of the instrument is so great that a very long time is required to reach equilibrium, can a voltmeter be used for this purpose. An *ideal* voltmeter has an *infinite* resistance, and although an *electrometer* does have a resistance that can be considered infinite, a moving-coil galvanometer can be deflected only by a current in its coil, and its resistance must be finite.

A moving-coil galvanometer can be used to measure the potential difference between the terminals of a *source*, or between *two points of a circuit containing a source*, because the source *maintains* a difference of potential between the points. However, complications arise here also.

We have shown that when a source is on *open* circuit, the potential difference between its terminals equals its emf. It would seem, therefore, that to measure the emf we need only measure this potential difference. But when the terminals of a galvanometer are connected to those of a source, the galvanometer and source form a *closed* circuit in which there is a current. The potential difference *after* the galvanometer is connected, although it is correctly indicated by the instrument, is not equal to ε, but to $\varepsilon - Ir$, and is less than it was *before* the instrument was connected. Again, the measuring instrument alters the quantity it is intended to measure. It is evidently desirable that the resistance of a voltmeter, even though not infinite, should be as large as possible.

Furthermore, the *range* of the galvanometer in our example, if used without modification, is limited to a maximum value of 20 mv. The range can be extended, and at the same time the equivalent resistance can be increased, by connecting a high-resistance R_s in *series* with the moving coil, as in Fig. 29–5(b).

Suppose we wish to modify the galvanometer for use as a voltmeter with a range of 0–10 volts. That is, the coil is to deflect full scale when the potential difference between the terminals of the instrument is 10 volts. In other words, the current in the instrument is to be 1 ma when the potential difference between its terminals is 10 volts.

The terminal potential difference is

$$V_{ab} = I(R_c + R_s),$$

and the necessary series resistance is

$$R_s = \frac{V_{ab}}{I} - R_c = \frac{10 \text{ volt}}{0.001 \text{ amp}} - 20 \text{ ohms} = 9980 \text{ ohms}.$$

The equivalent resistance R is

$$R = R_c + R_s = 10{,}000 \text{ ohms}.$$

Thus we have a high-resistance instrument with the desired range of 0–10 volts.

The resistance of a resistor equals the potential difference V_{ab} between its terminals, divided by the current I:

$$R = \frac{V_{ab}}{I},$$

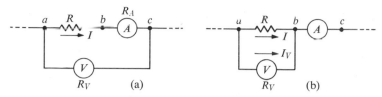

Fig. 29–6. Ammeter-voltmeter method for measuring resistance or power.

and the power input to any portion of a circuit equals the product of the potential difference across this portion and the current:

$$P = V_{ab}I.$$

The most straightforward method of measuring R or P is therefore to measure V_{ab} and I *simultaneously.*

In Fig. 29–6(a), ammeter A reads correctly the current I in the resistor R. Voltmeter V, however, reads the *sum* of the potential difference V_{ab} across the resistor and the potential difference V_{bc} across the ammeter.

If we transfer the voltmeter terminal from c to b, as in Fig. 29–6(b), the voltmeter reads correctly the potential difference V_{ab} but the ammeter now reads the *sum* of the current I in the resistor and the current I_V in the voltmeter. Thus whichever connection is used, we must correct the reading of one instrument or the other to obtain the true values of V_{ab} or I (unless, of course, the corrections are small enough to be neglected).

29-4 The Wheatstone bridge

The Wheatstone bridge circuit, shown in Fig. 29–7, is widely used for the rapid and precise measurement of resistance. It was invented in 1843 by the English scientist Charles Wheatstone. M, N, and P are adjustable resistors which have been previously calibrated, and X represents the unknown resistance. To use the bridge, switches K_1 and K_2 are closed and the resistance of P is adjusted until the galvanometer G shows no deflection. Points b and c must then be at the same potential or, in other words, the potential drop from a to b equals that from a to c. Also, the drop from b to d equals that from c to d. Since the galvanometer current is zero, the current in M equals that in N, say I_1, and the current in P equals that in X, say I_2. Then, since $V_{ab} = V_{ac}$, it follows that

$$I_1N = I_2P,$$

and since $V_{bd} = V_{cd}$,

$$I_1M = I_2X.$$

When the second equation is divided by the first, we find

$$X = \frac{M}{N}P.$$

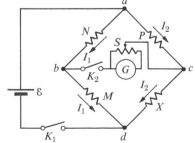

Fig. 29–7. Wheatstone bridge circuit.

Hence if M, N, and P are known, X can be computed. The ratio M/N is usually set at some integral power of 10, such as 0.01, 1, 100, etc., for simplicity in computation.

During preliminary adjustments, when the bridge may be far from balance and V_{bc} large, the galvanometer must be protected by the shunt S. A resistor whose resistance is large compared with that of the galvanometer is permanently connected across the galvanometer terminals. When the sliding contact is at the left end of the resistor, none of the current in the path between b and c passes through the galvanometer. In a position such as that shown, that portion of the resistor at the right of the sliding contact is in series with the galvanometer, and this combination is shunted by that portion of the resistor at the left of the contact. Hence only a fraction of the current passes through the galvanometer. With the sliding contact at the right of the resistor, all the current passes through the galvanometer except the small fraction bypassed by the resistor. The galvanometer is therefore fully protected when the contact is at the left end of the resistor and practically full galvanometer sensitivity is attained when the contact is at the right end.

If any of the resistances are inductive, the potentials V_b and V_c may attain their final values at different rates when K_1 is closed, and the galvanometer, if connected between b and c, would show an initial deflection even though the bridge were in balance. Hence K_1 and K_2 are frequently combined in a double key which closes the battery circuit first and the galvanometer circuit a moment later, after the transient currents have died out.

Portable bridges are available having a self-contained galvanometer and dry cells. The ratio M/N can be set at any integral power of 10 between 0.001 and 1000 by a single dial switch, and the value of P can be adjusted by four dial switches.

29–5 The ohmmeter

Although not a precision instrument, the ohmmeter is a useful device for rapid measurement of resistance. It consists of a galvanometer, a resistor, and a source (usually a flashlight cell) connected in series, as in Fig. 29–8. The resistance R to be measured is connected between terminals x and y.

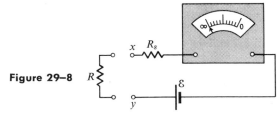

Figure 29–8

The series resistance R_s is chosen so that when terminals x and y are short-circuited (that is, when $R = 0$) the galvanometer deflects full scale. When the circuit between x and y is open (that is, when $R = \infty$) the galvanometer shows no deflection. For a value of R between zero and infinity, the galvanometer deflects to some intermediate point depending on the value of R, and hence the galvanometer scale can be calibrated to read the resistance R.

29-6 The potentiometer

The potentiometer is an instrument which can be used to measure the emf of a source without drawing any current from the source. It also has a number of other useful applications. Essentially, it balances an unknown potential difference against an adjustable, measurable potential difference.

The principle of the potentiometer is shown schematically in Fig. 29-9. A resistance wire ab is permanently connected to the terminals of a source of emf $\mathcal{E}_1$. A sliding contact c is connected through the galvanometer G to a second source whose emf $\mathcal{E}_2$ is to be measured. Contact c is moved along the wire until a position is found at which the galvanometer shows no deflection. (This necessitates that $V_{ab} \geq \mathcal{E}_2$.) If we then write the expression for V_{cb} for two paths between these points, we have

$$V_{cb} = IR_{cb}, \qquad \text{(resistance wire path)}$$

$$V_{cb} = (r_g + r)I_2 - (-\mathcal{E}_2) = \mathcal{E}_2, \qquad \text{(galvanometer path)}$$

where the last step is possible because *we have adjusted I_2 to be equal to zero*.

Hence IR_{cb} is *exactly* equal to the emf $\mathcal{E}_2$, and $\mathcal{E}_2$ can be computed if I and R_{cb} are known. No correction need be made for the "Ir" term, since the current in $\mathcal{E}_2$ is zero.

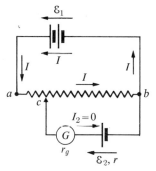

Fig. 29-9. Principle of the potentiometer.

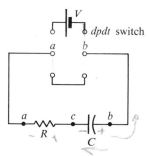

Figure 29-10

29-7 The R-C series circuit

Figure 29-10 represents a circuit in which a capacitor C may be charged or discharged through a resistor R. The resistor and the capacitor are connected in series to the center terminals of a double pole, double throw (*dpdt*) switch. The upper terminals of the switch are connected to a source of constant terminal voltage V. The lower terminals are connected together by a wire of zero resistance. The capacitor is initially uncharged.

When the switch is thrown in the "up" position, the capacitor eventually becomes charged to a potential difference V, but it does not acquire its final charge instantaneously. If the switch is thrown to the "down" position after the capacitor has acquired a charge, the capacitor eventually becomes discharged, but again the process is not instantaneous. We wish to study the current and charge during the charge and discharge processes.

Let q represent the charge on the capacitor and i the charging current at some instant after the switch is thrown in the "up" position. The instantaneous potential differences v_{ac} and v_{cb} are

$$v_{ac} = iR, \qquad v_{cb} = q/C. \tag{29–6}$$

Therefore

$$V_{ab} = V = v_{ac} + v_{cb} = iR + q/C, \tag{29–7}$$

where $V = $ constant. The current i is then

$$i = \frac{V}{R} - \frac{q}{RC}. \tag{29–8}$$

At the instant connections are made, $q = 0$ and the *initial current* $I_0 = V/R$, which equals the steady current if the capacitor is not present.

As the charge q increases, the term q/RC becomes larger, and the current decreases and eventually becomes zero. When $i = 0$,

$$\frac{V}{R} = \frac{q}{RC}, \qquad q = CV = Q_f,$$

where Q_f is the final charge.

Several procedures are available for finding the expressions for i, q, v_{ac}, and v_{cb}, as functions of time. We can replace i in Eq. (29–8) by dq/dt, obtaining

$$\frac{dq}{dt} = \frac{V}{R} - \frac{q}{RC}. \tag{29–9}$$

After collecting terms in q and integrating, we have $q(t)$. The current $i(t)$ can then be found by differentiation, since $i = dq/dt$.

Another procedure is to first differentiate Eq. (29–8) with respect to t, and replace dq/dt with i. Then

$$\frac{di}{dt} = -\frac{i}{RC}. \tag{29–10}$$

Integration gives $i(t)$, and when i is replaced by dq/dt a second integration gives $q(t)$. When $i(t)$ and $q(t)$ have been found, $v_{ac}(t)$ and $v_{cb}(t)$ are given by Eq. (29–6).

It is left as a problem to show that

$$i = I_0 e^{-t/RC}, \tag{29–11}$$

$$q = Q_f(1 - e^{-t/RC}). \tag{29–12}$$

The current and charge are therefore both *exponential* functions of time. Figure 29–11(a) is a graph of Eq. (29–11), and Fig. 29–11(b) is a graph of Eq. (29–12).*

---

* Objections may be raised that the graph in Fig. 29–11(a) is not physically realistic, because the current cannot jump suddenly and *discontinuously* at $t = 0$ from a value zero to a value I_0 without going through all intermediate values. This objection is correct, and we shall show in a later chapter that when the effect of *inductance* in the circuit is taken into account the current does not actually have a discontinuity at $t = 0$.

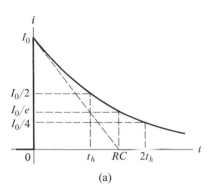

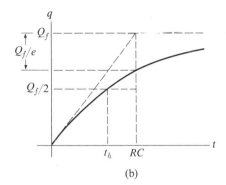

(a)   (b)

Figure 29–11

At a time $t = RC$, the current has decreased to $1/e$ th of its initial value and the charge has increased to *within* $1/e$ th of its final value. The product RC is called the *time constant*, or the *relaxation time*, of the circuit. It is the time in which the current *would* decrease to zero, if it continued to decrease at its initial rate.

The *half-life* of the circuit, t_h, is the time for the current to decrease to half its initial value, or for the capacitor to acquire half its final charge. Setting $i = I_0/2$ in Eq. (29–11), we find

$$t_h = RC \ln 2.$$

The half-life depends only on the time constant RC, and not on the initial current. Thus if the current decreases from I_0 to $I_0/2$ in a time t_h, as shown in Fig. 29–11(a), it decreases to half this value, or to $I_0/4$, in another half-life, and so on.

EXAMPLE.   A resistor of resistance $R = 10$ megohms is connected in series with a capacitor of capacitance 1 μf. The time constant is

$$RC = 10 \times 10^6 \text{ ohms} \times 10^{-6} \text{ f} = 10 \text{ sec},$$

and the half-life is

$$t_h = 10 \text{ sec} \times \ln 2 = 6.9 \text{ sec}.$$

On the other hand, if $R = 10$ ohms the time constant is only 10×10^{-6} sec, or 10 μsec.

Suppose next that the capacitor has acquired a charge Q_0 and that the switch is thrown to the "down" position. The capacitor then discharges through the resistor and its charge eventually decreases to zero. (We designate the charge by Q_0 because this is the *initial* charge in the discharge process. It is not necessarily equal to the charge Q_f defined above.)

Again let i and q represent the current and charge at some instant after the switch is thrown. Since V_{ab} is now zero, we have from Eq. (29–7)

$$0 = v_{ac} + v_{cb}.$$

The direction of the current in the resistor is now from c to a, so $v_{ca} = iR$ and

$$i = \frac{q}{RC}. \qquad (29\text{--}13)$$

When $t = 0$, $q = Q_0$ and the initial current I_0 is

$$I_0 = \frac{Q_0}{RC} = \frac{V_0}{R},$$

where V_0 is the initial potential difference across the capacitor. As the capacitor discharges, both q and i decrease.

The same procedures as above can be followed to obtain $i(t)$ and $q(t)$. If we replace i in Eq. (29–13) by $-dq/dt$ (the charge q is now *decreasing*), we get

$$\frac{dq}{dt} = -\frac{q}{RC}. \qquad (29\text{--}14)$$

Integration of this equation gives $q(t)$, and by differentiation we find $i(t)$.

Alternatively, differentiation of Eq. (29–13) gives

$$\frac{di}{dt} = -\frac{i}{RC}, \qquad (29\text{--}15)$$

from which we can get $i(t)$ and, by a second integration, get $q(t)$. It is left as a problem to show that

$$i = I_0 e^{-t/RC}, \qquad (29\text{--}16)$$

$$q = Q_0 e^{-t/RC}. \qquad (29\text{--}17)$$

Both the current and the charge decrease exponentially with time.

29–8 The sweep circuit

In the operation of a cathode-ray oscilloscope (see Section 26–10) an electron beam passes between two sets of metal plates on its way to a fluorescent screen, where it produces a bright spot of light. Variations in the electric field between one set of plates cause horizontal motion of the electron beam, whereas variations in the field between the other set of plates cause vertical motion. If the field intensity between the first set of plates is made to increase linearly with the time, and then to become zero almost instantaneously, repeating this cycle over and over again with any desired

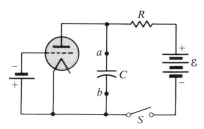

Fig. 29–12. Thyratron tube sweep circuit for producing sawtooth voltage wave.

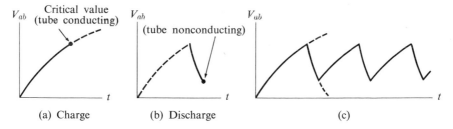

Fig. 29–13. (a) Slow increase of V_{ab} (large time constant). (b) Rapid decrease of V_{ab} (small time constant). (c) Sawtooth voltage.

frequency, the electron beam will sweep horizontally in one direction across the fluorescent screen with uniform linear motion, return to the starting point, and repeat this motion with the same frequency.

A convenient circuit for accomplishing this purpose, called a *sweep circuit*, is shown in Fig. 29–12. The three-element tube at the left is a small gas-filled *thyratron* which operates as follows. The tube is originally nonconducting. When switch S is closed, the capacitor C charges through the resistor R and the potential difference V_{ab} increases as shown in Fig. 29–13(a). Both C and R may be varied, and therefore the time constant RC may be adjusted to any desired value. When the potential difference V_{ab} across the capacitor reaches a critical value, the tube suddenly "breaks down" and becomes conducting. The capacitor discharges rapidly through the tube, the time constant RC being small because of the low resistance of the tube. The potential difference V_{ab} therefore decreases very quickly to a smaller value, at which the thyratron is no longer conducting.

The cycle is then repeated, giving rise to a sawtooth voltage across the capacitor, as shown in Fig. 29–13(c). The number of cycles per second may be varied by changing either C or R. In practice, coarse changes in frequency are produced by changing C and fine adjustments by varying R.

29-9 Displacement current

In the circuit of Fig. 29–10 there is a *conduction* current in the resistor and leads only; the conduction current in the region between the capacitor plates is zero. Maxwell pointed out that by extending the definition of "current" one can say that the current is the same at *all* cross sections of a circuit.

Consider the parallel-plate capacitor in Fig. 29–14, which is being charged by a conduction current i_C. We assume that the entire circuit is immersed in a homogeneous nonconducting dielectric. If q is the charge on either plate at any instant, the current i_C equals the rate of change of the charge q.

$$i_C = \frac{dq}{dt} = \dot{q}.$$

Although the surface density of charge is greatest on the inner, opposing surfaces of the plates, the charge q is actually distributed over the entire surface of each plate,

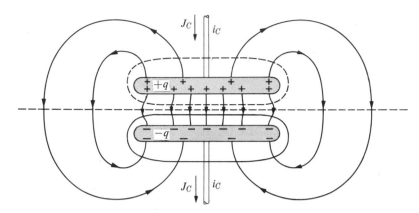

Fig. 29–14. Parallel-plate capacitor immersed in a homogeneous nonconducting dielectric being charged by a conduction current i_C.

as shown. Consider a closed surface such as that shown by the dotted line surrounding the upper plate. The lines of the **D**-field cross this surface in an outward direction and, as we have shown, the surface integral of **D** over the surface equals the enclosed free charge q:

$$\Psi_D = \oint \mathbf{D} \cdot d\mathbf{A} = q.$$

If q is changing, **D** is changing also, and hence

$$\dot{\Psi}_D = \oint \dot{\mathbf{D}} \cdot d\mathbf{A} = \dot{q} = i_C.$$

Maxwell proposed that the vector $\dot{\mathbf{D}}$ at any point be called the *displacement current density*, $\mathbf{J}_D$, at the point. The integral above can then be written as

$$\oint \mathbf{J}_D \cdot d\mathbf{A} = i_C.$$

The surface integral of the displacement current density $\mathbf{J}_D$ is the *total displacement current i_D* across the surface, and hence

$$i_D = i_C.$$

That is, the *outward displacement current* across the surface equals the *inward conduction current*, and the *net* current into the region within the surface is zero, just as is the case for any portion of a circuit within which there are conduction currents only.

The field of the capacitor actually extends outward indefinitely. (We assume that the remainder of the circuit is very far away.) Hence at the midplane of the capacitor the cross section of the circuit is the infinite dotted plane. It will be seen that *every* line of the **D**-field crosses this plane in a downward direction, so that the total displacement current across this section is equal to that across the closed surface and is equal to i_C. We can therefore say that even when a circuit is "open," in the sense that it contains a capacitor between whose plates there is no conduction current, *the current is the same at all cross sections.*

The *total* current density $\mathbf{J}$ at any point is defined as the sum of the conduction current density $\mathbf{J}_C$ and the displacement current density $\mathbf{J}_D$:

$$\mathbf{J} = \mathbf{J}_C + \mathbf{J}_D.$$

In the special case considered above, $\mathbf{J}_D = 0$ in the leads to the capacitor and $\mathbf{J}_C = 0$ in the space around the capacitor. In the general case, both types of current may exist simultaneously. For example, if the dielectric surrounding the plates in Fig. 29–14 is not a perfect insulator, there will be a *conduction* current from one plate to the other, as well as a *displacement* current.

Maxwell's generalized definition of current may appear simply as an artifice introduced in order to be able to say that "the current is the same at all cross sections of a circuit."* However, when we consider, in a later chapter, the *magnetic* field set up by a current, we shall see that displacement currents contribute to this field in precisely the same way as conduction currents.

The general definition of displacement is

$$\mathbf{D} = \epsilon_0 \mathbf{E} + \mathbf{P}.$$

Hence the displacement current density is

$$\mathbf{J}_D = \dot{\mathbf{D}} = \epsilon_0 \dot{\mathbf{E}} + \dot{\mathbf{P}}.$$

The term $\dot{\mathbf{P}}$, the rate of change of polarization in a dielectric, does represent an actual motion of charge across an area, since during the time that the polarization is changing there is a shift of *bound* charges across the area. The term $\epsilon_0 \dot{\mathbf{E}}$ does not represent any motion of charge. In a vacuum, where $\mathbf{P} = 0$, there is still a displacement current equal to $\epsilon_0 \dot{\mathbf{E}}$.

---

* "When *I* use a word," Humpty Dumpty said, in rather a scornful tone, "it means just what I choose it to mean—neither more nor less."

"The question is," said Alice, "whether you *can* make words mean so many different things."

"The question is," said Humpty Dumpty, "which is to be master—that's all."

Problems

29–1. Prove that when two resistors are connected in parallel the equivalent resistance of the combination is always smaller than that of either resistor.

29–2. (a) A resistance R_2 is connected in parallel with a resistance R_1. What resistance R_3 must be connected in series with the combination of R_1 and R_2 so that the equivalent resistance is equal to the resistance R_1? Draw a diagram. (b) A resistance R_2 is connected in series with a resistance R_1. What resistance R_3 must be connected in parallel with the combination of R_1 and R_2 so that the equivalent resistance is equal to R_1? Draw a diagram.

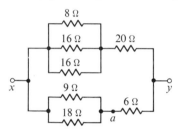

Figure 29–15

29–3. (a) Calculate the equivalent resistance of the circuit of Fig. 29–15 between x and y. (b) What is the potential difference between x and a if the current in the 8-ohm resistor is 0.5 amp?

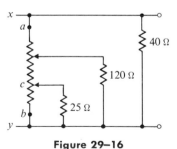

Figure 29–16

29–4. (a) The long resistor between a and b in Fig. 29–16 has a resistance of 300 ohms and is tapped at the one-third points. What is the equivalent resistance between

x and y? (b) The potential difference between x and y is 320 volts. What is the potential difference between b and c?

29–5. Each of the three resistors in Fig. 29–17 has a resistance of 2 ohms and can dissipate a maximum of 18 watts without becoming excessively heated. What is the maximum power the circuit can dissipate?

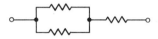

Figure 29–17

29–6. Two lamps, marked "60 watts, 120 volts" and "40 watts, 120 volts," are connected in series across a 120-volt line. What power is consumed in each lamp? Assume that the resistance of the filaments does not vary with current.

29–7. Three equal resistors are connected in series. When a certain potential difference is applied across the combination the total power consumed is 10 watts. What power would be consumed if the three resistors were connected in parallel across the same potential difference?

29–8. (a) The power rating of a 10,000-ohm resistor is 2 watts. (The power rating is the maximum power the resistor can safely dissipate without too great a rise in temperature.) What is the maximum allowable potential difference across the terminals of the resistor? (b) A 20,000-ohm resistor is to be connected across a potential difference of 300 volts. What power rating is required? (c) It is desired to connect a resistance of 1000 ohms across a potential difference of 200 volts. A number of 10-watt, 1000-ohm resistors are available. How should they be connected?

29–9. (a) Find the resistance of the network in Fig. 29–18, between the terminals a and b. (b) What potential difference between a and b will result in a current of 1 amp in the 4-ohm resistor?

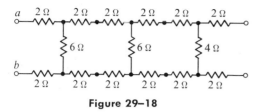

Figure 29-18

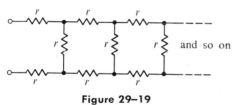

Figure 29-19

29-10. Prove that the resistance of the infinite network shown in Fig. 29-19 is equal to $(1 + \sqrt{3})r$.

29-11. (a) In Fig. 29-20(a), what is the potential difference V_{ab} when switch S is open? (b) What is the current through switch S when it is closed? (c) In Fig. 29-20(b), what is the potential difference V_{ab} when switch S is open? (d) What is the current through switch S when it is closed? What is the equivalent resistance of the circuit in Fig. 29-20(b), (e) when switch S is open? (f) When switch S is closed?

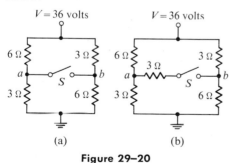

Figure 29-20

29-12. (a) What is the potential difference between points a and b in Fig. 29-21 when switch S is open? (b) Which point, a or b, is at the higher potential? (c) What is the final potential of point b when switch S is closed? (d) How much charge flowed through switch S when it was closed?

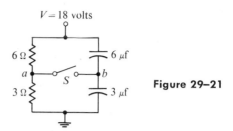

Figure 29-21

29-13. (a) What is the potential difference between points a and b in Fig. 29-22 when switch S is open? (b) Which point, a or b, is at the higher potential? (c) What is the final potential of point b when switch S is closed? (d) How much does the charge on each capacitor change when S is closed?

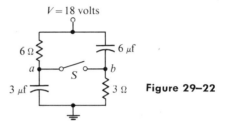

Figure 29-22

29-14. Calculate the three currents indicated in the circuit diagram of Fig. 29-23.

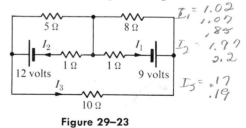

Figure 29-23

29-15. Find the emf's $\mathcal{E}_1$ and $\mathcal{E}_2$ in the circuit of Fig. 29-24, and the potential difference between points a and b.

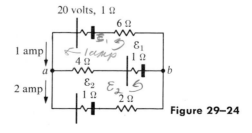

Figure 29-24

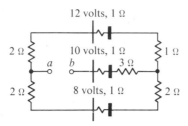

Figure 29–25

29–16. (a) Find the potential difference between points a and b in Fig. 29–25. (b) If a and b are connected, find the current in the 12-volt cell.

29–17. A 600-ohm resistor and a 400-ohm resistor are connected in series across a 90-volt line. A voltmeter across the 600-ohm resistor reads 45 volts. (a) Find the voltmeter resistance. (b) Find the reading of the same voltmeter if connected across the 400-ohm resistor.

29–18. Point a in Fig. 29–26 is maintained at a constant potential of 300 volts above ground. (a) What is the reading of a voltmeter of the proper range, and of resistance 3×10^4 ohms, when connected between point b and ground? (b) What would be the reading of a voltmeter of resistance 3×10^6 ohms? (c) Of a voltmeter of infinite resistance?

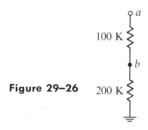

Figure 29–26

29–19. Two 150-volt voltmeters, one of resistance 15,000 ohms and the other of resistance 150,000 ohms, are connected in series across a 120-volt DC line. Find the reading of each voltmeter.

29–20. A 150-volt voltmeter has a resistance of 20,000 ohms. When connected in series with a large resistance R across a 110-volt line, the meter reads 5 volts. Find

the resistance R. (This problem illustrates one method of measuring large resistances.)

29–21. A 100-volt battery has an internal resistance of 5 ohms. (a) What is the reading of a voltmeter having a resistance of 500 ohms when placed across the terminals of the battery? (b) What maximum value may the ratio r/R_V have if the error in the reading of the emf of a battery is not to exceed 5%?

29–22. The resistance of a galvanometer coil is 50 ohms and the current required for full-scale deflection is 500 μa. (a) Show in a diagram how to convert the galvanometer to an ammeter reading 5 amp full scale, and compute the shunt resistance. (b) Show how to convert the galvanometer to a voltmeter reading 150 volts full scale, and compute the series resistance.

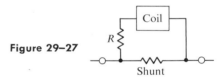

Figure 29–27

29–23. The resistance of the coil of a pivoted-coil galvanometer is 10 ohms, and a current of 0.02 amp causes it to deflect full scale. It is desired to convert this galvanometer to an ammeter reading 10 amp full scale. The only shunt available has a resistance of 0.03 ohm. What resistance R must be connected in series with the coil? (See Fig. 29–27.)

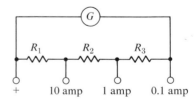

Figure 29–28

29–24. The resistance of the moving coil of the galvanometer G in Fig. 29–28 is 25 ohms and it deflects full scale with a current of 0.010 amp. Find the magnitudes of the resistances R_1, R_2, and R_3, to convert the galvanometer to a multirange ammeter deflecting full scale with currents of 10 amp, 1 amp, and 0.1 amp.

29–25. Figure 29–29 shows the internal wiring of a "three-scale" voltmeter whose binding posts are marked +, 3 volts, 15 volts, 150 volts. The resistance of the moving coil, R_G, is 15 ohms, and a current of 1 ma in the coil causes it to deflect full scale. Find the resistances R_1, R_2, R_3, and the over-all resistance of the meter on each of its ranges.

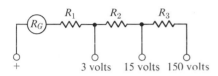

Figure 29–29

29–26. A certain DC voltmeter is said to have a resistance of "one thousand ohms per volt of full-scale deflection." What current, in milliamperes, is required for full-scale deflection?

29–27. Let V and A represent the readings of the voltmeter and ammeter, respectively, shown in Fig. 29–6, and R_V and R_A their equivalent resistances. (a) When the circuit is connected as in Fig. 29–6(a), show that $R = V/A - R_A$. (b) When the connections are as in Fig. 29–6(b), show that $R = V/[A - (V/R_V)]$. (c) Show that the power delivered to the resistor in part (a) is $AV - A^2R_A$, and in part (b) is $AV - (V^2/R_V)$.

29–28. A certain galvanometer has a resistance of 200 ohms and deflects full scale with a current of 1 ma in its coil. It is desired to replace this with a second galvanometer whose resistance is 50 ohms and which deflects full scale with a current of 50 μa in its coil. Devise a circuit incorporating the second galvanometer such that (a) the equivalent resistance of the circuit equals the resistance of the first galvanometer, and (b) the second galvanometer will deflect full scale when the current into and out of the circuit equals the full-scale current of the first galvanometer.

29–29. Suppose the galvanometer of the ohmmeter in Fig. 29–8 has a resistance of 50 ohms and deflects full scale with a current of 1 ma in its coil. The emf $\mathcal{E} = 1.5$ volts. (a) What should be the value of the series resistance R_s? (b) What values of R correspond to galvanometer deflections of $\frac{1}{4}$, $\frac{1}{2}$, and $\frac{3}{4}$ full scale? (c) Does the ohmmeter have a linear scale?

29–30. In the ohmmeter in Fig. 29–30, M is a 1-ma meter having a resistance of 100 ohms. The battery B has an emf of 3 volts and negligible internal resistance. R is so chosen that when the terminals a and b are shorted ($R_x = 0$) the meter reads full scale. When a and b are open ($R_x = \infty$) the meter reads zero. (a) What should be the value of the resistor R? (b) What current would indicate a resistance R_x of 600 ohms? (c) What resistances correspond to meter deflections of $\frac{1}{4}$, $\frac{1}{2}$, and $\frac{3}{4}$ full scale?

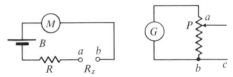

Figure 29–30   **Figure 29–31**

29–31. Figure 29–31 shows a resistor with a movable tap. The galvanometer has a resistance of 90 ohms. P has a resistance of 75 ohms. What is the resistance between a and b if the current in the galvanometer is to be $\frac{1}{3}$ the current in line bc?

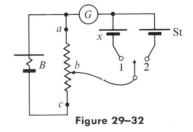

Figure 29–32

29–32. Figure 29–32 shows a potentiometer set up to measure the emf of cell x. B is a battery whose emf is approximately 3 volts and whose internal resistance is unknown. St is a standard cell of 1.0183 volt emf. The switch is set at point 2, placing the standard cell in the galvanometer circuit. When the tap b is 0.36 of the distance from a to c the galvanometer G reads zero. (a) What is the difference of potential across the entire length of resistor ac? (b) The switch is then set at point 1 and a new zero reading of the galvanometer is obtained when b is 0.47 of the distance from a to c. What is the emf of cell x?

29–33. (a) The differential equation for the instantaneous charge q of a capacitor after it has been connected to a source of terminal voltage V_{ab} through a resistance R is given by Eq. (29–9), namely,

$$\frac{dq}{dt} = \frac{V_{ab}}{R} - \frac{q}{RC}.$$

Show that

$$q = Q_f(1 - e^{-t/RC}).$$

(b) The current in the circuit of part (a) is given by Eq. (29–10), namely,

$$\frac{di}{dt} = -\frac{i}{RC}.$$

Show that

$$i = I_0 e^{-t/RC}.$$

29–34. (a) The differential equation for the instantaneous charge q of a capacitor a moment after its terminals have been disconnected from a source and connected to a resistance R is given by Eq. (29–14), namely,

$$\frac{dq}{dt} = -\frac{q}{RC}.$$

Show that

$$q = Q_0 e^{-t/RC}.$$

(b) The current in the circuit of part (a) is given by Eq. (29–15), namely,

$$\frac{di}{dt} = -\frac{i}{RC}.$$

Show that

$$i = I_0 e^{-t/RC}.$$

29–35. In Fig. 29–10, let $V = 100$ volts, $R = 10$ megohms, $C = 2\ \mu f$. The capacitor is initially uncharged. The switch is thrown to the up position for 20 sec and then quickly reversed to the down position. (a) Construct graphs of i, q, v_{ac}, and v_{cb} for a time interval of 60 sec after the switch is first thrown. (b) How much energy is eventually dissipated in the resistor?

29–36. Suppose that the parallel plates in Fig. 29–14 have an area of 2 m² and are separated by a sheet of dielectric 1 mm thick, of dielectric coefficient 3. Neglect edge effects. At a certain instant, the potential difference between the plates is 100 volts and the current I_C equals 2 ma. (a) What is the charge Q on each plate? (b) What is the rate of change of charge on the plates, $\dot{Q}$? (c) What is the displacement current $\dot{\Psi}_D$ in the dielectric?

CHAPTER 30

The Magnetic Field

30-1 Magnetism

The first magnetic phenomena to be observed were undoubtedly those associated with so-called "natural" magnets, rough fragments of an ore of iron found near the ancient city of Magnesia (whence the term "magnet"). These natural magnets have the property of attracting to themselves unmagnetized iron, the effect being most pronounced at certain regions of the magnet known as its *poles*. It was known to the Chinese as early as 121 A.D. that an iron rod, after being brought near a natural magnet, would acquire and retain this property of the natural magnet, and that such a rod when freely suspended about a vertical axis would set itself approximately in the north-south direction. The use of magnets as aids to navigation can be traced back at least to the eleventh century.

The study of magnetic phenomena was confined for many years to magnets made in this way. Not until 1819 was there shown to be any connection between electrical and magnetic phenomena. In that year the Danish scientist Hans Christian Oersted (1777–1851) observed that a pivoted magnet (a compass needle) was deflected when in the neighborhood of a wire carrying a current. Twelve years later, after attempts extending over a period of several years, Michael Faraday (1791–1867), an English physicist, found that a momentary current existed in a circuit while the current in a nearby circuit was being started or stopped. Shortly afterward followed the discovery that the motion of a magnet toward or away from the circuit would produce the same effect. Joseph Henry (1797–1878), an American scientist who later became the first director of the Smithsonian Institution, had anticipated Faraday's discoveries by about twelve months, but since Faraday was the first to publish his results he is usually assigned the credit for them. The work of Oersted thus demonstrated that magnetic effects could be produced by moving electric charges, and that of Faraday and Henry that currents could be produced by moving magnets.

It is believed at the present time that all so-called magnetic phenomena result from forces between electric charges in motion. That is, charges in motion relative to an observer set up a *magnetic* field as well as an *electrostatic* field, and this magnetic field exerts a force on a second charge in motion relative to the observer. Since the electrons in atoms are in motion about the atomic nuclei, and since each electron appears to be in continuous rotation about an axis passing through it, all atoms can be expected to exhibit magnetic effects and, in fact, such is found to be the case. The possibility that the magnetic properties of matter were the result of tiny atomic currents was first suggested by Ampere in 1820. Not until recent years has the verification of these ideas been possible.

The medium in which the charges are moving may have a pronounced effect on the observed magnetic forces between them. In the present chapter we shall assume the charges or conductors to be in otherwise empty space. For all practical purposes the results will apply equally well to charges and conductors in air.

30-2 Charges, currents, and relativity

The principles of special relativity are intimately related to the properties of electric and magnetic fields. One of the subjects discussed by Einstein in his first paper on special relativity, published in 1905, was the different ways in which electric and magnetic fields would be described by two observers in uniform relative motion.

We now show that *the existence of a magnetic field around a wire carrying a current is a necessary consequence of the laws of electrostatics, and the principles of special relativity.*

Figure 30-1(a) represents a portion of a positively charged wire. We wish to consider the fields around the wire from the standpoint of observer D, at rest relative to the charges, and of observer A, moving relative to D with velocity $\mathbf{v}$.

In D's system, the charge per unit length in the wire, averaged over a distance large compared with the separation d_D of the charges, is

$$\lambda_D = \frac{q}{d_D}.$$

It follows from Coulomb's law (or Gauss's law) that the wire sets up an electric field $\mathbf{E}_D$ directed radially outward from the wire and whose magnitude at a distance r from the wire is

$$E_D = 2k \frac{\lambda_D}{r}.$$

The force on a charge q', at rest in D's system, is

$$F_{eD} = q'E_D.$$

The subscript eD means that this is an *electrical* force, observed in D's system.

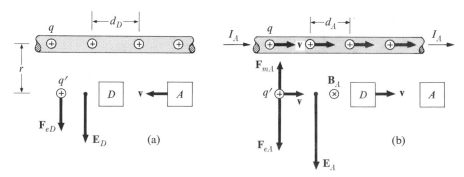

Fig. 30-1. (a) In the system of observer D, at rest relative to the charges in a wire, the charges set up an electrostatic field $\mathbf{E}_D$; (b) in the system of observer A, moving relative to D, the charges set up an electrostatic field $\mathbf{E}_A$ and also a magnetic field $\mathbf{B}_A$.

Figure 30–1(b) represents the same system from A's viewpoint. The charges in the wire, according to A, have a velocity $\mathbf{v}$ toward the right. Because of the relativistic length contraction (see Section 4–11), the distance d_A between the charges is *smaller* than d_D, or

$$d_A = d_D\sqrt{1 - (v^2/c^2)} = d_D\cos\alpha,$$

where the angle α (the angle between the space or time axes in a Brehme diagram) is defined by the equation

$$\sin\alpha = v/c.$$

The line density of charge in A's system is therefore

$$\lambda_A = \frac{q}{d_A} = \frac{q}{d_D}\frac{1}{\sqrt{1 - (v^2/c^2)}} = \frac{q}{d_D\cos\alpha},$$

or

$$\lambda_A = \frac{\lambda_D}{\sqrt{1 - (v^2/c^2)}} = \frac{\lambda_D}{\cos\alpha}.$$

Multiplying both sides of this equation by $2k/r$, we get

$$\frac{2k\lambda_A}{r} = \frac{2k\lambda_D/r}{\cos\alpha}, \quad\text{or}\quad E_A = \frac{E_D}{\cos\alpha}.$$

The electrical force F_{eA} on the charge q' which is moving with speed v in A's system is $q'E_A$, and the electrical force in D's system is $F_{eD} = q'E_D$. Therefore, multiplying both sides of the preceding equation by q', we get

$$F_{eA} = \frac{F_{eD}}{\cos\alpha},$$

which says that, on the basis of relativity and electrical forces *only*, the force on q' in A's system is *greater* than the force on q' in D's system.

But it was shown in Section 8–10 that relativity requires that

$$F_A = F_D\cos\alpha,$$

or that F_A should be *less* than F_D! We are therefore confronted with a dilemma: Relativity requires that $F_A < F_D$, whereas *relativity in conjunction with electrical forces alone* yields the result that $F_A > F_D$. To make these two results agree, we must conclude that in A's system there exists on q' *another force* of nonelectrical character in a direction opposite that of F_{eA}, that is, *toward* the wire. Observer A calls this a *magnetic* force, F_{mA}. The resultant force F_A is

$$F_A = F_{eA} - F_{mA},$$

and the principles of relativity require that

$$F_{eA} - F_{mA} = F_{eD}\cos\alpha.$$

Hence

$$F_{mA} = F_{eA} - F_{eD} \cos \alpha = \frac{F_{eD}}{\cos \alpha} - F_{eD} \cos \alpha$$

$$= F_{eD} \frac{1 - \cos^2 \alpha}{\cos \alpha} = F_{eD} \frac{\sin^2 \alpha}{\cos \alpha} = F_{eD} \frac{v^2}{c^2} \frac{1}{\cos \alpha} .$$

But

$$F_{eD} = q'E_D = q' \left(2k \frac{\lambda_D}{r} \right) = q'2k \frac{\lambda_A}{r} \cos \alpha.$$

Hence

$$F_{mA} = \frac{q'2k\lambda_A \cos \alpha}{r} \frac{v^2}{c^2} \frac{1}{\cos \alpha} ,$$

or

$$F_{mA} = q'v \left(\frac{2k}{c^2} \frac{\lambda_A v}{r} \right) . \qquad (30\text{--}1)$$

The moving charges in the wire, having a line density λ_A and moving with velocity v relative to A, constitute a current I in the wire, given by

$$I = nqAv = \lambda_A v.$$

Equation (30–1) can therefore be written as

$$F_{mA} = q'v \left(\frac{2k}{c^2} \frac{I}{r} \right) . \qquad (30\text{--}2)$$

That is, in A's system, there is a force F_{mA} on the charge q' proportional jointly to its charge, to its velocity v relative to A, and to the quantity in parentheses.

In electrostatics, we defined the *electric intensity E* as the ratio of the force on a charge at rest, to the magnitude of the charge.

$$E = \frac{F}{q'} .$$

Here, since the force depends on the velocity as well as on the charge, we define the *magnetic induction B* as *the ratio of the force on a* **moving** *charge, to the product of the charge and the velocity.*

$$B = \frac{F}{q'v} . \qquad (30\text{--}3)$$

It follows from Eq. (30–2) that the magnetic induction B set up by a long straight wire, at a distance r from the wire, is

$$B = 2 \frac{k}{c^2} \frac{I}{r} . \qquad (30\text{--}4)$$

The mksc unit of B is 1 n/amp·m. Other units will be introduced later.

It is a more complicated problem to assign a *direction* to the magnetic induction; we *cannot* define this direction as the direction of the force on a moving charge.

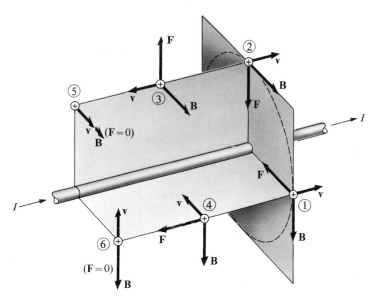

Fig. 30–2.   The force on a charge q moving with a velocity $\mathbf{v}$ in a magnetic field of induction $\mathbf{B}$ is $\mathbf{F} = q(\mathbf{v} \times \mathbf{B})$.

Figure 30–2 shows the forces that observer A would find on a test charge q at various points, and moving in various directions. Point 1 corresponds to Fig. 30–1(b); the test charge is moving parallel to the current in the wire with a velocity $\mathbf{v}$, and the magnetic force $\mathbf{F}$ is toward the wire.

At point 2, where the velocity is also parallel to the current, the force is still toward the wire, although it is at right angles to the force at point 1. The same result would be found at any point of the dotted circle; the force would be radially inward toward the wire.

At point 3, the velocity is parallel to the wire but *opposite* to the current. The force has the same magnitude as at points 1 and 2, but it is now radially *outward* from the wire.

At point 4, the test charge is moving radially inward, toward the wire. Again the force has the same magnitude as at points 1, 2, and 3, but it is now *parallel* to the wire.

At points 5 and 6, the charge is moving at right angles to the wire and the force on it is found to be zero.

We can bring order out of this apparent chaos of velocities and forces if we assign a direction to the **B**-vector at every point such that the force vector $\mathbf{F}$ (for a positive charge q) is in the direction of the *vector product* $\mathbf{v} \times \mathbf{B}$.

$$\mathbf{F} = q(\mathbf{v} \times \mathbf{B}). \qquad\qquad (30\text{–}5)$$

(If the charge q is *negative*, the force $\mathbf{F}$ is *opposite* to $\mathbf{v} \times \mathbf{B}$.)

The general expression for the magnitude of **F** is then

$$F = qvB \sin \theta,$$

where θ is the angle between **v** and **B**. The general expression for the magnitude of **B** is

$$B = \frac{F}{qv \sin \theta},$$

of which Eq. (30–3) is a special case where $\sin \theta = 1$.

It will be seen that at every point in Fig. 30–2, the force vector **F** is in the direction of **v** × **B**. In particular, at points 5 and 6, where **v** and **B** are parallel or antiparallel, $\sin \theta = 0$ and **F** $= 0$. *The direction of a **B**-field can therefore be described as that of the velocity of a moving charge which experiences* **no** *magnetic force.*

For simplicity in the diagram, the velocities of the charges in Fig. 30–2 were all either perpendicular or parallel to **B**. In the general case, the force is *perpendicular to the plane* of **v** and **B**.

Thus the principles of special relativity require that electric charges in motion relative to an observer shall set up a field, over and above their electrostatic field, and which we call a *magnetic* field. Had Oersted been aware of the principles of relativity, he might have performed his experiment to *verify* the prediction that a magnetic field should exist around a wire carrying a current.

In most cases of practical interest, a conductor in which there is a current appears electrically neutral to an observer at rest relative to the conductor. That is, the conductor contains equal quantities of positive and negative charge per unit volume (or per unit length). Any charges in the conductor that are in motion relative to the observer appear to him to set up a *magnetic* field, but because the conductor has no *excess* charge, it does not set up an *electric* field. Hence a test charge moving relative to the observer is acted on by a magnetic field but not by an electric field. To simplify the preceding derivation, we assumed that the wire contained charges of one sign only.

However, if a conductor carrying a current appears neutral to one observer, it appears charged to a second observer moving relative to the first, and to this observer it appears to set up an electric field as well as a magnetic field. See Problem 1 at the end of this chapter.

30–3 Experimental study of magnetic fields

An unknown *electric* field can be "explored" by measuring the magnitude and direction of the force on a test charge at rest relative to the observer. To "explore" an unknown *magnetic* field, we must measure the magnitude and direction of the force on a *moving* test charge.

The cathode-ray tube is a convenient experimental device for studying, at least in a qualitative way, the behavior of moving charges in a magnetic field. At one end of this tube is an electron gun which shoots out a narrow electron beam at a speed that can be controlled and calculated. At the other end is a fluorescent screen which emits light at the point where the electron beam strikes it. Let us suppose that our cathode-ray tube is small, that it is not surrounded by iron, and that it can be carried around the room easily. If the spot of light is always in the same place on the screen as we move the tube, we may conclude that there is no detectable magnetic field. If, on the other hand, as we move the tube around the room, the spot of light changes its position by virtue of the deflection of the electron beam, we conclude that we are in a magnetic field. Since the cathode-ray tube is imagined to be small, rotating the tube about any axis through its center, without shifting the position of its center, will provide information concerning the magnetic field in a small region at the center or, roughly, the magnetic field at a point.

At a given point in a magnetic field, the electron beam will, in general, be deflected. By rotating the cathode-ray tube, however, there will be found one direction in which no deflection takes place. This determines the direction of the field, but not its sense.

We next orient the cathode-ray tube so that the electron beam moves in a plane perpendicular to the direction of the field. The beam is then deflected at right angles to its velocity and from an observation of the deflection of the spot on the end of the tube the magnitude and direction of the transverse force can be deduced. Because the electron charge is *negative*, the force $e(\mathbf{v} \times \mathbf{B})$ on an electron is *opposite* to the vector product $\mathbf{v} \times \mathbf{B}$, and hence both the magnitude and sense of the $\mathbf{B}$-vector can be determined.

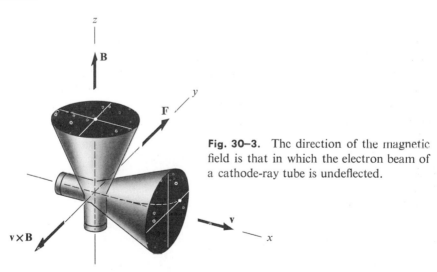

Fig. 30–3. The direction of the magnetic field is that in which the electron beam of a cathode-ray tube is undeflected.

EXAMPLE.   Suppose the electron beam of the cathode ray tube in Fig. 30–3 is undeflected when the beam is parallel to the z-axis. The $\mathbf{B}$-vector then points either up or down. When the tube axis is parallel to the x-axis, the beam is deflected in the positive y-direction. The deflecting force $\mathbf{F}$ is therefore in this direction and the $\mathbf{B}$-vector points *upward*. The vector $\mathbf{F}$ is then opposite to $\mathbf{v} \times \mathbf{B}$.

30–4 Lines of induction. Magnetic flux

A magnetic field can be represented by lines called *lines of induction*, whose direction at every point is that of the magnetic induction vector. In a uniform magnetic field, where the **B**-vector has the same magnitude and direction at all points, the lines of induction are straight and parallel. If the pole pieces of an electromagnet are large and close together, there is a region between them where the magnetic field is approximately uniform.

The *magnetic flux* Φ across a surface is defined in the same way as the electric flux Ψ, that is, as *the surface integral of the normal component of* **B** over the surface. Thus the flux $d\Phi$ across an area dA is

$$d\Phi = B_n \, dA = \mathbf{B} \cdot d\mathbf{A}, \qquad (30\text{–}6)$$

and the total flux across a finite area is

$$\Phi = \int B_n \, dA = \int \mathbf{B} \cdot d\mathbf{A}.$$

In the special case in which **B** is uniform and normal to a finite area A, the flux across the area is

$$\Phi = BA.$$

The mksc unit of magnetic induction B is 1 n/amp·m, and hence the unit of magnetic flux in this system is 1 n·m/amp. In honor of Wilhelm Weber (1804–1890), 1 n·m/amp is called 1 *weber*.

If the element of area dA in Eq. (30–6) is at right angles to the lines of induction, $B_n = B$ and hence

$$B = \frac{d\Phi}{dA_n}.$$

That is, the magnetic induction equals the *flux per unit area*, across an area at right angles to the magnetic field. Since the unit of flux is *one weber*, the unit of induction is called *one weber per square meter*. The magnetic induction **B** is often referred to as the *flux density*.

If the number of lines of induction, per unit area normal to their direction, is made numerically equal to the magnitude of **B**, one line of induction represents one weber. The total flux across a surface can then be pictured as *the number of lines of induction crossing the surface*, and the induction (the flux density) as the *number of lines per unit area*.

In one of a number of systems of electrical and magnetic units based on the cgs mechanical units, the unit of magnetic flux is called 1 *maxwell* and the corresponding unit of flux density, 1 maxwell/cm², is called 1 *gauss*. (Instruments for measuring flux density are often referred to as "gaussmeters.") The gauss and the weber/m² are related by the equation

$$1 \text{ w/m}^2 = 10^4 \text{ gauss}.$$

30-5 Orbits of charged particles in magnetic fields

Let a positively charged particle at point O in a uniform magnetic field of flux density **B** be given a velocity **v** in a direction at right angles to the field (Fig. 30–4). An upward force **F**, equal to qvB, is exerted on the particle at this point. Since the force is at right angles to the velocity, it will not affect the magnitude of this velocity but will merely alter its direction. At points such as P and Q the directions of force and velocity will have changed as shown, the magnitude of the force remaining constant, since the magnitudes of q, v, and B are constant. The particle therefore moves under the influence of a force whose magnitude is constant but whose direction is always at right angles to the velocity of the particle. The orbit of the particle is therefore a *circle* described with constant tangential speed v, the force **F** being the *centripetal force*. Since

$$\text{Centripetal acceleration} = \frac{v^2}{R},$$

we have, from Newton's second law,

$$qvB = m\frac{v^2}{R},$$

where m is the mass of the particle. The radius of the circular orbit is

$$R = \frac{mv}{Bq}. \tag{30–7}$$

If the direction of the initial velocity is not perpendicular to the field, the particle moves in a helix.

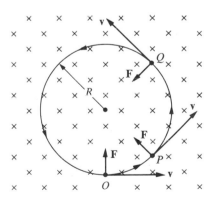

Fig. 30–4. The orbit of a charged particle in a uniform magnetic field is a circle when the initial velocity is perpendicular to the field.

Note that the radius is proportional to the *momentum* of the particle, mv. Note also that the *work* of the magnetic force acting on a charged particle is always *zero*, because the force is always at *right angles* to the motion. The only effect of a magnetic force is to change the *direction* of motion, never to increase or decrease the magnitude of the velocity.

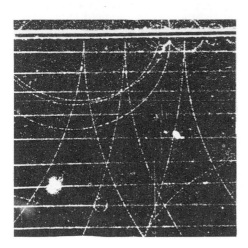

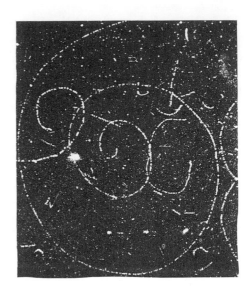

Fig. 30–5. Cloud-chamber tracks of three electron-positron pairs in a magnetic field. Three gamma-ray photons entering at the top materialize into pairs within a lead sheet. The coiled tracks are due to low-energy photoelectrons ejected from the lead. (Courtesy of Radiation Laboratory, University of California)

Fig. 30–6. A 4-Mev electron slowing down in a liquid hydrogen bubble chamber traversed by a magnetic field. The shape of the path shows how the radius of curvature decreases with velocity. (Courtesy of Radiation Laboratory, University of California)

Figure 30–5 is a photograph of the circular tracks made in a cloud chamber by charged particles moving in a magnetic field perpendicular to the plane of the paper. The photograph shows three pairs of tracks originating at common points but curving in opposite directions. A study of the density of droplets along the paths shows that both particles ionize like electrons, but since the tracks curve in opposite directions the charges must be of opposite sign. These tracks are in fact made by *electron-positron pairs*, created at the points from which the tracks originate by the annihilation of a high-energy gamma ray in the process known as *pair production.*

The other tracks at the top of the photograph are portions of the circular paths of photoelectrons, ejected from the lead sheet crossing the chamber. One complete circular track appears in the lower part of the photograph.

The spiral in Fig. 30–6 is the track made by a 4-Mev electron as it slows down in a liquid hydrogen bubble chamber in which there is a magnetic field. Many more ions are produced per unit length in a liquid than in a gas, so that although an electron may pass completely through a cloud chamber without appreciable energy loss, as in Fig. 30–5, the electron in Fig. 30–6 loses all its energy and comes to rest at the end of the spiral. The shape of the path shows in a striking way how the radius of curvature decreases as the velocity decreases.

30–6 Thomson's measurement of e/m

We are now ready to consider how Thomson measured the ratio of charge to mass, e/m, for what he called "cathode corpuscles" but which we now call electrons. His apparatus (Fig. 30–7) consisted of a highly evacuated glass tube into which several metal electrodes were sealed. Electrode C is the cathode from which the electrons emerged. Electrode A is the anode, which was maintained at a high positive potential. Most of the electrons hit electrode A, but there was a small hole in A through which some of them passed. They were further restricted by an electrode A' in which there was another hole. Thus a narrow beam of electrons passed into the region between the two plates P and P'. After passing between the plates, the electrons struck the end of the tube, where they caused fluorescent material at S to glow.

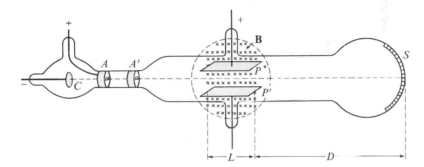

Fig. 30–7. Thomson's apparatus for measuring the ratio e/m for cathode rays.

The deflection plates P and P' were separated a known distance, so that when they were at a known difference of potential the electric field between them could be computed. We shall assume that the field was uniform for a distance L between the plates and zero outside them. When the upper plate P was made positive, the electric field deflected the negative electrons upward. After leaving the region between the plates, the electrons then coasted through the field-free region beyond the plates to the fluorescent screen at S. The deflection was discussed in detail in Chapter 26, where we obtained the result:

$$y_E = \frac{eEL}{mv^2}\left(D + \frac{L}{2}\right).\tag{30–8}$$

To obtain this equation, eliminate the accelerating voltage V_1 between Eqs. (26–22) and (26–26), and replace V_2/l by E, the electric field between the deflecting plates. The subscript E in y_E indicates that the deflection is produced by an electric field. The subscript a has been dropped from v.

If e/m is regarded as a single unknown, then there are two unknowns in this equation. The initial velocity v must be determined before e/m can be found. We need another equation involving the initial velocity v, so that this unknown velocity can be eliminated between the new equation and Eq. (30–8).

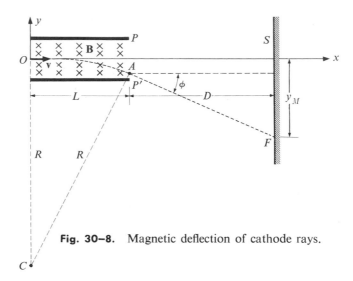

Fig. 30–8. Magnetic deflection of cathode rays.

Thomson obtained another equation by applying a magnetic field perpendicular to both the electron beam and the electric field. It is represented in Fig. 30–7 as being into the page and uniform everywhere within the ×-marked area. Thus the electrons experienced electric and magnetic forces in the same geometric space.

Figure 30–8 shows the situation when the magnetic field alone is present. The negative electrons experience an initial force downward, but this force is not constant in direction, and so the electrons move in a circular path. The equation of this path, taking the origin at C, the center of the curvature, is

$$R = \frac{mv}{qB}.$$

It follows from this equation and the geometry of the apparatus (we will not give details of the calculation) that the deflection y_M produced by the magnetic field is

$$y_M = -\frac{eBL}{mv}\left(D + \frac{L}{2}\right). \tag{30–9}$$

It may be mentioned at this point that the electron beam in all modern television "picture" tubes is deflected by *magnetic* fields, as in Fig. 30–8. To produce a given picture size using electrical deflection, either excessively large deflecting voltages or a much longer tube would be required.

Equation (30–9) is similar to Eq. (30–8). It contains e/m and v, together with measurable quantities, so that v can be eliminated and e/m found. It is interesting, however, to follow Thomson's procedure for determining v by the *simultaneous* application of electric and magnetic fields. If these are adjusted so that there is *no* deflection on the screen, the force of the electric field on an electron is balanced by that of the magnetic field. Then

$$qE = qvB, \quad \text{or} \quad v = \frac{E}{B}. \tag{30–10}$$

For this particular ratio of the fields, the electron goes straight through both fields. It is undeflected, and therefore the measurement of v does not depend on the geometry of the tube. The velocity thus determined may then be substituted into Eq. (30–8).

Thomson measured e/m for his "cathode corpuscles" and found a unique value for this quantity which was independent of the cathode material and the residual gas in the tube. This independence indicated that cathode corpuscles are a common constituent of all matter. The modern accepted value of e/m is $(1.758897 \pm 0.000032) \times 10^{11}$ coulombs per kilogram. Thus Thomson is credited with discovery of the first subatomic particle, the electron. He also found that the velocity of the electrons in the beam was about one-tenth the velocity of light, much larger than any previously measured material particle velocity.

Since the electron charge e is 1.602×10^{-19} coul and the charge-to-mass ratio e/m is 1.759×10^{11} coul/kgm, it follows that the electron mass is

$$m = \frac{1.602 \times 10^{-19} \text{ coul}}{1.759 \times 10^{11} \text{ coul/kgm}} = 9.108 \times 10^{-31} \text{ kgm}.$$

30–7 Positive rays

In 1886, Goldstein observed that if slots were cut in the cathode of a discharge tube, streaks of light appeared in the gas on the side away from the anode. These channels of light, first called "canal rays," were easily shown to be due to charged particles. They moved in the direction of the electric field which was producing the discharge, and they were deflected by electric and magnetic fields in directions that proved that their charge was positive. Attempts were made to measure q/m, the ratio of the charge to the mass, of these *positive rays*. It was soon discovered that q/m for positive rays was much less than for electrons and that it depended on the kind of residual gas in the tube. The velocities of the positive rays were found to be nonuniform and much smaller than electron velocities.

Thomson devised a different method for measuring q/m of these positive rays having nonuniform velocities. Figure 30–9(a) shows the apparatus he used. The main discharge took place in the large bulb A at the left, where K is the cathode and D is the anode. The gas under study was slowly admitted through the tube at L and was simultaneously pumped out at F. Thus a very low gas pressure was maintained. Most of the positive rays produced in the bulb hit the cathode and heated it. The cathode had a "canal" through it, so that some of the positive rays passed into the right half of the apparatus. Just to the right of the cathode are M and N, the poles of an electromagnet. The pole pieces of this magnet were electrically insulated by sheets, I, so that the magnetic pole pieces could also be used as the plates of a capacitor for the establishment of an electric field. With neither electric nor magnetic fields, the positive rays passed straight through the chamber C to the sensitive layer at S. This layer was either the emulsion on a photographic plate or a fluorescent screen. The beam was well defined because of the narrow tunnel in the cathode through which it had to pass. Instead of crossed fields, as in the electron apparatus, the fields in this apparatus were perpendicular to the rays but parallel to each other. The electric field is directed downward and the magnetic induction is upward, so that in Fig.

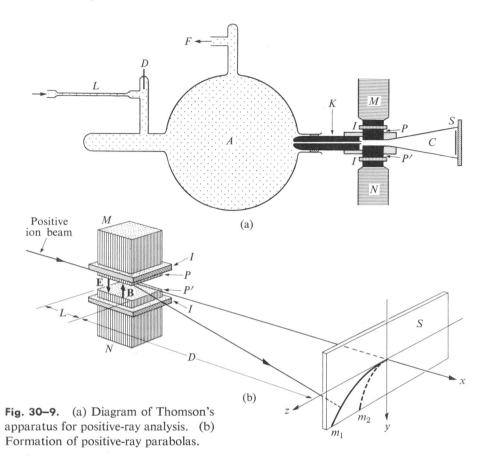

Fig. 30–9. (a) Diagram of Thomson's apparatus for positive-ray analysis. (b) Formation of positive-ray parabolas.

30–9(b) the electric force is toward the bottom of the page along the y-axis and the magnetic force is out of the page toward the reader along the z-axis.

Let a particle of unknown q/m enter the region between the electric plates with an unknown velocity v_x along the x-axis. If the length of its path in each field between the plates is L, the particle will have a downward acceleration qE/m for a time L/v_x, so that its downward velocity when leaving the plates is

$$v_y = \frac{qEL}{mv_x} \, .$$

Since the particle is also moving in the magnetic field, it will be accelerated in the z-direction an amount $qv_x B/m$ for a time L/v_x. It will therefore acquire a velocity in the z-direction given by

$$v_z = \frac{qv_x BL}{mv_x} = \frac{qBL}{m} \, .$$

The time required for the particles to travel a distance D in the field-free space beyond the plates is D/v_x. Knowing the time and the velocities and assuming $D \gg L$, we can compute the y- and z-coordinates of the point where the particle will hit. They are

$$y = \frac{qELD}{mv_x^2},$$

$$z = \frac{qBLD}{mv_x}.$$

These are the parametric equations of a *parabola*, where v_x is the parameter. Since v_x is different for different particles of the same kind, the pattern on the screen is not a point but a locus of points. Elimination of v_x between these two equations leads to

$$z^2 = \frac{q}{m}\frac{B^2LD}{E}y,$$

which is the equation of the parabola.

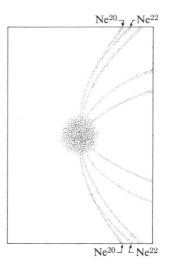

Fig. 30–10. The parabolas of neon.

Some of the parabolas obtained by Thomson's method are shown in Fig. 30–10. That a single experiment discloses several values of q/m is evident from the fact that there are several parabolas. It is apparent that the method is not capable of great precision because the parabolas are not sharp.

Thomson assumed that each particle of the positive rays carried a charge equal and opposite to the electronic charge, and he attributed the different parabolas to differences in mass. He assumed that the positive rays were positive because each had lost one electron. Thomson could identify particular parabolas with particular ions. Thus for atomic hydrogen, he could verify that the q/m he measured was equal to the value one would expect from dividing the electronic charge by the mass per atom. The reason that positive particles move more slowly than electrons and have lower values of q/m than electrons is now clear: the positive particles are much more massive. The largest q/m for positive particles is that for the lightest element, hydrogen. From the value of q/m it was found that the mass of the *hydrogen ion* or *proton* is 1836.13 ± 0.01 times the mass of an electron. Electrons contribute only a small amount to the mass of material objects.

30–8 Isotopes

The most striking thing that was shown by the Thomson parabolas was that certain chemically pure gases had more than one value of q/m. Most notable was the case of neon, of atomic weight 20.2. Neon exhibited a parabola corresponding to a particle of atomic weight 20, but it also had a parabola which indicated an atomic weight of 22. Since the next heavier element, sodium, has an atomic weight of 23.0, efforts to explain away the unexpected value of q/m failed at first. Finally, it was concluded that there must be two kinds of neon, with different masses but chemically identical. The proof of this interpretation was given by Aston, one of Thomson's students.

Aston used a principle which we discussed in Chapter 20. We pointed out there that the average kinetic energy of a molecule in a gas is $3kT/2$. Different gases mixed together in a container must be at the same temperature, and hence the average kinetic energy of each kind of molecule must be the same. If two gases have different molecular masses, the lighter molecules must have the higher average velocity, and these will make more collisions per unit time with the walls of the container than the heavier molecules. Therefore if these molecules are allowed to diffuse through a porous plug from one container into another, the number of lighter molecules passing through the plug will be greater than the number of heavier, slower ones. Aston took chemically pure neon gas and passed part of it through such a plug. Since one such pass accomplishes only a slight separation, the process had to be repeated many times. He ended with two very small amounts of gas. One fraction had been through the plug many times and the other had been "left behind" many times. He measured the atomic weight of each fraction and found values of 20.15 for the former and 20.28 for the latter. The difference was not great, but it was enough to show that there are indeed two kinds of neon. Many other elements have since been shown to exist in forms which are chemically identical but different in mass. Such forms of an element are called *isotopes*.

The discovery of isotopes solved several problems. It explained the two parabolas observed by Thomson. It also gave a logical explanation of the fact that the atomic weight of neon, 20.2, departs so far from an integral value. If chemical neon is a mixture of neon of atomic weight 20 and of neon of atomic weight 22, then there is some proportion of the two which, when mixed, will have an average atomic weight of 20.2.

30–9 Mass spectroscopy

A detailed search for the isotopes of all the elements required a more precise technique. Aston built the first of many instruments called *mass spectrometers* in 1919. His instrument had a precision of one part in 10,000, and he found that many elements have isotopes. Rather than discuss his instrument, however, we shall describe a more elegant one built by Bainbridge. The Bainbridge mass spectrometer (Fig. 30–11) has a source of ions (not shown) situated above S_1. The ions under study pass through slits S_1 and S_2 and move down into the electric field between the two plates P and P'. In the region of the electric field there is also a magnetic field **B**, perpendicular to the paper. Thus the ions enter a region of

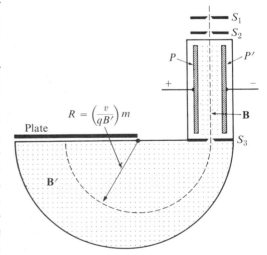

Fig. 30–11. Bainbridge's mass spectrograph, utilizing a velocity selector.

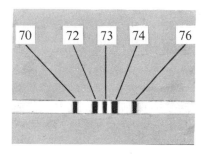

Fig. 30–12. The mass spectrum of germanium, showing the isotopes of mass numbers 70, 72, 73, 74, 76.

crossed electric and magnetic fields like those used by Thomson to measure the velocity of electrons in his determination of e/m. Those ions whose velocity is E/B pass undeviated through this region, but ions with other velocities are stopped by the slit S_3. All ions which emerge from S_3 have the same velocity. The region of crossed fields is called a *velocity selector*. Below S_3 the ions enter a region where there is another magnetic field $\mathbf{B}'$, perpendicular to the page, but no electric field. Here the ions move in circular paths of radius R. From Eq. (30–7), we find that

$$m = \frac{qB'R}{v}.$$

Assuming equal charges on each ion, and since B' and v are the same for all ions, we find that the masses of the ions are proportional to the radii of their paths. Ions of different isotopes converge at different points on the photographic plate. The relative abundance of the isotopes is measured from the densities of the photographic images they produce. Figure 30–12 shows the mass spectrum of germanium. The numbers shown beside the isotope images are not the atomic weights of the isotopes but the integers nearest the atomic weights. These integers are called *mass numbers*, and isotopes are written with the mass number as a superscript to the chemical symbol. Thus the isotopes shown would be written Ge^{70}, Ge^{72}, etc. The mass number is represented by the letter A.

As in the case of neon, the discovery of the isotopes of the various elements largely accounted for the fact that many chemical atomic weights are not integers. If germanium has mass numbers 70, 72, 73, 74, and 76, it is no wonder that a mixture of isotopes of germanium has a chemical atomic weight of 72.6.

30–10 Atomic weights. The atomic mass unit

One of the first discoveries in the field of mass spectroscopy was that oxygen, as found in air, oxides, sulphates, etc., is a mixture of three isotopes. The atomic weight of this mixture was arbitrarily assigned a value of exactly 16, and this number served for many years as the basis for atomic weights. In the 1920's and 1930's, however, mass spectrometers were developed by Aston, Dempster, Bainbridge, and others, that were capable of such precise measurements that it was found necessary to assign the number 16 to only the most abundant isotope of oxygen, the other two isotopes being designated by O^{17} and O^{18}. The chemists did not follow suit, so that there were two different systems of atomic weights in use at the same time, differing by some

275 parts per million. In addition, universal constants, such as Avogadro's number and the universal gas constant, had different values depending on which basis was chosen.

After much confusion and many international conferences, the chemists and physicists agreed in 1961 to use the same scale based upon the arbitrary *assignment of the number* 12 *to the lightest most abundant stable isotope of carbon.* The unit of atomic masses, called the *atomic mass unit* (amu), is by definition $\frac{1}{12}$ of the mass of C^{12}. Since the mass of an atom is equal to its atomic weight divided by Avogadro's number, it follows from the definition that 1 amu is equal to

$$1 \text{ amu} = \frac{\frac{1}{12} \times 12 \text{ gm/mole}}{6.02 \times 10^{23} \text{ atoms/mole}} = 1.66 \times 10^{-24} \frac{\text{gm}}{\text{atom}}.$$

The mass of a neutral atom expressed in amu is called its *isotopic mass.* The values given under the chemical symbols in the boxes of the periodic table at the end of this book are based on the C^{12} system.

30–11 The cyclotron

The cyclotron is an instrument developed in 1931 by Drs. Ernest O. Lawrence and M. Stanley Livingston at the University of California at Berkeley, for the purpose of securing a beam of charged atomic particles traveling at high speed. Despite its size and complexity, the basic theory of its operation is quite simple.

The heart of the cyclotron is a pair of metal chambers shaped like the halves of a pillbox that has been cut along one of its diameters. (See Fig. 30–13.) These hollow chambers, referred to as "dees" or "D's" because of their shape, have their diametric edges parallel and slightly separated from each other. A source of ions—the positively charged nuclei of heavy hydrogen (deuterons) are commonly used—is located near the midpoint of the gap between the dees. The latter are connected to the terminals of an electric circuit of the same sort as that used in a radio transmitter. The potential between the dees is thus caused to alternate rapidly, some millions of times per second, so the electric field in the gap between the dees is directed first toward one and then toward the other. But because of the electrical shielding effect of the dees, the space within each is a region of zero electric field.

The two dees are enclosed within, but insulated from, a somewhat larger cylindrical metal container from which the air is exhausted, and the whole apparatus is placed between the poles of a powerful electromagnet which provides a magnetic field whose direction is perpendicular to the ends of the cylindrical container.

Consider an ion of charge $+q$ and mass m, emitted from the ion source S at an instant when D_1 in Fig. 30–13 is positive. The ion is accelerated by the electric field in the gap between the dees and enters the (electric) field-free region within D_2 with a speed, say, of v_1. Since its motion is at right angles to the magnetic field, the ion will travel in a circular path of radius

$$r_1 = \frac{mv_1}{Bq}.$$

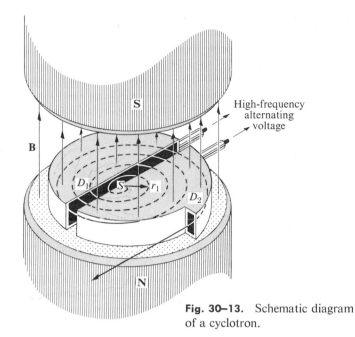

Fig. 30–13. Schematic diagram of a cyclotron.

If now, in the time required for the ion to complete a half-circle, the *electric* field has reversed so that its direction is toward D_1, the ion will again be accelerated as it crosses the gap between the dees and will enter D_1 with a greater velocity v_2. It therefore moves in a half circle of larger radius within D_1 to emerge again into the gap.

The angular velocity ω of the ion is

$$\omega = \frac{v}{r} = B\frac{q}{m}.$$

Hence the angular velocity is *independent of the speed of the ion and of the radius of the circle* in which it travels, depending only on the magnetic induction and the charge-to-mass ratio (q/m) of the ion. If, therefore, the electric field reverses at regular intervals, each equal to the time required for the ion to make a half revolution, the field in the gap will always be in the proper direction to accelerate an ion each time the gap is crossed. It is this feature of the motion, that the time of rotation is independent of the radius, which makes the cyclotron feasible, since the regularly timed reversals are accomplished automatically by the "radio" circuit to which the dees are connected.

The path of an ion is a sort of spiral, composed of semicircular arcs of progressively larger radius connected by short segments along which the radius is increasing. If R represents the outside radius of the dees and $v_{\max}$ the speed of the ion when traveling in a path of this radius,

$$v_{\max} = BR\frac{q}{m},$$

and the corresponding kinetic energy of the ion is

$$\frac{1}{2} m v_{max}^2 = \frac{1}{2} m \left(\frac{q}{m}\right)^2 B^2 R^2.$$

The potential difference V which would be required to produce the same kinetic energy in a single step, as in the Van de Graaff generator, can be found from

$$\tfrac{1}{2} m v_{max}^2 = qV,$$

or

$$V = \frac{1}{2} \frac{q}{m} B^2 R^2.$$

If the ions are deuterons,

$$\frac{q}{m} = 4.8 \times 10^7 \frac{coul}{kgm}.$$

In the M.I.T. cyclotron, B is about 1.8 w/m^2 and $R = 0.48$ m. Hence

$$V = \tfrac{1}{2} \times 4.8 \times 10^7 \times (1.8)^2 \times (0.48)^2$$
$$= 18 \times 10^6 \text{ volts, or 18 million volts,}$$

and the deuterons have the same speed as if they had been accelerated through a potential difference of 18 million volts.

Problems

30–1. The wire in Fig. 30–14 contains *two* sets of line charges, each charge of magnitude q and each set lying on the axis of the wire. The positive charges are at rest in D's system, and the negative charges have a velocity v toward the left, relative to D. Both sets of charges have the same separation d in D's system, so that in this system the wire is electrically neutral. A test charge q' is at rest in D's system. An observer A also has a velocity v toward the left, relative to D.

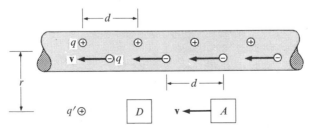

Figure 30–14

(a) What is the force on the test charge q' in D's system?

(b) What is the current I_D in the wire, in D's system?

(c) What is the separation of the positive charges, in A's system?

(d) What is the separation of the negative charges in A's system?

(e) What is the net line density of charge in A's system?

(f) What is the electrical force F_{eA} on the test charge q' in A's system?

(g) What is the current in the wire, in A's system?

(h) What is the magnetic force on the test charge q', in A's system?

(i) What is the resultant force on the charge q', in A's system?

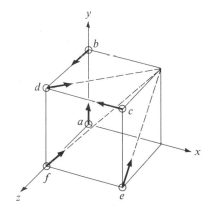

Figure 30–15

30–2. Each of the lettered circles at the corners of the cube in Fig. 30–15 represents a positive charge q moving with a velocity of magnitude v in the directions indicated. The region in the figure is a uniform magnetic field of flux density **B**, parallel to the x-axis and directed toward the right. Copy the figure, find the magnitude and direction of the force on each charge, and show the force in your diagram.

30–3. The magnetic induction or flux density **B** in a certain region is 2 w/m² and its direction is that of the positive x-axis in Fig. 30–16. (a) What is the magnetic flux across the surface $abcd$ in the figure? (b)

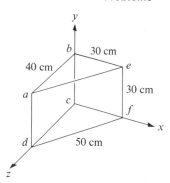

Figure 30–16

What is the magnetic flux across the surface $becf$? (c) What is the magnetic flux across the surface $aefd$?

30–4. A particle having a mass of 0.5 gm carries a charge of 2.5×10^{-8} coul. The particle is given an initial horizontal velocity of 6×10^4 m/sec. What is the magnitude and direction of the minimum magnetic field that will keep the particle moving in a horizontal direction?

30–5. A deuteron, an isotope of hydrogen whose mass is very nearly 2 amu, travels in a circular path of radius 40 cm in a magnetic field of flux density 1.5 w/m². (a) Find the speed of the deuteron. (b) Find the time required for it to make one-half a revolution. (c) Through what potential difference would the deuteron have to be accelerated to acquire this velocity?

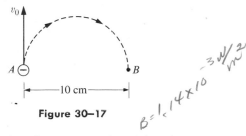

Figure 30–17

30 6. An electron at point A in Fig. 30–17 has a velocity v_0 of 10^7 m/sec. Find (a) the magnitude and direction of the magnetic induction that will cause the electron to follow the semicircular path from A to B; (b) the time required for the electron to move from A to B.

$\frac{\pi R}{V} = t$

$16 \times 10^{-3}\ M\,sec$

$B = 1.14 \times 10^{-3}\ W/m^2$

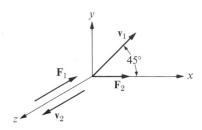

Figure 30–18

30–7. A particle carries a charge of 4×10^{-9} coul. When it moves with a velocity v_1 of 3×10^4 m/sec at 45° above the x-axis in the xy-plane a uniform magnetic field exerts a force F_1 along the z-axis. When the particle moves with a velocity v_2 of 2×10^4 m/sec along the z-axis there is a force F_2 of 4×10^{-5} newton exerted on it along the x-axis. What are the magnitude and direction of the magnetic induction? (See Fig. 30–18.)

30–8. An electron moves in a circular path of radius 1.2 cm perpendicular to a uniform magnetic field. The velocity of the electron is 10^6 m/sec. What is the total magnetic flux encircled by the orbit?

30–9. An electron and an alpha particle (a doubly ionized helium atom) both move in circular paths in a magnetic field with the same tangential velocity. Compare the number of revolutions they make per second. The mass of the alpha particle is 6.68×10^{-27} kgm.

30–10. For a particular parabola in Thomson's mass spectrograms, what physical quantity is different for the ions which land close to the origin than for those landing farther away? Why does this difference exist, since the accelerating voltage is the same for all the ions?

30–11. What must be the direction of the electric intensity **E** and the magnetic induction **B** in Fig. 30–9(b) so that the segment of the positive-ion parabola will be in (a) the lower right quadrant, (b) the upper right quadrant, and (c) the upper left quadrant as viewed from the right of the diagram?

30–12. (a) If the ion beam in Fig. 30–9(b) contains two types of ions having equal charges but different masses, which of the two parabolic segments will have those of greater mass? (b) If the masses are equal but the charges different, which segment will contain those having the larger charge?

30–13. (a) What is the velocity of a beam of electrons when the simultaneous influence of an electric field of intensity 34×10^4 volts/m and a magnetic field of flux density 2×10^{-3} w/m², both fields being normal to the beam and to each other, produces no deflection of the electrons? (b) Show in a diagram the relative orientation of the vectors **v**, **E**, and **B**. (c) What is the radius of the electron orbit when the electric field is removed?

30–14. A singly charged Li^7 ion has a mass of 1.16×10^{-23} gm. It is accelerated through a potential difference of 500 volts and then enters a magnetic field of flux density 0.4 w/m², moving perpendicular to the field. What is the radius of its path in the magnetic field?

30–15. Suppose the electric intensity between the plates P and P' in Fig. 30–11 is 150 volts/cm, and the magnetic induction in both magnetic fields is 0.5 w/m². If the source contains the three isotopes of magnesium, $_{12}Mg^{24}$, $_{12}Mg^{25}$, and $_{12}Mg^{26}$, and the ions are singly charged, find the distance between the lines formed by the three isotopes on the photographic plate. Assume the atomic weights of the isotopes equal to their mass numbers.

30–16. The electric field between the plates of the velocity selector in a Bainbridge mass spectrograph is 1200 volts/cm and the magnetic induction in both magnetic fields is 0.6 w/m². A stream of singly charged neon ions moves in a circular path of 7.28 cm radius in the magnetic field. Determine the mass number of the neon isotope.

30–17. A particle of mass m and charge $+q$ starts from rest at the origin in Fig. 30–19. There is a uniform electric field E

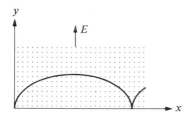

Figure 30–19

in the positive y-direction and a uniform magnetic field B directed toward the reader. It is shown in more advanced books that the path is a cycloid whose radius of curvature at the top point is twice the y-coordinate at that point.

(a) Explain why the path has a cycloidal shape and why it is repetitive.

(b) Prove that the speed at any point is equal to $\sqrt{2qEy/m}$.

(c) Applying Newton's second law at the top point, prove that the speed at this point is $2E/B$.

30–18. Two positive ions having the same charge q but different masses, m_1 and m_2, are accelerated horizontally from rest through a potential difference V. They

then enter a region where there is uniform magnetic induction **B** normal to the plane of the trajectory.   (a) Show that if the beam entered the magnetic field along the x-axis, the value of the y-coordinate for each at any time t is approximately

$$y = Bx^2(q/8mV)^{1/2}.$$

(b) Can this arrangement be used for isotope separation?

30–19. The magnetic induction in a cyclotron which is accelerating protons is 1.5 w/m^2. (a) How many times per second should the potential across the dees reverse?   (b) The maximum radius of the cyclotron is 0.35 m. What is the maximum velocity of the proton? (c) Through what potential difference would the proton have to be accelerated to give it the maximum cyclotron velocity?

30–20. Deuterons in a cyclotron describe a circle of radius 32.0 cm just before emerging from the D's. The frequency of the applied alternating voltage is 10 Mc/sec. Find (a) the flux density of the magnetic field, and (b) the energy and speed of the deuterons upon emergence.

6.64×10

Magnetic Forces on
Current-Carrying Conductors

31–1 Force on a current-carrying conductor

Figure 31–1 represents a portion of a conducting wire of length l and cross-sectional area A, in which the current density $\mathbf{J}$ is from left to right. The wire is in a magnetic field of flux density $\mathbf{B}$, perpendicular to the plane of the diagram. A positive charge q_1 within the wire, moving with its drift velocity $\mathbf{v}_1$, is acted on by an upward force $\mathbf{F}_1$ of magnitude q_1v_1B. The drift velocity $\mathbf{v}_2$ of a negative-charge carrier q_2 is opposite to $\mathbf{v}_1$ and the force $\mathbf{F}_2$ on it is q_2v_2B. Forces $\mathbf{F}_1$ and $\mathbf{F}_2$ are both upward, because the signs of both q_2 and v_2 are opposite to those of q_1 and v_1, respectively.

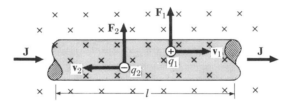

Fig. 31–1. Forces on the moving charges in a current-carrying conductor. The forces on both positive and negative charges are in the same directions.

Let n_1 and n_2 represent the numbers of positive and negative charge carriers per unit volume. The numbers of carriers in the portion are then n_1Al and n_2Al, and the total force $\mathbf{F}$ on all carriers (and hence the total force on the wire) is

$$F = (n_1Al)(q_1v_1B) + (n_2Al)(q_2v_2B)$$
$$= (n_1q_1v_1 + n_2q_2v_2)AlB.$$

But $n_1q_1v_1 + n_2q_2v_2$ (or more generally, $\sum nqv$) equals the current density J, and the product JA equals the current I, so finally,

$$F = IlB.$$

In the general case, where a conductor may be of any shape and make any arbitrary angle with the field, the force on a single carrier is $q(\mathbf{v} \times \mathbf{B})$. The force on an element of a conductor of length dl is then

$$d\mathbf{F} = I(d\mathbf{l} \times \mathbf{B}), \tag{31–1}$$

694

and the force on a straight conductor of length l is

$$\boxed{\mathbf{F} = I(\mathbf{l} \times \mathbf{B}).}$$ (31–2)

The vectors $d\mathbf{l}$ and $\mathbf{l}$ are in the direction of the current density $\mathbf{J}$, and Eqs. (31–1) and (31–2) describe both the *magnitude* and *direction* of the force.

31–2 The Hall effect

The reality of the forces on the moving charges in a conductor in a magnetic field is strikingly demonstrated by the *Hall effect*. The conductor in Fig. 31–2 is in the form of a flat strip. The current carriers within it are driven toward the upper edge of the strip by the magnetic force qvB exerted on them.

This force is an example of the *non*electrostatic forces $\mathbf{F}_n$ discussed in Chapter 28, and in this case the equivalent *non*electrostatic field $\mathbf{E}_n$, or the force per unit charge, has the magnitude

$$E_n = vB.$$

If the charge carriers are electrons, an excess negative charge accumulates at the upper edge of the strip, leaving an excess positive charge at its lower edge, until (as described in Section 28–4) the transverse electro*static* field $\mathbf{E}_e$ within the conductor is equal and opposite to the *non*electrostatic field $\mathbf{F}_n$. Because the final transverse current is zero, the conductor is on "open circuit" in the transverse direction, and the potential difference between the edges of the strip, which can be measured with a potentiometer, is equal to the *Hall emf* in the strip. The study of this Hall emf has provided much information regarding the conduction process. It is found that for the metals, the upper edge of the strip in Fig. 31–2 *does* become charged negatively relative to the lower, which justifies our belief that the charge carriers in a metal are negative electrons.

Suppose, however, that the charge carriers are *positive*. Then *positive* charge accumulates at the upper edge, and the potential difference is *opposite* to that resulting from the deflection of negative charges. Soon after the discovery of the Hall effect, in 1879, it was observed that many materials, notably the *semiconductors*, exhibited

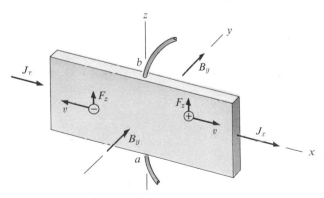

Fig. 31–2. Forces on charge carriers in a conductor in a magnetic field.

a Hall emf opposite to that of the metals, *as if* their charge carriers were positively charged. We now believe that these materials conduct by a process known as *hole conduction*. There are points within the material that would normally be occupied by an electron but because of a defect in the crystal structure they are actually empty, and a *missing negative* charge is equivalent to a *positive* charge. When an electron moves in one direction to fill a hole, it leaves another hole behind it and the result is that the *hole*, equivalent to a positive charge, migrates in the direction opposite to that of the electron.

In terms of the set of coordinate axes in Fig. 31–2, the electrostatic field E_e is in the z-direction, and we write it as E_z. The magnetic field is in the y-direction, and we write it as B_y. The nonelectrostatic field E_n (also in the z-direction) equals vB_y. The current density, J_x, is in the x-direction.

In the final steady state, when the fields $\mathbf{E}_e$ and $\mathbf{E}_n$ are equal,

$$E_z = vB_y.$$

The current density J_x is

$$J_x = nqv.$$

When v is eliminated, we have

$$nq = \frac{J_x B_y}{E_z}. \tag{31–3}$$

Thus from measurements of J_x, B_y, and E_z, one can compute the product nq.

31–3 Force and torque on a complete circuit. Magnetic moment

In Fig. 31–3 there is shown a rectangular loop of wire the lengths of whose sides are a and b. The normal to the plane of the loop makes an angle α with the direction of a uniform magnetic field $\mathbf{B}$, and the loop carries a current I. (Provision must be made for leading the current into and out of the loop, or for inserting a source. This is omitted from the diagram for simplicity.)

The force $d\mathbf{F}$ on the element $d\mathbf{l}$ equals $I(d\mathbf{l} \times \mathbf{B})$ and its direction is parallel to the x-axis toward the right. The magnitude of the total force $\mathbf{F}$ on the side of length a is

$$F = IaB.$$

This force is in reality distributed along the entire length of this side; the vector $\mathbf{F}$ is the *resultant* force. A force of the same magnitude but in the opposite direction acts on the opposite side.

The forces on the sides of length b, represented by the vectors $\mathbf{F'}$, are of magnitude $IbB \cos \alpha$. The lines of action of both lie along the y-axis.

The resultant *force* on the loop is evidently zero. The forces on the sides of length a, however, do not have the same line of action, and constitute a *couple* of moment

$$\Gamma = Fb \sin \alpha = I\,ab\,B \sin \alpha.$$

But ab is the area A of the loop, so

$$\Gamma = IAB \sin \alpha,$$

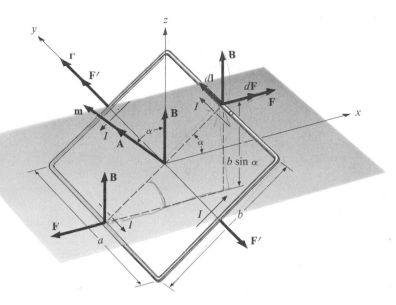

Fig. 31–3.   Forces on the sides of a current-carrying loop in a magnetic field. The resultant of the set of forces is a couple of moment $\Gamma = I(\mathbf{A} \times \mathbf{B})$.

or, in vector form,

$$\Gamma = I(\mathbf{A} \times \mathbf{B}), \tag{31–4}$$

where $\mathbf{A}$ is the vector area of the loop. The torque vector Γ is in the direction of the vector product $\mathbf{A} \times \mathbf{B}$ and points along the positive y-axis. The loop need not be rectangular; Eq. (31–4) gives the torque on a plane loop of *any* shape having an area $\mathbf{A}$.

The product $I\mathbf{A}$ is called the *magnetic moment* $\mathbf{m}$ of the loop. (It is analogous to the *electric moment* of an electric dipole.) Hence the result obtained above can be expressed by the simple equation

$$\Gamma = \mathbf{m} \times \mathbf{B}, \tag{31–5}$$

which is the analogue of the equation (see Section 26–7) for the torque on a dipole in an electric field,

$$\Gamma = \mathbf{p} \times \mathbf{E}.$$

The effect of the torque Γ is to rotate the loop toward its equilibrium position in which it lies in the xy-plane and its vector magnetic moment $\mathbf{m}$ is in the same direction as the field $\mathbf{B}$.

A helical winding of wire, such as that obtained by winding wire around the surface of a mailing tube, is called a *solenoid*. If the windings are closely spaced, the solenoid can be approximated by a number of circular loops lying in planes at right angles to its long axis. The total torque on a solenoid in a magnetic field is simply the sum of the torques on the individual turns. Hence for a solenoid of N turns in a uniform field of flux density B,

$$\Gamma = NIAB \sin \alpha, \tag{31-6}$$

where α is the angle between the axis of the solenoid and the direction of the field· The torque is a maximum when the magnetic field is parallel to the planes of the individual turns or perpendicular to the long axis of the solenoid. The effect of this torque, if the solenoid is free to turn, is to rotate it into a position in which each turn is perpendicular to the field and the axis of the solenoid is parallel to the field.

Although little has been said thus far regarding permanent magnets, everyone will probably recognize that the behavior of the solenoid as described above is the same as that of a bar magnet or compass needle, in that both the solenoid and the magnet will, if free to turn, set themselves with their axes parallel to a magnetic field. The behavior of a bar magnet or compass is often explained by ascribing the torque on it to magnetic forces exerted on "poles" at its ends. We see, however, that no such interpretation is demanded in the case of the solenoid. May it not be, therefore, that the spinning electrons (see Section 31–4) in a bar of magnetized iron are equivalent to the current in the windings of a solenoid, and that the observed torque arises from the same cause in both instances? We shall return to this question later.

EXAMPLE. Consider the electron of a hydrogen atom, revolving in the first Bohr orbit as discussed in Example 2 at the end of Section 24–6. The orbit is equivalent to a current loop of radius r and area πr^2. The average charge per unit time passing a point of the orbit, or the average current I, equals e/T, where T is the time of one revolution, equal to $2\pi r/v$. The magnetic moment of the loop is called 1 *Bohr magneton* and is represented by μ_B. Thus

$$\mu_B = IA = \tfrac{1}{2}evr.$$

But according to Bohr's theory, the angular momentum mvr is equal to $h/2\pi$, or

$$vr = \frac{h}{2\pi m}.$$

Therefore

$$\mu_B = \frac{h}{4\pi} \cdot \frac{e}{m} = \frac{6.62 \times 10^{-34} \text{ joule·sec} \times 1.76 \times 10^{11} \text{ coul/kgm}}{12.57}$$

$$= 9.27 \times 10^{-24} \text{ amp·m}^2.$$

31-4 The spinning electron

Electrons are characterized not only by their electric charge e, but by the fact that they have both a *magnetic moment* and an *angular momentum*, as would be the case if both their charge and their mass were distributed throughout a spherical volume and this sphere were spinning about an axis through its center. The magnetic moment and the angular momentum of an electron are indestructible properties, and we can do nothing to change their magnitudes. We can, however, change the *direction* of the spin axis by means of the torque exerted on the electron by a magnetic field.

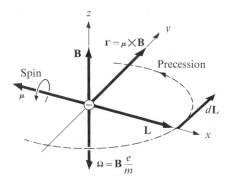

Fig. 31–4. A spinning electron of magnetic moment μ and angular momentum $\mathbf{L}$ is acted on by a torque $\mathbf{\Gamma} = \mu \times \mathbf{B}$ whose effect is to produce a precession of the spin axis.

The magnitude of the spin angular momentum $\mathbf{L}$ of an electron is $h/4\pi$, where h is Planck's constant, 6.62×10^{-34} joule·sec. It is found that the magnetic moment of a *spinning* electron is equal to that of an electron revolving in the first Bohr orbit of atomic hydrogen, or 1 Bohr magneton, μ_B.

$$\mu_B = \frac{h}{4\pi}\frac{e}{m}.$$

Figure 31–4 represents an electron whose spin axis is along the x-axis. Suppose an external magnetic field $\mathbf{B}$ is established in the direction of the z-axis. The torque on the electron is then $\mathbf{\Gamma} = \mu_B \times \mathbf{B}$, and if the electron had no angular momentum the effect of the torque would be to rotate the magnetic moment vector into parallelism with $\mathbf{B}$, as explained above. But the electron does have an angular momentum $\mathbf{L}$, and since the change in angular momentum $d\mathbf{L}$ produced by the torque is in the direction of the torque vector and hence at right angles to $\mathbf{L}$, the result is to cause the spin axis to *precess* about the direction of $\mathbf{B}$. That is, the electron behaves like a tiny *gyroscope*, acted on by a vector torque at right angles to its vector angular momentum. The angular velocity of precession, Ω, is

$$\Omega = \frac{\Gamma}{L} = \frac{\mu B}{L} = \frac{(h/4\pi)\cdot(e/m)}{h/4\pi}B = \frac{e}{m}B.$$

Nucleons, as well as electrons, have a magnetic moment and an angular momentum and behave in the same way as electrons in a magnetic field. The study of the precessional motions of electrons and nucleons is an important field of present-day experimental physics.

31–5 The galvanometer

Any device used for the detection or measurement of current is called a *galvanometer*. The earliest form of galvanometer was simply the apparatus of Oersted, namely a compass needle placed below the wire in which the current was to be measured. Wire and needle were both aligned in the north-south direction, with no current in the wire. The deflection of the needle when a current was sent through the wire was then a measure of the current. The sensitivity of this form of galvanometer was increased

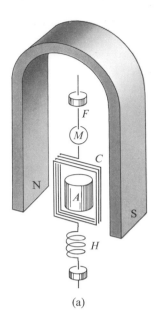

(a)   (b)

Fig. 31–5. (a) Principle of the D'Arsonval galvanometer. (b) D'Arsonval galvanometer. (Courtesy of Leeds and Northrup)

by winding the wire into a coil in a vertical plane with the compass needle at its center, and instruments of this type were developed by Lord Kelvin in the 1890's to a point where their sensitivity is scarcely exceeded by any available at the present time.

Practically all galvanometers used today, however, are of the D'Arsonval moving-coil or pivoted-coil type, in which the roies of magnet and coil are interchanged. The magnet is made much larger and is stationary, while the moving element is a light coil swinging in the field of the magnet.* The construction of a moving-coil galvanometer is illustrated in Fig. 31–5(a), and a photograph of one type of high-sensitivity galvanometer is shown in Fig. 31–5(b). The magnetic field of a horseshoe magnet whose poles are designated by N and S is concentrated in the vicinity of the coil C by the soft iron cylinder A. The coil consists of from 10 to 20 turns, more or less, of insulated copper wire wound on a rectangular frame and suspended by a fine conducting wire or thin flat strip F which provides a restoring torque when the coil is deflected from its normal position, and which also serves as one current lead to the coil. The other terminal of the coil is connected to the loosely wound helix H which serves as the second lead, but which exerts a negligible control on the coil.

When a current is sent through the coil, horizontal and oppositely directed side-thrusts are exerted on its vertical sides, producing a couple about a vertical axis through its center. The coil rotates in the direction of this couple and eventually comes

---

* The magnetic field surrounding a permanent magnet is discussed more fully in Chapter 34. For our present purposes, we may take it for granted that in the region between the magnet poles of Fig. 31–5(a) there does exist a field whose general direction is from N to S.

to rest in such a position that the restoring torque exerted by the upper suspension equals the deflecting torque due to the side-thrust. The angle of deflection is observed with the aid of a beam of light reflected from a small mirror M cemented to the upper suspension, the light beam serving as a weightless pointer. Since light incident on the mirror is reflected at an angle of reflection equal to the angle of incidence, rotation of the mirror through an angle θ deflects the light beam through an angle 2θ. It is standard practice to observe the reflected beam on a scale at a distance of one meter from the galvanometer.

Because of the geometry of the field in which the moving coil swings, the deflections of a D'Arsonval galvanometer are not directly proportional to the current in the galvanometer coil except for relatively small angles. Hence these instruments are used chiefly as *null* instruments, that is, in connection with circuits such as those of a Wheatstone bridge or a potentiometer, in which other circuit elements are to be adjusted so that the galvanometer current is zero.

31–6 The pivoted-coil galvanometer

The pivoted-coil galvanometer, while essentially the same in principle as the D'Arsonval instrument, differs from the latter in two respects. One is that the moving coil, instead of being suspended by a fine fiber, is pivoted between two jewel bearings. The instrument may hence be used in any position and is much more rugged and conveniently portable. The second difference is that the permanent magnetic field is modified by the use of soft iron pole pieces attached to the permanent magnet as shown in Fig. 31–6, so that the coil swings in a field which is everywhere radial. The side-thrusts on the coil are therefore always perpendicular to the plane of the coil, and the angular deflection of the coil is directly proportional to the current in it. The restoring torque is provided by two hairsprings, which serve also as current leads. A length of aluminum tubing, flattened at its tip in a vertical plane, serves as a pointer.

The frictional torque of the jewel bearings, while small, is greater than that of a supporting fiber. Since the deflecting and restoring torques must both be considerably larger than the friction torque, pivoted-coil instruments cannot be made as sensitive as the D'Arsonval type. The smallest currents which can be read on such an instrument are of the order of magnitude of 0.1 μa.

Fig. 31–6. Pivoted-coil galvanometer, modified for use as an ammeter or a voltmeter. Series resistor may be seen at left. (Courtesy of Houghton Mifflin Co.)

31–7 The ballistic galvanometer

A ballistic galvanometer is used for measuring the *quantity of charge* displaced by a current of short duration, as for example in the charging or discharging of a capacitor. While any moving-coil galvanometer can be used ballistically, instruments designed specifically for the purpose have coils with somewhat larger moments of inertia, and suspensions with somewhat smaller torque constants, than are found in instruments designed primarily for current measurement.

Consider a galvanometer coil of N turns, of area A, and moment of inertia I' suspended from a torsion wire whose torque constant (torque per unit angle) is k'. Suppose a current pulse is sent through the coil. The current is at first zero, then rises to a maximum, and then comes down to zero in such a short time that the coil does not move through an appreciable angle *while the current pulse exists*, but rotates only after the current has ceased. The torque at any moment of time *during the current pulse* is given by $\Gamma = NiAB$, and the angular impulse is this torque integrated with respect to time over the time interval of the current pulse. Since the angular impulse is equal to the change of angular momentum, we have

$$\int NiAB \, dt = I'\omega,$$

where ω is the angular velocity at the start of the galvanometer deflection.

The initial kinetic energy of the coil is converted to elastic potential energy of the torsion fiber, so that

$$\tfrac{1}{2} I'\omega^2 = \tfrac{1}{2}k'\theta_{max}^2,$$

where θ_{max} is the maximum angle of deflection. When ω is eliminated between these equations, we get

$$NAB \int i \, dt = \sqrt{k'I'} \, \theta_{max}.$$

But $\int i \, dt$ is the total charge Q transferred through the coil. Hence

$$Q = \frac{\sqrt{k'I'}}{NAB} \cdot \theta_{max},$$

which shows that the charge sent through a ballistic galvanometer coil is proportional to the maximum angle of deflection. The process is analogous to that which takes place when a ballistic pendulum is struck by a bullet. (See Section 8–4.)

31–8 The direct-current motor

The direct-current motor is illustrated schematically in Fig. 31–7. The armature, A, is a cylinder of soft steel mounted on a shaft so that it can rotate about its axis. Embedded in longitudinal slots in the surface of the armature are a number of copper conductors C. Current is led into and out of these conductors through graphite brushes making contact with a cylinder on the shaft called the commutator (not shown in Fig. 31–7). The commutator is an automatic switching arrangement which maintains the currents in the conductors in the directions shown in the figure, whatever the position of the armature.

The current in the field coils F and F' sets up a magnetic field which because of the shape of the pole pieces P and P' is essentially radial in the gap between them and the armature. The motor frame M provides a path for the magnetic field. Some of the lines of induction are indicated by the dotted lines in the figure.

With the relative directions of field and armature currents as shown, the side-thrust on each conductor is such as to produce a counterclockwise torque on the armature. When the motor is running, the armature develops mechanical energy at the expense of electrical energy. It must therefore be a source, in which there is an emf. This is an "induced" emf and is discussed further in Chapter 33. The field windings, however, are static and behave like a pure resistance.

If the armature and the field windings are connected in series we have a *series* motor; if they are connected in parallel, a *shunt* motor. In some motors the field windings are in two parts, one in series with the armature and the other in parallel with it; the motor is then *compound*.

EXAMPLE. A series-wound DC motor has an internal resistance of 2.0 ohms. When running at full load on a 120-volt line, a current of 4.0 amp is drawn.

(a) What is the emf in the armature?

$$V_{ab} = IR - \mathcal{E},$$
$$120 \text{ volts} = 2.0 \text{ ohms} \times 4.0 \text{ amp} - \mathcal{E},$$
$$\mathcal{E} = -112 \text{ volts}.$$

Since $\mathcal{E}$ is negative it is often called a "back emf."

(b) What is the power delivered to the motor?

$$P = IV_{ab}$$
$$= 4.0 \text{ amp} \times 120 \text{ volts} = 480 \text{ watts}.$$

(c) What is the rate of dissipation of energy in the motor?

$$P = I^2R$$
$$= (4.0 \text{ amp})^2 \times 2.0 \text{ ohms} = 32 \text{ watts}.$$

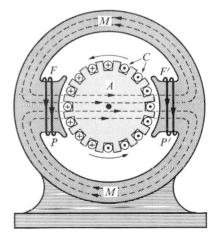

Fig. 31–7. Schematic diagram of a DC motor.

(d) What is the mechanical power developed?

$$\text{Mechanical power} = \text{total power} - \text{rate of dissipation of energy}.$$
$$480 \text{ watts} - 32 \text{ watts} = 448 \text{ watts}.$$

The mechanical power may also be calculated from the relation

$$\text{Mechanical power} = \text{back emf} \times \text{current} = 112 \text{ volts} \times 4.0 \text{ amp} = 448 \text{ watts}.$$

31–9 The electromagnetic pump

The heat developed in a nuclear reactor is, in some instances, transferred from the reactor core to the point where it is to be utilized by a circulating flow of liquid metal (sodium, lithium, bismuth, and sodium-potassium alloys have been used). The flow is maintained by an *electromagnetic pump*, one form of which is shown schematically in Fig. 31–8.

A current is sent transversely through the liquid metal, in a direction at right angles to a transverse magnetic field. The resulting side-thrust on the current-carrying metal drives it along the pipe in which it is contained. The system is completely sealed and the only moving part is the metal itself.

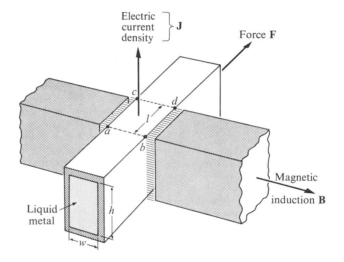

Problems

31–1. The cube in Fig. 31–9, 0.5 m on a side, is in a uniform magnetic field of 0.6 w/m², parallel to the x-axis. The wire *abcdef* carries a current of 4 amp in the direction indicated. Determine the magnitude and direction of the force acting on the segments *ab*, *bc*, *cd*, *de*, and *ef*.

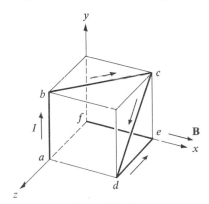

Figure 31–9

31–2. Figure 31–10 shows a portion of a silver ribbon with $y_1 = 2$ cm and $z_1 = 1$ mm, carrying a current of 200 amp in the positive x-direction. The ribbon lies in a uniform magnetic field, in the y-direction, of magnetic induction 1.5 w/m². If there are 7.4×10^{28} free electrons per m³, find (a) the drift velocity of the electrons in the x-direction, (b) the magnitude and direction of the electric field in the z-direction due to the Hall effect, (c) the Hall emf.

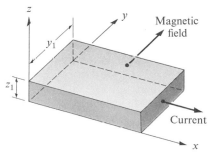

Figure 31–10

31–3. Let Fig. 31–10 represent a strip of copper of the same dimensions as those of the silver ribbon of the preceding problem. When the magnetic induction is 5 w/m² and the current is 100 amp, the Hall emf is found to be 2.28 μv. What is the concentration of free electrons?

31–4. The plane of a rectangular loop of wire 5 cm $\times$ 8 cm is parallel to a magnetic field whose flux density is 0.15 w/m². (a) If the loop carries a current of 10 amp, what torque acts on it? (b) What is the magnetic moment of the loop? (c) What is the maximum torque that can be obtained with the same total length of wire carrying the same current in this magnetic field?

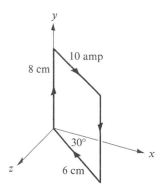

Figure 31–11

31–5. The rectangular loop in Fig. 31–11 is pivoted about the y-axis and carries a current of 10 amp in the direction indicated. (a) If the loop is in a uniform magnetic field of flux density 0.2 w/m², parallel to the x-axis, find the force on each side of the loop, in dynes, and the torque in dyne·cm required to hold the loop in the position shown. (b) Same as (a) except the field is parallel to the z-axis. (c) What torque would be required if the loop were pivoted about an axis through its center, parallel to the y-axis?

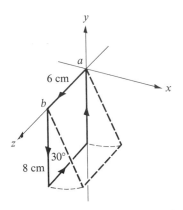

Figure 31–12

31–6. The rectangular loop of wire in Fig. 31–12 has a mass of 0.1 gm per centimeter of length, and is pivoted about side *ab* as a frictionless axis. The current in the wire is 10 amp in the direction shown. (a) Find the magnitude and sense of the magnetic field, parallel to the *y*-axis, that will cause the loop to swing up until its plane makes an angle of 30° with the *yz*-plane. (b) Discuss the case where the field is parallel to the *x*-axis.

31–7. As a naive guess, assume the charge of an electron to be distributed throughout a spherical volume of radius *a*, and the electron to possess electrical potential energy equal to ke^2/a. (a) Assuming this electrical potential energy to be equal to the rest mass energy m_0c^2, calculate the electron radius. (b) Compare this radius with that of a nucleus of an atom. Is it sensible to say that a nucleus contains electrons? (c) Calculate the moment of inertia of a spherically shaped, homogeneous electron. (d) Calculate the angular speed of a spinning electron. [*Warning:* Do not take the spherical electron too seriously.]

31–8. Calculate the angular velocity ω of an electron moving with any speed v perpendicular to a uniform magnetic field of induction B. Show that this "cyclotron frequency" is exactly the same as the angular velocity of precession, Ω, of a spinning electron in the same field.

31–9. (a) Calculate the angular velocity of precession of a spinning electron in a magnetic field of induction 0.5 w/m². (b) Calculate the same quantity for a proton in the same field, assuming that a proton spins with the same angular momentum as that of an electron and that the magnetic moment of a proton is 1.41×10^{-26} amp·m².

31–10. What is the maximum torque on a coil 5×12 cm, of 600 turns, when carrying a current of 10^{-5} amp in a uniform field where the flux density is 0.10 w/m²?

31–11. The coil of a pivoted-coil galvanometer has 50 turns and encloses an area of 6 cm². The magnetic induction in the region in which the coil swings is 0.01 w/m² and is radial. The torsional constant of the hairsprings is $k' = 0.1$ dyne·cm/deg. Find the angular deflection of the coil for a current of 1 ma.

31–12. A potential difference which varies with the time according to the equation

$$v = V \sin \frac{2\pi}{T} t$$

is established across a ballistic galvanometer coil of resistance R for a time interval of half a cycle, $T/2$. (a) What quantity of charge was transferred in the coil in this time interval? (b) Derive an expression for the maximum angle of deflection in terms of the physical constants of the galvanometer.

31–13. A 1-μf capacitor is connected to a dry cell of emf 1.5 volts and is then discharged through a ballistic galvanometer whose coil of 20 turns has an area of 4 cm² and swings in a magnetic field of 0.1 w/m². If the maximum angle of deflection is one-half a radian, what is the product of the torsion constant of the suspension and the moment of inertia of the coil?

31–14. In a shunt-wound DC motor the resistance of the field coils is 150 ohms and the resistance of the armature is 2 ohms. When a difference of potential of 120 volts is applied to the brushes, and the motor is running at full speed delivering mechanical power, the current supplied to it is 4.5 amp. (a) What is the current in the field coils? (b) What is the current in the armature? (c) What is the emf developed by the motor? (d) How much mechanical power is developed by this motor?

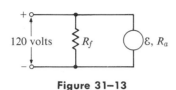

+ 120 volts R_f $\mathcal{E}, R_a$

Figure 31–13

31–15. Figure 31–13 is a diagram of a shunt-wound DC motor, operating from 120-volt DC mains. The resistance of the field windings, R_f, is 240 ohms. The resistance of the armature, R_a, is 3 ohms. When the motor is running the armature develops an emf $\mathcal{E}$. The motor draws a current of 4.5 amp from the line. Compute (a) the field current, (b) the armature current, (c) the emf $\mathcal{E}$, (d) the rate of development of heat in the field windings, (e) the

rate of development of heat in the armature, (f) the power input to the motor, (g) the efficiency of the motor, if friction and windage losses amount to 50 watts.

31–16. A horizontal tube of rectangular cross section (height h, width w) is placed at right angles to a uniform magnetic field of induction B, so that a length l is in the field. (See Fig. 31–8.) The tube is filled with liquid sodium and an electric current of density J is maintained in the third mutually perpendicular direction. (a) Show that the difference of pressure between a point in the liquid on a vertical plane through ab (Fig. 31–8) and a point in the liquid on another vertical plane through cd, under conditions in which the liquid is prevented from flowing, is

$$\Delta p = JlB.$$

(b) What current would be needed to provide a pressure difference between these two points of one atmosphere if $B = 1$ w/m^2 and $l = 0.1$ m?

CHAPTER 32

Magnetic Field of a Current

32–1 Magnetic field of a current-carrying circuit. The Biot law

It was shown at the beginning of Chapter 30 that the laws of electrostatics, together with the principles of special relativity, led to the result that the magnitude of the magnetic induction **B** in empty space, at a radial distance r from a long straight conductor in which there is a constant current I, is

$$B = 2k'\frac{I}{r},\tag{32–1}$$

where

$$k' = \frac{k}{c^2}.$$

The lines of the **B**-field are circles in planes perpendicular to the conductor.

From experimental studies of the magnetic fields around circuits of various shapes, the French physicist Jean Biot, in 1820, deduced an equation from which the **B**-field set up by a circuit of *any* shape can be calculated (except for possible mathematical difficulties). The circuit is to be divided, in imagination, into short elements of length dl, one of which is shown in Fig. 32–1. The remainder of the circuit, not shown, may be of any shape. The moving charges in the element set up a field at all points of space and the field of the entire circuit, at any point, is the resultant of the infinitesimal fields of all the elements of the circuit. The direction of the field $d\mathbf{B}$ set up at point P by the element of length dl is shown in Fig. 32–1. The vector $d\mathbf{B}$ lies in a plane per-

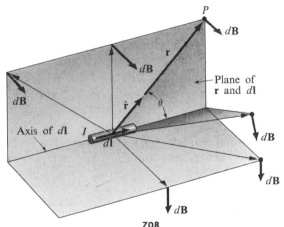

Figure 32–1

pendicular to the axis of dl and is itself perpendicular to the plane determined by dl and the line joining dl and P. The vector $d\mathbf{B}$ is given by

$$d\mathbf{B} = k' \frac{I \, dl \times \hat{\mathbf{r}}}{r^2}, \tag{32–2}$$

where r is the distance between dl and P, and $\hat{\mathbf{r}}$ is a unit vector in the direction from dl to P. The magnitude of $d\mathbf{B}$ is

$$dB = k' \frac{I \, dl \sin \theta}{r^2}. \tag{32–3}$$

The field $d\mathbf{B}$ due to a current element is zero at all points on the axis of the element, since $\sin \theta = 0$ at all such points. At a given distance r from the element, the field is a maximum in a plane through the element perpendicular to its axis, since $\theta = 90°$ and $\sin \theta = 1$ at all points in such a plane. Figure 32–1 shows the vectors $d\mathbf{B}$ at a number of different points.

The resultant flux density at any point of space, due to a complete circuit, is the *vector integral* of the values of $d\mathbf{B}$ due to all current elements of the circuit. Thus

$$\mathbf{B} = k' \int \frac{I \, d\mathbf{l} \times \hat{\mathbf{r}}}{r^2}. \tag{32–4}$$

It should be pointed out that it is impossible to verify Eq. (32–2) experimentally, since one can never obtain an isolated element of a current-carrying circuit. Only the *resultant* flux density $\mathbf{B}$, given by the integral in Eq. (32–4) can be measured experimentally. Equation (32–4) is the analytical formulation of *Biot's law*.

32–2 Magnetic field of a long straight conductor

Let us use the Biot law to compute the magnetic induction $\mathbf{B}$ at point P in Fig. 32–2, in the field of a long straight conductor carrying a current I. It will be convenient to change the notation (as we did when evaluating the *electric* field around the charged wire in Fig. 25–5) and let r represent the radial distance of point P from the wire and s the vector from a current element to P. Then in terms of the letters in Fig. 32–2,

$$\mathbf{B} = k'I \int \frac{d\mathbf{y} \times \hat{\mathbf{s}}}{s^2}.$$

This is a vector integral, but since the induction $d\mathbf{B}$ set up at P by any other element of the conductor is parallel to the vector $d\mathbf{B}$ in the diagram, the resultant induction is the algebraic sum or the ordinary integral of $d\mathbf{B}$. Then, since $\hat{\mathbf{s}}$ is a unit vector,

$$B = k'I \int_{-\infty}^{+\infty} \frac{\sin \theta}{s^2} \, dy.$$

Simplification results if θ is chosen as the integration variable. It will be seen from the diagram that

$$s = r \csc \theta, \qquad y = -r \cot \theta.$$

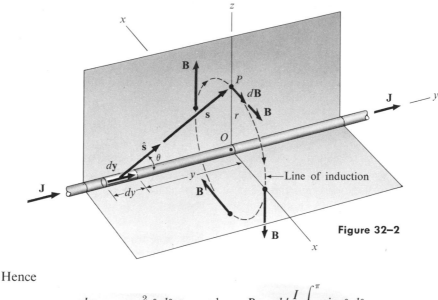

Figure 32–2

Hence

$$dy = r \csc^2 \theta \, d\theta \quad \text{and} \quad B = k' \frac{I}{r} \int_0^\pi \sin \theta \, d\theta.$$

The integration limits are from 0 to π, since the wire is assumed to be very long. (The remainder of the circuit is considered to be so far away that any contribution it makes to the field can be neglected.) On carrying out the integration, we find

$$B = 2k' \frac{I}{r}, \tag{32–5}$$

in agreement with Eq. (32–1).

This relation was deduced by Biot and Savart from experimental study of the field around a long straight conductor before the differential form [Eq. (32–2)] had been discovered. It is called the *Biot-Savart law*.

A portion of the magnetic field around a long straight conductor is shown in the cutaway view in Fig. 32–3. Unlike the electric field around a charged wire, which is radial, the lines of magnetic induction are *circles* concentric with the wire and lying in planes perpendicular to it. It will also be noted that in this special case each line of induction is a *closed* line, and that in this respect lines of induction differ from the lines of force in an electrostatic field, which terminate on positive or negative charges.

Figure 32–4 shows a portion of the field around a two-wire transmission line, in which the conductors are carrying equal currents in opposite directions. Each conductor sets up a field like that in Fig. 32–3, and the flux density at every point is the vector sum of the **B**-vectors due to the two conductors.

If a closed surface is constructed in a magnetic field, the number of lines of induction that emerge from the surface must equal the number that enter, because there are no free magnetic charges on which a line might terminate or originate. We have

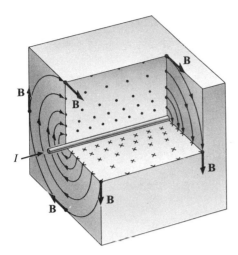

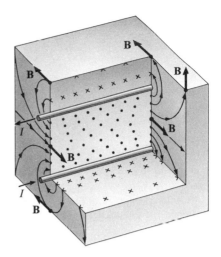

Fig. 32–3.   Magnetic field around a long straight conductor.

Fig. 32–4.   Magnetic field of two long straight conductors carrying currents in opposite directions.

shown that the number of lines of induction crossing a surface is proportional to the flux Φ across the surface. Hence in a magnetic field, the flux across any *closed* surface is zero, or

$$\oint B_n \, dA = \oint \mathbf{B} \cdot d\mathbf{A} = 0.$$

This should be compared with Gauss's law for electrostatic fields, in which the surface integral of $\mathbf{E}$ over a closed surface equals $1/\epsilon_0$ times the enclosed charge.

32–3 Force between parallel conductors. The ampere and the coulomb

Figure 32–5 shows a portion of two long straight parallel conductors separated by a distance r and carrying currents I and I', respectively, in the same direction. Since each conductor lies in the magnetic field set up by the other, each will experience a force. The diagram shows some of the lines of induction set up by the current in the *lower* conductor. The magnitude of $\mathbf{B}$ at the upper conductor is

$$B = 2k' \frac{I}{r}.$$

From Eq. (31–2), the force on a length l of the upper conductor is

$$F = I'lB = 2k'l\frac{II'}{r}$$

and the force per unit length is therefore

$$\frac{F}{l} = 2k' \frac{II'}{r}. \tag{32–6}$$

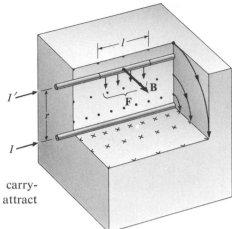

Fig. 32–5. Parallel conductors carrying currents in the same direction attract each other.

The direction of the force on the upper conductor is downward. There is an equal and opposite force per unit length on the lower conductor, as may be seen by considering the field set up by the upper conductor. Hence the conductors *attract* each other.

If the direction of either current is reversed, the forces reverse also. Parallel conductors carrying currents in *opposite* directions *repel* each other.

The fact that two straight parallel conductors exert forces of attraction or repulsion on each other is made the basis of the definition of the ampere in the mksc system. The ampere is defined as follows:

> *One ampere is that unvarying current which, if present in each of two parallel conductors of infinite length and one meter apart in empty space, causes each conductor to experience a force of exactly* 2×10^{-7} *newton per meter of length.*

It follows from this and the preceding equation that by definition the constant k' is *exactly* 10^{-7} n/amp^2. Since $k' = k/c^2$, it follows further that

$$k = k'c^2 = 10^{-7} \frac{\text{n}}{\text{amp}^2} \times 8.987 \times 10^{16} \frac{\text{m}^2}{\text{sec}^2} \approx 9 \times 10^9 \frac{\text{n·m}^2}{\text{coul}^2},$$

the value that was introduced in Chapter 24.

From the definition above, the ampere can be established, in principle, with the help of a meter stick and a spring balance. For the practical standardization of the ampere, coils of wire are used instead of straight wires and their separation is made only a few centimeters. The complete instrument, which is capable of measuring currents with a high degree of precision, is called a *current balance.*

Having defined the ampere, we can now define the coulomb as *the quantity of charge that in one second crosses a section of a circuit in which there is a constant current of one ampere.*

Mutual forces of attraction exist not only between *wires* carrying currents in the same direction, but between each of the longitudinal elements into which a single current-carrying conductor may be subdivided. If the conductor is a liquid or an

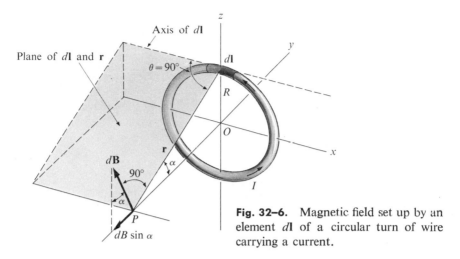

Fig. 32–6. Magnetic field set up by an element $d\mathbf{l}$ of a circular turn of wire carrying a current.

ionized gas (a plasma), these forces result in a constriction of the conductor as if its surface were acted on by an external, inward, pressure force. The constriction of the conductor is called the *pinch effect*, and attempts are being made to utilize the high temperature produced by the pinch effect in a plasma to bring about nuclear fusion.

32–4 Magnetic field of a circular turn

In many devices in which a current is used to establish a magnetic field, as in an electromagnet or a transformer, the wire carrying the current is wound into a coil of some sort. We therefore consider next the magnetic field set up by a single circular turn of wire carrying a current.

Figure 32–6 shows a circular turn of radius R carrying a current I and lying in the xz-plane. Point P is on the axis of the turn, at a distance y from its center O, and r is the distance from an element of the turn of length dl to point P. The plane determined by $d\mathbf{l}$ and $\mathbf{r}$ is shaded, and the induction $d\mathbf{B}$ set up at P by the current in the element $d\mathbf{l}$ is at right angles to this plane and lies in the yz-plane. The angle θ between $d\mathbf{l}$ and $\mathbf{r}$ is $90°$, so in terms of the symbols used in this diagram the Biot law becomes

$$dB = k'I\frac{dl}{r^2}.$$

Let α represent the angle between r and the y-axis. The vector $d\mathbf{B}$ can then be resolved into a component $dB \sin \alpha$ along the y-axis and a component $dB \cos \alpha$ at right angles to it. It will be seen by symmetry that each element contributes an equal component $dB \sin \alpha$, but that the components $dB \cos \alpha$ set up by diametrically opposite elements will cancel. Hence the resultant induction is along the y-axis, and is found by integration of the components $dB \sin \alpha$:

$$B = \int dB \sin \alpha = k'\frac{I \sin \alpha}{r^2} \int dl, \tag{32–7}$$

since $\sin \alpha$ and r are constants and may be taken outside the integral sign. The integral is merely the circumference of the turn, $2\pi R$, so finally

$$B = 2\pi k' \frac{IR \sin \alpha}{r^2}. \qquad (32\text{–}8)$$

At the center of the turn, $\alpha = 90°$ and $r = R$, so at the center

$$B = 2\pi k' \frac{I}{R}. \qquad (32\text{–}9)$$

If instead of a single turn, as in Fig. 32–6, we have a coil of N closely spaced turns all of essentially the same radius, each turn contributes equally to the field and Eq. (32–9) becomes

$$B = 2\pi k' \frac{NI}{R}.$$

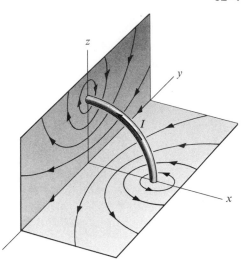

Fig. 32–7. Lines of induction surrounding a circular turn.

Since $\sin \alpha = R/r$, Eq. (32–8) can also be written

$$B = 2k' \frac{I(\pi R^2)}{r^3}.$$

But πR^2 is the area of the loop and $I(\pi R^2)$ is its magnetic moment m. Hence

$$B = k' \frac{2m}{r^3}.$$

At sufficiently large distances from the loop, r is very nearly equal to the *axial* distance from the center of the loop. Comparison with Eq. (26–19) will show that the axial **B**-field of the loop, at large distances, is like the E_r-field of an electric dipole, with the magnetic moment m of the loop corresponding to the electric moment p of the dipole. A complete analysis shows that at large distances this is the case for all other points as well. Close to the loop, or the dipole, the similarity breaks down. Some of the lines of induction surrounding a circular turn are shown in Fig. 32–7.

It was pointed out in Chapter 31 that a loop of wire of any shape and carrying a current is acted on by a torque when placed in an external magnetic field. The position of stable equilibrium is one in which the plane of the loop is perpendicular to the external field. Now we see that this position is such that *within the area enclosed by the loop, the loop's own* **B**-*field is in the same direction as that of the external field.* In other words, a loop, if free to turn, will set itself in such a plane that the flux passing through the area enclosed by it has its maximum possible value. This is found to be true in all instances and is a useful general principle. For example, if a current is sent through an irregular loop of *flexible* wire in an external magnetic field, the loop will assume a circular form with its plane perpendicular to the field and with its own flux adding to that of the field. The same conclusion can, of course, be drawn by analyzing the side-thrusts on the elements of the conductor.

32–5 Ampere's law ~~USE THIS~~

The relation known as Ampere's law has to do with an important general property of magnetic fields. We shall derive it for the special case of the field of one or more long straight parallel conductors.

The plane of the diagram in Fig. 32–8 is perpendicular to a conductor which carries a current I. The flux density $\mathbf{B}$ at any point is in the plane of the diagram and at right angles to the radius $\mathbf{r}$ from the wire to the point. The magnitude of $\mathbf{B}$ is

$$B = 2k'\frac{I}{r}.$$

The $\mathbf{B}$-vector makes an angle θ with an element ds of a closed path encircling the wire and the component of $\mathbf{B}$ in the direction of ds is $B_s = B\cos\theta$. From the small right "triangle" of which ds is the hypotenuse, we see that

$$r\,d\phi = ds\cos\theta,$$

or

$$ds = r\,d\phi/\cos\theta.$$

Therefore

$$B_s\,ds = \mathbf{B}\cdot d\mathbf{s} = B\cos\theta\,ds$$

$$= \left(2k'\frac{I}{r}\right)(\cos\theta)\frac{r\,d\phi}{\cos\theta}$$

$$= 2k'I\,d\phi.$$

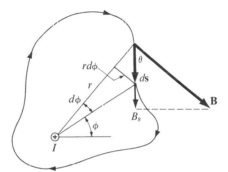

Fig. 32–8. The line integral of $\mathbf{B}$ around a closed path equals $4\pi k'$ times the net current through the area bounded by the path.

The line integral of $\mathbf{B}$ around the closed path is

$$\oint \mathbf{B}\cdot d\mathbf{s} = 2k'I\oint d\phi,$$

or,

$$\boxed{\oint \mathbf{B}\cdot d\mathbf{s} = 4\pi k'I,} \qquad (32\text{–}10)$$

Ampere's law

since the angle ϕ increases by 2π as we go once around the path.

The line integral does not depend on the shape of the path, or on the position of the wire within it. If the current in the wire were opposite to that shown, the integral would have the opposite sign. Hence if any number of long straight conductors pass through the surface bounded by the path, the line integral equals $4\pi k'$ times the *algebraic sum* of the currents.

If a closed path does not encircle the wire (or if a wire lies outside the path), the line integral of the $\mathbf{B}$-field of that wire is zero, because the angle ϕ then has the same value at the start and finish of any round trip. Hence if there are other conductors present that do not pass through a given path, they may contribute to the value of $\mathbf{B}$ at every point but the line integrals of their fields are zero.

It follows that if we interpret I in Eq. (32–10) to mean the algebraic sum of the currents across the area bounded by a closed path, this equation implies all of the statements above and is the analytic form of *Ampere's law: The line integral of the magnetic induction* **B** *around any closed path is equal to* $4\pi k'$ *times the net current across the area bounded by the path.*

Although derived only for the special case of the field of a number of long straight parallel conductors, the law is true for conductors and paths of any shape. The general derivation is no different in principle from that above, but it is complicated geometrically and will not be given.

The appearance of the factor 4π in Eq. (32–10) suggests that the form of certain magnetic equations can be simplified if we define a new constant μ_0 by the equation

$$4\pi k' = \mu_0.$$

Since k' is exactly 10^{-7} w/amp·m,

$$\mu_0 = 4\pi \times 10^{-7} \frac{w}{amp \cdot m} = 12.57 \times 10^{-7} \frac{w}{amp \cdot m}.$$

Hence Ampere's law can be written more compactly as

$$\oint \mathbf{B} \cdot ds = \mu_0 I. \tag{32–11}$$

In terms of μ_0, Eq. (32–4) becomes

$$\mathbf{B} = \frac{\mu_0}{4\pi} \int \frac{I \, d\mathbf{l} \times \hat{\mathbf{r}}}{r^2}. \tag{32–12}$$

32–6 Applications of Ampere's law

In some instances, *symmetry* considerations make it possible to use Ampere's law to compute the magnetic flux density. As was the case with similar applications of Gauss's law, we must be able to replace the *integral* in Eq. (32–11) by a *product*, thus obtaining an *algebraic* equation that can be solved for B. We consider three examples.

1. *Field of a solenoid.* A solenoid is constructed by winding wire in a helix around the surface of a cylindrical form, usually of circular cross section. The turns of the winding are ordinarily closely spaced and may consist of one or more layers. For simplicity, we have represented a solenoid in Fig. 32–9 by a relatively small number of circular turns, each carrying a current I. The resultant flux density at any point is the vector sum of the **B**-vectors due to the individual turns. The diagram shows the lines of induction in the *xy*- and *yz*-planes. Exact calculations show that for a long closely wound solenoid, half of the lines passing through a cross section at the center emerge from the ends and half "leak out" through the windings between center and end.

If the length of the solenoid is large compared with its cross-sectional diameter, the internal field near its center is very nearly uniform and parallel to the axis, and the external field near the center is very small. The internal field at or near the center can then be found by applying Ampere's law to the dotted rectangle in the *xy*-plane, of

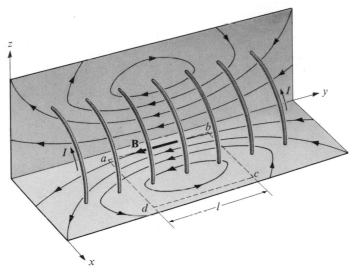

Fig. 32–9. Lines of induction surrounding a solenoid. The dotted rectangle *abcd* is used to compute the flux density *B* in the solenoid from Ampere's law.

length *l*, and neglecting any contribution of the external field to the line integral of **B**, which reduces simply to the product *Bl*.

Let *n* represent the number of turns per unit length in the windings. The number of turns in the length *l* is then *nl*. Each of these turns passes once through the rectangle *abcd* and carries a current *I*, where *I* is the current in the windings. The total current through the rectangle is then *nlI*, and from Ampere's law,

$$Bl = \mu_0 nlI,$$

$$B = \mu_0 nI. \tag{32–13}$$

We have assumed that each turn of the windings lies in a plane perpendicular to the axis. If the windings are helical there is a *longitudinal* as well as a *circumferential* current. Superposed on the external field shown in the diagram, therefore, is a circumferential field (due to the longitudinal component of current) like that surrounding any long straight conductor.

2. *Field of a toroid.* Figure 32–10(a) represents a toroid, wound with wire carrying a current *I*. The dotted lines in Fig. 32–10(b) are a number of paths to which we wish to apply Ampere's law. Consider first path 1. By symmetry, if there is any field at all in this region it will be tangent to the path at all points and its line integral will equal the product of *B* and the circumference of the path. The current through the path, however, is zero, and hence from Ampere's law (since the circumference is *not* zero) the flux density *B* must be zero.

Similarly, if there is any field at path 3 it will also be tangent to the path at all points. Each turn of the winding passes *twice* through the area bounded by this path, carrying equal currents in opposite directions. The *net* current through the area is

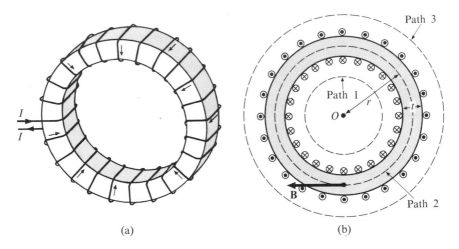

Fig. 32–10. (a) A toroidal winding. (b) Closed paths (dotted circles) used to compute the flux density B set up by a current in a toroidal winding. The field is very nearly zero at all points except those within the space enclosed by the windings.

therefore zero and hence $B = 0$ at all points of the path. The field of the toroid is therefore confined wholly to the space enclosed by the windings. The toroid may be thought of as a solenoid that has been bent into a circle.

Finally, consider path 2, a circle of radius r. Again by symmetry, the induction **B** is tangent to the path and the line integral of **B** equals $2\pi rB$. Each turn of the winding passes *once* through the area bounded by path 2, and the total current through the area is NI, where N is the number of turns in the winding. Then from Ampere's law,

$$2\pi rB = \mu_0 NI,$$

and

$$B = \frac{\mu_0}{2\pi} \cdot \frac{NI}{r}.$$

If the cross section of the toroid is sufficiently small, we can neglect variations in r and consider that $2\pi r$ is the circumferential length of the toroid and that $N/2\pi r$ is the number of turns per unit length, n. Then

$$B = \mu_0 nI,$$

as for a long solenoid.

We have again neglected the circumferential component of current and assumed that each turn of the windings is normal to the circumference. In an actual winding, the circumferential component of current gives rise to a magnetic field like that around a single turn of wire of radius r, carrying a current I.

3. *Field between parallel plates.* Figure 32–11 is a sectional view of two long parallel plates of width w. The plate on the left carries a current I toward the reader and that on the right carries an equal current away from the reader.

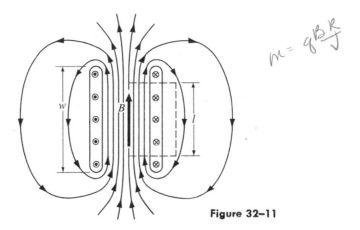

$\mu = q \frac{\mathcal{R}}{\delta} \vec{J}$

Figure 32-11

In the region between the plates and not too near their edges, the **B**-field is uniform. The field outside the plates is small, and becomes smaller as the width w is increased.

Let us apply Ampere's law to the dotted rectangle, and assume the field outside the plates to be zero. The line integral of **B** around the rectangle is Bl. If I is the total current in either plate, the current per unit width is I/w and the current through the rectangle is Il/w. Hence

$$Bl = \frac{\mu_0 Il}{w}, \qquad B = \frac{\mu_0 I}{w}. \tag{32-14}$$

We shall use this relation later, in developing the equation for the velocity of propagation of electromagnetic waves.

It is interesting to compare the nature of the magnetic field between two long current-carrying plates with the electric field between two large charged plates. Both fields are approximately uniform, the magnetic lines being parallel to the plates and the electric lines perpendicular. In the magnetic case $B = \mu_0(I/w)$, whereas in the electric case $E = (1/\epsilon_0)(Q/A)$.

32-7 Magnetic field of a displacement current   *NO*

Reference to Section 29-9 will call to mind that in a circuit containing a capacitor that is being charged or discharged, the *displacement* current I_D over any cross section between the capacitor plates is equal to the *conduction* current I_C in the leads. The concept of displacement current may appear of greater physical reality when it is pointed out that displacement currents set up magnetic fields in the same way as conduction currents. That is, in the expression for the magnetic field set up by a current element, the current I refers to the *total* current $I_C + I_D$, conduction current plus displacement current:

$$d\mathbf{B} = k'(I_C + I_D)\frac{d\mathbf{l} \times \hat{\mathbf{r}}}{r^2}. \tag{32-15}$$

In special cases, either I_C or I_D may be zero.

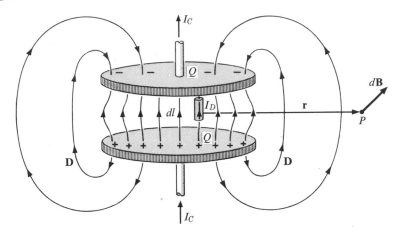

Figure 32–12

Figure 32–12 represents a pair of parallel plates, forming a portion of an electric circuit. The charge Q on the plates is increasing and hence the displacement $\mathbf{D}$ in the electric field of the plates is increasing also. The displacement current I_D in a filamentary element of length dl and cross-sectional area A equals $\dot{\mathbf{D}} \cdot \mathbf{A}$, and the magnetic field set up by this element at point P is

$$d\mathbf{B} = k'I_D \frac{d\mathbf{l} \times \hat{\mathbf{r}}}{r^2}. \tag{32–16}$$

Thus every portion of a circuit contributes to the magnetic field set up by the circuit, even though the circuit is not "closed" in the sense that every portion of it is a conductor in which there are moving charges. In other words, magnetic fields can be set up by *changing electric fields*, as well as by *moving electric charges*. We shall see later that the effect described here is basic to the propagation of an *electromagnetic wave*.

It should be pointed out that in the diagram of Fig. 32–12 the contributions to the **B**-field of *all* elements of displacement current sum to zero, so that the *resultant* **B**-field at any point is that due to conduction currents alone.

A necessary consequence of Eq. (32–15) is expressed by Ampere's law; that is, the line integral of **B** around a closed path equals μ_0 times the net current across any surface bounded by the path. We now see that the "net current" means *the conduction current plus the displacement current*, so the general form of Ampere's law is

$$\oint \mathbf{B} \cdot d\mathbf{s} = \mu_0(I_C + I_D). \tag{32–17}$$

EXAMPLE.   What is the flux density **B** in the region between the plates of a capacitor that is being charged?

Figure 32–13 represents a plane midway between the plates of the capacitor in Fig. 32–12. If the plates are circular, as in Fig. 32–12, then by symmetry the lines of induction are con-

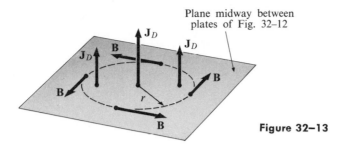

Plane midway between
plates of Fig. 32–12

Figure 32–13

centric circles and the line integral of **B** around a circular path of radius r reduces to $2\pi rB$. The displacement current density $\mathbf{J}_D = \dot{\mathbf{D}}$ at any point depends on the spacing of the capacitor plates, and without further information no specific values can be given. If r is less than the radius of the plates, the displacement current I_D across the shaded area is smaller than I_C because not *all* of the **D**-lines pass through the area. All we can say, then, is that at every radius r,

$$2\pi rB = \mu_0 I_D, \qquad B = \frac{\mu_0}{2\pi} \frac{I_D}{r}.$$

In the idealized case in which fringing fields are neglected, and r equals the radius of the plates, the displacement current equals the conduction current and

$$B = \frac{\mu_0}{2\pi} \frac{I_C}{r} = 2k' \frac{I_C}{r},$$

which is the same as the field at a distance r from an infinitely long straight conductor.

Problems

$$1 \frac{w}{m^2} = 1 \frac{n}{amp \cdot m}$$

$$k' = 10^{-7} \frac{n}{amp^2} = 10^{-7} \frac{w}{amp \cdot m}$$

$$\mu_0 = 4\pi k' = 12.57 \times 10^{-7} \frac{w}{amp \cdot m}$$

32–1. A long straight wire, carrying a current of 200 amp, runs through a cubical wooden box, entering and leaving through holes in the centers of opposite faces, as in Fig. 32–14. The length of each side of the box is 20 cm. Consider an element of the wire 1 cm long at the center of the box. Compute the magnitude of the magnetic induction ΔB produced by this element at the points lettered a, b, c, d, and e in Fig. 32–14. Points a, c, and d are at the centers of the faces of the cube, point b is at the midpoint of one edge, and point e is at a corner. Copy the figure and show by vectors the directions and relative magnitudes of the field vectors.

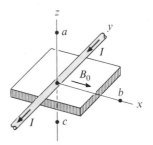

Figure 32–15

32–3. Figure 32–16 is an end view of two long parallel wires perpendicular to the xy-plane, each carrying a current I, but in opposite directions. (a) Copy the diagram, and show by vectors the **B**-field of each wire, and the resultant **B**-field, at point P. (b) Derive the expression for the magnitude of **B** at any point on the x-axis, in terms of the coordinate x of the point. (c) Construct a graph of the magnitude of **B** at any point on the x-axis. (d) At what value of x is B a maximum?

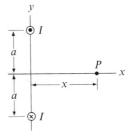

Figure 32–16

32–4. Same as Problem 32–3, except that the current in both wires is away from the reader.

32–5. Two long, straight, parallel wires are separated by a distance $2a$. If the wires carry equal currents in opposite directions, what is the flux density in the plane of the wires at a point (a) midway between them, and (b) at a distance a above the upper wire? If the wires carry equal currents in the

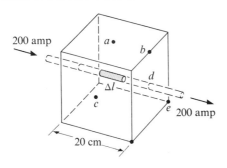

Figure 32–14

32–2. A long straight wire carries a current of 10 amp along the y-axis, as shown in Fig. 32–15. A uniform magnetic field whose flux density B_0 is 10^{-6} w/m² is directed parallel to the x-axis. What is the resultant magnetic field at the following points: (a) $x = 0, z = 2$ m, (b) $x = 2$ m, $z = 0$, (c) $x = 0, z = -0.5$ m?

same direction what is the flux density in the plane of the wires at a point (c) midway between them, and (d) at a distance a above the upper wire?

32–6. Two long, straight, parallel wires are 100 cm apart, as in Fig. 32–17. The upper wire carries a current I_1 of 6 amp into the plane of the paper. (a) What must be the magnitude and direction of the current I_2 for the resultant field at point P to be zero? (b) What is then the resultant field at Q? (c) At S?

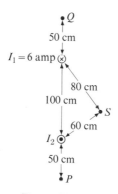

Figure 32–17

32–7. In Fig. 32–16 suppose a third long straight wire, parallel to the other two, passes through point P, and that each wire carries a current $I = 20$ amp. Let $a = 30$ cm and $x = 40$ cm. Find the magnitude and direction of the force per unit length on the third wire, (a) if the current in it is away from the reader, (b) if the current is toward the reader.

32–8. A long straight wire carries a current of 1.5 amp. An electron travels with a velocity of 5×10^6 cm/sec parallel to the wire, 10 cm from it, and in the same direction as the current. What force does the magnetic field of the current exert on the moving electron?

32–9. A long horizontal wire AB rests on the surface of a table. (See Fig. 32–18.) Another wire CD vertically above the first is 100 cm long and is free to slide up and down on the two vertical metal guides C

and D. The two wires are connected through the sliding contacts and carry a current of 50 amp. The mass of the wire CD is 0.05 gm/cm. To what equilibrium height will the wire CD rise, assuming the magnetic force on it to be due wholly to the current in the wire AB?

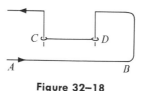

Figure 32–18

32–10. Two long parallel wires are hung by cords of 4 cm length from a common axis. The wires have a mass of 50 gm/m and carry the same current in opposite directions. What is the current if the cords hang at an angle of 6° with the vertical?

32–11. The long straight wire AB in Fig. 32–19 carries a current of 20 amp. The rectangular loop whose long edges are parallel to the wire carries a current of 10 amp. Find the magnitude and direction of the resultant force exerted on the loop by the magnetic field of the wire.

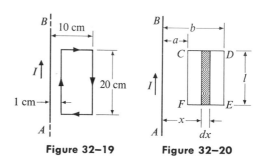

Figure 32–19   Figure 32–20

32–12. The long straight wire AB in Fig. 32–20 carries a constant current I. (a) What is the flux density at the shaded area at a perpendicular distance x from the wire? (b) What is the magnetic flux $d\Phi$ through the shaded area? (c) What is the flux Φ through the rectangular area $CDEF$, in terms of $I, l, a,$ and b?

32–13. Refer to Fig. 32–6. Sketch a graph of the magnitude of the flux density B on the axis of the coil, from $y = -3R$ to $y = +3R$.

32–14. Figure 32–21 is a sectional view of two circular coils of radius a, each wound with N turns of wire carrying a current I, circulating in the same direction in both coils. The coils are separated by a distance a equal to their radii. (a) Derive the expression for the flux density B at point P, midway between the coils. (b) Calculate the magnitude of $\mathbf{B}$ if $N = 100$ turns, $I = 5$ amp, $a = 30$ cm.

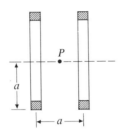

Figure 32–21

32–15. A closely wound coil has a diameter of 40 cm and carries a current of 2.5 amp. How many turns does it have if the magnetic induction at the center of the coil is 1.26×10^{-4} w/m²?

32–16. A thin disk of dielectric material, having a total charge $+Q$ distributed uniformly over its surface, and of radius a, rotates n times per second about an axis perpendicular to the surface of the disk and passing through its center. Find the magnetic induction at the center of the disk.

32–17. A solenoid is 30 cm long and is wound with two layers of wire. The inner layer consists of 300 turns, the outer layer of 250 turns. The current is 3 amp, in the same direction in both layers. What is the magnetic induction at a point near the center of the solenoid?

32–18. A wire of circular cross section and radius R carries a current I, uniformly distributed over its cross-sectional area. (a) In terms of I, R, and r_1, what is the current through a circular area of radius r_1, inside the wire? (b) Use Ampere's law to find the flux density B inside the wire, at a distance r_1 from the axis. (c) What is the flux density outside the wire, at a distance r_2 from the axis? (d) What would the flux density be at this distance if the current were concentrated in a very fine wire along the axis? (e) Sketch a graph of the magnitude of $\mathbf{B}$ as a function of r, from $r = 0$ to $r = 2R$.

32–19. A coaxial cable consists of a solid conductor of radius R_1, supported by insulating disks on the axis of a tube of inner radius R_2 and outer radius R_3. If the central conductor and the tube carry equal currents in opposite directions, find the magnetic flux density (a) at points outside the axial conductor but inside the tube, and (b) at points outside the tube.

CHAPTER 33

Induced Electromotive Force

33-1 Motional electromotive force

Figure 33–1(a) represents a conducting rod of length l in a uniform magnetic field of flux density $\mathbf{B}$, perpendicular to the plane of the diagram and directed away from the reader. The rod is moving toward the right with velocity $\mathbf{v}$, and a charge q within it is acted on by a force equal to $q\mathbf{v} \times \mathbf{B}$. Since this force is of nonelectrostatic origin, let us represent it by $\mathbf{F}_n$:

$$\mathbf{F}_n = q\mathbf{v} \times \mathbf{B}.$$

If, as in Chapter 28, we define the equivalent nonelectrostatic field $\mathbf{E}_n$ as the non-electrostatic force per unit charge, then

$$\mathbf{E}_n = \mathbf{v} \times \mathbf{B}.$$

As a result of this field, there is a displacement of the free charges within the rod until an electrostatic field $\mathbf{E}_e$ is set up such that at all points within the rod the magnitudes of $\mathbf{E}_e$ and $\mathbf{E}_n$ are equal, and the charges in the rod are in equilibrium. The resultant field $\mathbf{E}$ at all points in the rod is then zero.

Now suppose that the magnetic field is limited to the region within the dotted rectangle in Fig. 33–1(b). The left end of a closed conducting loop lies in the field and the loop is moving to the right with velocity $\mathbf{v}$. There will then be a nonelectrostatic field $\mathbf{E}_n = \mathbf{v} \times \mathbf{B}$ in the left end of the loop. (There will also be a field $\mathbf{E}_n$ in those portions of the sides of the loop that lie in the magnetic field, but it will be transverse to these sides.) It follows that there is an electromotive force $\mathcal{E}$ in the loop, given by

$$\mathcal{E} = \oint \mathbf{E}_n \cdot d\mathbf{s} = E_n l = vBl. \tag{33–1}$$

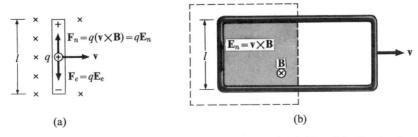

(a)   (b)

Fig. 33–1. (a) Conducting rod in a uniform magnetic field. (b) Conducting loop partially immersed in a magnetic field.

This emf is called a *motional electromotive force*. The field E_n is one example of the *non*electrostatic fields that were mentioned in Chapter 28.*

The left end of the loop can be considered as a *source* and the remainder of the loop as a conductor completing a closed circuit. As with every closed circuit containing a source, induced surface charges are developed on the loop such that the *resultant* field, $E = E_e + E_n$, is the same at all points within the material of the loop. These surface charges, and the field they set up, are not shown in Fig. 33-1(b). The field E_e makes no contribution to the emf, since its line integral is zero.

Equation (33-1) was derived for the special case in which v, B, and l are mutually perpendicular. The general expression for the motional emf $d\varepsilon$ in an element of a conductor of length dl is

$$d\varepsilon = E_n \cdot dl = (v \times B) \cdot dl. \qquad (33-2)$$

The motional emf in a circuit can be expressed in a different way. In a time dt, as the loop in Fig. 33-1(b) moves a distance $v\,dt$ to the right, the shaded area over which magnetic flux lines pass through the surface bounded by the loop *decreases* by an amount $lv\,dt$, and the flux through this surface changes by

$$d\Phi = -B(lv\,dt).$$

The *rate* of change of flux, $d\Phi/dt = \dot\Phi$, is

$$\dot\Phi = -vBl.$$

But vBl equals the emf ε, so

$$\varepsilon = -\dot\Phi. \qquad (33-3)$$

That is, *when a circuit moves in a magnetic field, the motional emf in the circuit is equal to the rate of decrease of flux across the area bounded by the circuit.* Any motional emf can be calculated either from Eq. (33-2) or Eq. (33-3).

Although Eq. (33-3) is often a convenient way of calculating the motional emf in a circuit, or the line integral of E_n, it provides no information regarding the magnitude and direction of the E_n-field itself, or the portion of a circuit in which there is such a field.

33-2 Induced electric fields

We now describe another process by which nonelectrostatic fields can be set up. It will be recalled (see Section 32-7) that an *electric* field which is changing with time sets up a *magnetic* field. The converse is also true: a *changing magnetic field* sets up an *electric field*. The electric intensity E in this field is related to the changing magnetic field that produces it in the same way that the magnetic flux density B is related to the changing electric field that produces it.

---

* The subscript n means that the field is *non*electrostatic. It does not refer to the normal component of E.

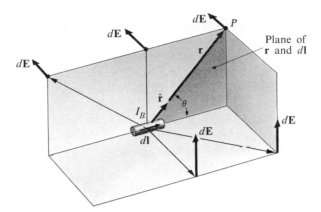

Fig. 33–2. Electric field at various points near a line element in which there is a changing magnetic field.

Let us review briefly the discussion in Section 32–7. If the displacement $\mathbf{D}$ in an element of length dl and cross-sectional area A is changing at a rate $\dot{\mathbf{D}}$, we call $\dot{\mathbf{D}}$ the *displacement current density* $\mathbf{J}_D$ in the element. The displacement *current* I_D is then

$$I_D = \mathbf{J}_D \cdot \mathbf{A} = \dot{\mathbf{D}} \cdot \mathbf{A} = \dot{\Psi}_D.$$

The element sets up a magnetic field given by the Biot law:

$$d\mathbf{B} = \frac{\mu_0}{4\pi} \frac{I_D \, d\mathbf{l} \times \hat{\mathbf{r}}}{r^2}. \qquad (33\text{–}4)$$

In an analogous manner, if the flux density $\mathbf{B}$ in an element of length dl and cross-sectional area A is changing at a rate $\dot{\mathbf{B}}$, we call $\dot{\mathbf{B}}$ the *magnetic displacement current density* $\mathbf{J}_B$ in the element. The *magnetic displacement current* I_B is then

$$I_B = \mathbf{J}_B \cdot \mathbf{A} = \dot{\mathbf{B}} \cdot \mathbf{A} = \dot{\Phi}. \qquad (33\text{–}5)$$

The element sets up an *electric* field given by an equation having the same form as the Biot law, but which has not received a name:

$$d\mathbf{E} = -\frac{1}{4\pi} \frac{I_B \, d\mathbf{l} \times \hat{\mathbf{r}}}{r^2}. \qquad (33\text{–}6)$$

Except for the coefficients $(\mu_0/4\pi)$ and $(-1/4\pi)$, Eqs. (33–4) and (33–6) have exactly the same form. Figure 33–2, which should be compared with Fig. 32–1, shows the vectors $d\mathbf{E}$ at a few points in the field of an element in which there is a magnetic displacement current $I_B \ (=\dot{\Phi})$. (Although Fig. 32–1 refers to the magnetic field set up by a *conduction* current I_C, it applies equally well to the magnetic field of a *displacement* current I_D.) The negative sign in Eq. (33–6) means that the vector $d\mathbf{E}$ is *opposite* to that of the vector product $d\mathbf{l} \times \hat{\mathbf{r}}$. Hence the vector $d\mathbf{E}$ at point P in Fig. 33–2 points to the left, while the vector $d\mathbf{B}$ at point P in Fig. 32–1 points to the right.

The electric field set up by a magnetic displacement current (or, what is the same thing, by a changing magnetic field) is called an *induced* electric field. Since it is not produced by bodies having an excess electric charge it is another example of a *non-electrostatic* field and can be written as $\mathbf{E}_n$.

Because of the identical forms of Eqs. (33–4) and (33–6), the *induced electric field* around any magnetic circuit in which the flux is changing is geometrically identical to the *magnetic* field around a current-carrying circuit of the same geometry. All of the results we have derived for *magnetic* fields around *electric* circuits can therefore be taken over without change (except for the difference in coefficients) for the *induced electric* fields around *magnetic* circuits.

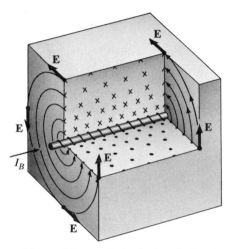

Fig. 33–3. Lines of force of the induced electric field around a long straight solenoid in which there is a magnetic displacement current $I_B = \dot{\Phi}$.

As an example, the induced *electric* field around a long slender solenoid in which the flux density is changing is like the *magnetic* field around a conductor having the same size and shape as the core of the solenoid, and in which there is a current. The field is shown in Fig. 33–3, which should be compared with Fig. 32–3. The lines of the induced electric field around the solenoid are (counterclockwise) circles concentric with the solenoid, and the magnitude of the electric intensity $\mathbf{E}_n$ at a radial distance r is

$$E_n = \frac{1}{2\pi}\frac{I_B}{r} = \frac{1}{2\pi}\frac{\dot{\Phi}}{r}.$$

Unlike the lines of force of an electro*static* field, which terminate on positive or negative charges, each line in Fig. 33–3 closes on itself.

As a second example, consider the conducting circuit of Fig. 33–4(a), in which there is a conduction current I_C. (Unless the ring is superconducting, a source of some sort, not shown, would be necessary to maintain the current.) The lines of the **B**-field around the circuit have the general shape shown.

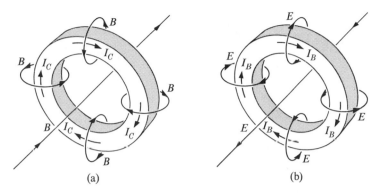

Fig. 33–4.   (a) Magnetic field around a current-carrying ring.   (b) Similarly shaped electric field about a toroid with a changing current in the windings.

Figure 33–4(b) represents the core of a toroid having the same size and shape as the circuit of part (a). (The windings of the toroid are not shown.) The current in the windings is changing in such a way that the magnetic displacement current I_B (or the changing flux $\dot{\Phi}$) is in the same direction as the current I_C in part (a). The core is then surrounded by an **E**-field in which the lines have the same shape as in part (a).

33–3 Induced electromotive force. The Faraday law

The **B**-field set up by a conduction or displacement current obeys Ampere's law:

$$\oint \mathbf{B} \cdot d\mathbf{s} = \mu_0(I_C + I_D) = \mu_0(I_C + \dot{\psi}_D). \tag{33–7}$$

Since induced electric fields are related to magnetic displacement currents (or changes in magnetic flux) in the same way that magnetic fields are related to conduction or displacement currents, they obey a law analogous to Ampere's law, namely,

$$\oint \mathbf{E}_n \cdot d\mathbf{s} = -I_B = -\dot{\Phi}. \tag{33–8}$$

Because there are no "free magnetic charges," a term corresponding to the term I_C in Eq. (33–7) does not appear in Eq. (33–8).

The line integral of $\mathbf{E}_n$ around a closed path, however, is by definition the electromotive force $\mathcal{E}$ in the path, so Eq. (33–8) can be written more compactly as

$$\mathcal{E} = -\dot{\Phi}. \tag{33–9}$$

That is, *the line integral of an induced electric field around a closed path, or the electromotive force $\mathcal{E}$ in the path, equals the time rate of change of magnetic flux across the area bounded by the path.*

Thus suppose that a conducting ring encircles the solenoid of Fig. 33–3, or links with the magnetic circuit of Fig. 33–4(b), as indicated in Fig. 33–5. It should be

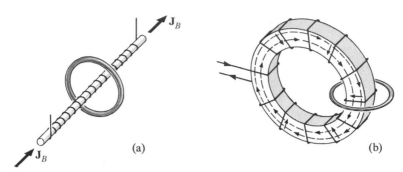

Fig. 33–5. An emf is induced in a ring surrounding (a) a straight solenoid and (b) a toroid, when the flux is changing.

evident from the general nature of the induced electric field that the line integral of this field around the loop will *not* be zero. That is, the induced field provides a driving force that sends free charges around the loop, and there is an *induced electromotive force* in the loop.

There is a common impression that induced emf's are always produced by the "cutting" of lines of magnetic flux. Although this expression is applicable to the *motional* emf in the loop of Fig. 33–1, where the left end of the moving loop does "cut" the lines of induction of the magnetic field, it obviously does not apply to the loops in Fig. 33–5, which not only are not *moving* in a magnetic field, but are not even *in* a magnetic field. We must distinguish between the nonelectrostatic field $\mathbf{E}_n = \mathbf{v} \times \mathbf{B}$ in a *moving* conductor, and the nonelectrostatic field $\mathbf{E}_n$ arising from a *changing magnetic field*, which can exist even in a stationary conductor. It is the former field that gives rise to the emf in the *rotating* armature of a generator, while the latter gives rise to the emf in the *stationary* windings of the secondary of a transformer.

The reader will have noticed that the emf arising from the motion of the boundary of a circuit in a magnetic field, and the emf in a *stationary* circuit, arising from an induced electric field, are both given by the same expression, $\mathcal{E} = -\dot{\Phi}$. Hence if we interpret the symbol $\dot{\Phi}$ to mean the *total* rate of change of flux, resulting from the motion of the circuit boundary or the time rate of change of flux density, or from both simultaneously, the emf can be found from the *single* equation

$$\mathcal{E} = -\dot{\Phi}. \qquad (33\text{--}10)$$

Although we have distinguished between a *motional* emf and an *induced* emf, it is customary to refer to either one as an "induced" emf. Hence we can say: *The induced electromotive force in a circuit equals the negative of the time rate of change of magnetic flux through the area bounded by the circuit.* The preceding statement is known as the *Faraday law*. It was discovered experimentally by Faraday in 1831, and complemented the discovery by Oersted that a magnetic field could be produced by an electric current.

Joseph Henry (1797–1878), an American who later became the first director of the Smithsonian Institution, had anticipated Faraday's discovery by about twelve months, but Faraday is usually assigned the credit, since he was the first to publish his results.

It should be noted, however, that although the emf in a circuit can always be calculated from the Faraday law if $\dot{\Phi}$ is known, this law in itself provides no information regarding the magnitude or location in the circuit of the nonelectrostatic fields. In other words, the *line integral* of $\mathbf{E}_n$ around the circuit, or the emf $\mathcal{E}$, can be found without any detailed information regarding $\mathbf{E}_n$ itself. A similar situation is encountered in mechanics, where the *work* of a force, or the *line integral* of the force, can be found if we know the change in kinetic energy of the body on which the force acts, without any detailed knowledge of the magnitude and direction of the force itself.

33–4 Lenz's law

H. F. E. Lenz (1804–1864) was a German scientist who, without knowledge of the work of Faraday and Henry, duplicated many of their discoveries nearly simultaneously. The law which goes by his name is a useful rule for predicting the direction of an induced current. It states:

The direction of an induced current is such as to oppose the cause producing it.

The "cause" of the current may be the motion of a conductor in a magnetic field, or it may be the change of flux through a stationary circuit. In the first case, the direction of the induced current in the moving conductor is such that the direction of the side-thrust exerted on the conductor by the magnetic field is opposite in direction to its motion. The motion of the conductor is therefore "opposed."

In the second case, the current sets up a magnetic field of its own which within the area bounded by the circuit is (a) *opposite* to the original field if this is *increasing*, but (b) is in the *same* direction as the original field if the latter is *decreasing*. Thus it is the *change in flux* through the circuit (not the flux itself) which is "opposed" by the induced current.

In order for there to be an induced current, we must have a closed circuit. If a conductor does not form a closed circuit, then we mentally complete the circuit between the ends of the conductor and use Lenz's law to determine the direction of the current. The polarity of the ends of the open-circuited conductor may then be deduced.

EXAMPLE 1.   The rectangular loop in Fig. 33–6, of length a and width b, is rotating with uniform angular velocity ω about the y-axis. The entire loop lies in a uniform, constant **B**-field, parallel to the z-axis. We wish to calculate the motional emf in the loop, both from Eq. (33–2) and Eq. (33–10).

The velocity v of the long sides of the loop is

$$v = \omega \frac{b}{2}.$$

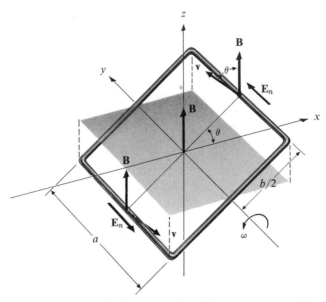

Fig. 33-6.   Rectangular loop rotating with constant angular velocity in a uniform magnetic field.

The direction of the motional field E_n ($= v \times B$) in each of the sides of length a is shown
in the diagram. Its magnitude is

$$E_n = vB \sin \theta = \omega \frac{b}{2} B \sin \theta.$$

The motional fields in the other two sides of the loop are transverse to these sides and contribute nothing to the emf. The line integral of E_n around the loop reduces to $2E_n a$, so

$$\varepsilon = \oint E_n \cdot ds = 2E_n a = \omega(ab)B \sin \theta.$$

The product ab equals the area A of the loop, and if the loop lies in the xy-plane at $t = 0$,
then $\theta = \omega t$. Hence

$$\varepsilon = \omega AB \sin \omega t. \tag{33-11}$$

The emf therefore varies sinusoidally with the time. The *maximum* emf ε_m, which occurs
when $\sin \omega t = 1$, is

$$\varepsilon_m = \omega AB,$$

so we can write Eq. (33-11) as

$$\varepsilon = \varepsilon_m \sin \omega t. \tag{33-12}$$

The rotating loop is the prototype of the *alternating current generator*, or *alternator;* we
say it develops a *sinusoidal alternating emf.*
     The emf is a maximum (in absolute value) when $\theta = 90°$ or $270°$ and the long sides are
moving at right angles to the field. The emf is zero when $\theta = 0$ or $180°$ and the long sides

are moving parallel to the field. The emf depends only on the *area A* of the loop and not on its shape.

We next compute the emf from Eq. (33–10). The flux through the loop equals that through its projected area on the *xy*-plane (shaded in Fig. 33–6).

$$\Phi = \mathbf{B} \cdot \mathbf{A} = BA \cos \theta = BA \cos \omega t.$$

Then

$$\dot{\Phi} = \frac{d\Phi}{dt} = -\omega BA \sin \omega t$$

and

$$\mathcal{E} = -\dot{\Phi} = \omega BA \sin \omega t,$$

in agreement with Eq. (33–11).

Notice that the maximum value of $\mathcal{E}$ occurs when $\theta = 90°$ and the flux through the loop is zero, and that $\mathcal{E} = 0$ when $\theta = 0$ and the flux is a maximum. That is, the emf depends not on the flux through the loop, but on its *rate of change*.

The rotating loop in Fig. 33–6 can be utilized as the source in an external circuit by making connections to *slip rings S, S*, which rotate with the loop as shown in Fig. 33–7(a). Stationary brushes bearing against the rings are connected to the output terminals *a* and *b*. The instantaneous terminal voltage v_{ab}, on open circuit, equals the instantaneous emf. Figure 33–7(b) is a graph of v_{ab} as a function of time.

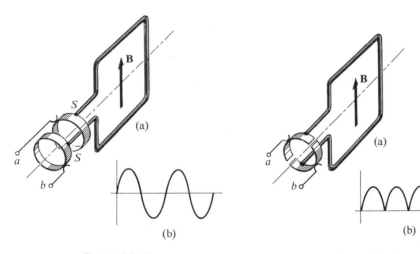

Figure 33–7   Figure 33–8

A terminal voltage that always has the same sign, although it fluctuates in magnitude, can be obtained by connecting the loop to a split ring or *commutator*, as in Fig. 33–8(a). At the position in which the emf reverses, the connections to the external circuit are interchanged. Figure 33–8(b) is a graph of the terminal voltage, and the device is the prototype of a DC generator.

Commercial DC generators have a large number of coils and commutator segments, and their terminal voltage is not only unidirectional but also practically constant. The connections are complicated, and a discussion of them properly belongs in a text on DC machinery.

EXAMPLE 2.   A disk of radius R, shown in Fig. 33–9, lies in the xz-plane and rotates with uniform angular velocity ω about the y-axis. The disk is in a uniform, constant **B**-field parallel to the y-axis. Consider a short portion of a narrow radial segment of the disk, of length dr. Its velocity is $v = \omega r$, and since **v** is at right angles to **B**, the motional field E_n in the segment is

$$E_n = vB = \omega r B.$$

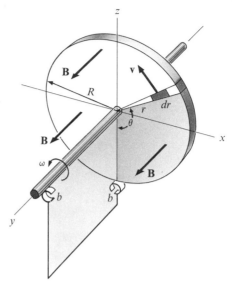

Figure 33–9

The direction of E_n is radially outward.
    The emf between center and rim is

$$\mathcal{E} = \int_0^R \mathbf{E}_n \cdot d\mathbf{r} = \omega B \int_0^R r\, dr = \omega B R^2/2.$$

All of the radial segments of the disk are in *parallel*, so the emf between center and rim equals that in any radial segment. The entire disk can therefore be considered a *source* for which the emf between center and rim equals $\omega B R^2/2$. The source can be included in a closed circuit by completing the circuit through sliding contacts or *brushes b, b*.
    The emf in such a disk was studied by Faraday, and the device is called a *Faraday disk dynamo*.
    To compute the emf from Eq. (33–10), we consider the circuit to be the periphery of the shaded areas in Fig. 33–9. The rectangular portion in the yz-plane is fixed. The area of the shaded sector in the xz-plane is $\frac{1}{2}R^2\theta$, and the flux through it is

$$\Phi = \tfrac{1}{2}BR^2\theta.$$

As the disk rotates, the shaded area increases and the magnitude of the emf in the circuit is

$$\mathcal{E} = \dot{\Phi} = \tfrac{1}{2}BR^2\dot{\theta} = \omega B R^2/2,$$

which agrees with the previous result.

EXAMPLE 3.   The long solenoid in Fig. 33–5(a) is wound with 1000 turns per meter, and the current in its windings is increasing at the rate of 100 amp/sec. The cross-sectional area of the solenoid is 4 cm² $= 4 \times 10^{-4}$ m².
    The flux Φ in the solenoid, not too near its ends, is

$$\Phi = BA = \mu_0 n I A.$$

The rate of change of flux, or the magnetic displacement current, is

$$I_B = \dot{\Phi} = \mu_0 n A \frac{dI}{dt}$$

$$= 4\pi \times 10^{-7}\ \frac{\text{w}}{\text{amp·m}} \times 1000\ \frac{\text{turns}}{\text{m}} \times 4 \times 10^{-4}\ \text{m}^2 \times 100\ \frac{\text{amp}}{\text{sec}}$$

$$= 16\pi \times 10^{-6}\ \text{w/sec}.$$

The induced electric field at a distance of $10 \text{ cm} = 10^{-1} \text{ m}$ from the axis of the solenoid is

$$E_n = \frac{1}{2\pi} \frac{I_B}{r} = \frac{1}{2\pi} \frac{\dot{\Phi}}{r}$$

$$= 8 \times 10^{-5} \frac{\text{w}}{\text{m·sec}} = 8 \times 10^{-5} \frac{\text{v}}{\text{m}} \cdot$$

The line integral of E_n around a circular path of this radius, or the emf in the path, is

$$\mathcal{E} = \oint \mathbf{E}_n \cdot d\mathbf{s} = E_n \cdot 2\pi r$$

$$= 16\pi \times 10^{-6} \text{ v} = 16\pi \ \mu\text{v}.$$

Hence if a circular loop of wire of radius 10 cm encircles the solenoid concentrically, an emf of $16\pi \ \mu\text{v}$ is induced in it.

The induced emf is of course equal to the rate of change of flux, $\dot{\Phi}$, and could have been computed directly from the Faraday law without calculating $\mathbf{E}_n$.

The same emf will be induced in a loop of *any* size and shape encircling the solenoid, since the line integral of $\mathbf{E}_n$ depends only on the rate of change of flux through the loop, and not on its size or shape.

If instead of a single turn of wire, the solenoid is encircled by a coil of N turns, the emf in the coil will be N times as great as that computed above.

33–5 The search coil

A useful experimental method of measuring the flux density at a point in a magnetic field will now be described. The apparatus consists of a ballistic galvanometer connected by flexible leads to the terminals of a small, closely wound coil called a *search coil* or a *snatch coil*. Assume first, for simplicity, that the search coil is placed with its plane perpendicular to a magnetic field of flux density B. If the area enclosed by the coil is A, the flux Φ through it is $\Phi = BA$. Now if the coil is quickly given a quarter-turn about one of its diameters so that its plane becomes parallel to the field, or if it is quickly snatched from its position to another where the field is known to be zero, the flux through it decreases rapidly from BA to zero. During the time that the flux is decreasing, an emf of short duration is induced in the coil and a "kick" is imparted to the ballistic galvanometer. The maximum deflection of the galvanometer is noted.

The galvanometer current at any instant is

$$i = \mathcal{E}/R,$$

where R is the combined resistance of galvanometer and search coil, $\mathcal{E}$ is the instantaneous induced emf, and i the instantaneous current. Since $i = \mathcal{E}/R$, the instantaneous current is

$$i = -\frac{N}{R} \frac{d\Phi}{dt},$$

and

$$\int_0^t i \, dt = -\frac{N}{R} \int_\Phi^0 d\Phi.$$

But
$$\int_0^t i\,dt = Q, \qquad \int_\Phi^0 d\Phi = -\Phi,$$

so
$$Q = \frac{N\Phi}{R}, \qquad \Phi = \frac{RQ}{N},$$

and
$$B = \frac{\Phi}{A} = \frac{RQ}{NA}. \tag{33–13}$$

The maximum deflection of a ballistic galvanometer is proportional to the quantity of charge displaced through it. (See Section 31–7.) Hence, if this proportionality constant is known, Q may be found, and from Q we can obtain Φ and B.

Strictly speaking, while this method gives correctly the total flux through the coil, it is only the *average* flux density over the area of the coil which is measured. However, if the area is sufficiently small, this approximates closely the flux density at, say, the center of the coil.

The preceding discussion assumed the plane of the coil to be initially perpendicular to the direction of the field. If one is "exploring" a field whose direction is not known in advance, the same apparatus may be used to find the direction by performing a series of experiments in which the coil is placed at a given point in the field in various orientations, and snatched out of the field from each orientation. The deflection of the galvanometer will be a maximum for the particular orientation in which the plane of the coil was perpendicular to the field. Thus the magnitude and direction of an unknown field can both be found by this method.

Since the search coil is permanently connected to the galvanometer terminals, the galvanometer will be highly damped and must either be calibrated with the search coil connected, or the corrections mentioned in the next section must be applied.

33–6 Galvanometer damping

Suppose a ballistic galvanometer is connected as in Fig. 33–10(a) to measure the quantity of charge on a capacitor. Let the switch S be closed momentarily, allowing the capacitor to discharge through the galvanometer, and then immediately opened. The surge of charge starts the galvanometer coil swinging and, since it is rotating in a magnetic field, an emf is induced in it. The current through it is zero, however, since the switch has been opened and there is no closed circuit. The motion of the coil is controlled solely by the suspension and friction. If the latter were entirely absent, the coil would oscillate indefinitely with angular harmonic motion.

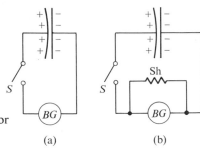

Fig. 33–10. Discharge of a capacitor though a ballistic galvanometer.

(a)   (b)

Now let the shunt resistor Sh in Fig. 33–10(b) be connected across the galvanometer terminals and the experiment repeated. The motion of the galvanometer will be affected for two reasons. First, a part of the discharge current of the capacitor will be bypassed by the shunt and the impulse imparted to the coil will be correspondingly less. Second, the galvanometer and shunt now form a closed circuit even when switch S is opened, so that there will now be a current in the swinging coil. The side-thrusts on this current give rise to a torque on the coil, and from Lenz's law the direction of this torque is such as to oppose the motion of the coil and aid in bringing it to rest. From the energy standpoint, a part of the kinetic energy of the swinging coil is dissipated as an I^2R "loss." The motion of the coil is *damped harmonic*.

It should be evident that the smaller the shunt resistance, the larger will be the induced current and the greater the damping. With a sufficiently small shunt resistance the motion ceases to be oscillatory; the galvanometer makes but one swing and returns slowly to its zero position. The particular resistance for which the motion just ceases to be oscillatory is called the *critical external damping resistance (CXDR)* and when shunted by its *CXDR* the galvanometer is said to be *critically damped*. With more resistance it is *underdamped* and with less it is *overdamped*.

Since the presence of damping reduces the maximum swing of a ballistic galvanometer, the simple theory in Section 31–7, which assumes that all of the initial kinetic energy of the coil is converted to potential energy of the suspension, must be extended if damping is present. The complete analysis shows that the quantity of charge displaced is still proportional to the maximum angle of swing, although with a modified proportionality constant. However, if the galvanometer is calibrated with the same external resistance as that with which it is to be used, the modified constant is automatically determined.

In many pivoted-coil instruments, such as portable ammeters and voltmeters, the necessary amount of damping is "built into" the moving coil, so to speak, by winding this coil on a light aluminum frame. The frame itself then forms a closed circuit and the currents induced in this circuit quickly bring the swinging coil to rest.

33–7 Eddy currents

Thus far we have considered only instances in which the currents resulting from induced emf's were confined to well-defined paths provided by the wires and apparatus of the external circuit. In many pieces of electrical equipment, however, one finds masses of metal moving in a magnetic field or located in a changing magnetic field, with the result that induced currents circulate throughout the volume of the metal. Because of their general circulatory nature, these are referred to as *eddy currents*.

Consider a disk rotating in a magnetic field perpendicular to the plane of the disk but confined to a limited portion of its area, as in Fig. 33–11(a). Element Ob is moving across the field and has an emf induced in it. Elements Oa and Oc are not in the field, but, in common with all other elements located outside the field, provide return conducting paths along which charges displaced along Ob can return from b to O. A general eddy current circulation is therefore set up in the disk somewhat as sketched in Fig. 33–11(b).

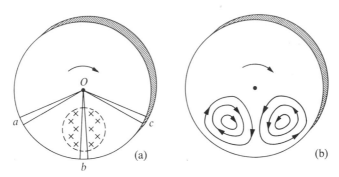

Fig. 33–11. Eddy currents in a rotating disk.

The currents in the neighborhood of radius Ob experience a side-thrust which opposes the motion of the disk, while the return currents, since they lie outside the field, do not experience such a thrust. The interaction between the eddy currents and the field therefore results in a braking action on the disk. The apparatus finds some technical applications and is known as an "eddy current brake."

As a second example of eddy currents, consider the core of an alternating current transformer, shown in Fig. 33–12. The alternating current in the transformer windings sets up an alternating flux within the core, and an induced emf develops in the secondary windings because of the continual change in flux through them. The iron core, however, is also a conductor, and any section such as that at AA can be thought of as a number of closed conducting circuits, one within the other. The flux through each of these circuits is continually changing, so that there is an eddy current circulation in the entire volume of the core, the lines of flow lying in planes perpendicular to the flux. These eddy currents are very undesirable both because of the energy which they dissipate, and because of the flux which they themselves set up.

In all actual transformers the eddy currents are nearly, although not completely, eliminated by the use of a *laminated* core, that is, one built up of thin sheets or laminae. The electrical resistance between the surfaces of the laminations (due either to a natural coating of oxide or to an insulating varnish) effectively confines the eddy

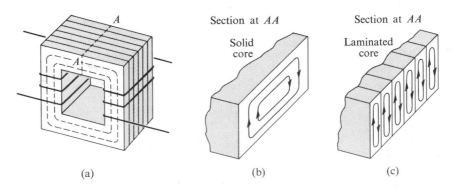

Fig. 33–12. Reduction of eddy currents by use of a laminated core.

currents to individual laminae. The resulting length of path is greatly increased, with consequent increase in resistance. Hence, although the induced emf is not altered, the currents and their heating effects are minimized.

In open-core transformers or spark coils a bundle of iron wires is often used as a core. Powdered iron formed into a core under high pressure is also used in small transformers where eddy-current loss must be kept to an absolute minimum.

33–8 The betatron

The *magnetic induction accelerator*, or *betatron*, is one of the family of machines designed for the purpose of accelerating charged particles to high energies. It was invented in 1941 by Donald W. Kerst of the University of Illinois. The following description refers to a machine constructed in 1945 by the General Electric Company, which could accelerate electrons to an energy of 100 million electron volts. Although the betatron has now been superseded by other machines (the Cambridge electron accelerator, completed in 1962, accelerates electrons to energies of 6.5 billion electron volts!) it is nevertheless of interest to us at this point because it affords an excellent example of the induced electric field set up by a varying magnetic field.

Figure 33–13 is a photograph of the toroidal vacuum tube of the 1945 machine. The tube is placed horizontally between the pole faces of a large electromagnet. (The magnet is not shown in the photograph.) Alternating current at a frequency of 60 cycles/sec is sent through the windings of the electromagnet so that the magnetic flux through the plane of the toroid reverses from a maximum in one direction to a maximum in the opposite direction in 1/120 sec. Electrons accelerated through

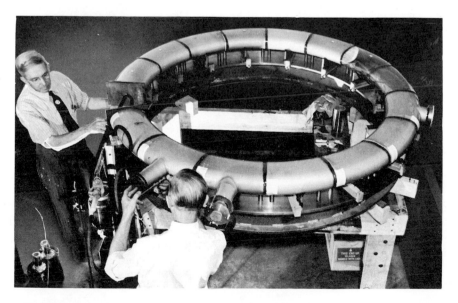

Fig. 33–13. Assembling the vacuum tube of the betatron. (Courtesy of General Electric Company.)

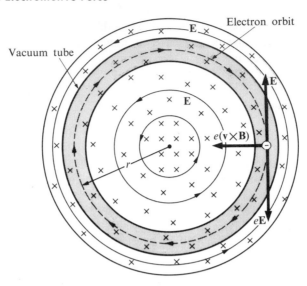

Fig. 33–14. An electron in the vacuum tube of a betatron is accelerated by the induced electric field **E** and forced to move in a circle by the magnetic field **B**.

approximately 50,000 volts by an electron gun are shot tangentially into the tube and are caused by the magnetic field to circle around within the tube in an orbit about 5 ft in diameter or about 5 m in circumference.

Figure 33–14 is a top view of the tube at an instant when the magnetic field **B** is into the plane of the diagram, and is increasing. For reasons that will be explained later, the magnetic flux density near the center is larger than that near the periphery. The field is symmetrical, however, so the lines of force of the induced electric field are *circles*, and the line integral of $\mathbf{E}_n$ around a circular path of radius r within the tube is

$$\varepsilon = \oint \mathbf{E}_n \cdot d\mathbf{s} = 2\pi r E_n.$$

By the Faraday law, this equals the rate of change of flux through the path and, disregarding algebraic signs,

$$2\pi r E_n = \dot{\Phi}, \qquad E_n = \frac{\dot{\Phi}}{2\pi r}.$$

Note that there would be an *electric* field at the vacuum tube, even if the *magnetic* field were limited to a small region near the axis. The values of $\dot{\Phi}$ and r are such that the electric field E_n is about 80 n/coul or 80 volts/m. The emf in the path is

$$\varepsilon = 2\pi r E_n = 80 \frac{\text{volts}}{\text{m}} \times 5\,\text{m} = 400\,\text{volts} = 400\,\text{j/coul}.$$

Because there *is* a magnetic field at the electron orbit, an electron is acted on by a centripetal force $e(\mathbf{v} \times \mathbf{B})$, which constrains it in a circular path. As the electron is accelerated by the E-field, its velocity **v** increases and a larger **B**-field is necessary to provide the requisite centripetal force. It is not difficult to show that if the value of **B** *at* the orbit is always just half as great as the *average* value of **B** over the area bounded by the orbit, the increasing **B**-field will be just large enough to provide the increasing centripetal force required because of the increasing velocity. Hence the value of **B** near the axis must be greater than that at the orbit, as mentioned earlier.

If a loop of wire were inserted in the field at the same place as the vacuum tube, the electrons in the wire would be acted on by the same electric field as those in the tube, and in each journey around the loop they would acquire 400 electron volts of energy. Their motion, however, would be a series of accelerations followed by decelerations as they collided with the fixed particles in the wire. At each collision they would give up the energy acquired in the interval following the preceding collision, and their average velocity would be only the relatively small drift velocity.

The electrons in the vacuum tube of the betatron, however, instead of being confined in a wire, are forced to move in a circle by the magnetic field. In each revolution they also acquire 400 electron volts of energy, but they can accelerate continuously without making collisions and the energy gain is *cumulative*. During the interval while the flux increases from zero to its maximum value an electron makes 250,000 revolutions and hence gains 250,000 × 400 ev or 100 million ev of energy.

The accelerator may be compared to an ordinary transformer with the secondary replaced by the electrons in the evacuated tube. The electrons are accelerated by the *induced electric field* set up by the *changing magnetic field*, and at the same time are forced to move in a circular orbit by the *existence* of the magnetic field.

At any desired stage in the accelerating process, an additional surge or pulse of current may be sent through the magnet coils. This causes the electrons to spiral out of their circular path and strike a target on which is mounted some material whose interaction with high-energy electrons we wish to study.

Note that the relativistic increase of mass with velocity, which prevents the acceleration of electrons to high velocities in a cyclotron, does not preclude their acceleration in this apparatus, since they gain their final energy in less than one cycle of the varying field and do not have to remain in phase with the field for a large number of cycles.

33–9 Mutual inductance

An emf is induced in a stationary circuit whenever the magnetic flux through the circuit varies with time. If the variation in flux is brought about by a varying current in a second circuit, it is convenient to express the induced emf in terms of the varying *current*, rather than in terms of the varying *flux*.

Figure 33–15 is a sectional view of two closely wound coils of wire. A current in coil 1 sets up a magnetic field, as indicated by the dotted lines, and some of these lines pass through coil 2. Let us represent the flux through coil 2, produced by a current i_1 in coil 1, by Φ_{21}. The *mutual inductance* M_{21} of the coils is defined as the ratio of the product $N_2\Phi_{21}$ to the current i_1, where N_2 is the number of turns in coil 2:

$$M_{21} = \frac{N_2\Phi_{21}}{i_1}, \quad \text{or} \quad N_2\Phi_{21} = M_{21}i_1. \tag{33–14}$$

The product $N_2\Phi_{21}$ is called the number of *flux linkages* with coil 2.

If no ferromagnetic materials are present, the flux Φ_{21} is directly proportional to the current i_1 and the mutual inductance is a constant, independent of i_1. Equation (33–14) defines the mutual inductance, however, whether or not M_{21} is a constant.

If the current i_1 varies with time,

$$N_2 \frac{d\Phi_{21}}{dt} = M_{21}\frac{di_1}{dt}.$$

The left side of this equation is the negative of the induced emf $\mathcal{E}_2$ in coil 2, so

$$\mathcal{E}_2 = -M_{21}\frac{di_1}{dt}. \qquad (33\text{–}15)$$

From this point of view, the mutual inductance can be considered as *the induced emf in coil 2, per unit rate of change of current in coil 1.*

It can be shown that the same emf is induced in either of two circuits between which there is mutual inductance, when the current in the other changes at a given rate. That is,

$$\frac{N_2\Phi_{21}}{i_1} = \frac{N_1\Phi_{12}}{i_2}.$$

We can therefore drop the subscripts from M_{21} and write

$$\mathcal{E}_2 = -M\frac{di_1}{dt},$$

$$\mathcal{E}_1 = -M\frac{di_2}{dt}.$$

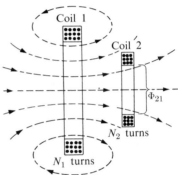

Fig. 33–15. A portion of the flux set up by a current in circuit 1 links with circuit 2.

The mksc unit of mutual inductance is 1 volt/(amp/sec). This is called 1 *henry*, in honor of Joseph Henry.

EXAMPLE. A long solenoid of length l and cross-sectional area A is closely wound with N_1 turns of wire. A small coil of N_2 turns surrounds it at its center, as in Fig. 33–16. A current I_1 in the solenoid sets up a **B**-field at its center, of magnitude

$$B = \frac{\mu_0 N_1 I_1}{l}$$

The flux through the central section is equal to BA, and since all of this flux links with the small coil the mutual inductance is

$$M = \frac{N_2\Phi_{21}}{I_1} = \frac{\mu_0 A N_1 N_2}{l}.$$

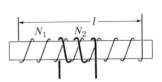

Figure 33–16

If $l = 0.50$ m, $A = 10$ cm^2 $= 10^{-3}$ m^2, $N_1 = 1000$ turns, $N_2 = 10$ turns,

$$M = \frac{4\pi \times 10^{-7} \times 10^{-3} \times 10^3 \times 10}{0.50}$$

$$\approx 25 \times 10^{-6} \text{ henry} \approx 25 \ \mu\text{h}.$$

33–10 Self-inductance

In the preceding section, the source of the magnetic field linking a circuit was independent of the circuit in which the induced emf appeared. But whenever there is a current in any circuit, this current sets up a magnetic field which itself links with the circuit and which varies when the current varies. Hence any circuit in which there is a varying current has induced in it an emf, because of the variation in its own magnetic field. Such an emf is called a *self-induced electromotive force*.

Suppose a circuit has N turns of wire and that a flux Φ passes through each turn, as in Fig. 33–17. The number of flux linkages per unit current is called the *self-inductance* of the circuit, L:

$$L = \frac{N\Phi}{i}. \tag{33–16}$$

The self-inductance of a circuit depends on its size, shape, number of turns, etc. It also depends on the magnetic properties of the material in which a magnetic field exists. For example, the self-inductance of a solenoid of given dimensions is much greater if it has an iron core than if it is in vacuum. If no *ferro*magnetic materials are present, the self-inductance is a constant, independent of the current, since then the flux density at any point is directly proportional to the current. When ferromagnetic materials are present, the self-inductance varies in a complicated way as the current varies, because of the variations in permeability. For simplicity, we shall consider only circuits of constant self-inductance.

Equation (33–16) can be written as

$$N\Phi = Li.$$

Differentiating both sides with respect to t gives

$$N\frac{d\Phi}{dt} = L\frac{di}{dt},$$

and since the self-induced emf ε is

$$\varepsilon = -N\frac{d\Phi}{dt},$$

it follows that

$$\varepsilon = -L\frac{di}{dt}. \tag{33–17}$$

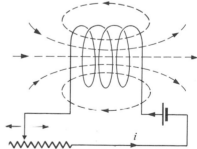

Fig. 33–17. A flux Φ linking a coil of N turns. When the current in the circuit changes, the flux changes also, and a self-induced emf appears in the circuit.

The self-inductance of a circuit is therefore *the self-induced emf per unit rate of change of current*. The mksc unit of self-inductance is 1 henry.

A circuit or part of a circuit which has inductance is called an *inductor*. An inductor is represented by the symbol ‑000‑ .

The direction of a self-induced (nonelectrostatic) field can be found from Lenz's law. We consider the "cause" of this field, and hence of the emf associated with it, to be the *changing current* in the conductor. If the current is *increasing*, the direction of the induced field is *opposite* to that of the current. If the current is *decreasing*, the induced field is in the *same* direction as the current. Thus it is the *change* in current, not the current itself, that is "opposed" by the induced field.

EXAMPLE.   An air-core toroid of cross-sectional area A and mean circumferential length l is closely wound with N turns of wire. The flux density in the toroid is

$$B = \frac{\mu_0 N I}{l}$$

and the flux is

$$\Phi = BA = \frac{\mu_0 N I A}{l}.$$

Since all of the flux links with each turn, the self-inductance is

$$L = \frac{N\Phi}{I} = \frac{\mu_0 N^2 A}{l}.$$

Thus if $N = 100$ turns, $A = 10 \text{ cm}^2 = 10^{-3} \text{ m}^2$, $l = 0.50 \text{ m}$,

$$L = \frac{4\pi \times 10^{-7} \times (100)^2 \times 10^{-3}}{0.50}$$

$$\approx 25 \times 10^{-6} \text{ henry.}$$

33–11 Energy associated with an inductor

Consider an inductor carrying a current i which is increasing at the rate di/dt. This changing current results in an emf $L(di/dt)$, so that power P is supplied to the inductor, where

$$P = \mathcal{E}i = Li\frac{di}{dt}.$$

The energy dW supplied in time dt is $P\,dt$, or

$$dW = Li\,di,$$

and the total energy supplied while the current increases from zero to I is

$$W = L\int_0^I i\,di = \tfrac{1}{2}LI^2. \tag{33–18}$$

After the current has reached its final steady value, $di/dt = 0$, and the power input is zero. The energy that has been supplied to the inductor is used to establish the magnetic field around the inductor, where it is "stored" as a form of potential energy so long as the current is maintained. When the circuit is opened the magnetic field collapses and this energy is returned to the circuit. It is this release of energy that maintains the arc often seen when a switch is opened in an inductive circuit.

Consider an inductor in the form of a closely wound toroid. From the preceding example, the self-inductance of the toroid is

$$L = \frac{\mu_0 N^2 A}{l},$$

and the energy stored in the toroid when the current in the windings is I is

$$W = \frac{1}{2} LI^2 = \frac{1}{2} \frac{\mu_0 N^2 A}{l} I^2.$$

We can think of this energy as localized in the volume enclosed by the windings, equal to lA. The energy per unit volume is then

$$\frac{W}{lA} = \frac{1}{2} \mu_0 \frac{N^2 I^2}{l^2}.$$

But $N^2 I^2 / l^2 = B^2 / \mu_0^2$, so

$$\frac{W}{lA} = \frac{1}{2} \frac{B^2}{\mu_0}, \tag{33-19}$$

which is the analogue of the expression for the energy per unit volume in the electric field of an air capacitor, $\frac{1}{2}\epsilon_0 E^2$.

33-12 The R-L circuit

Every inductor necessarily has some resistance (unless its windings are super-conducting). To distinguish between the effects of the resistance R and the self-inductance L, we represent the inductor as in Fig. 33-18, replacing it with an ideal resistanceless inductor in series with a noninductive resistor. The same diagram can also represent a resistor in series with an inductor, in which case R is the *total* resistance of the combination. By means of the *dpdt* switch, the R-L circuit may be connected to a source of constant terminal voltage V, or it may be shorted by the conductor across the lower switch terminals.

Suppose the switch in the diagram is suddenly closed in the "up" position. Then

$$V = V_{ab} = v_{ac} + v_{cb} = iR + L\frac{di}{dt} = \text{constant},$$

$$\frac{di}{dt} = \frac{V}{L} - \frac{R}{L} i. \tag{33-20}$$

When the circuit is first closed, $i = 0$ and the initial rate of increase of current is

$$\left(\frac{di}{dt}\right)_0 = \frac{V}{L}.$$

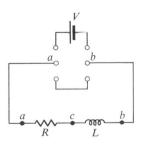

Figure 33-18

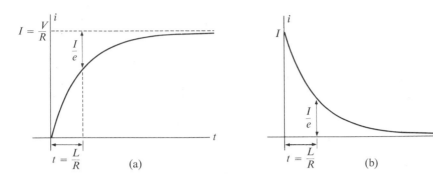

Fig. 33–19. (a) Growth of current in a circuit containing inductance and resistance. (b) Decay of current in a circuit containing inductance and resistance.

As the current increases, the term Ri/L increases and di/dt decreases. Eventually, the current becomes constant, $di/dt = 0$, and

$$i = \frac{V}{R} = I.$$

The final current I is the same as if the inductor were not present.

To find the expression for the current as a function of time, collect terms in i in Eq. (33–20) and integrate. The result is

$$i = I(1 - e^{-Rt/L}). \qquad (33\text{–}21)$$

The current therefore increases in the same way as does the charge on a capacitor in an R-C circuit. (See Section 29–7.) The time constant of an R-L circuit is L/R and the half life is $(L/R)\ln 2$. Figure 33–19 is a graph of i versus t.

If a current I_0 is established in the circuit of Fig. 33–18, and the switch is very quickly thrown to the "down" position, the current decreases exponentially according to the relation

$$i = I_0 e^{-Rt/L}, \qquad (33\text{–}22)$$

which is plotted in Fig. 33–19(b).

The energy necessary to maintain the current is provided by the energy stored in the magnetic field of the inductor.

33–13 The L-C circuit

The behavior of an R-C circuit was discussed in Section 29–7, and that of an R-L circuit in Section 33–12. We now consider the L-C circuit shown in Fig. 33–20, a resistanceless inductor connected between the terminals of a charged capacitor. At the instant connections are made, in Fig. 33–20(a), the capacitor starts to discharge through the inductor. At a later instant, represented in Fig. 33–20(b), the capacitor has completely discharged and the potential difference between its terminals (and those of the inductor) has decreased to zero. The current in the inductor has meanwhile established a magnetic field in the space around it. This magnetic field now decreases,

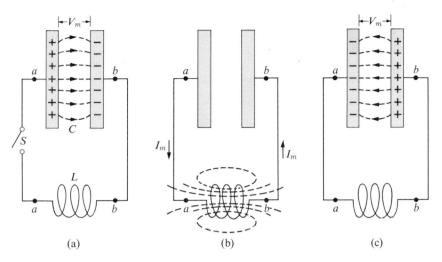

Fig. 33–20. Energy transfer between electric and magnetic fields in an oscillating *L-C* circuit.

inducing an emf in the inductor in the same direction as the current. The current therefore persists, although with diminishing magnitude, until the magnetic field has disappeared and the capacitor has been charged in the opposite sense to its initial polarity, as in Fig. 33–20(c). The process now repeats itself in the reversed direction, and in the absence of energy losses the charges on the capacitor will surge back and forth indefinitely. This process is called an *electrical oscillation*.

The frequency of the electrical oscillations of a circuit containing inductance and capacitance only may be calculated in exactly the same way as the frequency of oscillation of a body suspended from a spring. (See Chapter 11.)

In the mechanical problem, a body of mass m is attached to a spring of force constant k. Because the system is conservative, the sum of the kinetic and elastic potential energies is constant and is equal to the elastic potential energy when the body has its maximum displacement A. The steps in the derivation of the equation of motion are given in the left column of Table 33–1. The motion is simple harmonic, with an angular frequency ω given by

$$\omega = \sqrt{k/m}.$$

The electrical circuit in Fig. 33–20 is also a conservative system, provided the resistance of the circuit is zero. The sum of the energy associated with the magnetic field of the inductor, $\frac{1}{2}Li^2$, and the energy associated with the electric field of the capacitor, $\frac{1}{2}(q^2/C)$, is constant and equal to the energy of the capacitor when it has its maximum charge Q. The way in which the charge on the capacitor varies with time is given in the right column of Table 33–1. The angular frequency of the electrical oscillations is

$$\omega = \sqrt{1/LC}. \tag{33–23}$$

This is called the *natural frequency* of the *L-C* circuit.

TABLE 33–1

OSCILLATION OF A MASS ON A SPRING COMPARED WITH THE
ELECTRICAL OSCILLATION IN AN *L-C* CIRCUIT

Mass on a spring	Circuit containing inductance and capacitance
$\frac{1}{2}mv^2 + \frac{1}{2}kx^2 = \frac{1}{2}kA^2$	$\frac{1}{2}Li^2 + \frac{1}{2}\frac{q^2}{C} = \frac{1}{2}\frac{Q^2}{C}$
$v = \sqrt{\frac{k}{m}}\sqrt{A^2 - x^2}$	$i = \sqrt{\frac{1}{LC}}\sqrt{Q^2 - q^2}$
$v = \frac{dx}{dt}$	$i = \frac{dq}{dt}$
$\int \frac{dx}{\sqrt{A^2 - x^2}} = \sqrt{\frac{k}{m}}\int dt$	$\int \frac{dq}{\sqrt{Q^2 - q^2}} = \sqrt{\frac{1}{LC}}\int dt$
$\sin^{-1}\frac{x}{A} = \sqrt{\frac{k}{m}}\,t$	$\sin^{-1}\frac{q}{Q} = \sqrt{\frac{1}{LC}}\,t$
$x = A\sin\sqrt{\frac{k}{m}}\,t$	$q = Q\sin\sqrt{\frac{1}{LC}}\,t$
$\omega = 2\pi f = \sqrt{\frac{k}{m}}$	$\omega = 2\pi f = \sqrt{\frac{1}{LC}}$
$x = A\sin\omega t$	$q = Q\sin\omega t$

The equations in Table 33–1 correspond to setting $t = 0$ at the instant shown in part (b) of Fig. 33–20, so that $q = 0$ when $t = 0$. If we set $t = 0$ at the instant shown in part (a), then $q = Q$ when $t = 0$ and

$$q = Q\cos\omega t.$$

33–14 The R-L-C circuit

Every real circuit contains at least one turn and hence has some *self-inductance*. There is also some *capacitance* between those portions of a circuit at different potentials, and every real conductor (except a superconductor) has some *resistance*. (There is an energy loss by *radiation* from an oscillating circuit even if it has zero resistance.) We therefore consider next two examples of *R-L-C* circuits, in which all three types of circuit elements are present.

Suppose an inductor of self-inductance L and resistance R is connected across the terminals of a capacitor. If the capacitor is initially charged, it starts to discharge at the instant the connections are made but, because of i^2R losses in the resistor, the energy of the inductor, when the capacitor is completely discharged, is less than the

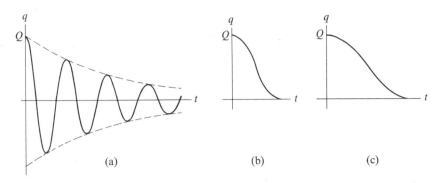

Fig. 33–21. Graphs of q versus t in an *R-L-C* circuit. (a) Small damping. (b) Critically damped. (c) Overdamped.

original energy of the capacitor. In the same way, the energy of the capacitor when the magnetic field has collapsed is still smaller, and so on.

If the resistance R is relatively small, the circuit oscillates, but with *damped harmonic motion* as illustrated in Fig. 33–21(a). As R is increased, the oscillations die out more rapidly. At a sufficiently large value of R the circuit no longer oscillates and is said to be *critically damped*, as in Fig. 33–21(b). For still larger resistances it is *overdamped*, as in Fig. 33–21(c).

With the proper electronic circuitry, energy can be fed *into* an *R-L-C* circuit at the same rate as that at which it is dissipated by i^2R or radiation losses. In effect, a *negative resistance* is inserted in the circuit so that its total resistance is zero. The circuit then oscillates with *sustained* oscillations, as does the idealized circuit discussed in Section 33–13.

As a second example, we consider the process of charging a capacitor, which was discussed in Section 29–7 on the assumption that the circuit was a pure *R-C* circuit. We now take into account the self-inductance L which, although it may be small, is always present. We shall assume that the resistance R is sufficiently large so that the circuit is overdamped. Then instead of the circuit of Fig. 29–10 we have that of Fig. 33–22.

Let i and q represent the current and the charge on the capacitor at some instant after the switch is closed. Then

$$V_{ab} = iR + L\frac{di}{dt} + \frac{q}{C} = \text{constant.}$$

When this equation is differentiated with respect to t, and dq/dt is replaced with i, we get

$$R\frac{di}{dt} + L\frac{d^2i}{dt^2} + \frac{i}{C} = 0,$$

or

$$\frac{d^2i}{dt^2} + \frac{R}{L}\frac{di}{dt} + \frac{1}{LC}i = 0. \qquad (33\text{–}24)$$

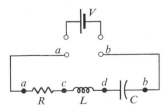

Figure 33–22

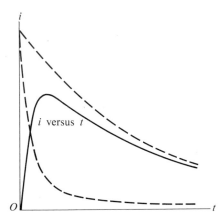

Fig. 33–23. The solid curve represents the charging current of a capacitor in an *R-L-C* circuit. It should be compared with Fig. 29–11, which is the graph when the self-inductance *L* of the circuit is neglected.

Thus when *all* of the electrical properties of a circuit are taken into account, the current as a function of time is the solution of a *second-order* differential equation.* We shall not give the complete solution, but only state that the current is given by the *difference* between two exponential curves such as those shown by dotted lines in Fig. 33–23. It will be seen that the current does not change discontinuously from zero to a finite value, as in Fig. 29–11(a) where the effect of self-inductance was ignored, but increases continuously from zero to a maximum and then decreases. In many practical cases, however, the self-inductance of a circuit is so small that the analysis in Section 29–7 is a satisfactory approximation.

----

* A more rigorous mathematical treatment shows that even when *L* is neglected, we still must solve a second-order differential equation. Thus in Section 29–7, if we write the basic equation, Eq. (29–7), as

$$V_{ab} = R\frac{dq}{dt} + \frac{q}{C},$$

and differentiate with respect to *t*, we get

$$\frac{d^2q}{dt^2} + \frac{1}{RC}\frac{dq}{dt} = 0$$

as the equation to be solved for $q(t)$.

Problems

33–1. In Fig. 33–1(a), let $l = 1.5\,\mathrm{m}$, $B = 0.5\,\mathrm{w/m^2}$, $v = 4\,\mathrm{m/sec}$. (a) Find the magnitude and direction of the equivalent nonelectrostatic field $\mathbf{E}_n$ in the rod. (b) Find the magnitude and direction of the electrostatic field $\mathbf{E}_e$ in the rod. (c) What is the motional emf in the rod? (d) What is the potential difference between its terminals? Which end is at the higher potential?

33–2. The cube in Fig. 33–24, one meter on a side, is in a uniform magnetic field of flux density $0.2\,\mathrm{w/m^2}$, directed along the y-axis. Wires A, C, and D move in the directions indicated, each with a velocity of $50\,\mathrm{cm/sec}$. (a) What is the magnitude of the equivalent nonelectrostatic field $\mathbf{E}_n$ in each wire? (b) What is the motional emf in each wire? (c) What is the potential difference between the terminals of each?

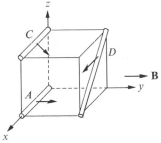

Figure 33–24

33–3. In Fig. 33–1(b), let the loop be a square 1.5 m on a side, and let $B = 0.5\,\mathrm{w/m^2}$, $v = 4\,\mathrm{m/sec}$, and let the resistance of the loop be 0.2 ohm. (a) Find the magnitude and direction of the equivalent nonelectrostatic field $\mathbf{E}_n$ in the left end of the loop. (b) Find the motional emf in the loop. (c) Find the current in the loop. (d) Find the electrostatic field $\mathbf{E}_e$ in the left end of the loop, and in the remainder of the loop. (e) Find the potential difference between the upper and lower left-hand corners of the loop. (f) Find the magnitude and direction of the external force $\mathbf{F}$ required to maintain

the loop in motion with constant velocity. (g) Compare the rate at which mechanical work is done by this force with the rate of dissipation of energy in the loop.

33–4. A square loop of wire is moved at constant velocity v across a uniform magnetic field confined to a square region whose sides are twice the length of those of the square loop. (See Fig. 33–25.) (a) Sketch a graph of the external force F needed to move the loop at constant velocity, as a function of the distance x, from $x = -2l$ to $x = +2l$. (b) Sketch a graph of the induced current in the loop as a function of x, plotting clockwise currents upward and counterclockwise currents downward.

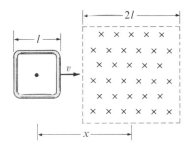

Figure 33–25

33–5. The long rectangular loop in Fig. 33–26, of width l, mass m, and resistance R, starts from rest in the position shown and is acted on by a constant force F. At all points to the right of the dotted line there is a uniform magnetic field of flux density $\mathbf{B}$, perpendicular to the plane of the diagram. (a) Sketch a graph of the velocity of the loop as a function of time. (b) Find the terminal velocity. (c) Derive the equation for the velocity as a function of time.

Figure 33–26

33–6. A slender rod one meter long rotates about an axis through one end and perpendicular to the rod, with an angular velocity of 2 rev/sec. The plane of rotation of the rod is perpendicular to a uniform magnetic field of flux density 0.5 w/m². (a) What are the magnitude and direction of the equivalent nonelectrostatic field in the rod, at its mid point? (b) What is the induced emf in the rod? (c) What is the potential difference between its terminals?

33–7. The rectangular loop in Fig. 33–27, of area A and resistance R, rotates at uniform angular velocity ω about the y-axis. The loop lies in a uniform magnetic field of flux density $\mathbf{B}$ in the direction of the x-axis. Sketch the following graphs: (a) the flux Φ through the loop as a function of time (let $t = 0$ in the position shown in Fig. 33–27); (b) the rate of change of flux, $\dot{\Phi}$; (c) the induced emf in the loop; (d) the torque Γ needed to keep the loop rotating at constant angular velocity; (e) the induced emf if the angular velocity is doubled. (Neglect the self-inductance of the loop.)

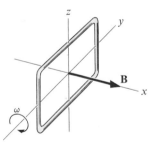

Figure 33–27

33–8. In Problem 33–7 and Fig. 33–27, let $A = 400$ cm², $R = 2$ ohms, $\omega = 10$ rad/sec, $B = 0.5$ w/m². Find (a) the maximum flux through the loop, (b) the maximum induced emf, (c) the maximum torque. (d) Show that the work of the external torque in one revolution is equal to energy dissipated in the loop.

33–9. Suppose the loop in Fig. 33–27 is (a) rotated about the z-axis; (b) rotated about the x-axis; (c) rotated about an edge parallel to the y-axis. What is the maximum induced emf in each case if the angular velocity is the same as in Problem 33–8?

33–10. A flexible circular loop 10 cm in diameter lies in a magnetic field of flux density 1.2 w/m², directed into the plane of the diagram in Fig. 33–28. The loop is pulled at the points indicated by the arrows, forming a loop of zero area in 0.2 sec. (a) Find the induced emf in the circuit. (b) What is the direction of the current in R?

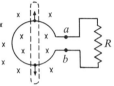

Figure 33–28

33–11. The flux density within a long, straight solenoid of circular cross section and radius R is increasing at a rate $\dot{B}$. (a) What is the magnetic displacement current through a circle of radius r_1 inside the solenoid, normal to the axis of the solenoid, and with center on the solenoid axis? (b) Find the induced electric field $\mathbf{E}_n$ inside the solenoid, at a distance r_1 from its axis. Show the direction of this field in a diagram. (c) What is the induced electric field *outside* the solenoid, at a distance r_2 from the axis? (d) Sketch a graph of the magnitude of $\mathbf{E}_n$ as a function of the distance r from the axis, from $r = 0$ to $r = 2R$. Compare with part (e) of Problem 32–18. (e) What is the induced emf in a circular turn of radius $R/2$? (f) Of radius R? (g) Of radius $2R$?

33–12. A long, straight solenoid of cross-sectional area 6 cm² is wound with 10 turns of wire per centimeter, and the windings carry a current of 0.25 amp. A secondary winding of 2 turns encircles the solenoid. When the primary circuit is opened, the magnetic field of the solenoid becomes zero in 0.05 sec. What is the average induced emf in the secondary?

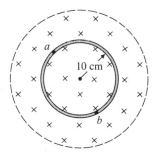

Figure 33–29

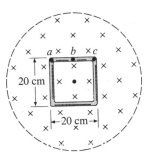

Figure 33–30

33–13. The flux density B at all points within the dotted circle of Fig. 33–29 equals 0.5 w/m². It is directed into the plane of the diagram and is decreasing at the rate of 0.1 (w/m²)/sec. (a) What is the shape of the lines of force of the induced E_n-field in Fig. 33–29, within the dotted circle? (b) What are the magnitude and direction of this field at any point of the circular conducting ring of radius 10 cm, and what is the emf in the ring? (c) What is the current in the ring, if its resistance is 2 ohms? (d) What is the potential difference between points a and b of the ring? (e) How do you reconcile your answers to (c) and (d)? (f) If the ring is cut at some point and the ends separated slightly, what will be the potential difference between the ends?

33–14. A square conducting loop, 20 cm on a side, is placed in the same magnetic field as in Problem 33–13 (see Fig. 33–30). (a) Copy Fig. 33–30, and show by vectors the directions and relative magnitudes of the induced electric field E_n at points a, b, and c. (b) Prove that the component of E_n along the loop has the same value at every point of the loop and is equal to that at the ring of Fig. 33–29. (c) What is the current in the loop, if its resistance is 2 ohms? (d) What is the potential difference between points a and b?

33–15. A square conducting loop, 20 cm on a side, is placed in the same magnetic field as in Problem 33–13 with side ac along a diameter and with point b at the center of the field. (See Fig. 33–31.) (a) Copy Fig.

33–31, and show by vectors the directions and relative magnitudes of the induced electric field E_n at the lettered points. (b) What is the induced emf in side ac? (c) What is the induced emf in the loop? (d) What is the current in the loop, if its resistance is 2 ohms? (e) What is the potential difference between points a and c? Which is the higher potential?

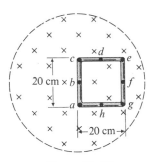

Figure 33–31

33–16. (a) Find the induced field E_n in each side of the square loop in Problem 33–15 and Fig. 33–31. (b) Find the induced emf in each side. (c) Find the electro*static* field E_e in each side. (d) Find the potential differences V_{ac}, V_{ce}, V_{eg}, and V_{ga}. What should be the sum of these potential differences?

33–17. (a) What is the direction of the drift velocity of an electron at point b in the wire loop of Fig. 33–31? (b) What would be the direction of the drift velocity if the loop were at the left side of the center line instead of at the right side? (c) What would be the direction of the force on an electron if it were at rest at the center of the magnetic field, with no wire loop present? (d) How do you reconcile the answers to (a), (b), and (c)?

33–18. The magnetic flux in a toroid of small cross-sectional area and radius R is increasing at a constant rate $\dot{\Phi}$. (a) What are the magnitude and direction of the induced $\mathbf{E}_n$-field at a point on the axis of the toroid at a distance x from its center? (See Section 32–4 for the corresponding expression for the $\mathbf{B}$-field at a point on the axis of a circular turn of wire carrying a constant current.) (b) Sketch a graph of the magnitude of $\mathbf{E}_n$ as a function of x. (c) Evaluate $\int_{-\infty}^{+\infty} E_n \, dx$ to find the induced emf in a wire that extends along the axis of the toroid from $x = -\infty$ to $x = +\infty$. (d) If the ends of the wire are joined by a conductor very far from the toroid, what is the induced emf in this circuit? (e) What is the induced emf in a ring that links the toroid closely, like that in Fig. 33–5?

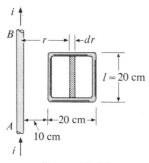

Figure 33–32

33–19. The current in the wire AB of Fig. 33–32 is upward, and is increasing steadily at the rate of 2 amp/sec. (a) At an instant when the current is i, what are the magnitude and direction of the flux density $\mathbf{B}$ at a distance r from the wire? (b) What is the flux $d\Phi$ through the narrow shaded strip? (c) What is the total flux through the square loop of wire, 20 cm on

a side? (d) What is the induced emf in the loop?

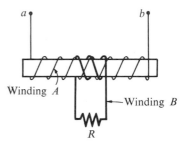

Figure 33–33

33–20. A cardboard tube is wound with two windings of insulated wire, as in Fig. 33–33. Terminals a and b of winding A may be connected to a battery through a reversing switch.

State whether the induced current in the resistor R is from left to right, or from right to left, in the following circumstances: (a) the current in winding A is from a to b and is increasing; (b) the current is from b to a and is decreasing; (c) the current is from b to a and is increasing.

33–21. Using Lenz's law, determine the direction of the current in resistor ab of Fig. 33–34 when (a) switch S is opened, (b) coil B is brought closer to coil A, (c) the resistance of R is decreased.

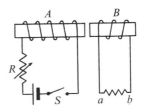

Figure 33–34

33–22. The cross-sectional area of a closely wound search coil having 20 turns is 1.5 cm^2 and its resistance is 4 ohms. The coil is connected through leads of negligible resistance to a ballistic galvanometer of resistance 16 ohms. Find the quantity of charge displaced through the galvanometer when the coil is pulled quickly out of a region where $B = 1.8$ w/m^2 to a point where the magnetic field is zero. The plane of the coil, when in the field, made an angle of 90° with the magnetic induction.

33–23. A solenoid 50 cm long and 8 cm in diameter is wound with 500 turns. A closely wound coil of 20 turns of insulated wire surrounds the solenoid at its midpoint, and the terminals of the coil are connected to a ballistic galvanometer. The combined resistance of coil, galvanometer, and leads is 25 ohms. (a) Find the quantity of charge displaced through the galvanometer when the current in the solenoid is quickly decreased from 3 amp to 1 amp. (b) Draw a sketch of the apparatus, showing clearly the directions of winding of the solenoid and coil, and of the current in the solenoid. What is the direction of the current in the coil when the solenoid current is decreased?

33–24. A closely wound search coil has an area of 4 cm^2, 160 turns, and a resistance of 50 ohms. It is connected to a ballistic galvanometer whose resistance is 30 ohms. When the coil is rotated quickly from a position parallel to a uniform magnetic field to one perpendicular to the field, the galvanometer indicates a charge of 4×10^{-5} coul. What is the flux density of the field?

33–25. The orbit of an electron in a betatron is a circle of radius R. Suppose the electron is revolving in this orbit with a tangential velocity v. (a) What flux density is required to maintain the electron in this orbit if the magnitude of its velocity is constant? (b) If the flux density is uniform over the plane of the orbit, and is increasing at a rate dB/dt, what is the equivalent voltage accelerating the electron in each revolution?

33–26. In the diagram of the toroidal tube of the betatron, Fig. 33–14, a magnetic field is directed into the plane of the diagram and is increasing. An electron is moving clockwise. (a) Show that the emf induced around the electron's orbit is such as to accelerate the electron. (b) Show

that the increasing radial force on the electron due to the magnetic field tends to prevent the electron from going to larger orbits.

33–27. A coaxial cable consists of a small solid conductor of radius r_a supported by insulating disks on the axis of a thin-walled tube of inner radius r_b. Show that the self-inductance of a length l of the cable is

$$ L = l \frac{\mu_0}{2\pi} \ln \frac{r_b}{r_a}. $$

Assume the inner and outer conductors to carry equal currents in opposite directions. (*Hint:* Use Ampere's law to find the flux density at any point in the space between the conductors. Write the expression for the flux $d\Phi$ through a narrow strip of length l parallel to the axis, of width dr, at a distance r from the axis of the cable and lying in a plane containing the axis. Integrate to find the total flux linking a current i in the central conductor.)

33–28. (a) Show that the two expressions for self-inductance, namely,

$$ \frac{N\Phi}{i} \quad \text{and} \quad \frac{\mathcal{E}}{di/dt}, $$

have the same units. (b) Show that L/R and RC both have the units of time. (c) Show that 1 weber per second equals 1 volt.

33–29. The current in a resistanceless inductor is caused to vary with time as in the graph of Fig. 33–35. (a) Sketch the pattern that would be observed on the screen of an oscilloscope connected to the terminals of the inductor. (The oscilloscope spot sweeps horizontally across the screen at constant speed, and its vertical deflection is proportional to the potential dif-

Figure 33–35

ference between the inductor terminals.)
(b) Explain why the inductor can be described as a "differentiating circuit."

33–30. An inductor of inductance 3 henrys and resistance 6 ohms is connected to the terminals of a battery of emf 12 volts and of negligible internal resistance. Find: (a) the initial rate of increase of current in the circuit, (b) the rate of increase of current at the instant when the current is 1 amp, (c) the current 0.2 sec after the circuit is closed, (d) the final steady-state current.

33–31. The resistance of a 10-henry inductor is 200 ohms. The inductor is suddenly connected across a potential difference of 10 volts. (a) What is the final steady current in the inductor? (b) What is the initial rate of increase of current? (c) At what rate is the current increasing when its value is one-half the final current? (d) At what time after the circuit is closed does the current equal 99% of its final value? (e) Compute the current at the following times after the circuit is closed: 0, 0.025 sec, 0.05 sec, 0.075 sec, 0.10 sec. Show the results in a graph.

33–32. An inductor of resistance R and self-inductance L is connected in series with a noninductive resistor of resistance R_0 to a constant potential difference V (Fig. 33–36). (a) Find the expression for the potential difference v_{cb} across the inductor at any time t after switch S_1 is closed. (b) Let $V = 20$ volts, $R_0 = 50$ ohms, $R = 150$ ohms, $L = 5$ henrys. Compute a few points, and construct graphs of v_{ac} and v_{cb} over a time interval from zero to twice the time constant of the circuit.

33–33. After the current in the circuit of Fig. 33–36 has reached its final steady value the switch S_2 is closed, thus short-circuiting the inductor. What will be the magnitude and direction of the current in S_2, 0.01 sec after S_2 is closed?

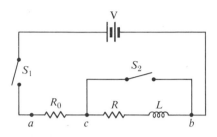

Figure 33–36

33–34. Refer to Problem 33–30. (a) What is the power input to the inductor at the instant when the current in it is 0.5 amp? (b) What is the rate of dissipation of energy at this instant? (c) What is the rate at which the energy of the magnetic field is increasing? (d) How much energy is stored in the magnetic field when the current has reached its final steady value?

33–35. The maximum capacitance of a variable air capacitor is 35 pf. (a) What should be the self-inductance of a coil to be connected to this capacitor if the natural frequency of the L-C circuit is to be 550 $\times$ 10^3 cycles/sec, corresponding to one end of the broadcast band? (b) The frequency at the other end of the broadcast band is 1550 $\times$ 10^3 cycles/sec. What must be the minimum capacitance of the capacitor if the natural frequency is to be adjustable over the range of the broadcast band?

CHAPTER 34

Magnetic Properties of Matter

34–1 Equivalent surface currents

In the preceding chapters we discussed the magnetic fields set up by moving charges or by currents in conductors, when the charges or conductors are in air (or, strictly speaking, in a vacuum). However, pieces of technical equipment, such as transformers, motors, generators, or electromagnets, always incorporate iron or an iron alloy in their structures, both for the purpose of increasing the magnetic flux and for confining it to a desired region. The magnetic field of a galvanometer or loudspeaker is set up by a *permanent* magnet, which produces this field without any apparent circulation of charge. The coating on magnetic tape makes a record of information supplied to it by the extent to which it becomes permanently magnetized.

We therefore turn next to a consideration of the magnetic properties which make iron and a few other ferromagnetic materials so useful. We shall find that magnetic properties are not confined to ferromagnetic materials but are exhibited (to a much smaller extent, to be sure) by *all* substances. A study of the magnetic properties of materials affords another means of gaining an insight into the nature of matter in general.

The existence of the magnetic properties of a substance can be demonstrated by supporting a small spherically shaped specimen by a fine thread and placing it near the poles of a powerful electromagnet. If the specimen is of iron or one of the *ferromagnetic* substances, it will be attracted into the strong part of the magnetic field. Not so familiar is the fact that any substance whatever will be influenced by the field, although to an extent which is extremely small compared with a substance like iron. Some substances will, like iron, be forced into the strong part of the field, while others will be urged to move toward the weak part of the field. The first type is called *paramagnetic*; the second, *diamagnetic*. All substances, including liquids and gases, fall into one or the other of these classes. Liquids and gases must, of course, be enclosed within some sort of container, and due allowance must be made for the properties of the container as well as those of the medium (usually air) in which the specimens are immersed.

In Chapter 27, our treatment of the properties of a dielectric substance was based on a specimen in the form of a flat slab, inserted in the field between oppositely charged parallel plates. The electric field is wholly confined to the region between the plates if their separation is small, and therefore a flat slab between the plates will completely occupy all points of space at which an electric field exists. A specimen of this shape is not as well suited for a study of magnetic effects, however, because there is no way

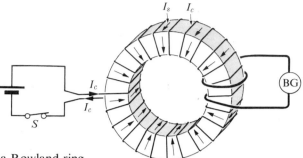

Fig. 34–1. A toroid; a Rowland ring.

of producing a magnetic field which is confined to the region between two closely spaced surfaces. The magnetic field within a closely spaced toroidal winding, however, is wholly confined to the space enclosed by the winding. We shall accordingly use such a field on which to base our discussion of magnetic properties, the specimen being in the form of a ring on whose surface the wire is wound. Such a specimen is often called a *Rowland ring* after J. H. Rowland, who made much use of it in his experimental and theoretical work on electricity and magnetism. The winding of wire around the specimen is called the *magnetizing winding*, and the conduction current in the winding is called the *magnetizing current*, I_c.

The magnetic flux density within the space enclosed by a toroidal winding *in vacuum* is

$$B = \mu_0 \frac{NI_c}{l}. \tag{34–1}$$

It will simplify the notation if we represent the quantity NI_c/l, the total magnetizing current per unit of circumferential length, by the symbol j_c:

$$j_c = \frac{NI_c}{l}.$$

The **B**-field set up by the magnetizing current is then

$$B_c = \mu_0 j_c.$$

Suppose now that a second winding is placed on the ring as in Fig. 34–1, with its terminals connected to a ballistic galvanometer. The flux density within the ring may be measured, as explained in Section 33–5, by opening switch S and quickly reducing the magnetizing current to zero. If this is done, the flux density computed from the ballistic galvanometer deflection will not agree with that computed from Eq. (34–1). If the core is ferromagnetic, the measured flux density will be tremendously larger, if paramagnetic, very slightly larger, and if diamagnetic, it will be very slightly smaller than the calculated value. The differences in the two latter cases are, in fact, so small that this method is not a practical one for investigating these substances, but its principle is simpler than that of other methods, so we shall ignore experimental difficulties.

The result is the same as if there were, in addition to the magnetizing current I_c, an additional current I_s around the *surface* of the ring, as indicated by the short arrows in Fig. 34–1. This current is in such a direction as to set up a field of its own which *adds* to the B_c-field if the ring is paramagnetic or ferromagnetic, and *subtracts* from it if the ring is diamagnetic. That is, in the former case I_s is in the same direction as I_c, and in the latter case, it is opposite to I_c.

These *equivalent surface currents* contribute to the **B**-field in the same way as conduction currents, so the complete expression for the flux density **B** at a point, due to both types of current, is

$$\mathbf{B} = \frac{\mu_0}{4\pi} \int \frac{I_c \, d\mathbf{l} \times \hat{\mathbf{r}}}{r^2} + \frac{\mu_0}{4\pi} \int \frac{I_s \, d\mathbf{l} \times \hat{\mathbf{r}}}{r^2}. \tag{34–2}$$

In the most general case the conduction and surface currents will not have the same geometry, but in a Rowland ring, where both circulate around the surface of the ring, they contribute in the same way to the **B**-field. Hence the flux density in the ring is

$$B = B_c + B_s = \mu_0(j_c + j_s). \tag{34–3}$$

The *surface current per unit length*, j_s, is analogous to the *bound charge per unit area*, σ_b, on the surface of a dielectric in an electric field.

The obvious generalization of Ampere's law, for a path which encloses both conduction and surface currents, is

$$\oint \mathbf{B} \cdot d\mathbf{s} = \mu_0(I_c + I_s). \tag{34–4}$$

If there are displacement currents present, we must also include the term $I_D = \dot{\Psi}$.

34–2 Molecular theory of dia- and paramagnetism

The earliest speculations as to the origin of the magnetic properties of a piece of lodestone, or of a permanent magnet, were that such a substance was composed of, or at least contained, a number of particles each of which was itself a tiny magnet. In an unmagnetized body, the magnets were oriented at random and the process of magnetizing a body consisted of aligning these elementary magnets. When it was discovered that magnetic effects could also be produced by currents, Ampere proposed the theory that the magnetic properties of a body arose from a multitude of tiny closed current loops within the body. The currents in these loops were assumed to continue indefinitely, as if there were no resistance. At the time the theory was proposed it was highly speculative, since no currents were known that would continue indefinitely of themselves. We now believe the theory to be essentially correct, the elementary current loops consisting of electrons spinning about their axes or revolving in orbits around nuclei.

The theory of *diamagnetism* is based on the Faraday law. The electrons in an atom can be thought of as revolving in orbits about their parent nuclei, and hence their paths are equivalent to current loops of zero resistance, since their motion goes on indefinitely. When a magnetic field is established in a material, the increasing flux

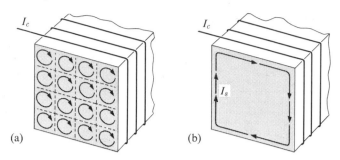

Fig. 34–2. (a) Alignment of atomic current loops. (b) Surface current equivalent to part (a).

gives rise to an emf in each loop and the electrons are accelerated or decelerated, depending on their direction of revolution. (The process is like that taking place in a betatron.) The end result is the same as if a current were induced in each loop, opposite to the current in the windings setting up the original field. In Fig. 34–2(a), these induced currents are represented by the small circles. At interior points the currents are in opposite directions and cancel. The outer portions of the outside loops, however, are uncompensated and the entire assembly of loops is equivalent to a current I_s circulating around the outside of the body, as in Fig. 34–2(b). These equivalent surface currents have essentially the same shape as a magnetizing winding around the body, and since they are opposite to the magnetizing current their effect is to *decrease* the field set up by the current in the windings.

Since all atoms contain electron current loops, the phenomenon of diamagnetism is present in all substances. In many materials, the molecular currents in one direction are just equal to those in the other and in the absence of an external field the molecules have no net magnetic moment. The phenomenon of *paramagnetism* results when the molecules of a substance have a *permanent magnetic moment*, corresponding to the molecules of a *polar* dielectric. The effect of a magnetic field on a molecule with a permanent magnetic moment, as we have seen in Section 31–4, is to cause the magnetic moment vector to *precess* around the direction of the field, and if this were all that happened there would be no *alignment* of molecular moments with the field. Interactions with other molecules, however, resulting from thermal agitation, disturb the regular precessional motion and after a certain time (very short in most instances) the molecular magnetic moments do become aligned with the field. We have shown that in its equilibrium position, the flux through a current loop is in the same direction as that of the external field, so that in this case the molecular field *adds* to the external field.

As with the induced current loops in a diamagnetic material, the aligned loops in a paramagnetic substance are equivalent to a surface current around the periphery of a magnetized body, with the difference that they are now in the *same* direction as the magnetizing current.

Paramagnetic effects are small, but if they exist at all they always outweigh the diamagnetic effect which is present in every substance, and the material appears paramagnetic.

34-3 Magnetization. Magnetic intensity

The *magnetization* **M** in a material is defined as the *magnetic moment per unit volume*. It is a vector quantity and is the magnetic analogue of the *polarization* **P** in a dielectric. The mksc unit of magnetization is 1 $(amp{\cdot}m^2)/m^3 = 1\ amp/m$.

Let $\mathfrak{M}$ represent the *total* magnetic moment of a body of volume V, in which there are N current loops all aligned in the same direction. The magnetization is then

$$\mathbf{M} = \frac{\mathfrak{M}}{V} = \frac{N}{V}\frac{\mathfrak{M}}{N}.$$

But N/V is the number of current loops per unit volume, which we represent by n, and $\mathfrak{M}/N$ is the magnetic moment per current loop, represented by **m**, so we can also write

$$\mathbf{M} = n\mathbf{m}.$$

For the special case of a Rowland ring of small cross section, the magnetization vector **M** has the same magnitude at all points. In other cases it may vary from point to point and the magnetization at any point is given by the preceding equation, letting n and **m** refer to a small volume including the point.

Consider a portion of the toroidal core in Fig. 34-1, of length l. The total surface current around the portion is $I_s = j_s l$, and the total magnetic moment $\mathfrak{M}$ of the portion is $I_s A = j_s l A$. But lA is the volume of the portion, so the magnetization M, or the magnetic moment per unit volume, is

$$M = j_s.$$

In this special case, then, the surface current per unit length equals the magnetization. More generally, the surface current per unit length at any point of the surface of a magnetized body is equal to the *tangential* component of **M** at the surface.

Since the B_s-field of the surface currents in a Rowland ring is equal to $\mu_0 j_s$, we can also write

$$\mathbf{B}_s = \mu_0\mathbf{M}.$$

That is, the B_s-field set up by the surface currents is proportional to the magnetization.

The *resultant* flux density B in a Rowland ring is the sum of the flux densities B_c and B_s. Since $B_c = \mu_0 j_c$ and $B_s = \mu_0 M$, we have

$$B = \mu_0(j_c + M),$$

or

$$\frac{B}{\mu_0} = j_c + M.$$

In our discussion of electric fields in matter, it was convenient to introduce the concept of *displacement*, defined as $\mathbf{D} = \epsilon_0\mathbf{E} + \mathbf{P}$. When dealing with *magnetic* fields in matter, we find it useful to define a similar concept, called the *magnetic intensity* **H**, as the *vector difference* between **B**/μ_0 and the magnetization **M**.

$$\mathbf{H} = \frac{\mathbf{B}}{\mu_0} - \mathbf{M}.$$ (34–5)

The mksc unit of **H** is the same as that of **M**, 1 amp/m. In free space, where **M** = 0, **H** = **B**/μ_0.

In a Rowland ring, where $B/\mu_0 = j_c + M$, the magnetic intensity is

$$H = \frac{B}{\mu_0} - M = j_c = \frac{NI_c}{l}.$$ (34–6)

Thus in this special case the magnetic intensity H is equal to the *conduction* current per unit length in the magnetizing windings.

The general expression for the H-field set up by a conduction current I_c is

$$\mathbf{H} = \frac{1}{4\pi} \int \frac{I_c \, d\mathbf{l} \times \hat{\mathbf{r}}}{r^2}.$$ (34–7)

That is, the "sources" of the **H**-field, in this case, are *conduction* currents only; surface currents are not included. The lines of an **H**-field are related *geometrically* to the current producing it in the same way as are those of a **B**-field. An **H**-field is analogous to a **D**-field in that surface currents do not contribute to **H**, and bound surface charges do not contribute to **D**.

It follows at once from Eq. (34–7) that in a Rowland ring,

$$H = \frac{NI_c}{l} = j_c.$$ (34–8)

We shall show later that Eq. (34–7) is not the *complete* expression for **H**, but that a term must be added to include the contribution of *magnetic poles*. This term need not be considered here because no poles are present.

34–4 Magnetic susceptibility, permeability, and magnetic coefficient

The magnetization **M** in a material depends on the magnetic intensity **H** and on the nature of the material. We define a property of a material called its *magnetic susceptibility* χ_m as the ratio of the magnetization to the magnetic intensity:

$$\chi_m = \frac{M}{H}, \quad \text{or} \quad \mathbf{M} = \chi_m \mathbf{H}.$$ (34–9)

That is, the magnetic susceptibility is the *magnetization per unit magnetic intensity*. (Compare the corresponding definition of electric susceptibility.) The magnetic susceptibility of a vacuum is zero, because only a material substance can become magnetized. Magnetic susceptibility is a pure number, since the units of **M** and **H** are both 1 amp/m.

TABLE 34–1

MAGNETIC SUSCEPTIBILITIES OF PARAMAGNETIC
AND DIAMAGNETIC MATERIALS

Materials	Temperature, °C	$\chi_m = K_m - 1$
Paramagnetic		
Iron ammonium alum	−269	4830 × 10^{-5}
Iron ammonium alum	−183	213
Oxygen, liquid	−183	152
Iron ammonium alum	+20	66
Uranium	20	40
Platinum	20	26
Aluminum	20	2.2
Sodium	20	0.72
Oxygen gas	20	0.19
Diamagnetic		
Bismuth	20	−16.6 × 10^{-5}
Mercury	20	−2.9
Silver	20	−2.6
Carbon (diamond)	20	−2.1
Lead	20	−1.8
Rock salt	20	−1.4
Copper	20	−1.0

The magnetic susceptibility of a paramagnetic material is positive and that of a diamagnetic material is negative. Some representative values are given in Table 34–1.

The orienting influence of a magnetic field on the molecules of a paramagnetic material is opposed by the disorienting effect of thermal agitation, which is greater, the higher the temperature. Hence the magnetic susceptibility of a paramagnetic material *decreases* with increasing temperature. For many materials, the temperature dependence is satisfactorily represented by the *Curie law*,

$$\chi_m = \frac{C}{T},$$

where C is a constant called the *Curie constant* and T is the kelvin temperature. Diamagnetic susceptibilities are independent of temperature.

When Eq. (34–5) is combined with Eq. (34–9), we get

$$H = \frac{B}{\mu_0} - \chi_m H,$$

or

$$B = \mu_0(1 + \chi_m)H. \tag{34–10}$$

TABLE 34–2

Magnetic (Rowland ring)	Electric (Dielectric between parallel plates)
$B = B_c + B_s$	$E = E_f + E_b$
$\quad = \mu_0 j_c + \mu_0 j_s$	$\quad = \dfrac{\sigma_f}{\epsilon_0} - \dfrac{\sigma_b}{\epsilon_0}$
$j_c = \dfrac{I_c}{l}$	$\sigma_f = \dfrac{q_f}{A}$
$j_s = \dfrac{I_s}{l}$	$\sigma_b = \dfrac{q_b}{A}$
$M = j_s$	$P = \sigma_b$
$H = \dfrac{B}{\mu_0} - M = j_c$	$D = \epsilon_0 E + P = \sigma_f$
$B = \mu_0(H + M)$	$E = \dfrac{1}{\epsilon_0}(D - P)$
$\chi_m = \dfrac{M}{H}$	$\epsilon_0 \chi = \dfrac{P}{E}$
$\mu = \mu_0(1 + \chi_m)$	$\epsilon = \epsilon_0(1 + \chi)$
$B = \mu H$	$D = \epsilon E$
$K_m = \dfrac{\mu}{\mu_0} = 1 + \chi_m$	$K = \dfrac{\epsilon}{\epsilon_0} = 1 + \chi$

The quantity $\mu_0(1 + \chi_m)$ also represents a property of the material called its *permeability μ*:

$$\mu = \mu_0(1 + \chi_m). \qquad (34\text{–}11)$$

In a vacuum, where $\chi_m = 0$, $\mu = \mu_0$ and the quantity μ_0 is often referred to as "the permeability of a vacuum," or "the permeability of free space." The mksc unit of permeability is the same as that of μ_0, 1 n/amp^2 or 1 w/amp·m.

Equation (34–10) can now be written

$$B = \mu H. \qquad (34\text{–}12)$$

The ratio μ/μ_0 is called the *relative permeability K_m*, or the *magnetic coefficient*,

$$K_m = \frac{\mu}{\mu_0}. \qquad (34\text{–}13)$$

Relative permeability is evidently a pure number.

It follows from Eqs. (34–11) and (34–13) that

$$K_m = 1 + \chi_m, \quad \text{or} \quad \chi_m = K_m - 1. \tag{34–14}$$

The "relative permeability of a vacuum," where $\chi_m = 0$, is equal to 1. The relative permeability of a paramagnetic substance is slightly greater than 1 and that of a diamagnetic substance is slightly less than 1.

We can now see the reason (or one of the reasons) for introducing the magnetic intensity **H**. Given the number of turns per unit length in the windings of a Rowland ring and the current I_c in the windings, we can compute H from Eq. (34–8), and if the permeability μ of the material of the ring is known, the resultant flux density B can be found from Eq. (34–12), $B = \mu H$, without having first to calculate the magnetization M or the equivalent surface currents.

This is analogous to the procedure in Section 27–9, where the displacement D can be calculated from a knowledge of the *free* charges only and the resultant **E**-field in a dielectric can be found from the equation $E = D/\epsilon$.

The first column in Table 34–2 summarizes the important relations that have been developed in this chapter and compares them with the analogous relations for electric fields in the second column.

34–5 Ferromagnetism

The flux density in a Rowland ring of iron may be hundreds or even thousands of times as great as that due to the magnetizing current alone. Furthermore, the flux density B is not a linear function of the magnetic intensity H or, in other words, the permeability μ is not a constant. To complicate matters even further, the permeability depends on the past history (magnetically speaking) of the iron, a phenomenon known as *hysteresis*. In fact, a flux may exist in the iron even in the absence of any external field; when in this state the iron is called a *permanent magnet*.

Any substance which exhibits the properties above is called *ferromagnetic*. Iron, nickel, cobalt, and gadolinium are the only ferromagnetic *elements* at room temperature, but a number of elements at low temperatures and alloys whose components are not ferromagnetic also show these effects.

Because of the complicated relation between the flux density B and the magnetic intensity H in a ferromagnetic material, it is not possible to express B as an analytic function of H. Instead, the relation between these quantities is either given in tabular form or is represented by a graph of B versus H, called the *magnetization curve* of the material.

The initial magnetization curve of a specimen of annealed iron is shown in Fig. 34–3 in the curve labeled B versus H. The permeability μ, equal to the ratio of B to H, can be found at any point of the curve by dividing the flux density B, at the point, by the corresponding magnetic intensity H. For example, when $H = 150$ amp/m, $B = 1.01$ w/m^2 and

$$\mu = \frac{B}{H} = \frac{1.01 \text{ w/m}^2}{150 \text{ amp/m}} = 67,500 \times 10^{-7} \text{ w/amp·m}.$$

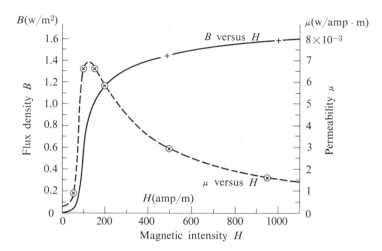

Fig. 34–3. Magnetization curve and permeability curve of annealed iron.

It is evident that the permeability is not a constant. The curve labeled μ versus H in Fig. 34–3 is a graph of μ as a function of H.

Table 34–3 covers a wider range of values for the same specimen, and also includes values of the flux density B_c set up by the current in the magnetizing windings, the flux density B_s set up by the surface currents, and the relative permeability K_m.

The data in Table 34–3 are plotted in Fig. 34–4 where, because of the wide range of values of H, the horizontal scale has been compressed beyond $H = 1000$ amp/m. It will be seen that when H is small, practically all of the flux is due to the equivalent surface currents. Beyond the point where H is of the order of 100,000 amp/m there is little further increase in B_s and the iron is said to become *saturated*. Further increases in B are due almost entirely to increases in B_c, resulting from the increased current in the windings.

34–6 Magnetization of iron.   Magnetic domains

The electrons in most of the metallic ions which form the lattice structure of a metal are paired off, with half spinning one way and half the other way. The ion is thus "magnetically neutral." The ions of the ferromagnetic elements, iron, nickel, cobalt, etc., are exceptions. In particular, that of iron has an excess of two uncompensated electrons and the magnetization of a sample of iron is due almost entirely to the alignment of the magnetic moments of these electrons. When a sample of iron is magnetically *saturated*, all of the uncompensated electrons are spinning with their axes in the direction of the magnetizing field.

We can now understand the reason for the shape of the graph of B_s versus H in Fig. 34–4. Since $B_s = \mu_0 M$, this curve (to a different vertical scale) is also the graph of M versus H. As H is increased from zero, more and more of the spinning electrons become aligned with the **H**-field and M increases steadily. When H is about 100,000 amp/m, practically all of the electrons have lined up with the **H**-field. No further increase in M can occur, and the iron is saturated.

TABLE 34–3

MAGNETIC PROPERTIES OF ANNEALED IRON

Magnetic intensity	Total flux density	Flux density due to current in windings	Flux density due to surface currents	Permeability	Relative permeability
H, amp $\overline{m}$	B, webers $\overline{m^2}$	B_c, webers $\overline{m^2}$	B_s, webers $\overline{m^2}$	$\mu = B/H$, webers $\overline{amp \cdot m}$	$K_m = \mu/\mu_0$
0	0	0	0	$3,100 \times 10^{-7}$	250
10	0.0042	.000013	0.0042	4,200	330
20	.010	.000025	.010	5,000	400
40	.028	.000050	.028	7,000	560
50	.043	.000063	.043	8,600	680
60	.095	.000078	.095	16,000	1270
80	.45	.000104	.45	56,000	4500
100	.67	.00013	.67	67,000	5300
150	1.01	.00019	1.01	67,500	5350
200	1.18	.00025	1.18	59,000	4700
500	1.44	.00063	1.44	28,800	2300
1,000	1.58	.0013	1.58	15,800	1250
10,000	1.72	.013	1.71	1,720	137
100,000	2.26	.13	2.13	226	18
800,000	3.15	1.00	2.15	39	3.1

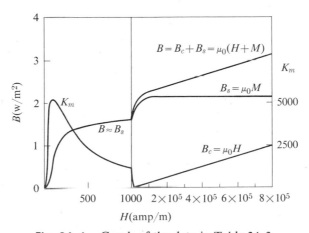

Fig. 34–4.   Graph of the data in Table 34–3.

The magnetic moment of a spinning electron is 1 Bohr magneton, of moment

$$\mu_B = 0.927 \times 10^{-23} \text{ amp·m}^2.$$

Reference to Fig. 34–4 shows that in saturated iron the field $B_s = \mu_0 M$ is about 2.15 w/m^2, so that the saturation magnetization is

$$M = \frac{B_s}{\mu_0} = 1.71 \times 10^6 \text{ amp·m}.$$

The density of iron is 7.8 gm/cm^3 and its atomic weight is 56 gm/gm-mole. The volume of 1 gm-mole is therefore 7.18 cm^3 and since there are 6.02×10^{23} atoms in a gram-mole, the number of atoms per cubic centimeter is 8.38×10^{22} and the number per cubic meter is 8.38×10^{28}. The magnetic moment per atom, in saturated iron, is therefore

$$\frac{1.71 \times 10^6 \text{ amp·m}}{8.38 \times 10^{28} \text{ atoms/m}^3} = 2.04 \times 10^{-23} \frac{\text{amp·m}^2}{\text{atom}},$$

which is almost exactly equal to two Bohr magnetons!

This result, however, should not give the impression that our simple theory is quite as simple as it might appear. In none of the ferromagnetic elements is the saturation magnetization per atom *exactly* equal to some *integral* number of Bohr magnetons. Nevertheless, we are quite confident that the main features of the problem are as described above.

This is not the whole story, however. If the effect described above were all, iron would be *para*magnetic but not *ferro*magnetic. Ferromagnetism results because of a spontaneous, self-aligning, cooperative interaction among relatively large numbers of iron atoms.

Recent experimental and theoretical work has led to a fairly complete understanding of the nature of these interactions, but the problem is far from simple, and even a reasonably complete description would take us beyond the scope of this book. It must suffice to state that there exist in ferromagnetic materials small regions called *domains*, in each of which, as a result of molecular interactions, the molecular magnetic moments are all aligned parallel to one another. In other words, each domain is *spontaneously magnetized to saturation* even in the absence of any external field. The directions of magnetization in different domains are not necessarily parallel to one another, so that in an unmagnetized specimen the resultant magnetization is zero. When the specimen is placed in a magnetic field the resultant magnetization may increase in two different ways, either by an increase in the volume of those domains which are favorably oriented with respect to the field at the expense of unfavorably oriented domains, or by the rotation of the direction of magnetization toward the direction of the field. These two methods are shown in Fig. 34–5(a).

In weak fields, the magnetization usually changes by means of domain boundary displacements, so that the favorably oriented domains increase in size. In strong fields the magnetization usually changes by rotation of the direction of magnetization. The curve in Fig. 34–5(b) shows the regions in which each process is dominant. In

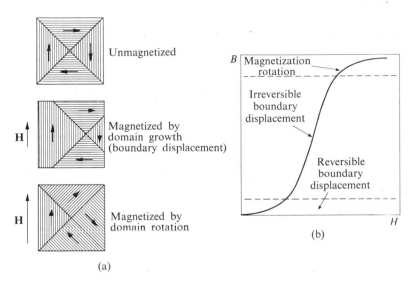

Fig. 34–5. Schematic diagram showing magnetization by domain growth and domain rotation.

small fields the changes are reversible. That is, the boundaries return to their original positions when the field is removed. In stronger fields the changes are irreversible and the substance remains magnetized when the external field is removed.

The sizes of the domains can be studied by spreading a finely divided magnetic powder on the surface of the specimen, a technique first developed by F. H. Bitter. The powder particles collect along the boundaries between domains and may be examined under a microscope. The size of the domains may vary widely, depending on the size of the specimen and whether it is a single crystal or is polycrystalline. Typical values are from 10^{-6} to 10^{-2} cm^3, which means that a domain may contain from 10^{17} to 10^{21} molecules.

The *Barkhausen effect*, which is most pronounced along the steeply rising portion of the magnetization curve, is believed to be caused by the irregular motion of domain boundaries. If a rod of ferromagnetic material is surrounded by a search coil connected to an audio amplifier, and the rod is placed in a magnetic field that can be steadily increased or decreased, a crackling sound is heard from a speaker connected to the amplifier. As the domain boundaries change in size, each change induces a sudden short rush of current through the search coil and these surges are heard as noise from the speaker.

34–7 Hysteresis

A magnetization curve such as that in Fig. 34–3 expresses the relation between the flux density B in a ferromagnetic material and the corresponding magnetic intensity H, *provided the sample is initially unmagnetized and the magnetic intensity is steadily increased from zero.* Thus in Fig. 34–6, if the magnetizing current in the windings of an unmagnetized ring sample is steadily increased from zero until the magnetic

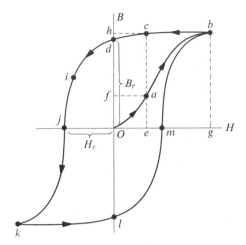

Fig. 34–6. Hysteresis loop.

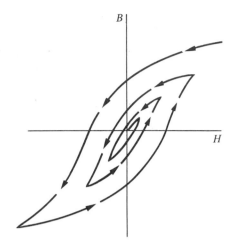

Fig. 34–7. Successive hysteresis loops during the operation of demagnetizing a ferromagnetic sample.

intensity H corresponds to the abscissa Oe, the flux density B is given by the ordinate Of. If, starting from the same unmagnetized state, the magnetic intensity is first increased from zero to Og and then *decreased* to Oe, the magnetic state of the sample follows the path $Oabc$. The flux density, when the magnetic intensity has been reduced to Oe, is represented by the ordinate Oh rather than Of. If the magnetizing current is now reduced to zero, the curve continues to point d, where the flux density is Od.

The flux density in the sample is seen to depend not on the magnetic intensity alone, but on the *magnetic history* of the sample as well. The sample has a magnetic "memory," so to speak, and "remembers" that it has been magnetized to point b even after the magnetizing current has been cut off. At point d it has become a *permanent magnet*. This behavior of the material, as evidenced by the fact that the B–H curve for decreasing H does not coincide with that for increasing H, is called *hysteresis*. The term means literally, "to lag behind."

In many pieces of electrical apparatus, such as transformers and motors, masses of iron are located in magnetic fields whose direction is continually reversing. That is, the magnetic intensity H increases from zero to a certain maximum in one direction, then decreases to zero, increases to the same maximum but in the opposite direction, decreases to zero, and continues to repeat this cycle over and over. The flux density B within the iron reverses also, but in the manner indicated in Fig. 34–6, tracing out a closed curve in the B–H plane known as a *hysteresis loop*.

Positive values of H or B in Fig. 34–6 indicate that the respective directions of these quantities are, say, clockwise in a Rowland ring, while negative values mean that the directions are counterclockwise. The magnitude and direction of H are determined solely by the current in the winding, while those of B depend on the magnetic properties of the sample and its past history. Note that at points in the second and fourth quadrants, B and H are opposite in direction.

TABLE 34–4

RETENTIVITY AND COERCIVE FORCE OF PERMANENT
MAGNET MATERIALS

Material	Composition, percent	B_r, w/m^2	H_c, amp/m
Carbon steel	98 Fe, 0.86 C, 0.9 Mn	0.95	3.6×10^3
Cobalt steel	52 Fe, 36 Co, 7 W, 3.5 Cr, 0.5 Mn, 0.7 C	0.95	18×10^3
Alnico 2	55 Fe, 10 Al, 17 Ni, 12 Co, 6 Cu	0.76	42×10^3
Alnico 5	51 Fe, 8 Al, 14 Ni, 24 Co, 3 Cu	1.25	44×10^3

The ordinate *Od* in Fig. 34–6 represents the flux density remaining in the specimen when the magnetic intensity has been reduced to zero. It is called the *retentivity* or *remanence* of the specimen and is designated by B_r. The abscissa *Oj* represents the reversed magnetic intensity needed to reduce the flux density to zero after the specimen has been magnetized to saturation in the opposite direction, and it is called the *coercive force* or the *coercivity*, H_c.

The magnetization curve *Oab* in Fig. 34–6 shows the sample initially unmagnetized. One may wonder how this can be accomplished, since cutting off the magnetizing current does not reduce the flux density in the material to zero. A sample may be demagnetized by reversing the magnetizing current a number of times, decreasing its magnitude with each reversal. The sample is thus carried around a hysteresis curve which winds more and more closely about the origin (see Fig. 34–7).

Hysteresis effects introduce a similar difficulty in measuring the flux in a sample. In the absence of hysteresis, the flux falls to zero when the magnetizing current is cut off, and a ballistic galvanometer connected to a search coil around the specimen indicates the flux previously present in the specimen. But since *B* does not become zero when *H* is reduced to zero, ballistic galvanometer deflections indicate only the *changes* in flux corresponding to changes in the magnetizing force. Hence in practice the complete hysteresis loop must be traced out in stepwise fashion, measuring the changes in flux accompanying changes in magnetizing current.

It is evidently desirable that a material for permanent magnets should have both a large retentivity so that the magnet will be "strong" and a large coercive force so that the magnetization will not be wiped out by stray external fields. Some typical values are given in Table 34–4. Alnico 5 is one of the most recently developed alloys for permanent magnets. Its superiority to carbon steel, which was the material used for many years, is evident.

One consequence of the phenomenon of hysteresis is the dissipation of energy within a ferromagnetic material each time the material is caused to traverse its hysteresis loop. This results from the irreversible motion of domain boundaries. It can be shown that the energy dissipated per unit volume, in each cycle, is proportional to the area enclosed by the hysteresis loop. Hence if a ferromagnetic material is to be subjected to a field which is continually reversing its direction (the core of a transformer, for example) it is desirable that the hysteresis loop of the material shall be narrow to minimize losses. Fortunately, iron or iron alloys are available which combine high permeability with small hysteresis loss.

The self-inductance L of a coil can be defined as the number of flux-linkages per unit current in the coil. If a magnetic material of permeability μ replaces a vacuum at all points of the magnetic field set up by a coil, the flux density at every point is increased by a factor K_m over its value in empty space. The number of flux-linkages, and hence the self-inductance, increases in the same ratio. Another way of stating this is that in any expression for the self-inductance in vacuum, the term μ_0 is to be replaced by $\mu = K_m\mu_0$. Thus the self-inductance of a closely wound toroid on a magnetic core (see example in Section 33–10) is

$$L = \frac{\mu N^2 A}{l}.$$

Thus the self-inductance of an iron-core coil is very much larger than that of the same winding in vacuum. On the other hand, since the permeability of a ferromagnetic material is not constant, the self-inductance of such a coil is not constant either, but depends on the current in the coil and on its magnetic history.

The expression for the energy density in a magnetic field is modified in the same way. It was shown in Section 33–11 that the energy density in a magnetic field in vacuum equals $\frac{1}{2}B^2/\mu_0$. In a magnetic material of permeability μ, the energy density is $\frac{1}{2}B^2/\mu$, and since $B = \mu H$ this can also be written as

$$\text{Energy density} = \frac{1}{2}\frac{B^2}{\mu} = \frac{1}{2}\mu H^2 = \frac{1}{2}BH.$$

34–8 Magnetic poles

Magnetic fields can be set up by magnetized matter, as well as by currents in conductors. Figure 34–8 is a sectional view of a thin circular disk, of radius R and thickness t, that has been permanently magnetized in a direction perpendicular to its flat end faces. The magnetization $\mathbf{M}$ (magnetic moment per unit volume) is uniform within the disk and is zero at points outside the disk.

Part (b) of the diagram shows the $\mathbf{B}$-field of the disk. Since there are no conduction currents, the $\mathbf{B}$-field is due wholly to the equivalent surface currents circulating around the rim of the disk in the narrow shaded zone. The lines of the $\mathbf{B}$-field are continuous and are from left to right through the disk.

Now consider the $\mathbf{H}$-field, shown in part (c). The values of $\mathbf{H}$, $\mathbf{B}$, and $\mathbf{M}$, at every point, are related by the equation

$$\mathbf{H} = \frac{\mathbf{B}}{\mu_0} - \mathbf{M}.$$

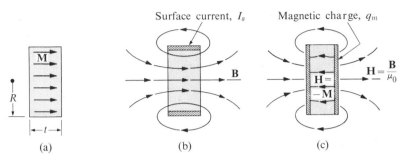

Surface current, I_s Magnetic charge, q_m

Fig. 34-8. (a) A uniformly magnetized disk. (b) *B*-field of the disk.
(c) *H*-field of the disk.

Outside the disk, where $\mathbf{M} = 0$, $\mathbf{H} = \mathbf{B}/\mu_0$. Since this is a *vector* equation, the *direction* of the **H**-field at external points is the same as that of the **B**-field, and the *magnitude* of **H** at every point equals B/μ_0.

Inside the disk, where $M \neq 0$, the magnetic intensity **H** equals the vector *difference* $\mathbf{B}/\mu_0 - \mathbf{M}$. Let us compute B/μ_0 at the center of the disk. The surface current per unit length, j_s, is equal to M and the surface current I_s is therefore

$$I_s = j_s t = Mt.$$

The **B**-field at the center of a circular current loop is

$$B = \frac{\mu_0}{2} \frac{I_s}{R} = \frac{\mu_0}{2} \frac{Mt}{R}.$$

Therefore at the center

$$H = \frac{B}{\mu_0} - M = M\left(\frac{t}{2R} - 1\right).$$

If the thickness t is *very* small compared with the radius R, the term $t/2R$ is very much less than 1 and can be neglected. Hence at the center

$$H = -M.$$

The H-field at the center is therefore *opposite* to **M**, or is from right to left, and is numerically equal to M. Thus the lines of the H-field must be as shown in Fig. 34-8(c). Because the vector difference $\mathbf{B}/\mu_0 - \mathbf{H}$ must equal the constant value **M** at every point, the lines of **H** within the disk, except on the axis, are curved as indicated.

A complete calculation shows that the H-field is geometrically identical to the E-field between a pair of oppositely charged parallel plates, as shown in Fig. 25-19. We might therefore postulate (for the purpose of calculating the H-field of a magnetized body) the existence of hypothetical positive and negative *magnetic charges*, which set up a radial inverse square **H**-field in the same way that *electric charges* set up a radial inverse square **E**-field. For the disk in Fig. 34-8, these charges are distributed in thin layers over the flat end faces of the disk, as suggested by the shading in part (c). The **H**-field set up by a hypothetical magnetic charge dq_m is given by

$$\mathbf{H} = \frac{1}{4\pi} \int \frac{dq_m \hat{\mathbf{r}}}{r^2}.$$

The analogue of Gauss's law for **H** is

$$\oint \mathbf{H} \cdot d\mathbf{A} = q_m. \tag{34–15}$$

That is, *the surface integral of* **H** *over a closed surface equals the net magnetic charge inside the surface.* Symmetry considerations applied to the two layers of magnetic charge in Fig. 34–8 lead to the result that within the disk

$$H = \sigma_m,$$

where σ_m is the surface density of magnetic charge. This equation is the analogue of Eq. (27–19) for electric fields.

But we have shown that within a thin permanently magnetized disk

$$H = -\mathbf{M},$$

so that the surface density of magnetic charge is related to the magnetization by the equation

$$\sigma_m = -M.$$

In summary, to compute the **B**- and **H**-fields set up by the magnetized disk, we proceed as follows.

(1) To find the **B**-field, we consider the disk to be replaced by *equivalent surface currents around its rim,* having a line density

$$j_s = M.$$

The *B*-field is then calculated from the equation

$$\mathbf{B} = \int \frac{I_s \, d\mathbf{l} \times \hat{\mathbf{r}}}{r^2}.$$

(2) To find the **H**-field, we consider the disk to be replaced by *equivalent surface magnetic charges on its end faces,* having a surface density

$$\sigma_m = -M.$$

The **H**-field is then calculated from the equation

$$\mathbf{H} = \frac{1}{4\pi} \int \frac{dq_m \hat{\mathbf{r}}}{r^2}.$$

Although the term "magnetic charge" is an appropriate one, the term "magnetic pole" is ordinarily used. A *north magnetic pole* (an N-pole) corresponds to a positive magnetic charge, and a *south magnetic pole* (an S-pole) to a negative magnetic charge. We would say that N-poles are distributed over the right face of the disk in Fig. 34–8, and S-poles over its left face. Unnecessary and often confusing geographical implications can be avoided by speaking of these simply as "enn-poles" and "ess-poles."

It will be seen from Fig. 34–8 that we find *equivalent surface currents* at points where the **M**-vector is *parallel* to the outer surface of a magnetized body, and *magnetic charges* or *poles* where the **M**-vector is *perpendicular* to the surface. For a magnetized body in vacuum, the general relations between **M** and the surface currents and charges are

$$j_s = M_{||}, \qquad \sigma_m = -M_\perp,$$

where $M_{||}$ and $M_\perp$ are the components of **M**, parallel and perpendicular to the surface.

Although isolated magnetic poles have never been observed, the "poles" of a magnetized body nevertheless have a physical reality if we define them simply as *those portions of the surface of the body where the **M**-vector has a component perpendicular to the surface.*

The complete expression for **H**, then, including the effects of any conduction currents as well as that of magnetic poles, is

$$\mathbf{H} = \frac{1}{4\pi} \int \frac{I_c \, d\mathbf{l} \times \hat{\mathbf{r}}}{r^2} + \frac{1}{4\pi} \int \frac{dq_m \hat{\mathbf{r}}}{r^2}. \tag{34–16}$$

Because the line integral of any radial inverse square field is zero around a closed path, the second term in Eq. (34–16) contributes nothing to such an integral and

$$\oint \mathbf{H} \cdot d\mathbf{s} = I_c. \tag{34–17}$$

34–9 Demagnetizing fields

The **H**-field inside the disk in Fig. 34–8 (and in fact inside any permanent magnet) is *opposite* to the magnetization **M** and to the flux density **B**. It is called a *demagnetizing* field.

The three parts of Fig. 34–9 represent schematically the fields within a thin disk as it is being magnetized to form a permanent magnet. The disk is originally unmag-

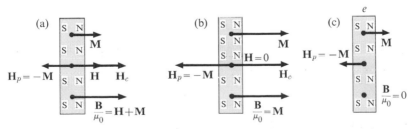

Fig. 34–9. Three stages in the process of permanently magnetizing a thin disk. Parts (a), (b), and (c) correspond, respectively, to points *a*, *c*, and *e* in Fig. 34–10. The thickness of the disk has been greatly exaggerated.

netized. In part (a), an external H-field, $\mathbf{H}_c$, set up by a current in an external circuit, has been applied. The magnetization has increased to $\mathbf{M}$, and the poles of the disk have set up an internal demagnetizing H-field, $\mathbf{H}_p$. The resultant field is $\mathbf{H} = \mathbf{H}_c - \mathbf{H}_p$. In the *M-H* diagram of Fig. 34–10, the state of the disk is represented by some point such as *a*.

Suppose the external field is increased until the state of the disk is represented by point *b*, and is then decreased. At point *c* in the *M-H* diagram, corresponding to part (b) of Fig. 34–9, the fields $\mathbf{H}_c$ and $\mathbf{H}_p$ are equal and opposite and $\mathbf{H} = 0$.

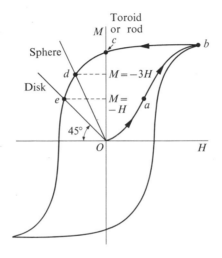

Figure 34–10

If the external field $\mathbf{H}_c$ is now reduced to zero, there remains only the $\mathbf{H}_p$-field of the disk, directed toward the left. The state of the disk is represented in Fig. 34–9(c), which corresponds to point *e* in Fig. 34–10. Since $\mathbf{H}_p = -\mathbf{M}$ in a thin disk, this point lies on a line through the origin at an angle of 45° with the axes, whatever the shape of the hysteresis loop.

The demagnetizing field in a body depends on the shape of the body, and in general varies in magnitude and direction from point to point. Within a uniformly magnetized sphere, the demagnetizing field equals $-M/3$ and the state of a permanently magnetized sphere is represented by point *d* in Fig. 34–10. At a point within a long, slender rod, not too near its ends, the demagnetizing field is very small, and point *c* represents the state of the rod. The same point represents the state of a magnetized toroid, because such a body has no magnetic poles (there are no points where $\mathbf{M}$ is perpendicular to the surface) and hence it sets up no demagnetizing field.

It will be appreciated that the magnetic state of, say, a bar magnet or a horseshoe magnet is extremely complicated and in general the problem is not capable of an exact analytical solution.

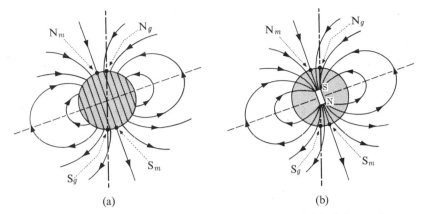

(a)   (b)

Fig. 34–11. Simplified diagram of the magnetic field of the earth.

34–10 The magnetic field of the earth

To a first approximation, the magnetic field of the earth is the same as that outside a uniformly magnetized sphere. Figure 34–11(a) represents a section through the earth. The dot-dash line is its axis of rotation, and the *geographic* north and south poles are lettered N_g and S_g. The direction of the (presumed) internal magnetization makes an angle of about 15° with the earth's axis. The dashed line indicates the plane of the magnetic equator, and the letters N_m and S_m represent the so-called *magnetic* north and south poles. Note carefully that lines of induction emerge from the earth's surface over the entire southern magnetic hemisphere and enter its surface over the entire northern magnetic hemisphere. Hence if we wish to attribute the earth's field to magnetic poles we must assume, on the basis of this hypothesis about the earth's internal magnetic state, that magnetic N-poles are distributed over the entire *southern* magnetic hemisphere, and magnetic S-poles over the entire *northern* magnetic hemisphere. This can be very confusing. The north and south magnetic poles, considered as points on the earth's surface, are simply those points where the field is vertical. The former is located at latitude 70°N, longitude 96°W.

It is interesting to note that the same field at *external* points would result if the earth's magnetism were due to a short bar magnet near its center, as in Fig. 34–11(b), with the S-pole of the magnet pointing toward the north magnetic pole. The field within the earth is different in the two cases, but for obvious reasons experimental verification of either hypothesis is impossible.

Except at the magnetic equator, the earth's field is not horizontal. The angle which the field makes with the horizontal is called the *angle of dip* or the *inclination*. At Cambridge, Mass. (about 45°N lat.), the magnitude of the earth's field is about 5.8×10^{-5} w/m^2 and the angle of dip about 73°. Hence the horizontal component at Cambridge is about 1.7×10^{-5} w/m^2 and the vertical component about 5.5×10^{-5} w/m^2. In northern magnetic latitudes the vertical component is directed downward, in southern magnetic latitudes it is upward. The angle of dip is, of course, 90° at the magnetic poles.

The angle between the horizontal component and the true north-south direction is called the *variation* or *declination*. At Cambridge, Mass., the declination at present is about 15°W, that is, a compass needle points about 15° to the west of true north.

The magnetic field of the earth is not as symmetrical as one might be led to suspect from the idealized drawing of Fig. 34–11. It is in reality very complicated; the inclination and the declination vary irregularly over the earth's surface, and also vary with the time.

34–11 The magnetic circuit

Figure 34–12 is a schematic diagram of an *electromagnet*. The vertical portions of the iron core are wound with coils of wire carrying a current I, and experiments can be performed in the magnetic field in the air gap.

The magnetic state of such a magnet is very complex. Most of the lines of the **B**-field (shown by dotted lines) are confined to the core and the air gap, but some close on themselves via air paths (the "leakage flux"). N- and S-poles are found at all points of the surface of the core where **M** has a component perpendicular to the surface. The pole strength per unit area is greatest, however, at the ends facing the gap (the pole faces). There is some fringing of the lines as they cross the air gap.

The **H**-field due to the current I in the coils ($\mathbf{H}_c$) is everywhere clockwise in the core, but does not have the same magnitude at all points. The poles set up a demagnetizing field $\mathbf{H}_p$ which at all points in the core is opposite to $\mathbf{H}_c$. For example, the N- and S-poles at the pole faces set up fields $\mathbf{H}_N$ and $\mathbf{H}_S$ at point P, and their resultant $\mathbf{H}_p$ is opposite to $\mathbf{H}_c$.

An exact analytic solution of the problem is impossible. A very rough approximation can be made as follows. We neglect any leakage flux, that is, we assume that the flux Φ is the same over all cross sections of the core and the air gap. We consider the core to have the same cross section A_1 at all points, and take fringing into account by

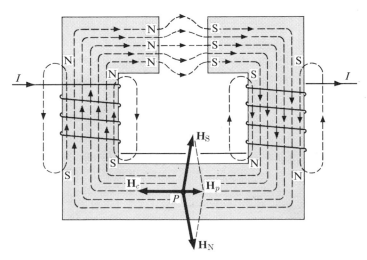

Figure 34–12

assuming the gap to have a larger cross section A_2. The flux densities in the core and the gap are then

$$B_1 = \frac{\Phi}{A_1}, \qquad B_2 = \frac{\Phi}{A_2}.$$

The corresponding values of H are

$$H_1 = \frac{B_1}{\mu_1} = \frac{\Phi}{\mu_1 A_1}, \qquad H_2 = \frac{B_2}{\mu_2} = \frac{\Phi}{\mu_2 A_2}.$$

We now form the line integral of **H** around a closed path through the core and air gap. If l_1 and l_2 are the path lengths in the core and the gap, respectively,

$$\oint \mathbf{H} \cdot d\mathbf{l} = H_1 l_1 + H_2 l_2.$$

The **H**-field at every point is the resultant of the fields-$\mathbf{H}_c$ and $\mathbf{H}_p$. The line integral of the $\mathbf{H}_p$-field is zero and that of the $\mathbf{H}_c$-field equals the product NI, where N is the total number of turns in the windings. Hence

$$\oint \mathbf{H} \cdot d\mathbf{l} = \int \mathbf{H}_c \cdot d\mathbf{l} = NI.$$

It follows from the preceding three equations that

$$\Phi = \frac{NI}{(l_1/\mu_1 A_1) + (l_2/\mu_2 A_2)}. \qquad (34\text{–}18)$$

This equation is closely analogous to the *circuit equation* for an electric circuit, and the electromagnet is referred to as a *magnetic circuit*, although of course there is nothing in the nature of a *flow* around it. The magnetic intensity $\mathbf{H}_c$ corresponds to the nonelectrostatic field $\mathbf{E}_n$, and the line integral of $\mathbf{H}_c$ around the circuit is called the *magnetomotive force* $\mathfrak{M}$, abbreviated mmf:

$$\mathfrak{M} = \oint \mathbf{H}_c \cdot d\mathbf{l} = NI.$$

(This is analogous to the definition of emf, $\mathcal{E} = \oint \mathbf{E}_n \cdot d\mathbf{l}$.) The *resistance* R of an electrical conductor is

$$R = \frac{l}{\sigma A},$$

where σ is the electrical conductivity. The terms in the denominator of Eq. (34–18) have the same form, and we define the *reluctance* $\mathfrak{R}$ of a portion of a magnetic circuit as

$$\mathfrak{R} = \frac{l}{\mu A}.$$

Hence we can write Eq. (34–18) as

$$\Phi = \frac{\mathfrak{M}}{\mathfrak{R}_1 + \mathfrak{R}_2},$$

in which form it is exactly analogous to the electric circuit equation for two resistances in series:

$$I = \frac{\mathcal{E}}{R_1 + R_2} \cdot$$

EXAMPLE 1.   The mean length of a Rowland ring is 50 cm and its cross section is 4 cm^2. Use the permeability curve of Fig. 34–3 to compute the magnetomotive force needed to establish a flux of 4×10^{-4} weber in the ring. What current is required if the ring is wound with 200 turns of wire?

The desired flux density B is

$$B = \frac{\Phi}{A} = \frac{4 \times 10^{-4} \text{ w}}{4 \times 10^{-4} \text{ m}^2} = 1 \text{ w/m}^2.$$

From Fig. 34–3, the permeability at this flux density is about 65×10^{-4} w/amp·m. Hence the reluctance $\mathcal{R}$ is

$$\mathcal{R} = \frac{l}{\mu A} = \frac{0.5 \text{ m}}{65 \times 10^{-4} \text{ (w/amp·m)} \times 4 \times 10^{-4} \text{ m}^2} = 1.92 \times 10^5 \text{ amp/w},$$

and since $\mathcal{M} = \Phi\mathcal{R}$, the required magnetomotive force is

$$\mathcal{M} = 4 \times 10^{-4} \text{ w} \times 1.92 \times 10^5 \text{ (amp/w)} = 77 \text{ amp-turns}.$$

If the ring is wound with 200 turns, the current required is 0.385 amp.

EXAMPLE 2.   If an air gap one millimeter in length is cut in the ring, what current is required to maintain the same flux?

The reluctance of the air gap is

$$\mathcal{R} = \frac{l}{\mu_0 A} = \frac{10^{-3} \text{ m}}{12.57 \times 10^{-7} \text{ (w/amp·m)} \times 4 \times 10^{-4} \text{ m}^2} = 20 \times 10^5 \text{ amp/weber}.$$

Neglecting the small change in length of the iron, its reluctance is the same as before, or 1.92×10^5 amp-turns/w. Thus although the gap is only 1 mm long, its reluctance is ten times as great as that of the iron portion of the circuit. The reluctance of the entire circuit is now $(20 \times 10^5 + 1.92 \times 10^5)$ amp/w $= 22 \times 10^5$ amp/w.   The number of ampere turns required is 880 and the corresponding current is 4.4 amp.

Problems

$$\mu_0 = 12.57 \times 10^{-7} \frac{\text{w}}{\text{amp·m}}$$

34-1. Experimental measurements of the magnetic susceptibility of iron ammonium alum are given in Table 34-5. Make a graph of $1/\chi_m$ against kelvin temperature and determine whether Curie's law holds. If so, what is the Curie constant?

TABLE 34-5

t, °C	χ_m
−258	75.4×10^{-4}
−173	11.3×10^{-4}
−73	5.65×10^{-4}
27	3.77×10^{-4}

34-2. A Rowland ring having 500 turns of wire and a mean circumferential length of 50 cm carries a current of 0.3 amp. The relative permeability of the core is 600. (a) What is the flux density in the core? (b) What is the magnetic intensity? (c) What part of the flux density is due to surface currents?

34-3. The current in the windings on a Rowland ring is 2.0 amp. There are 400 turns and the mean circumferential length is 40 cm. With the aid of a search coil and ballistic galvanometer, the magnetic induction is found to be 1.0 weber/m². Calculate (a) the magnetic intensity, (b) the magnetization, (c) the magnetic susceptibility, (d) the equivalent surface current, and (e) the magnetic coefficient (relative permeability).

34-4. Each of the two preceding coils has a cross-sectional area of 8 cm². Calculate the self-inductance L of each coil.

34-5. In 1911, Kamerlingh-Onnes discovered that at low temperatures some metals lose their electrical resistance and become superconductors. Thirty years later, Meissner showed that the magnetic induction inside a superconductor is zero. If a superconductor in the form of a Rowland ring has a toroidal winding and the current is increased, a critical value H_c may be reached at which the metal suddenly becomes normal with practically zero magnetization. (a) Plot a graph of B/μ_0 against H from $H = 0$ to $H = 2H_c$. (b) Plot a graph of M against H in the same range. (c) Is a superconductor paramagnetic, diamagnetic, or ferromagnetic? (d) If the current in the windings is 10 amp, how large are the surface currents on the superconducting ring and in what direction? (e) What happens when you try to place a small permanent magnet on a superconducting plate?

34-6. Table 34-6 lists corresponding values of H and B for a specimen of commercial hot-rolled silicon steel, a material

TABLE 34-6

MAGNETIC PROPERTIES
OF SILICON STEEL

Magnetic intensity H, amp-turns/m	Flux density B, w/m²
0	0
10	0.050
20	0.15
40	0.43
50	0.54
60	0.62
80	0.74
100	0.83
150	0.98
200	1.07
500	1.27
1,000	1.34
10,000	1.65
100,000	2.02
800,000	2.92

widely used in transformer cores. (a) Construct graphs of B and μ as functions of H, in the range from $H = 0$ to $H = 1000$ amp-turns/m.   (b) What is the maximum permeability? (c) What is the initial permeability ($H = 0$)?   (d) What is the permeability when

$$H = 800{,}000 \text{ amp-turns/m}?$$

34–7. Construct graphs of $\mu_0 H$, $\mu_0 M$, and K_m against H, like those in Fig. 34–4 for the specimen of silicon steel in Table 34–4.

34–8. Suppose the ordinate of the point b in Fig. 34–6 corresponds to a flux density of 1.6 w/m^2, and the abscissa to a magnetic intensity H of 1000 amp/m. Approximately what is the relative permeability at points a, b, c, d, i, and j?

34–9. A bar magnet has a coercivity of 4×10^3 amp/m. It is desired to demagnetize it by inserting it inside a solenoid 12 cm long and having 60 turns. What current should be carried by the solenoid?

34–10. An iron disk 6 cm in diameter and 4 mm thick is uniformly magnetized in a direction perpendicular to its end faces. The magnetization $M = 1.5 \times 10^6$ amp/m. (a) What is the equivalent surface current around the rim of the disk? (b) What is the flux density B at the center of the disk?   (c) What is the magnetic intensity H at the center of the disk? What is its direction relative to that of B? (d) What is the relative permeability of the disk? (e) What is the surface density of magnetic charge on the end faces? (f) What is the magnetic moment of the disk?

34–11. The horizontal component of the flux density of the earth's magnetic field at Cambridge, Mass., is 1.7×10^{-5} w/m^2. What is the horizontal component of the magnetic intensity?

34–12. Show that for a continuous Rowland ring (no air gap) Eq. (34–18) reduces to $B = \mu H$, where $H = NI/l$.

34–13. An iron Rowland ring has a mean circumferential length of 40 cm and an area of 5 cm^2. The ring is wound with 350 turns of wire and carries a current of 0.2 amp. (a) What is the magnetomotive force in the ring? (b) What is the magnetic intensity in the ring?   (c) Using the permeability curve of Fig. 34–3, determine the permeability of iron at this value of magnetic intensity. (d) What is the reluctance of the magnetic circuit? (e) What is the total flux in the ring?

34–14. A gap 0.5 mm wide is cut in the ring of Problem 34–13. (a) What is the reluctance of the magnetic circuit?   (b) What is now the flux in the ring?

CHAPTER 35

Alternating Currents

35–1 Introduction

A coil of wire, rotating with constant angular velocity in a magnetic field, develops a sinusoidal alternating emf as explained in Section 33–4. This simple device is the prototype of the commercial alternating current generator, or *alternator*. An *L-C* circuit, as explained in Section 33–13, oscillates sinusoidally, and with the proper circuitry provides an alternating potential difference between its terminals having a frequency, depending on the purpose for which it is designed, that may range from a few cycles per second to many millions of cycles per second.

We consider next a number of circuits connected to an alternator or oscillator which maintains between its terminals a sinusoidal alternating potential difference

$$v = V \sin \omega t,$$

where V is the maximum potential difference or the *voltage amplitude*, v is the *instantaneous* potential difference, and ω the *angular frequency*, equal to 2π times the frequency f. For brevity, the alternator or oscillator will be referred to as an "AC source," although this is not the best English usage, since "AC" is an abbreviation for "alternating current." The symbol for an AC source is $\bigodot$.

Because sine curves are not easy to draw, we shall make frequent use of *rotor* diagrams (see Section 11–4) in which the instantaneous value of a quantity is represented by the projection onto a vertical axis of a rotor of length corresponding to the amplitude of the quantity and rotating counterclockwise at an angular velocity ω.

When an AC source is first connected to a circuit, *transient* currents like those discussed in Sections 29–7 and 33–12 are set up. These die out exponentially and the current settles down to a *steady state*. The analyses that follow apply only to the final steady-state current. They also apply only to circuits in which the frequency is sufficiently low so that the time required for a disturbance to travel the length of the circuit with speed c (see Section 36–1) is very small compared with the period $T = 1/f$.

35–2 Circuits containing resistance, inductance, or capacitance

Let a resistor of resistance R be connected between the terminals of an AC source as in Fig. 35–1. The instantaneous potential difference between points a and b is $v_{ab} = V \sin \omega t$, and the instantaneous current in the resistor is

$$i = \frac{v_{ab}}{R} = \frac{V}{R} \sin \omega t.$$

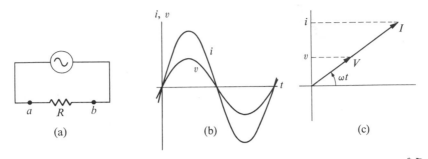

Fig. 35–1. (a) Resistance R connected across an AC source. (b) Graphs of instantaneous voltage and current. (c) Rotor diagram; current and voltage in phase.

The maximum current I, or the *current amplitude*, is evidently

$$I = \frac{V}{R} \tag{35–1}$$

and we can therefore write

$$i = I \sin \omega t. \tag{35–2}$$

The current and voltage both vary with $\sin \omega t$, so the current is *in phase* with the voltage. The current and voltage amplitudes, from Eq. (35–1), are related in the same way as in a DC circuit.

Figure 35–1(b) shows graphs of i and v as functions of time. (The fact that the *curve* representing the current has the greater amplitude in the diagram is of no significance because the choice of vertical scales for i and v is arbitrary.) The corresponding rotor diagram is given in Fig. 35–1(c). Because i and v are in phase and have the same frequency, the current and voltage rotors rotate together.

The current density in a wire carrying alternating current is not uniform over the cross section of the wire but is greater near the surface, a phenomenon known as "skin effect." The effective cross section of the wire is therefore reduced and its resistance is larger than when the current is constant. Skin effect results from self-induced emf's set up by the variation in the internal flux in the conductor, and is greater the higher the frequency. Unless the frequency is extremely high, however (of the order of some millions of cycles per second), the change in resistance is not large and we shall assume the resistance to be independent of frequency.

Next, suppose that a capacitor of capacitance C is connected across the source, as in Fig. 35–2. The instantaneous charge q on the capacitor is

$$q = Cv_{ab} = CV \sin \omega t,$$

and the current i is

$$i = \frac{dq}{dt} = \omega CV \cos \omega t.$$

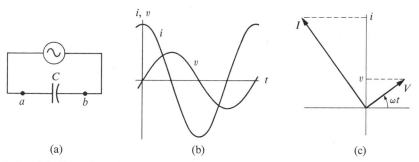

Fig. 35–2. (a) Capacitor C connected across an AC source. (b) Graphs of instantaneous voltage and current. (c) Rotor diagram; current leads voltage by 90°.

The maximum current is evidently

$$I = \omega CV, \tag{35-3}$$

and we can write

$$i = I \cos \omega t. \tag{35-4}$$

Thus if the voltage is represented by a *sine* function, the current is represented by a *cosine* function, as shown in Fig. 35–2(b). The current is *not* in phase with the voltage. The current and voltage rotors are shown in Fig. 35–2(c). Remembering that these rotate counterclockwise, and that their projections on the vertical axis represent instantaneous values, it will be seen that the current goes through its sequence of values 90° *earlier* than does the voltage. We say that the current *leads* the voltage by 90°. (One could equally well say that the voltage *lags* the current by 90°.)

The expression for the maximum current can be put in the same form as that for the current in a resistor if we write Eq. (35–3) as

$$I = \frac{V}{1/\omega C},$$

and define a quantity X_C, called the *capacitive reactance* of the capacitor, as

$$X_C = \frac{1}{\omega C}. \tag{35-5}$$

Then

$$I = \frac{V}{X_C}. \tag{35-6}$$

It will be seen from Eq. (35–6) that the unit of capacitive reactance is 1 volt/amp, or 1 ohm.

The reactance of a capacitor is inversely proportional both to the capacitance C and to the angular frequency ω; the greater the capacitance, and the higher the frequency, the *smaller* is the reactance X_C.

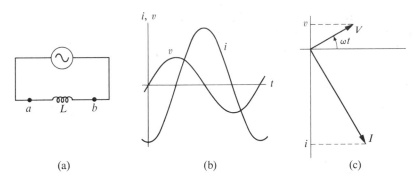

Fig. 35-3. (a) Inductance L connected across an AC source. (b) Graphs of instantaneous voltage and current. (c) Rotor diagram; current lags voltage by 90°.

EXAMPLE. At an angular frequency of 1000 rad/sec, the reactance of a 1-μf capacitor is

$$X_C = \frac{1}{\omega C} = \frac{1}{(10^3 \text{ rad/sec}) \times 10^{-6} \text{ f}} = 1000 \text{ ohms.}$$

At a frequency of 10,000 rad/sec the reactance of the same capacitor is only 100 ohms, and at a frequency of 100 rad/sec it is 10,000 ohms.

Finally, suppose a pure inductor of zero resistance and having a self-inductance L is connected to an AC source as in Fig. 35-3. Since the potential difference between the terminals of an inductor equals $L \, di/dt$, we have

$$L \frac{di}{dt} = V \sin \omega t$$

and

$$di = \frac{V}{L} \sin \omega t \, dt.$$

Integration of both sides gives

$$i = -\frac{V}{\omega L} \cos \omega t.$$

The maximum current is

$$I = \frac{V}{\omega L}, \tag{35-7}$$

and

$$i = -I \cos \omega t. \tag{35-8}$$

If the voltage is represented by a sine curve, the current is given by a *negative cosine* curve, as in Fig. 35-3(b). The rotor diagram in Fig. 35-3(c) shows that the current goes through its sequence of values 90° *later* than the voltage, and we say that the current *lags* the voltage by 90°.

The *inductive reactance* X_L of an inductor is defined as

$$X_L = \omega L, \tag{35–9}$$

and Eq. (35–7) can also be written in the same form as that for a resistor:

$$I = \frac{V}{X_L}. \tag{35–10}$$

The unit of inductive reactance is also 1 ohm.

The reactance of an inductor is directly proportional both to its inductance L and to the angular frequency ω; the greater the inductance, and. the higher the frequency, the *larger* is the reactance. If there is any iron associated with an inductor its self-inductance is not constant, but for simplicity we shall ignore this variation.

EXAMPLE.   At an angular frequency of 1000 rad/sec, the reactance of a 1-henry inductor is

$$X_L = \omega L = 10^3 \frac{\text{rad}}{\text{sec}} \times 1\ \text{h} = 1000\ \text{ohms}.$$

At a frequency of 10,000 rad/sec the reactance of the same inductor is 10,000 ohms, while at a frequency of 100 rad/sec it is only 100 ohms.

The graphs in Fig. 35–4 summarize the variations with frequency of the resistance of a resistor, and of the reactances of an inductor and of a capacitor. As the frequency increases, the reactance of the inductor approaches infinity and that of the capacitor

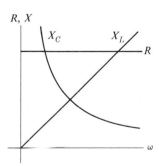

Fig. 35–4.   Graphs of R, X_L, and X_C, as functions of frequency.

approaches zero. As the frequency decreases, the inductive reactance approaches zero and the capacitive reactance approaches infinity. The limiting case of zero frequency corresponds to a DC circuit.

The generic term *reactor* is used to refer either to an inductor or to a capacitor.

35-3 The *R-L-C* series circuit

In many instances, AC circuits include resistance, inductive reactance, and capacitive reactance. A simple series circuit is shown in Fig. 35–5(a). We shall analyze the circuit by constructing its rotor diagram, shown in Fig. 35–5(b).

Provided the frequency is not too high, the instantaneous current i has the same value at all points of the circuit. Thus a *single* rotor I, of length proportional to the current amplitude, suffices to represent the current in each circuit element.

Let us use the symbols v_R, v_L, and v_C for the instantaneous voltages across R, L, and C, and V_R, V_L, and V_C for their maximum values. The instantaneous and maximum voltages across the source will be represented by v and V. Then $v = v_{ab}$, $v_R = v_{ac}$, $v_L = v_{cd}$, and $v_C = v_{db}$.

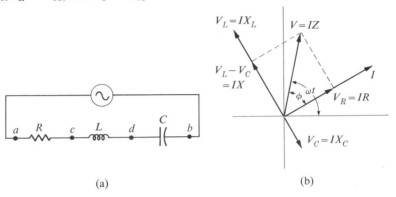

(a)   (b)

Fig. 35–5.   (a) A series *R-L-C* circuit.   (b) Rotor diagram.

We have shown that the potential difference between the terminals of a resistor is *in phase* with the current in the resistor and that its maximum value V_R is

$$V_R = IR.$$

Thus the rotor V_R in Fig. 35–5(b), in phase with the current rotor, represents the voltage across the resistor. Its projection on the vertical axis, at any instant, gives the instantaneous potential difference v_R.

The current in an inductor *lags* the voltage by 90° or, what is the same thing, the voltage *leads* the current by 90°. The voltage amplitude is

$$V_L = IX_L.$$

The rotor V_L in Fig. 35–5(b) represents the voltage across the inductor, and its projection at any instant onto the vertical axis equals v_L.

The current in a capacitor *leads* the voltage by 90°, or, the voltage *lags* the current by 90°. The voltage amplitude is

$$V_C = IX_C.$$

The rotor V_C in Fig. 35–5(b) represents the voltage across the capacitor and its projection at any instant onto the vertical axis equals v_C.

The instantaneous potential difference v between terminals a and b equals at every instant the (algebraic) sum of the potential differences v_R, v_L, and v_C. That is, it equals the sum of the projections of the rotors V_R, V_L, and V_C. But the *projection* of the *vector sum* of these rotors is equal to the *sum* of their *projections*, so this vector sum V must be the rotor that represents the terminal voltage. To form the vector sum, we first subtract the rotor V_C from the rotor V_L (since these always lie in the same straight line), giving the rotor $V_L - V_C$. Since this is at right angles to the rotor V_R, the magnitude of the rotor V is

$$V = \sqrt{V_R^2 + (V_L - V_C)^2}$$
$$= \sqrt{(IR)^2 + (IX_L - IX_C)^2}$$
$$= I\sqrt{R^2 + (X_L - X_C)^2}.$$

The notation can be simplified by defining a quantity X, the *net reactance* of the circuit, as

$$X = X_L - X_C. \tag{35-11}$$

Then

$$V = I\sqrt{R^2 + X^2}.$$

Finally, we define the *impedance* Z of the circuit as

$$Z = \sqrt{R^2 + X^2}, \tag{35-12}$$

so we can write

$$V = IZ, \quad \text{or} \quad I = \frac{V}{Z}. \tag{35-13}$$

Thus the *form* of the equation relating current and voltage *amplitudes* is the same as that for a DC circuit, the impedance Z playing the same role as the resistance R of the DC circuit. Note, however, that the impedance is actually a function of R, L, and C, as well as of the frequency ω. The complete expression for Z, for a series circuit, is

$$Z = \sqrt{R^2 + (X_L - X_C)^2} = \sqrt{R^2 + [\omega L - (1/\omega C)]^2}. \tag{35-14}$$

The unit of impedance, from Eq. (35-14), is evidently 1 volt/amp or 1 ohm.

The expressions for the impedance Z of (a) an R-L series circuit, (b) an R-C series circuit, and (c) an L-C series circuit can be obtained from Eq. (35-14) by letting (a) $X_C = 0$, (b) $X_L = 0$, and (c) $R = 0$.

Equation (35-14) gives the impedance Z only for a series R-L-C circuit. But whatever the nature of an R-L-C network, its impedance can be defined by Eq. (35-13) as the ratio of the voltage amplitude to the current amplitude.

The angle ϕ, in Fig. 35-5(b), is the phase angle between the line voltage V and the line current I. It should be evident from the diagram that

$$\tan \phi = \frac{V_L - V_C}{V_R} = \frac{I(X_L - X_C)}{IR} = \frac{X}{R}. \tag{35-15}$$

Hence if the line voltage is represented by a sine function,

$$v = V \sin \omega t,$$

the line current lags by an angle ϕ and its equation is

$$i = I \sin (\omega t - \phi).$$

Figure 35–5 has been constructed for a circuit in which $X_L > X_C$. If $X_L < X_C$, rotor V lies on the opposite side of the current rotor I and the current *leads* the voltage. In this case, $X = X_L - X_C$ is a negative quantity and tan ϕ is negative.

To summarize, we can say that the *instantaneous* potential differences in an AC series circuit add *algebraically*, just as in a DC circuit, while the voltage *amplitudes* add *vectorially*.

EXAMPLE.   In the series circuit of Fig. 35–5, let $R = 300$ ohms, $L = 0.9$ h, $C = 2.0$ μf, and $\omega = 1000$ rad/sec. Then

$$X_L = \omega L = 900 \text{ ohms}, \qquad X_C = \frac{1}{\omega C} = 500 \text{ ohms}.$$

The reactance X of the circuit is

$$X = X_L - X_C = 400 \text{ ohms},$$

and the impedance Z is

$$Z = \sqrt{R^2 + X^2} = 500 \text{ ohms}.$$

If connected across an AC source of voltage amplitude 50 volts, the current amplitude is

$$I = \frac{V}{Z} = 0.10 \text{ amp.}$$

The lag angle ϕ is

$$\phi = \tan^{-1} \frac{X}{R} = 53°.$$

The voltage amplitude across the resistor is

$$V_R = IR = 30 \text{ volts.}$$

The voltage amplitudes across the inductor and capacitor are, respectively,

$$V_L = IX_L = 90 \text{ volts}, \qquad V_C = IX_C = 50 \text{ volts.}$$

35–4 Average and root-mean-square values.   AC instruments

The *instantaneous* potential difference between two points of an AC circuit can be measured by connecting a calibrated oscilloscope between the points, and the instantaneous current by connecting an oscilloscope across a resistor in the circuit. The usual moving coil galvanometer, however, has too large a moment of inertia to follow the instantaneous values of an alternating current. It averages out the fluctuating torque on its coil, and its deflection is proportional to the *average* current.

The average value of any quantity that varies with time, $f(t)$, over a time interval from t_1 to t_2, is defined as

$$f_{av} = \frac{1}{t_2 - t_1} \int_{t_1}^{t_2} f(t)\, dt, \qquad f_{av}(t_2 - t_1) = \int_{t_1}^{t_2} f(t)\, dt.$$

The average has the following graphical interpretation. The integral $\int_{t_1}^{t_2} f(t)\, dt$ is the *area* under a graph of $f(t)$ versus t, between vertical lines at t_1 and t_2. The product $f_{av}(t_2 - t_1)$ is the area of a rectangle of height f_{av} and base $(t_2 - t_1)$. From the definition of f_{av}, these areas are equal.

Let us apply this definition to a sinusoidally varying quantity, for example, a current given by

$$i = I \sin \omega t.$$

The average value of the current for the *half-cycle* from $t = 0$ to $t = \pi/\omega$ is

$$I_{av} = \frac{\omega}{\pi} \int_0^{\pi/\omega} I \sin \omega t\, dt = \frac{2I}{\pi}.$$

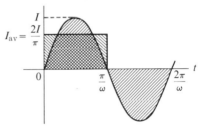

That is, the average current is $2/\pi$ (about $\frac{2}{3}$) times the maximum current, and the area under the rectangle in Fig. 35–6 equals the area under one loop of the sine curve.

Fig. 35–6. The average value of a sinusoidal current over a half-cycle is $2I/\pi$. The average over a complete cycle is zero.

The average current for a *complete cycle* (or any number of complete cycles) is

$$I_{av} = \frac{\omega}{2\pi} \int_0^{2\pi/\omega} I \sin \omega t\, dt = 0,$$

as would be expected, since the *positive* area of the loop between 0 and π/ω is equal to the *negative* area of the loop between π/ω and $2\pi/\omega$. Hence if a sinusoidal current is sent through a moving-coil galvanometer, the meter reads zero.

Such a meter can be used in an AC circuit, however, if it is connected in the *full-wave* rectifier circuit shown in Fig. 35–7(a). As explained in Section 28–6, an ideal rectifier

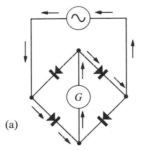

(a)

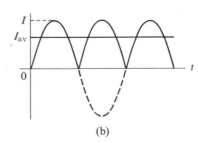

(b)

Fig. 35–7. (a) A full-wave rectifier. (b) Graph of a full-wave rectified current and its average value.

offers a constant finite resistance to current in the forward direction and an infinite resistance to current in the opposite direction. By tracing through the circuit, it will be seen that when the line current is in the direction shown, two of the rectifiers are conducting and two are nonconducting, and the current in the galvanometer is upward. When the line current is in the opposite direction, the rectifiers that are non-conducting in Fig. 35–7(a) carry the current and the current in the galvanometer is still upward. Thus if the line current alternates sinusoidally, the current in the galvanometer has the waveform shown in Fig. 35–7(b). Although pulsating, it is always in the same direction and its average value is not zero. The galvanometer must, of course, be provided with the necessary series resistances or shunts, as for any DC voltmeter or ammeter.

The average value of the rectified current, in any number of complete cycles, is the same as the average current in the first half-cycle in Fig. 35–6, or it is $2/\pi$ times the maximum current I. Hence if the meter deflects full scale with a steady current I_0 through it, it will also deflect full scale when the average value of the rectified current, $2I/\pi$, is equal to I_0. The current amplitude I, when the meter deflects full scale, is then

$$I = \frac{\pi I_0}{2}.$$

For example, if $I_0 = 1$ amp, $I = 1.57$ amp.

Most AC meters are calibrated to read not the maximum value of the current or voltage, but the *root-mean-square* value, that is, the *square root* of the *average* value of the *square* of the current or voltage, abbreviated as the rms value.

Figure 35–8 shows graphs of a sinusoidally varying current and of its square. [The graph of i^2 has the same form if the current is fully rectified, as in Fig. 35–7(b).] If $i = I \sin \omega t$, then

$$i^2 = I^2 \sin^2 \omega t = I^2 \tfrac{1}{2}(1 - \cos 2\omega t) = \tfrac{1}{2}I^2 - \tfrac{1}{2}I^2 \cos 2\omega t.$$

The *average* value of i^2, or the *mean square current*, is equal to the constant term $\tfrac{1}{2}I^2$, since the average value of $\cos 2\omega t$, over any number of complete cycles, is zero.

$$(I^2)_{av} = \frac{I^2}{2}.$$

The root mean square current is the square root of this, or

$$I_{rms} = \sqrt{(I^2)_{av}} = \frac{I}{\sqrt{2}}.$$

In the same way, the root mean square value of a sinusoidal voltage is

$$V_{rms} = \frac{V}{\sqrt{2}}.$$

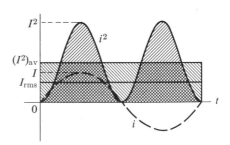

Fig. 35–8. The average value of the square of a sinusoidally varying current, over any number of half-cycles, is $I^2/2$. The root-mean-square value is $I/\sqrt{2}$.

Voltages and currents in power distribution systems are always referred to in terms of their rms values. Thus when we speak of our household power supply as "115-volt AC," this means that the rms voltage is 115 volts. The voltage amplitude is

$$V = \sqrt{2}\, V_{rms} = 163 \text{ volts.}$$

When the rectifier meter described above reads full scale, the current amplitude I equals $\pi I_0/2$. The corresponding rms current is then

$$I_{rms} = \frac{I}{\sqrt{2}} = \frac{\pi}{2\sqrt{2}} I_0 = 1.11 I_0.$$

If the meter deflects full scale with a steady current I_0 of 1 amp, the corresponding rms current for full-scale deflection is

$$I_{rms} = 1.11 \text{ amp.}$$

35–5 Power in AC circuits

The instantaneous power input to an AC circuit is

$$p = vi,$$

where v is the instantaneous potential difference between the terminals of the circuit, and i is the instantaneous current. We consider first some special cases.

If the circuit consists of a pure resistance R, as in Fig. 35–1, i and v are *in phase*. The graph representing p is obtained by multiplying together at every instant the ordinates of the graphs of v and i in Fig. 35–1(b), and it is shown by the full curve in Fig. 35–9(a). (The product vi is positive when v and i are both positive or both negative.) That is, energy is supplied *to* the resistor at all instants, whatever the direction of the current, although the *rate* at which it is supplied is not a constant.

The power curve is symmetrical about a value equal to one-half its maximum ordinate VI, so the average power P is

$$P = \tfrac{1}{2}VI.$$

The same result can be obtained analytically as follows. The equation of the power curve is

$$p = V \sin \omega t \times I \sin \omega t = VI \sin^2 \omega t. \tag{35–16}$$

But

$$\sin^2 \omega t = \tfrac{1}{2}(1 - \cos 2\omega t),$$

so

$$p = \tfrac{1}{2}VI - \tfrac{1}{2}VI \cos 2\omega t.$$

The average power is equal to the constant term $\tfrac{1}{2}VI$, since the average value of the second term, over any number of complete cycles, is zero.

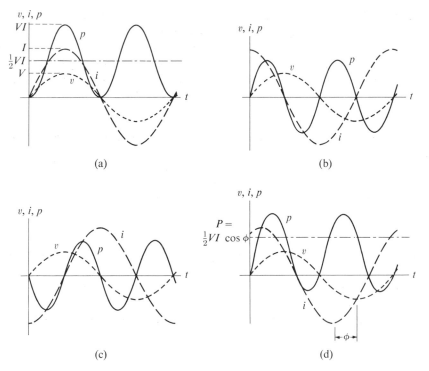

Fig. 35–9. (a) Instantaneous power input to a resistor. The average power is $\frac{1}{2}VI$. (b) Instantaneous power input to a capacitor. The average power is zero. (c) Instantaneous power input to a pure inductor. The average power is zero. (d) Instantaneous power input to an arbitrary AC circuit. The average power is $\frac{1}{2}VI \cos \phi = V_{\mathrm{rms}}I_{\mathrm{rms}} \cos \phi$.

The average power can also be written

$$P = \frac{V}{\sqrt{2}} \frac{I}{\sqrt{2}} = V_{\mathrm{rms}} I_{\mathrm{rms}}. \qquad (35\text{--}17)$$

Furthermore, since $V_{\mathrm{rms}} = I_{\mathrm{rms}}R$, we have

$$P = I_{\mathrm{rms}}^2 R. \qquad (35\text{--}18)$$

Note that Eqs. (35–17) and (35–18) have the same *form* as those for a DC circuit.

Suppose next that the circuit consists of a capacitor, as in Fig. 35–2. The current and voltage are then 90° out of phase. When the curves of v and i are multiplied together (the product vi is *negative* when v and i have *opposite* signs) the power curve in Fig. 35–9(b) is obtained, and is symmetrical about the horizontal axis. The average power is therefore zero.

To see why this is so, we recall that positive power means that energy is supplied *to* a device and that negative power means that energy is supplied *by* a device. The process we are considering is merely the charge and discharge of a capacitor. During the intervals when p is positive, energy is supplied to charge the capacitor, and when p is negative the capacitor is discharging and returning energy to the source.

The expression for the average power can also be obtained as follows. The instantaneous power is

$$p = V \sin \omega t \times I \cos \omega t = \tfrac{1}{2} VI \sin 2\omega t.$$

The average value of $\sin 2\omega t$ is zero over any number of complete cycles.

Figure 35–9(c) is the power curve for a pure inductor. As for a capacitor, the current and voltage are out of phase by 90°, and the average power is zero. Energy is supplied to establish a magnetic field around the inductor and is returned to the source when the field collapses.

In the most general case, current and voltage differ in phase by an angle ϕ and

$$p = V \sin \omega t \times I \sin (\omega t - \phi). \tag{35–19}$$

The instantaneous power curve has the form shown in Fig. 35–9(d). The area under the positive loops is greater than that under the negative loops and the net average power is positive.

The preceding analyses have shown that when v and i are *in phase* the average power equals $\tfrac{1}{2} VI$, and when v and i are 90° *out of phase* the average power is zero. Hence we might expect that in the general case, when v and i differ by an angle ϕ, the average power would equal $\tfrac{1}{2} V$, multiplied by $I \cos \phi$, the component of I that is *in phase* with V. That is,

$$P = \tfrac{1}{2} VI \cos \phi.$$

This can be shown analytically as follows. Making use of the relation

$$\sin (\omega t - \phi) = \sin \omega t \cos \phi - \cos \omega t \sin \phi,$$

Eq. (35–19) can be written as

$$p = VI \cos \phi \sin^2 \omega t - VI \sin \phi \sin \omega t \cos \omega t.$$

The average value of the second term is zero. The first term, except for the factor $\cos \phi$, has the same form as Eq. (35–16) and hence the average power is

$$P = \tfrac{1}{2} VI \cos \phi = V_{\text{rms}} I_{\text{rms}} \cos \phi. \tag{35–20}$$

This is the general expression for the power input to *any* AC circuit. The term $\cos \phi$ is called the *power factor* of the circuit. For a pure resistance, $\phi = 0$, $\cos \phi = 1$, and $P = V_{rms}I_{rms}$. For a capacitor or inductor, $\phi = 90°$, $\cos \phi = 0$, and $P = 0$.

If the circuit is *passive*, $V = IZ$ and $\cos \phi = R/Z$. Then in this case,

$$P = \tfrac{1}{2}VI \cos \phi = \tfrac{1}{2}IZ \times I \times (R/Z) = \tfrac{1}{2}I^2 R,$$

and all of the power input is dissipated in the resistor, and produces either a rise of temperature or a flow of heat to the surroundings. If the circuit is not passive but contains a motor, for example, the power is still given correctly by Eq. (35–20) but it is no longer true that $V = IZ$ and $\cos \phi = R/Z$, so that the power input is *not* all dissipated.

35–6 Series resonance

The impedance of an *R-L-C* series circuit depends on the frequency, since the inductive reactance is directly, and the capacitive reactance is inversely, proportional to the frequency. This dependence is illustrated in Fig. 35–10(a), where a logarithmic frequency scale has been used because of the wide range of frequencies covered. Note that there is one particular frequency at which X_L and X_C are numerically equal. At this frequency, $X = X_L - X_C$ is zero. Hence the impedance Z, equal to $\sqrt{R^2 + X^2}$, is a *minimum* at this frequency and is equal to the resistance R.

If an AC source of constant voltage amplitude but variable frequency is connected across the circuit, the current amplitude I varies with frequency as shown in Fig. 35–10(b), and is a *maximum* at the frequency at which the impedance Z is a *minimum*. The same diagram also shows the phase difference ϕ as a function of frequency. At low frequencies, where capacitive reactance X_C predominates, the current leads the voltage. At the frequency where $X = 0$, the current and voltage are in phase, and at high frequencies, where X_L predominates, the current lags the voltage.

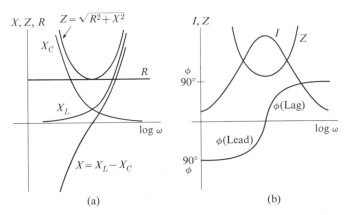

(a)   (b)

Fig. 35–10.   (a) Reactance, resistance, and impedance as functions of frequency (logarithmic frequency scale). (b) Impedance, current, and phase angle as functions of frequency (logarithmic frequency scale).

The behavior of the current in an AC series circuit, as the source frequency is varied, is exactly analogous to the response of a spring-mass system having a viscous damping force as the frequency of the driving force is varied. The frequency ω_0 at which the current is a maximum is called the *resonant frequency* and is easily computed from the fact that at this frequency $X_L = X_C$:

$$X_L = X_C, \qquad \omega_0 L = 1/\omega_0 C, \qquad \omega_0 = \sqrt{1/LC}.$$

Note that this is equal to the natural frequency of oscillation of an L-C circuit, as derived in Section 33–13.

If the inductance L or the capacitance C of a circuit can be varied, the resonant frequency can be varied also. This is the procedure by which a radio or television receiving set may be "tuned" to receive the signal from a desired station.

EXAMPLE. The series circuit in Fig. 35-11 is connected to the terminals of an AC source of variable frequency but whose rms terminal voltage is constant and equal to 100 volts. At the resonant frequency, $X_L = X_C = 2000$ ohms, and $R = 500$ ohms. The impedance Z is then equal to the resistance R and the rms current is

$$I = \frac{V}{Z} = \frac{V}{R} = 0.20 \text{ amp.}$$

The rms potential difference across the resistor is

$$V_R = IR = 100 \text{ volts.}$$

The potential differences across the inductor and capacitor are, respectively,

$$V_L = IX_L = 400 \text{ volts}, \qquad V_C = IX_C = 400 \text{ volts.}$$

The potential difference across the inductor-capacitor combination (V_{cb}) is

$$V = IX = I(X_L - X_C) = 0.$$

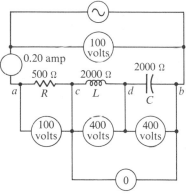

Fig. 35–11. Series resonant circuit.

This is because the instantaneous potential differences across the inductor and the capacitor are 180° out of phase. Although the effective values of each may be large, their resultant at each instant is zero.

35–7 Circuits in parallel

Circuit elements connected in parallel across an AC source can be analyzed by the same procedure as for elements in series. The rotor diagram for the circuit in Fig. 35–12(a) is given in Fig. 35–12(b). In this case, the instantaneous potential difference across each element is the same, and a *single* rotor V represents the common terminal voltage. The rotor I_R, of amplitude V/R and in phase with V, represents the current in the resistor. Rotor I_L, of amplitude V/X_L and lagging V by 90°, repre-

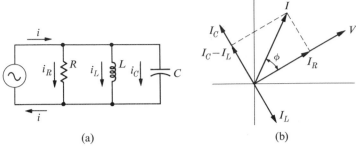

Figure 35–12

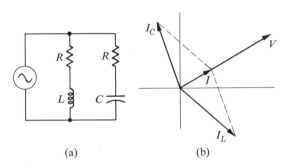

Figure 35–13

sents the current in the inductor, and rotor I_C, of amplitude V/X_C and leading V by 90°, represents the current in the capacitor.

The instantaneous line current i, by Kirchhoff's point rule, equals the (algebraic) sum of the instantaneous currents i_R, i_L, and i_C, and is represented by the rotor I, the vector sum of rotors I_R, I_L, and I_C. Angle ϕ is the phase angle between line current and line voltage.

Although the principles of parallel circuits are straightforward, the algebraic analysis of such circuits is more complicated than is that of series circuits and will not be given. The special case of *parallel resonance*, however, is important enough to be considered further. Figure 35–13 represents a circuit having two branches in parallel. We shall assume that the resistance R is the same in each branch, that $X_L = X_C$, and that X_L and X_C are large compared with R. The currents I_L and I_C are then equal and the former lags the voltage by nearly 90°, while the latter leads by nearly 90°. The line current I is in phase with the line voltage V but is very much *smaller* than either I_L or I_C. This means that the equivalent impedance of the parallel circuit is very much *larger* than the reactances X_L and X_C.

35–8 The transformer

For reasons of efficiency, it is desirable to transmit electrical power at high voltages and small currents, with consequent reduction of I^2R heating in the transmission line. On the other hand, considerations of safety and of insulation of moving parts require relatively low voltages in generating equipment and in motors and household

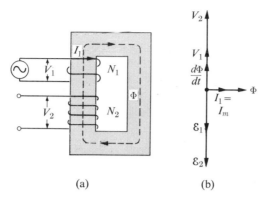

(a)   (b)

Fig. 35–14. (a) Schematic diagram of a transformer with secondary open. (b) Corresponding rotor diagram.

appliances. One of the most useful features of AC circuits is the ease and efficiency
with which voltages (and currents) may be changed from one value to another by
transformers.

In principle, the transformer consists of two coils electrically insulated from each
other and wound on the same iron core. An alternating current in one winding sets
up an alternating flux in the core, and the induced electric field produced by this
varying flux (see Section 33–3) induces an emf in the other winding. Energy is thus
transferred from one winding to another via the core flux and its associated induced
electric field. The winding to which power is supplied is called the *primary*; that from
which power is delivered is called the *secondary.* Either winding may be used as the
primary. The symbol for an iron core transformer is ⧦⧦ .

The power output of a transformer is necessarily less than the power input because
of unavoidable losses. These losses consist of I^2R losses in the primary and secondary
windings (copper losses) and hysteresis and eddy-current losses in the core (core
losses). Hysteresis losses are minimized by the use of iron having a narrow hysteresis
loop, and eddy currents are minimized by laminating the core. In spite of these
losses, transformer efficiencies are usually well over 90% and in large installations
may reach 99%.

For simplicity, we shall consider only an idealized transformer in which there are
no losses and in which all of the flux is confined to the iron core, so that the same flux
links both primary and secondary. The transformer is shown schematically in
Fig. 35–14(a). A primary winding of N_1 turns and a secondary winding of N_2 turns
both encircle the core in the same sense. An AC source of voltage amplitude V_1 is
connected to the primary and, to begin with, we assume the secondary to be open, so
that there is no secondary current. The primary winding then functions merely
as an inductor.

Figure 35–14(b) is the rotor diagram of the transformer.* Rotor V_1 represents the
primary voltage. Since the primary is assumed of zero resistance, the primary current

---

*To help understand Figs. 35–14(b) and 35–15(b), the reader should construct his own
diagrams, following the sequence of steps given in the text.

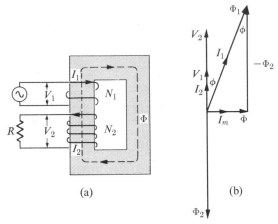

Fig. 35-15. (a) Schematic diagram of a transformer with a resistance R connected across the secondary. (b) Corresponding rotor diagram.

I_1, referred to also as the *magnetizing* current I_m, lags the primary voltage by 90°. Its magnitude is V_1/X_1, where X_1 is the reactance of the primary. The magnetizing current sets up a flux of amplitude Φ in the core, in phase with the current and equal to $N_1I_1/\mathfrak{R}$, where $\mathfrak{R}$ is the reluctance of the core, assumed constant. The rotor $d\Phi/dt$ represents the rate of change of flux, and it leads the flux by 90°. (If the flux is represented by $\Phi \sin \omega t$, then $d\Phi/dt = \omega\Phi \cos \omega t$.) By Faraday's law, the induced emf's in the primary and secondary are

$$\mathcal{E}_1 = -N_1 \frac{d\Phi}{dt}, \qquad \mathcal{E}_2 = -N_2 \frac{d\Phi}{dt}, \qquad (35\text{-}21)$$

and because of the minus sign are 180° out of phase with $d\Phi/dt$. Since both primary and secondary are of zero resistance, $V_1 = -\mathcal{E}_1$ and $V_2 = -\mathcal{E}_2$. Hence rotors V_1 and V_2 are *in phase* with the rotor $d\Phi/dt$. It follows from Eq. (35-21) that the ratio of the secondary to the primary voltage is

$$\frac{V_2}{V_1} = \frac{N_2}{N_1}. \qquad (35\text{-}22)$$

If $N_2 > N_1$, $V_2 > V_1$ and we have a *step-up* transformer; if $N_2 < N_1$, then we have a *step-down* transformer. The power input to the ideal transformer, with the secondary open-circuited, is zero.

In Fig. 35-15(a), a resistance R is connected across the secondary, and Fig. 35-15(b) is the corresponding rotor diagram. Because the primary voltage V_1 is fixed, the rate of change of flux $d\Phi/dt$ must be the same as in Fig. 35-14. Hence the core flux Φ and the secondary voltage V_2 must also be the same. The core flux, however, is now set up both by the primary current I_1 and by the secondary current I_2. We do not as yet know the magnitude or phase of the primary current, but since a pure resistance R is connected across the secondary, the secondary current I_2 is in phase with the secondary voltage V_2 and its magnitude is V_2/R. (In general, the secondary current equals

V_2/Z_2, where Z_2 is the impedance of the external secondary circuit, and it lags or
leads V_2 depending on the nature of this circuit.) With the sign convention we are
using, the flux Φ_2 set up by the secondary current is opposite in phase to this current,
as shown. Then, since the net core flux Φ is the vector sum of Φ_1 and Φ_2, the primary
flux Φ_1 is the vector sum of Φ and $-\Phi_2$. The primary current I_1 is in phase with Φ_1
as shown and its magnitude is $\Phi_1\mathfrak{R}/N_1$.

Thus the effect of completing the secondary circuit is twofold; the primary current
is increased in magnitude from I_m to I_1 (Fig. 35–15), and it lags the primary voltage
V_1 by an angle ϕ less than 90°. The power input to the primary is now

$$P = V_1 I_1 \cos \phi.$$

But

$$\cos \phi = \frac{\Phi_2}{\Phi_1} = \frac{N_2 I_2/\mathfrak{R}}{N_1 I_1/\mathfrak{R}} = \frac{N_2}{N_1} \frac{I_2}{I_1},$$

and

$$V_1 = \frac{N_1}{N_2} V_2, \tag{35–23}$$

so

$$P = \frac{N_1}{N_2} V_2 \times I_1 \times \frac{N_2}{N_1} \frac{I_2}{I_1} = V_2 I_2.$$

But $V_2 I_2$ equals the power *output*, so the power input equals the power output, as it
must for an ideal transformer with no losses. Equating the power input to the power
output, we get

$$\frac{I_2}{I_1} = \frac{V_1}{V_2} \cos \phi = \frac{N_1}{N_2} \cos \phi. \tag{35–24}$$

In power transformers operating at rated load, the magnetizing current I_m is very
small compared with the current I_1, the angle ϕ is small, and $\cos \phi \approx 1$. To this
approximation, the ratio of secondary to primary current equals the *inverse* of the
turns ratio.

From the equation $I_2 = V_2/R$, together with Eqs. (35–23) and (35–24), it follows
to within the approximation above that

$$I_1 = \frac{V_1}{(N_1/N_2)^2 R}.$$

Thus when the secondary circuit is completed through a resistance R, the result is
the same as if the *source* had been connected directly to a resistance equal to R
multiplied by the reciprocal of the *square* of the turns ratio. In other words, the transformer "transforms" not only voltages and currents, but resistances (more generally,
impedances) as well. Problem 28–25 shows that maximum power is supplied by a
source to a resistor when its resistance equals the internal resistance of the source.
The same principle applies in AC circuits, with resistance replaced by impedance.
When a high-impedance AC source must be connected to a low-impedance circuit, as
when an audio amplifier is connected to a loudspeaker, the impedance of the source
can be matched to that of the circuit by the insertion of a transformer of the correct
turns ratio.

Problems

35–1. A 1-μf capacitor is connected across an AC source whose voltage amplitude is kept constant at 50 volts, but whose frequency can be varied. Find the current amplitude when the angular frequency is (a) 100 rad/sec, (b) 1000 rad/sec, (c) 10,000 rad/sec. (d) Construct a log-log plot of current amplitude versus frequency.

35–2. The voltage amplitude of an AC source is 50 volts and its angular frequency is 1000 rad/sec. Find the current amplitude if the capacitance of a capacitor connected across the source is (a) 0.01 μf, (b) 1.0 μf, (c) 100 μf. (d) Construct a log-log plot of current amplitude versus capacitance.

35–3. An inductor of self-inductance 10 h and of negligible resistance is connected across the source of Problem 35–1. Find the current amplitude when the angular frequency is (a) 100 rad/sec, (b) 1000 rad/sec, (c) 10,000 rad/sec. (d) Construct a log-log plot of current amplitude versus frequency.

35–4. Find the current amplitude if the self-inductance of a resistanceless inductor connected across the source of Problem 35–2 is (a) 0.01 h, (b) 1.0 h, (c) 100 h. (d) Construct a log-log plot of current amplitude versus self-inductance.

35–5. The expression for the impedance Z of an *R-L* series circuit can be obtained from Eq. (35–14) by setting $X_C = 0$, which corresponds to $C = \infty$. Explain.

35–6. In the series circuit of Fig. 35–5, the source has a constant voltage amplitude of 50 volts and a frequency of 1000 rad/sec. $R = 300$ ohms, $L = 0.9$ h, and $C = 2.0$ μf.

Suppose a series circuit contains only the resistor and the inductor in series. (a) What is the impedance of the circuit? (b) What is the current amplitude? (c) What are the voltage amplitudes across the resistor and across the inductor? (d) What is the phase angle ϕ? Does the current lag or lead? (e) Construct the rotor diagram.

35–7. Same as Problem 35–6, except that the circuit consists of the resistor and the capacitor of Fig. 35–5 in series.

35–8. Same as Problem 35–6, except that the circuit consists of the inductor and capacitor of Fig. 35–5 in series.

35–9. Construct graphs of i, v_R, v_L, and v_C, as functions of time, for the circuit in Fig. 35–5 and in the example at the end of Section 35–3.

35–10. (a) Compute the impedance of the circuit in Fig. 35–5 at an angular frequency of 500 rad/sec. (b) Describe how the current amplitude varies as the frequency of the source is slowly reduced from 1000 rad/sec to 500 rad/sec. (c) What is the phase angle when $\omega = 500$ rad/sec? (d) Construct the rotor diagram when $\omega = 500$ rad/sec. See the example at the end of Section 35–3 for data.

35–11. Five infinite impedance voltmeters, calibrated to read rms values, are connected as shown in Fig. 35–16 to the circuit of Fig. 35–5. What does each voltmeter read? See the example at the end of Section 35–3 for data.

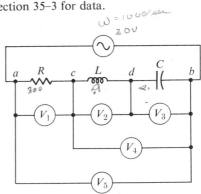

Figure 35–16

35–12. What is the reading of each voltmeter in Fig. 35–16 if the angular frequency $\omega = 500$ rad/sec? See the example at the end of Section 35–3 for data.

35–13. Refer to Fig. 35–5 and the data at the end of Section 35–3. (a) Construct graphs of i, v, and p as functions of time. (b) What is the average power input to the circuit? (c) What are the values of i and v at the instants when the power p is an (absolute) maximum? .

35–14. Same as Problem 35–13, except that the circuit consists of the resistor and inductor of Fig. 35–5 in series.

35–15. Same as Problem 35–13, except that the circuit consists of the resistor and capacitor of Fig. 35–5 in series.

35–16. Same as Problem 35–13, except that the circuit consists of the inductor and capacitor of Fig. 35–5 in series.

35–17. (a) Construct a graph of the current amplitude in the circuit of Fig. 35–5 as the angular frequency of the source is increased from 500 rad/sec to 1000 rad/sec. (b) At what frequency is the circuit in resonance? (c) What is the power factor at resonance? (d) What is the reading of each voltmeter in Fig. 35–16 when the frequency equals the resonant frequency? (e) What would be the resonant frequency if the resistance were reduced to 100 ohms? (f) What would then be the rms current at resonance? See the example at the end of Section 35–3 for data.

35–18. (a) At what frequency is the voltage amplitude across the inductor in an R-L-C series circuit a maximum? (b) At what frequency is the voltage amplitude across the capacitor a maximum?

35–19. In the parallel resonant circuit in Fig. 35–17, $R = 14.1\,\Omega$, $X_L = X_C = 120\,\Omega$. The voltage amplitude V of the source is 130 volts and A_1, A_2, and A_3 are ideal (zero impedance) AC ammeters cali-

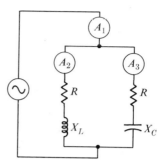

Figure 35–17

brated to read root mean square currents. (a) Compute the impedance of each of the parallel branches. (b) Compute the readings of ammeters A_2 and A_3. (c) Construct the rotor diagram corresponding to Fig. 35–13(b), and find the reading of ammeter A_1. (d) Find the equivalent impedance of the circuit.

35–20. A resistor of 500 ohms and a capacitor of 2 μf are connected in parallel to an AC generator supplying a constant voltage amplitude of 282 volts and having an angular frequency of 374 rad/sec. Find (a) the current amplitude in the resistor, (b) the current amplitude in the capacitor, (c) the phase angle, and (d) the line current amplitude.

35–21. The internal resistance of an AC source is 10,000 ohms. (a) What should be the turns ratio of a transformer to match the source to a load of resistance 10 ohms? (b) If the voltage amplitude of the source is 100 volts, what is the voltage amplitude of the secondary on open circuit?

CHAPTER 36

Electromagnetic Waves

36–1 Introduction

Before the mksc system of units was developed, it was customary to express electrical quantities in terms of the so-called *electrostatic* system of units, and magnetic quantities in terms of the units of a different system called the *electromagnetic* system. The electrostatic unit of charge (now called the *statcoulomb*) was defined in terms of the electrostatic force of repulsion between point charges in vacuum, and the electromagnetic unit of charge (now called the *abcoulomb*) was defined in terms of the magnetic force between two current-carrying wires in vacuum. It was well known that the ratio of the electromagnetic unit of *any* electrical quantity to the electrostatic unit of that quantity had the dimensions of length divided by time, or *velocity*.

In 1856, Weber and Kohlrausch made a careful measurement of the ratio of the abcoulomb to the statcoulomb and found the value 3×10^{10} cm/sec, which they knew to be equal to the speed of light. Physicists regarded this as an extraordinary coincidence, and had no idea as to its explanation. It was the search for the explanation of this result that led Maxwell, in 1864, to prove by theoretical reasoning that an electrical disturbance should propagate in free space with a speed equal to that of light, and hence to postulate that light waves were electromagnetic waves.

It remained for Heinrich Hertz, in 1887, to first produce electromagnetic waves with the aid of oscillating circuits and to receive and detect these waves with other circuits tuned to the same frequency. Hertz then produced stationary electromagnetic waves and measured the distance between adjacent nodes, to measure the wavelength. Knowing the frequency of his resonators, he then found the velocity of the waves from the fundamental wave equation $c = f\lambda$, and directly verified Maxwell's theoretical value.

The possible use of electromagnetic waves for purposes of long-distance communication does not seem to have occurred to Hertz. It remained for the enthusiasm and energy of Marconi and others to make "wireless telegraphy" a familiar household phenomenon.

36–2 Propagation of an electromagnetic wave

Figure 36–1 represents a region near one end of a long two-wire line in empty space and of zero resistance. At time $t = 0$ the reversing switch S is thrown to the right so that the upper wire is connected to the positive terminal of a source of constant terminal voltage V, and the lower wire is connected to its negative terminal. The

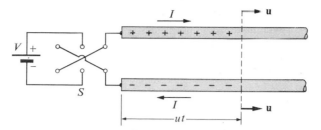

Fig. 36–1. Propagation of an electric disturbance along a two-wire line of zero resistance in a vacuum.

entire line does not become charged instantaneously, nor is the current I set up instantaneously at all points. Instead, as shown in the figure, there exists a boundary plane, shown by the dotted line, which travels to the right along the line with a constant velocity **u**. At a time t after the source has been connected, this plane has advanced a distance ut. At the left of the plane there is a current I, toward the right in the upper wire and toward the left in the lower. Within the same portion of the line the upper wire has a positive charge and the lower wire, a negative charge. To the right of the plane there is no current and no excess charge. This portion has not as yet received the news that the source has been connected.

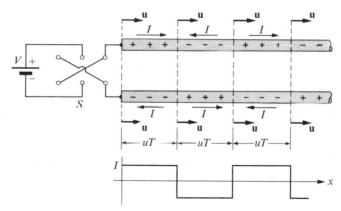

Fig. 36–2. Propagation of an electromagnetic wave along a two-wire line.

Suppose next that after being connected to the source for a time interval T, the switch S is reversed instantaneously. The region of charge and current that was first established *continues* to travel toward the right, and a second region is established behind the first, in which the charges and currents are opposite to those in the first. This region also travels to the right with velocity **u**. If the switch is reversed periodically, at equal time intervals T, a succession of regions, one behind the other, each of length uT, travel along the line as in Fig. 36–2. We say that an *electromagnetic wave* travels along the line, and we wish to calculate its velocity of propagation, **u**. Instead of formulating the problem in terms of currents and charges, we shall consider the more fundamental quantities, the electric and magnetic fields.

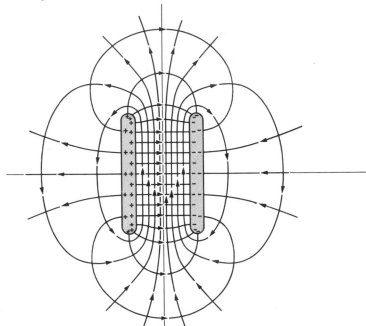

Fig. 36–3.   End view of a line consisting of two plane parallel conducting plates.

Also, our problem will be simplified geometrically if, instead of two parallel wires, we consider a line consisting of two plane parallel conducting plates, as in Fig. 36–3, which is an end view of the line. The left plate is positively charged and carries a current toward the reader. The right plate is negatively charged and carries a current away from the reader. The electric field between the plates was discussed in Section 25–5 and illustrated in Fig. 25–19(a). The magnetic field was discussed in Section 32–6 and illustrated in Fig. 32–11. Figure 36–3 shows *both* the electric and magnetic fields.

If the plates are large compared with the distance between them, the **E**- and **H**-fields are very nearly uniform at points not too near the edges. Figure 36–4 is an enlarged cutaway view of such a portion. It includes the first two consecutive regions at the left end of the line. There is an electric field **E** in the *y*-direction, directed away from the positively charged portions and toward the negatively charged portions. There is also a magnetic field **H** in the *z*-direction, downward in the left-hand portion and upward in the right-hand portion. Each of these "blocks" or "chunks" of combined electric and magnetic fields travels toward the right with velocity **u** and there is a *traveling electromagnetic wave* in the space between the plates. The wave is *transverse*, because the directions of **E** and **H** are at right angles to the direction of propagation of the wave. The wave is also said to be *linearly polarized*, which means that the **E**-vector (or the **H**-vector) is always parallel (or antiparallel) to a fixed direction in space.

We now apply Faraday's law and Ampere's law to the dotted rectangles *abcd* and *efgh*. Both rectangles are fixed in space, relative to the plates. Rectangle *abcd* is parallel to the *xy*-plane, with its left portion, of area A_1, in the region in which **E** is

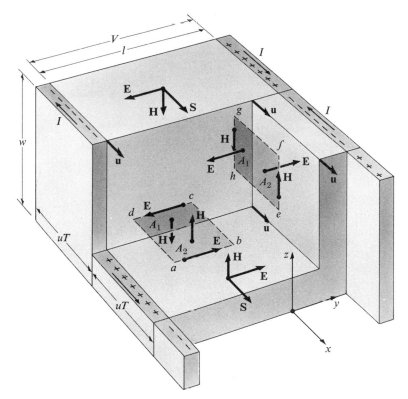

Fig. 36–4. Directions of **E**- and **H**-vectors in an electromagnetic wave between two plane parallel conducting plates.

to the left and **H** is downward, and its right portion, of area A_2, in the region in which **E** is to the right and **H** is upward. The net magnetic flux through the rectangle in the positive z-direction is

$$\Phi = \mu_0 H A_2 - \mu_0 H A_1 = \mu_0 H (A_2 - A_1).$$

As the wave advances and the boundary line between A_1 and A_2 moves to the right, the area A_1 increases and the area A_2 decreases. The rate of change of flux is

$$\frac{d\Phi}{dt} = \mu_0 H \left(\frac{dA_2}{dt} - \frac{dA_1}{dt} \right).$$

The rate of increase of the area A_1 equals the product of the length s of side cd and the velocity u of the boundary line. Also, the rate of *increase* of A_1 equals the rate of *decrease* of A_2, so

$$\frac{dA_1}{dt} = su = -\frac{dA_2}{dt},$$

and hence

$$\frac{d\Phi}{dt} = -2\mu_0 H s u.$$

The line integral of **E** around the rectangle is $2Es$, so from Faraday's law,

$$2Es = 2\mu_0 Hsu,$$

$$E = \mu_0 Hu. \tag{36-1}$$

The rectangle $efgh$ is parallel to the xz-plane. The flux of displacement through it in the positive y-direction is

$$\Psi_D = \epsilon_0 E(A_2 - A_1)$$

and

$$\frac{d\Psi_D}{dt} = \epsilon_0 E\left(\frac{dA_2}{dt} - \frac{dA_1}{dt}\right) = -2\epsilon_0 Esu.$$

The line integral of **H** around the rectangle is $-2Hs$, and from Ampere's law,

$$-2Hs = -2\epsilon_0 Esu,$$

$$H = \epsilon_0 Eu. \tag{36-2}$$

When Eqs. (36–1) and (36–2) are multiplied, we get

$$EH = (\mu_0 Hu)(\epsilon_0 Eu),$$

or, after cancelling the product EH,

$$u = \sqrt{1/\epsilon_0 \mu_0}.$$

But

$$\epsilon_0 = 1/4\pi k, \qquad \mu_0 = 4\pi k',$$

and

$$\frac{1}{\epsilon_0 \mu_0} = \frac{k}{k'} = c^2,$$

where c is the velocity of light, so finally

$$u = c. \tag{36-3}$$

That is, the boundary plane advances with a velocity equal to the velocity of light in free space! The conclusion that light is an electromagnetic wave seems inescapable. When Eq. (36–1) is divided by Eq. (36–2), we get

$$\frac{E}{H} = \sqrt{\mu_0/\epsilon_0} = 4\pi\sqrt{kk'}. \tag{36-4}$$

On inserting the numerical values of k and k', we find

$$\frac{E}{H} = 377 \frac{\text{volts/m}}{\text{amp/m}} = 377 \text{ ohms}. \tag{36-5}$$

Thus the *ratio* of the electric and magnetic field intensities is independent of the size or spacing of the plates and depends only on the constants ϵ_0 and μ_0 (or k and k').

The potential difference between the plates is

$$V = El,$$

where l is the distance between the plates.

The magnetic intensity H equals I/w, where w is the vertical width of the plates [see Eq. (32–14)], and therefore

$$I = Hw.$$

Although the plates themselves are assumed resistanceless, the current I is the same *as if* the line had a resistance R, given by

$$R = \frac{V}{I} = \frac{l}{w}\frac{E}{H} = \frac{l}{w} \times 377 \text{ ohms.}$$

This is called the *characteristic impedance* of the line.

If we consider two opposite strips 1 m wide, in two very large parallel plates 1 m apart (so that $l = 1$ m, $w = 1$ m) the strips appear to have a resistance

$$R = \frac{E}{H} = \sqrt{\frac{\mu_0}{\epsilon_0}} = 377 \text{ ohms.}$$

This quantity is called the *characteristic impedance of free space.*

The electrical energy density in the region in which electric and magnetic fields exist is

$$\tfrac{1}{2}\epsilon_0 E^2$$

and the magnetic energy density is

$$\tfrac{1}{2}\mu_0 H^2.$$

But

$$H = E\sqrt{\epsilon_0/\mu_0}, \quad \text{so} \quad \tfrac{1}{2}\mu_0 H^2 = \tfrac{1}{2}\epsilon_0 E^2.$$

The electric and magnetic energy densities are therefore equal and the total energy density is

$$\epsilon_0 E^2 = \mu_0 H^2. \tag{36–6}$$

EXAMPLE. Let the plates in Fig. 36–4 be 1 m wide and have a separation of 1 cm, so that $l = 10^{-2}$ m, $w = 1$ m. Neglect edge effects. The plates extend indefinitely in the x-direction.

The characteristic impedance of the plates is

$$R = \frac{l}{w} \times 377 \text{ ohms} = 3.77 \text{ ohms.}$$

If $V = 20$ volts, the current I is

$$I = \frac{V}{R} = \frac{20 \text{ volts}}{3.77 \text{ ohms}} = 5.30 \text{ amp.}$$

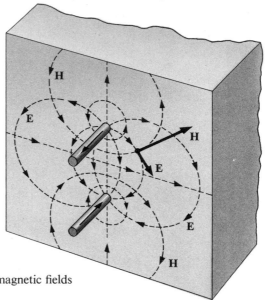

Fig. 36–5.   Electric and magnetic fields near a two-wire line.

The electric intensity between the plates is

$$E = \frac{V}{l} = 2 \times 10^3 \, \frac{\text{volts}}{\text{m}}.$$

The electromagnetic energy density is

$$\epsilon_0 E^2 = 8.85 \times 10^{-12} \times (2 \times 10^3)^2 = 35.4 \times 10^{-6} \, \text{joule/m}^3.$$

At a time of 1 μsec $= 10^{-6}$ sec after the source is connected, the boundary plane has advanced a distance

$$ut = ct = 3 \times 10^8 \, \frac{\text{m}}{\text{sec}} \times 10^{-6} \, \text{sec} = 300 \, \text{m}.$$

The volume of the region between the plates at the left of the plane is

$$300 \, \text{m} \times 10^{-2} \, \text{m} \times 1 \, \text{m} = 3 \, \text{m}^3$$

and the total electromagnetic energy in this volume is

$$35.4 \times 10^{-6} \, \frac{\text{joule}}{\text{m}} \times 3 \, \text{m}^3 = 106 \times 10^{-6} \, \text{joule}.$$

The power input to the line from the source is

$$P = VI = 20 \, \text{volts} \times 5.3 \, \text{amp} = 106 \, \text{watts}$$

and the energy input in 10^{-6} sec is

$$106 \, \text{watts} \times 10^{-6} \, \text{sec} = 106 \times 10^{-6} \, \text{joule}.$$

Thus all of the energy input goes to establish the electromagnetic field.

Let us now return to the open two-wire line described at the beginning of the section. Figure 36–5 is an end view. The upper wire is positively charged and the lower wire is negatively charged. The current in the upper wire is toward the reader and that in the lower wire is away from the reader. Although in this case the electric and magnetic fields are not uniform, it will be seen from the diagram that at every point the **E**- and **H**-vectors are mutually perpendicular, as in Fig. 36–4. It is not difficult to show that the ratio E/H, at every point, is also equal to $\sqrt{\mu_0/\epsilon_0}$, as in Fig. 36–4, and that the boundary planes between regions in which the currents and fields are in opposite directions also advance with a velocity $u = c$.

The *complete* electromagnetic field of the line extends outward indefinitely. Only a limited portion is shown in Fig. 36–5.

36–3 Electromagnetic waves in matter

Suppose that the space between the plates of Fig. 36–4, or around the wires of Fig. 36–5, is not empty but is filled by a material substance. Electromagnetic waves can still travel through it provided that it is a dielectric. (If it is a conductor, the electric field sets up currents and the wave is rapidly damped out by "I^2R" losses.) If the substance has a permittivity $\epsilon = K\epsilon_0$ and a permeability $\mu = K_m\mu_0$, the velocity of propagation is

$$u = \sqrt{1/\epsilon\mu} = \sqrt{1/\epsilon_0\mu_0}\ \sqrt{1/KK_m} = c\ \sqrt{1/KK_m}.$$

The magnetic coefficient of all dielectrics is so nearly equal to 1 that for all practical purposes we can say that in a dielectric

$$u = c\ \sqrt{1/K}.$$

Because K is always greater than 1, the velocity of electromagnetic waves in a material substance is always less than c.

36–4 The Poynting vector

It was shown in Section 25–5 that the electric field just outside the surface of a charged conductor is at right angles to the surface *when the charges in the conductor are at rest.* The proof was based on the fact that $\mathbf{E} = 0$ inside the conductor. But when there is a *current* in a conductor, the charges in it are *not* at rest and there *is* a field $\mathbf{E}_i$ inside the conductor, equal to $\rho\mathbf{J}$.

Figure 36–6 represents a portion of the surface of a conductor within which there is a current density $\mathbf{J}$ and an electric field $\mathbf{E}_i$. (We consider only the case of a conductor in which the field is wholly electrostatic.) As explained earlier, there is in general a surface charge on a conductor forming a part of a circuit, dis-

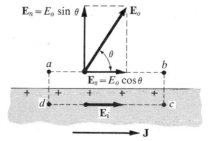

Fig. 36–6. Electric field near the surface of a current-carrying conductor.

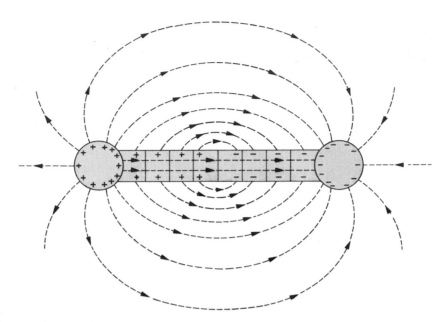

Fig. 36–7. The electric field around a uniform straight current-carrying conductor between spherical terminals maintained at fixed potentials.

tributed in such a way that the current in the conductor has the same value at all cross sections. Let σ represent the surface density of charge, and $\mathbf{E}_o$ the electric intensity just outside the conductor, making an angle θ with the surface.

Let the dotted rectangle represent first a closed *path* in the plane of the diagram. Since the line integral of $\mathbf{E}$ must be zero around this path, and since the sides bc and ad are of negligible length, it follows that the component $\mathbf{E}_s$, equal to $\mathbf{E}_o \cos\theta$, equals the field $\mathbf{E}_i$ inside the surface. Hence the external field $\mathbf{E}_o$ is *not* at right angles to the surface.

If we now let the rectangle represent a side view of a small gaussian surface like that in Fig. 25–20, it follows from Gauss's law that the component $\mathbf{E}_n$, equal to $\mathbf{E}_o \sin\theta$, is equal to σ/ϵ_0. It is directed outward if σ is positive and inward if σ is negative.

The distribution of surface charge is extremely complicated for a circuit of irregular shape, but is relatively simple for the circuit shown in Fig. 36–7, where a uniform straight conductor connects two spheres maintained at fixed potentials. The spheres are assumed of zero resistance, and the dotted lines of force intersect them at right angles. The left half of the conductor has an excess positive surface charge and the right half an excess negative surface charge. The component of $\mathbf{E}_o$ just outside the surface and parallel to the surface is in the direction of $\mathbf{E}_i$ at all points. The component at right angles to the surface points outward where σ is positive and inward where σ is negative.

In our previous discussion of electric circuits we have considered that energy is transported by the circulating charges, which acquire potential energy in a source and give up this energy in other portions of a circuit. Another very fruitful point of view is that the energy is carried not by the moving charges, but by the *electromagnetic field* associated with them. In fact, when we consider the flow of energy from the sun, a radiant heater, or a radio antenna, where the energy must be transported by electromagnetic waves without any motion of charged particles, this viewpoint seems a necessary one to adopt.

Consider the parallel-plate transmission line of Fig. 36–4. The power input to the line is $P = VI$. But as we have shown,

$$V = El, \quad I = Hw,$$

so

$$P = VI = (EH)(lw).$$

The product lw equals the cross-sectional area A of the electromagnetic field between the plates, so

$$\frac{P}{A} = EH.$$

This equation can be interpreted to mean that energy is transported along the line by way of the electromagnetic field, and that the flow of energy across any cross section of the field, per unit area and per unit time, is equal to the product EH. This viewpoint was first proposed by J. H. Poynting, and the *Poynting vector* **S** is defined as the vector product of **E** and **H**.

$$\boxed{\mathbf{S} = \mathbf{E} \times \mathbf{H}.} \tag{36–7}$$

Reference to Fig. 36–4 will show that the Poynting vector **S** is in the direction of propagation of the wave at every point, so that the *magnitude* of **S** equals the flow of energy, per unit area and per unit time, and the *direction* of **S** is in the direction of propagation.

This point of view regarding the transport of energy is applicable to DC circuits also. Consider a portion of a wire of resistance R in which there is a current I. The rate of dissipation of energy in the wire equals I^2R, and from one point of view we can consider that this energy is "delivered" to the wire by the flowing electrons, which gain potential energy in a source and give it up within the wire as they make inelastic collisions. We can also consider that energy flows out of the source into the electromagnetic field surrounding the circuit, and flows from the field into the wire.

Figure 36–8(a) shows the same conductors as Fig. 36–7. There is a current in the rod from left to right and it is surrounded by a magnetic as well as by an electric field, with the **H**-vector toward the reader at points in the diagram above the rod, and away from the reader at points below the rod. Only two of the electric lines of force are shown, and the Poynting vector **S** has been constructed at a few points on these lines. It will be seen that there is a flow of energy inward toward the rod at all points.

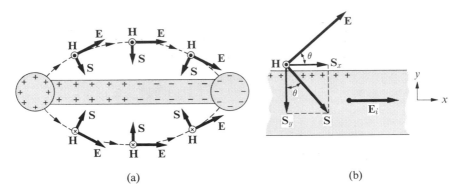

(a)   (b)

Fig. 36–8. (a) Electric and magnetic fields near a current-carrying rod. (b) Enlarged view of a portion of the rod.

Figure 36–8(b) is an enlarged view of a portion of the rod. The magnetic intensity H just outside the surface is

$$H = \frac{1}{2\pi}\frac{I}{r},$$

where I is the current in the rod and r is its radius.

The electric intensity E just outside the rod makes an angle θ with the rod and the Poynting vector S makes the same angle with the normal to the surface. The component S_y, which represents the energy flow *into* the rod across its surface, is

$$S_y = S \cos \theta = EH \cos \theta.$$

The electric intensity E_i at all points *inside* the rod (including points at its surface)

$$E_i = \rho J = \rho \frac{I}{\pi r^2},$$

where ρ is the resistivity of the rod, and r is its radius. Just outside the surface, the component of E parallel to the surface, $E \cos \theta$, is equal to the intensity E_i inside, so

$$E \cos \theta = E_i = \rho \frac{I}{\pi r^2}.$$

The surface area A of a length l of the rod is $2\pi r l$, and the rate of flow of energy into this portion across its surface is

$$S_y A = E \cos \theta H A = \left(\rho \frac{I}{\pi r^2}\right)\left(\frac{1}{2\pi}\frac{I}{r}\right)(2\pi r l) = I^2 \frac{\rho l}{\pi r^2}.$$

But $\rho l / \pi r^2$ equals the resistance R of the portion, so finally

$$S_y A = I^2 R,$$

and the rate of flow of energy into the portion across its surface is equal to the rate of dissipation of energy within the portion.

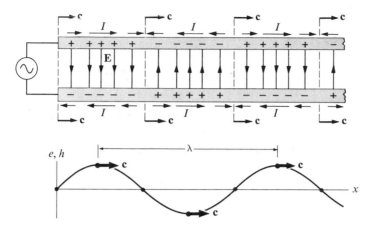

Fig. 36–9. Current and charge distribution in a line consisting of a pair of parallel plates at one moment during the propagation of a sinusoidal electromagnetic wave.

36–5 Sinusoidal waves

A switch such as that in Fig. 36–1 cannot, of course, be reversed instantaneously. However, if the source and switch are replaced with a high-frequency oscillating circuit, the voltage across the line will be reversed automatically and continuously. We shall assume that the source provides a sinusoidal alternating voltage, in which case a *sinusoidal electromagnetic wave* propagates along the line. The frequency f, the wavelength λ, and the velocity of propagation c are related by the fundamental equation applicable to any sort of wave motion, namely, $c = f\lambda$. If the frequency f is the power line frequency of 60 cycles/sec, the wavelength is

$$\lambda = \frac{c}{f} = \frac{3 \times 10^8 \text{ m/sec}}{60 \text{ cycles/sec}} = 5 \times 10^6 \text{ m} = 5000 \text{ km},$$

which is of the order of the earth's radius! Hence at this frequency a line even many miles in length includes only a small fraction of a wavelength. On the other hand, if the frequency is 10^8 cycles/sec (or 100 megacycles/sec) the wavelength is

$$\lambda = \frac{3 \times 10^8 \text{ m/sec}}{10^8 \text{ cycles/sec}} = 3 \text{ m},$$

and a line of only moderate length can include a number of complete waves.

The upper part of Fig. 36–9 is a top view of a portion of a line consisting of a pair of parallel plates. The arrows above and below the plates indicate the magnitudes and directions of the current at various points. The + and − signs indicate by their spacing the charge densities on the plates, and the lines between the plates represent the electric intensity. (The lines of the **H**-field are not shown.) Instead of changing their directions discontinuously as in Fig. 36–2, the fields alternate in direction sinusoidally. The entire pattern in the diagram travels to the right with speed c.

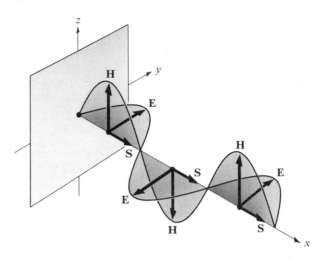

Fig. 36–10. E-, H-, and S-vectors in a sinusoidal electromagnetic wave traveling in the positive x-direction.

Figure 36–10 represents schematically the magnitudes and directions of the E- and H-fields in planes perpendicular to the x-axis. In those planes in which the E-vector is in the direction of the positive y-axis, the H-vector is in the direction of the positive z-axis. Where E is in the direction of the negative y-axis, H is in the direction of the negative z-axis.

It will be recalled that the equation of a transverse wave traveling to the right along a stretched string is $y = Y \sin (\omega t - kx)$, where y is the transverse displacement from its equilibrium position, at the time t, of a point of the string whose coordinate is x. The quantity Y is the maximum displacement or the *amplitude* of the wave, ω is its *angular frequency*, equal to 2π times the frequency f, and k is the *propagation constant*, equal to $2\pi/\lambda$, where λ is the wavelength.

Let e and h represent the instantaneous values, and E and H the maximum values or amplitudes, of the electric and magnetic fields in Fig. 36–9. The equations of the traveling electromagnetic wave are then

$$e = -E \sin (\omega t - kx), \qquad h = -H \sin (\omega t - kx). \qquad (36\text{–}8)$$

The sine curve in the lower part of Fig. 36–9 represents instantaneous values of either e or h, as functions of x at the time $t = 0$. The wave travels to the right with speed c.

The instantaneous value s of the Poynting vector is

$$s = eh = EH \sin^2 (\omega t - kx)$$
$$= \tfrac{1}{2}EH[1 - \cos 2(\omega t - kx)].$$

The time average value of $\cos 2(\omega t - kx)$ is zero, so the average value $\bar{S}$ of the Poynting vector, or the average power transmitted per unit area, is

$$\bar{S} = \tfrac{1}{2}EH. \qquad (36\text{–}9)$$

36–6 Stationary waves

Suppose the line in Fig. 36–9 does not extend indefinitely to the right, but is of finite length. Waves traveling to the right may then be *reflected* or *absorbed* at the far end, depending on the way in which the line is terminated. If the line is *open* or is *shorted*, the waves will be very nearly completely reflected. If the ends of the line are connected by a resistor equal to the characteristic impedance of the line, the waves will be completely *absorbed*. The problem is closely analogous to that of a tube with a source of sound waves at one end, where the nature of the reflection at the other end depends on whether the end is open or closed. The superposition of incident and reflected waves gives rise to *stationary* waves on the line.

Figure 36–11 represents schematically the electric and magnetic fields of a wave traveling in the *negative* x-direction. At points where **E** is in the positive y-direction, **H** is in the *negative* z-direction, and where **E** is in the negative y-direction, **H** is in the positive z-direction. The Poynting vector **S** = **E** × **H** is in the negative x-direction at all points. (Compare with Fig. 36–10, which represents a wave traveling in the *positive* x-direction.) The equations of the wave are

$$e = E \sin (\omega t + kx), \qquad h = -H \sin (\omega t + kx). \qquad (36\text{--}10)$$

Assume that we have an *incident* wave traveling to the right, and also a *reflected* wave of the same amplitude traveling to the left. Let the subscripts 1 and 2 refer to the incident and reflected waves, respectively. From the principle of superposition, the resultant **E**- and **H**-fields are

$$e = e_1 + e_2,$$
$$\qquad \qquad (36\text{--}11)$$
$$h = h_1 + h_2.$$

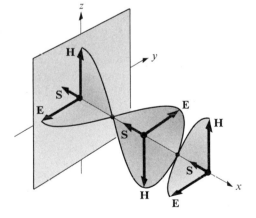

Then from Eqs. (36–8) and (36–10),

$$e = 2E \cos \omega t \sin kx,$$
$$h = -2H \sin \omega t \cos kx.$$

The electric field is zero at all times in those planes for which $\sin kx = 0$, or at which

$$x = 0, \ \frac{\lambda}{2}, \ 2\frac{\lambda}{2}, \ 3\frac{\lambda}{2}, \ \text{etc.}$$

Fig. 36–11. Electric and magnetic fields of a wave traveling in the negative x-direction.

These are the *nodal planes* of the **E**-field.

The magnetic field is zero at all times in those planes for which $\cos kx = 0$, or at which

$$x = \frac{\lambda}{4}, \ 3\frac{\lambda}{4}, \ 5\frac{\lambda}{4}, \ \text{etc.}$$

These are the nodal planes of the **H**-field. The nodal planes of one field are midway between those of the other, and the nodal planes of either field are separated by

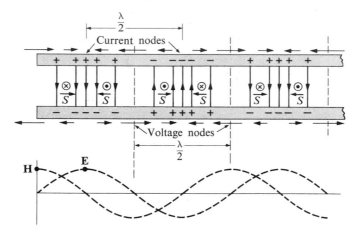

Fig. 36–12. Stationary waves on a transmission line.

one-half a wavelength. The fields are shown in Fig. 36–12 at a time at which $\omega t = \pi/4$.

The electric field is a *cosine* function of t and the magnetic field is a *sine* function of t. The fields are therefore 90° out of phase. At times at which $\cos \omega t = 0$ the electric field is zero *everywhere* and the magnetic field is a maximum. When $\sin \omega t = 0$, the magnetic field is zero *everywhere* and the electric field is a maximum.

The potential difference between the plates, at any plane, is proportional to the **E**-field in that plane. Hence the nodal planes of the **E**-field are also *voltage nodes*; the potential difference between the plates is always zero at these planes.

The current, at any plane, is proportional to the **H**-field. Hence the nodal planes of the **H**-field are also *current nodes*; the current is always zero at these planes. The current nodes lie midway between the voltage nodes.

The existence of these current and voltage nodes can be demonstrated by the use of an open two-wire line; the wires are called *Lecher wires*. If a source whose frequency is of the order of 10^8 cycles/sec (100 megacycles/sec) is connected across one end of the line, the wavelength of electromagnetic waves on the line is 3 m.

If the line is of finite length, waves will be reflected at its far end and stationary waves will be set up, with current nodes and voltage nodes separated by half a wavelength or 1.5 meters. If the far end of the line is open, the current at that end must be zero and the end will be a *current node*. If the end is shorted by a conductor of zero resistance, the potential difference between the ends must be zero and the end will be a *voltage node*.

Just as with a stretched string, the line will *resonate* if its length is some integral number of half-wavelengths, and the current and voltage will be large at the respective antinodes.

The magnitude of the voltage between the wires (or of the E-field) can be demonstrated qualitatively by connecting a small neon lamp across the line. The lamp glows brightly at the voltage antinodes and not at all at the voltage nodes.

The magnitude of the current in the wires (or of the H-field) can be demonstrated with the help of an *L-C* circuit "tuned" to the frequency of the source. (Basically, this is a radio receiver called a *wavemeter*.) It consists of a single turn of wire whose terminals are connected to a small variable capacitor. The loop is placed between the Lecher wires so that the magnetic field passes through it. The magnitude of the induced current, which is proportional to that of the **H**-field, is indicated by a small flashlight lamp connected across the capacitor.

If a resistance equal to the characteristic impedance of the line is connected across its ends, all of the energy carried by the incident wave is absorbed. There are no reflected waves and hence no voltage or current nodes. If the resistance has some value other than zero, infinity, or the characteristic impedance, the incident wave will be *partially* reflected and the amplitude of the reflected wave will be smaller than that of the incident wave. The current and voltage will exhibit maxima and minima, but will not be *zero* at the minima. That is, there will be no true nodes.

36–7 Radiation of electromagnetic waves from an antenna

In our discussion of stationary waves on a two-wire line, one important aspect of the problem was ignored, namely, that electromagnetic waves (and the energy they transport) not only travel back and forth along the line, but also spread outward in all directions. We say that energy is *radiated* by the line.

A complete analysis of the radiation from a transmission line is a long and complicated problem, and except in special cases one cannot obtain an exact solution. We shall describe only the general nature of the radiation process from a *half-wave antenna*, consisting of a single wire with an alternating source at its center, as in Fig. 36–13. The length of the wire is one-half a wavelength and its ends are therefore *current nodes*.

Figure 36–13 illustrates schematically the current and charge distributions, and the **E**- and **H**-fields, at some instant. The current, from right to left, is a maximum at the center and decreases to zero at the ends. The lines of the **H**-field are circles concentric with the antenna and, near the antenna, are clockwise when we look along the antenna

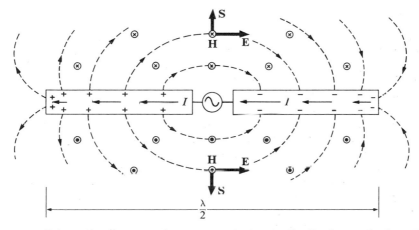

Fig. 36–13. Schematic diagram of current and charge distribution, and of the **E**- and **H**-fields around a half-wave antenna, at one particular instant.

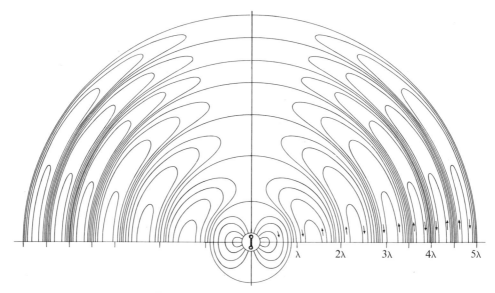

Fig. 36–14.   Electric field lines produced by an oscillating dipole.

in the direction of the current.   At a given radial distance from the antenna the H-field is a maximum in a plane through the midpoint of the antenna.   It is zero at all points on the antenna axis.

The two halves of the antenna are oppositely charged.   The charge density is a maximum at the ends and zero at the center.   The lines of the E-field have the general shape shown, from the + charges to the − charges.

The Poynting vector **S** is shown at two points and is radially outward.   That is, energy is flowing outward from the antenna at these points and at this instant.

As time goes on, and the **E**- and **H**-fields alternate in direction, the Poynting vector near the antenna is alternately outward and inward.   The phase relations of **E** and **H** in this region, however, are such that the average outward flow exceeds the average inward flow, so there is a net radiation of energy outward.   In other words, near the antenna a net outward flow of energy is superposed on an alternating in-and-out surge of energy.

At distances from the antenna greater than several wavelengths, the **E**- and **H**-fields are in phase and the energy flow is outward at all points and all times.   The **E**- and **H**-vectors are at right angles to each other, with the **E**-vector in a plane passing through the antenna.   The ratio E/H equals $\sqrt{\mu_0/\epsilon_0}$, as in a wave between parallel plates.   The magnitudes of **E** and **H** are greatest in the midplane of the antenna, and the radiated power per unit area is greatest in this plane.   No power is radiated in the direction of the antenna axis.

The antenna can be approximated by an *oscillating dipole*, that is, a pair of equal and opposite point charges whose charge alternates sinusoidally with time.   The lines of force of the *electric* field of an oscillating dipole are shown in Fig. 36–14. Accurate scale has been sacrificed in order that the fields near the dipole, and at a distance of several wavelengths from it, may be shown in the same drawing.

Problems

36–1. Suppose that the two long plates of width w and separation l shown in Fig. 36–4 are connected to a source of constant potential difference V for a short time t and a current I exists in a length ct. (a) What is the capacitance of this length? (b) What is the inductance of this length? (c) What is the energy stored in the capacitor? (d) What is the energy stored in the magnetic field? (e) Show that these two expressions are equal and that the sum is the energy supplied by the source. (f) Show that $c = \sqrt{1/L'C'}$, where L' is the inductance per unit length and C' is the capacitance per unit length.

36–2. Consider a transmission line consisting of an inner solid conducting cylinder of radius r_a and a coaxial outer hollow conducting cylinder of inner radius r_b. A constant potential difference V has been established across this coaxial cable for a short time t, so that a constant current I exists in one direction in the inner cylinder and the same current I is in the opposite direction in the outer cylinder for a distance ut measured from the source. Consider the portion of the line of length ut. (a) If C' is the capacitance per unit length, show that $I = C'uV$. (b) If L' is the inductance per unit length, show that $V = L'uI$. (c) Show that $u = \sqrt{1/L'C'}$. (d) Show that $C' = 1/2k \ln (r_b/r_a)$. (e) Show that $L' = 2k' \ln (r_b/r_a)$. (f) Show that $u = c$.

36–3. Refer to Fig. 36–4 and the example in Section 36–2. (a) What is the magnetic intensity H between the plates? (b) What is the energy density $\mu_0 H^2$? (c) What is the magnitude of the Poynting vector $\mathbf{S}$?

36–4. A bar magnet is mounted on an insulating support, as in the side and end views of Fig. 36–15(a) and (b), and is given a positive electric charge. Copy the diagram, sketch the lines of the **E**- and **H**-fields around the magnet, and draw the Poynting vector at a number of points. Is it correct to regard $\mathbf{E} \times \mathbf{H}$ *always* as

the energy flowing per unit time, per unit area? Is it correct to regard $\int \mathbf{E} \times \mathbf{H} \, dA$ over the entire surrounding space as the total energy per unit time?

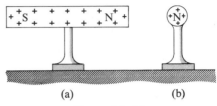

(a)   (b)

Figure 36–15

36–5. A cylindrical conductor of circular cross section has a radius a and a resistivity ρ and carries a constant current I. (a) What are the magnitude and direction of the E-vector at a point inside the wire, at a distance r from the axis? (b) What are the magnitude and direction of the H-vector at the same point? (c) What are the magnitude and direction of the Poynting vector $\mathbf{S}$ at the same point? (d) Compare your answer to (c) with the rate of dissipation of energy within a volume of the conductor of length l and radius r.

36–6. A wire of radius 1 mm whose resistance per unit length is 3×10^{-3} ohm/m carries a current of 25.1 amp. At a point very near the surface of the wire, calculate (a) the magnitude of **H**, (b) the component of **E** parallel to the wire, (c) the component of **S** perpendicular to the wire.

36–7. The inner and outer conductors of a coaxial cable are of zero resistance and carry equal currents in opposite directions. Figure 36 16 is a diagram showing the directions of **E**, **H**, and **S** at a point between the inner and outer conductors, assumed in vacuum. (a) Prove that the ratio E/H is the same as in the field between two parallel conducting plates. (b) Show that the rate of flow of energy in the electromagnetic field, across any section of the cable, is equal to the product VI, where V

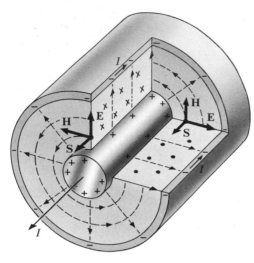

Figure 36–16

is the potential difference between inner and outer conductors and I is the current in either.

36-8. Assume that 10% of the power input to a 100-watt lamp is radiated uniformly as light of wavelength 500 nm (1 nm = 10^{-9} m). At a distance of 2 m from the source, the electric and magnetic intensities vary sinusoidally according to the equations $e = E \sin(\omega t + \phi)$ and $h = H \sin(\omega t + \phi)$. Calculate E and H.

36-9. A capacitor has two circular plates of radius r separated by a distance l, with a vacuum in between. Neglecting fringing, show that, while the capacitor is being charged, (a) the Poynting vector points everywhere radially into the space between the plates, (b) the rate at which energy flows into this space is equal to the rate at which the electrostatic energy increases.

36-10. A very long solenoid of n turns per unit length and radius a carries an increasing current i. (a) Calculate the induced electric field at a point at a distance r from the solenoid axis. (b) Compute the magnitude and direction of the Poynting vector at this point. (c) Consider a portion of length l of the space inside the solenoid. Show that the rate at which energy flows into this volume is equal to $d(\frac{1}{2}Li^2)/dt$, where L is the inductance of length l of the solenoid.

36-11. A television antenna radiates a power of 10 kilowatts at a wavelength of 300 m. Assume for simplicity that the radiated power is confined to, and is uniform over, a hemisphere with the antenna at its center. What are the amplitudes of E and H in the radiation field at a distance of 10 km from the antenna?

CHAPTER 37

The Nature and Propagation of Light

37-1 The nature of light

Until about the middle of the 17th century, it was generally believed that light consisted of a stream of corpuscles. These corpuscles were emitted by light sources, such as the sun or a candle flame, and traveled outward from the source in straight lines. They could penetrate transparent materials and were reflected from the surfaces of opaque materials. When the corpuscles entered the eye, the sense of sight was stimulated.

By the middle of the 17th century, while most workers in the field of optics accepted the corpuscular theory, the idea had begun to develop that light might be a wave motion of some sort. Christian Huygens, in 1678, showed that the laws of reflection and refraction could be explained on the basis of a wave theory and that such a theory furnished a simple explanation of the recently discovered phenomenon of double refraction. The wave theory failed of immediate acceptance, however. For one thing, it was objected that if light were a wave motion one should be able to see around corners, since waves can bend around obstacles in their path. We know now that the wavelengths of light waves are so short that the bending, while it does actually take place, is so small that it is not ordinarily observed. As a matter of fact, the bending of a light wave around the edges of an object, a phenomenon known as *diffraction*, was noted by Grimaldi in a book published in 1665, but the significance of his observations was not realized at the time.

In the first quarter of the 19th century the experiments of Thomas Young and Augustin Fresnel, on interference, and the measurements of the velocity of light in liquids by Leon Foucault at a somewhat later date, conclusively demonstrated the existence of optical phenomena for whose explanation a corpuscular theory was inadequate. The phenomena of interference and diffraction will be discussed further in Chapter 41, where it will be shown that they are only what would be expected if light is a wave motion. Young's experiments enabled him to measure the wavelength of the waves and Fresnel showed that the rectilinear propagation of light, as well as the diffraction effects observed by Grimaldi and others, could be accounted for by the behavior of waves of short wavelength.

The next great forward step in the theory of light was the work of Maxwell, discussed in the previous chapter. In 1873, Maxwell showed that an oscillating electrical circuit should radiate electromagnetic waves. The velocity of propagation of the waves could be computed from purely electrical and magnetic measurements, and it turned out to be very nearly 3×10^8 m/sec. Within the limits of experimental error, this was equal to the measured velocity of propagation of light. The evidence seemed inescapable that light consisted of electromagnetic waves of extremely short wavelength. Fifteen years after this discovery by Maxwell, Heinrich Hertz, using an oscillating circuit of small dimensions, succeeded in producing short wavelength waves (we would speak of them today as microwaves) of undoubted electromagnetic origin and showed that they possessed all the properties of light waves. They could be reflected, refracted, focused by a lens, polarized, and so on, just as could waves of light. Maxwell's electromagnetic theory of light and its experimental justification by Hertz constituted one of the triumphs of physical science. By the end of the 19th century it was the general belief that little, if anything, would be added in the future to our knowledge of the nature of light. Such was not to be the case.

The classical electromagnetic theory failed to account for the phenomenon of photoelectric emission, that is, the ejection of electrons from a conductor by light incident on its surface. In 1905, Einstein extended an idea proposed five years earlier by Planck and postulated that the energy in a light beam, instead of being distributed through space in the electric and magnetic fields of an electromagnetic wave, was concentrated in small packets or *photons*. A vestige of the wave picture was retained, in that a photon was still considered to have a frequency and the energy of a photon was proportional to its frequency. The mechanism of the photoelectric effect consisted in the transfer of energy from a photon to an electron. Experiments by Millikan showed that the kinetic energies of photoelectrons were in excellent agreement with the formula proposed by Einstein.

Still another striking confirmation of the photon nature of light is the Compton effect. A. H. Compton, in 1921, succeeded in determining the motion of a photon and a single electron, both before and after a "collision" between them, and found that they behaved like material bodies having kinetic energy and momentum, both of which were conserved in the collision. The photoelectric effect and the Compton effect, then, both seem to demand a return to a corpuscular theory of light.

The present standpoint of physicists, in the face of apparently contradictory experiments, is to accept the fact that light appears to be dualistic in nature. The phenomena of light propagation may best be explained by the electromagnetic wave theory, while the interaction of light with matter, in the processes of emission and absorption, is a corpuscular phenomenon.

37–2 Sources of light

The electromagnetic waves whose energy depends only upon the temperature and the nature of the surface of a body constitute what is known as *thermal radiation*. This radiation is a mixture of different wavelengths. At a temperature of 300°C the most intense of these waves has a wavelength of 5000×10^{-9} m or 5000 nm, which is in the *infrared* region. At a temperature of 800°C a body emits enough visible radiant energy to be self-luminous and appears "red hot." By far the larger part of the energy emitted, however, is still carried by infrared waves. At 3000°C, which is about the temperature of an incandescent lamp filament, the radiant energy contains enough of the "visible" wavelengths, between 400 nm and 700 nm, that the body appears nearly "white hot."

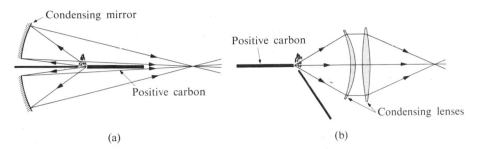

Fig. 37–1.   Two types of carbon arcs.   (a) With condensing mirror, for moderately sized motion picture theaters.   (b) With condensing lenses for large motion picture theaters.

In modern incandescent lamps, the filament is a coil of fine tungsten wire.   An inert gas such as argon is introduced to reduce evaporation of the filament.   Incandescent lamps vary in size from one no larger than a grain of wheat to one with a power input of 5000 watts, used for illuminating airfields.

The brightest source of light is the *carbon arc*.   Rods of carbon from 6 to 12 inches in length and from $\frac{1}{4}$ to $\frac{1}{2}$ inch in diameter are placed either horizontally, as shown in Fig. 37–1(a), or at an angle, as shown in Fig. 37–1(b).   Sometimes the carbon rods are copper coated to improve electrical conductivity.   To start a carbon arc, the two carbons are connected to a 110–volt or 220-volt DC source, are allowed to touch momentarily, and are then withdrawn.   Intense electron bombardment of the positive carbon causes an extremely hot crater to form at the end of the positive carbon.   This end, at a temperature of about 4000°C, is the source of light.   An electric motor or a clockwork mechanism is used to keep the carbons close to each other as they burn away.   Carbon arcs are used in all motion picture theaters, where they operate on from 50 to several hundred amperes.

A common laboratory source of light is provided by a mercury arc.   A glass or quartz tube has tungsten electrodes sealed in each end.   A pool of mercury surrounds the negative electrode.   A difference of potential is established across the electrodes and the tube is tilted until the mercury makes contact between the two electrodes.   Some mercury is vaporized, and when the tube is restored to its vertical position an electric discharge is maintained by electrons and positive mercury ions.   When the mercury is at low pressure the mercury atoms emit a characteristic light consisting of only yellow, green, blue, and violet.   A didymium filter may be used to absorb the yellow, and a yellow glass filter to absorb the blue and violet, leaving an intense green light consisting of a very small band of wavelengths whose average value is 546 nm.   Low-pressure mercury arcs containing only one isotope of mercury, of atomic weight 198, are obtainable from the United States National Bureau of Standards.   The green light from these lamps consists of an extremely narrow band of wavelengths, and is a close approach to *monochromatic* light.

If the current through a quartz mercury arc lamp is allowed to increase, the temperature rises greatly and the vapor pressure of the mercury rises to between 50 and 100 atmospheres.   Such a lamp requires water cooling, and when operating is a very intense source of white light.

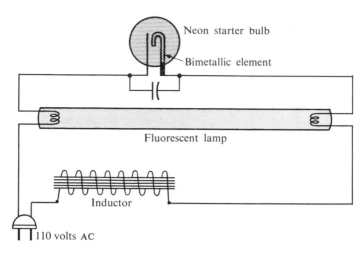

Fig. 37–2. Circuit consisting of a neon starter bulb and a series inductor for starting a fluorescent lamp.

An intense source of yellow light of average wavelength 589.3 nm is provided by a sodium arc lamp. This is usually made of a special kind of glass that is not attacked by sodium and into which electrodes are sealed. Each electrode is a filament for providing electrons to maintain an electric discharge through an inert gas. After the inert gas discharge has taken place for a few minutes, the temperature rises to a value at which the vapor pressure of the sodium is great enough to provide sufficient sodium atoms to emit the characteristic yellow sodium light. Sodium lamps are often used for street lighting because of their economy and because great visual acuity results from the absence of chromatic aberration of the eye when almost monochromatic light is used.

A very important development in illumination engineering is provided by the fluorescent lamp. This consists of a glass tube containing argon and a droplet of mercury. The electrodes consist of tungsten filaments. When an electric discharge takes place in the mercury-argon mixture, only a small amount of visible light is emitted by the mercury and argon atoms. There is, however, considerable *ultraviolet* light (light of wavelength shorter than that of visible violet). This ultraviolet light is absorbed in a thin layer of material, called a *phosphor*, with which the interior walls of the glass tube are coated. The phosphor has the property of *fluorescence*, which means that it emits visible light when illuminated by light of shorter wavelength. Lamps may be obtained which will fluoresce with any desired color, depending on the nature of the phosphor. Phosphors commonly used are cadmium borate for pink, zinc silicate for green, calcium tungstate for blue, and a mixture for white.

A method commonly employed to start a fluorescent lamp embodies some interesting physical principles. Consider, for example, the fluorescent lamp depicted in Fig. 37–2. When 110 volts AC are established across the lamp, the full line voltage exists across the electrodes of a small neon starter bulb which is usually mounted in the base of the lamp. The neon glows and warms up the electrodes, one of which is a bimetallic element. The bimetal expands and touches the other electrode, thereby short-circuiting the neon lamp and causing an appreciable current to exist in the two filaments of the fluorescent lamp. In a short time the filaments get hot and the neon lamp cools off. Then the bimetal contracts and breaks the circuit in the neon lamp, creating a voltage surge in the line because of the presence of an inductor. This momentary increase of voltage causes an electric discharge to take place in the mercury-argon mixture between the two filaments. Once this discharge is maintained, the potential difference across the fluorescent lamp, which is the same as the potential difference across the neon starter bulb, is too small to create a discharge in the neon bulb itself.

37–3 Waves, wavefronts, and rays

It is convenient to represent a train of waves of any sort by means of *wavefronts*. *A wavefront is defined as the locus of all points at which the phase of vibration or harmonic variation of a physical quantity is the same.* Thus in the case of sound waves spreading out in all directions from a point source, any spherical surface concentric with the source is a possible wavefront. Some of these spherical surfaces are the loci of points at which the pressure is a maximum, others where it is a minimum, and so on, but the phase of the pressure variations is the same over any spherical surface. It is customary to draw only a few wavefronts, usually those which pass through the maxima and minima of the disturbance. Such wavefronts are separated from one another by one-half a wavelength.

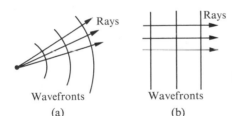

Fig. 37–3.   Wavefronts and rays.

If the wave is a light wave, the quantity which corresponds to the pressure in a sound wave is the electric or magnetic intensity. It is usually unnecessary to indicate in a diagram either the magnitude or direction of the intensity, but simply to show the *shape* of the wave by drawing the wavefronts or their intersections with some reference plane. For example, the electromagnetic waves radiated by a small light source may be represented by spherical surfaces concentric with the source or, as in Fig. 37–3(a), by the intersections of these surfaces with the plane of the diagram. At a sufficiently great distance from the source, where the radii of the spheres have become very large, the spherical surfaces can be considered planes and we have a train of plane waves as in Fig. 37–3(b).

Figure 37–4(a) illustrates the electric and magnetic field distributions in a train of plane electromagnetic waves at any one instant. The waves are advancing along the x-axis toward the right. The electric lines of force are drawn in gray and the magnetic lines in black. Where the lines are close together the intensities are large; where they

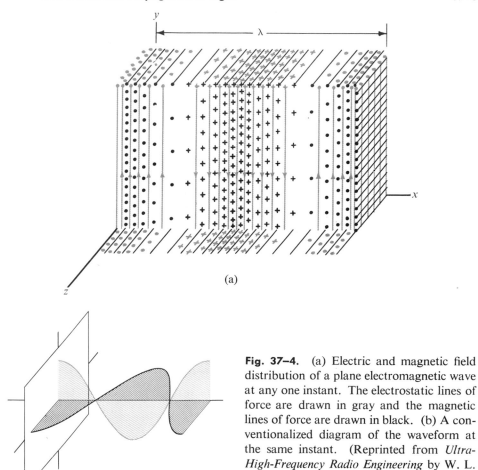

(a)

(b)

Fig. 37–4. (a) Electric and magnetic field distribution of a plane electromagnetic wave at any one instant. The electrostatic lines of force are drawn in gray and the magnetic lines of force are drawn in black. (b) A conventionalized diagram of the waveform at the same instant. (Reprinted from *Ultra-High-Frequency Radio Engineering* by W. L. Emery, by permission of the Macmillan Company.)

are far apart the intensities are small. The directions of the electric and magnetic fields are shown by arrows and by the usual convention of dots and crosses. A more conventional diagram of the waveform is shown in Fig. 37–4(b).

A train of light waves may often be represented more simply by means of *rays* than by wavefronts. In a corpuscular theory, a ray is simply the path followed by a light corpuscle. From the wave viewpoint, a *ray is an imaginary line drawn in the direction in which the wave is traveling*. Thus in Fig. 37–3(a) the rays are the radii of the spherical wavefronts and in Fig. 37–3(b) they are straight lines perpendicular to the wavefronts. In fact, in every case in which the waves are traveling in a homogeneous isotropic medium, the rays are straight lines, normal to the wavefronts. At a boundary surface between two media, such as the surface between a glass plate and the air outside it, the direction of a ray may change suddenly but it is a straight line both in the air and in the glass. If the medium is not homogeneous, for instance, if one is considering the passage of light through the earth's atmosphere, where the density and

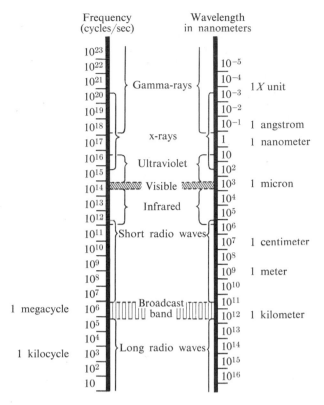

Fig. 37–5.   A chart of the electromagnetic spectrum.

hence the velocity vary with elevation, the rays are curved but are still normal to the wavefronts. If the medium is anisotropic, as is the case in certain crystals, the direction of rays is not always normal to the wavefronts. This problem will be considered in more detail in Chapter 42.

A narrow cone of rays diverging from a common point is called a *pencil*. The entire group of pencils originating at all points of a surface of finite extent is called a *beam*.

The wavelength of electromagnetic waves capable of affecting the sense of sight lies between 0.00004 cm and 0.00007 cm. Because these wavelengths are so small, it is convenient to express them in terms of a small unit of length.

Three such units are commonly used: the *micron*, the *nanometer* (accent on the *first* syllable), and the *angstrom*. One micron (1 μ) is a millionth of a meter, one nanometer (nm) is one one-thousandth of a micron, and one angstrom (1 A) is one ten-thousandth of a micron:

$$1\,\mu = 10^{-6}\,\text{m} = 10^{-4}\,\text{cm},$$

$$1\,\text{nm} = 10^{-9}\,\text{m} = 10^{-7}\,\text{cm},$$

$$1\,\text{A} = 10^{-10}\,\text{m} = 10^{-8}\,\text{cm}.$$

Most workers in the fields of optical instrument design, color, and physiological optics express wavelengths in *nanometers*. For example, the wavelength of the yellow light from a sodium flame is 589 nm. A spectroscopist, however, would specify the wavelengths present in this same yellow light to be 5889.963 A and 5895.930 A.

Figure 37–5 is a chart of the electromagnetic spectrum. Although waves of different wavelengths must be excited by different methods, all are alike so far as their fundamental nature is concerned. Note the relatively small portion occupied by the visible spectrum.

Different parts of the visible spectrum evoke the sensations of different colors. Very approximately: from 400 to 450 nm, violet; from 450 to 500 nm, blue; from 500 to 550 nm, green; from 550 to 600 nm, yellow; from 600 to 650 nm, orange; and from 650 to 700 nm, red. By the use of special sources or special filters, it is possible to limit the wavelength spread to a small band, say from 1 to 10 nm. Such light is called roughly *monochromatic light*, meaning light of a single color. Light consisting of only one wavelength is an idealization that is useful in theoretical calculations but represents an experimental impossibility. When the expression "monochromatic light of wavelength 550 nm" is used in theoretical discussions, it refers to one wavelength, but in descriptions of laboratory experiments it means a small band of wavelengths *around* 550 nm.

37-4 The speed of light

The speed of light in free space is one of the fundamental constants of nature. Its magnitude is so great (about 186,000 mi/sec or 3×10^8 m/sec) that it evaded experimental measurement until 1676. Up to that time it was generally believed that light traveled with an infinite speed.

The first attempt to measure the speed of light involved a method proposed by Galileo. Two experimenters were stationed on the tops of two hills about a mile apart. Each was provided with a lantern, the experiment being performed at night. One man was first to uncover his lantern and, observing the light from this lantern, the second was to uncover his. The velocity of light could then be computed from the known distance between the lanterns and the time elapsing between the instant when the first observer uncovered his lantern and when he observed the light from the second. While the experiment was entirely correct in principle, we know now that the speed is too great for the time interval to be measured in this way with any degree of precision.

In 1676, the Danish astronomer Olaf Roemer, from astronomical observations made on one of the satellites of the planet Jupiter, obtained the first definite evidence that light is propagated with a finite speed. Jupiter has twelve small satellites or moons, four of which are sufficiently bright to be seen with a moderately good telescope or a pair of field glasses. The satellites appear as tiny bright points at one side or the other of the disk of the planet. These satellites revolve about Jupiter just as does our moon about the earth and, since the plane of their orbits is nearly the same as that in which the earth and Jupiter revolve, each is eclipsed by the planet during a part of every revolution.

Roemer was engaged in measuring the time of revolution of one of the satellites by taking the time interval between consecutive eclipses (about 42 hr). He found, by a comparison of results over a long period of time, that while the earth was receding from Jupiter the period times were all somewhat longer than the average, and that while it was approaching Jupiter the times were all somewhat shorter. He concluded rightly that the cause of these variations was the varying distance between Jupiter and the earth.

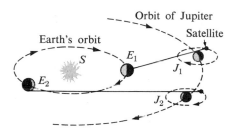

Fig. 37–6. Roemer's method for deducing the velocity of light.

Figure 37–6, not to scale, illustrates the case. Let observations be started when the earth and Jupiter are in the positions E_1 and J_1. Since Jupiter requires about 12 years to make one revolution in its orbit, then by the time the earth has moved to E_2 (about five months later) Jupiter has moved only to J_2. During this interval the distance between the planets has been continually increasing. Hence at each eclipse, the light from the satellite must travel a slightly greater distance than at the preceding eclipse, and the observed time of revolution is slightly larger than the true time.

Roemer concluded from his observations that a time of about 22 minutes was required for light to travel a distance equal to the diameter of the earth's orbit. The best figure for this distance, in Roemer's time, was about 172,000,000 miles. Although there is no record that Roemer actually made the computation, had he used the data above he would have found a speed of about 130,000 mi/sec or 2.1×10^8 m/sec.

The first successful determination of the speed of light from purely terrestrial measurements was made by the French scientist Fizeau in 1849. A schematic diagram of his apparatus is given in Fig. 37–7. Lens L_1 forms an image of the light source S at

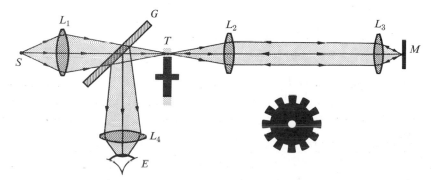

Fig. 37–7. Fizeau's toothed-wheel method for measuring the velocity of light. S is a light source, L_1, L_2, L_3, and L_4 are lenses, T is the toothed wheel, M is a mirror, and G is a glass plate.

a point near the rim of a toothed wheel T, which can be set into rapid rotation. G is an inclined plate of clear glass. Suppose first that the wheel is stationary and the light passes through one of the openings between the teeth. Lenses L_2 and L_3, which are separated by about 8.6 km, form a second image on the mirror M. The light is reflected from M, retraces its path, and is in part reflected from the glass plate G through the lens L_4 into the eye of an observer at E.

If the wheel T is set in rotation, the light from S is "chopped up" into a succession of wave trains of limited length. If the speed of rotation is such that by the time the front of one wave train has traveled to the mirror and returned, an opaque segment of the wheel has moved into the position formerly occupied by an open portion, no reflected light will reach the observer E. At twice this angular velocity, the light transmitted through any one opening will return through the next and an image of S will again be observed. From a knowledge of the angular velocity and radius of the wheel, the distance between openings, and the distance from wheel to mirror, the speed of light may be computed. Fizeau's measurements were not of high precision. He obtained a value of 3.15×10^8 m/sec.

Fizeau's apparatus was modified by Foucault, who replaced the toothed wheel with a rotating mirror. By introducing between the wheel and the mirror a tube filled with water, he proved that the speed of light in water is less than in air. A corpuscular theory demands that it shall be greater, and at the time these measurements were made they were taken as conclusive proof that a corpuscular theory was untenable.

The most precise measurements by the Foucault method were made by the American physicist Albert A. Michelson (1852–1931). His first experiments were performed in 1878 while he was on the staff of the Naval Academy at Annapolis. The latest, which were under way at the time of his death, were completed in 1935 by Pease and Pearson.

In an analysis of all measurements up to 1955, Cohen, DuMond, Layton, and Rollett report that the best value is

$$c = 2.997930 \times 10^8 \text{ m/sec},$$

which they believe correct within ± 300 m/sec.

37–5 The laws of reflection and refraction

Most of the objects we see are visible because they reflect light into our eyes. In the most common class of reflection, called *diffuse reflection*, light is reflected in all directions. A book on a table in a room lighted only by a point source of light can be seen from any part of the room. This type of reflection occurs whenever the roughness of the reflecting body has "dimensions" large compared with the wavelength of the reflected wave. In the other class of reflection, called *regular* or *specular reflection*, a narrow beam or *pencil* of light is reflected in one direction only. This type of reflection occurs from smooth surfaces whose irregularities are small compared with the wavelength of the reflected wave. For example, reflection from a blotter is diffuse, whereas reflection from a mirror is specular. Reflection from a polished automobile is intermediate, in that the reflected light is both diffuse and specular. Our main

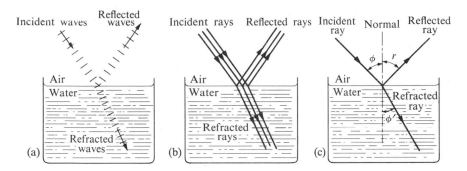

Fig. 37–8. (a) A train of plane waves is in part reflected and in part refracted at the boundary between two media. (b) The waves in (a) are represented by rays. (c) For simplicity, only one example of incident, reflected, and refracted rays is drawn.

interest is in specular reflection, and in what follows, the word "reflection" will mean "specular reflection."

Figure 37–8(a) shows a narrow train of plane waves of light incident from the upper left on a plane surface separating two transparent substances, *a* and *b*. For concreteness, let the upper medium be air and the lower, water. The path of the light, indicated by a narrow beam of rays in Fig. 37–8(b), can be clearly seen if there is some smoke or dust in the air, and if the water contains a small amount of fluorescent dye. A part of the incident light is *reflected* at the surface and a part passes into the water, or is *refracted.*

The directions of the incident, reflected, and refracted beams of light are specified in terms of the angles they make with the normal to the surface at the point of incidence. For this purpose it is sufficient to indicate merely one ray, as in Fig. 37–8(c), although a single ray of light is a geometrical abstraction. A careful experimental study of the directions of the incident, reflected, and refracted beams leads to the following results:

(1) *The incident, reflected, and refracted rays, and the normal to the surface, all lie in the same plane.* Thus, if the incident ray is in the plane of the diagram, and the surface of separation is perpendicular to this plane, the reflected and refracted rays are in the plane of the diagram.

(2) *The angle of reflection r is equal to the angle of incidence ϕ for all colors and any pair of substances.* Thus

$$r = \phi. \tag{37–1}$$

The experimental result that $r = \phi$, and that the incident and reflected rays and the normal all lie in the same plane, is known as the *law of reflection.*

(3) For monochromatic light and for a given pair of substances, *a* and *b*, on opposite sides of the surface of separation, *the ratio of the sine of the angle ϕ_a (between the ray in substance a and the normal) and the sine of the angle ϕ_b (between the ray in*

substance b and the normal) *is a constant.* Thus

$$\frac{\sin \phi_a}{\sin \phi_b} = \text{constant}. \tag{37-2}$$

The experimental result that $\sin \phi_a / \sin \phi_b$ is a *constant* for a given pair of substances and for monochromatic light, together with the fact that the incident and refracted rays, and the normal to the surface, all lie in the same plane, is known as the *law of refraction.* The discovery of this law is usually credited to Willebrord Snell (1591–1626), although there appears to be some doubt that it was actually original with him. It is commonly referred to as *Snell's law.*

The laws of reflection and refraction relate only to the *directions* of the corresponding rays but say nothing about an equally important question, namely, the fraction of the incident light that is reflected and the fraction that is refracted. These fractions depend also on the angle of incidence, and for the present we shall state only that the fraction reflected is smallest at *normal* incidence (where it is about 4% for an air-water surface) and that it increases with increasing angle of incidence (to almost 100% for an air-water surface at grazing incidence, or when $\phi_a = 90°$).

Suppose next that a ray of light is directed from *below* the air-water surface in Fig. 37–8. Again, we find that reflected and refracted rays exist, and that these, together with the incident ray and the normal, all lie in the same plane. The same law of reflection applies as when the ray is originally traveling in air, and the same law of refraction, Eq. (37–2). *The passage of a ray of light in going from one medium to another is reversible.* It follows the same path in going from b to a as when going from a to b. Also, in going from b to a, when the incident ray is normal to the surface, the same fraction of the incident light is reflected as when normal to the surface from above (about 4% for a water-air surface). As the angle between the ray in water and the normal is increased, the fraction reflected increases, but according to a different law from that applying in the direction from a to b.

37–6 Index of refraction

If a beam of monochromatic light is traveling *in a vacuum* and makes an angle of incidence ϕ_v with the normal to the surface of a substance a, and an angle of refraction ϕ_a in the substance, then Snell's law becomes

$$\frac{\sin \phi_v}{\sin \phi_a} = n_a, \tag{37-3}$$

and n_a is called the *index of refraction* of the substance a. The index of refraction depends not only on the substance but on the wavelength of the light. If no wavelength is stated, the index is usually assumed to be that corresponding to the yellow light from a sodium flame, of wavelength 589 nm.

The index of refraction of most of the common glasses used in optical instruments lies between 1.46 and 1.96. There are only a very few substances having indices larger than this value, diamond being one, with an index of 2.42, and rutile (crystalline titanium dioxide), with an index of 2.7, another. The values for a number of solids and liquids are given in Table 37–1.

TABLE 37–1

INDEX OF REFRACTION FOR YELLOW SODIUM LIGHT
($\lambda = 589$ nm)

Substance	Index of refraction	Substance	Index of refraction
Solids:		Liquids at 20°C:	
Ice (H$_2$O)	1.309	Methyl alcohol (CH$_3$OH)	1.3290
Fluorite (CaF$_2$)	1.434	Water (H$_2$O)	1.3330
Rock salt (NaCl)	1.544	Ethyl alcohol (C$_2$H$_5$OH)	1.3618
Quartz (SiO$_2$)	1.544	Carbon tetrachloride (CCl$_4$)	1.4607
Zircon (ZrO$_2$·SiO$_2$)	1.923	Turpentine	1.4721
Diamond (C)	2.417	Glycerine	1.4730
Fabulite (SrTiO$_3$)	2.409	Benzene	1.5012
Rutile (TiO$_2$)	$\begin{cases} 2.616 \\ 2.903 \end{cases}$	Carbon disulfide (CS$_2$)	1.6276

The index of refraction of air at standard conditions, for violet light of wavelength 436 nm, is 1.0002957, while for red light of wavelength 656 nm, the index is 1.0002914. It follows that for most purposes the *index of refraction of air can be assumed unity.* The index of refraction of a gas increases uniformly as the density of the gas is increased.

It follows from Eq. (37–3) that the angle of refraction ϕ_a is always less than the angle of incidence ϕ_v for a ray passing from a vacuum into one of the materials listed in Table 37–1, where all indices are seen to be greater than unity. In such a case, the ray is bent *toward* the normal. If the light is traveling in the opposite direction, the reverse is true and the ray is bent *away from* the normal.

Consider two parallel-sided plates of substances *a* and *b* placed parallel to each other with an arbitrary space between them, as shown in Fig. 37–9(a). Let the medium surrounding both plates be a vacuum, although the behavior of light would be practically the same if the plates were surrounded by air. If a ray of monochromatic light starts at the lower left of the figure and makes an angle of incidence ϕ_v, the angle between ray and normal in substance *a* is ϕ_a, and the light emerges from substance *a* at an angle ϕ_v equal to its incident angle. The light ray therefore enters plate *b* with an angle of incidence ϕ_v, makes an angle ϕ_b in substance *b*, and emerges again at an angle ϕ_v. Exactly the same path would be traversed if the same light ray were to start at the upper right and enter substance *b* at an angle ϕ_v. Moreover, *this behavior is independent of the thickness of the space between the two plates*, and exists when the space shrinks to nothing, as in Fig. 37–9(b).

Applying Snell's law to the refractions that take place at the surface between vacuum and substance *a*, and also at the surface between vacuum and substance *b*, we have

$$\frac{\sin \phi_v}{\sin \phi_a} = n_a, \qquad \frac{\sin \phi_v}{\sin \phi_b} = n_b.$$

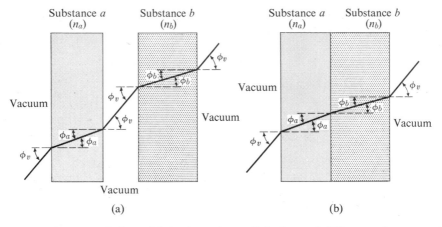

Fig. 37–9. The transmission of light through parallel plates of different substances. The incident and emerging rays are parallel, regardless of direction and regardless of the thickness of the space between adjacent slabs.

Dividing the second equation by the first, we get

$$\frac{\sin \phi_a}{\sin \phi_b} = \frac{n_b}{n_a},\qquad(37\text{--}4)$$

which shows that the *constant of Snell's law for the refraction between substances a and b is the ratio of the indices of refraction.* From Eq. (37–4) we see that the simplest and most symmetrical way of writing Snell's law for any two substances *a* and *b, and for any direction* is

$$\boxed{n_a \sin \phi_a = n_b \sin \phi_b.}\qquad(37\text{--}5)$$

Problems

37–1. What is the wavelength in meters, microns, nanometers, and angstrom units of (a) soft x-rays of frequency 2×10^{17} cycles/sec? (b) green light of frequency 5.6×10^{14} cycles/sec?

37–2. The visible spectrum includes a wavelength range from about 400 nm to about 700 nm. Express these wavelengths in inches.

37–3. Assuming the radius of the earth's orbit to be 92,900,000 miles, and taking the best value of the speed of light, compute the time required for light to travel a distance equal to the diameter of the earth's orbit. Compare with Roemer's value of 22 minutes.

37–4. Fizeau's measurements of the speed of light were continued by Cornu, using Fizeau's apparatus but with the distance between mirrors increased to 22.9 km. One of the toothed wheels used was 40 mm in diameter and had 180 teeth. Find the angular velocity at which it should rotate so that light transmitted through one opening will return through the next.

37-5. A ray of light traveling with speed c leaves point 1 of Fig. 37-10 and is reflected to point 2. Show (a) that the time required for the light to travel from 1 to 2 is $(y_1 \sec \theta_1 + y_2 \sec \theta_2)/c$, and (b) that this time is a minimum when $\theta_1 = \theta_2$. (Note that $l = y_1 \tan \theta_1 + y_2 \tan \theta_2$.)

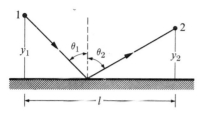

Figure 37-10

37-6. Prove that a ray of light reflected from a plane mirror rotates through an angle 2θ when the mirror rotates through an angle θ about an axis perpendicular to the plane of incidence.

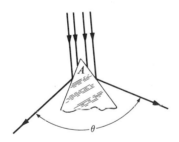

Figure 37-11

37-7. A parallel beam of light is incident on a prism, as shown in Fig. 37-11. Part is reflected from one face and part from the other. Show that the angle θ between the two reflected beams is twice the angle A between the two reflecting surfaces.

37-8. The density of the earth's atmosphere increases as the surface of the earth is approached. (a) Draw a diagram showing how the light from a star or planet is bent as it goes through the atmosphere. (b) Indicate the apparent position of the light source. (c) Explain how one can see the sun after it has set. (d) Explain why the setting sun appears flattened.

37-9. (a) Why does the surface of a smooth highway under hot sun appear wet when it is seen at a glancing angle? (b) Account for a mirage in the desert.

37-10. A parallel beam of light makes an angle of 30° with the surface of a glass plate having a refractive index of 1.50. (a) What is the angle between the refracted beam and the surface of the glass? (b) What should be the angle of incidence ϕ with this plate for the angle of refraction to be $\phi/2$?

37-11. Light strikes a glass plate at an angle of incidence of 60°, part of the beam being reflected and part refracted. It is observed that the reflected and refracted portions make an angle of 90° with each other. What is the index of refraction of the glass?

37-12. A ray of light is incident on a plane surface separating two transparent substances of indices 1.60 and 1.40. The angle of incidence is 30° and the ray originates in the medium of higher index. Compute the angle of refraction.

37-13. A parallel-sided plate of glass having a refractive index of 1.60 is held on the surface of water in a tank. A ray coming from above makes an angle of incidence of 45° with the top surface of the glass. (a) What angle does the ray make with the normal in the water? (b) How does this angle vary with the refractive index of the glass?

Index of refract of air = 1

CHAPTER 38

Reflection and Refraction at Plane Surfaces

38–1 Huygens' principle

The equation representing the propagation of a spherical, electromagnetic wave from a point source through a homogeneous medium is

$$e = E \sin (\omega t - kr),$$

where e is the instantaneous value of the electric intensity, E is the amplitude, ω is the angular frequency $2\pi f$, k is the propagation constant $2\pi/\lambda$, and r is the distance from the source (very much larger than λ). If the wave is entirely unobstructed, the value of e at any time t and at any point r is obtained by substituting the appropriate numerical values into the wave equation. But waves are almost always obstructed. When light enters a telescope, only that portion of a wavefront equal to the diameter of the objective lens is admitted. When light passes through a narrow slit almost the entire wavefront is absorbed by the screen and only a small portion goes through. The fundamental problem of wave propagation is to determine the amplitude, the phase, and the polarization of the light arriving at a point when only a portion of a wavefront is exposed. This can be an extraordinarily difficult problem when the exposed portion of the wavefront has an unusual shape, and when the electrical and magnetic characteristics of the obstructing screen have to be taken into account to determine the polarization. If, however, the direction of the **E**-vector is unimportant, a scalar theory may be used and the mathematical equations become somewhat simpler. The technique of finding the intensity and phase of the light at any point when only a portion of a wavefront is exposed is called *Huygens' principle*. (The dipthong "uy" is pronounced like the French sound "euille" and the g is guttural.)

The principle, as stated originally by Huygens, is a geometrical method for finding, from the known shape of a portion of a wavefront at some instant, what the shape will be at some later instant. It is assumed that *every point of a wavefront may be considered the source of small secondary wavelets, which spread out in all directions with a speed equal to the speed of propagation of the waves.* The new wavefront is then found by constructing a surface tangent to the secondary wavelets or, as it is called, the *envelope* of the wavelets.

Huygens' principle is illustrated in Fig. 38–1. The original wavefront, AA', is traveling as indicated by the small arrows. We wish to find the shape of the wavefront after a time interval t. Let v represent the speed of propagation. Construct a number of circles (traces of spherical wavelets) of radius $r = vt$, with centers along AA'. The trace of the envelope of these wavelets, which is the new wavefront, is the curve BB'. The speed v has been assumed the same at all points and in all directions.

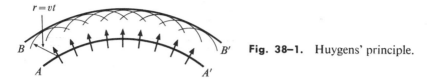

Fig. 38–1. Huygens' principle.

The original form of Huygens' principle is adequate to account for the reflection and refraction of waves. When we come to the phenomena of interference and diffraction in Chapter 41, the principle will be extended to include the concept of phase. The further extension of the principle into a complete scalar theory, first done by Kirchhoff, and the further development by Sommerfeld into a vector theory are beyond the scope of this book.

The fact that any point on a wavefront may be regarded as a source of a secondary wavelet may be demonstrated convincingly with the aid of a ripple tank, mentioned briefly in Section 21–6. If plane wavefronts are produced in the water in a shallow tank and these wavefronts come to a narrow slit, instead of a parallel beam issuing from the slit, a complete circular wave is formed, as shown in Fig. 38–2.

Fig. 38–2. Demonstration of a Huygens wavelet with the aid of water waves in a shallow tank. (Reproduced from *Ripple Tank Studies of Wave Motion* with permission of W. Llowarch, the Clarendon Press, Oxford.)

38–2 Derivation of the law of reflection from Huygens' principle

Consider the trace of a plane wave surface AA', called the incident *wavefront*, which is just making contact with the reflecting surface MM' along a line through A perpendicular to the plane of the diagram (Fig. 38–3). The planes of the wavefront and the reflecting surface are also normal to the plane of the figure. The position of the wavefront after a time interval t may be found by applying Huygens' principle. With points on AA' as centers, draw a number of secondary wavelets of radius vt, where v is the speed of propagation in the medium near the surface. Those wavelets originating near the upper end of AA' spread out unhindered, and their envelope gives that portion of the new wave surface OB'. The wavelets originating near the lower end of AA', however, strike the reflecting surface. If the latter had not been there, they would have occupied the positions shown by the dotted circular arcs. The effect of the reflecting surface is to reverse the direction of travel of those wavelets which strike it, so that that part of a wavelet which would have penetrated the surface actually lies to the left of it, as shown by the full lines. The envelope of these reflected wavelets is then that portion of the wavefront OB. The trace of the entire wavefront at this instant is the broken line BOB'. A similar construction gives the line CPC' for the wavefront after another interval t.

The angle ϕ between the incident wavefront and the surface is the same as that between the incident ray and the normal to the surface, and is therefore the angle of incidence. Similarly, r is the angle of reflection. To find the relation between these angles, consider Fig. 38–4, which is the same as a portion of Fig. 38–3. From O, draw $OP = vt$, perpendicular to AA'. Now OB, by construction, is tangent to a circle of

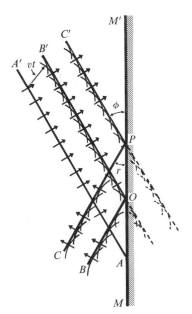

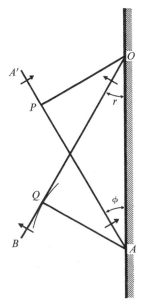

Fig. 38–3. Successive positions of a plane wave AA' as it is reflected from a plane surface.

Fig. 38–4. A portion of Fig. 38–3.

radius vt with center at A. Hence if AQ is drawn from A to the point of tangency, the triangles APO and AQO are equal (right triangles with the side AO in common and with $AQ = OP$). The angle ϕ therefore equals the angle r, and we have the law of reflection.

38–3 Derivation of Snell's law from Huygens' principle

Consider the trace of a plane wavefront AA' (Fig. 38–5) which is just making contact with the surface MM' along a line through A perpendicular to the plane of the diagram. MM' represents a boundary surface between two transparent media of different indices of refraction. The reflected waves are not shown in the figure, as they proceed exactly as in Fig. 38–3. Let us apply Huygens' principle to find the position of the refracted wavefront after a time t.

With points on AA' as centers, draw a number of secondary wavelets. Those originating near the upper end of AA' travel with speed v and after a time interval t are spherical surfaces of radius vt. The wavelet originating at point A, however, is traveling in the lower medium with speed v' and in time t is a spherical surface of radius $v't$. The envelope of the wavelets from the original wavefront is the plane whose trace is the broken line BOB'. A similar construction leads to the trace CPC' after a second interval t.

The angles ϕ and ϕ' between the surface and the incident and refracted wavefronts are, respectively, the angle of incidence and the angle of refraction. To find the relation between these angles refer to Fig. 38–6, which is the same as a portion of Fig. 38–5. Draw $OQ = vt$, perpendicular to AQ, and draw $AB = v't$, perpendicular to BO.

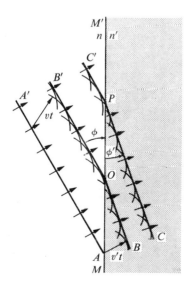

Fig. 38–5. Successive positions of a plane wavefront AA' as it is refracted by a plane surface.

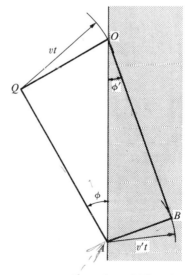

Fig. 38–6. A portion of Fig. 38–5.

From the right triangle AOQ,

$$\sin \phi = \frac{vt}{AO},$$

and from the right triangle AOB,

$$\sin \phi' = \frac{v't}{AO}.$$

Hence

$$\frac{\sin \phi}{\sin \phi'} = \frac{v}{v'}. \qquad (38\text{--}1)$$

Since v/v' is a constant, Eq. (38–1) expresses Snell's law, and we have derived Snell's law from a wave theory.

The most general form of Snell's law is given by Eq. (37–4), namely

$$\frac{\sin \phi}{\sin \phi'} = \frac{n'}{n},$$

whence

$$\frac{v}{v'} = \frac{n'}{n},$$

and

$$nv = n'v'.$$

When either medium is a vacuum, the index is 1 and the speed is c. Hence

$$\boxed{n = \frac{c}{v}, \qquad n' = \frac{c}{v'},} \qquad (38\text{--}2)$$

showing that the *index of refraction of any medium is the ratio of the speed of light in a vacuum to the speed in the medium.*

It was shown in Chapter 36 that the speed of an electromagnetic wave in a vacuum is given by

$$c = \sqrt{1/\epsilon_0 \mu_0}.$$

When the same calculation is made for a light wave in a *material* medium of permittivity ϵ and permeability μ, the speed v is

$$v = \sqrt{1/\epsilon\mu} = \sqrt{1/K\epsilon_0 K_m \mu_0} = c\sqrt{1/KK_m}.$$

Most transparent substances show a magnetic behavior that differs only slightly from that of a vacuum. The quantity K_m is therefore very close to 1, and $v = c/\sqrt{K}$, or

$$\boxed{n = \sqrt{K}.} \qquad (38\text{--}3)$$

The values of K listed in Table 27–1 are *static* values, obtained by measurements with nonvarying electric fields. When the electric field varies rapidly, as it does in a light wave, K is found to depend on the frequency. The index of refraction, therefore, cannot be calculated from the values in Table 27–1.

In Fig. 38–5 the spacing of the incident wavefronts is arbitrary. If t is chosen to be the period T of the wave, the spacing would be vT, which is the wavelength λ. Figure 38–5 shows that the wavelength in the second medium is smaller, since the wave speed is smaller. When a light wave proceeds from one medium to another, where the speed is different, the wavelength changes but *not the frequency*. Since

$$v = f\lambda \qquad \text{and} \qquad v' = f\lambda',$$

$$\frac{\lambda}{v} = \frac{\lambda'}{v'} \qquad \text{and} \qquad \lambda\frac{c}{v} = \lambda'\frac{c}{v'}.$$

Therefore

$$\lambda n = \lambda'n'.$$

If either medium is a vacuum, the index is 1 and the wavelength in a vacuum is represented by λ_v. Hence

$$\lambda = \frac{\lambda_v}{n}, \qquad \lambda' = \frac{\lambda_v}{n'}, \tag{38–4}$$

showing that *the wavelength in any medium is the wavelength in a vacuum divided by the index of refraction of the medium.*

38–4 Total internal reflection

Figure 38–7 shows a number of rays diverging from a point source P in a medium of index n and striking the surface of a second medium of index n', where $n > n'$. From Snell's law,

$$\sin \phi' = \frac{n}{n'} \sin \phi.$$

Since n/n' is greater than unity, $\sin \phi'$ is larger than $\sin \phi$ and evidently equals unity (i.e., $\phi' = 90°$) for some angle ϕ less than 90°. This is illustrated by ray 3 in the dia-

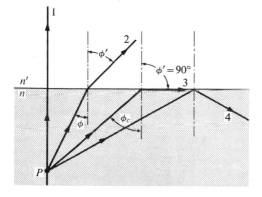

Fig. 38–7. Total internal reflection. The angle of incidence ϕ_c, for which the angle of refraction is 90°, is called the critical angle.

gram, which emerges just grazing the surface at an angle of refraction of 90°. The angle of incidence for which the refracted ray emerges tangent to the surface is called the *critical angle* and is designated by ϕ_c in the diagram. If the angle of incidence is greater than the critical angle, the sine of the angle of refraction, as computed by Snell's law, is greater than unity. This may be interpreted to mean that beyond the critical angle the ray does not pass into the upper medium but is *totally internally reflected* at the boundary surface. Total internal reflection can occur only when a ray is incident on the surface of a medium whose index is *smaller* than that of the medium in which the ray is traveling.

The critical angle for two given substances may be found by setting $\phi' = 90°$ or $\sin \phi' = 1$ in Snell's law. We then have

$$\sin \phi_c = \frac{n'}{n} \cdot \qquad (38\text{–}5)$$

The critical angle of a glass-air surface, taking 1.50 as a typical index of refraction of glass, is

$$\sin \phi_c = \frac{1}{1.50} = 0.67, \qquad \phi_c = 42°.$$

This angle, very conveniently, is slightly less than 45°, which makes possible the use in many optical instruments of prisms of angles 45°–45°–90° as totally reflecting surfaces. The advantages of totally reflecting prisms over metallic surfaces as reflectors are, first, that the light is *totally* reflected, while no metallic surface reflects 100% of the light incident on it, and second, the reflecting properties are permanent and not affected by tarnishing. Offsetting these is the fact that there is some loss of light by reflection at the surfaces where light enters and leaves the prism, although recently discovered methods of coating the surfaces with so-called "nonreflecting" films can reduce this loss considerably.

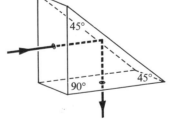

Fig. 38–8. A totally reflecting prism.

The simplest type of reflecting prism is shown in Fig. 38–8. Its angles are 45°–45°–90°. Light incident normally on one of the shorter faces strikes the inclined face at an angle of incidence of 45°. This is greater than the critical angle, so the light is totally internally reflected and emerges from the second of the shorter faces after undergoing a deviation of 90°.

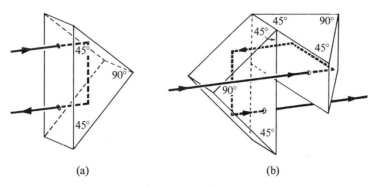

Fig. 38–9. (a) A Porro prism. (b) A combination of two Porro prisms.

A 45°–45°–90° prism, used as in Fig. 38–9(a), is called a *Porro* prism. Light enters and leaves at right angles to the hypotenuse and is reflected at each of the shorter faces. The deviation is 180°. Two Porro prisms are often combined as in Fig. 38–9(b).

38–5 Refraction by a prism

The prism, in one or another of its many forms, is second only to the lens as the most useful piece of optical apparatus. Totally reflecting prisms have been mentioned briefly. We consider now the *deviation* and the *dispersion* produced by a prism.

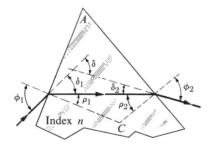

Fig. 38–10.   Deviation by a prism.

Consider a light ray incident at an angle ϕ_1 on one face of a prism, as in Fig. 38–10. Let the index of the prism be n, the included angle at the apex be A, and let the medium on either side of the prism be air. It is desired to find the *angle of deviation*, δ. The deviation produced by the first refraction is δ_1 and by the second, δ_2. Hence

$$\delta = \delta_1 + \delta_2 = \phi_1 - \rho_1 + \phi_2 - \rho_2$$

or

$$\delta = \phi_1 + \phi_2 - (\rho_1 + \rho_2).$$

But the sum $\rho_1 + \rho_2$ is supplementary to angle C. The same is true of angle A. Therefore $\rho_1 + \rho_2 = A$, and $\delta = \phi_1 + \phi_2 - A$. From a laboratory standpoint, the fundamental independent variable is the angle of incidence ϕ_1. When δ is measured as a function of ϕ_1 it is found that as ϕ_1 increases, δ first decreases, reaches a minimum, and then increases. To find the condition that exists when δ is a minimum, it is sufficient merely to set the first derivative of δ with respect to ϕ_1 equal to zero. But since ρ_1 is a function of ϕ_1, we may consider with equal justification that ϕ_1 is a function of ρ_1 and express δ as a function of ρ_1. To do this, we first apply Snell's law to the first refraction:

$$\sin \phi_1 = n \sin \rho_1, \qquad \phi_1 = \text{arc sin } (n \sin \rho_1).$$

The second refraction yields

$$\sin \phi_2 = n \sin \rho_2 = n \sin (A - \rho_1), \qquad \phi_2 = \text{arc sin } [n \sin (A - \rho_1)].$$

Hence

$$\delta = \text{arc sin } (n \sin \rho_1) + \text{arc sin } [n \sin (A - \rho_1)] - A,$$

$$\frac{d\delta}{d\rho_1} = \frac{n \cos \rho_1}{\sqrt{1 - n^2 \sin^2 \rho_1}} - \frac{n \cos (A - \rho_1)}{\sqrt{1 - n^2 \sin^2 (A - \rho_1)}} = 0,$$

which says that a function of ρ_1 is equal to the *same* function of $A - \rho_1$. It follows that $\rho_1 = A - \rho_1$, and therefore $\rho_1 = A/2$. Since $\rho_1 + \rho_2 = A$, it follows that

$$\rho_1 = \frac{A}{2} = \rho_2 \text{ (for minimum } \delta). \qquad (38\text{–}6)$$

Also,

$$\delta_1 = \delta_2, \quad \text{and} \quad \phi_1 = \phi_2 \text{ (for minimum } \delta), \qquad (38\text{–}7)$$

so that, at minimum deviation, the ray emerges at the same angle at which it entered. If the base of the prism were such that Fig. 38–10 became an isosceles triangle, at minimum deviation the ray would pass through the prism *symmetrically*.

If we designate the angle of minimum deviation by the symbol δ_m, then $\delta_m = 2\phi_1 - A$, and

$$\phi_1 = \frac{A + \delta_m}{2}, \qquad \rho_1 = \frac{A}{2}.$$

Since $n = \sin \phi_1 / \sin \rho_1$, we get

$$n = \frac{\sin \frac{1}{2}(A + \delta_m)}{\sin \frac{1}{2}A}. \qquad (38\text{–}8)$$

By making use of this equation, the index of refraction of a transparent solid may be measured. The specimen whose index is desired is ground into the form of a prism. The angle of the prism A and the angle of minimum deviation δ_m are measured with the aid of a spectrometer. Since these angles may be determined with a high degree of precision, this method is an extremely accurate one and by means of it indices of refraction may be measured to the sixth place of decimals.

If the angle of the prism is small, the angle of minimum deviation is small also and we may replace the sines of the angles by the angles.

One then obtains

$$n = \frac{A + \delta_m}{A},$$

or

$$\delta_m = (n - 1)A, \qquad (38\text{–}9)$$

a useful approximate relation.

38–6 Dispersion

Most light beams are a mixture of waves whose wavelengths extend throughout the visible spectrum. While the speed of light waves in a vacuum is the same for all wavelengths, the speed in a material substance is different for different wavelengths. Hence the index of refraction of a substance is a function of wavelength. The dependence of wave speed on wavelength was first mentioned in connection with water waves, in Section 21–6. A substance in which the speed of a wave varies with wavelength is said to exhibit *dispersion*. Figure 38–11 is a diagram showing the variation of index of refraction with wavelength for a number of the more common optical materials.

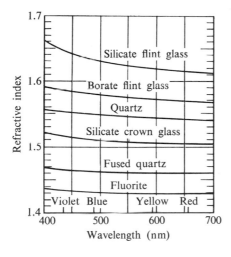

Fig. 38–11. Variation of index with wavelength.

Consider a ray of white light, a mixture of all visible wavelengths, incident on a prism as in Fig. 38–12. Since the deviation produced by the prism increases with increasing index of refraction, violet light is deviated most and red least, with other colors occupying intermediate positions. On emerging from the prism, the light is spread out into a fan-shaped beam as shown. The light is said to be *dispersed* into a spectrum.

When white light is dispersed by a prism, it can be seen from Fig. 38–12 that the whole fan-shaped beam is deviated from the incident direction. A convenient measure

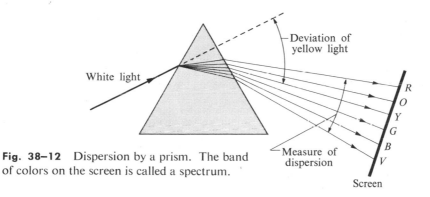

Fig. 38–12 Dispersion by a prism. The band of colors on the screen is called a spectrum.

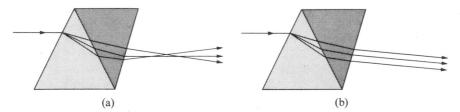

Fig. 38–13. (a) A direct-vision prism. (b) An achromatic prism.

of this deviation is provided by the angle of deviation of yellow light, since yellow is roughly midway between red and violet. A simple measure of the dispersion is provided by the angular separation of the red and violet rays. Since deviation and index of refraction are related, the deviation of the entire spectrum is controlled by the index of refraction for yellow light, whereas the dispersion depends on the *difference* between the index for violet light and that for red light. From the graphs of Fig. 38–11 it can be seen that for a substance like fluorite, whose index for yellow light is small, the difference between the indices for red and violet is also small. On the other hand, in the case of silicate flint glass, both the index for yellow light and the difference between extreme indices are large. In other words, for most transparent materials the greater the deviation, the greater the dispersion.

The brilliance of diamond is due in part to its large dispersion. In recent years synthetic crystals of titanium dioxide and of strontium titanate, with about eight times the dispersion of diamond, have been produced.

Because of the shape of the curves in Fig. 38–11, the dispersions produced by two prisms of equal angles are not exactly proportional to the mean deviations. It is therefore possible to combine two (or more) prisms of different materials in such a way that there is no net deviation of a ray of some chosen wavelength, while there remains an outstanding dispersion of the spectrum as a whole. Such a device, illustrated in Fig. 38–13(a), is known as a *direct-vision prism*. Two prisms may also be designed so that the dispersion of one is offset by the dispersion of the other, although the deviation is not. A compound prism of this sort is called *achromatic* (without color). See Fig. 38–13(b).

38–7 The rainbow

The rainbow is produced by the combined effects of refraction, dispersion, and internal reflection of sunlight by drops of rain. When conditions for its observation are favorable, two bows may be seen, the inner being called the primary bow and the outer the secondary bow. The inner bow, which is the brighter, is red on the outside and violet on the inside, while in the more faint outer bow the colors are reversed. The primary bow is produced in the following manner. Assume that the sun's rays are horizontal, and consider a ray striking a raindrop, as in Fig. 38–14(a). This ray is refracted at the first surface and is in part reflected at the second surface, passing out again at the front surface as shown. The French scientist Descartes computed the paths of some thousands of rays incident at different points on the surface of a raindrop and showed that if a ray of any given color were incident at such a point that its

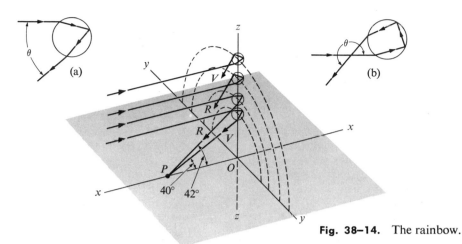

Fig. 38–14. The rainbow.

deviation was a maximum, all other rays of the same color which struck the surface of the drop in the immediate neighborhood of this point would be reflected in a direction very close to that of the first. Hence each color is strongly reflected in the direction of maximum deviation of that particular color. The angle of maximum deviation of red light is 138°, or the angle θ in Fig. 38–14(a) is $180° - 138° = 42°$. The corresponding angle for violet light is 40°, while that for other colors lies between these.

Consider now an observer at P, Fig. 38–14. The xy-plane is horizontal and sunlight is coming from the left parallel to the x-axis. All drops which lie on a circle subtending an angle of 42° at P, and with the center at O, will reflect red light strongly to P. All those on a circle subtending 40° at P will reflect violet light strongly, while those occupying intermediate positions will reflect the intermediate colors of the spectrum.

The point O, the center of the circular arc of the bow, may be considered the shadow of P on the yz-plane. As the sun rises above the horizon the point O moves down, and hence with increasing elevation of the sun a smaller and smaller part of the bow is visible. Evidently an observer at ground level cannot see the primary bow when the sun is more than 42° above the horizon. If the observer is in an elevated position, however, the point O moves up and more and more of the bow may be seen. In fact, it is not uncommon for a complete circular rainbow to be seen from an airplane.

The secondary bow is produced by two internal reflections, as shown in Fig. 38–14(b). As before, the light which is reflected in any particular direction consists largely of the color for which that direction is the angle of maximum deviation. Since the angle of deviation is here the angle θ, and since the violet is deviated more than the red, the violet rays in the secondary bow are deflected down at a steeper angle than the red and the secondary bow is red on the inside and violet on the outside edge. The corresponding angles are 50.5° for red and 54° for violet.

The preceding discussion applies when the drops producing a rainbow are relatively large. When the drops are small, diffraction plays just as important a role as dispersion and reflection, and red light, for example, is received in appreciable amounts from drops lying on circles other than those subtending an angle of 42°. The bow is then a complicated mixture of colors and its appearance depends on the size of the drops.

Problems

38–1. (a) What is the speed of light of wavelength 500 nm (in vacuum), in glass whose index at this wavelength is 1.50? (b) What is the wavelength of these waves in the glass?

38–2. A glass plate 3 mm thick, of index 1.50, is placed between a point source of light of wavelength 600 nm (in vacuum) and a screen. The distance from source to screen is 3 cm. How many waves are there between source and screen?

38–3. The speed of light of wavelength 656 nm in heavy flint glass is 1.60×10^8 m/sec. What is the index of refraction of this glass?

38- 4. Light of a certain frequency has a wavelength in water of 442 nm. What is the wavelength of this light when it passes into carbon disulfide?

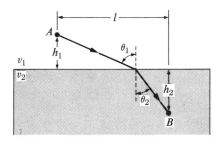

Figure 38–15

38–5. A ray of light goes from point A in a medium where the velocity of light is v_1 to point B in a medium where the velocity is v_2, as in Fig. 38–15. Show (a) that the time required for the light to go from A to B is

$$t = \frac{h_1 \sec \theta_1}{v_1} + \frac{h_2 \sec \theta_2}{v_2},$$

and (b) that this time is minimum when the relation between the angles is $n_1 \sin \theta_1 = n_2 \sin \theta_2$. (Note that $l = h_1 \tan \theta_1 + h_2 \tan \theta_2$.)

38–6. A point light source is 2 in. below a water-air surface. Compute the angles of refraction of rays from the source making angles with the normal of 10°, 20°, 30°, and 40°, and show these rays in a carefully drawn full-size diagram.

38–7. A glass cube in air has a refractive index of 1.50. Parallel rays of light enter the top obliquely and then strike a side of the cube. Is it possible for the rays to emerge from this side?

38–8. A point source of light is 8 in. below the surface of a body of water. Find the diameter of the largest circle at the surface through which light can emerge from the water.

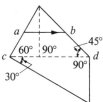

Figure 38–16

38–9. The index of refraction of the prism shown in Fig. 38–16 is 1.56. A ray of light enters the prism at point a and follows in the prism the path ab which is parallel to the line cd. (a) Sketch carefully the path of the ray from a point outside the prism at the left, through the glass, and out some distance into the air again. (b) Compute the angle between the original and final directions in air. (Dotted lines are construction lines only.)

38–10. Light is incident normally on the short face of a 30°-60°-90° prism, as in Fig. 38–17. A drop of liquid is placed on the hypotenuse of the prism. If the index of the prism is 1.50, find the maximum index the liquid may have if the light is to be totally reflected.

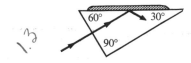

Figure 38–17

38–11. A 45°-45°-90° prism is immersed in water. What is the minimum index of refraction the prism may have if it is to reflect totally a ray incident normally on one of its shorter faces?

✗38–12. The velocity of a sound wave is 1100 ft/sec in air and 4400 ft/sec in water. (a) What is the critical angle for a sound wave incident on the surface between air and water? (b) Which medium has the higher "index of refraction" for sound?

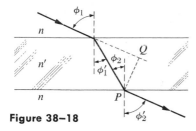

Figure 38–18

38-13. Light is incident at an angle ϕ_1 (as in Fig. 38–18) on the upper surface of a transparent plate, the surfaces of the plate being plane and parallel to each other. (a) Prove that $\phi_1 = \phi_2'$. (b) Show that this is true for any number of different parallel plates. (c) Prove that the lateral displacement of the emergent beam is given by the relation

$$PQ = t\,\frac{\sin(\phi_1 - \phi_1')}{\cos\phi_1'},$$

where t is the thickness of the plate.

38–14. A parallel beam of light containing wavelengths A and B is incident on the face of a triangular glass prism having a refracting angle of 60°. The indices of refraction are $n_A = 1.40$ and $n_B = 1.60$. If beam A goes through the prism at minimum deviation, find (a) the angle of emergence of each beam and (b) the angle of deviation of each.

38–15. A ray of light is incident at an angle of 60° on one surface of a glass plate 2 cm thick, of index 1.50. The medium on either side of the plate is air. Find the transverse displacement between the incident and emergent rays.

✗38–16. The prism of Fig. 38–19 has a refractive index of 1.414, and the angles A are 30°. Two light rays m and n are parallel as they enter the prism. What is the angle between them after they emerge?

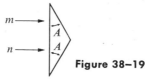

Figure 38–19

✗38–17. What is the angle of minimum deviation of an equiangular prism having a refractive index of 1.414?

38 18. An equiangular prism is constructed of the silicate flint glass whose index of refraction is given in Fig. 38–11. Find the angles of minimum deviation for light of wavelength 400 nm and 700 nm.

✗38–19. A silicate crown prism of apex angle 15° is to be combined with a prism of silicate flint so as to result in no net deviation of light of wavelength 550 nm. (See Fig. 38–11 for indices of refraction.) Find the angle of the flint prism. Assume that light passes through both prisms at the angle of minimum deviation.

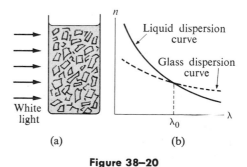

Figure 38–20

38–20. The glass vessel shown in Fig. 38–20(a) contains a large number of small, irregular pieces of glass and a liquid. The dispersion curves of the glass and of the liquid are shown in Fig. 38–20(b). Explain the behavior of a parallel beam of white light as it traverses the vessel. (This is known as a *Christiansen filter*.)

CHAPTER 39

Images Formed by a Single Reflection or Refraction

39–1 Introduction

In the preceding chapter we discussed the reflection and refraction of rays of light at a surface separating two substances of different index, but considered only a single ray or bundles of parallel rays. We now take up the problem of tracing the paths of a large number of rays, all of which diverge from some one point of an object which is either self-luminous or has a rough surface capable of reflecting light in all directions. Such a point is represented by P in Fig. 39–1. At the right of P is a plane surface like that of a block of glass. A ray incident on any point of the surface is in part transmitted and in part reflected. The direction of the reflected ray is given by the law of reflection and that of the transmitted or refracted ray by Snell's law. These two principles suffice to determine the directions of all rays after they encounter a surface of any shape. We shall first consider the reflected rays only, from both plane and spherical surfaces, and then discuss refraction at plane and spherical surfaces. A discussion of surfaces other than plane and spherical is beyond the scope of this book.

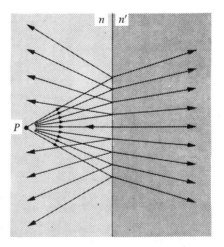

Fig. 39–1. Reflection and refraction of rays at a plane surface.

39–2 Reflection at a plane mirror

While some light is reflected at any surface separating two substances of different index, it is often desirable that the fraction reflected shall be as large as possible. By making the surface of highly polished metal, or by applying a thin metallic coat to a polished surface, the fraction of the light reflected can be made nearly 100%. A highly reflecting smooth surface is called a *mirror*, and we shall speak of the reflecting

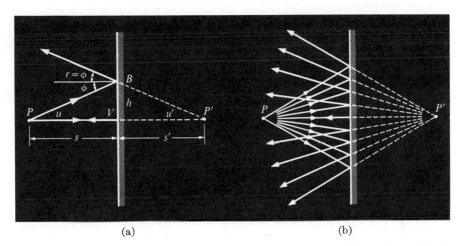

(a)   (b)

Fig. 39–2. Rays diverging from point P appear to diverge from point P' after reflection at a plane surface.

surfaces in the sections to follow as mirrors, although the equations to be derived will apply to smooth surfaces from which the light is only partially reflected, such as the surface of a pane of window glass, or that of a lens.

Figure 39–2(a) shows two rays diverging from a point P at a distance s at the left of a plane mirror. We call P the *object point* and s the *object distance*. In measuring the object distance we shall always *start at the reflecting surface and proceed toward the object point. If this direction is opposite to the direction of the oncoming (incident) light, the object distance s is positive.* In Fig. 39–2(a) it is evident that s is positive. The ray PV, incident normally on the mirror, returns along its original path. The ray PB, making an arbitrary angle u with PV, strikes the mirror at an angle of incidence $\phi = u$ and is reflected at an angle $r = \phi = u$.

Extend the reflected rays by dotted lines at the right of the mirror, as shown. These dotted lines intersect at P', at a distance s' to the right of the mirror. We shall prove in a moment that *all* rays diverging from P will give rise to reflected rays which, when prolonged backward into the region behind the mirror, intersect at the point P', as shown in Fig. 39–2(b). If one looks toward the mirror from the left, his eye treats the diverging reflected rays as if they had actually originated at the point P'. We say that P' is the *image* of point P and we call s' the *image distance*. In measuring the image distance we shall always *start at the reflecting surface and proceed toward the image point. If this direction is the same as that of the ongoing (reflected) light, the image distance s' is positive.*

In Fig. 39–2(a) it is evident that s' is negative. The angle u' is equal to r and hence is equal to u. Let h represent the distance VB. Then from the triangles PBV and $P'BV$,

$$\tan u = \frac{h}{s}, \qquad \tan u' = \frac{h}{-s'},$$

and since $u = u'$, it follows that

$$s = -s'. \tag{39–1}$$

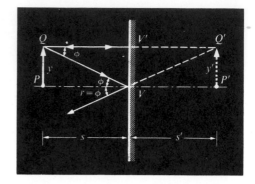

Fig. 39-3. Construction for determining the height of an image formed by reflection at a plane surface.

This result is true whatever the value of the angle u. For the special case of a plane mirror, we see that the image of an object point lies on the extension of the normal from the object point to the mirror, and that the object distance and image distance are equal in absolute value.

Now consider an object of finite size and parallel to the mirror, represented by the arrow PQ in Fig. 39-3. Point P', the image of P, is found as in Fig. 39-2(a). Two of the rays from Q are shown in Fig. 39-3, and all rays from Q appear to diverge from its image Q' after reflection. Other points of the object PQ are imaged between P' and Q'. Let y and y' represent the lengths of object and image, respectively. These lengths are *measured from the axis* PP', *and are positive when this direction is up*. The ratio y'/y is called the *magnification m*:

$$m = \frac{y'}{y}.$$

From the triangles PQV and $P'Q'V$,

$$\tan \phi = \frac{y}{s} = \frac{y'}{-s'},$$

and since $s = -s'$, it follows that $y' = y$ and hence for a plane mirror the magnification is unity.

The image $P'Q'$ in Fig. 39-3 is called *virtual*, meaning that the reflected rays *appear* to diverge from the image, although they do not actually do so. Virtual images are represented by dotted lines.

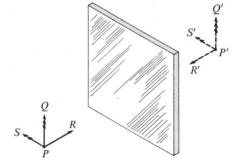

Fig. 39-4. A plane mirror forms a three-dimensional perverted image of a three-dimensional object.

The three-dimensional virtual image of a three-dimensional object, formed by a plane mirror, is shown in Fig. 39–4. The image of every object point lies on the normal from that point to the mirror, and the distances from object and image to the mirror are equal. Thus while the images $P'Q'$ and $P'S'$ are parallel to their objects, $P'R'$ is reversed relative to PR. The object and its image are related in the same way as are a left hand and a right hand. To verify this, point your thumbs along PR and $P'R'$, your forefingers along PQ and $P'Q'$, and your middle fingers along PS and $P'S'$. When an object and image are related in this way the image is called *perverted*. When the transverse dimensions of object and image are in the same direction, the image is *erect*. Thus a plane mirror forms an erect but perverted image.

39–3 Reflection at a spherical mirror

Figure 39–5 shows a spherical mirror of radius of curvature R, with its concave side toward the left. The center of curvature of the surface is at C. In measuring the radius of curvature we shall always *start at the reflecting surface and proceed toward the center of curvature. If this direction is the same as that of the ongoing (reflected) light, the radius of curvature is positive.* In Fig. 39–5, R is positive. Point P is an object point. Since the direction from the mirror to P is opposite that for the oncoming light, the object distance s is positive. The ray PV, passing through C, strikes the mirror normally and is reflected back along itself. Point V is called the *vertex*, and the line PCV the *axis*.

Ray PB, at an arbitrary angle u with the axis, strikes the surface at B, where the angle of incidence is ϕ and the angle of reflection is $r = \phi$. The rays reflected at V and B intersect at the image point P' at a distance s' from the mirror. Since the direction from the mirror to P' is the same as that of the ongoing light, s' is positive. We wish to derive an expression for s'.

Making use of the fact that an exterior angle of a triangle equals the sum of the two opposite interior angles, and considering the triangles PBC and $P'BC$ of Fig. 39–5, we have

$$\theta = u + \phi, \qquad u' = \theta + \phi.$$

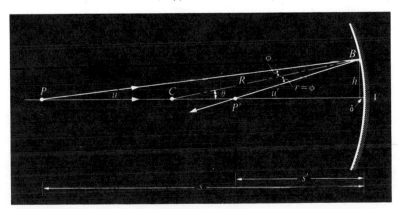

Fig. 39–5. Construction for finding the position of the image P' of a point object P, formed by a concave spherical mirror.

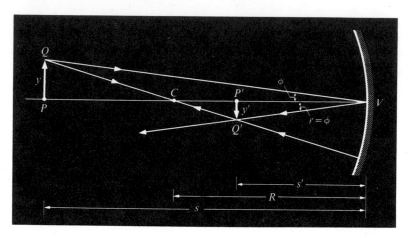

Fig. 39–6. Construction for determining the height of an image formed by a concave spherical mirror.

Eliminating ϕ between these equations gives

$$u + u' = 2\theta. \tag{39-2}$$

Let h represent the height of B above the axis, and δ the short distance from V to the foot of this vertical line. Now write the expressions for the tangents of u, u', and θ:

$$\tan u = \frac{h}{s - \delta}, \qquad \tan u' = \frac{h}{s' - \delta}, \qquad \tan \theta = \frac{h}{R - \delta}.$$

Evidently, these trigonometric equations cannot be solved as simply as the corresponding equations for a plane mirror. However, if the angle u is small, the angles u' and θ will be small also. Since the tangent of a small angle is nearly equal to the angle (in radians), we can replace $\tan u'$ by u', etc., in the equations above. Also, if u is small, the distance δ can be neglected compared with s', s, and R. Hence *approximately, for small angles,*

$$u = \frac{h}{s}, \qquad u' = \frac{h}{s'}, \qquad \theta = \frac{h}{R}.$$

Substituting in Eq. (39–2) and canceling h, we get

$$\frac{1}{s} + \frac{1}{s'} = \frac{2}{R} \tag{39-3}$$

as a general relation among the three quantities s, s', and R. The significant feature of the equation above is that *it does not contain the angle u.* This means that *all* rays from P *making sufficiently small angles with the axis* will, after reflection, intersect at P'. Such rays, nearly parallel to the axis, are called *paraxial* rays. As the angle increases, the point P' moves closer to the vertex, and a spherical mirror, unlike a plane mirror, does not form a point image of a point object. This property of a spherical mirror is called *spherical aberration.*

If $R = \infty$ the mirror becomes plane and Eq. (39–3) reduces to Eq. (39–1), previously derived for this special case.

Now suppose we have an object of finite size, represented by the arrow PQ in Fig. 39–6, perpendicular to the axis PV. The image of P formed by paraxial rays is at P'. Since the object distance for point Q is a trifle greater than that for the point P, the image $P'Q'$ is not a straight line but is curved, another aberration of spherical surfaces, called *curvature of field*. However, if the height PQ is not too great, the image is nearly straight and perpendicular to the axis, and we shall assume this to be the case.

We now compute the magnification m. The ray QCQ', incident normally, is reflected back on itself. The ray QV makes an angle of incidence ϕ and an angle of reflection $r = \phi$. From the triangles PQV and $P'Q'V$,

$$\tan \phi = \frac{y}{s} = \frac{-y'}{s'}.$$

Hence

$$m = \frac{y'}{y} = -\frac{s'}{s}. \tag{39–4}$$

For a plane mirror, $s = -s'$ and hence $y' = y$, as we have already shown.

39–4 Sign conventions

In general, an object point may lie on either side of a reflecting or refracting surface. The same is true of an image point, and of the center of curvature of a spherical surface. (If the latter lies at the left of the surface, the concave side of the surface faces toward the left.) Also, objects and images of finite size may extend either above or below the axis of a surface. By adopting a convention of algebraic signs for s, s', R, y, and y', it becomes unnecessary to derive special formulas for a large number of special cases. A single formula can cover all cases and the algebraic sign of a quantity will tell us whether it lies at the right or left of a surface, etc. Many sign conventions are in common use. The one that we have been using is due to R. E. Worley and applies equally well to reflecting and refracting surfaces, giving rise to the same relation between s and s' for both a mirror and a lens. In summary:

1. All distances are measured along the axis *from* the reflecting or refracting surface *to* the point in question.
2. An object distance s is positive if the direction from the surface to the object is *opposite* to that of the *oncoming* light.
3. An image distance s' is positive if the direction from the surface to the image is the *same* as that of the *ongoing* light.
4. A radius of curvature R is positive if the direction from the surface to the center of curvature is the *same* as that of the *ongoing* light.
5. An object or image dimension *above* the axis is positive.

To illustrate the use of these conventions, let us derive for a convex mirror the relation between the object and image distance, and the expression for the magnification.

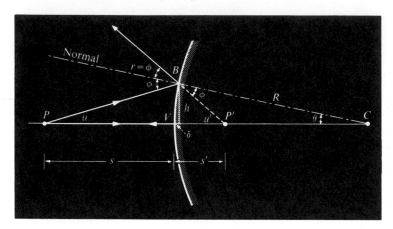

Fig. 39–7. Construction for finding the position of the image P' of a point object P, formed by a convex spherical mirror.

In Fig. 39–7, the object distance s is positive, the image distance s' is negative, and R is negative. Making use of the triangles PBC and $P'BC$, we get

$$\phi = u + \theta, \qquad u' = \phi + \theta$$

or

$$u - u' = -2\theta. \tag{39-5}$$

Also

$$\tan u = \frac{h}{s + \delta}, \qquad \tan u' = \frac{h}{-s' - \delta}, \qquad \tan \theta = \frac{h}{-R - \delta}.$$

Assuming the angles u, u', and θ to be small (rays are paraxial) and that δ is very small compared with s, s', and R, the preceding equations become

$$u = \frac{h}{s}, \qquad u' = \frac{h}{-s'}, \qquad \theta = \frac{h}{-R},$$

and when these are substituted into Eq. (39–5), we get

$$\frac{1}{s} + \frac{1}{s'} = \frac{2}{R},$$

which is exactly the same formula as that obtained for a concave mirror (Eq. 39–3).

Figure 39–8 shows the image of a finite object formed by a convex mirror. From the triangles PQV and $P'Q'V$,

$$\tan \phi = \frac{y}{s} = \frac{y'}{-s'}.$$

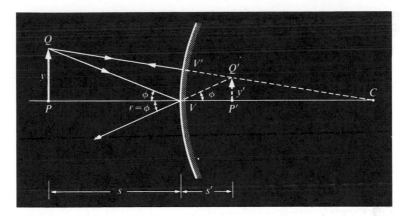

Fig. 39–8. Construction for determining the height of an image formed by a convex spherical mirror.

Hence, just as for a concave mirror (Eq. 39–4),

$$m = \frac{y'}{y} = -\frac{s'}{s}.$$

The image $P'Q'$ formed by the concave mirror in Fig. 39–6 is determined by actual rays of light that intersect at all the points lying between P' and Q'. Such an image is a *real image* and may be formed on a screen. In Fig. 39–8, however, the image formed by the convex mirror consists of points from which the reflected rays of light appear to be coming. Actually no real light exists in the space behind the mirror. This image is therefore a *virtual image. A virtual image has a negative image distance.*

EXAMPLE 1. (a) What type of mirror is required to form an image, on a wall 3 m from the mirror, of the filament of a headlight lamp 10 cm in front of the mirror? (b) What is the height of the image if the height of the object is 5 mm?

(a) $s = 10$ cm, $s' = 300$ cm.

$$\frac{1}{10 \text{ cm}} + \frac{1}{300 \text{ cm}} = \frac{2}{R},$$

$$R = 19.4 \text{ cm.}$$

Since the radius is positive, a concave mirror is required.

(b) $m = -\frac{s'}{s} = -\frac{300 \text{ cm}}{10 \text{ cm}} = -30.$

The image is therefore inverted (m is negative) and is 30 times the height of the object, or $30 \times 5 = 150$ mm.

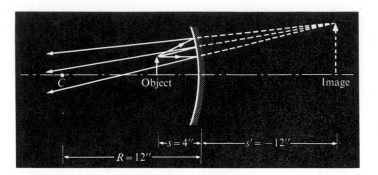

Figure 39-9

EXAMPLE 2.   A small object lies 4 in. to the left of the vertex of a concave mirror of radius of curvature 12 in. Find the position and magnification of the image.

$$s = 4 \text{ in.,} \qquad R = 12 \text{ in.,}$$

$$\frac{1}{4 \text{ in.}} + \frac{1}{s'} = \frac{2}{12 \text{ in.}},$$

$$s' = -12 \text{ in.,}$$

$$m = -\frac{s'}{s} = -\frac{-12 \text{ in.}}{4 \text{ in.}} = 3.$$

The image is therefore 12 in. to the right of the vertex (s' is negative), is virtual (s' is negative), erect (m is positive), and 3 times the height of the object. See Fig. 39-9.

39-5 Focal point and focal length

When an object point is at a very large distance from a mirror, all rays from that point that strike the mirror are parallel to one another. The object distance $s = \infty$, and from Eq. (39-3)

$$\frac{1}{\infty} + \frac{1}{s'} = \frac{2}{R}, \qquad s' = \frac{R}{2}.$$

The image distance s' then equals one-half the radius of curvature and has the same sign as R. This means that if R is positive, as in Fig. 39-10(a), the image point F lies to the left of the mirror and is real, while if R is negative, as in (b), the image point F lies at the right of the mirror and is virtual.

Conversely, if the image distance s' is very large, the object distance s is

$$\frac{1}{s} + \frac{1}{\infty} = \frac{2}{R}, \qquad s = \frac{R}{2}.$$

The object distance then equals half the radius of curvature. If R is positive, as in Fig. 39-11(a), s is positive. If R is negative, as in Fig. 39-11(b), s is negative and the *object is behind* the mirror. That is, rays previously made converging by some other surface are converging toward F.

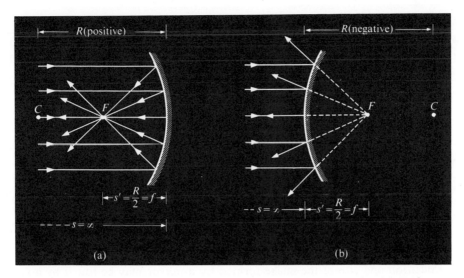

Fig. 39–10. Incident rays parallel to the axis (a) converge to the focal point F of a concave mirror, (b) diverge as though coming from the focal point F of a convex mirror.

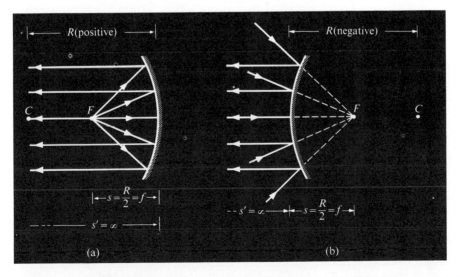

Fig. 39–11. Rays from a point object at the focal point of a spherical mirror are parallel to the axis after reflection. The object in part (b) is virtual.

The point F in Figs. 39–10 and 39–11 is called the *focal point* of the mirror. It may be considered either as the image point of an infinitely distant object point on the mirror axis, or as the object point of an infinitely distant image point. Thus the mirror of an astronomical telescope forms at its focal point an image of a star on the axis of the mirror.

The distance between the vertex of a mirror and the focal point is called the *focal length* of the mirror and is represented by f. The magnitude of the focal length, from the preceding discussion, equals one-half the radius of curvature. We shall see in the next chapter that a lens also has a focal length, and that the focal length of a lens which *converges* parallel rays to a real image is a positive quantity. A concave mirror, which behaves like a converging lens, has a positive focal length:

$$f = \frac{R}{2}.$$

(39–6)

The relation between object and image distances, Eq. (39–3), for a mirror may now be written as

$$\frac{1}{s} + \frac{1}{s'} = \frac{1}{f}.$$

(39–7)

39–6 Graphical methods

The position and size of the image formed by a mirror may be found by a simple graphical method. This method consists of finding the point of intersection, after reflection from the mirror, of a few rays diverging from some point of the object *not* on the mirror axis. Then (neglecting aberrations) *all* rays from this point which strike the mirror will intersect at the same point. Three rays whose paths may readily be traced are shown in Fig. 39–12.

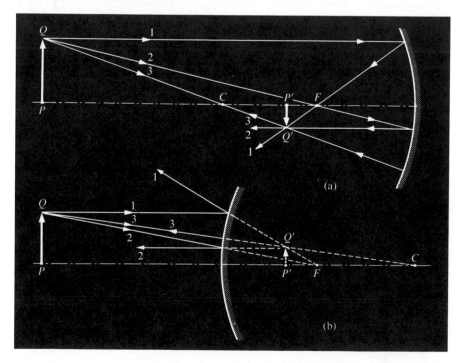

Fig. 39–12. Rays used in the graphical method of locating an image.

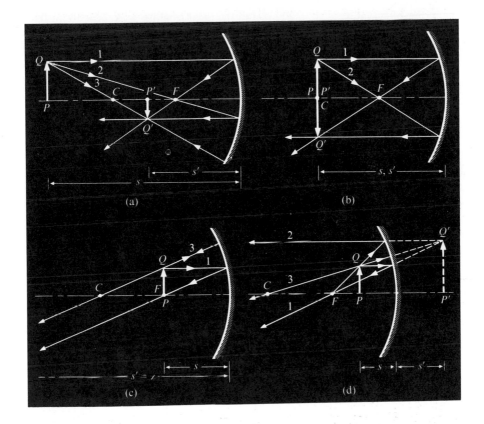

Fig. 39–13. Image of an object at various distances from a concave mirror.

1. *A ray parallel to the axis.* After reflection, this ray passes through the focal point of a concave mirror or appears to come from the focal point of a convex mirror.

2. *A ray from (or proceeding toward) the focal point.* This ray is reflected parallel to the axis.

3. *A ray along the radius* (extended if necessary). This ray intersects the surface normally and is reflected back along its original path.

Since the position of the image point has been found by means of the intersection of any two of the rays 1, 2, 3, the paths of all other rays from the same point may be drawn.

EXAMPLE.   A concave mirror has a radius of curvature of magnitude 20 in. Find graphically the image of an object in the form of an arrow perpendicular to the axis of the mirror and at the following object distances: 30 in., 20 in., 10 in., 5 in. Check the construction by computing the size and magnification of the image.

The graphical construction is indicated in the four parts of Fig. 39–13. [Note that in (b) and (c) only two of the three rays can be used.] The calculations are given below.

The radius of curvature is $R = 20$ in., and the focal length $f = R/2 = 10$ in. Hence

$$\frac{1}{s} + \frac{1}{s'} = \frac{1}{f} = \frac{1}{10 \text{ in.}}.$$

(a)
$$\frac{1}{30 \text{ in.}} + \frac{1}{s'} = \frac{1}{10 \text{ in.}}, \qquad s' = 15 \text{ in.},$$

$$m = -\frac{s'}{s} = -\frac{15 \text{ in.}}{30 \text{ in.}} = -\frac{1}{2}.$$

(b)
$$\frac{1}{20 \text{ in.}} + \frac{1}{s'} = \frac{1}{10 \text{ in.}}, \qquad s' = 20 \text{ in.},$$

$$m = -\frac{s'}{s} = -\frac{20 \text{ in.}}{20 \text{ in.}} = -1.$$

(c)
$$\frac{1}{10 \text{ in.}} + \frac{1}{s'} = \frac{1}{10 \text{ in.}}, \qquad s' = \infty,$$

$$m = -\frac{s'}{s} = -\frac{\infty}{10 \text{ in.}} = -\infty.$$

(d)
$$\frac{1}{5 \text{ in.}} + \frac{1}{s'} = \frac{1}{10 \text{ in.}}, \qquad s' = -10 \text{ in.},$$

$$m = -\frac{s'}{s} = -\frac{-10 \text{ in.}}{5 \text{ in.}} = 2.$$

39–7 Refraction at a plane surface

The method of finding the image of a point object formed by rays refracted at a plane or spherical surface is essentially the same as for reflection, the only difference being that Snell's law replaces the law of reflection. In every case, we let n represent the index of the medium on one side of the surface and n' that of the medium on the other side. The same convention of signs is used as in reflection.

Consider first a plane surface, shown in Fig. 39–14, and assume $n' > n$. A ray from the object point P toward the vertex V is incident normally and passes into the second medium without deviation. A ray making an angle u with the axis is incident at B with an angle of incidence $\phi = u$. The angle of refraction, ϕ', is found from Snell's law,

$$n \sin \phi = n' \sin \phi'.$$

The two rays both appear to come from point P' after refraction. From the triangles PVB and $P'VB$,

$$\tan \phi = \frac{h}{s}, \qquad \tan \phi' = \frac{h}{-s'}. \qquad (39\text{–}8)$$

[We must write $-s'$, since the direction *from* the surface *to* the image is not the same as that of the ongoing (refracted) light.]

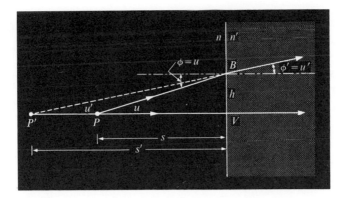

Fig. 39–14. Construction for finding the position of the image P' of a point object P, formed by refraction at a plane surface.

If the angle u is small, the angles ϕ, u', and ϕ' are small also, and therefore, approximately,

$$\tan \phi = \sin \phi, \quad \tan \phi' = \sin \phi'.$$

Then Snell's law can be written as

$$n \tan \phi = n' \tan \phi',$$

and from Eq. (39–8), after canceling h, we have

$$\frac{n}{s} = -\frac{n'}{s'}, \quad \text{or} \quad \frac{s'}{s} = -\frac{n'}{n}. \tag{39–9}$$

This is an *approximate* relation, *good for paraxial rays only.* That is, a plane refracting surface does *not* image all rays from a point object at the same image point.

Consider next the image of a finite object, as in Fig. 39–15. The two rays shown diverging from point Q appear to diverge from its image Q' after refraction. From the

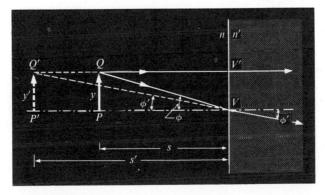

Fig. 39–15. Construction for determining the height of an image formed by refraction at a plane surface.

triangles PQV and $P'Q'V$,

$$\tan \phi = \frac{y}{s}, \qquad \tan \phi' = \frac{y'}{-s'}.$$

Combining with Snell's law and using the small-angle approximation, $\sin \phi = \tan \phi$, $\sin \phi' = \tan \phi'$, we get

$$\frac{ny}{s} = -\frac{n'y'}{s'},$$

and hence

$$m = \frac{y'}{y} = -\frac{ns'}{n's}. \qquad (39\text{–}10)$$

However, from Eq. (39–9), $ns' = -n's$, so

$$m = \frac{y'}{y} = 1. \quad \text{(plane refracting surface)},$$

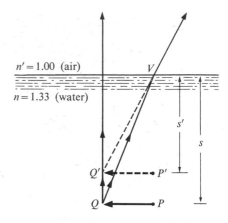

Fig. 39–16. Arrow $P'Q'$ is the image of the underwater object PQ.

in agreement with Fig. 39–15. The image distance is greater than the object distance, but image and object are the same height.

A common example of refraction at a plane surface is afforded by looking vertically downward into the quiet water of a pond or a swimming pool; the apparent depth is less than the actual depth. Figure 39–16 illustrates this case. Two rays are shown diverging from a point Q at a distance s below the surface. Here, n' (air) is less than n (water) and the ray incident at V is deviated *away from* the normal. The rays after refraction appear to diverge from Q', and the arrow PQ, to an observer looking vertically downward, appears lifted to the position $P'Q'$. From Eq. (39–9),

$$s' = -\frac{n'}{n}s = -\frac{1.00}{4/3}s = -\frac{3}{4}s.$$

The apparent depth s' is therefore only three-fourths of the actual depth s. The same phenomenon accounts for the apparent sharp bend in an oar when a portion of it extends below a water surface. The submerged portion appears lifted above its actual position.

39–8 Refraction at a spherical surface

Finally, we consider refraction at a spherical surface. In Fig. 39–17, P is an object point at a distance s to the left of a spherical surface of radius R. The indices at the left and right of the surface are n and n', respectively. Ray PV, incident normally, passes into the second medium without deviation. Ray PB, making an angle u with the axis, is incident at an angle ϕ with the normal and is refracted at an angle ϕ'. These rays intersect at P' at a distance s' to the right of the vertex. From the triangles PBC and $P'BC$,

$$\phi = \theta + u, \qquad \theta = u' + \phi'. \qquad (39\text{–}11)$$

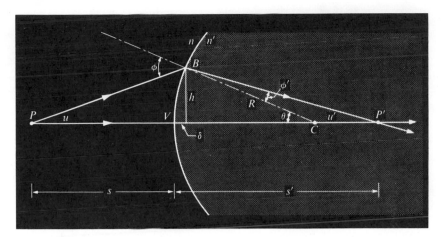

Fig. 39–17. Construction for finding the position of the image P' of a point object P, formed by refraction at a spherical surface.

From Snell's law,

$$n \sin \phi = n' \sin \phi'.$$

Also, the tangents of u, u', and θ are

$$\tan u = \frac{h}{s + \delta}, \qquad \tan u' = \frac{h}{s' - \delta}, \qquad \tan \theta = \frac{h}{R - \delta}. \qquad (39\text{–}12)$$

For paraxial rays we may approximate both the sine and tangent of an angle by the angle itself, and neglect the small distance δ. Snell's law then becomes

$$n\phi = n'\phi',$$

and combining with the first of Eqs. (39–11), we get

$$\phi' = \frac{n}{n'}(u + \theta).$$

Substituting this in the second of Eqs. (39–11) gives

$$nu + n'u' = (n' - n)\theta.$$

Using the small-angle approximations of Eqs. (39–12) and canceling h, this becomes

$$\boxed{\frac{n}{s} + \frac{n'}{s'} = \frac{n' - n}{R}.} \qquad (39\text{–}13)$$

If the surface is plane, $R = \infty$ and this equation reduces to Eq. (39–9), already derived for the special case of a plane surface.

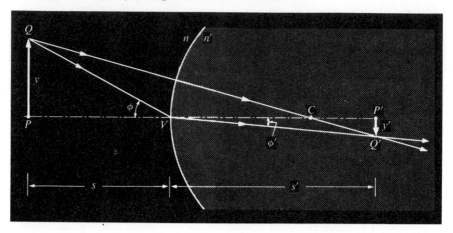

Fig. 39–18. Construction for determining the height of an image formed by refraction at a spherical surface.

The magnification is found from the construction in Fig. 39–18. From point Q draw two rays, one through the center of curvature C and the other incident at the vertex V. From the triangles PQV and $P'Q'V$,

$$\tan \phi = \frac{y}{s}, \qquad \tan \phi' = \frac{-y'}{s'},$$

and from Snell's law,

$$n \sin \phi = n' \sin \phi'.$$

For small angles,

$$\tan \phi = \sin \phi, \qquad \tan \phi' = \sin \phi',$$

and hence

$$\frac{ny}{s} = -\frac{n'y'}{s'},$$

or

$$m = \frac{y'}{y} = -\frac{ns'}{n's}, \qquad (39\text{–}14)$$

which agrees with the relation previously derived for a plane surface.

Equations (39–13) and (39–14) can be applied to both convex and concave refracting surfaces when a consistent sign convention is used, and they apply whether n' is greater or less than n. The reader should construct diagrams like Figs. 39–17 and 39–18, when R is negative and $n' < n$, and use them to derive Eqs. (39–13) and (39–14).

The concepts of focal point and focal length can also be applied to a refracting surface. Such a surface is found to have *two* focal points. The first is the object point when the image is at infinity, the second is the image point of an infinitely distant object. These points lie on opposite sides of the surface and at different distances from it, so that a single refracting surface has two focal lengths. The positions of the focal points can readily be found from Eq. (39–13) by setting s or s' equal to infinity.

TABLE 39-1

	Plane mirror	Curved mirror	Plane refracting surface	Curved refracting surface
Object and image distances	$\dfrac{1}{s} + \dfrac{1}{s'} = 0$	$\dfrac{1}{s} + \dfrac{1}{s'} = \dfrac{2}{R} = \dfrac{1}{f}$	$\dfrac{n}{s} + \dfrac{n'}{s'} = 0$	$\dfrac{n}{s} + \dfrac{n'}{s'} = \dfrac{n'-n}{R}$
Magnification	$m = -\dfrac{s'}{s} = 1$	$m = -\dfrac{s'}{s}$	$m = -\dfrac{ns'}{n's} = 1$	$m = -\dfrac{ns'}{n's}$

39-9 Summary

The results of this chapter are summarized in Table 39-1. Note that by letting $R = \infty$, the equation for a plane surface follows immediately from the appropriate equation for a curved surface.

EXAMPLE 1. One end of a cylindrical glass rod (Fig. 39-19) is ground to a hemispherical surface of radius $R = 20$ mm. Find the image distance of a point object on the axis of the rod, 80 mm to the left of the vertex. The rod is in air.

$$n = 1, \qquad n' = 1.5,$$

$$R = +20 \text{ mm}, \qquad s = +80 \text{ mm}.$$

$$\frac{1}{80 \text{ mm}} + \frac{1.5}{s'} = \frac{1.5 - 1}{+20 \text{ mm}},$$

$$s' = +120 \text{ mm}.$$

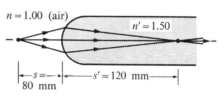

Figure 39-19

The image is therefore formed at the right of the vertex (s' is positive) and at a distance of 120 mm from it. Suppose that the object is an arrow 1 mm high, perpendicular to the axis. Then

$$m = -\frac{ns'}{n's} = -\frac{1 \times 120 \text{ mm}}{1.5 \times 80 \text{ mm}} = -1.$$

That is, the image is the same height as the object, but is inverted.

EXAMPLE 2. Let the same rod be immersed in water of index 1.33, the other quantities having the same values as before. Find the image distance (Fig. 39-20).

$$\frac{1.33}{80 \text{ mm}} + \frac{1.5}{s'} = \frac{1.5 - 1.33}{+20 \text{ mm}}, \quad s' = -180 \text{ mm}.$$

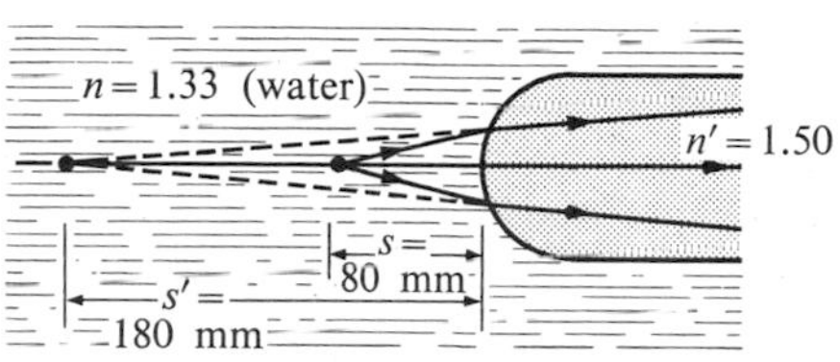

Figure 39-20

The fact that s' is a negative quantity means that the rays, after refraction by the surface, are not converging but appear to diverge from a point 180 mm to the left of the vertex. We have met a similar case before in the refraction of spherical waves by a plane surface and have called the point a *virtual image*. In this example, then, the surface forms a virtual image 180 mm to the left of the vertex.

Problems

39-1. (a) Prove that a ray of light travels the shortest possible distance in going from point A to point B after reflection from the plane mirror M in Fig. 39-21. [*Hint:* Draw a straight line connecting B and the image of A.] (b) What is the size of the smallest vertical plane mirror in which an observer standing erect can see his full-length image?

Figure 39-21

~~not sofit~~

39-2. The image of a tree just covers the length of a 2-in. plane mirror when the mirror is held 1 ft from the eye. The tree is 300 ft from the mirror. What is its height?

39-3. An object is placed between two mirrors arranged at right angles to each other. (a) Locate all of the images of the object. (b) Draw the paths of rays from the object to the eye of an observer.

39-4. An object 1 cm high is 20 cm from the vertex of a concave spherical mirror whose radius of curvature is 50 cm. Compute the position and size of the image. Is it real or virtual? Erect or inverted?

39-5. A concave mirror is to form an image of the filament of a headlight lamp on a screen 4 m from the mirror. The filament is 5 mm high, and the image is to be 40 cm high. (a) What should be the radius of curvature of the mirror? (b) How far in front of the vertex of the mirror should the filament be placed?

39-6. The diameter of the moon is 2160 mi and its distance from the earth is 240,000 mi. Find the diameter of the image of the moon formed by a spherical concave telescope mirror of focal length 12 ft.

39-7. A spherical concave shaving mirror has a radius of curvature of 1 ft. What is the magnification when the face is 4 in. from the vertex of the mirror?

39-8. A concave spherical mirror has a radius of curvature of 10 cm. Make a diagram of the mirror to scale, and show rays incident on it parallel to the axis and at distances of 1, 2, 3, 4, and 5 cm from the mirror. Using a protractor, construct the reflected rays and indicate the points at which they cross the axis.

39-9. An object is 6 in. from the center of a silvered spherical glass Christmas tree ornament 3 in. in diameter. What are the position and magnification of its image?

39-10. A tank whose bottom is a mirror is filled with water to a depth of 20 cm. A small object hangs motionless 8 cm under the surface of the water. What is the apparent depth of its image when viewed at normal incidence?

39-11. A ray of light in air makes an angle of incidence of 45° at the surface of a sheet of ice. The ray is refracted within the ice at an angle of 30°. (a) What is the critical angle for the ice? (b) A speck of dirt is embedded $\frac{3}{4}$ in. below the surface of the ice. What is its apparent depth when viewed at normal incidence?

39-12. A microscope is focused on the upper surface of a glass plate. A second plate is then placed over the first. In order to focus on the bottom surface of the second plate, the microscope must be raised 1 mm. In order to focus on the upper surface it must be raised 2 mm *farther*. Find the index of refraction of the second plate. (This problem illustrates one method of measuring index of refraction.)

39-13. A layer of ether ($n = 1.36$) 2 cm deep floats on water ($n = 1.33$) 4 cm deep. What is the apparent distance from the ether surface to the bottom of the water layer, when viewed at normal incidence?

39-14. The end of a long glass rod 8 cm in diameter has a hemispherical surface 4 cm in radius. The refractive index of the glass is 1.50. Determine each position of the image if an object is placed on the axis of the rod at the following distances from

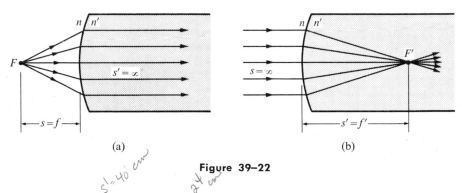

Figure 39–22

its end: (a) infinitely far, (b) 16 cm, (c) 4 cm.

39–15. The rod of Problem 39–14 is immersed in a liquid. An object 60 cm from the end of the rod and on its axis is imaged at a point 100 cm inside the rod. What is the refractive index of the liquid?

39–16. What should be the index of refraction of a transparent sphere in order that paraxial rays from an infinitely distant object will be brought to a focus at the vertex of the surface opposite the point of incidence?

39–17. The left end of a long glass rod 10 cm in diameter, of index 1.50, is ground and polished to a convex hemispherical surface of radius 5 cm. An object in the form of an arrow 1 mm long, at right angles to the axis of the rod, is located on the axis 20 cm to the left of the vertex of the convex surface. Find the position and magnification of the image of the arrow formed by paraxial rays incident on the convex surface.

39–18. A transparent rod 40 cm long is cut flat at one end and rounded to a hemispherical surface of 12 cm radius at the

other end. A small object is embedded within the rod along its axis and halfway between its ends. When viewed from the flat end of the rod the apparent depth of the object is 12.5 cm. What is its apparent depth when viewed from the curved end?

39–19. A solid glass hemisphere having a radius of 10 cm and a refractive index of 1.50 is placed with its flat face downward on a table. A parallel beam of light of circular cross section 1 cm in diameter travels directly downward and enters the hemisphere along its diameter. What is the diameter of the circle of light formed on the table?

39–20. A small tropical fish is at the center of a spherical fish bowl 1 ft in diameter. Find its apparent position and magnification to an observer outside the bowl. The effect of the thin walls of the bowl may be neglected.

39–21. In Fig. 39–22(a) the first focal length f is seen to be the value of s corresponding to $s' = \infty$. In (b) the second focal length f' is the value of s' when $s = \infty$. (a) Prove that $n/n' = f/f'$. (b) Prove that $f/s + f'/s' = 1$.

CHAPTER 40

Lenses and Optical Instruments

40-1 Images as objects

Most optical systems include more than one reflecting or refracting surface. The image formed by the first surface serves as the object for the second; the image formed by the second surface serves as the object for the third; etc. Figure 40–1 illustrates the various situations which may arise, and the following discussion of them should be thoroughly understood.

In Fig. 40–1, the arrow at point O represents a small object at right angles to the axis. A narrow cone of rays diverging from the head of the arrow is traced through the system. Surface 1 forms a real image of the arrow at point P. Distance V_1O is the object distance for the first surface and distance V_1P is the image distance. Both of these are positive.

The image at P, formed by surface 1, serves as the object for surface 2. The object distance is V_2P and is positive, since the direction from V_2 to P is opposite that of the oncoming light. The second surface forms a virtual image at point Q. The image distance is V_2Q and is negative because the direction from V_2 to Q is opposite that of the ongoing light.

The image at Q, formed by surface 2, serves as the object for surface 3. The object distance is V_3Q and is positive. The image at Q, although virtual, constitutes a *real object* so far as surface 3 is concerned. The rays incident on surface 3 are rendered converging and, except for the interposition of surface 4, would converge to a real image at point R. Even though this image is never formed, distance V_3R is the image distance for surface 3 and is positive.

The rays incident on surfaces 1, 2, and 3 have all been diverging and the object distance has been the distance from the surface to the point from which the rays were

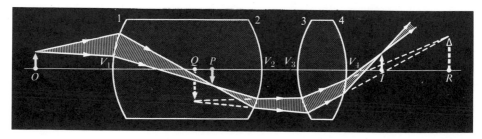

Fig. 40–1. The object for each surface, after the first, is the image formed by the preceding surface.

872

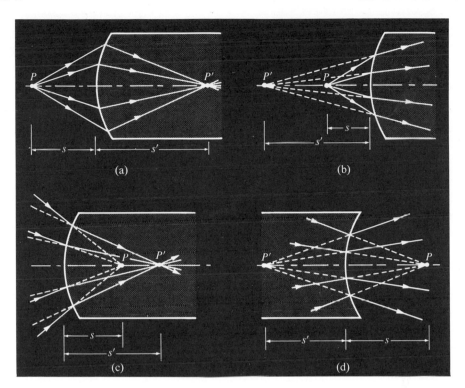

Fig. 40–2. (a) A real image of a real object. (b) A virtual image of a real object. (c) A real image of a virtual object. (d) A virtual image of a virtual object.

actually or apparently diverging. The rays incident on surface 4, however, are *converging* and there is no point at the left of the vertex from which they diverge or appear to diverge. *The image at R, toward which the rays are converging*, is the object for surface 4, and since this image is reached by proceeding in the direction of the oncoming light, the object distance V_4R is negative. The image at R is called a *virtual object* for surface 4. In general, whenever a *converging* cone of rays is incident on a surface, the point toward which the rays are converging serves as the object, the object distance is negative, and the point is called a virtual object.

Finally, surface 4 forms a real image at I, the image distance being V_4I and positive.

The meaning of virtual object and of virtual image are further exemplified by Fig. 40–2.

40–2 The thin lens

A lens is an optical system bounded by two refracting surfaces. The general problem of refraction by a lens is solved by applying the methods of Section 40–1 to each surface in turn, the object for the second surface being the image formed by the first. Figure 40–3 shows a pencil of rays diverging from point Q of an object PQ. The first surface of lens L forms a virtual image of Q at Q'. This virtual image serves as a

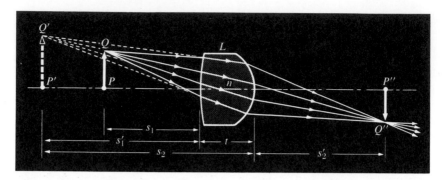

Fig. 40-3. The image formed by the first surface of a lens serves as the object for the second surface.

real object for the second surface of the lens, which forms a real image of Q' at Q''. Distance s_1 is the object distance for the first surface; s_1' is the corresponding image distance. The object distance for the second surface is s_2, equal to the sum of s_1' and the lens thickness t, and s_2' is the image distance for the second surface.

If, as is often the case, the lens is so thin that its thickness t is negligible in comparison with the distances s_1, s_1', s_2, and s_2', we may assume that s_1' equals s_2, and measure object and image distances from either vertex of the lens. We shall also assume the medium on both sides of the lens to be air, with index of refraction 1.00. For the first refraction, Eq. (39–13) becomes

$$\frac{1}{s_1} + \frac{n}{s_1'} = \frac{n-1}{R_1}.$$

Refraction at the second surface yields the equation

$$\frac{n}{s_2} + \frac{1}{s_2'} = \frac{1-n}{R_2}.$$

Adding these two equations, and remembering that the lens is so thin that $s_2 = -s_1'$, we get

$$\frac{1}{s_1} + \frac{1}{s_2'} = (n-1)\left(\frac{1}{R_1} - \frac{1}{R_2}\right).$$

Since s_1 is the object distance for the thin lens and s_2' is the image distance, the subscripts may be omitted, and we get finally

$$\frac{1}{s} + \frac{1}{s'} = (n-1)\left(\frac{1}{R_1} - \frac{1}{R_2}\right). \tag{40-1}$$

The usual sign conventions apply to this equation. Thus, in Fig. 40–4, s, s', and R_1 are positive quantities, but R_2 is negative.

The *focal length* f of a thin lens may be defined either as (a) the object distance of a point object on the lens axis whose image is at infinity, or (b) the image distance of a

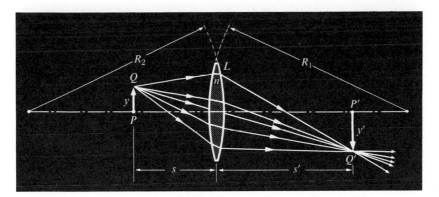

Fig. 40–4.   A thin lens.

point object on the lens axis at an infinite distance from the lens. When we set either
s or s' equal to infinity in Eq. (40–1) we find for the focal length

$$\frac{1}{f} = (n - 1)\left(\frac{1}{R_1} - \frac{1}{R_2}\right),\qquad (40\text{–}2)$$

which is known as the *lensmaker's equation*.

Substituting Eq. (40–2) in Eq. (40–1), the thin lens equation becomes

$$\frac{1}{s} + \frac{1}{s'} = \frac{1}{f}.\qquad (40\text{–}3)$$

This is known as the *gaussian* form of the thin lens equation, after Karl F. Gauss, the
same mathematician responsible for the law in electrostatics bearing his name. Note
that Eq. (40–3) has exactly the same form as the equation for a spherical mirror.

The object point for which the image is at infinity is called the *first focal point* of the
lens and is lettered F in Fig. 40–5(a). The image point for an infinitely distant object
is called the *second focal point* and is lettered F' in Fig. 40–5(b). The focal points of a
thin lens lie on opposite sides of the lens at a distance from it equal to its focal length.

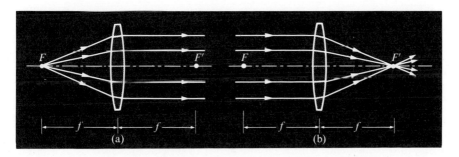

Fig. 40–5.   First and second focal points of a thin lens.

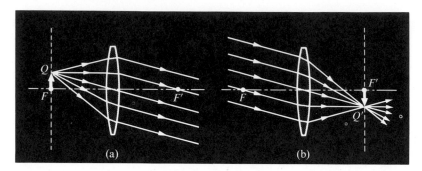

Fig. 40–6. Planes through the focal points of a lens are called focal planes.

Figure 40–6 corresponds to Fig. 40–5, except that it is drawn for object and image points not on the axis of the lens. Planes through the first and second focal points of a lens, perpendicular to the axis, are called the first and second *focal planes*. Paraxial rays from point Q in Fig. 40–6(a), in the first focal plane of the lens, are parallel to one another after refraction. In other words, they converge to an infinitely distant image of point Q. In Fig. 40–6(b) a bundle of parallel rays from an infinitely distant point, not on the lens axis, converges to an image Q' lying in the second focal plane of the lens.

The three-dimensional image of a three-dimensional object, formed by a lens, is shown in Fig. 40–7. Since point R is nearer the lens than point P, its image, from Eq. (40–3), is farther from the lens than is point P', and the image $P'R'$ points in the same direction as the object PR. Arrows $P'S'$ and $P'Q'$ are reversed in space, relative to PS and PQ. Although we speak of the image as "inverted," only its transverse dimensions are reversed.

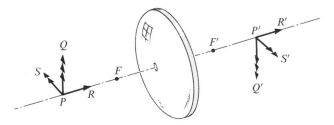

Fig. 40–7. A lens forms a three-dimensional image of a three-dimensional object.

Figure 40–7 should be compared with Fig. 39–4, showing the image formed by a plane mirror. Note that the image formed by a lens, although it is inverted, is not perverted. That is, if the object is a left hand, its image is a left hand also. This may be verified by pointing the left thumb along PR, the left forefinger along PQ, and the left middle finger along PS. A rotation of 180° about the thumb as an axis then brings the fingers into coincidence with $P'Q'$ and $P'S'$. In other words, *inversion* of an image is equivalent to a rotation of 180° about the lens axis.

The magnification produced by a lens is the product of the magnification at each of its surfaces. The magnification due to the first refraction is, from Eq. (39–14),

$$m_1 = -\frac{1 \times s_1'}{ns_1},$$

and that due to the second refraction is

$$m_2 = -\frac{ns_2'}{1 \times s_2}.$$

The over-all magnification m of the lens is therefore

$$m = \left(-\frac{1 \times s_1'}{ns_1}\right)\left(-\frac{ns_2'}{1 \times s_2}\right).$$

Since the lens is thin, $s_2 = -s_1'$, and

$$m = -\frac{s'}{s}. \qquad\qquad\qquad (40\text{--}4)$$

A simpler derivation of this equation may be obtained merely by inspection of Fig. 40–4, where the object PQ, the image $P'Q'$, and the lines PP' and QQ' form two similar triangles. Hence

$$\frac{-y'}{y} = \frac{s'}{s},$$

and since m, as usual, is y'/y, we get

$$m = -\frac{s'}{s},$$

in agreement with Eq. (40–4).

Although Eqs. (40–3) and (40–4) were derived for the special case of rays making small angles with the axis and, in general, do not apply to rays making large angles, they may be used for any lens which has been corrected so that all rays are imaged at the same point. They are therefore two of the most important equations in geometrical optics.

40–3 Diverging lenses

A bundle of parallel rays incident on the lens shown in Figs. 40–5 and 40–6 converges to a real image after passing through the lens. The lens is called a *converging lens*. Its focal length, as computed from Eq. (40–2), is a positive quantity and therefore the lens is also called a *positive lens*.

A bundle of parallel rays incident on the lens in Fig. 40–8 becomes diverging after refraction and the lens is called a *diverging lens*. Its focal length, computed by Eq. (40–2), is a negative quantity and therefore the lens is also called a *negative lens*. The focal points of a negative lens are reversed, relative to those of a positive lens. The

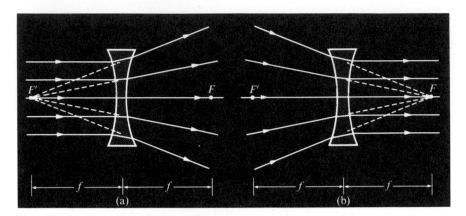

Fig. 40–8. Focal points of a diverging lens.

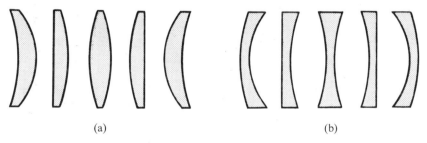

(a)   (b)

Fig. 40–9. (a) Meniscus, plano-convex, and double-convex converging lenses. (b) Meniscus, plano-concave, and double-concave diverging lenses.

second focal point, F', of a negative lens is the point from which rays, originally parallel to the axis, appear to diverge after refraction, as in Fig. 40–8(a). Incident rays converging toward the first focal point F, as in Fig. 40–8(b), emerge from the lens parallel to its axis. That is, just as for a positive lens, the second focal point is the (virtual) image of an infinitely distant object on the axis of the lens, while the first focal point is the object point (a virtual object if the lens is diverging) for which an image is formed at infinity. Equations (40–2) through (40–6) apply both to negative and to positive lenses. Various types of lenses, both converging and diverging, are illustrated in Fig. 40–9.

In addition to lenses having spherical surfaces, use is frequently made of *cylindrical* lenses, particularly in spectacles, to correct a defect of vision known as *astigmatism*. One or both surfaces of a cylindrical lens are portions of cylinders (Fig. 40–10). Since defects of vision other than astigmatism are frequently present also, a spectacle lens may be cylindrical at one surface and spherical at the other, or one of its surfaces may be a combined sphere and cylinder.

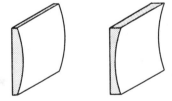

Fig. 40–10. Cylindrical lenses.

40–4 Graphical methods

The position and size of the image of an object formed by a thin lens may be found by a simple graphical method. This method consists of finding the point of intersection, after passing through the lens, of a few rays diverging from some chosen point of the object. Then (neglecting lens aberrations) all rays from this point which pass through the lens will intersect at the same point. In using the graphical method, the entire deviation of any ray is assumed to take place at a plane through the center of the lens. Three rays whose paths may readily be traced are shown in Fig. 40–11.

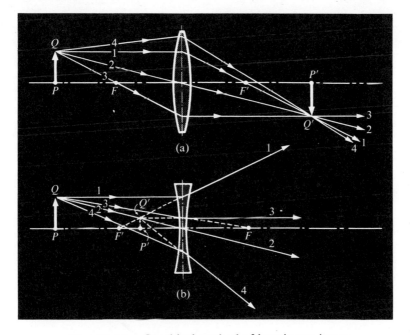

Fig. 40–11.   Graphical method of locating an image.

1. *A ray parallel to the axis.* After refraction by the lens, this ray passes through the second focal point of a converging lens, or appears to come from the second focal point of a diverging lens.

2. *A ray through the center of the lens.* This ray is not appreciably deviated, since the two lens surfaces through which the central ray passes are very nearly parallel if the lens is thin. We have seen that a ray passing through a plate with parallel faces is not deviated, but only displaced. For a thin lens, the displacement may be neglected.

3. *A ray through (or proceeding toward) the first focal point.* This ray emerges parallel to the axis.

Since the position of the image point has been found by means of the intersection of any two of the rays 1, 2, 3, the paths of all other rays from the same point, such as ray 4 in Fig. 40–11, may be drawn. A few examples of this procedure are given in Fig. 40–12.

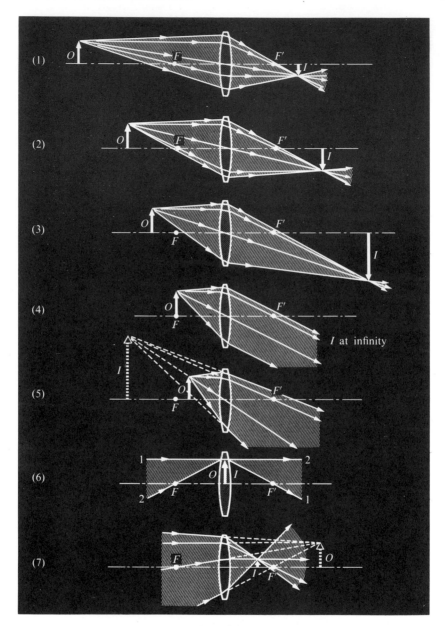

Fig. 40–12. Formation of an image by a thin lens.

40–5 Images as objects for lenses

It was shown in Section 40–1 and Fig. 40–1 how the image formed by any one *surface* in an optical system serves as the object for the next surface. In the majority of optical systems employing lenses, more than one lens is used and the image formed by any one *lens* serves as the object for the next lens. Figure 40–13 illustrates the

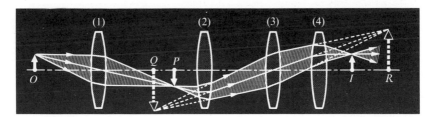

Fig. 40–13. The object for each lens, after the first, is the image formed by the preceding lens.

various possibilities. Lens 1 forms a real image at P of a real object at O. This real image serves as a real object for lens 2. The virtual image at Q formed by lens 2 is a real object for lens 3. If lens 4 were not present, lens 3 would form a real image at R. Although this image is never formed, it serves as a virtual object for lens 4, which forms a final real image at I.

40–6 Lens aberrations

The relatively simple equations we have derived connecting object and image distances, focal lengths, radii of curvature, etc., were based upon the approximation that all rays made small angles with the axis. In general, however, a lens is called upon to image not only points on its axis, but points which lie off the axis as well. Furthermore, because of the finite size of the lens, the cone of rays which forms the image of any point is of finite size. Nonparaxial rays proceeding from a given object point do not, in general, all intersect at the same point after refraction by a lens. Consequently, the image formed by these rays is not a sharp one. Furthermore, the focal length of a lens depends upon its index of refraction, which varies with wavelength. Therefore, if the light proceeding from an object is not monochromatic, a lens forms a number of colored images which lie in different positions and are of different sizes, even if formed by paraxial rays.

The departures of an actual image from the predictions of simple theory are called *aberrations*. Those caused by the variation of index with wavelength are the *chromatic aberrations*. The others, which would arise even if the light were monochromatic, are the *monochromatic aberrations*. Lens aberrations are not caused by any faulty construction of the lens, such as the failure of its surfaces to conform to a truly spherical shape, but are simply consequences of the laws of refraction at spherical surfaces.

40–7 The eye

Since the purpose of most optical instruments is to enable us to see better, the logical place to begin a discussion of such instruments is with the eye. The essential parts of the eye, considered as an optical system, are shown in Fig. 40–14.

The eye is very nearly spherical in shape, and about an inch in diameter. The front portion is somewhat more sharply curved, and is covered by a tough, transparent membrane C, called the *cornea*. The region behind the cornea contains a liquid A

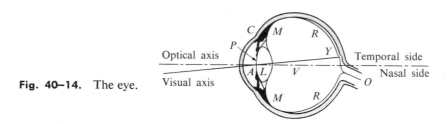

Fig. 40–14. The eye.

called the *aqueous humor*. Next comes the *crystalline lens*, L, a capsule containing a fibrous jelly hard at the center and progressively softer at the outer portions. The crystalline lens is held in place by ligaments which attach it to the ciliary muscle *M*. Behind the lens, the eye is filled with a thin jelly *V* consisting largely of water, called the *vitreous humor*. The indices of refraction of both the aqueous humor and the vitreous humor are nearly equal to that of water, about 1.336. The crystalline lens, while not homogeneous, has an "average" index of 1.437. This is not very different from the indices of the aqueous and vitreous humors, so that most of the refraction of light entering the eye is produced at the cornea.

A large part of the inner surface of the eye is covered with a delicate film of nerve fibers, *R*, called the *retina*. A cross section of the retina is shown in Fig. 40–15(a). Nerve fibers branching out from the *optic nerve O* terminate in minute structures called rods and cones. The rods and cones, together with a bluish liquid called the visual purple, which circulates among them, receive the optical image and transmit it along the optic nerve to the brain. There is a slight depression in the retina at *Y* called the yellow spot or macula. At its center is a minute region, about 0.25 mm in diameter, called the *fovea centralis*, which contains cones exclusively. Vision is much more acute at the fovea than at other portions of the retina, and the muscles controlling the eye always rotate the eyeball until the image of the object toward which attention is

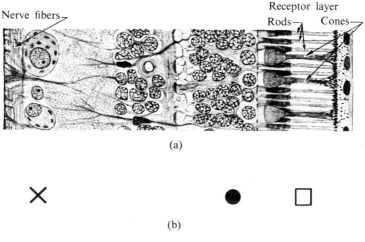

(a)

(b)

Fig. 40–15. (a) Section of the human retina (500×). Light is incident from the left. (b) Figure for demonstrating the blind spot.

directed falls on the fovea. The outer portion of the retina merely serves to give a general picture of the field of view. The fovea is so small that motion of the eye is necessary to focus distinctly two points as close together as the dots in a colon (:).

There are no rods or cones at the point where the optic nerve enters the eye and an image formed at this point cannot be seen. This region is called the *blind spot*. The existence of the blind spot can be demonstrated by closing the left eye and looking with the right eye at the cross in Fig. 40–15(b). When the diagram is about 10 inches from the eye, the square disappears. At a smaller distance, the square reappears while the circle disappears. At a still smaller distance, the circle again appears.

In front of the crystalline lens is the iris, at the center of which is an opening P called the *pupil*. The function of the pupil is to regulate the quantity of light entering the eye, the pupil automatically dilating if the brightness of the field is low, and contracting if the brightness is increased. This process is known as *adaptation*. However, the range of pupillary diameter is only about fourfold (hence the range in area is about sixteenfold) over a range of brightness which is 100,000-fold. The relatively enormous variation in light entering the eye is far from compensated for by the change in size of the pupil, the receptive mechanism of the retina being able to adapt itself to large differences in quantity of light.

To see an object distinctly, a sharp image of it must be formed on the retina. If all the elements of the eye were rigidly fixed in position there would be but one object distance for which a sharp retinal image would be formed, while in fact the normal eye can focus sharply on an object at any distance from infinity up to about 10 inches in front of the eye. This is made possible by the action of the crystalline lens and the ciliary muscle to which it is attached. When relaxed, the normal eye is focused on objects at infinity, i.e., the second focal point is at the retina. When it is desired to view an object nearer than infinity, the ciliary muscle tenses and the crystalline lens assumes a more nearly spherical shape. This process is called *accommodation*.

The extremes of the range over which distinct vision is possible are known as the *far point* and the *near point* of the eye. The far point of a normal eye is at infinity. The position of the near point evidently depends on the extent to which the curvature of the crystalline lens may be increased in accommodation. The range of accommodation gradually diminishes with age as the crystalline lens loses its flexibility. For this reason the near point gradually recedes as one grows older. This recession of the near point with age is called *presbyopia*, and should not be considered a defect of vision, since it proceeds at about the same rate in all normal eyes. The following is a table of the approximate position of the near point at various ages.

Age (years)	Near point (cm)
10	7
20	10
30	14
40	22
50	40
60	200

40-8 The magnifier

The apparent size of an object is determined by the size of its retinal image, which, in turn, if the eye is unaided, depends upon the angle subtended by the object at the eye. When one wishes to examine a small object in detail one brings it close to the eye, in order that the angle subtended and the retinal image may be as large as possible. Since the eye cannot focus sharply on objects closer than the near point, a given object subtends the maximum possible angle at an unaided eye when placed at this point. (We shall assume hereafter that the near point is 25 cm from the eye.) By placing a converging lens in front of the eye, the accommodation may, in effect, be increased. The object may then be brought closer to the eye than the near point and will subtend a correspondingly larger angle. A lens used for this purpose is called a *magnifying glass, a simple microscope,* or a *magnifier.* The magnifier forms a virtual image of the object and the eye "looks at" this virtual image. Since a (normal) eye can focus sharply on an object anywhere between the near point and infinity, the image can be seen equally clearly if it is formed anywhere within this range. We shall assume that the image is formed at infinity.

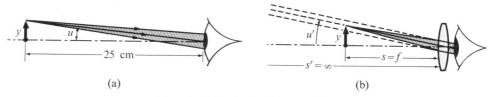

(a) (b)

Fig. 40-16. A simple magnifier.

The magnifier is illustrated in Fig. 40–16. In (a), the object is at the near point, where it subtends an angle u at the eye. In (b), a magnifier in front of the eye forms an image at infinity, and the angle subtended at the magnifier is u'. The *angular magnification M* (not to be confused with the *lateral magnification m*) is defined as the ratio of the angle u' to the angle u. The value of M may be found as follows:

From Fig. 40–16(a) and (b),

$$u = \frac{y}{25} \text{ (approximately)}, \qquad u' = \frac{y}{f} \text{ (approximately)}.$$

Hence

$$M = \frac{u'}{u} = \frac{y/f}{y/25} = \frac{25}{f} \quad (f \text{ in centimeters}). \tag{40-5}$$

While it appears at first as if the angular magnification may be made as large as desired by decreasing the focal length f, the aberrations of a simple double convex

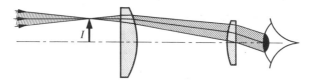

Fig. 40-17. The Ramsden ocular.

lens set a limit to M of about $2\times$ or $3\times$. If these aberrations are corrected, the magnification may be carried as high as $20\times$.

An *ocular* or *eyepiece* is a magnifier used for viewing an image formed by a lens or lenses preceding it in an optical system. The Ramsden ocular is illustrated in Fig. 40–17. It is constructed of two plano-convex lenses of equal focal length, separated by a distance of about $\frac{2}{3}$ of this length. The image to be examined is shown at I; the final image is at infinity. Since four refracting surfaces are available, the aberrations of a simple magnifier can be greatly reduced.

40–9 The camera

The essential elements of a camera are a lens, a light-tight box, and a sensitized plate or film for receiving the image. In contrast with a telescope objective, for which the field of view is limited to a range of about 6°, a photographic objective is called upon to cover a field of 50° or even more. Furthermore, the aperture of the lens must be large, in order that it may collect sufficient light to permit short exposures. The combination of wide field and large aperture makes the problem of correcting a photographic lens a difficult

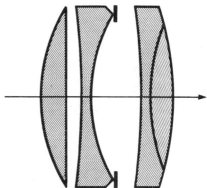

Fig. 40–18. Zeiss "Tessar" lens.

one. Nevertheless, even the simplest lenses, such as those used in Brownie cameras, are corrected for chromatic aberration and curvature of field. Most modern high-speed, short-focal length lenses are modifications of the Zeiss "Tessar" lens, illustrated in Fig. 40–18.

The light-gathering power of a photographic objective is usually stated in terms of its $f/$-number, which is determined by the focal length of the lens and by its diameter or the diameter of the aperture which effectively determines the lens area. Thus the notation $f/4.5$ means that the focal length of the lens is 4.5 times its effective diameter. The smaller the $f/$-number, the larger the lens diameter for a given focal length, and the greater the light-gathering power or "speed" of the lens. Extremely fast lenses may have $f/$-numbers as small as $f/1.9$ or $f/1.5$. That of the Brownie lens is approximately $f/11$. The required time of exposure increases with the square of the $f/$-number.

For a given position of the photographic plate, only those objects lying in the plane conjugate to that of the plate are sharply focused upon it, objects at a greater or less distance appearing somewhat blurred. However, because of lens aberrations, a point of a given object will be imaged as a small circle, called the *circle of confusion*, even with the best focusing. The circles of confusion of points at other distances will be larger. If extremely sharp definition of the image is not essential, there is evidently a certain range of object distances, called the *depth of field*, such that all objects within this range are simultaneously "in focus" on the plate. That is, the circles of confusion of points within this range are not so large that the image is unsatisfactory. The so-called *fixed-focus* camera is one with a large depth of field, so that all objects beyond a certain distance are simultaneously in satisfactory focus.

40–10 The projection lantern

The optical system of the projection lantern, or the motion picture projector, is illustrated in Fig. 40–19. The arrow at the left represents the light source; for example, the filament of a projection lamp. For simplicity, the slide to be projected is represented as opaque except for a single transparent aperture.

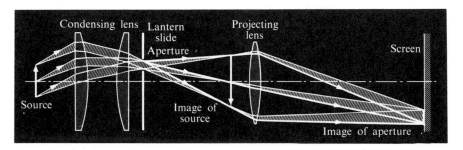

Fig. 40–19.   The projection lantern.

Of course, light is emitted from all points of the source and in all directions. The diagram traces the course of three pencils of rays originating at the ends and at the midpoint of the source. The function of the condensing lens is to deviate the light from the source inward, so that it can pass through the projecting lens. If the condensing lens were omitted, light passing through the outer portions of the slide would not strike the projecting lens and only a small portion of the slide near its center would be imaged on the screen.

A study of the figure will show that (a) for the three selected points of the source, only those rays within the shaded pencils can pass through the aperture, all others striking the condensing lens being intercepted by the opaque portions of the slide, and (b) similar pencils of rays could be drawn from all other points of the source.

Each of these pencils converges, after passing through the aperture, to form an image of its point of origin just to the left of the projecting lens. In practice, this image would be formed *at* the projecting lens, but for clarity in the diagram the image and the lens have been displaced slightly. The focal length of the condensing lens should be such that the image of the source just fills the projecting lens. If the image of the source is larger than the projecting lens, some of the light passing through the slide is wasted. If it is smaller, the area of the projecting lens is not being fully utilized. Thus, in the diagram, the outer portions of the projecting lens serve no useful purpose.

Three rays tangent to the upper edge of the aperture have been emphasized in the figure. These rays originate at *different* points of the source. Hence, although they intersect at the edge of the aperture, this point of intersection does not constitute an image of any point of the source. But these three rays diverge from a common point of the *lantern slide*, and therefore this point of the slide is imaged as shown on the screen. Similarly, rays tangent to any point of the edge of the aperture are imaged at a conjugate point on the screen. Thus if the aperture is circular, a circular spot of light appears on the screen.

Note that light from *all* points of the source illuminates *every* point of the image of the aperture, and would do the same were the aperture at any other point of the slide.

The preceding discussion has explained the conditions that determine the *focal length* of the condensing lens and the *diameter* of the projecting lens (the image of the source formed by the condensing lens should just fill the projecting lens). The *diameter* of the condensing lens must evidently be at least as great as the diagonal of the largest slide to be projected, while the *focal length* of the projecting lens is determined by the magnification desired between the slide and its image, and the distance of the lantern from the screen.

40–11 The microscope

When an angular magnification higher than that attainable with a simple magnifier is desired, it is necessary to use a *compound microscope*, usually called merely a *microscope*. The essential elements of a microscope are illustrated in Fig. 40–20. The object O to be examined is placed just beyond the first focal point F_1 of the *objective* lens, which forms a real and enlarged image I. This image lies just within the first focal point F_2 of the ocular, which forms a virtual image of I at I'. As was stated earlier, the position of I' may be anywhere between the near and far points of the eye. While both the objective and ocular of an actual microscope are highly corrected compound lenses, they are shown as simple thin lenses for simplicity.

Since the objective merely forms an enlarged real image which is examined by the ocular, the over-all magnification M of the compound microscope is the product of the lateral magnification m_1 of the objective and the angular magnification M_2 of the ocular. It may be shown (see Problem 40–18) that

$$m_1 = -\frac{x'}{f_1},$$

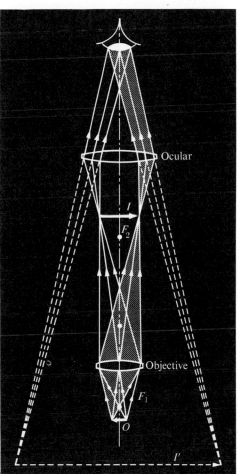

Fig. 40–20. The microscope.

where f_1 is the focal length of the objective and x' is the image distance measured from its second focal point. The angular magnification of the ocular (considered as a simple lens) is $M_2 = 25/f_2$, where f_2 is the focal length of the ocular. Hence the over-all magnification M of the compound microscope is

$$M = m_1 \times M_2 = - \frac{x'}{f_1} \times \frac{25}{f_2} \quad (x', f_1, f_2, \text{ in cm}). \qquad (40\text{–}6)$$

It has become customary among microscope manufacturers to specify the values of m_1 and M_2, rather than the focal lengths of objective and ocular.

40–12 The telescope

A telescope is illustrated in Fig. 40–21. In practice, the objects examined by a telescope are at such large distances from the instrument that the image I is formed very nearly at the second focal point of the objective. Furthermore, if the final image I' is at infinity, the image I is at the first focal point of the ocular. The distance between objective and ocular, or the length of the telescope, is therefore the sum of the focal lengths of objective and ocular, $f_1 + f_2$.

The *angular magnification* of a telescope is defined as the ratio of the angle subtended at the eye by the final image I', to the angle subtended at the (unaided) eye by the object. This ratio may be expressed in terms of the focal lengths of objective and ocular as follows. In Fig. 40–21, the ray passing through F_1, the first focal point of the objective, and through F_2', the second focal point of the ocular, has been emphasized. The object (not shown) subtends an angle u at the objective and would subtend essentially the same angle at the unaided eye. Also, since the observer's eye is placed just to the right of the focal point F_2', the angle subtended at the eye by the final image is very nearly equal to the angle u'. The distances ab and cd are evidently equal to each other and to the height y' of the image I. Since both u and u' are small, they may be approximated by their tangents. From the right triangles F_1ab and $F_2'cd$, $u = -y'/f_1$, $u' = y'/f_2$. Hence

$$M = \frac{u'}{u} = - \frac{y'/f_2}{y'/f_1} = - \frac{f_1}{f_2}. \qquad (40\text{–}7)$$

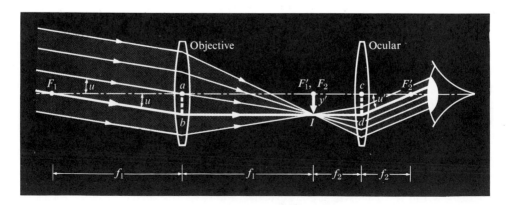

Fig. 40–21.   Telescope, final image at infinity.

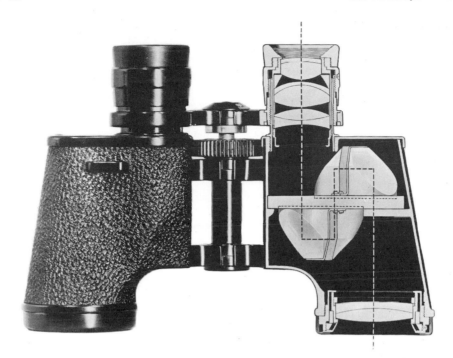

Fig. 40–22. The prism binocular. (Courtesy of Bausch & Lomb Optical Co.)

The angular magnification of a telescope is therefore equal to the ratio of the focal length of the objective to that of the ocular. The minus sign denotes an inverted image. While an inverted image is not a disadvantage if the instrument is to be used for astronomical observations, it is desirable that a terrestrial telescope shall form an erect image. This is accomplished in the *prism binocular*, of which Fig. 40–22 is a cutaway view, by a pair of 45°-45°-90° totally reflecting prisms inserted between objective and ocular. The image is inverted by the four reflections from the inclined faces of the prisms. It is customary to stamp on a flat metal surface of a binocular two numbers separated by a multiplication sign, thus, 7 × 50. The first number is the magnification and the second is the diameter of the objective lenses in millimeters.

Problems

40–1. A thin-walled glass sphere of radius R is filled with water. An object is placed a distance $3R$ from the surface of the sphere. Determine the position of the final image. The effect of the glass wall may be neglected.

40–2. A transparent rod 40 cm long is cut flat at one end and rounded to a hemispherical surface of 12 cm radius at the other end. An object is placed on the axis of the rod, 10 cm from the hemispherical end. (a) What is the position of the final image? (b) What is its magnification? Assume the refractive index to be 1.50.

40–3. Both ends of a glass rod 10 cm in diameter, of index 1.50, are ground and polished to convex hemispherical surfaces of radius 5 cm at the left end and radius 10 cm at the right end. The length of the rod between vertices is 60 cm. An arrow 1 mm long, at right angles to the axis and 20 cm to the left of the first vertex, constitutes the object for the first surface. (a) What constitutes the object for the second surface? (b) What is the object distance for the second surface? (c) Is the object real or virtual? (d) What is the position of the image formed by the second surface? (e) What is the height of the final image?

40–4. The same rod as in Problem 40–3 is now shortened to a distance of 10 cm between its vertices, the curvatures of its ends remaining the same. (a) What is the object distance for the second surface? (b) Is the object real or virtual? (c) What is the position of the image formed by the second surface? (d) Is the image real or virtual? Erect or inverted, with respect to the original object? (e) What is the height of the final image?

40–5. A glass rod of refractive index 1.50 is ground and polished at both ends to hemispherical surfaces of 5 cm radius. When an object is placed on the axis of the rod and 20 cm from one end the final image is formed 40 cm from the opposite end. What is the length of the rod?

40–6. A solid glass sphere of radius R and index 1.50 is silvered over one hemisphere, as in Fig. 40–23. A small object is located on the axis of the sphere at a distance $2R$ from the pole of the unsilvered hemisphere. Find the position of the final image after all refractions and reflections have taken place.

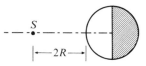

Figure 40–23

40–7. A narrow beam of parallel rays enters a solid glass sphere in a radial direction. At what point outside the sphere are these rays brought to a focus? The radius of the sphere is 3 cm and its index is 1.50.

40–8. A glass plate 1 in. thick, of index 1.50, having plane parallel faces, is held with its faces horizontal and its lower face 4 in. above a printed page. Find the position of the image of the page, formed by rays making a small angle with the normal to the plate.

40–9. (a) Show that the equation $(1/s) + (1/s') = 1/f$ is that of an equilateral hyperbola having as asymptotes the lines $x = f$ and $y = f$. (b) Construct a graph with object distance (s) as abscissa, and image distance (s') as ordinate, for a lens of focal length f, and for object distances from 0 to ∞. (c) On the same set of axes construct a graph of magnification (ordinate) *vs.* object distance.

40–10. A converging lens has a focal length of 10 cm. For object distances of 30 cm, 20 cm, 15 cm, and 5 cm determine (a) image position, (b) magnification, (c) whether image is real or virtual, (d) whether image is erect or inverted.

40–11. Sketch the various possible thin lenses obtainable by combining two surfaces whose radii of curvature are, in absolute magnitude, 10 cm and 20 cm. Which

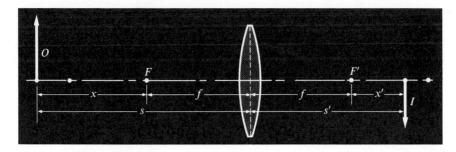

Figure 40–24

are converging and which are diverging? Find the focal length of each lens if made of glass of index 1.50.

40–12. The radii of curvature of the surfaces of a thin lens are +10 cm and +30 cm. The index is 1.50. (a) Compute the position and size of the image of an object in the form of an arrow 1 cm high, perpendicular to the lens axis, 40 cm to the left of the lens. (b) A second similar lens is placed 160 cm to the right of the first. Find the position of the final image. (c) Same as (b) except the second lens is 40 cm to the right of the first. (d) Same as (c) except the second lens is diverging, of focal length −40 cm.

40–13. An object is placed 18 cm from a screen. (a) At what points between object and screen may a lens of 4 cm focal length be placed to obtain an image on the screen? (b) What is the magnification of the image for these positions of the lens?

40–14. An object is imaged by a lens on a screen placed 12 cm from the lens. When the lens is moved 2 cm farther from the object the screen must be moved 2 cm closer to the object to refocus it. What is the focal length of the lens?

40–15. Three thin lenses, each of focal length 20 cm, are aligned on a common axis and are separated by 30 cm. Find the position of the image of a small object on the axis, 60 cm to the left of the first lens.

40–16. An equiconvex thin lens made of glass of index 1.50 has a focal length in air of 30 cm. The lens is sealed into an opening in one end of a tank filled with water (index = 1.33). At the end of the tank opposite the lens is a plane mirror, 80 cm distant from the lens. Find the position of the image formed by the lens-water-mirror system, of a small object outside the tank on the lens axis and 90 cm to the left of the lens. Is the image real or virtual? Erect or inverted?

40–17. A diverging meniscus lens of 1.48 refractive index has spherical surfaces whose radii are 2.5 and 4 cm. What would be the position of the image if an object were placed 15 cm in front of the lens?

40–18. Figure 40–24 shows an object O and its image I formed by a thin lens. The object and image distances, measured from the lens, are s and s', respectively. Let x and x' represent the distances of object and image *measured from the corresponding focal points* F and F'. (a) Derive the *Newtonian form* of the thin lens equation, $xx' = f^2$. (b) Prove that $m = -f/x = -x'/f$.

40–19. A plano-convex lens is 2 cm thick along its axis. The refractive index is 1.50 and the radius of curvature of the convex surface is 10 cm. The convex surface faces toward the left. (a) Find the distance from the first focal point to the vertex of the convex surface. (b) Find the distance from the vertex of the plane surface to the second focal point.

40–20. When an object is placed at the proper distance in front of a converging lens, the image falls on a screen 20 cm from the lens. A diverging lens is now placed halfway between the converging lens and the screen, and it is found that the screen must be moved 20 cm farther away from the lens to obtain a sharp image. What is the focal length of the diverging lens?

40–21. (a) Prove that when two thin lenses of focal lengths f_1 and f_2 are placed *in contact*, the focal length f of the combination is given by the relation

$$1/f = 1/f_1 + 1/f_2.$$

(b) A converging meniscus lens has an index of refraction of 1.50 and the radii of its surfaces are 5 and 10 cm. The concave surface is placed upward and filled with water. What is the focal length of the water-glass combination?

40–22. Two thin lenses, both of 10 cm focal length, the first converging, the second diverging, are placed 5 cm apart. An object is placed 20 cm in front of the first (converging) lens. (a) How far from this lens will the image be formed? (b) Is the image real or virtual?

40–23. Rays from a lens are converging toward a point image P, as in Fig. 40–25. What thickness t of glass of index 1.50 must be interposed as in the figure in order that the image shall be formed at P'?

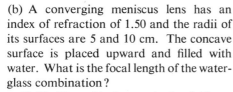

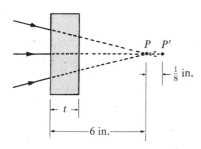

Figure 40–25

40–24. An object 10 ft in front of a camera lens is sharply imaged on a photographic film 6 in. behind the lens. A glass plate 0.5 in. thick, of index 1.50, having plane parallel faces, is interposed between

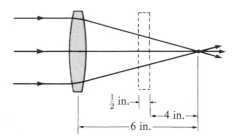

Figure 40–26

lens and plate as shown in Fig. 40–26. (a) Find the new position of the image. (b) At what distance in front of the lens will an object be in sharp focus on the film with the plate in place, the distance from lens to film remaining 6 in.? Consider the lens as a simple thin lens.

40–25. An ocular consists of two similar positive thin lenses having focal lengths of 2 in., separated by a distance of 1 in. Where are the focal points of the ocular?

40–26. A thin lens of focal length 10 cm is used as a simple magnifier. (a) What angular magnification is obtainable with the lens? (b) When an object is examined through the lens, how close may it be brought to the eye?

40–27. The focal length of a simple magnifier is 10 cm. (a) How far in front of the magnifier should an object to be examined be placed if the image is formed at the observer's near point, 25 cm in front of his eye? (b) If the object is 1 mm high, what is the height of its image formed by the magnifier? Assume the magnifier to be a thin lens.

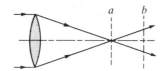

Figure 40–27

40–28. A camera lens is focused on a distant point source of light, the image forming on a screen at a (Fig. 40–27).

When the screen is moved backward a distance of 2 cm to *b*, the circle of light on the screen has a diameter of 4 mm. What is the *f*/-number of the lens?

40–29. Camera *A*, having an *f*/8 lens 2.5 cm in diameter, photographs an object using the correct exposure of 1/100 sec. What exposure should camera *B* use in photographing the same object if it has an *f*/4 lens 5 cm in diameter?

40–30. The focal length of an *f*/2.8 camera lens is 8 cm. (a) What is the diameter of the lens? (b) If the correct exposure of a certain scene is 1/200 sec at *f*/2.8, what would be the correct exposure at *f*/5.6?

40–31. The dimensions of a lantern slide are 3″ × 4″. It is desired to project an image of the slide, enlarged to 6′ × 8′, on a screen 30 ft from the projection lens. (a) What should be the focal length of the projection lens? (b) Where should the slide be placed?

40–32. The image formed by a microscope objective of focal length 4 mm is 180 mm from its second focal point. The ocular has a focal length of 31.25 mm. (a) What is the magnification of the microscope? (b) The unaided eye can distinguish two points as separate if they are about 0.1 mm apart. What is the minimum separation, using this microscope?

40–33. A certain microscope is provided with objectives of focal lengths 16 mm, 4 mm, and 1.9 mm, and with oculars of angular magnifications 5× and 10×. What is (a) the largest, (b) the least over-all magnification obtainable? Each objective forms an image 160 mm beyond its second focal point.

40–34. The focal length of the ocular of a certain microscope is 2.5 cm. The focal length of the objective is 16 mm. The distance between objective and ocular is 22.1 cm. The final image formed by the ocular is at infinity. Treat all lenses as thin. (a) What should be the distance from the objective to the object viewed? (b) What is the linear magnification produced by the objective? (c) What is the over-all magnification of the microscope?

40–35. A microscope with an objective of focal length 9 mm and an ocular of focal length 5 cm is used to project an image on a screen 1 m from the ocular. What is the lateral magnification of the image? Let $x' = 18$ cm.

40–36. The moon subtends an angle at the earth of approximately $\frac{1}{2}°$. What is the diameter of the image of the moon produced by the objective of the Lick Observatory telescope, a refractor having a focal length of 58 ft?

40–37. The ocular of a telescope has a focal length of 10 cm. The distance be-

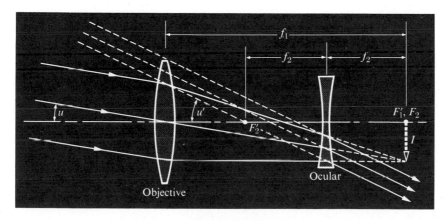

Figure 40–28

tween objective and ocular is 2.1 m. What is the angular magnification of the telescope?

40–38. A crude telescope is constructed of two spectacle lenses of focal lengths 100 cm and 20 cm respectively. (a) Find its angular magnification. (b) Find the height of the image formed by the objective of a building 200 ft high and distant one mile.

40–39. Figure 40–28 is a diagram of a *Galilean telescope*, or opera glass, with both the object and its final image at infinity. The image I serves as a virtual object for the ocular. The final image is virtual and erect. Prove that the angular magnification $M = -f_1/f_2$.

40–40. A Galilean telescope is to be constructed, using the same objective as in Problem 40–38. (a) What type and focal length lens should be used as an ocular, if the telescopes are to have the same magnification? (b) Compare the lengths of the telescopes.

Interference and Diffraction

41–1 Principles of interference. Coherent sources

We have seen that the position and magnification of the image formed by a mirror or lens can be computed on the assumption that light travels in a straight line in a homogeneous medium, and that rays of light are deviated through definite angles at the surfaces separating two different media. The location of an image was seen to be a problem in geometry, and the methods used are those of *geometrical optics*.

In this chapter we shall discuss the phenomena of *interference* and *diffraction*, for whose understanding the principles of geometrical optics do not suffice. Instead, we must return to the more fundamental point of view that light is a wave motion, and that the effect of a number of wave trains arriving at one point depends upon the phases of the waves as well as upon their amplitudes. This part of the subject is called *physical optics*.

At any point where two or more trains of waves cross one another they are said to *interfere*. This does not mean that any wave train is impeded by the presence of the others, but refers to the combined effect of them all at the point in question. The *principle of superposition*, first introduced in connection with sound waves in Section 22–2, states that the resultant displacement at any point and at any instant may be found by adding the instantaneous displacements that would be produced at the point by the individual wave trains if each were present alone. The term "displacement" as used here is a general one. If one is considering surface ripples on a liquid, the displacement means the actual displacement of the surface above or below its normal level. If the waves are sound waves, the term refers to the excess or deficiency of pressure. If the waves are electromagnetic, the displacement means the magnitude of the electric or magnetic field intensity.

The fundamental problem under consideration is the effect at one point when light waves coming from different sources arrive at this point. Suppose, for the sake of simplicity, that we have two point sources. If the waves leaving these sources start in phase, travel different paths, and then come together, they *may* arrive in phase. If this is the case, they will reinforce each other. But this reinforcement may last only a very short time, for one of the sources may undergo a sudden phase shift, after which the two wave trains from the two sources will not start in phase. When these new waves arrive together, they may not reinforce. It is a fundamental property of the atoms or molecules of a source of light that they are continually undergoing transitions which produce frequent haphazard phase changes in the light which they emit.

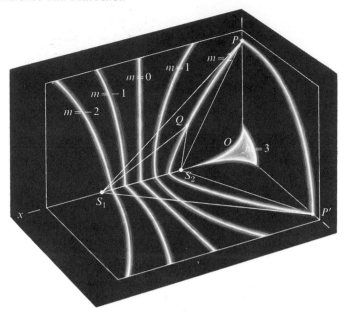

Fig. 41–1. Curves of maximum intensity in the interference pattern of two monochromatic point sources.

To produce observable interference effects, *it is necessary to have two sources emitting light waves which, at the start, are always in phase. This can never be accomplished with two separate sources or from two separate points of the same source.* Even if the light waves from separate sources were in phase at one moment, they would shortly get out of phase. To ensure the existence of two light waves leaving two points always in phase, *it is necessary to start with only one light wave* and to split this wave into two parts, each of which travels a different path, the two waves eventually meeting at the same point. In these circumstances, any haphazard changes of phase which the original light wave undergoes are shared by the two parts, which therefore leave their respective starting points always in phase. Two sources of this sort are called *coherent sources.*

Let S_1 and S_2 in Fig. 41–1 represent two coherent *point* sources on the line xO, and P a point in a vertical plane for which the path difference $PS_1 - PS_2$ is some whole number of wavelengths $m\lambda$. The vibrations at P due to the two waves will therefore be in phase and the two waves will reinforce each other at this point. Reinforcement will also take place at point P' in a horizontal plane if $P'S_1 = PS_1$ and $P'S_2 = PS_2$. In fact, at all points of the circle through P and P', with center at O, the waves from the two sources will reinforce, and a bright circular region of reinforcement will appear on a vertical screen through P and P', perpendicular to the line xO. Close to this region of maximum reinforcement will be circular regions of lesser intensity where the waves come together neither in phase nor in opposite phase. These regions are terminated by a black circle where there is complete destructive interference because the waves arrive in opposite phase. The intensity distribution on a screen from dark to bright to dark again is called an *interference fringe.*

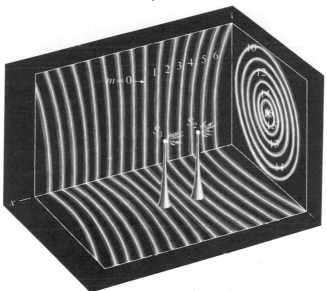

Fig. 41–2. Hyperbolic (almost straight) interference fringes, and also circular fringes formed when the distance between the two coherent point sources S_1 and S_2 is 16 wavelengths.

Point Q in Fig. 41–1 is another point for which the path difference $QS_1 - QS_2$ is also $m\lambda$, and the curve passing through P and Q is the locus of all such points in the vertical plane passing through xO. This curve is a hyperbola, a curve which has the property that the difference between the distances from any point on it to two fixed points is a constant. If we imagine this hyperbola to be rotated about the line xO as an axis, it sweeps out a surface called a *hyperboloid*, and we see that the waves from S_1 and S_2 will arrive at *all* points of this surface so as to reinforce each other.

The diagram of Fig. 41–1 has been drawn for the simple case where the distance from S_1 to S_2 is 3λ, and where the path difference

$$PS_1 - PS_2 = 2\lambda \quad (m = 2).$$

The hyperbola lettered $m = 1$ is the locus of points in a vertical plane for which the path difference is λ. The locus of all points for which the path difference is zero $(m = 0)$ is a line passing through the midpoint of $S_1 S_2$. Hyperbolas for which $m = -1$ and $m = -2$ are also shown. Rotation of these curves about xO gives rise, in this case, to five hyperboloids. Bright lines will appear on a screen in any position, along those curves where the hyperboloids intersect the screen.

If the distance between the sources is many wavelengths, there will be a large number of surfaces over which the waves reinforce, and a large number of alternate bright and dark hyperbolic (almost straight) fringes will be formed on a screen parallel to the line joining the sources. Also, a great number of alternate bright and dark circular fringes will be formed on a screen perpendicular to the line joining the sources, as shown in Fig. 41–2.

The experimental realization of these ideas will be described in Section 41–2.

41-2 Young's double slit and Pohl's mica sheet

The wave theory of light became fully established in the early nineteenth century, when an English physician, Thomas Young, and a French engineer, Augustin Fresnel, gave simple and fairly complete explanations of interference and diffraction on the basis of wave theory. Today, a phenomenon is believed to be a wave or, at least, to have wave characteristics when and only when interference effects can be produced. The wave characteristics of electrons were believed only when electrons were shown to produce interference effects.

In the field of microwaves of wavelength, say, 10 cm, a source whose dimensions are 1 or 2 cm (much less than a wavelength) is a good approximation to a point source. In optics, however, where wavelengths are of the order of 5×10^{-5} cm, there are no point sources. The best one can do is to illuminate a narrow slit (or hole) S_0 of width about 10^{-2} cm and divide the light issuing from this opening into two parts. The light from *each point* of the slit S_0, after being subdivided, gives rise to its own set of interference fringes. If all these sets of interference fringes amount to a distribution of light intensity on a screen, which has marked regions of light and darkness, that is, great contrast, then the slit or hole may be regarded as a good approximation to a point source. In other words, a "point source" of visible light is one which produces (with some kind of interferometer) many sets of interference fringes which do not overlap to the point where they obscure one another.

In Young's interferometer, shown in Fig. 41-3(a), the monochromatic light issuing from a narrow slit S_0 is divided into two parts by falling upon a screen in which are

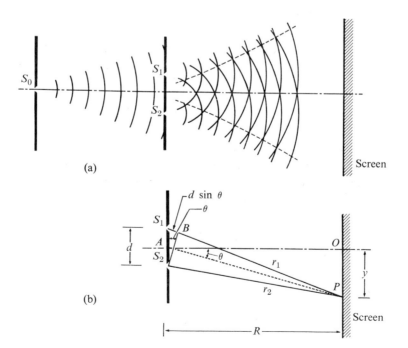

Fig. 41-3.   Interference of light waves passing through two slits. Young's experiment.

cut two other narrow slits S_1 and S_2, very close together. The dimensions in this figure are grossly distorted for reasons of clarity. The distance from the source slit S_0 to the screen containing S_1 and S_2 is anywhere from 20 cm to 100 cm. The distance from the double slit screen to the final screen is usually from 1 m to 5 m. The slits are anywhere from 0.1 mm to 0.2 mm wide and the separation of the slits S_1 and S_2 is less than 1 mm. In short, all slit widths and slit separations are fractions of millimeters; all other distances are hundreds or thousands of millimeters.

According to Huygens' principle, cylindrical wavelets spread out from slit S_0 and reach slits S_1 and S_2 at the same instant. A train of Huygens wavelets diverges from both of these slits, which therefore act as coherent sources. Let d represent the distance between the slits, and consider a point P on the screen, in a direction making an angle θ with the axis of the system [Fig. 41–3(b)]. With P as a center and PS_2 as radius, strike an arc intersecting PS_1 at B. If the distance R from slits to screen is large in comparison with the distance d between the slits, the arc S_2B can be considered a straight line at right angles to PS_2, PA, and PS_1. Then the triangle BS_1S_2 is a right triangle, similar to POA, and the distance S_1B equals $d \sin \theta$. This latter distance is the difference in path length $r_1 - r_2$ between the waves reaching P from the two slits. The waves spreading out from S_1 and S_2 necessarily start in phase, but they will not be in phase at P because of this difference in length of path. According to the principles discussed in the preceding section, complete reinforcement will take place at the point P, that is, P will lie at the center of a bright fringe, when the path difference $d \sin \theta$ is some integral number of wavelengths, say $m\lambda$ ($m = 0, 1, 2, 3$, etc.). Thus

$$d \sin \theta = m\lambda, \quad \text{or} \quad \sin \theta = \frac{m\lambda}{d}.$$

Now λ is of the order 5×10^{-5} cm, while d cannot be made much smaller than about 10^{-2} cm. As a rule, only the first five to ten fringes are bright enough to be seen, so that m is at most, say, 10. Therefore the very largest value of $\sin \theta$ is

$$\sin \theta \text{ (maximum)} = \frac{10 \times 5 \times 10^{-5} \text{ cm}}{10^{-2} \text{ cm}} = 0.05,$$

which corresponds to an angle of only $3°$.

The central bright fringe at point O, or zeroth fringe ($m = 0$), corresponds to zero path difference, or $\sin \theta = 0$. If point P is at the center of the mth fringe, the distance y_m from the zeroth to the mth fringe is, from Fig. 41–3(b),

$$y_m = R \tan \theta_m.$$

Since, however, the angle θ_m for all values of m is extremely small,

$$y_m = R \sin \theta_m.$$

Therefore

$$y_m = R \frac{m\lambda}{d},$$

and

$$\lambda = \frac{y_m d}{mR}. \tag{41-1}$$

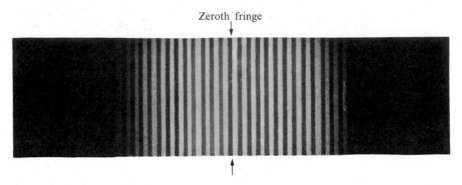

Fig. 41-4.   Interference fringes produced by Young's double-slit interferometer.

Hence, by measuring the distance d between the slits, the distance R to the screen, and the distance y_m from the center of the zeroth fringe to the center of the mth fringe on either side, the wavelength of the light producing the interference pattern may be computed.

EXAMPLE.   With two slits spaced 0.2 mm apart, and a screen at a distance of one meter, the third bright fringe is found to be displaced 7.5 mm from the central fringe.   Find the wavelength of the light used.

Let λ be the unknown wavelength.   Then

$$\lambda = \frac{y_m d}{m R} = \frac{0.75 \text{ cm} \times 0.02 \text{ cm}}{3 \times 100 \text{ cm}} = 5 \times 10^{-5} \text{ cm} = 500 \times 10^{-9} \text{ m} = 500 \text{ nm}.$$

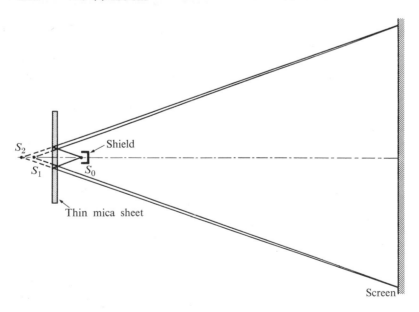

Fig. 41-5.   Pohl's mica-sheet interferometer.

Fig. 41–6. Circular interference fringes produced by Pohl's mica interferometer. The dark rectangle is the shadow of the mercury arc housing.

The fringes obtained with the aid of Young's double-slit interferometer are shown in Fig. 41–4. Note that the zeroth fringe in the middle and three or four fringes on each side are roughly of the same intensity. Farther on, the fringes decrease markedly in brightness. This effect is due to the finite width of each of the interferometer slits S_1 and S_2. The wider these slits are, the sooner the fringes darken as you proceed away from the zeroth fringe. This variation of intensity of the fringes is due to the phenomenon of diffraction and will be discussed in Section 41–10.

Circular interference fringes may be produced very easily with the aid of simple apparatus suggested by Robert Pohl and shown in Fig. 41–5. A small arc lamp S_0 is placed a few inches away from a sheet of mica of thickness about 0.002 in. Some light is reflected from the first surface, as though it were issuing from the virtual image S_1. An approximately equal amount of light is reflected from the back surface as though it were coming from the virtual image S_2. The circular interference fringes formed by the light issuing from these two coherent sources may be shown on the entire wall of a room, as shown in Fig. 41–6. One of the most interesting features of Pohl's interferometer is that the condition of nonoverlapping of sets of interference fringes, which determines whether the source S_0 may be regarded as a point source, is satisfied quite well when the aperture of the arc lamp is as large as 1 cm. One has therefore a large amount of light at his disposal.

41-3 Intensity distribution in interference fringes

Since a light wave in the visible region has a wavelength between 4 and 7×10^{-5} cm, any point of observation is bound to be many wavelengths away from the source. At such a point, the electric and magnetic vectors are not only in phase but they are proportional to each other. When two or more electromagnetic waves arrive together, however, experiments indicate that photochemical processes, such as the blackening of a photographic plate, or the stimulation of the retina of the eye, depend upon the square of the *resultant amplitude* of the *electric vector E*, not of the magnetic vector. The energy arriving per unit time per unit area, or the *intensity* of the light, is proportional to E^2. It is therefore customary in optics to deal with the electric vector.

Suppose we have the two coherent point sources S_1 and S_2 of Fig. 41-3(b) which emit monochromatic light of frequency f in all directions. If the electric vector at each source varies sinusoidally with the time, then the electric vector at a point is the sum of the two contributions

$$e_1 = E_1 \sin (\omega t - kr_1),$$

$$e_2 = E_2 \sin (\omega t - kr_2),$$

where $\omega = 2\pi f$, $k = 2\pi/\lambda$, and r_1 and r_2 are the respective distances of the point P from each source. These harmonic variations may be represented by the projections on the vertical axis of two *rotors* of length E_1 and E_2 rotating with angular velocity ω about the z-axis. Rotors were first mentioned in Section 11-4, and were used extensively with alternating currents in Chapter 35. The two rotors are shown in Fig. 41-7(a), and the sum of the two projections on the y-axis is seen to be the projection of the rotor E_P which is the vector sum of E_1 and E_2. The angle $k(r_1 - r_2)$ is the phase difference δ between the two electric vectors at P, or

$$\delta = k(r_1 - r_2) = \frac{2\pi}{\lambda}(r_1 - r_2). \tag{41-2}$$

It is generally true that, in any *one* medium, the phase difference between two vibrations at a point due to two waves that have traveled different paths (having started

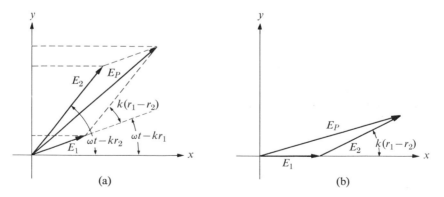

Fig. 41-7.   Rotor diagram of the variations of the electric vector at a point P where two waves meet.

in phase) is given by the relation

$$\text{Phase difference} = \frac{2\pi}{\lambda} \text{(path difference)}, \qquad (41\text{-}3)$$

provided that λ is the wavelength *in the medium*.

To find E_P in the simplest possible manner, it suffices to lay off one electric amplitude along the x-axis, and the other at the *end* of the first, making an exterior angle $k(r_1 - r_2)$, as shown in Fig. 41-7(b). From Fig. 41-7 either (a) or (b) it is evident that

$$E_P^2 = E_1^2 + E_2^2 + 2E_1 E_2 \cos \delta.$$

When the two coherent sources S_1 and S_2 are made equally intense, $E_1 = E_2 = E$, and

$$E_P^2 = 2E^2 + 2E^2 \cos \delta = 2E^2(1 + \cos \delta)$$

$$= 4E^2 \cos^2 \frac{\delta}{2}.$$

The interference fringes therefore consist of gradations of light intensity varying with the cosine squared of *half* the phase difference. Fringes formed by only two interfering rays are called "cosine-squared" fringes.

Since

$$\delta = k(r_1 - r_2) = \frac{2\pi}{\lambda} d \sin \theta,$$

and

$$y = R \tan \theta = R \sin \theta,$$

we get

$$\frac{\delta}{2} = \left(\frac{\pi d}{\lambda R}\right) y.$$

If I is the intensity of the light at any value of y and I_0 the intensity at the point where $y = 0$, we get finally

$$I = I_0 \cos^2 \left(\frac{\pi d}{\lambda R}\right) y, \qquad (41\text{-}4)$$

which enables us to calculate the intensity of light at any point.

41-4 Phase change in reflection. Lloyd's mirror

When a train of waves of amplitude E whose direction is shown by the ray in Fig. 41-8(a) is incident upon the surface of a medium in which it travels more slowly, both a reflected train and a refracted train are produced, each with an amplitude less than E. Let r and t be fractions such that rE is the reflected amplitude in the fast medium and tE is the amplitude in the slow medium. In the following calculation, due to Stokes, we consider the conclusions to be drawn from the fact that a ray of light is *reversible*, that is, it retraces its path if its direction is reversed. With reference to Fig. 41–8(a), reversibility means that two trains of waves of amplitudes rE and tE, arriving at the surface, should combine to form a single train of amplitude E leaving the surface. But a train of amplitude rE in the fast medium, arriving at the surface as in Fig. 41–8(b), gives rise to both a reflected train of amplitude rrE and a transmitted train trE. Similarly, the train of amplitude tE gives rise to a reflected amplitude $r'tE$ and a transmitted amplitude $t'tE$, where r' refers to reflection in the slow medium, and t' to transmission from the slow to the fast medium.

The conditions for reversibility are

$$rrE + t'tE = E,$$

or

$$t't = 1 - r^2, \qquad (41\text{–}5)$$

and

$$trE + r'tE = 0,$$

or

$$r = -r'. \qquad (41\text{–}6)$$

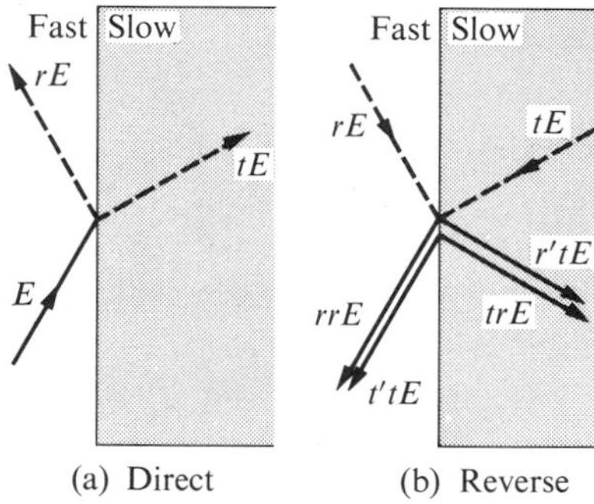

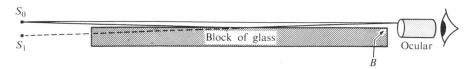

Fast | Slow

Fast | Slow

(a) Direct   (b) Reverse

Fig. 41–8. Stokes' treatment of reflection and refraction.

The negative sign in the second result, $r = -r'$, means that *either the ray reflected in the fast medium or the ray reflected in the slow medium undergoes a phase change of π.* The Stokes treatment is unable to tell which of these possibilities takes place.

The decision can be made with the aid of an interferometer known as Lloyd's mirror. This is depicted in Fig. 41–9. In this arrangement, the two coherent sources are the actual source slit S_0 and its virtual image S_1. The fringes formed by interference between the light waves from these coherent sources may be viewed on a ground glass screen placed anywhere beyond the mirror. If an ocular of high magnification is used to view the fringes that form in space in a plane passing through the edge B, the fringe nearest this edge is seen to be black. This is the fringe corresponding to zero path difference, and if the two wave trains giving rise to this fringe had both traveled in air or had both been reflected from glass, this fringe would have been bright. Of the two wave trains forming the zeroth fringe, however, one had undergone reflection from the glass and one had proceeded directly from S_1. The fact that the zeroth fringe is black indicates that *light waves traveling in air and reflected from glass have undergone a phase shift of π.* In other words, the coefficient r is negative and r' is positive.

S_0

S_1

Block of glass

Ocular

B

Fig. 41–9. Lloyd's mirror. When the ocular is focused on the edge B of the glass block, the fringe nearest the edge is black.

41–5 The Michelson interferometer

Young's double slit and Lloyd's mirror are examples of optical interferometers in which a wavefront from a very narrow source slit is subdivided into two wavefronts by reflecting or transmitting regions of the interferometer. The wavefront subdivision that takes place in Pohl's interferometer does not require as small a source as in the other two cases, but it would be difficult to achieve clean interference fringes with a source much larger than one centimeter in width.

There are several important interferometers that can be used in conjunction with a large extended source. Of these, the Michelson interferometer has been most important in the past and is still of some importance. Figure 41–10 shows the principal features of the Michelson interferometer. Consider one ray from an extended source of monochromatic light at the left. A very thin coating of silver on the right side of the glass plate C is used to provide a transmitted ray 1 and a reflected ray 2 of very nearly equal intensity. This plate serves as a beam splitter. Ray 1 proceeds to a stationary mirror M_1, is reflected back to P and thence to the eye. Ray 2 goes to a movable mirror M_2, is reflected, passes through the beam splitter and then enters the eye. The purpose of the compensator plate D is to ensure that ray 1 passes through three thicknesses of glass, like ray 2. The beam splitter and the compensator plate are made from the same plate of glass in order that their thicknesses should not differ by more than a small fraction of a wavelength. The whole apparatus is mounted on a heavy rigid frame and a fine, very accurate screw thread is used to move the mirror M_2. A diagram of a common commercial model of the interferometer is shown in Fig. 41–11. The source is placed to the left and the observer is directly in front of the handle that turns the screw.

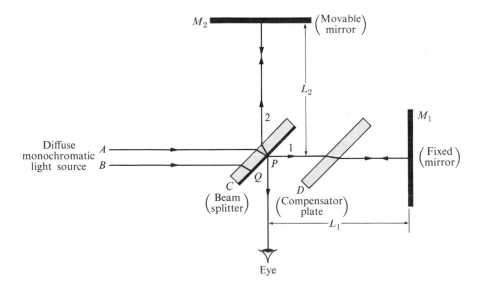

Fig. 41–10. The Michelson interferometer.

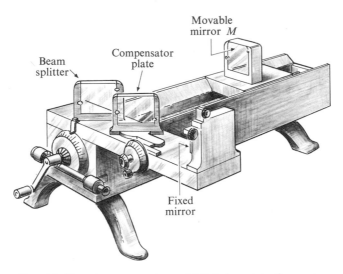

Fig. 41–11. A common type of Michelson interferometer.

The ray *AP* shown in Fig. 41–10 comes from *one* point of the diffuse source and produces on the retina of the eye of the observer a point of light whose intensity depends on the path difference between rays 1 and 2. Similarly, another ray *BQ* is split at *Q* into two rays which travel different paths and arrive at another point on the retina of the eye. If the stationary mirror M_1 and the movable mirror M_2 make an angle that departs slightly from a right angle, the path differences that result from the splitting of the various rays from different points of the source vary continuously from one end of the field of view to the other, producing on the retina the familiar "cosine squared" fringes. The sets of interfering rays in the Young, Pohl, and Lloyd interferometers are produced by *wavefront division* (reflection from mirrors, transmission through slits, etc.), whereas the sets of interfering rays in the Michelson interferometer are produced by what is known as *amplitude division*.

Suppose the angle between the fixed and movable mirrors is such that five or six vertical fringes are present in the field of view. If the mirror M_2 is now moved slowly either backward or forward a distance $\lambda/2$, the path difference between two rays such as 1 and 2 in Fig. 41–10 will change by λ, and each of the fringes will move either to the right or to the left a distance equal to the spacing of the fringes. If the field of view is provided with a stationary vertical line, the observer will note that one fringe will cross this line. If the observer views the fringes through a telescope whose ocular is equipped with a crosshair, and counts *m* fringes that cross the crosshair when the mirror is moved a distance *x* (as measured on the micrometer scale), then

$$2x = m\lambda, \quad \text{or} \quad \lambda = \frac{2x}{m}. \tag{41–7}$$

If *m* is several thousand, *x* can be measured accurately and a good value of λ can be obtained.

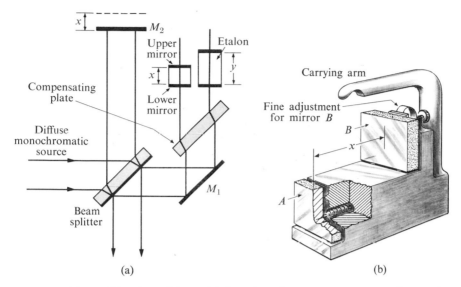

Fig. 41-12. (a) Modification of the Michelson interferometer to measure the number of wavelengths in the distance x between the mirrors of an etalon shown in (b).

One of the most important uses of the Michelson interferometer is to measure the number of wavelengths of the light from atoms of krypton 86, the world-standard source, in a given distance. For this purpose the interferometer is modified as shown in Fig. 41–12. With this modification one can measure not only the number of waves in the distance x, but the number of x's and waves in the distance y between the mirrors of a larger etalon. Proceeding in this manner, the number of waves in a meter was first measured. Now, of course, the meter is defined in terms of wavelength.

41-6 The Michelson-Morley experiment

Before the electromagnetic theory of light became established and before Einstein's theory of special relativity was formulated, every physicist firmly believed in the existence of a medium for light waves, called the ether. Although the ether was assumed to be very rigid in order to propagate waves with the enormous speed of light, it was assumed also to be very tenuous in order to allow the planets to move freely through it. The ether was assumed to be at rest with respect to the sun, and it was believed possible to perform an experiment showing the motion of the earth through the ether, or what amounts to the same thing, the ether "breeze" past the earth in the opposite direction.

Suppose a wave W is moving through a medium M (the ether) with a velocity $\mathbf{v}_{WM}$ relative to the medium. If the velocity of the medium relative to the earth E is $\mathbf{v}_{ME}$, then according to the principles of Newtonian mechanics the velocity of the wave with respect to the earth, $\mathbf{v}_{WE}$, is given by the "domino rule" (Section 4–9):

$$\mathbf{v}_{WE} = \mathbf{v}_{WM} + \mathbf{v}_{ME}. \tag{41-8}$$

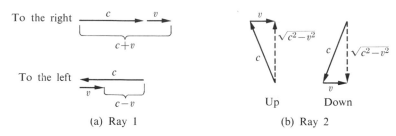

(a) Ray 1   (b) Ray 2

Fig. 41–13. Velocity diagrams according to Newtonian mechanics for rays 1 and 2 in the Michelson interferometer of Fig. 41–10, when the ether is moving with speed v from left to right.

If the wave is a light wave, then $v_{WM} = c$. Also, v_{ME} is the orbital speed v of the earth around the sun. When the ether breeze is in the same direction as the light wave, the speed of light relative to the earth is $c + v$, and when it is in the opposite direction, v_{WE} is $c - v$. This point of view has been substantiated so many times with water waves and with sound waves that it seemed obvious that the same result should hold for light waves.

In 1887 Michelson and Morley utilized the Michelson interferometer in an attempt to detect the relative motion of the earth and the ether. Suppose the interferometer in Fig. 41–10 is placed on a rotatable platform (or floated on mercury) and placed so that the direction from left to right coincides with the direction of the ether breeze. In these circumstances ray 1 traverses a path that is first in the direction of motion of the ether and then opposite, as shown on the velocity diagrams of Fig. 41–13(a). The time $t_{||}$ for ray 1 to travel a distance L from the beam splitter and back again is given by

$$t_{||} = \frac{L}{c+v} + \frac{L}{c-v} = \frac{2cL}{c^2 - v^2} = \frac{2L}{c}\left(1 - \frac{v^2}{c^2}\right)^{-1}.$$

In order for ray 2 to go from point P in Fig. 41–10 back to P again while the ether is moving with speed v to the right, it would have to move first with speed c in a direction slightly upstream, as shown in Fig. 41–13(b), so that the vector sum of its two velocities would be exactly perpendicular to the line of the earth's motion. This means that ray 2 would have a speed $\sqrt{c^2 - v^2}$ on the way to the mirror M_2 and the same speed on the way back. The time to go a distance L would then be

$$t_{\perp} = \frac{2L}{\sqrt{c^2 - v^2}} = \frac{2L}{c}\left(1 - \frac{v^2}{c^2}\right)^{-1/2}.$$

The difference between $t_{||}$ and $t_{\perp}$ is given by

$$\Delta t = \frac{2L}{c}\left[\left(1 - \frac{v^2}{c^2}\right)^{-1} - \left(1 - \frac{v^2}{c^2}\right)^{-1/2}\right].$$

Since the orbital speed v of the earth is given by $v = 3 \times 10^4$ m/sec, and $c = 3 \times 10^8$ m/sec, the ratio $v/c = 10^{-4}$ and $v^2/c^2 = 10^{-8}$. If a number ϵ is much smaller than 1, the following relations hold:

$$(1 - \epsilon)^{-1} \approx 1 + \epsilon, \qquad (1 - \epsilon)^{-1/2} \approx 1 + \frac{\epsilon}{2}.$$

Therefore

$$\Delta t \approx \frac{2L}{c}\left[\left(1 + \frac{v^2}{c^2}\right) - \left(1 + \frac{v^2}{2c^2}\right)\right],$$

or

$$\Delta t \approx \frac{Lv^2}{c^3}. \tag{41–9}$$

According to Newtonian mechanics, then, the motion of the earth through the ether produces a time difference Δt between rays 1 and 2, and this in turn produces a path difference $\Delta x = c\,\Delta t$, where, from Eq. (41–9),

$$\Delta x = c\,\Delta t \approx \frac{Lv^2}{c^2}. \tag{41–10}$$

A path difference x would involve a shift of m fringes, where $2x = m\lambda$. A slight change Δx in x would involve a fringe shift of Δm, where

$$\Delta m = \frac{2\,\Delta x}{\lambda}.$$

Therefore, from Eq. (41–10),

$$\Delta m \approx \frac{2Lv^2}{\lambda c^2}. \tag{41–11}$$

By making rays 1 and 2 undergo many reflections back and forth, Michelson was able to make L equal to about eleven meters. Therefore, with

$$L = 11 \text{ m}, \qquad v^2/c^2 = 10^{-8}, \qquad \text{and} \qquad \lambda = 5.5 \times 10^{-7} \text{ m} \quad \text{(green light)},$$

we get

$$\Delta m \approx \frac{2 \times 11 \text{ m} \times 10^{-8}}{5.5 \times 10^{-7} \text{ m}} = 0.4,$$

that is, four-tenths of a fringe.

On rotating the interferometer through 90°, a shift of 0.4 of a fringe should take place. Since the interferometer was capable of detecting a shift much smaller than this, the fact that no shift at all was observed was most baffling, and to this day the Michelson-Morley experiment is the most significant "negative result" ever obtained.

At first it did not occur to physicists to give up the notion of the ether. Lorentz and, independently, Fitzgerald realized that the negative result of the Michelson-Morley experiment could be explained if a linear object like a rod or a portion of the interferometer moving parallel to itself through the ether with speed v were to undergo a shortening by a factor $\sqrt{1 - v^2/c^2}$. *Merely by virtue of its motion through the ether*, a length L of the interferometer should be contracted to $L\sqrt{1 - v^2/c^2}$. Since

$$t_{\parallel} = \frac{2L/c}{1 - v^2/c^2} \qquad \text{and} \qquad t_{\perp} = \frac{2L/c}{\sqrt{1 - v^2/c^2}},$$

such a contraction would provide that

$$t_{\parallel} = \frac{\frac{2}{c}L\sqrt{1 - v^2/c^2}}{1 - v^2/c^2},$$

which is equal to $t_{\perp}$. This would indeed "explain" the negative result of Michelson-Morley, but such an assumption has three disadvantages: (1) It is *ad hoc*, that is, it is constructed to explain *one* phenomenon only. (2) It does not explain other effects. (3) It is not based on any general theory or set of assumptions. Although the "Lorentz-Fitzgerald contraction" $\sqrt{1 - v^2/c^2}$ has the same mathematical form as the "relativistic length contraction" introduced in Chapter 4, the two equations refer to very different concepts. In the Lorentz-Fitzgerald equation v is the speed of a rod *relative to the ether*, while in the relativistic equation it is the speed *relative to an observer*.

In 1905 Einstein realized that the Newtonian equation for the speed of a wave with respect to the earth,

$$v_{WE} = v_{WM} + v_{ME},$$

is the basic weakness in the analysis of the Michelson-Morley experiment, and that a negative result would be expected if this equation were replaced by the *relativistic equation for relative velocities*,

$$v_{WE} = \frac{v_{WM} + v_{ME}}{1 + (v_{WM}v_{ME}/c^2)}.$$

To see how this comes about, it should first be noted that when v_{WM} is very small compared with c the term $v_{WM}v_{ME}/c^2$ is negligible, and the relativistic equation reduces to the classical one. When, however, the wave is a light wave, with $v_{WM} = c$, then

$$v_{WE} = \frac{c + v_{ME}}{1 + (cv_{ME}/c^2)} = c,$$

regardless of the relative motion of the earth and the ether. It follows from this relativistic equation that the speed of light, relative to the Michelson-Morley interferometer, is c, whether it is moving with the ether, against the ether, or perpendicular to the ether. There is therefore no time difference between any two interfering rays and hence no fringe shift when the interferometer is rotated.

Since the relative motion of the earth and the ether plays no role in the measurement of the speed of light, the very concept of the ether has been given up, and the underlying principle in the theory of special relativity may be stated as follows: there is no preferred frame of reference for the measurement of the speed of light; the speed is the same for every observer, without regard to the magnitude or direction of his motion.

41-7 Interference in thin films. Newton's rings

The brilliant colors that are often seen when light is reflected from a soap bubble or from a thin layer of oil floating on water are produced by interference effects between the two trains of light waves reflected at opposite surfaces of the thin films of soap solution or of oil. In Fig. 41–14, the line ab is one ray in a beam of monochromatic light incident on the upper surface of a thin film. A part of the incident light is reflected at the first surface, as indicated by ray bc, and a part, represented by bd, is transmitted. At the second surface a part is again reflected, and, of this, a part emerges as represented by ray ef. The rays bc and ef come together at a point on the retina of the eye, provided the film is thin enough to allow both rays to enter the pupil of the eye. Needless to say, the thickness of the film and the spacing of the interfering rays are greatly exaggerated in Fig. 41–14.

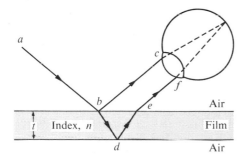

Fig. 41–14. Interference between rays reflected from the upper and lower surfaces of a thin film.

If an extended monochromatic source is used, there are many rays like ab which give rise to two rays that enter the eye. Interference fringes are therefore formed. If the film has parallel surfaces and is illuminated normally, the fringes are circular and appear in space. If, on the other hand, the film is wedge-shaped, the fringes are fairly straight and seem to be localized near the film itself. At the apex of the wedge, where the path difference is zero, destructive interference takes place for all wavelengths because, of the two interfering rays, the one reflected in air from the film undergoes a phase reversal, whereas the other ray does not. At the apex, therefore, the edge of the fringe is black. At a distance from the apex such that the film thickness is one-quarter of a wavelength, it will be bright. Where the thickness equals one-half a wavelength it will be dark, and so on. If the film is illuminated first by blue, then by red light, the spacing of the red fringes is greater than that of the blue, as is to be expected from the greater wavelength of the red light. The fringes produced by intermediate wavelengths occupy intermediate positions. If the film is illuminated by white light, its color at any point is that due to the mixture of those colors which may be reflected at that point, while the colors for which the thickness is such as to result in destructive interference are absent. Just those colors which are absent in the reflected light, however, are found to predominate in the transmitted light. At any point, the color of the film by reflected light is complementary to its color by transmitted light.

If the convex surface of a lens is placed in contact with a plane glass plate, as in Fig. 41–15, a thin film of air is formed between the two surfaces. The thickness of this

Fig. 41-15. Air film between a
convex and a plane surface.

film is very small at the point of contact, gradually increasing as one proceeds outward. The loci of points of equal thickness are circles concentric with the point of
contact. Such a film is found to exhibit interference colors, produced in the same way
as the colors in a thin soap film. The interference bands are circular, concentric with
the point of contact. When viewed by reflected light, the center of the pattern is black,
as is a thin soap film. Note that in this case there is no phase reversal of the light
reflected from the upper surface of the film (which here is of smaller index than that
of the medium in which the light is traveling before reflection), but the phase of the
wave reflected from the lower surface is reversed. When viewed by transmitted light,
the center of the pattern is bright. If white light is used, the color of the light reflected
from the film at any point is complementary to the color transmitted.

These interference bands were studied by Newton, and are called after him, *Newton's
rings.* Figure 41-16 is a photograph of Newton's rings, formed by the air film between
a convex and a plane surface.

The surface of an optical part which is being ground to some desired curvature
may be compared with that of another surface, known to be correct, by bringing the
two in contact and observing the interference fringes. For example, if a plane surface
(an "optical flat") is desired, a glass plate whose lower surface is accurately plane is
placed over the surface to be tested. If both surfaces are accurately plane, and if contact between them is made at one edge, a series of straight interference fringes, parallel
to the line of contact, will be observed. If the surface being ground is not plane, the

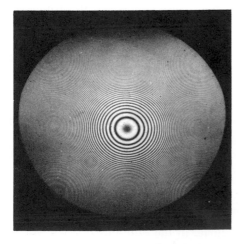

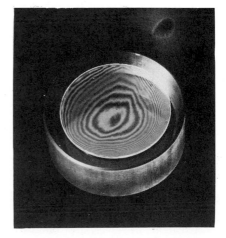

Fig. 41-16. Newton's rings formed by interference in the air film between a convex
and a plane surface. (Courtesy of Bausch &
Lomb Optical Co.)

Fig. 41-17. The surface of a telescope objective under inspection during manufacture.
(Courtesy of Bausch & Lomb Optical Co.)

interference bands will be curved. By noting the shape and separation of the fringes, the departure of the surface from the desired form may be determined.

Figure 41–17 is a photograph made at one stage of the process of manufacturing a telescope objective. The lower, larger diameter, thicker disk is the master. The smaller upper disk is the objective under test. The "contour lines" are Newton's interference fringes, and each one indicates an additional departure of the specimen from the master of one-half a wavelength of light. That is, at 10 lines from the center spot the space between the specimen and master is 5 wavelengths, or about 0.0002 inch. This specimen is very poor.

41–8 Thin coatings on glass

The phenomenon of interference is utilized in the production of so-called "non-reflecting" glass. A thin layer or film of hard transparent material is deposited on the surface of the glass, as in Fig. 41–18. If the index of refraction of the coating is equal to the square root of the index of the glass, equal quantities of light will be reflected from its outer surface, and from the boundary surface between it and the glass. (A proof of this will follow.) Furthermore, since in both reflections the light is reflected from a medium of greater index than that in which it is traveling, the same phase change occurs in each reflection. It follows that if the film thickness is one-quarter of the wavelength *in the film* (normal incidence is assumed), the light reflected from the first surface will be 180° out of phase with that reflected from the second, and complete destructive interference will result.

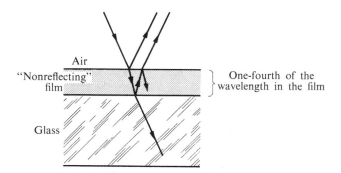

Fig. 41–18. Destructive interference results when the film thickness is one-quarter of the wavelength in the film.

The thickness can, of course, be one-quarter wavelength for one particular wavelength only. This is usually chosen in the yellow-green portion of the spectrum, where the eye is most sensitive. Some reflection then takes place at both longer and shorter wavelengths and the reflected light has a purple hue. The over-all reflection from a lens or prism surface can be reduced in this way from 4 or 5 percent to a fraction of 1 percent. The treatment is extremely effective in eliminating stray reflected light and increasing the contrast in an image formed by highly corrected lenses having a large number of air-glass surfaces.

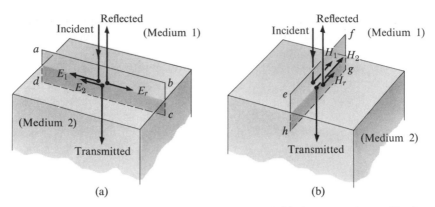

Fig. 41–19.   Behavior of (a) the electric amplitude and (b) the magnetic amplitude at the boundary of two transparent dielectric media in an electromagnetic wave at normal incidence.

To find the condition that must hold for the fraction of the incident electric amplitude that is reflected from the film to be equal to the fraction that is reflected from the glass, consider Fig. 41–19.   Part (a) represents the electric amplitude of a wave arriving at the boundary of two dielectric media at normal incidence.   Note that, in agreement with Stokes' treatment of reflection, the reflected amplitude has a direction opposite to that of the incident one.   The point where the three rays meet at the boundary has been drawn as though there were three separate points, for clarity.   Imagine a rectangular path *abcd* with the line *ab* in medium 1 and *cd* in medium 2, and with the lengths *bc* and *da* vanishingly small.   Since there is no emf in these parts of the two media, it follows that the line integral around the rectangle,

$$\int \mathbf{E} \cdot d\mathbf{s} = 0,$$

or

$$E_1 - E_r = E_2. \tag{41–12}$$

Now consider part (b) of Fig. 41–19.   The directions of the magnetic amplitudes of the three waves at the boundary are such as to make the directions of the Poynting vectors $\mathbf{E} \times \mathbf{H}$ agree with the directions of the corresponding rays.   Imagine a rectangular path *efgh* with the line *ef* in medium 1 and *gh* in medium 2, and with lengths *fg* and *he* vanishingly small.   Since there are no currents within this rectangle, Ampere's law requires that

$$\int \mathbf{H} \cdot d\mathbf{s} = 0,$$

or

$$H_1 + H_r = H_2. \tag{41–13}$$

It was shown in Chapter 36 that, for an electromagnetic wave in a vacuum,

$$\sqrt{\mu_0}\, H = \sqrt{\epsilon_0}\, E.$$

In a transparent dielectric, the magnetic properties are practically the same as those of a vacuum, but the permittivity is $K\epsilon_0$. Hence, for media 1 and 2

$$\sqrt{\mu_0}\,H_1 = \sqrt{K_1\epsilon_0}\,E_1, \qquad \sqrt{\mu_0}\,H_2 = \sqrt{K_2\epsilon_0}\,E_2.$$

Therefore, Eq. (41–13) becomes

$$\sqrt{K_1}\,E_1 + \sqrt{K_1}\,E_r = \sqrt{K_2}\,E_2. \tag{41–14}$$

But the index of refraction of a medium is

$$n = \frac{c}{v} = \frac{\sqrt{1/\mu_0\epsilon_0}}{\sqrt{1/\mu_0 K\epsilon_0}} = \sqrt{K},$$

and therefore Eq. (41–14) becomes

$$n_1 E_1 + n_1 E_r = n_2 E_2. \tag{41–15}$$

Multiplying Eq. (41–12) by n_2, we get

$$n_2 E_1 - n_2 E_r = n_2 E_2. \tag{41–16}$$

Eliminating E_2 from the last two equations, we get

$$(n_2 - n_1)E_1 = (n_2 + n_1)E_r$$

or

$$r_{12} = \frac{E_r}{E_1} = \frac{n_2 - n_1}{n_2 + n_1}. \tag{41–17}$$

Now let n_a, n_c, and n_g be, respectively, the indices of refraction of air, coating, and glass. Then the fraction of the amplitude reflected in air from the coating, r_{ac}, is

$$r_{ac} = \frac{n_c - n_a}{n_c + n_a},$$

and the fraction reflected in the coating from the glass, r_{cg}, is

$$r_{cg} = \frac{n_g - n_c}{n_g + n_c}.$$

In order that

$$r_{ac} = r_{cg},$$

$$\frac{n_c - n_a}{n_c + n_a} = \frac{n_g - n_c}{n_g + n_c},$$

or

$$n_c = \sqrt{n_a n_g}. \tag{41–18}$$

Taking the index of refraction of air to be 1 and that of glass to be 1.5, $n_c = 1.22$. Unfortunately, a hard, transparent material with such a low index that can be easily evaporated and condensed on glass has not yet been found. The best approximation

TABLE 41–1

INCREASED REFLECTION OF MULTIPLE LAYERS

Number of layers	Percentage reflection	Equivalent refractive index of the combination
1	33.97	2.4000
3	71.23	4.2353
5	89.70	7.4740
7	96.57	13.189
9	98.88	23.275
11	99.65	41.074
13	99.89	72.482
15	99.96	127.91

is magnesium fluoride, MgF_2, with an index of 1.38. With this coating, the wavelength of green light in the coating is

$$\lambda_c = \frac{\lambda_a}{n_c} = \frac{5.5 \times 10^{-5} \text{ cm}}{1.38}$$

$$= 4 \times 10^{-5} \text{ cm},$$

and the thickness of a "nonreflecting" film of MgF_2 is 10^{-5} cm.

If a material whose index of refraction is *greater* than that of glass is deposited on glass with a thickness of one-quarter of a wavelength, then the reflectivity is *increased*. For example, a coating of index 2.5 will allow 38% of the incident energy to be reflected, instead of the usual 4% when there is no coating. With the aid of multiple coatings it is possible to achieve an equivalent index of refraction of greater than 100, in which case the reflectivity is almost 100% for a particular wavelength, as shown in Table 41–1, compiled by Vašíček.

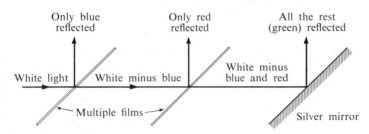

Fig. 41–20. Television beam-splitter. The entire light flux of the incident white light is utilized.

A practical application of multiple films that reflect selectively without absorption is in the field of color television as a beam-splitter, as shown in Fig. 41–20.

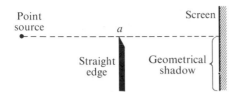

Fig. 41–21. Geometrical shadow of a straight edge.

41–9 Fresnel diffraction

According to geometrical optics, if an opaque object is placed between a point light source and a screen, as in Fig. 41–21, the edges of the object will cast a sharp shadow on the screen. No light will reach the screen at points within the geometrical shadow, while outside the shadow the screen will be uniformly illuminated. The photograph reproduced in Fig. 41–22 was made by placing a razor blade halfway between a pinhole illuminated by monochromatic light and a photographic film, so that the film made a record of the shadow cast by the blade. Figure 41–23 is an enlargement of a region near the shadow of an edge of the blade. The boundary of the *geometrical* shadow is indicated by the short arrows. Note that a small amount of light has "bent" around the edge, into the geometrical shadow, which is bordered by alternating bright and dark bands. Note also that in the first bright band, just outside the geometrical shadow, the illumination is actually greater than in the region of uniform illumination at the extreme left.

Fig. 41–22. Shadow of a razor blade.

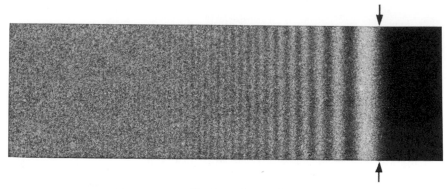

Fig. 41–23.   Shadow of a straight edge.

This simple experimental setup serves to give some idea of the true complexity of what is often considered the most elementary of optical phenomena, the shadow cast by a small source of light.

The reason that a diffraction pattern like that of Fig. 41–22 is not commonly observed in the shadow of an object is merely that most light sources are not point sources. If a shadow of a razor blade is cast by a frosted bulb incandescent lamp, for example, the light from every point of the surface of the lamp forms its own diffraction pattern, but these overlap to such an extent that no individual pattern can be observed.

The term *diffraction* is applied to problems in which one is concerned with *the resultant effect produced by a limited portion of a wave surface*. Since in most diffraction problems some light is found within the region of geometrical shadow, diffraction is sometimes defined as "the bending of light around an obstacle." It should be emphasized, however, that the process by which diffraction effects are produced is going on continuously in the propagation of every wave. Only if a part of the wave is cut off by some obstacle are the effects commonly called "diffraction effects" observed. But since every optical instrument does in fact make use of only a limited portion of a wave (a telescope, for example, utilizes only that portion of a wave admitted by the objective lens), it is evident that a clear comprehension of the nature of diffraction is essential for a complete understanding of practically all optical phenomena.

The main features observed in diffraction effects can be predicted with the help of Huygens' principle, according to which every point of a wave surface can be considered the source of a secondary wavelet which spreads out in all directions. However, instead of finding the new wave surface by the simple process of constructing the envelope of all the secondary wavelets, we must combine these wavelets according to the principles of interference. That is, at every point we must combine the displacements that would be produced by the secondary wavelets, taking into account their amplitudes and relative phases. The mathematical operations are often quite complicated.

A circular *opening* in an opaque screen transmits only a small circular patch of a wave surface; the remainder of the wave is obscured. An interesting effect is observed

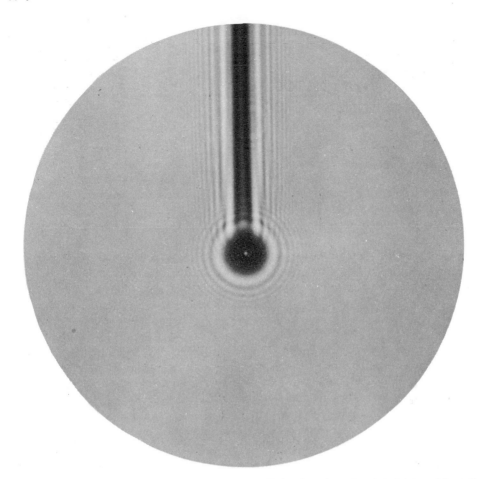

Fig. 41–24. Fresnel diffraction pattern of a small circular obstacle. A bright spot is at the center of the shadow.

if we reverse this procedure and insert a small circular *obstacle* in the light from a distant point source. A small circular patch of the wave is then obscured, while the remainder is allowed to proceed. Figure 41–24 is a photograph of the shadow of a small ball bearing, supported from the tip of a magnetized sewing needle. Constructive interference of the wavelets from the unobstructed portion of the incident wave results in the small bright spot at the center of the geometrical shadow.

In Fig. 41–21, the distance from the source to the obstacle that cuts off part of the wavefront is several meters, and the same is true of the distance from the obstacle to the screen. No lenses are used. This type of diffraction is known as *Fresnel diffraction* (Augustin Jean Fresnel, 1788–1827) and the distribution of light intensity on the screen is known as a Fresnel *diffraction pattern*. When a lens is used and the diffraction pattern appears on a screen in the second focal plane of the lens, the phenomenon is called *Fraunhofer diffraction* (Joseph von Fraunhofer, 1787–1826).

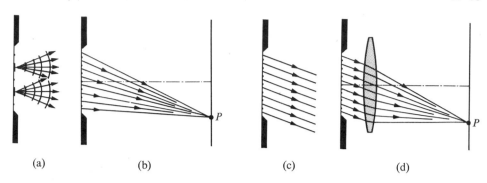

Fig. 41–25. Transition from Fresnel diffraction to Fraunhofer diffraction by a single slit.

41–10 Fraunhofer diffraction by a single slit

Consider a plane wavefront at the moment it reaches the space between the edges of a slit such as that shown in section in Fig. 41–25(a). Small elements of area are obtained by subdividing the wavefront into narrow strips, parallel to the long edges of the slit, perpendicular to the page. From each of these strips, secondary Huygens wavelets spread out in all directions, as shown.

In Fig. 41–25(b), a screen is placed at the right of the slit and P is one point on a line in the screen, the line being parallel to the long edges of the slit and perpendicular to the plane of the diagram. The light reaching a point on the line is calculated by applying the principle of superposition to all the wavelets arriving at the point, from all the elementary strips of the original wave surface. Because of the varying distances to the point, and the varying angles with the original direction of the light, the amplitudes and phases of the wavelets at the point will be different.

The problem is greatly simplified when the screen is sufficiently distant, or the slit sufficiently narrow, so that all rays from the slit to a point on the screen can be considered parallel, as in Fig. 41–25(c). The former case, where the screen is relatively close to the slit (or the slit is relatively wide) is Fresnel diffraction, whereas the latter is Fraunhofer diffraction. There is, of course, no difference in the *nature* of the diffraction process in the two cases, and Fresnel diffraction merges gradually into Fraunhofer diffraction as the screen is moved away from the slit, or as the slit width is decreased.

Fraunhofer diffraction occurs also if a lens is placed just beyond the slit, as in Fig. 41–25(d), since the lens brings to a focus, in its second focal plane, all light traveling in a specified direction. That is, the lens forms in its focal plane a reduced image of the pattern that would appear on an infinitely distant screen in the absence of the lens. The photograph in Fig. 41–28(b) is a Fraunhofer diffraction pattern of a single slit.

To find the distribution of light intensity on a screen due to diffraction by a single slit of width a, it is necessary to imagine a plane wavefront at the slit subdivided into a large number of strips each of which sends out rays in *all* directions toward the lens, shown in Fig. 41–26. If we choose an arbitrary point P on a screen in the focal plane of the lens, only those rays making an angle θ with the axis of the lens will arrive at P. Point O on the screen is the special point at which all rays making the angle $\theta = 0$

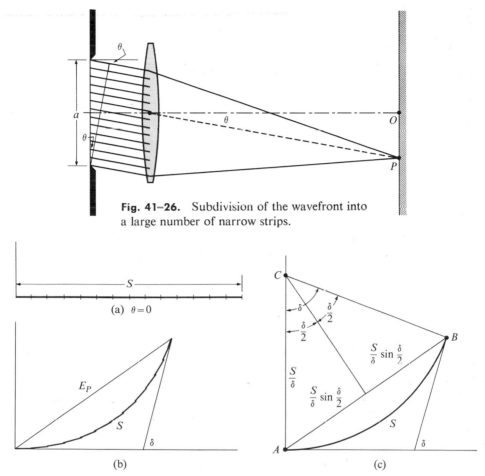

Fig. 41–26. Subdivision of the wavefront into a large number of narrow strips.

(a) $\theta=0$

E_P

(b)

(c)

Fig. 41–27. (a) Rotor diagram when all elementary electric intensities are in phase $(\theta = 0, \delta = 0)$. (b) Rotor diagram when each elementary electric intensity differs in phase slightly from the preceding one. (c) Limit reached by the rotor diagram when the slit is subdivided infinitely.

arrive. Figure 41–27(a) is the rotor diagram showing that when the slit is subdivided into 14 sections and each section emits a Huygens wavelet at the angle $\theta = 0$, all wavelets arrive in phase. The resultant amplitude of the electric intensity at O is denoted by S.

Keeping the same subdivision of the wavefront into 14 strips and considering the wavelets that make the angle θ and arrive at P, there will be a slight phase difference between the electric intensity at P due to each succeeding wavelet, and the appropriate rotor diagram is shown in Fig. 41–27(b). The sum S is now the perimeter of a portion of a many-sided polygon and E_P, the amplitude of the resultant electric intensity at P, is the chord. The angle δ is the phase difference between the ray from the bottom strip of Fig. 41–26 and the ray from the top strip.

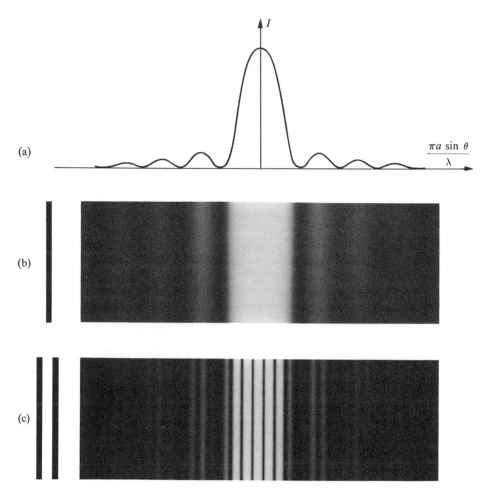

Fig. 41–28. (a) Intensity distribution. (b) Photograph of the Fraunhofer diffraction pattern of a single slit. (c) Fraunhofer diffraction pattern of a double slit.

In the limit, as the number of strips into which the slit is subdivided is increased, the rotor diagram becomes an *arc of a circle*, as shown in Fig. 41–27(c), with the length of arc S equal to a constant. Constructing perpendiculars at A and B, the center of the circular arc C is found. The radius of the circle of which S is an arc is S/δ and the resultant amplitude E_P (distance AB) is $2(S/\delta)\sin\delta/2$. We have then

$$E_P = S\frac{\sin\delta/2}{\delta/2},$$

where δ is the phase difference between the two rays at the extreme edges of the slit. The phase difference between the vibrations at a point due to the arrival of two waves starting in phase at the same source and traveling different paths is $2\pi/\lambda$ times the path difference. We see from Fig. 41–26 that the path difference between the ray from the top of the slit and that from the bottom is $a \sin \theta$. Therefore

$$\delta = \frac{2\pi}{\lambda} a \sin \theta, \tag{41–19}$$

and

$$E_P = S \frac{\sin (\pi a \sin \theta / \lambda)}{\pi a \sin \theta / \lambda}.$$

Since the intensity I is proportional to the square of the amplitude,

$$I = I_0 \left[\frac{\sin (\pi a \sin \theta / \lambda)}{\pi a \sin \theta / \lambda} \right]^2, \tag{41–20}$$

where I_0 is easily seen to be the intensity at O in Fig. 41–26 where $\theta = 0$.

Equation (41–20) is plotted in Fig. 41–28(a) and a photograph of the diffraction pattern is shown directly underneath. Note that most of the light exists in the region close to the point where $\theta = 0$, or the geometrical focus. From Eq. (41–20), the smallest value of $\pi a \sin \theta / \lambda$ at which the intensity becomes zero is the value π. This corresponds to a value of θ equal to θ_1 and given by

$$\sin \theta_1 = \frac{\lambda}{a}.$$

Since λ is of the order of 5×10^{-5} cm, and a typical slit width is 10^{-2} cm, $\sin \theta_1$ is seen to be so small that $\sin \theta_1 = \theta_1$, so that

$$\theta_1 = \frac{\lambda}{a}.$$

When a is several centimeters, θ_1 is so small that one can consider practically all the light to be concentrated at the geometrical focus.

The photograph in Fig. 41–28(c) shows the Fraunhofer diffraction pattern of two slits each of the same width a as the one above, but separated by a distance $d = 4a$. Note that the interference fringes due to cooperation between the slits have intensities that follow the diffraction pattern of each separate slit. The "cosine-squared" interference fringes are modulated by the shape of the curve shown in part (a) of the figure. This is the effect of the finite width of the slits S_1 and S_2 to which reference was made in Section 41–2.

41–11 The plane diffraction grating

Suppose that instead of a single slit, or two slits side by side as in Young's experiment, we have a very large number of parallel slits all of the same width and spaced at regular intervals. Such an arrangement, known as a *diffraction grating*, was first constructed by Fraunhofer. The earliest gratings were of fine wires, 0.04 mm to 0.6 mm in diameter, spaced at intervals of from 0.0528 mm to 0.6866 mm. Gratings are now made by ruling, with a diamond point, a large number of equidistant grooves on a glass or metal surface.

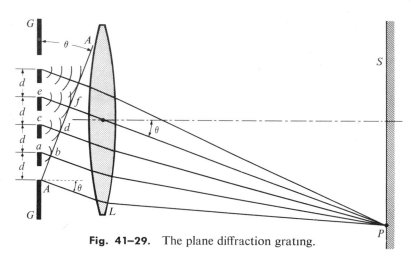

Fig. 41–29. The plane diffraction grating.

Let GG, in Fig. 41–29, represent the grating, the slits of which are perpendicular to the plane of the paper. While only five slits are shown in the diagram, an actual grating contains several thousand, with a grating spacing d of the order of one ten-thousandth of an inch. Let a train of plane waves be incident normally on the grating from the left. The problem of finding the intensity of the light transmitted by the grating then combines the principles of interference and diffraction. That is, each slit gives rise to a diffracted beam whose nature, as we have seen, depends on the slit width. These diffracted beams then interfere with one another to produce the final pattern.

Let us assume that the slits are so narrow that the diffracted beam from each spreads out over a sufficiently wide angle for it to interfere with all the other diffracted beams. Consider first the light proceeding from elements of infinitesimal width at the lower edges of each opening, and traveling in a direction making an angle θ with that of the incident beam, as in Fig. 41–29. A lens at the right of the grating forms in its focal plane a diffraction pattern similar to that which would appear on a screen at infinity.

Suppose the angle θ in Fig. 41–29 is taken so that the distance $ab = \lambda$, the wavelength of the incident light. Then $cd = 2\lambda$, $ef = 3\lambda$, etc. The waves from all of these elements, since they are in phase at the plane of the grating, are also in phase along the plane AA and therefore reach the point P in phase. The same holds true for any set of elements in corresponding positions in the various slits.

If the angle θ is increased slightly, the disturbances from the grating elements no longer arrive at AA in phase with one another, and even an extremely small change in angle results in almost complete destructive interference between them, provided there is a large number of slits in the grating. Hence the maximum at the angle θ is an extremely sharp one, differing from the rather broad maxima and minima which result from interference or diffraction effects with a small number of openings.

As the angle θ is still further increased, a position is eventually reached in which the distance ab in Fig. 41–29 becomes equal to 2λ. Then cd equals 4λ, cf equals 6λ, and so on. The disturbances at AA are again all in phase, the path difference between them

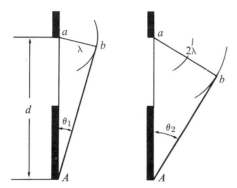

Fig. 41–30. First-order maximum when $ab = \lambda$, second-order maximum when $ab = 2\lambda$.

now being 2λ, and another maximum results. Evidently still others will appear when $ab = 3\lambda$, 4λ, ... Maxima will also be observed at corresponding angles on the opposite side of the grating normal, as well as along the normal itself, since in the latter position the phase difference between disturbances reaching AA is zero.

The angles of deviation for which the maxima occur may readily be found from Fig. 41–30. Consider the right triangle Aba. Let d be the distance between successive grating elements, called the "grating spacing." The necessary condition for a maximum is that $ab = m\lambda$, where $m = 0, 1, 2, 3$, etc. It follows that

$$\sin \theta = m\frac{\lambda}{d} \qquad (41\text{--}21)$$

is the necessary condition for a maximum. The angle θ is also the angle by which the rays corresponding to the maxima have been *deviated* from the direction of the incident light.

In practice, the parallel beam incident on the grating is usually produced by a lens at the first focal point of which is a narrow illuminated slit. Each of the maxima is then a sharp image of the slit, of the same color as that of the light illuminating the slit, assumed thus far to be monochromatic. If the slit is illuminated by light consisting of a mixture of wavelengths, the lens will form a number of images of the slit in different positions, every wavelength in the original light giving rise to a set of slit images deviated by the appropriate angles. If the slit is illuminated with white light, a continuous group of images is formed side by side or, in other words, the white light is dispersed into continuous spectra. In contrast with the single spectrum produced by a prism, a grating forms a number of spectra on either side of the normal. Those which correspond to $m = 1$ in Eq. (41–21) are called *first-order*, those which correspond to $m = 2$ are called *second-order*, and so on. Since for $m = 0$ the deviation is zero, all colors combine to produce a white image of the slit in the direction of the incident beam.

In order that an appreciable deviation of the light may be produced, it is necessary that the grating spacing be of the same order of magnitude as the wavelength of light. Gratings for use in or near the visible spectrum are ruled with from 10,000 to 30,000 lines per inch.

The diffraction grating is widely used in spectrometry, instead of a prism, as a means of dispersing a light beam into spectra. If the grating spacing is known, then from a measurement of the angle of deviation of any wavelength, the value of this wavelength may be computed. In the case of a prism this is not so; the angles of deviation are not related in any simple way to the wavelengths but depend on the characteristics of the material of which the prism is constructed. Since the index of refraction of optical glass varies more rapidly at the violet than at the red end of the spectrum, the spectrum formed by a prism is always spread out more at the violet end than it is at the red. Also, while a prism deviates red light the least and violet the most, the reverse is true of a grating, since in the latter case the deviation increases with increasing wavelength.

EXAMPLE 1.   The limits of the visible spectrum are approximately 400 nm to 700 nm. Find the angular breadth of the first-order visible spectrum produced by a plane grating having 15,000 lines per inch, when light is incident normally on the grating.

The grating spacing, d, in centimeters, is

$$d = \frac{2.54 \text{ cm/in.}}{15,000 \text{ lines/in.}} = 1.69 \times 10^{-4} \text{ cm.}$$

The angular deviation of the violet is

$$\sin \theta = \frac{4 \times 10^{-5} \text{ cm}}{1.69 \times 10^{-4} \text{ cm}} = 0.237,$$

$$\theta = 13° \, 40'.$$

The angular deviation of the red is

$$\sin \theta = \frac{7 \times 10^{-5} \text{ cm}}{1.69 \times 10^{-4} \text{ cm}} = 0.415,$$

$$\theta = 24° \, 30'.$$

Hence the first-order visible spectrum includes an angle of

$$24° \, 30' - 13° \, 40' = 10° \, 50'.$$

EXAMPLE 2.   Show that the violet of the third-order spectrum overlaps the red of the second-order spectrum.

The angular deviation of the third-order violet is

$$\sin \theta = \frac{3 \times (4 \times 10^{-5} \text{ cm})}{d}$$

and of the second-order red it is

$$\sin \theta = \frac{2 \times (7 \times 10^{-5} \text{ cm})}{d}.$$

Since the first angle is smaller than the second, whatever the grating spacing, the third order will always overlap the second.

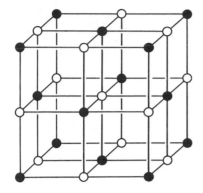

Fig. 41–31. Model of arrangement of ions in a crystal of NaCl. Black circles, Na; open circles, Cl.

41–12 Diffraction of x-rays by a crystal

Although x-rays were discovered by Roentgen in 1895, it was not until 1913 that x-ray wavelengths were measured with any degree of precision. Experiments had indicated that these wavelengths might be of the order of 10^{-8} cm, which is about the same as the interatomic spacing in a solid. It occurred to Laue in 1912 that if the atoms in a crystal were arranged in a regular way, a crystal might serve as a three-dimensional diffraction grating for x-rays. The experiment was performed by Friederich and Knipping and it succeeded, thus verifying in a single stroke both the hypothesis that x-rays *are* waves (or at any rate wavelike in some of their properties) and that the atoms in a crystal are arranged in a regular manner. Since that time, the phenomenon of x-ray diffraction by a crystal has proved an invaluable tool of the physicist, both as a method of measuring x-ray wavelengths and of studying the structure of crystals.

Figure 41–31 is a diagram of a simple type of crystal, that of sodium chloride (NaCl). The black circles represent the sodium, and the open circles the chlorine ions. Figure 41–32 is a diagram of a section through the crystal. Planes such as those parallel to *aa*, *bb*, *cc*, etc., can be constructed through the crystal in such a way that they pass through relatively large numbers of atoms.

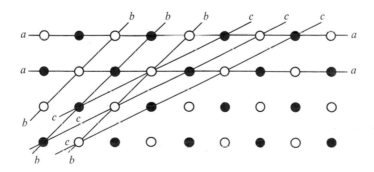

Fig. 41–32. Crystal planes such as *aa*, *bb*, and *cc* serve as a three-dimensional diffraction grating for *x*-rays.

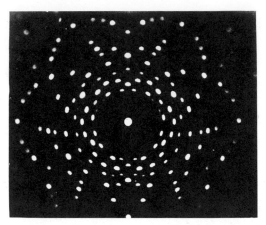

Fig. 41-33. Laue diffraction patterï. formed by directing a beam of x-rays at a thin section of quartz crystal. (Courtesy of Dr. B. E. Warren)

Figure 41-33 is a photograph made by directing a narrow beam of x-rays at a thin section of a crystal of quartz and allowing the diffracted beams to strike a photographic plate. Each spot corresponds to the diffraction by a particular set of crystal planes.

41-13 The resolving power of optical instruments

The expressions for the magnification of a telescope or a microscope (except for certain numerical factors) involved only the focal lengths of the lenses making up the optical system of the instrument. It appears at first sight as though any desired magnification might be attained by a proper choice of these focal lengths. Beyond a certain point, however, while the image formed by the instrument becomes larger (or subtends a larger angle) it does not gain in detail, even though all lens aberrations have been corrected. This limit to the useful magnification is set by the fact that light is a wave motion and the laws of geometrical optics do not hold strictly for a wave surface of limited extent. Physically, the image of a point source is not the intersection of *rays* from the source, but the diffraction pattern of those *waves* from the source that pass through the lens system.

It is an important experimental fact that the light from a point source, diffracted by a circular opening, is focused by a lens not as a geometrical point, but as a disk of finite radius surrounded by dark and bright rings. The larger the wave surface admitted (i.e., the larger the lenses or diaphragms in an optical system), the smaller the diffraction pattern of a point source and the closer together may two point sources be before their diffraction disks overlap and become indistinguishable. An optical system is said to be able to *resolve* two point sources if the corresponding diffraction patterns are sufficiently small or sufficiently separated to be distinguished. The numerical measure of the ability of the system to resolve two such points is called its *resolving power*.

Figure 41-34(a) is a photograph of four point sources made with the camera lens "stopped down" to an extremely small aperture. The nature of the diffraction patterns is clearly evident and it is obvious that further magnification, or enlargement of the

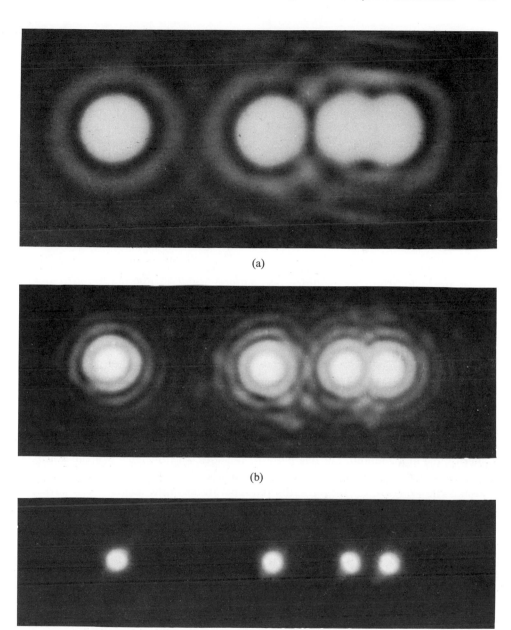

(a)

(b)

(c)

Fig. 41–34. Diffraction patterns of four "point" sources, with a circular opening in front of the lens. In (a), the opening is so small that the patterns at the right are just resolved, by Rayleigh's criterion. Increasing the aperture decreases the size of the diffraction patterns, as in (b) and (c).

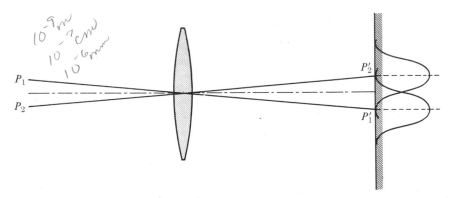

Fig. 41–35. Two point sources are just resolved if the maximum of the diffraction pattern of one source just coincides with the first minimum of the other (Rayleigh's criterion).

picture, would not aid in resolving the sources. What is necessary is not to make the image *larger*, but to make the diffraction patterns *smaller*. Figures 41–34(b) and (c) show how the resolving power of the lens is increased by increasing its aperture. In (b) the diffraction patterns are sufficiently small for all four sources to be distinguished. In (c) the full aperture of the lens was utilized.

An arbitrary criterion proposed by Lord Rayleigh is that two point sources are just resolvable if the central maximum of the diffraction pattern of one source just coincides with the first minimum of the other. Let P_1 and P_2 in Fig. 41–35 be the central rays in the two parallel beams coming from two very distant point sources. Let P_1' and P_2' be the centers of their diffraction patterns, formed by some optical instrument such as a microscope or telescope, which for simplicity is represented in the diagram as a single lens. If the images are just resolved, that is, if according to Rayleigh's criterion the first minimum of one pattern coincides with the center of the other, the separation of the centers of the patterns equals the radius of the central bright disk. From a knowledge of the focal lengths and separations of the lenses in any particular instrument, one can compute the corresponding distance between the two point objects. This distance, the minimum separation of two points that can just be resolved, is called the *limit of resolution* of the instrument. The smaller this distance, the greater is said to be the *resolving power*. The resolving power increases with the solid angle of the cone of rays intercepted by the instrument, and is inversely proportional to the wavelength of the light used. It is as if the light waves were the "tools" with which our optical system is provided, and the smaller the tools the finer the work which the system can do.

Problems

41–1. Two slits are spaced 0.3 mm apart and are placed 50 cm from a screen. What is the distance between the second and third dark lines of the interference pattern when the slits are illuminated with light of 600 nm wavelength?

41–2. Young's experiment is performed with sodium light. Fringes are measured carefully on a screen 100 cm away from the double slit, and the center of the 20th fringe is found to be 11.78 mm from the center of the zeroth fringe. What is the separation of the two slits?

41–3. In the case of the double slit, show that (a) the intensity of light on a screen is given by $I = I_0 \cos^2 (\pi d \sin \theta / \lambda)$; (b) the first minimum occurs at the angle $\theta_1 = \lambda/2d$. If there are two extremely narrow *source* slits S_0 and S_0' subtending an angle α at the center of the double slit there are two sets of interference fringes whose zeroth fringes also subtend an angle α. (c) Sketch the two sets of fringes when $\alpha \gg \theta_1$, $\alpha = \theta_1$, and $\alpha \ll \theta_1$.

41–4. Light of wavelength 500 nm is incident perpendicularly from air on a film 10^{-4} cm thick and of 1.375 refractive index. Part of the light enters the film and is reflected back at the second face. (a) How many waves are contained along the path of this light in the film? (b) What is the phase difference between these waves as they leave the film and as they enter it?

41–5. A glass plate 0.40 micron thick is illuminated by a beam of white light normal to the plate. The index of refraction of the glass is 1.50. What wavelengths within the limits of the visible spectrum ($\lambda = 400$ nm to $\lambda = 700$ nm) will be intensified in the reflected beam?

41–6. Figure 41–36 shows an interferometer known as *Fresnel's biprism*. The magnitude of the prism angle A is extremely small. (a) If S_0 is a very narrow source slit, show that the separation of the two virtual coherent sources S_1 and S_2 is given by $d = 2aA(n - 1)$, where n is the index of refraction of the material of the prism. (b) Calculate the spacing of the fringes of green light of wavelength 500 nm on a screen 2 m from the biprism. Take $a = 20$ cm and $n = 1.5$.

41–7. In Lloyd's mirror, the source slit S_0 and its virtual image S_1 lie in a plane 20 cm behind the left edge of the mirror. (See Fig. 41–9.) The mirror is 30 cm long and a ground glass screen is placed at the right edge. Calculate the distance from this edge to the first light maximum, if the perpendicular distance from S_0 to the mirror is 2 mm and $\lambda = 7.2 \times 10^{-5}$ cm.

41–8. How far must the mirror M_2 of the Michelson interferometer be moved in order that 3000 fringes of krypton 86 light ($\lambda = 606$ nm) move across a line in the field of view?

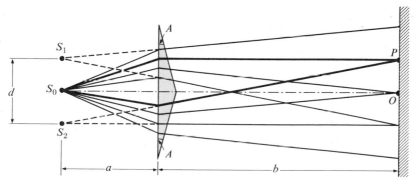

Fig. 41–36. The Fresnel biprism.

41–9. Two rectangular pieces of plane glass àre laid one upon the other on a table. A thin strip of paper is placed between them at one edge so that a very thin wedge of air is formed. The plates are illuminated by a beam of sodium light at normal incidence. Interference fringes are formed, there being ten per centimeter length of wedge measured normal to the edges in contact. Find the angle of the wedge.

41–10. A sheet of glass 10 cm long is placed in contact with a second sheet, and is held at a small angle with it by a metal strip 0.1 mm thick placed under one end. The glass is illuminated from above with light of 546 nm wavelength. How many interference fringes are observed per cm in the reflected light?

41–11. The radius of curvature of the convex surface of a plano-convex lens is 120 cm. The lens is placed convex side down on a plane glass plate, and illuminated from above with red light of wavelength 650 nm. Find the diameter of the third bright ring in the interference pattern.

41–12. What is the thinnest film of 1.40 refractive index in which destructive interference of the violet component (400 nm) of an incident white beam in air can take place by reflection? What is then the residual color of the beam?

41–13. The surfaces of a prism of index 1.52 are to be made "nonreflecting" by coating them with a thin layer of transparent material of index 1.30. The thickness of the layer is such that at a wavelength of 550 nm (in vacuum), light reflected from the first surface is one-half a wavelength out of phase with that reflected from the second surface. Find the thickness of the layer.

41–14. (a) Is a thin film of quartz suitable as a nonreflecting coating for fabulite? (See Table 37–1.) (b) If so, how thick should the film be?

41–15. Parallel rays of green mercury light of wavelength 546 nm pass through a slit of width 0.437 mm covering a lens of focal length 40 cm. In the focal plane of

the lens, what is the distance from the central maximum to the first minimum?

41–16. A slit of width a was placed in front of a lens of focal length 80 cm. The slit was illuminated by parallel light of wavelength 600 nm and the diffraction pattern of Fig. 41–28(b) was formed on a screen in the second focal plane of the lens. If the photograph of Fig. 41–28(b) represents an enlargement to twice the actual size, what was the slit width?

41–17. The intensity of light in the Fraunhofer diffraction pattern of a single slit is

$$I = I_0 \left(\frac{\sin \beta}{\beta} \right)^2,$$

where

$$\beta = (\pi a \sin \theta)/\lambda.$$

Show that the equation for the values of β at which I is a maximum is $\tan \beta = \beta$. How can you solve such an equation graphically?

41–18. Plane monochromatic waves of wavelength 600 nm are incident normally on a plane transmission grating having 500 lines/mm. Find the angles of deviation in the first, second, and third orders.

41–19. A plane transmission grating is ruled with 4000 lines/cm. Compute the angular separation in degrees, in the second-order spectrum, between the α and δ lines of atomic hydrogen, whose wavelengths are respectively 656 nm and 410 nm. Assume normal incidence.

41–20. (a) What is the wavelength of light which is deviated in the first order through an angle of 20° by a transmission grating having 6000 lines/cm? (b) What is the second-order deviation of this wavelength? Assume normal incidence.

41–21. What is the longest wavelength that can be observed in the fourth order for a transmission grating having 5000 lines/cm? Assume normal incidence.

41–22. In Fig. 41–37, two point sources of light, a and b, at a distance of 50 m from lens L and 6 mm apart, produce images at

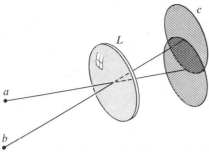

Figure 41–37

c which are just resolved by Rayleigh's criterion. The focal length of the lens is 20 cm. What is the diameter of the diffraction circles at *c*?

41–23. A telescope is used to observe two distant point sources 1 foot apart. (λ = 500 nm.) The objective of the telescope is covered with a slit of width 1 mm. What is the maximum distance in feet at which the two sources may be distinguished as two?

CHAPTER 42

Polarization

42–1 Polarization

The phenomena of interference and diffraction can occur with any sort of waves, such as sound waves or surface waves on a liquid. In this chapter we consider some optical phenomena that depend not merely on the fact that light is a wave motion, but that the waves are *transverse*. These are called *polarization* effects. They can be observed only with transverse waves and cannot be duplicated with sound waves because the latter are longitudinal.

Let us recall for a moment the nature of the electromagnetic waves radiated by a radio antenna, as described in Section 36–7. Suppose the antenna is vertical, and we consider a portion of a wavefront in a vertical plane and not too near the antenna, as in Fig. 42–1. The electric field intensity **E** at all points of this wavefront is in a vertical direction, as indicated. If in the wavefront in the diagram the electric intensity is a maximum in the upward direction, then in wavefronts one-half a wavelength ahead of or behind this one the intensity is a maximum in a downward direction. At all points of any plane fixed in space, the electric vector oscillates up and down along a vertical line and the wave is said to be *linearly* polarized. (Waves of this sort are also described as plane polarized, or merely as polarized.)

To avoid confusion, the magnetic intensity **H** is not shown in Fig. 42–1. It is always at right angles to the electric intensity **E**.

The "antennas" that radiate light waves are the molecules of which light sources are composed. The electrically charged particles in the molecules acquire energy in some way, and radiate this energy as electromagnetic waves of short wavelength. Presumably the waves from any one molecule are linearly polarized, like those from a radio antenna. But since any actual light source contains a tremendous number of

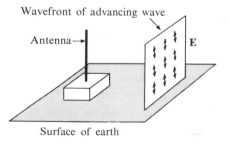

Fig. 42–1. The electromagnetic waves radiated by an antenna are linearly polarized.

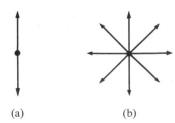

(a) (b)

Fig. 42–2. Schematic diagrams of (a) linearly polarized light, and (b) ordinary light.

molecules, oriented at random, the light emitted is a mixture of waves linearly polarized in all possible transverse directions. Let the plane of the diagram in Fig. 42–2(a)
represent a wavefront in a beam of light advancing toward the reader, and the dot an
end view of one ray in this beam. A linearly polarized light wave is represented
schematically by the double arrow, which indicates that the electric field oscillates in
the vertical direction only. A beam of natural light is represented as in part (b), in
which the arrows indicate a mixture of waves, linearly polarized in all possible transverse directions.

42–2 Polarization by reflection

There are a number of methods by which the vibrations in one particular direction
can be "sorted out," in whole or in part, from a beam of natural light. One of these
is the familiar process of reflection. When natural light strikes a reflecting surface,
there is found to be a preferential reflection for those waves in which the electric
vector is vibrating perpendicular to the plane of incidence. (The plane of incidence is
the plane containing the incident ray and the normal to the surface. See Fig. 42–3.)
An exception is that at normal incidence all directions of polarization are reflected
equally. At one particular angle of incidence, known as the *polarizing angle*, ϕ_p, no
light whatever is reflected except that in which the electric vector is perpendicular
to the plane of incidence. This case is illustrated in Fig. 42–3.

The situation depicted in Fig. 42–3 calls for somewhat more explanation. The
heavy double arrow lettered E in Fig. 42–4 represents the amplitude of the electric
field in a linearly polarized wave advancing toward the reader, the direction of vibration making an angle θ with the x-axis. This wave can be resolved into two component

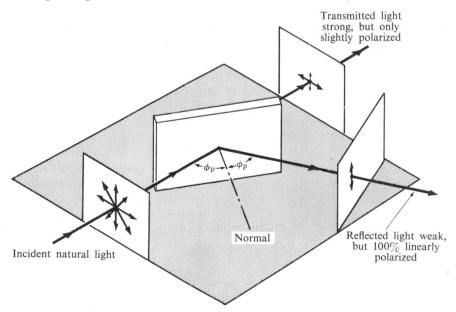

Fig. 42–3. When light is incident at the polarizing angle, the reflected light is linearly
polarized.

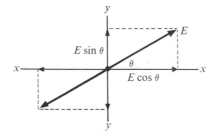

Fig. 42–4. Linearly polarized light resolved into two linearly polarized components.

waves (that is, it is equivalent to these two waves) linearly polarized along the x- and y-axes, and of amplitudes $E \cos \theta$ and $E \sin \theta$. In the same way, each linearly polarized component in the incident beam of natural light in Fig. 42–3, as represented by the "star" of vectors, can be resolved into two components, one perpendicular and the other parallel to the plane of incidence.

We can describe the reflection of light at the surface by stating what happens to each component of an arbitrary linearly polarized wave in the incident light. When incident at the polarizing angle, *none* of the components parallel to the plane of incidence is reflected; that is, each is 100% transmitted in the *refracted* beam. Of the components perpendicular to the plane of incidence, about 15% are reflected if the reflecting surface is glass. (The fraction reflected depends on the index of the reflecting material.) Hence the *reflected* light is weak and *completely* linearly polarized. The *refracted* light is a mixture of the parallel components, all of which are refracted, and the remaining 85% of the perpendicular component. It is therefore strong, but only *partially* polarized.

At angles of incidence other than the polarizing angle some of the components parallel to the plane of incidence are reflected, so that except at the polarizing angle the reflected light is not completely linearly polarized.

To increase the intensity of the reflected light, a pile of thin glass plates is often used. Due to the many rays reflected at the polarizing angle from the various surfaces, there is not only an increase in intensity of the reflected light, but also an increase in the polarization of the transmitted light, which now contains much less of the perpendicular component.

In 1812, Sir David Brewster noticed that when the angle of incidence became equal to ϕ_p, the reflected ray and the refracted ray were perpendicular to each other, as shown in Fig. 42–5. When this is the case, the angle of refraction ϕ' becomes the complement of ϕ_p, so that $\sin \phi' = \cos \phi_p$. Since $n \sin \phi_p = n' \sin \phi'$, we get

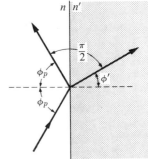

$$n \sin \phi_p = n' \cos \phi_p,$$

and

$$\tan \phi_p = \frac{n'}{n}, \qquad (42\text{--}1)$$

a relation known as *Brewster's law*.

Fig. 42–5. At the polarizing angle the reflected and transmitted rays are perpendicular to each other.

42–3 Double refraction

The progress of a wave train through a homogeneous isotropic medium, such as glass, may be determined graphically by Huygens' construction. The secondary wavelets in such a medium are spherical surfaces. There exist, however, many transparent crystalline substances which, while homogeneous, are *anisotropic*. That is, the velocity of a light wave in them is not the same in all directions. Crystals having this property are said to be *doubly refracting*, or *birefringent*. *Two* sets of Huygens wavelets propagate from every wave surface in such a crystal, one set being spherical and the other ellipsoidal. The two sets are tangent to each other in one direction, called the *optic axis* of the crystal.

Figure 42–6(a) shows the traces of the Huygens wavelets from a point source O within a doubly refracting crystal. The complete wave surfaces are obtained by rotating the diagram about axis AA. The direction of line AOA is the optic axis. (The optic axis is a *direction* in the crystal, not just one line. Any other line parallel to AOA is also an optic axis.)

Parts (b), (c), and (d) of Fig. 42–6 show the wavefronts in three sections cut from the crystal in different directions, when light is incident normally on the surface of the section. It will be seen that two sets of wavefronts travel through the crystal, one formed by the tangents to the spheres and the other by the tangents to the ellipsoids.

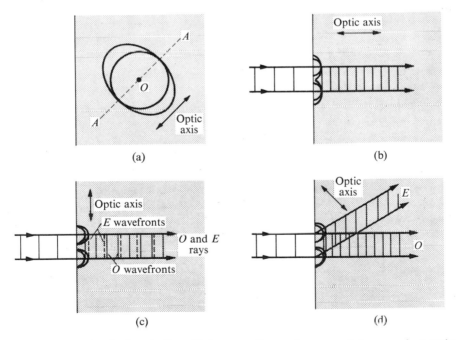

(a) (b)

(c) (d)

Fig. 42–6. (a) Spherical and ellipsoidal waves diverge from a point source in a uniaxial crystal. (b) In the direction of the optic axis there is no distinction between O- and E-beams. (c) Perpendicular to the optic axis there is the maximum difference in the speed and the wavelength of the O- and E-beams. (d) At an arbitrary angle to the optic axis the O- and E-beams differ in direction, speed, and wavelength.

TABLE 42–1

INDICES OF REFRACTION OF DOUBLY REFRACTING CRYSTALS

(For light of wavelength 589 nm)

Material	n_O	n_E
Calcite	1.6583	1.4864
Quartz	1.544	1.553
Tourmaline	1.64	1.62
Ice	1.306	1.307

It may be seen in Fig. 42–6(d) that a ray incident normally is broken up into two rays in traversing the crystal. The ray which corresponds to wave surfaces tangent to the spherical wavelets is undeviated and is called the *ordinary ray*. The ray corresponding to the wave surfaces tangent to the ellipsoids is deviated even though the incident ray is normal to the surface, and is called the *extraordinary ray*. If the crystal is rotated about the incident ray as an axis, the ordinary ray remains fixed but the extraordinary ray revolves around it, as shown in Fig. 42–7. Furthermore, for angles of incidence other than 0°, Snell's law (i.e., $\sin\phi/\sin\phi' = $ constant) holds for the ordinary but not for the extraordinary ray, since evidently the velocity of the latter is different in different directions.

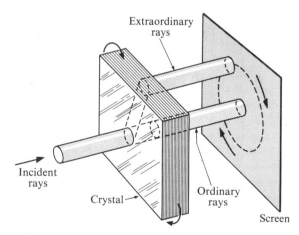

Fig. 42–7. A narrow beam of natural light can be split into two beams by a doubly refracting crystal.

The index of refraction for the extraordinary ray is therefore a function of direction. It is customary to state the index for the direction at right angles to the optic axis, in which the velocity is a maximum or a minimum. Some values of n_O and n_E, the indices for the ordinary and extraordinary rays, are listed in Table 42–1.

Figure 42–6 is drawn for a crystal in which the velocity of the ellipsoidal waves is greater than that of the spherical waves, except in the direction of the optic axis. In some crystals the velocity of the ellipsoidal waves is less than that of the spherical waves except along the optic axis, where the two are equal. Both this type of crystal and that described above are called *uniaxial*. In some crystals there are two different directions in which the velocities are equal. These crystals are called *biaxial*, but since all of the doubly refracting crystals used in optical instruments (chiefly quartz and calcite) are uniaxial, we shall concentrate on this type.

42–4 Polarization by double refraction

Experiment shows that the ordinary and extraordinary waves in a doubly refracting crystal are linearly polarized in mutually perpendicular directions. Consequently, if some means can be found to separate one wave from the other, a doubly refracting crystal may be used to obtain linearly polarized light from natural light. There are a number of ways in which this separation may be accomplished.

One method of separating the two components is by means of a *Nicol prism* or one of its modifications. The Nicol prism is a crystal of Iceland spar or calcite ($CaCO_3$), whose natural shape is shown by the full lines in Fig. 42–8(a). To make a Nicol prism, the end faces of the crystal are cut at a more obtuse angle, as shown by the dotted lines. The crystal is then cut along the shorter diagonal $b'd'$ and cemented together again with Canada balsam. The index of Canada balsam has such a value that the ordinary ray is totally reflected, while the extraordinary ray is transmitted as in Fig. 42–8(b).

Certain doubly refracting crystals exhibit *dichroism;* that is, one of the polarized components is absorbed much more strongly than the other. Hence if the crystal is cut of the proper thickness, one of the components is practically extinguished by absorption, while the other is transmitted in appreciable amount, as indicated in Fig. 42–9. Tourmaline is one example of such a dichroic crystal.

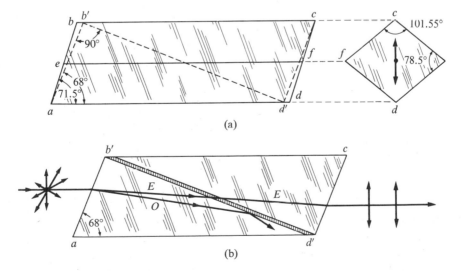

Fig. 42–8. (a) Natural crystal of Iceland spar. (b) A Nicol prism.

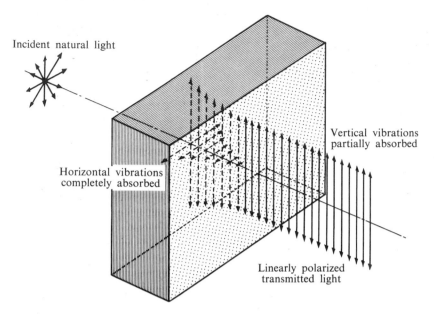

Incident natural light

Vertical vibrations
partially absorbed

Horizontal vibrations
completely absorbed

Linearly polarized
transmitted light

Fig. 42–9.   Linearly polarized light transmitted by a dichroic crystal.

An early form of polaroid, invented by Edwin H. Land in 1928, consists of a thin layer of tiny needlelike dichroic crystals of herapathite (iodoquinine sulfate), in parallel orientation, embedded in a plastic matrix and enclosed for protection between two transparent plates. A more recent modification, developed by Land in 1938 and known as an *H*-sheet, is a molecular polarizer. It consists of long polymeric molecules of polyvinyl alcohol (PVA) that have been given a preferred direction by stretching, and have been stained with an ink containing iodine that causes the sheet to exhibit dichroism. The PVA sheet is laminated to a support sheet of cellulose acetate butyrate.

Polaroid does not polarize all wavelengths equally. When two polaroids are crossed, a small amount of red and of violet (the two ends of the visible spectrum) are transmitted. When white light passes through one polaroid, the transmitted light is slightly colored. The large area of such plates, however, and their moderate cost more than compensate for these small deficiencies. The existence of polaroid sheets has stimulated the development and applications of polarized light to an extent that was out of the question when reflecting surfaces, Nicol prisms, and other costly devices had to be used.

42–5 Percentage polarization.   Malus' law

When light is incident on a polarizer, as in Fig. 42–10, linear light only is transmitted. The polarizer may be a pile of plates, a Nicol prism, or a sheet of polaroid. It is represented as a polaroid disk in Fig. 42–10. The dotted line across the polarizer indicates the direction of the electric vector in the transmitted light. The transmitted light falls on a photocell, and the current in a microammeter connected to the cell is proportional to the quantity of light incident on it.

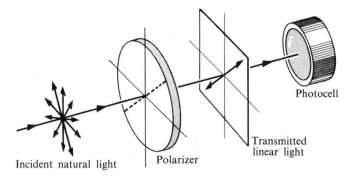

Fig. 42–10.   The intensity of the transmitted linear light is the same at all azimuths of the polarizer.

If the incident light is unpolarized, then as the polarizer is rotated about the incident ray as an axis, the reading of the microammeter remains constant. The polarizer transmits the components of the incident waves in which the E-vector is parallel to the transmission direction of the polarizer, and by symmetry the components are equal for all azimuths.

If there is any variation in the meter reading as the polarizer is rotated, the incident light is not natural light and is said to be *partially* polarized. (But just what kind of light it is cannot be determined from this experiment alone.) Suppose the meter reading does vary. Let I_{max} and I_{min} represent the maximum and minimum values of the quantity of light incident on the photocell, or the maximum and minimum meter readings, since the two are proportional. The *percentage polarization* of the incident light is defined as

$$\text{Percent polarization} = \frac{I_{max} - I_{min}}{I_{max} + I_{min}} \times 100. \qquad (42\text{–}2)$$

Suppose now that a second polaroid is inserted in the light between polarizer and photocell, as in Fig. 42–11. Let the transmission direction of the second polaroid, or

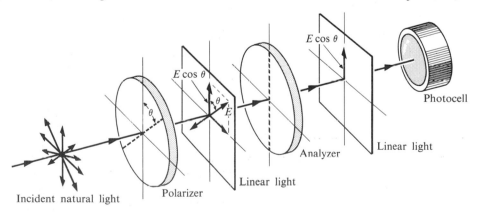

Fig. 42–11. The analyzer transmits only that component of the linear light parallel to its transmission direction.

analyzer, be vertical, and let that of the polarizer make an angle θ with the vertical. The linear light transmitted by the polarizer may be resolved into two components as shown, one parallel and the other perpendicular to the transmission direction of the analyzer. Evidently only the parallel component, of amplitude $E \cos \theta$, will be transmitted by the analyzer. The transmitted light is a maximum when $\theta = 0$, and is zero when $\theta = 90°$, or when polarizer and analyzer are *crossed*. At intermediate angles, since the quantity of energy is proportional to the square of the amplitude, we have

$$I = I_{\max} \cos^2 \theta, \tag{42–3}$$

where $I_{\max}$ is the maximum amount of light transmitted and I is the amount transmitted at the angle θ. This relation, which was discovered experimentally by Etienne Louis Malus in 1809, is called *Malus' law*.

Evidently, the significance of the angle θ, in general, is the angle between the transmission directions of polarizer and analyzer. If either the analyzer or the polarizer is rotated, the amplitude of the transmitted beam varies with the angle between them according to Eq. (42–3).

Polaroid is now widely used in "sun glasses" where, from the standpoint of its polarizing properties, it plays the role of the analyzer in Fig. 42–11. We have seen that when unpolarized light is reflected, there is a preferential reflection for light polarized perpendicular to the plane of incidence. When sunlight is reflected from a horizontal surface, the plane of incidence is vertical. Hence in the reflected light there is a preponderance of light polarized in the horizontal direction, the proportion being greater the nearer the angle of incidence is to the polarizing angle. The transmission direction of the polaroid in the sun glasses is vertical, so none of the horizontally polarized light is transmitted.

Apart from this polarizing feature, these glasses serve the same purpose as any dark glasses absorbing 50% of the incident light, since even in an unpolarized beam, half the light can be considered as polarized horizontally and half vertically. Only the vertically polarized light is transmitted.

42–6 The scattering of light

The sky is blue. Sunsets are red. Skylight is largely linearly polarized, as can readily be verified by looking at the sky directly overhead through a polarizing plate. It turns out that one and the same phenomenon is responsible for all three of the effects noted above.

In Fig. 42–12, sunlight (unpolarized) comes from the left along the z-axis and passes over an observer looking vertically upward along the y-axis. One of the molecules of the earth's atmosphere is located at point O. The electric field in the beam of sunlight sets the electric charges in the molecule in vibration. Since light is a transverse wave, the direction of the electric field in any component of the sunlight lies in the xy-plane and the motion of the charges takes place in this plane. There is no field, and hence no vibration, in the direction of the z-axis.

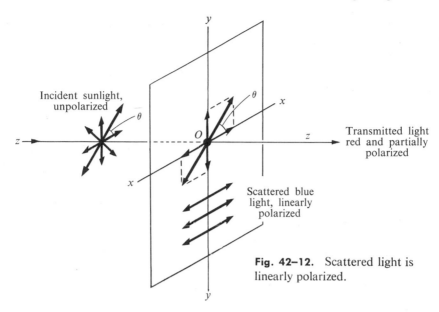

Fig. 42–12. Scattered light is linearly polarized.

An arbitrary component of the incident light, vibrating at an angle θ with the x-axis, sets the electric charges in the molecule vibrating in the same direction, as indicated by the heavy line through point O. In the usual way, we can resolve this vibration into two, one along the x- and the other along the y-axis. The result, then, is that each component in the incident light produces the equivalent of two molecular "antennas," oscillating with the frequency of the incident light, and lying along the x- and y-axes.

It has been explained in Section 36–7 that an antenna does not radiate in the direction of its own length. Hence the antenna along the y-axis does not send any light to the observer directly below it. It does, of course, send out light in other directions. The only light reaching the observer comes from the component of vibration along the x-axis and, as is the case with the waves from any antenna, this light is linearly polarized, with the electric field parallel to the antenna. The vectors on the y-axis below point O show the direction of vibration of the light reaching the observer.

The process described above is called *scattering*. The energy of the scattered light is abstracted from the original beam, which becomes weakened in the process.

The vibration of the charges in the molecule is a *forced* vibration, like the vibration of a mass on a spring when the upper end of the spring is moved up and down with simple harmonic motion. It is well known that the amplitude of the forced vibrations is greater, the closer the driving frequency approaches the natural frequency of vibration of the spring-mass system. Now the natural frequency of the electric charges in a molecule is the same as that of wavelengths in the ultraviolet. The frequencies of the waves in visible light are less than the natural frequency, but the higher their frequency, or the shorter their wavelength, the closer is the driving frequency to the natural frequency, the greater the amplitude of vibration, and the greater the intensity of the scattered light. In other words, blue light is scattered more than red, with the result that the hue of the scattered light is blue.

Toward evening, when sunlight has to travel a large distance through the earth's atmosphere to reach a point over or nearly over an observer, a large proportion of the blue light in sunlight is removed from it by scattering. White light minus blue light is yellow or red in hue. Thus when sunlight, with the blue component removed, is incident on a cloud, the light reflected from the cloud to the observer has the yellow or red hue so commonly seen at sunset.

From the explanation above, it follows that if the earth had no atmosphere we would receive no skylight at the earth's surface, and the sky would appear as black in the daytime as it does at night. This conclusion is borne out by observations at high altitudes, where there is less atmosphere above the observer.

42–7 Circular and elliptic polarization

Linearly polarized light represents a special and relatively simple type of polarization. When the ordinary and extraordinary rays in a doubly refracting crystal are separated, each ray taken alone is linearly polarized, but with the directions of vibration at right angles. When, however, the crystal is cut with its faces parallel to the optic axis, so that light, incident normally on one of its faces, traverses the crystal in a direction perpendicular to the optic axis, as shown in Fig. 42–6(c), the ordinary and extraordinary rays are not separated. *They traverse the same path, but with different speeds.* Upon emerging from the second face of the crystal, the ordinary and extraordinary rays are out of phase with each other and give rise to either elliptically polarized, circularly polarized, or linearly polarized light, depending upon a number of factors which we shall proceed to discuss now.

Since in the ordinary ray the direction of vibration is perpendicular to that in the extraordinary ray, we have to consider a fundamental problem which, for the sake of simplicity, may be discussed in mechanical terms: What sort of vibration results from the combination of two simple harmonic vibrations at right angles to each other and differing in phase? The solution may be reached in a variety of ways: (1) with the aid of mechanical equipment, (2) by using two rotor diagrams for plotting two simple harmonic motions at right angles, (3) by establishing alternating potential differences on the horizontal and vertical plates of a cathode-ray oscilloscope, and (4) by mathematical calculation (see Problem 42–16).

In Fig. 42–13 are shown the results obtained by combining a horizontal and a vertical simple harmonic motion of the same frequency and the same amplitude, for nine different phase differences. It is at once evident that *two simple harmonic motions*

0	$\frac{\pi}{4}$	$\frac{\pi}{2}$	$\frac{3\pi}{4}$	π	$\frac{5\pi}{4}$	$\frac{3\pi}{2}$	$\frac{7\pi}{4}$	2π

Fig. 42–13. Vibrations which result from the combination of a horizontal and a vertical simple harmonic motion of the same frequency and the same amplitude, for various values of the phase difference.

at right angles to each other never produce destructive interference, no matter what the phase difference.

1. When the phase difference is 0, 2π, or any even multiple of π, the result is a linear vibration at 45° to both original vibrations.

2. When the phase difference is π, 3π, or any odd multiple of π, the result is also a linear vibration, but at right angles to those corresponding to even multiples of π.

3. When the phase difference is $\pi/2$, $3\pi/2$, or any odd multiple of $\pi/2$, the resulting vibration is a circle.

4. At all other phase differences, the resulting vibration is an ellipse.

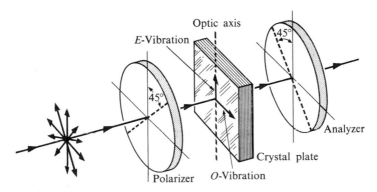

Fig. 42–14. Crystal plate between crossed polaroids. Since the optic axis makes an angle of 45° to the vibration direction of the linearly polarized light transmitted by the polarizer, the amplitudes of the *O*- and *E*-vibrations in the crystal are equal.

With these facts in mind, consider the optical apparatus shown in Fig. 42–14. After unpolarized light traverses the polarizer, it is linearly polarized, with the vibration direction along the dotted line drawn on the polarizer. This linear light then enters a crystal plate cut so that the light travels in a direction perpendicular to the optic axis. The crystal plate has been rotated about the light beam until the optic axis makes an angle of 45° with the direction of vibration of the linear light incident upon it. Since the *E*-vibration is, in this case, parallel to the optic axis, and the *O*-vibration is perpendicular to it, it follows that the amplitudes of the *E*- and *O*-beams are identical. The *E*- and *O*-beams travel through the crystal along the same path but with different speeds and, as they are about to emerge from the second crystal face, they combine to form one of the vibrations depicted in Fig. 42–13, depending on the phase difference.

The phase difference between the *E*- and *O*-vibrations at the second face of the crystal depends on the following: (1) the frequency of the light, (2) the indices of refraction of the crystal for *E*- and *O*-light, (3) the thickness of the crystal.

If a given crystal has such a thickness as to give rise to a phase difference of $\pi/2$ for a given frequency, then, according to Fig. 42–13, a circular vibration results and the light emerging from this crystal is said to be *circularly polarized light*. The crystal itself is called a *quarter-wave plate*. If the crystal plate shown in Fig. 42–14 is a quarter-wave plate, the intensity of light transmitted by the analyzer will remain constant as the analyzer is rotated. In other words, if an analyzer alone is used to analyze circularly polarized light, it will give the same result as when used to analyze unpolarized light.

A quarter-wave plate for, say, green light is not a quarter-wave plate for any other color. Other colors have different frequencies and different E- and O-indices. Hence the phase difference would not be $\pi/2$. (See Problem 42–13.)

If the crystal has such a thickness as to give rise to a phase difference of π for a given frequency, then, according to Fig. 42–13, a linear vibration perpendicular to the incident vibration direction results. The light that emerges from this crystal is linearly polarized and, by rotating the analyzer, a position of the analyzer may be found at which this light will be completely stopped. A crystal plate of this sort is called a *half-wave plate* for the given frequency of light. For any other frequency it would not be a half-wave plate.

If the phase difference produced by a crystal plate is such as to produce an elliptical vibration, the emerging light is said to be *elliptically polarized*.

42–8 Production of colors by polarized light

Consider, for the sake of definiteness, a crystal plate which is a half-wave plate for red light. If red light, linearly polarized at 45° to the optic axis, is allowed to traverse the plate, it will emerge from the plate as linearly polarized light with the vibration direction perpendicular to that of the incident light. An analyzer which is crossed with the polarizer will therefore transmit this red light.

Now suppose the incident radiation is *white* light. Only the red component of the white light will emerge from the half-wave plate as linearly polarized light. All the other wavelengths will emerge as either elliptically or circularly polarized light. When the analyzer is in a position to transmit the red, linearly polarized light completely, it will cut out a small amount of all the other wavelengths. The light transmitted by the analyzer will therefore predominate in red, and will have a pinkish hue. When the analyzer is rotated through 90°, so as to cut the red light out completely, the other wavelengths will be transmitted to some extent and the resulting hue will be the complement of pink, that is, a blue-green.

Now suppose that we have a crystal plate of nonuniform thickness, such as a rough strip of selenite (gypsum). A small piece of the strip may have the proper thickness to act as a half-wave plate for red light, another piece may serve as a half-wave plate for yellow light, and so on. When a projecting lens is used to project an image of the selenite on a screen, the rest of the apparatus being the same as that in Fig. 42–14, the image will show patches of different colors, corresponding to regions of different thickness. These colors will change into the complementary values when the analyzer is rotated through 90°.

Ordinary cellophane, such as that used for wrapping cigarette packages, is doubly refracting. Striking color effects can be obtained by inserting various thicknesses of cellophane, or a crumpled ball of the material, between a polarizer and an analyzer.

42–9 Optical stress analysis.

When a polarizer and an analyzer are mounted in the "crossed" position, i.e., with their transmission directions at right angles to each other, no light is transmitted through the combination. But if a doubly refracting crystal is inserted between polarizer and analyzer, the light after passing through the crystal is, in general, elliptically polarized, and some light will be transmitted by the analyzer. Thus the field of view, dark in the absence of the crystal, becomes light when the crystal is inserted.

Some substances, such as glass, celluloid, and Bakelite, while not normally doubly refracting, become so when subjected to mechanical stress. From a study of the specimen between crossed polaroids, much information regarding the stresses can be obtained. Improperly annealed glass, for example, may be internally stressed to an extent which might cause it later to develop cracks. It is evidently important that optical glass should be free from such a condition before it is subjected to expensive grinding and polishing. Hence such glass is always examined between crossed polaroids before grinding operations are begun.

The double refraction produced by stress is the basis of the science of *photoelasticity*. The stresses in opaque engineering materials, such as girders, boiler plates, gear teeth, etc., can be analyzed by constructing a transparent model of the object, usually of a plastic, and examining it between crossed polaroids. Very complicated stress distributions, such as those around a hole or a gear tooth, which it would be practically impossible to analyze mathematically, may thus be studied by optical methods. Figure 42–15 is a photograph of a photoelastic model under stress.

Liquids are not normally doubly refracting, but some become so when an electric field is established within them. This phenomenon is known as the *Kerr effect*. The existence of the Kerr effect makes it possible to construct an electrically controlled "light valve." A cell with transparent walls contains the liquid between a pair of parallel plates. The cell is inserted between crossed polaroids. Light is transmitted when an electric field is set up between the plates and is cut off when the field is removed.

Fig. 42–15. Photoelastic stress analysis. (Courtesy of Dr. W. M. Murray, M.I.T.)

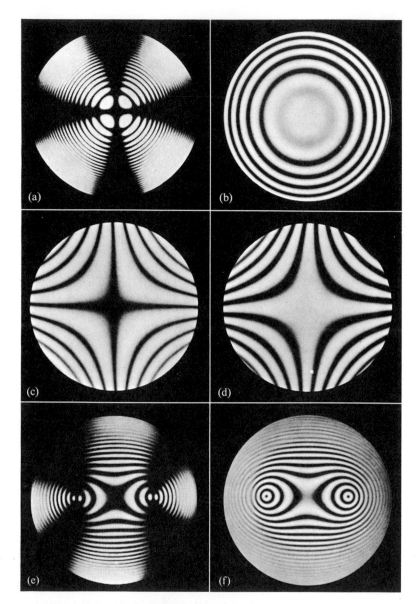

Fig. 42–16. Figures obtained with convergent polarized light. (a) Uniaxial crystal cut perpendicular to the optic axis, crossed polaroids. (b) Same crystal, parallel polaroids, with quarter-wave plates to eliminate brushes. (c) Uniaxial crystal cut parallel to the optic axis, crossed polaroids. (d) Same crystal, parallel polaroids. (e) Biaxial crystal, crossed polaroids. (f) Same crystal with quarter-wave plates to eliminate brushes. (Photographed by H. Hauswaldt, Magdeburg, 1902.)

42–10 Study of crystals by convergent polarized light

Polarized light is used extensively in the field of mineralogy. A transparent specimen of rock or crystal is cut into a thin plate and mounted on the stage of a *polarizing microscope*, which has a polarizer below the substage condenser and an analyzer above the objective lens. The substage condenser serves to converge the polarized light onto the specimen, from which it diverges to the objective lens. When monochromatic light is used, the image formed in the focal plane of the objective is found to have a pattern which indicates whether (a) the crystal is uniaxial or biaxial, (b) if uniaxial, where the optic axis is, and (c) if biaxial, the angle between the optic axes. Some of the polarization figures obtained with convergent polarized light are shown in Fig. 42–16. If white light is used, these patterns are brilliantly colored.

The figure obtained with a uniaxial crystal cut with its faces perpendicular to the optic axis consists of concentric colored rings, and when the polarizer and analyzer are crossed, a black cross is superimposed on the rings. The elements of the black cross are called brushes. When circularly polarized light is used, the cross may be eliminated.

Polarizing ring sights are constructed from a plate of crystal, two polaroids, two quarter-wave plates, and two protecting plates of glass. When mounted on a gun perpendicular to the barrel and viewed with the eye, colored rings appear in space and move with the gun. Aiming the gun is accomplished by getting the target within the center of the ring system.

42–11 Optical activity

When a beam of linearly polarized light is sent through certain types of crystals and certain liquids, the direction of vibration of the emerging linearly polarized light is found to be different from the original direction. This phenomenon is called *rotation of the plane of polarization*, and substances which exhibit the effect are called *optically active*. Those which rotate the plane of polarization to the right, looking along the advancing beam, are called dextrorotatory or right-handed; those which rotate it to the left, laevorotatory or left-handed.

Optical activity may be due to an asymmetry of the molecules of a substance, or it may be a property of a crystal as a whole. For example, solutions of cane sugar are dextrorotatory, indicating that the optical activity is a property of the sugar molecule. The rotation of the plane of polarization by a sugar solution is used commercially as a method of determining the proportion of cane sugar in a given sample. Crystalline quartz is also optically active, some natural crystals being right-handed and others left-handed. Here the optical activity is a consequence of the crystalline structure, since it disappears when the quartz is melted and allowed to resolidify into a glassy noncrystalline state called fused quartz.

Problems

42–1. A beam of light is incident on a liquid of 1.40 refractive index. The reflected rays are completely polarized. What is the angle of refraction of the beam?

42–2. The critical angle of light in a certain substance is 45°. What is the polarizing angle?

42–3. (a) At what angle above the horizontal must the sun be in order that sunlight reflected from the surface of a calm body of water shall be completely polarized? (b) What is the plane of the E-vector in the reflected light?

42–4. A parallel beam of "natural" light is incident at an angle of 58° on a plane glass surface. The reflected beam is completely linearly polarized. (a) What is the angle of refraction of the transmitted beam? (b) What is the refractive index of the glass?

42–5. Canada balsam has a refractive index of 1.528. What is the minimum angle of incidence that the ordinary ray may make with the Canada balsam layer of a Nicol prism to be totally reflected at this layer?

42–6. A parallel beam of linearly polarized light of wavelength 589 nm (in vacuum) is incident on a calcite crystal as in Fig. 42–6(c). Find the wavelengths of the ordinary and extraordinary waves in the crystal.

42–7. A polarizer and an analyzer are oriented so that the maximum amount of light is transmitted. To what fraction of its maximum value is the intensity of the transmitted light reduced when the analyzer is rotated through (a) 30°, (b) 45°, (c) 60°?

42–8. A beam of linearly polarized light strikes a calcite crystal, the direction of the electric vector making an angle of 60° with the optic axis. (a) What is the ratio of the amplitude of the two refracted beams? (b) What is the ratio of their intensities?

42–9. Refer to Table 42–1 and draw Fig. 42–6(a), (c), and (d) for quartz.

42–10. Figure 42–17 represents a Wollaston prism made of two prisms of quartz cemented together. The optic axis of the right-hand prism is perpendicular to the page, whereas that of the left-hand prism is parallel. The incident light is normal to the surface and gives rise to O- and E-beams which travel in the left-hand prism along the same path but with different speeds. Copy Fig. 42–17 and show on your diagram how the O- and E-beams are bent in going into the right-hand prism and thence into the air.

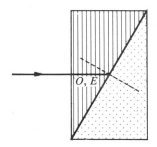

Figure 42–17

42–11. A beam of light, after passing through the Nicol prism N_1 in Fig. 42–18, traverses a cell containing a scattering medium. The cell is observed at right angles through another Nicol, N_2. Originally, the Nicols are oriented until the brightness of the field seen by the observer is a maximum. (a) Prism N_2 is rotated through 90°. Is

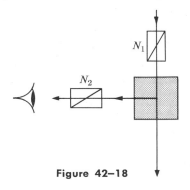

Figure 42–18

extinction produced? (b) Prism N_1 is now rotated through 90°. Is the field bright or dark? (c) Prism N_2 is then restored to its original position. Is the field bright or dark?

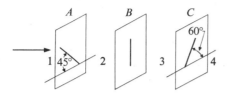

Figure 42–19

42–12. In Fig. 42–19, A and C are sheets of polaroid whose transmission directions are as indicated. B is a sheet of doubly refractive material whose optic axis is vertical. All three sheets are parallel. Unpolarized light enters from the left. Discuss the state of polarization of the light at points 2, 3, and 4.

42–13. The phase difference δ between the E- and O-rays after traversing a crystal plate such as that in Fig. 42–14 is given by

$$\delta = \frac{2\pi}{\lambda} t(n_O - n_E),$$

where λ is the wavelength in air and t is the thickness of the crystal. (a) Show that the minimum thickness of a quarter-wave plate is given by $t = \lambda/4(n_O - n_E)$. (b) What is this minimum thickness for a quarter-wave calcite plate and light of 400 nm wavelength?

42–14. What is the state of polarization of the light transmitted by a quarter-wave plate when the electric vector of the incident linearly polarized light makes an angle of 30° with the optic axis?

42–15. Assume the values of n_O and n_E for quartz to be independent of wavelength. A certain quartz crystal is a quarter-wave plate for light of wavelength 800 nm (in vacuum). What is the state of polarization of the transmitted light when linearly polarized light of wavelength 400 nm (in vacuum) is incident on the crystal, the direction of polarization making an angle of 45° with the optic axis?

42–16. Consider two vibrations, one along the y-axis, $y = a \sin(\omega t - \alpha)$, and the other along the z-axis of equal amplitude and frequency, but differing in phase, $z = a \sin(\omega t - \beta)$. Let us write them as follows:

$$\frac{y}{a} = \sin \omega t \cos \alpha - \cos \omega t \sin \alpha, \quad (1)$$

$$\frac{z}{a} = \sin \omega t \cos \beta - \cos \omega t \sin \beta. \quad (2)$$

(a) Multiply Eq. (1) by $\sin \beta$ and Eq. (2) by $\sin \alpha$ and then subtract the resulting equations. (b) Multiply Eq. (1) by $\cos \beta$ and Eq. (2) by $\cos \alpha$ and then subtract the resulting equations. (c) Square and add the results of (a) and (b). (d) Derive the equation $y^2 + z^2 - 2yz \cos \delta = a^2 \sin^2 \delta$, where $\delta = \alpha - \beta$. (e) Justify the diagrams in Fig. 42–13.

CHAPTER 43

Atoms, Electrons, and Photons

43-1 Conduction in gases

Unlike a metal or an electrolyte, a gas free from external influences contains no free charges to serve as carriers in an electric field. Gases may be rendered conducting, however, in a variety of ways, in all of which some of the molecules become ionized by the detachment of one or more of their outer electrons. Some of these electrons may then attach themselves to neutral molecules, forming negative ions, so that in an ionized gas both positive and negative ions and free electrons are usually present.

In order to ionize a molecule, energy must be supplied to it in some way. This may come about as a result of a collision with a rapidly moving molecule, ion, or electron, or by interaction with a quantum of radiation (a photon). Some common ionizing agents are cosmic rays, radioactive emanations, photons, x-rays, electrons, positive ions, and high-speed atoms.

Ionization by collision is the chief means of producing ions in most instances of gaseous conduction. Positive and negative ions and electrons are accelerated by the electric field in the gas and may acquire sufficient energy to ionize a neutral molecule when a collision takes place. A current in a gas is referred to as a *discharge*.

The type of discharge in a neon sign and a fluorescent lamp is called a *glow discharge*. Glow discharges take place at pressures of a few millimeters of mercury. Figure 43-1 represents a tube with electrodes sealed in at its ends and containing a gas at low pressure. Because of the few ions formed by cosmic rays or other means, the gas will be very slightly conducting even at low voltages. When the critical voltage is reached, the current increases very rapidly and the gas in the tube becomes luminous, whence the term "glow discharge."

A marked difference in the appearance of the gas near the cathode and anode will be noted after the glow discharge sets in. The surface of the cathode is covered with

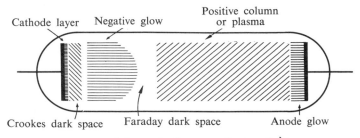

Fig. 43-1. Schematic diagram of a gas discharge.

a thin layer of luminous gas called the *cathode layer*. Immediately beyond it is a relatively nonluminous region called the *Crookes dark space* (after Sir William Crookes, one of the early workers in this field). Beyond the Crookes dark space is a second luminous region, blue if the discharge is in air, called the *negative glow*. Following this is another relatively dark region, the *Faraday dark space*, and beyond this is the *positive column* or *plasma*, which occupies the remainder of the tube. When the pressure is reduced to about 0.1 mm, the positive column is often broken up into alternating luminous and nonluminous portions called *striations*. Most of the light emitted by the gas comes from the positive column.

The electrical phenomena whose study constituted the beginning of modern atomic physics take place when the gas pressure is reduced to about 0.001 mm. At this pressure the positive column and the negative glow disappear but the inner walls of the discharge tube itself start to glow with a greenish fluorescence. An obstacle such as a metal disk placed between the negative electrode and the glass wall opposite casts a sharp shadow and indicates that something is emitted by the negative electrode. What were originally called cathode rays are now known to be electrons, and an account of the measurements of J. J. Thomson and of Millikan of the electronic charge and mass has been given in Chapter 30.

Electrons are produced occasionally even today by a gaseous discharge at low pressure. The disadvantage of this method lies in the fact that it is difficult to control and vary independently the number of electrons emitted per second and the velocity of the electrons. Both of these quantities increase, as a rule, when the voltage is raised. A more convenient method of generating electrons whose rate of production and velocity are independently controllable is provided by the Edison effect, described in the next section.

43–2 Thermionic emission

During the course of his experiments on electric light bulbs, Thomas Edison, in 1883, observed a phenomenon which is fundamental to the science known today as *electronics*. A glassblower had sealed into the bulb of an ordinary filament lamp an extra metal electrode or plate, shown in Fig. 43–2. The glass bulb was then exhausted and the filament was heated as usual. When the plate was connected through a galvanometer to the positive terminal of the 110-volt DC source, a galvanometer deflection indicated the existence of a current, whereas no appreciable current existed when the

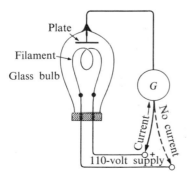

Fig. 43–2. Edison's original experiment.

plate was connected to the negative terminal. Edison paid great attention to this effect but neither he nor anyone else at the time could explain it.

The explanation of the Edison effect is as follows. Electrons are liberated (or evaporated) from the hot filament and are attracted to a positively charged plate, but repelled by a negatively charged one. The liberation of electrons from a hot wire is called *thermionic emission* or the *thermionic effect*. There is a certain minimum energy, different for different metals, which an electron must have in order to be able to get out of the metal. At low temperatures very few electrons have this amount of energy, but as the temperature is raised the energies of the electrons increase and the number capable of escaping increases rapidly.

The escape of electrons from the surface of an isolated metallic conductor leaves the conductor positively charged. The electrons which have escaped are therefore attracted by the conductor and form a "cloud" of negative charge outside its surface. This cloud is called a *space charge*. If a second nearby conductor is at a higher potential than the first, the electrons in the cloud are attracted to it, and so long as the potential difference between the conductors is maintained there will be a steady drift of electrons from the emitter or *cathode* to the other body, which is called the plate or *anode*.

In the common thermionic tube the cathode and anode (and often other electrodes as well) are enclosed within an evacuated glass or metal container, and leads to the various electrodes are brought out through the base or walls of the tube. We shall first describe the characteristics of a simple thermionic tube in which the only electrodes are the cathode and anode. Such a tube is called a *diode*.

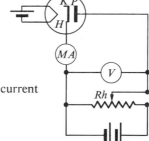

Fig. 43–3. Circuit for measuring plate current and plate voltage in a vacuum diode.

The diode is shown schematically in Fig. 43–3. The cathode and plate are represented by K and P. The cathode is often in the form of a hollow cylinder, which is heated by a fine resistance wire H within it. Electrons emitted from the outer surface of the cathode are attracted to the plate, which is a larger cylinder surrounding the cathode and coaxial with it. The electron current to the plate is read on the milliammeter MA. The potential difference between plate and cathode can be controlled by the slide wire and read on voltmeter V.

If the potential difference between cathode and anode is small (a few volts), only a few of the emitted electrons reach the plate, the majority penetrating a short distance

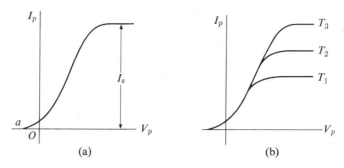

Fig. 43–4. (a) Plate current-plate voltage characteristic of a diode. (b) Plate current curves at three different cathode temperatures. $T_3 > T_2 > T_1$.

into the cloud of space charge and then returning to the cathode. As the plate potential is increased, more and more electrons are drawn to it, and with sufficiently high potentials (of the order of 100 volts), all of the emitted electrons arrive at the plate. Further increase of plate potential does not increase the plate current, which is then said to become *saturated*.

A graph of plate current, I_p, versus plate potential V_p is shown in Fig. 43–4(a). Note that I_p is not zero even when V_p is zero. This is because the electrons leave the cathode with an initial velocity and the more rapidly moving ones may penetrate the cloud of space charge and reach the plate even with no accelerating field. In fact, a *retarding* field is necessary to prevent their reaching the plate, an effect which may be used to measure their velocities of emission.

The saturation current I_s in Fig. 43–4(a) is equal to the current from the cathode, and for a given tube its magnitude depends markedly on the cathode temperature. Figure 43–4(b) shows three plate current curves at three different temperatures, where $T_3 > T_2 > T_1$. The relation between saturation current and temperature was first derived by O. E. Richardson and later in a slightly different form by S. Dushman. The Dushman equation is

$$J_s = AT^2 e^{-\phi/kT}, \tag{43–1}$$

where J_s is the saturation current density at the cathode surface, A is a constant characteristic of the emitting surface, T is the kelvin temperature of the emitter, k is the Boltzmann constant, and ϕ is the *work function* of the surface, a quantity related to the energy required for an electron to leave the surface.

The work function ϕ of a surface may be considerably reduced by the presence of impurities. A small amount of thorium, for example, reduces the work function of pure tungsten by about 50%. Since the smaller the work function the larger the current density at a given temperature (or the lower the temperature at which a given emission can be attained), most vacuum tubes now use cathodes having composite surfaces.

43-3 The triode

Lee de Forest, in 1907, discovered that if a third electrode, called a *grid*, is inserted between the cathode and plate of a thermionic tube, and is maintained at a *negative* potential with respect to the cathode, it draws a negligible current but its potential exerts much more control over the plate current than does the potential of the plate itself. The grid is usually an open mesh or a helix of fine wire which allows most of the electrons to pass through its openings. In the symbol for a triode, the grid is represented by a dashed line, as shown in Fig. 43–5.

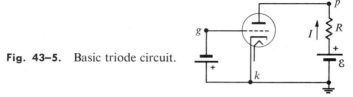

Fig. 43–5. Basic triode circuit.

Commercial tubes are invariably operated at potentials much lower than would be required to draw saturation currents. The currents to various electrodes cannot be represented by any simple equation and are best expressed by graphs. In particular, the current to an electrode is rarely a linear function of the potential of that electrode. The tube therefore does not obey Ohm's law and is a *nonlinear* circuit element. The plate current in a triode depends both on the plate potential and on the grid potential, and the curves in Fig. 43–6 give plate current as a function of plate potential (relative to the cathode), for various values of the grid potential (relative to the cathode).

The cathode of the triode in Fig. 43–5 is grounded so that its potential $V_k = 0$. The grid is maintained at a negative potential V_g by a battery, and a battery of emf ε and a resistor R are connected between plate and ground. The combination of plate battery and plate resistor is equivalent to a source of emf ε and internal resistance R, and the potential V_p of the plate is, therefore, $V_p = \varepsilon - IR$.

Suppose that $\varepsilon = 400$ volts and $R = 2000\ \Omega$. The short-circuit current is then 200 ma and, as explained in Section 28–6, the straight line in Fig. 43–6 is the current-voltage graph of the source.

If the grid potential $V_g = -40$ volts, the operating point of the triode is at point *a* in Fig. 43–6. The plate current I is 75 ma and the plate potential V_p is 250 volts. If the grid potential is changed to -20 volts, the operating point shifts to point *b*. The plate current increases to 110 ma and the plate potential decreases to 190 volts. Hence a *change* in grid potential of 20 volts produces a *change* in plate potential of 60 volts. It is this property of the triode that enables it to function as an *amplifier*.

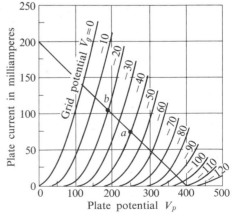

Fig. 43–6. Plate characteristics of a triode.

43–4 The photoelectric effect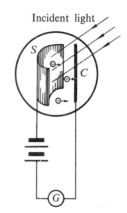

In the thermionic emission of electrons from metals, the energy needed by an electron to escape from the metal surface is furnished by the energy of thermal agitation. Electrons may also acquire enough energy to escape from a metal, even at low temperatures, if the metal is illuminated by light of sufficiently short wavelength. This phenomenon is called the *photoelectric effect*. It was first observed by Heinrich Hertz in 1887, who noticed that a spark would jump more readily between two spheres when their surfaces were illuminated by the light from another spark. Hall-wachs investigated the effect more fully the following year, and it is usually known by his name.

A modern phototube is shown schematically in Fig. 43–7. A beam of light, indicated by the arrows, falls on a photosensitive surface *S*. Electrons emitted by the surface are drawn to the collector *C*, normally maintained at a positive potential with respect to the emitter. Emitter and collector are enclosed in an eva-cuated container. The photoelectric current can be read on the galvanometer *G*.

It is found that with a given material as emitter, the wavelength of the light must be shorter than a critical value, different for different surfaces, in order that any photoelectrons at all may be emitted. This critical wavelength, or the corresponding frequency, is called the *threshold frequency* of the particular surface. The

Fig. 43–7. Schematic diagram of a photocell circuit.

threshold frequency for most metals is in the ultra-violet (critical wavelength 200 to 300 nm), but for potassium and cesium oxide it lies in the visible spectrum (400 to 700 nm).

Just as in the case of thermionic emission, the photoelectrons form a cloud of space charge around the emitter *S*. That some of the electrons are emitted with an initial velocity is shown by the fact that even with no emf in the external circuit a few electrons penetrate the cloud of space charge and reach the collector, causing a small current in the external circuit. The velocity of the most rapidly moving electrons can be deduced by measuring the reversed voltage (negative potential of collector) required to reduce the current to zero. This potential is known as the *stopping potential*.

A remarkable feature of photoelectric emission is the relation between the number and maximum velocity of escaping electrons on the one hand, and the intensity and wavelength of the incident light on the other. Surprisingly enough, it is found that the maximum velocity of emission is *independent of the intensity* of the light, but does depend on its wavelength. It is true that the photoelectric current increases as the light intensity is increased, but only because more electrons are emitted. With light of a given wavelength, no matter how feeble it may be, the maximum velocity of the photoelectrons from a given surface is always the same, provided, of course, that the frequency is above the threshold frequency.

The explanation of the photoelectric effect was given by Einstein in 1905, although his theory was so radical that it was not generally accepted until 1916, when it was confirmed by experiments performed by Millikan. Extending a proposal made two years earlier by Planck, Einstein postulated that a beam of light consisted of small bundles of energy which are now called *light quanta* or *photons*. The energy W of a photon is proportional to its frequency f, or is equal to its frequency multiplied by a constant. That is,

$$W = hf, \tag{43–2}$$

where h is a universal constant called Planck's constant whose value is 6.63×10^{-34} joule·sec. When a photon collides with an electron at or just within the surface of a metal, it may transfer its energy to the electron. This transfer is an "all-or-none" process, the electron getting all the photon's energy or none at all. The photon then simply drops out of existence. The energy acquired by the electron may enable it to escape from the surface of the metal if it is moving in the right direction.

In leaving the surface of the metal the electron loses energy in amount ϕ (the work function of the surface). Some electrons may lose more than this if they start at some distance below the metal surface, but the maximum energy with which an electron can emerge is the energy gained from a photon minus the work function. Hence the maximum kinetic energy of the photoelectrons ejected by light of frequency f is

$$\tfrac{1}{2}mv^2_{\max} = hf - \phi. \tag{43–3}$$

This is Einstein's photoelectric equation, and it was in exact agreement with Millikan's experimental results.

The currents obtainable with vacuum phototubes are extremely small, of the order of microamperes. These currents may be increased by a factor of 5 to 10 if a small quantity of gas is left in the tube. The electrons ionize the gas and more current-carriers are available.

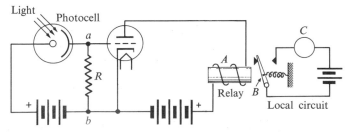

Fig. 43–8.   Principle of the photoelectric relay.

One of the most important uses of the photoelectric cell is to operate a relay which opens or closes a local circuit to accomplish some useful purpose. In this connection the photocell is called an *electric eye*. A simple photoelectric relay circuit is shown in Fig. 43–8. While the light is incident upon the photoelectric surface there is a photo-electric current in the resistor R and the potential of point a is the potential of point b

Photosensitive surface

Fig. 43–9. Photronic cell.

plus the "iR" drop in the resistor R. The grid of the vacuum tube, which is connected to a, is therefore only slightly negative, and the plate current is sufficient to actuate the electromagnet A, thereby attracting the armature B and keeping the local circuit open. When the light is cut off, the point a (and therefore the grid) becomes more negative in the absence of an iR drop in R and the plate current is reduced. The armature then springs back and closes the local circuit. A wide variety of industrial operations are performed in this way.

Figure 43–9 is a photograph of another type of photoelectric cell, called a barrier-layer or photronic cell. A layer of copper oxide is deposited on a copper disk, with an extremely thin layer of metal on top of the oxide. Light passing through the thin metal layer drives electrons from the oxide into this layer, producing between the copper disk and the metal layer a potential difference which depends upon the amount of light striking the cell.

43–5 Line spectra

We have seen how a prism or grating spectrograph functions to disperse a beam of light into a spectrum. If the light source is an incandescent solid or liquid, the spectrum is *continuous*; that is, light of all wavelengths is present. If, however, the source is a gas through which an electrical discharge is passing, or a flame into which a volatile salt has been introduced, the spectrum is of an entirely different character. Instead of a continuous band of color, only a few colors appear, in the form of isolated parallel lines. (Each "line" is an image of the spectrograph slit, deviated through an angle dependent on the frequency of the light forming the image.) A spectrum of this sort is termed a *line spectrum*. The wavelengths of the lines are characteristic of the element emitting the light. That is, hydrogen always gives a set of lines in the same position, sodium another set, iron still another, and so on. The line structure of the spectrum extends into both the ultraviolet and infrared regions, where photographic or other means are required for its detection.

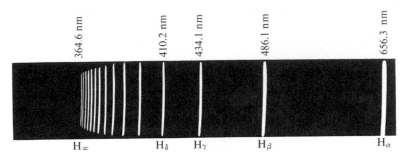

Fig. 43-10. The Balmer series of atomic hydrogen. (Reproduced by permission from *Atomic Spectra and Atomic Structures* by Gerhard Herzberg. Copyright 1937 by Prentice-Hall, Inc.)

It might be expected that the frequencies of the light emitted by a particular element would be arranged in some regular way. For instance, a radiating atom might be analogous to a vibrating string, emitting a fundamental frequency and its harmonics. At first sight there does not seem to be any semblance of order or regularity in the lines of a typical spectrum, and for many years unsuccessful attempts were made to correlate the observed frequencies with those of a fundamental and its overtones. Finally, in 1885, Johann Jakob Balmer (1825–1898) found a simple formula which gave the frequencies of a group of lines emitted by atomic hydrogen. Since the spectrum of this element is relatively simple, and fairly typical of a number of others, we shall consider it in more detail.

Under the proper conditions of excitation, atomic hydrogen may be caused to emit the sequence of lines illustrated in Fig. 43–10. This sequence is called a *series*. There is evidently a certain order in this spectrum, the lines becoming crowded more and more closely together as the limit of the series is approached. The line of longest wavelength or lowest frequency, in the red, is known as H_α, the next, in the blue-green, as H_β, the third as H_γ and so on. Balmer found that the wavelengths of these lines were given accurately by the simple formula,

$$\frac{1}{\lambda} = R\left(\frac{1}{2^2} - \frac{1}{n^2}\right), \tag{43-4}$$

where λ is the wavelength, R is a constant called the Rydberg constant, and n may have the integral values 3, 4, 5, etc. If λ is in meters,

$$R = 1.097 \times 10^7 \text{ m}^{-1}.$$

Letting $n = 3$ in Eq. (43–4), one obtains the wavelength of the H_α line:

$$1/\lambda = 1.097 \times 10^7 \text{ m}^{-1} \left(\tfrac{1}{4} - \tfrac{1}{9}\right) = 1.522 \times 10^6 \text{ m}^{-1},$$

whence

$$\lambda = 656.3 \text{ nm}.$$

If $n = 4$, one obtains the wavelength of the H_β line, etc. For $n = \infty$, one obtains the limit of the series, at $\lambda = 364.6$ nm. This is the shortest wavelength in the series.

Still other series spectra for hydrogen have since been discovered. These are known, after their discoverers, as the Lyman, Paschen, and Brackett series. The formulas for these are

$$\text{Lyman series:} \quad \frac{1}{\lambda} = R\left(\frac{1}{1^2} - \frac{1}{n^2}\right), \qquad n = 2, 3, \ldots$$

$$\text{Paschen series:} \quad \frac{1}{\lambda} = R\left(\frac{1}{3^2} - \frac{1}{n^2}\right), \qquad n = 4, 5, \ldots$$

$$\text{Brackett series:} \quad \frac{1}{\lambda} = R\left(\frac{1}{4^2} - \frac{1}{n^2}\right), \qquad n = 5, 6, \ldots$$

The Lyman series is in the ultraviolet, and the Paschen and Brackett series are in the infrared. The Balmer series evidently fits into the scheme between the Lyman and the Paschen series.

The Balmer formula, Eq. (43–4), may also be written in terms of the frequency of the light, recalling that

$$c = f\lambda \qquad \text{or} \qquad \frac{1}{\lambda} = \frac{f}{c}.$$

Thus Eq. (43–4) becomes

$$f = Rc\left(\frac{1}{2^2} - \frac{1}{n^2}\right) \tag{43–5}$$

or

$$f = \frac{Rc}{2^2} - \frac{Rc}{n^2}. \tag{43–6}$$

Each of the fractions on the right side of Eq. (43–6) is called a *term*, and the frequency of every line in the series is given by the difference between two terms.

There are only a few elements (hydrogen, singly ionized helium, doubly ionized lithium) whose spectra can be represented by a simple formula of the Balmer type. Nevertheless, it is possible to separate the more complicated spectra of other elements into series, and to express the frequency of each line in the series as the difference of two terms. The first term is constant for any one series, while the various values of the second term are found by assigning successive integral values to a quantity corresponding to n in Eq. (43–6), which appears in the (somewhat more complicated) expression for this term.

43–6 The Bohr atom

Einstein invoked the concept of light quanta, or photons, to account for the experimental facts of photoelectric emission. We shall now see how the Danish physicist Niels Bohr, in 1913, first applied the same ideas to the emission of light by atoms.

Experiments on the scattering of alpha particles by thin metallic foils were performed by Rutherford and his co-workers about 1906. These led to the hypothesis that atoms consisted of a relatively massive, positively charged nucleus, surrounded by a swarm of electrons. To account for the fact that the electrons in an atom remained at relatively large distances from the nucleus, in spite of the electrostatic force of attraction of the nucleus for them, Rutherford postulated that the electrons revolved about the nucleus, the force of attraction providing the requisite centripetal force to retain them in their orbits. This assumption, however, has an unfortunate consequence. A body moving in a circle is continuously accelerated toward the center of the circle, and according to classical electromagnetic theory an accelerated electron radiates energy. The total energy of the electrons would therefore gradually decrease, their orbits would become smaller and smaller, and eventually they would spiral into the nucleus and come to rest. Furthermore, according to classical theory, the frequency of the electromagnetic waves emitted by a revolving electron is equal to the frequency of revolution. As the electrons radiated energy their angular velocities would change continuously and they would emit a continuous spectrum (a mixture of all frequencies), in contradiction to the line spectrum which is observed.

Faced with the dilemma that electromagnetic theory predicted an unstable atom emitting radiant energy of all frequencies, while observation showed stable atoms emitting only a few frequencies, Bohr concluded that in spite of the success of electromagnetic theory in explaining large-scale phenomena, it could not be applied to processes on an atomic scale. Bohr's *first postulate*, therefore, was that *an electron in an atom can revolve in certain specified orbits without the emission of radiant energy*, contrary to the predictions of the classical electromagnetic theory. The first postulate therefore "explained" the stability of the atom.

A completely stable atom, however, is as unsatisfactory as an unstable one, since atoms *do* emit radiant energy. Bohr's *second postulate* incorporated into atomic theory the quantum concepts that had been developed by Planck and applied by Einstein to the photoelectric effect. The second postulate was that *an electron may suddenly "jump" from one of its specified nonradiating orbits to another of lower energy. When it does so, a single photon is emitted whose energy equals the energy difference between the initial and final states, and whose frequency f is given by the relation*

$$hf = W_1 - W_2, \tag{43-7}$$

where h is Planck's constant and W_1 and W_2 are the initial and final energies.

It remained to specify the radii of the nonradiating orbits. Bohr found that the frequencies of the spectral lines of atomic hydrogen, as computed from Eq. (43-7), were in agreement with observation provided the electron was permitted to rotate about the nucleus *only in those orbits for which the angular momentum is some integral multiple of $h/2\pi$*. It will be recalled that the angular momentum of a particle of mass m, moving with tangential velocity v in a circle of radius r, is mvr. Hence the quantum condition above may be stated

$$mvr = n\frac{h}{2\pi}, \tag{43-8}$$

where $n = 1, 2, 3$, etc.

The hydrogen atom consists of a single electron of charge $-e$, rotating about a single proton of charge $+e$. The electrostatic force of attraction between the charges,

$$F = \frac{1}{4\pi\epsilon_0}\frac{e^2}{r^2},$$

provides the centripetal force and, from Newton's second law,

$$\frac{1}{4\pi\epsilon_0}\frac{e^2}{r^2} = \frac{mv^2}{r}. \tag{43–9}$$

When Eqs. (43–8) and (43–9) are solved simultaneously for r and v, we obtain

$$r = \epsilon_0\frac{n^2h^2}{\pi me^2}, \tag{43–10}$$

$$v = \frac{1}{\epsilon_0}\frac{e^2}{2nh}.$$

Let

$$\epsilon_0\frac{h^2}{\pi me^2} = r_0. \tag{43–11}$$

Then Eq. (43–10) becomes

$$r = n^2 r_0,$$

and the permitted, nonradiating orbits are of radii r_0, $4r_0$, $9r_0$, etc. The appropriate value of n is called the *quantum number* of the orbit.

The numerical values of the quantities on the left side of Eq. (43–11) are

$$\epsilon_0 = 8.85 \times 10^{-12}\frac{\text{coul}^2}{\text{newton·m}^2},$$

$$h = 6.62 \times 10^{-34}\text{ joule·sec},$$

$$m = 9.11 \times 10^{-31}\text{ kgm},$$

$$e = 1.60 \times 10^{-19}\text{ coul}.$$

Hence r_0, the radius of the first Bohr orbit, is

$$r_0 = \frac{8.85 \times 10^{-12}\,(\text{coul}^2/\text{n·m}^2) \times (6.62 \times 10^{-34}\text{ joule·sec})^2}{3.14 \times 9.11 \times 10^{-31}\text{ kgm} \times (1.60 \times 10^{-19}\text{ coul})^2}$$

$$= 5.3 \times 10^{-11}\text{ m} = 0.53 \times 10^{-8}\text{ cm}.$$

This is in good agreement with atomic diameters as estimated by other methods, namely, about 10^{-8} cm.

The kinetic energy of the electron in any orbit is

$$E_k = \tfrac{1}{2}mv^2 = \frac{1}{\epsilon_0^2}\frac{me^4}{8n^2h^2},$$

and the potential energy is

$$E_p = -\frac{1}{4\pi\epsilon_0}\frac{e^2}{r} = -\frac{1}{\epsilon_0^2}\frac{me^4}{4n^2h^2}.$$

The total energy, W, is therefore

$$W = E_k + E_p = -\frac{1}{\epsilon_0^2}\frac{me^4}{8n^2h^2}. \tag{43--12}$$

The total energy has a negative sign because the reference level of potential energy is taken with the electron at an infinite distance from the nucleus. Since we are interested only in energy differences this is not of importance.

The energy of the atom is least when its electron is revolving in the orbit for which $n = 1$, for then W has its largest negative value. For $n = 2, 3, \ldots$ the absolute value of W is smaller, hence the energy is progressively larger in the outer orbits. The *normal state* of the atom is that of lowest energy, with the electron revolving in the orbit of smallest radius, r_0. As a result of collisions with rapidly moving electrons in an electrical discharge, or for other causes, the atom may temporarily acquire sufficient energy to raise the electron to some outer orbit. The atom is then said to be in an *excited state*. This state is an unstable one, and the electron soon falls or "jumps" back to a state of lower energy, emitting a photon in the process.

Let n be the quantum number of some excited state, and l the quantum number of the lower state to which the electron returns after the emission process. Then W_1, the initial energy, is

$$W_1 = -\frac{1}{\epsilon_0^2}\frac{me^4}{8n^2h^2},$$

and W_2, the final energy, is

$$W_2 = -\frac{1}{\epsilon_0^2}\frac{me^4}{8l^2h^2}.$$

The decrease in energy, $W_1 - W_2$, which we place equal to the energy hf of the emitted photon, is

$$W_1 - W_2 = hf = -\frac{1}{\epsilon_0^2}\frac{me^4}{8n^2h^2} + \frac{1}{\epsilon_0^2}\frac{me^4}{8l^2h^2},$$

or

$$f = \frac{1}{\epsilon_0^2}\frac{me^4}{8h^3}\left(\frac{1}{l^2} - \frac{1}{n^2}\right). \tag{43--13}$$

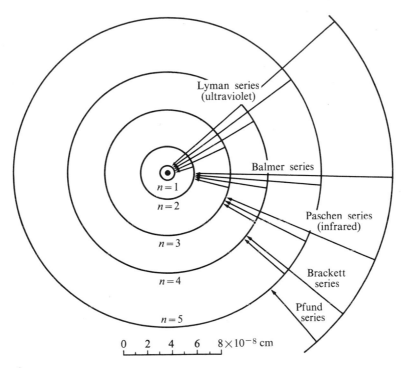

Fig. 43–11. "Permitted" orbits of an electron in the Bohr model of a hydrogen atom. The transitions or "jumps" responsible for some of the lines of the various series are indicated by arrows.

This equation is of precisely the same form as the Balmer formula (Eq. 43–5) for the frequencies in the hydrogen spectrum if we place

$$\frac{1}{\epsilon_0^2} \frac{me^4}{8h^3} = Rc, \tag{43–14}$$

and let $l = 1$ for the Lyman series, $l = 2$ for the Balmer series, etc. The Lyman series is therefore the group of lines emitted by electrons returning from some excited state to the normal state. The Balmer series is the group emitted by electrons returning from some higher state, but which stop in the second orbit instead of falling at once to that of lowest energy. That is, an electron returning from the third orbit ($n = 3$) to the second orbit ($l = 2$) emits the H_α line. One returning from the fourth orbit ($n = 4$) to the second ($l = 2$) emits the H_β line, etc. (See Fig. 43–11.)

The question naturally arises as to whether or not Eq. (43–14) is true, since every quantity in it may be determined quite independently of the Bohr theory, and apart from this theory we have no reason to expect these quantities to be related in this particular way. The quantities m and e, for instance, are found from experiments on free electrons, h may be found from the photoelectric effect, R by measurements of wavelengths, while c is the velocity of light. However, if we substitute in Eq. (43–14) the values of these quantities, obtained by such diverse means, we find that it does hold exactly, within the limits of experimental error.

43–7 Deuterium

The discovery of deuterium constitutes another triumph of Bohr's theory of the hydrogen atom. According to Bohr, an electron revolving about a stationary nucleus in an orbit characterized by the quantum number n has an energy given by Eq. (43–12); thus

$$W = - \frac{1}{\epsilon_0^2} \frac{me^4}{8n^2h^2} .$$

The nucleus of a hydrogen atom, a proton, has a mass 1840 times that of an electron, and therefore the assumption that the proton remains stationary while the electron revolves around it is a fair one if great accuracy is not desired. In devising a theory to explain spectral lines, however, the utmost refinements must be introduced because measurements of the wavelengths of spectral lines are among the most precise in all experimental physics. It is natural, therefore, to take into account the fact that both the electron and proton revolve about their common center of gravity. When this is done, the energy of an electron becomes

$$W = - \frac{1}{\epsilon_0^2} \frac{m}{1 + m/M} \frac{e^4}{8n^2h^2} ,$$

where M is the mass of the nucleus.

It was suspected in 1931 that ordinary hydrogen was a mixture of two isotopes, one consisting of an electron revolving about a proton, and the other consisting of an electron revolving about a nucleus consisting of a proton and a neutron and having a mass very nearly twice that of the proton. (See Section 44–9.)

If all of these atoms are excited in an electric discharge and the Balmer lines are measured carefully, the frequency of, say, the second Balmer line (H_β) would be slightly different for the two different hydrogens. Thus

$$f_1 = \frac{1}{\epsilon_0^2} \frac{m}{1 + m/M_1} \frac{e^4}{8h^3} \left(\frac{1}{2^2} - \frac{1}{4^2} \right) \quad \left(\begin{array}{l} \text{for a nucleus} \\ \text{of mass } M_1 \end{array} \right) ,$$

and

$$f_2 = \frac{1}{\epsilon_0^2} \frac{m}{1 + m/M_2} \frac{e^4}{8h^3} \left(\frac{1}{2^2} - \frac{1}{4^2} \right) \quad \left(\begin{array}{l} \text{for a nucleus} \\ \text{of mass } M_2 \end{array} \right) ,$$

where $m/M_1 = 1/1840$ and $m/M_2 = 1/3680$. The two different H_β's would be very close together because the wavelength difference corresponding to the frequency difference $f_1 - f_2$ is only 1.3 angstroms. Furthermore, the H_β line corresponding to the heavy isotope would be very much fainter than the other because in any ordinary sample of hydrogen there is presumably only a small percentage of heavy hydrogen

In spite of these difficulties, Urey, Murphy, and Brickwedde, in 1932, undertook the task of determining whether the heavy isotope of hydrogen existed. With the aid of a diffraction grating spectrograph they found the blue H_β line to consist of a very strong line and a faint companion. They then proceeded to prepare hydrogen with a higher percentage of the heavy isotope by allowing liquid hydrogen to evaporate and retaining the residue. With this residue in the discharge tube, the companion line was much stronger and its displacement from the other H_β line was in agreement with the value predicted by the Bohr theory. They called the heavier isotope *deuterium*.

43-8 Wave mechanics

The Bohr model of the atom was successful in explaining the observed spectra of atomic hydrogen and of a few other elements, but for atoms having a large number of orbital electrons, and for molecules, the theory was not as satisfactory. Furthermore, there seemed to be no good justification, except that it led to the right answer, for the hypothesis that only those orbits are permitted for which the angular momentum is equal to some integral multiple of $h/2\pi$. The next advance in atom-building, which followed the theory of Bohr by about ten years, was a suggestion by de Broglie that since light appeared to be dualistic in nature, behaving in some aspects like waves and in others like corpuscles, the same might be true of matter. That is, electrons and protons, which until that time had been thought to be purely corpuscular, might in some circumstances behave like waves. The rapid development of this idea in the hands of Heisenberg, Schroedinger, and many others, led to the so-called *wave mechanics* or *quantum mechanics*, which has placed atomic theory on what we believe to be a secure foundation.

A single section on "wave mechanics" cannot, of course, give the reader any adequate comprehension of this complex and highly mathematical subject, any more than the whole field of "Newtonian mechanics" could be covered in the same amount of space. We can point out only the main lines of thought in a nonmathematical way, describe some of the experimental evidence for the wave nature of material particles, and show how the quantum numbers that were introduced in such an artificial way by Bohr now enter naturally into the problem of atomic structure.

The essential feature of the new wave mechanics, as we have said, is that particles of matter are also endowed with wavelike properties. An electron, then, must be considered as some sort of wave, more or less spread out through space and not simply localized at a point. The idea that the electrons in an atom move in definite Bohr orbits such as those in Fig. 43-11 has been abandoned. Instead, the new theory specifies merely that there are certain *regions* in which an electron is more or less likely to be found. The orbits themselves, however, were never an essential part of Bohr's theory, since the only quantities that determined the frequencies of the emitted photons were the *energies* corresponding to the orbits. The new theory still assigns definite energy states to an atom. In the hydrogen atom the energies are the same as those given by Bohr's theory; in more complicated atoms where the Bohr theory did not work, the wave-mechanical picture is in excellent agreement with observation.

We shall illustrate how quantization arises in atomic structure by an analogy with the classical mechanical problem of a vibrating string fixed at its ends. When the string vibrates, the ends must be nodes, but nodes may occur at other points also, and the general requirement is that the length of the string shall equal some integral number of half-wavelengths. The point of interest is that the solution of the problem of the vibrating string leads to the appearance of *integral numbers*.

In a similar way, the principles of quantum mechanics lead to a wave equation (Schroedinger's equation) that must be satisfied by an electron in an atom, subject also to certain boundary conditions. Let us think of an electron as a wave extending in a circle around the nucleus. In order that the wave may "come out even," the circumference of this circle must include some *integral number* of wavelengths. The wavelength of a particle of mass m, moving with a velocity v, is given according to wave mechanics by the equation

$$\lambda = \frac{h}{mv}, \tag{43–15}$$

where λ is the wavelength and h is Planck's constant. Then if r is the radius and $2\pi r$ the circumference of the circle occupied by the wave, we must have

$$2\pi r = n\lambda,$$

where $n = $ 1, 2, 3, etc.

Since $\lambda = h/mv$, this equation becomes

$$2\pi r = n\frac{h}{mv}, \qquad mvr = n\frac{h}{2\pi}.$$

But mvr is the angular momentum of the electron, and we see that the wave-mechanical picture leads naturally to Bohr's postulate that the angular momentum equals some integral multiple of $h/2\pi$.

There is even more direct experimental evidence of the wavelike nature of electrons. We have described in Chapter 41 how the layers of atoms in a crystal serve as a diffraction grating for x-rays. An x-ray beam is strongly reflected when it strikes a crystal at such an angle that the waves reflected from the atomic layers combine to reinforce one another. The point of importance here is that the existence of these strong reflections is evidence of the wave nature of x-rays.

In 1927, Davisson and Germer, working in the Bell Telephone Laboratories, were studying the nature of the surface of a crystal of nickel by directing a beam of electrons at the surface and observing the electrons reflected at various angles. It might be expected that even the smoothest surface attainable would still look rough to an electron, and that the electron beam would therefore be diffusely reflected. But Davisson and Germer found that the electrons were reflected in almost the same way that x-rays would be reflected from the same crystal. The wavelengths of the electrons in the beam were computed from their known velocity, with the help of Eq. (43–15), and the angles at which strong reflection took place were found to be the same as those at which x-rays of the same wavelength would be reflected.

43–9 The electron microscope

The shorter the wavelength, the smaller is the limit of resolution of a microscope. Modern physical theories indicate that a moving electron can, for some purposes, be considered as a wave, and the wavelengths of electron waves can easily be made very much shorter than the wavelengths of visible light. Hence the limit of resolution of a microscope may be extended to a value several hundred times smaller than that

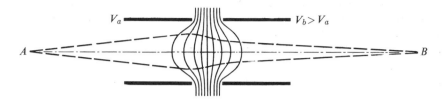

Fig. 43–12. An electrostatic electron lens. The cylinders are at different potentials, V_a and V_b. A beam of electrons diverging from point A is focused at point B.

obtainable with an optical instrument by using electrons, rather than light waves, to form an image of the object being examined.

A beam of electrons can be focused by either a magnetic or an electric field of the proper configuration, and both types are used in electron microscopes. Figure 43–12 illustrates an electrostatic lens. Two hollow cylinders are maintained at different potentials. A few of the equipotentials are indicated, and the trajectories of a beam of electrons traveling from left to right are shown by the dashed lines. The optical analog of this electrostatic lens is shown in Fig. 43–13. It will be evident without going into further details that by the proper design of such lenses the elements of an optical microscope, such as its condensing lens, objective, and ocular, can all be duplicated electronically.

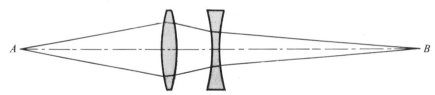

Fig. 43–13. Optical analog of the electron lens in Fig. 43–12.

The source of electrons in an electron microscope is a heated filament. Electrons emitted by the filament are accelerated by an electron gun and strike the object to be examined. This must necessarily be a thin section so that some of the electrons can pass through it. The thicker portions of the section absorb more of the electron stream than do the thinner portions, just as would a lantern slide in a projection lantern. Needless to say, the entire apparatus must be evacuated.

The final image may be formed on a photographic plate, or on a fluorescent screen which can be examined visually or photographed with a still further gain in magnification. Commercial electron microscopes give satisfactory definition at an over-all magnification, electronic followed by photographic, as great as 50,000×. Figure 43–14 is an electron micrograph of aluminum oxide, magnified 53,500 times.

It should be pointed out that the ability of the electron microscope to form an image does not depend on the wave properties of the electrons; their trajectories can be computed by treating them as charged particles, deflected by the electric or magnetic fields through which they move. It is only when considerations of resolving power arise that the electron wavelengths come into the picture. The situation is

Fig. 43–14. Electron micrograph of aluminum oxide, magnified 53,500 times. (Courtesy of Radio Corporation of America.)

analogous to that in the optical microscope. The paths of light rays through an optical microscope can be computed by the principles of geometrical optics, but the resolving power of the microscope is determined by the wavelength of the light used.

43–10 Absorption spectra

Although the precise picture of electronic orbits about the nucleus of an atom has been abandoned in modern physics, the concept of energy levels still remains. The fundamental problem of the spectroscopist is to determine the energy levels of an atom from the measured values of the wavelengths of the spectral lines emitted when the atom proceeds from one set of energy levels to another. In the case of complicated spectra emitted by the heavier atoms this is a task requiring tremendous ingenuity. Nevertheless, almost all spectra have been analyzed, and the resulting energy levels have been tabulated or plotted with the aid of diagrams similar to the one shown for sodium in Fig. 43–15.

The lowest energy level of the atom is called the *normal state*, and all higher levels are called *excited states*. As we have seen, a spectral line is emitted when an atom proceeds from an excited state to a lower state. The only means discussed so far for raising the atom from the normal state to an excited state has been with the aid of an electric discharge. Let us consider now another method, involving the absorption of radiant energy.

From Fig. 43–15 it may be seen that a sodium atom emits the characteristic yellow light of wavelengths 5890 and 5896 angstroms (the D_1 and D_2 lines) when it undergoes the transitions from the two levels marked *resonance levels* to the normal state. Suppose a sodium atom in the normal state were to absorb a quantum of radiant energy of wavelength 5890 or 5896 angstroms. It would then undergo a transition in the opposite direction and be raised to one of the resonance levels. After a short

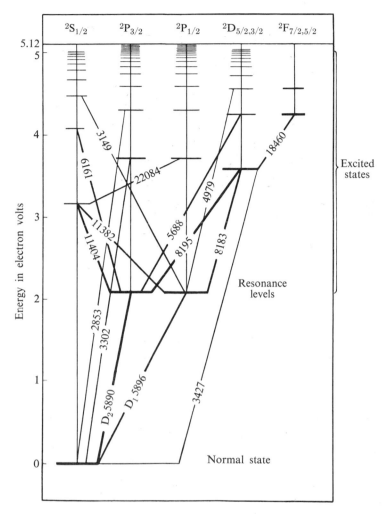

Fig. 43–15.   Energy levels of the sodium atom.   Numbers on the lines between levels are wavelengths in angstroms.

time, known as the *lifetime* of the excited state (which in the case of the resonance levels of the sodium atom has been found to be 1.6×10^{-8} sec), the atom returns to the normal state and emits this quantum. The emission process is called *resonance radiation* and may be easily demonstrated as follows. A strong beam of the yellow light from a sodium arc is concentrated on a glass bulb which has been highly evacuated and into which a small amount of pure metallic sodium has been distilled. If the bulb is gently warmed with a Bunsen burner to increase the sodium vapor pressure, resonance radiation will take place throughout the whole bulb, which glows with the yellow light characteristic of sodium.

A sodium atom in the normal state may absorb radiant energy of wavelengths other than the yellow resonance lines. All wavelengths corresponding to spectral lines emitted when the sodium atom returns to its normal state may be absorbed. Thus, from Fig. 43–15, wavelengths 3302, 2853, etc., may be absorbed by a normal sodium atom. If, therefore, the light from a carbon arc is sent through an absorption tube containing sodium vapor, and then examined with a spectroscope, there will be a series of dark lines corresponding to the wavelengths absorbed, as shown in Fig. 43–16. This is known as an *absorption spectrum*.

Fig. 43–16. Absorption spectrum of sodium.

The absorption of the resonance lines of sodium may be easily demonstrated with the aid of the apparatus depicted in Fig. 43–17. A large chunk of metallic sodium placed in an iron boat and heated with a battery of large Bunsen burners supplies sufficient concentration of sodium atoms to absorb the yellow light and create a thick dark line in the yellow part of the continuous spectrum. The slit of the spectroscope is usually too wide to show the presence of two dark lines close together.

The sun's spectrum is an absorption spectrum. The main body of the sun emits a continuous spectrum, whereas the cooler vapors in the sun's atmosphere emit line spectra corresponding to all the elements present. When the intense light from the main body of the sun passes through the cooler vapors the lines of these elements are absorbed. The light emitted by the cooler vapors is so small compared with the unabsorbed continuous spectrum that the continuous spectrum appears to be crossed by a myriad of faint dark lines. These were first observed by Fraunhofer and are therefore called *Fraunhofer lines*. They may be observed with any student spectroscope pointed toward any part of the sky.

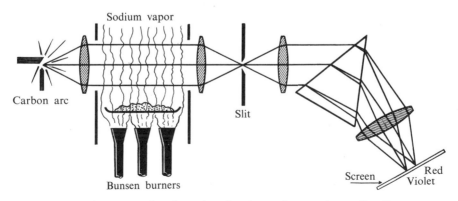

Fig. 43–17. Apparatus for observing the absorption spectrum of sodium vapor.

43–11 The laser

If the energy difference between the normal and the first excited state of an atom is W, the atom is capable of absorbing a photon whose frequency f is given by the Planck equation $W = hf$. The *absorption* of a photon by a normal atom N is depicted schematically in Fig. 43–18(a). After absorbing the photon the atom becomes an excited atom E. A short time later, *spontaneous emission* takes place and the excited atom becomes normal again by emitting a photon of the same frequency as that which was originally absorbed but in a random direction and with a random phase, as shown in Fig. 43–18(b). In 1917 Einstein found it necessary, in order to derive Planck's law of blackbody radiation (Section 17–7), to postulate the existence of a third process which he called *stimulated emission* and which is shown schematically in Fig. 43–18(c). *Stimulated emission takes place when a photon encounters an excited atom and forces it to emit another photon of the same frequency, in the same direction, and in the same phase.* The two photons go off together as two samples of *coherent* radiation.

Consider an absorption cell containing a large number of normal atoms of the type depicted in Fig. 43–18. In the absence of an external beam of radiation, there are only a few excited atoms present in the cell. The ratio of the number n_W of excited atoms to the number n_0 of normal atoms is given by *Boltzmann's equation*

$$\frac{n_W}{n_0} = e^{-W/kT}, \tag{43–16}$$

where k is Boltzmann's constant. For sodium vapor at, say, $400°K$, $W = 2.1$ ev $= 3.36 \times 10^{-19}$ joule, and $k = 1.38 \times 10^{-23}$ joule/K°. Therefore

$$\frac{W}{kT} = \frac{3.36 \times 10^{-19}}{1.38 \times 10^{-23} \times 400} = 61,$$

and since e^{-61} is extremely small, the number of excited atoms is negligible.

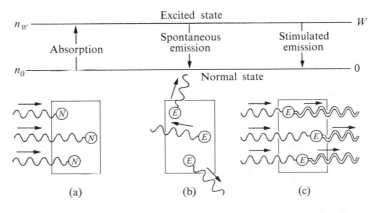

Fig. 43–18. Three interaction processes between an atom and radiation.

Now suppose a *parallel* beam of radiation of the frequency f that corresponds to the energy difference W is sent through the cell. The ratio of the numbers n_W and n_0, that is, the ratio of the *populations* of the energy levels, is increased. Since the population of the normal state was so much larger than that of the excited state, an enormously intense beam of light would be required to increase the population of the excited state to a value comparable with or greater than that of the normal state. Therefore the rate at which energy is extracted from the beam by absorption of normal atoms far outweighs the rate at which energy is added to the beam by stimulated emission of excited atoms.

There are a few atoms, however, that have an excited state near which there exists another excited state of long lifetime, a so-called *metastable* state. By making use of this metastable state as a "feeder," and by using a very strong beam of radiation to provide metastable atoms, a procedure known as "optical pumping," it has been found possible to produce a *population inversion*, that is, a ratio of n_W to n_0 *greater* than unity. When this is the case, the rate at which energy is added to the beam is greater than that at which it is extracted and *light amplification* results. The device for performing this feat is called a *laser*, the letters of which are the first letters of the words (neglecting prepositions) "light amplification through stimulated emission of radiation." A similar device for the amplification of microwaves is called a *maser*.

One type of solid state laser uses some of the energy levels of the chromium ion in a ruby rod. A population inversion is produced by a beam of light that is so intense that the source (a gaseous electrical discharge in a spiral glass tube surrounding the ruby rod) must be pulsed. Continuously operated lasers use a mixture of helium and neon atoms, and in both solid and gaseous lasers, the light beam is sent back and forth many times between two mirrors so as to encounter as many excited atoms as possible.

43–12 Band spectra

Up to this point we have confined our attention to spectra emitted by individual atoms. Many gases, however, have molecules consisting of two or more atoms held more or less tightly together. Thus hydrogen, oxygen, nitrogen, carbon monoxide, etc., are diatomic gases with molecules composed of two atoms each. To obtain the spectrum of atomic hydrogen or atomic oxygen, a heavy electrical discharge is needed to dissociate some of the molecules into atoms. If no dissociation takes place, the molecules themselves emit light which when analyzed with a spectroscope shows an enormous number of lines spaced so close together that they form what appear roughly to be bands. Hence the term *band spectrum*. Typical band spectra are shown in Fig. 43–19.

Fig. 43–19.   Typical band spectrum. (Courtesy of R. C. Herman.)

Each line in a band spectrum is the result of a transition between two energy levels of the molecule. The energy levels of molecules are much more numerous and much more complicated than those of atoms. They arise not only from different electron "orbits" but also from different energies of rotation and vibration. A whole set of bands corresponds to an electronic transition, a single band to a vibrational transition, and a single line in a band to a rotational transition.

43–13 The x-ray tube

X-rays are produced when rapidly moving electrons, which have been accelerated through potential differences of some tens or hundreds of thousands of volts, are allowed to strike a metal target. They were first observed by Wilhelm K. Roentgen (1845–1923) in 1895, and are also called "Roentgen rays."

X-rays are of the same nature as light or any other electromagnetic wave and, like light waves, they are governed by quantum relations in their interaction with matter. One may hence speak of x-ray photons or quanta, the energy of such a photon being given by the familiar relation $W = hf$. Wavelengths of x-rays range from 10^{-10} to 10^{-6} cm.

At present, practically all x-ray tubes are of the Coolidge type, invented by W. D. Coolidge of the General Electric laboratories in 1913. A diagram of a Coolidge tube is given in Fig. 43–20. A thermionic cathode and an anode are enclosed in a glass tube which has been pumped down to an extremely low pressure, so that electrons emitted from the cathode can travel directly to the anode with only a small probability of a collision on the way, reaching the anode with a speed corresponding to the full potential difference across the tube. X-radiation is emitted from the anode surface as a consequence of its bombardment by the electron stream.

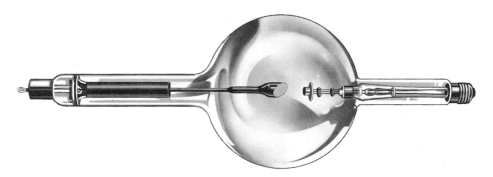

Fig. 43–20. Coolidge-type x-ray tube.

There appear to be two distinct processes going on when x-rays are emitted. Some of the electrons are stopped by the target and their kinetic energy is converted directly to x-radiation. Others transfer their energy in whole or in part to the atoms of the target, which retain it temporarily as "energy of excitation" but very shortly emit it as x-radiation. The latter is characteristic of the material of the target, while the former is not.

43–14 X-ray spectra

The elements of the periodic system may be arranged in sequence according to *atomic number*, that is, according to the number of electrons which surround the nucleus of the atom. The electrons group themselves in various "shells" about the nucleus. Each shell seems able to hold a certain maximum number of electrons. As we consider atoms of larger and larger atomic number, first the inner shell fills up to its maximum number, then the second shell, then the third, and so on. (This order is not exactly followed in all cases, but is nearly so.) The innermost shell, known as the *K*-shell, can contain at the most two electrons. The next outer shell, the *L*-shell, can contain eight. The third, the *M*-shell, has a capacity for 18 electrons, while the *N*-shell may hold 32. The sodium atom, for example, which contains 11 electrons, has two in the *K*-shell, eight in the *L*-shell, and a single electron in the *M*-shell. Molybdenum, with 42 electrons, has two in the *K*-shell, eight in the *L*-shell, 18 in the *M*-shell, and 14 in the *N*-shell.

The outer electrons of an atom, as the *M* electron of sodium, are the ones responsible for the optical spectra of the elements. Relatively small amounts of energy suffice to remove these to excited states, and on their return to their normal states wavelengths in or near the visible region are emitted. The inner electrons, such as those in the *K*-shell, require much more energy to displace them from their normal levels. As a result, we would expect a photon of much larger energy, and hence much higher frequency, to be emitted when the atom returns to its normal state after the displacement of an inner electron. This is in fact the case, and it is the displacement of the inner electrons which gives rise to the emission of x-rays.

On colliding with the atoms of the anode, some of the electrons accelerated in an x-ray tube, provided they have acquired sufficient energy, will dislodge one of the inner electrons of a target atom, say one of the *K* electrons. This leaves a vacant space in the *K*-shell, which is immediately filled by an electron from either the *L*-, *M*-, or *N*-shell. The readjustment of the electrons is accompanied by a decrease in the energy of the atom, and an x-ray photon is emitted with energy just equal to this decrease. Since the energy change is perfectly definite for atoms of a given element, we can predict definite frequencies for the emitted x-rays or, in other words, the x-ray spectrum should be a line spectrum also. We can predict further that there should be just three lines in the series, corresponding to the three possibilities that the vacant space may have been filled by an *L*, *M*, or *N* electron.

This is precisely what is observed. Figure 43–21 illustrates the so-called *K*-series of the elements tungsten, molybdenum, and copper. Each series consists of three lines, known as the K_α, K_β, and K_γ lines. The K_α line is produced by the transition of an *L* electron to the vacated space in the *K*-shell, the K_β line by an *M* electron, and the K_γ line by an *N* electron.

In addition to the *K*-series, there are other series known as the *L*-, *M*-, and *N*-series, produced by the ejection of electrons from the *L*-, *M*-, and *N*-shells rather than the *K*-shell. As would be expected, the electrons in these outer shells, being farther away from the nucleus, are not held as firmly as those in the *K*-shell. Consequently, the other series may be excited by more slowly moving electrons, and the photons emitted are of lower energy and longer wavelength.

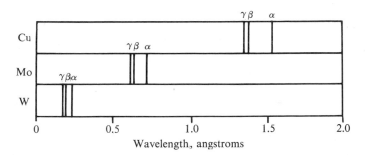

Fig. 43–21. Wavelengths of the K_α, K_β, and K_γ lines of copper, molybdenum, and tungsten.

In addition to the x-ray *line* spectrum there is a background of *continuous* x-radiation from the target of an x-ray tube. This is due to the sudden deceleration of those cathode rays which do not happen to eject an electron. The remarkable feature of the continuous spectrum is that while it extends indefinitely toward the long wavelength end, it is cut off very sharply at the short wavelength end. Again the quantum theory furnishes a satisfactory explanation of the short-wave limit of the continuous x-ray spectrum.

A bombarding electron may be brought to rest in a single process if the electron happens to collide head-on with an atom of the target, or it may make a number of collisions before coming to rest, giving up part of its energy each time. If we assume that the energy lost at each collision is radiated as an x-ray photon, these photons may be of any energy up to a certain maximum, namely, that of an electron which gives up all of its energy in a single collision. Hence there will be a short-wave limit to the spectrum. The frequency of this limit is found as usual by setting the energy of the electron equal to the energy of the x-ray photon:

$$hf = \tfrac{1}{2}mv^2. \tag{43–17}$$

This is precisely the same equation as that for the photoelectric effect except for the work function term, which is negligible here since the energies of the x-ray photons are so large. In fact, the emission of x-rays may be described as an *inverse photoelectric effect*. In photoelectric emission the energy of a photon is transformed into kinetic energy of an electron; here, the kinetic energy of an electron is transformed into that of a photon.

EXAMPLE. Compute the potential difference through which an electron must be accelerated in order that the short-wave limit of the continuous x-ray spectrum shall be exactly 1 angstrom.

The frequency corresponding to 1 angstrom (10^{-10} m) is given by

$$f = \frac{c}{\lambda} = \frac{3 \times 10^8 \text{ m/sec}}{10^{-10} \text{ m}} = 3 \times 10^{18} \text{ sec}^{-1}.$$

The energy of the photon is

$$hf = 6.62 \times 10^{-34} \text{joule·sec} \times 3 \times 10^{18} \text{sec}^{-1} = 19.9 \times 10^{-16} \text{joule}.$$

This must equal the kinetic energy of the electron, $\frac{1}{2}mv^2$, which is also equal to the product of the electronic charge and the accelerating voltage, V.

$$\tfrac{1}{2}mv^2 = eV = 19.9 \times 10^{-16} \text{joule}.$$

Since

$$e = 1.60 \times 10^{-19} \text{coulomb},$$

$$V = \frac{19.9 \times 10^{-16} \text{joule}}{1.60 \times 10^{-19} \text{coul}} = 12,400 \text{ volts}.$$

Problems

$$e = 1.60 \times 10^{-19} \text{coul}$$

$$m = 9.10 \times 10^{-31} \text{kgm}$$

$$h = 6.63 \times 10^{-34} \text{joule·sec}$$

$$N_0 = 6.03 \times 10^{26} \text{atoms/kgm-mole}$$

Energy equivalent of 1 amu $= 931$ Mev

$$e/m = 1.76 \times 10^{11} \text{coul/kgm}$$

$$k = 1.38 \times 10^{-23} \text{joule/K}°$$

1 electron volt $= 1.60 \times 10^{-19}$ joule

1 atomic mass unit
$$= 1.66 \times 10^{-27} \text{kgm/atom}$$

$$\epsilon_0 = 8.85 \times 10^{-12} \text{coul}^2/\text{n·m}^2$$

43–1. Figure 43–22 shows an alternating current generator connected to the primary of a transformer. One end of the secondary is connected to the plate of a diode and the other end to the cathode through a load

resistance R_L. Make a rough graph of the current in the load resistance as a function of the time (half-wave rectification).

43–2. Figure 43–23 shows a circuit for full-wave rectification, using two separate diodes. (a) Explain the operation of the circuit. (b) Make a rough graph of the current in the load resistance as a function of the time. (c) Draw a diagram of a circuit that would accomplish full-wave rectification with one tube containing two separate plates.

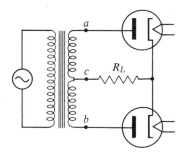

Figure 43–23

43–3. A triode whose static characteristics are given in Fig. 43–6 has its cathode connected to the negative terminal of a 200-volt battery and its plate to the positive terminal of the battery through an 800-ohm resistor. The grid potential is -10 volts. Find (a) the plate current, and (b) the plate potential.

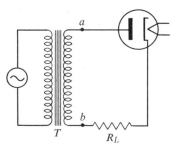

Figure 43–22

43–4. Suppose that the tube and the conditions of Problem 43–3 remain the same except that the grid potential is changed to -20 volts. What is the ratio of the change of plate potential to the change of grid potential?

43–5. In the photoelectric effect, what is the relation between the threshold frequency f_0 and the work function ϕ?

43–6. The photoelectric threshold wavelength of tungsten is 2.73×10^{-5} cm. Calculate the maximum kinetic energy of the electrons ejected from a tungsten surface by ultraviolet radiation of wavelength 1.80×10^{-5} cm. (Express the answer in electron volts.)

43–7. A photoelectric surface has a work function of 4.00 electron volts. What is the maximum velocity of the photoelectrons emitted by light of frequency 3×10^{15} sec^{-1}?

43–8. When ultraviolet light of wavelength 2.54×10^{-5} cm from a mercury arc falls upon a clean copper surface, the retarding potential necessary to stop the emission of photoelectrons is 0.59 volt. What is the photoelectric threshold wavelength for copper?

43–9. When a certain photoelectric surface is illuminated with light of different wavelengths, the stopping potentials in the table below are observed.

Wavelength, angstroms	Stopping potential, volts
3660	1.48
4050	1.15
4360	0.93
4920	0.62
5460	0.36
5790	0.24

Plot the stopping potential as ordinate against the frequency of the light as abscissa. Determine (a) the threshold frequency, (b) the threshold wavelength, (c) the photoelectric work function of the material, and (d) the value of Planck's constant h (the value of e being known).

43–10. The photoelectric work function of potassium is 2.0 ev. If light having a wavelength of 3600 A falls on potassium, find (a) the stopping potential, (b) the kinetic energy in ev of the most energetic electrons ejected, and (c) the velocities of these electrons.

43–11. What will be the change in the stopping potential for photoelectrons emitted from a surface if the wavelength of the incident light is reduced from 4000 A to 3600 A?

43–12. The photoelectric work functions for particular samples of certain metals are as follows: cesium, 2.00 ev; copper, 4.00 ev; potassium, 2.25 ev; and zinc, 3.60 ev. (a) What is the threshold wavelength for each metal? (b) Which of these metals could not emit photoelectrons when irradiated with visible light?

43–13. The light-sensitive compound on most photographic films is silver bromide, AgBr. We will assume that a film is exposed when the light energy absorbed dissociates this molecule into its atoms. (The actual process is more complex, but the quantitative result does not differ greatly.)

The energy of or heat of dissociation of AgBr is 23.9 kcal/gm-mole. Find (a) the energy in ev, (b) the wavelength, and (c) the frequency of the photon which is just able to dissociate a molecule of silver bromide. (d) What is the energy in ev of a quantum of radiation having a frequency of 100 megacycles? (e) Explain the fact that light from a firefly can expose a photographic film, whereas the radiation from a TV station transmitting 50,000 watts at 100 megacycles cannot. (f) Will photographic films stored in a light-tight container be ruined (exposed) by the radiowaves constantly passing through them? Explain.

43–14. (a) Show that the energy W (in electron volts) of a photon of wavelength λ (in angstroms) is given by W (ev) $= 12,400/\lambda$ (A). (b) What is the energy in ev of a photon having a wavelength of 912 A?

43–15. If 5% of the energy supplied to an incandescent light bulb is radiated as visible light, how many visible quanta are emitted per second by a 100-watt bulb? Assume the wavelength of all the visible light to be 5600 A.

43–16. The directions of emission of photons from a source of radiation are random. According to the wave theory, the intensity of radiation from a point source varies inversely as the square of the distance from the source. Show that the number of photons from a point source passing out through a unit area is also given by an inverse-square law.

43–17. Show that the angular speed of the electron of a hydrogen atom in its orbit is $\omega = \pi m e^4 / 2\epsilon_0^2 n^3 h^3$.

43–18. According to Bohr, the Rydberg constant R is equal to $me^4 / 8\epsilon_0^2 h^3 c$. Calculate R in m^{-1} and compare with the experimental value.

43–19. Calculate (a) the frequency, (b) the wavelength, and (c) the wave number of the H_β line of the Balmer series for hydrogen. This line is emitted in the transition from $n = 4$ to $l = 2$. Assume that the nucleus has infinite mass.

43–20. (a) What is the least amount of energy in ev that must be given to a hydrogen atom so that it can emit the H_β line (see Problem 43–19 and Fig. 43–11) in the Balmer series? (b) How many different possibilities of spectral line emission are there for this atom when the electron goes from $n = 4$ to the ground state?

43–21. (a) Show that the frequency of revolution of an electron in its circular orbit in the Bohr model of the hydrogen atom is $f = me^4 / 4\epsilon_0^2 n^3 h^3$. (b) Show that when n is very large, the frequency of revolution equals the radiated frequency calculated from Eq. (43–13) for a transition from $n = n' + 1$ to $l = n'$. (This problem illustrates Bohr's *correspondence principle*, which is often used as a check on quantum calculations. When n is small, quantum physics gives results which are very different from those of classical

physics. When n is large, the differences are not significant and the two methods then "correspond.")

43–22. A 10-kgm satellite circles the earth once every 2 hr in an orbit having a radius of 8000 km. (a) Assuming that Bohr's angular momentum postulate applies to satellites just as it does to an electron in the hydrogen atom, find the quantum number of the orbit of the satellite. (b) Show from Bohr's first postulate and Newton's law of gravitation that the radius of an earth-satellite orbit is directly proportional to the square of the quantum number, $r = kn^2$, where k is the constant of proportionality. (c) Using the result from part (b), find the distance between the orbit of the satellite in this problem and its next "allowed" orbit. (d) Comment on the possibility of observing the separation of the two adjacent orbits. (e) Do quantized and classical orbits correspond for this satellite? Which is the "correct" method for calculating the orbits?

43–23. Using the reduced mass equations, calculate the wavelength of the H_β line (see Problem 43–19) in the Balmer series for the three isotopes of hydrogen: H^1; deuterium, H^2; tritium, H^3.

43–24. (a) An electron is moving with a velocity of 3×10^8 cm/sec. What is its de Broglie wavelength? (b) A proton is moving with the same velocity. Determine its de Broglie wavelength.

43–25. The average kinetic energy of a neutron is kT. What is the de Broglie wavelength associated with the neutrons in thermal equilibrium with matter at 300°K? (The mass of a neutron is approximately 1 amu.)

43–26. Find the de Broglie wavelength of an electron in the second Bohr orbit of hydrogen.

43–27. What is the de Broglie wavelength of an electron which has been accelerated through a potential difference of 200 volts? Would you expect this electron to exhibit particle-like or wavelike characteristics on encountering an obstacle or opening 1 mm in diameter?

43–28. (a) What is the minimum potential difference between the filament and the target of an x-ray tube if the tube is to produce x-rays of wavelength 0.5 A? (b) What is the shortest wavelength produced in an x-ray tube operated at 2 million volts?

43–29. An electron in a certain x-ray tube is accelerated from rest through a potential difference of 180,000 volts in going from the cathode to the anode. When it arrives at the anode, what is its (a) kinetic energy in ev, (b) its relativistic mass, (c) its relativistic velocity, and (d) the value of e/m? (e) What is the velocity of the electron, calculated classically?

43–30. An x-ray tube is operating at 150,000 volts and 10 ma. (a) If only 1% of the electric power supplied is converted into x-rays, at what rate is the target being heated in calories per second? (b) If the target weighs 300 gm and has a specific heat of 0.035 cal/gm·°C, at what average rate would its temperature rise if there were no thermal losses? (c) What must be the physical properties of a practical target material? What would be some suitable target elements?

CHAPTER 44

Radioactivity and Nuclear Physics

44–1 Natural radioactivity

In studying the fluorescence and phosphorescence of compounds irradiated with visible light, Becquerel, in 1896, performed a crucial experiment which led to a deeper understanding of the properties of the nucleus of an atom. After illuminating some pieces of uranium-potassium sulfate with visible light, Becquerel wrapped them in black paper and separated the package from a photographic plate by a piece of silver. After several hours' exposure the photographic plate was developed and showed a blackening due to something that must have been emitted from the compound and was able to penetrate both the black paper and the silver.

Rutherford showed later that the emanations given off by uranium sulfate were capable of ionizing the air in the space between two oppositely charged metallic plates (an ionization chamber). The current registered by a galvanometer in series with the circuit was taken to be a measure of the "activity" of the compound.

A systematic study of the activity of various elements and compounds led Mme. Curie to the conclusion that it was an atomic phenomenon, and by the methods of chemical analysis, she and her husband, Pierre Curie, found that "ionizing ability" or "activity" was associated not only with uranium but with two other elements that they discovered, radium and polonium. The activity of radium was found to be more than a million times that of uranium. Since the pioneer days of the Curies, many more radioactive substances have been discovered.

The activity of radioactive material may be easily shown to be the result of three different kinds of emanations. A small piece of radioactive material is placed at the bottom of a long groove in a lead block, as shown in Fig. 44–1. Some distance above the lead block a photographic plate is placed, and the whole apparatus is highly evacuated. A strong magnetic field is applied at right angles to the plane of the diagram. After developing the plate, three distinct spots are found, one in the direct line of the groove in the lead block, one deflected to one side, and one to the other side. From a knowledge of the direction of the magnetic field, it is concluded that one of the emanations is positively charged (alpha particles), one is negatively charged (beta particles), and one is neutral (gamma rays).

Further investigation showed that not all three emanations are emitted simultaneously by all radioactive substances. Some elements emit alpha particles, others emit beta particles, while gamma rays sometimes accompany one and sometimes the other. Furthermore, no simple macroscopic physical or chemical process, such as raising or lowering the temperature, chemical combination with other nonradioactive

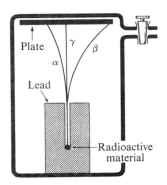

Fig. 44–1. The three emanations from a radioactive material and their paths in a magnetic field perpendicular to the plane of the diagram.

substances, etc., could change or affect in any way the activity of a given sample. As a result, it was suspected from the beginning that radioactivity is a *nuclear* process and that the emission of a charged particle from the nucleus of an atom results in leaving behind a different atom, occupying a different place in the periodic table. In other words, radioactivity involves the transmutation of elements.

44–2 Alpha particles

In the preceding section it was shown that alpha particles are positively charged. To determine the magnitude of the charge, experiments were first performed to determine the number of alpha particles emitted per second per unit mass of radioactive material. This was accomplished with the aid of a device called a *Geiger counter*, one of the most important instruments of modern physics.

As shown in Fig. 44–2, a Geiger counter consists of a metal cylinder and a wire along the axis. The cylinder contains a gas such as air or argon at a pressure of from 50 to 100 mm of mercury. A difference of potential slightly less than that necessary to produce a discharge is maintained between the wire and the cylinder wall. Alpha particles (or, for that matter, any particles to be studied) can enter through a thin glass or mica window. The particle entering the counter produces ionization of the gas molecules. These ions are accelerated by the electric field and produce more ions by collisions, causing the ionization current to build up rapidly. The current, however, decays rapidly since the circuit has a small time constant. There is therefore a momentary surge of current or a momentary potential surge across R which may be amplified and made to actuate a relay to advance a mechanical counter, or to produce a click in a loudspeaker.

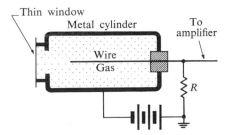

Fig. 44–2. Schematic diagram of a Geiger counter.

Placing a known mass of radium a known distance from the window of a Geiger counter, Rutherford and Geiger counted the number of alpha particles emitted in a known time interval. They found that 3.57×10^{10} alpha particles were emitted per second per gram of radium. They then allowed the alpha particles from the same source to fall upon a plate and measured its rate of increase of charge. Dividing the rate of increase of charge by the number emitted per second, Rutherford and Geiger determined the charge on an alpha particle to be 3.19×10^{-19} coulomb, or practically twice the charge on an electron, but opposite in sign.

The next problem was to determine the mass of an alpha particle. This was accomplished by measuring first the ratio of charge to mass by the electric and magnetic deflection method described in Chapter 30. The ratio was found by Rutherford and Robinson to be 4.82×10^{7} coulombs per kilogram. Combining this result with the charge of an alpha particle, the mass was found to be 6.62×10^{-27} kgm, almost exactly four times the mass of a hydrogen atom.

Since a helium atom has a mass four times that of a hydrogen atom and, stripped of its two outer electrons (as a bare nucleus), has a charge equal in magnitude and opposite in sign to two electrons, it seemed certain that alpha particles were helium nuclei. To make the identification certain, however, Rutherford and Royds collected the alpha particles in a glass discharge tube over a period of about six days and then established an electric discharge in the tube. Examining the spectrum of the emitted light, they identified the characteristic helium spectrum and established without doubt that alpha particles are helium nuclei.

The speed of an alpha particle emitted from a given radioactive source such as radium may be measured by observing the radius of the circle traversed by the particle in a magnetic field perpendicular to the motion. Such experiments show that alpha particles are emitted with very high speeds, of the order of 1.6×10^{7} m/sec or about 10,000 miles/sec. Because of the tremendous speeds of α-particles, they are capable of traveling several centimeters in air, or a few tenths or hundredths of a millimeter through solids, before they are brought to rest by collisions.

44–3 Rutherford's scattering experiment

Before the advent of the cyclotron and other more powerful "atom smashers," the only massive, high-speed particle available as a bombarding projectile was the alpha particle. In 1910, the alpha particle was used in one of the most important experiments of all time, conceived by Rutherford and performed with the aid of two of his students, Geiger and Marsden. The electron had been "discovered" in 1897 by Sir J. J. Thomson, and by 1910 its mass and charge were quite accurately known. It had also been well established that, with the sole exception of hydrogen, all atoms contain more than one electron. Thomson had proposed an atomic model consisting of a relatively large sphere of positive charge (about 2 or 3×10^{-8} cm in diameter) within which were embedded, like plums in a pudding, the electrons. What Rutherford and his co-workers did was to project alpha particles at the atoms under investigation, and from observations of the way in which the projected particles were deflected or *scattered*, they drew conclusions about the distribution of charge within the atoms at which the particles had been projected.

Fig. 44–3. The scattering of alpha particles by a thin metal foil.

The experimental setup is shown schematically in Fig. 44–3. A radioactive source at the left emits α-particles. Thick lead screens stop all particles except those in a narrow beam defined by small holes. The beam then passes through a thin metal foil (gold, silver, and copper were used) and strikes a plate coated with zinc sulfide. A momentary flash or scintillation can be observed on the screen whenever it is struck by an α-particle, and the number of particles that have been deflected through any angle from their original direction can therefore be determined.

According to the Thomson model, the atoms of a solid are packed together like marbles in a box. The experimental fact that an α-particle can pass right through a sheet of metal foil forces one to conclude, if this model is correct, that the α-particle is capable of actually penetrating the spheres of positive charge. Granted that this is possible, we can compute the deflection it would undergo. The Thomson atom is electrically neutral, so outside the atom no force would be exerted on the α-particle. Within the atom, the electrical force would be due in part to the electrons and in part to the sphere of positive charge. However, the mass of an α-particle is about 7400 times that of an electron, and from momentum considerations it follows that the α-particle can suffer only a negligible scattering as a consequence of forces between it and the much less massive electrons. It is only interactions with the positive charge, which makes up most of the atomic mass, that can deviate the α-particle.

The electrical force on an α-particle within a sphere of positive charge is like the gravitational force on a mass point within a sphere, except that gravitational forces are attractive, while the force between two positive charges is a repulsion. The gravitational intensity within a sphere is zero at the center and increases linearly with distance from the center, because that part of the mass of the sphere lying *outside* any radius exerts no force at interior points. The α-particle is therefore *repelled* from the center of

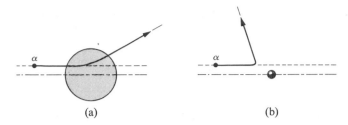

(a)   (b)

Fig. 44–4. (a) Alpha particle scattered through a small angle by the
Thomson atom. (b) Alpha particle scattered through a large angle by
the Rutherford nuclear atom.

the sphere with a force proportional to its distance from the center, and its trajectory
can be computed for any initial direction of approach such as that in Fig. 44–4(a).
On the basis of such calculations, Rutherford predicted the number of α-particles that
should be scattered at any angle with their original direction.

The experimental results did not agree with the calculations based on the Thomson
atom. In particular, many more particles were scattered through large angles than
were predicted. To account for the observed large-angle scattering, Rutherford concluded that the positive charge, instead of being spread through a sphere of atomic
dimensions (2 or 3 $\times$ 10^{-8} cm) was concentrated in a much smaller volume, which
he called a *nucleus*. When an α-particle approaches the nucleus, the entire nuclear
charge exerts a repelling effect on it down to extremely small separations, with the
consequence that much larger deviations can be produced. Figure 44–4(b) shows the
trajectory of an α-particle deflected by a Rutherford nuclear atom, for the same original path as that in part (a) of the figure.

Rutherford again computed the expected number of particles scattered through any
angle, assuming an inverse-square law of force between the α-particle and the nucleus
of the scattering atom. Within the limits of experimental accuracy, the computed
and observed results were in agreement down to distances of approach of about 10^{-12}
cm. We may therefore say that these experiments verify the Coulomb law for "point"
charges, and at the same time indicate that the size of the nucleus is about 10^{-12} cm.

44–4 Beta particles

Beta particles are negatively charged and are therefore deflected in an electric or
magnetic field. Deflection experiments similar to those described in Chapter 30 prove
conclusively that beta particles have the same charge and mass as electrons. They
are emitted with tremendous speeds, some reaching a value of 0.9995 that of light.

According to Einstein's special theory of relativity, the mass of a particle should
depend upon its speed acccording to the equation

$$m = \frac{m_0}{\sqrt{1 - v^2/c^2}},$$

where m_0 is the mass at zero speed (rest mass), v is the speed of the particle, and c is the speed of light. Assuming the charge to remain constant, the ratio of the charge e to the mass m of a beta particle should vary as follows:

$$\frac{e}{m} = \frac{e}{m_0}\sqrt{1 - v^2/c^2},$$

and therefore the value of e/m measured by deflection methods should depart considerably from the value e/m_0, since the values of v for beta particles approach so closely the value of c. Experiments to test these relativistic equations have been performed on the beta particles emitted by radium, and complete confirmation obtained.

Unlike alpha particles, which are emitted from a given nucleus with one or a few definite velocities, beta particles are emitted with a continuous range of velocities, from zero up to a maximum which depends on the nature of the emitting nucleus. If the principles of conservation of energy and of momentum are to hold in nuclear processes, it is necessary to assume that the emission of a beta particle is accompanied by the emission of another particle of negligible rest mass and with no charge. This particle, called the *neutrino*, is believed to have zero rest mass and zero charge and therefore, even in traversing the densest matter, would be expected to produce very little measurable effect. In spite of this, Reines and Cowan, in 1953 and again in 1956, succeeded in detecting its existence in a series of extraordinary experiments.

44–5 Gamma rays

Since gamma rays are not deflected by a magnetic field, they cannot consist of charged particles. They are, however, diffracted at the surface of a crystal in a manner similar to that of x-rays but with extremely small angles of diffraction. Experiments of this sort lead to the conclusion that "gamma rays" are actually electromagnetic waves of extremely short wavelength, about 1/100 that of x-rays.

The gamma-ray spectrum of any one element is a line spectrum, suggesting that a gamma-ray photon is emitted when a nucleus proceeds from a state of higher to a state of lower energy. This view is substantiated in the case of radium by the following facts. When alpha particles are emitted from radium they are found to consist of two groups, those with a kinetic energy of 48.79×10^5 electron volts and those with an energy of 46.95×10^5 electron volts. When a radium atom emits an alpha particle of the smaller energy, the resulting nucleus (which corresponds to the element *radon*) has a greater amount of energy than if the higher-speed alpha particle had been emitted. This represents an excited state of the radon nucleus. If now the radon nucleus undergoes a transition from this excited state to the lower energy state, a gamma-ray photon of energy $(48.79 - 46.95) \times 10^5 = 1.84 \times 10^5$ electron volts should be emitted. The measured energy of the gamma-ray photon emitted by radium is 1.89×10^5 electron volts, in excellent agreement.

Thus, by correlating alpha-particle energies and gamma-ray energies, it is possible in some cases to construct nuclear energy level diagrams similar to x-ray energy level diagrams.

TABLE 44–1

ATOMIC DATA*

Element	Atomic number, Z	Atomic mass in amu	Mass number, A
Hydrogen H	1	1.00783	1
Deuterium H	1	2.01410	2
Helium He	2	3.01603	3
Helium He	2	4.00260	4
Lithium Li	3	6.01513	6
Lithium Li	3	7.01601	7
Beryllium Be	4	8.00508	8
Beryllium Be	4	9.01219	9
Boron B	5	10.01294	10
Boron B	5	11.00931	11
Carbon C	6	12.00000	12
Carbon C	6	13.00335	13
Nitrogen N	7	14.00307	14
Nitrogen N	7	15.00011	15
Oxygen O	8	15.99491	16
Oxygen O	8	16.99913	17
Oxygen O	8	17.99916	18

*American Institute of Physics Handbook, 1963.

44–6 Radioactive transformations

Every atom is specified with the aid of three numbers:

1. The *atomic number Z*, or the positive charge of the nucleus, expressed as a multiple of the electronic charge.

2. The *atomic mass* or the mass of the atom expressed in atomic mass units (abbreviated amu), which are of such magnitude that the atomic mass of the most abundant isotope of carbon is taken arbitrarily to be exactly 12 amu.

3. The *mass number A*, or the nearest whole number to the actual atomic mass.

These numbers are given in Table 44–1 for a few of the light elements.

When a radioactive atom emits an alpha particle, the atomic number is reduced by 2 and the mass number reduced by 4, since an alpha particle is a helium nucleus with a charge of 2 units and a mass number 4. On the other hand, when a beta particle is emitted, the atomic number is increased by 1 but the mass number remains the same, since a beta particle is an electron with a charge of $-e$ and a negligible mass. The emission of gamma rays leaves both the atomic number and the mass number unaltered. In natural radioactivity either an alpha particle or a beta particle is emitted, and gamma rays may accompany either process.

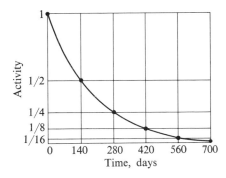

Fig. 44–5. Decay curve for the radioactive element polonium. Polonium has a half-life of 140 days.

Suppose a convenient mass of radioactive material is isolated by chemical methods, and its activity is measured as a function of the time. In all cases the "decay" curve has the appearance of the graph in Fig. 44–5. It is an exponential decay curve similar to that representing the discharge of a capacitor through a resistor. The fact that such a curve represents the activity of all known radioactive materials is interpreted as follows. The emission of an alpha or beta particle from a nucleus is a haphazard event, so that when a very large number of nuclei are present, the emission obeys the laws of probability. If it takes a time T for half the original nuclei to disintegrate, then in the next interval T, half of those remaining will disintegrate, and so on. The time for half the original atoms to undergo radioactive transformation is called the *half-life* of the atom, and it is one of the important constants to be measured. It is not necessary to wait until half the sample has disintegrated in order to measure the half-life. If the logarithm of the activity is plotted as a function of the time (on semilog paper), the resulting graph will be found to be a straight line, from whose slope the half-life may be obtained.

In studying radioactivity the following questions must be answered:

1. What is the parent nucleus?
2. What particle is emitted from this nucleus?
3. What is the half-life of the parent nucleus?
4. What is the resulting nucleus (called the product nucleus)?
5. Is the product nucleus radioactive and if so, what are the answers to questions 2, 3, and 4 for this nucleus, and so on?

Exhaustive investigations have been carried on in the last fifty years, and these questions have been answered for many nuclei. The results are most conveniently

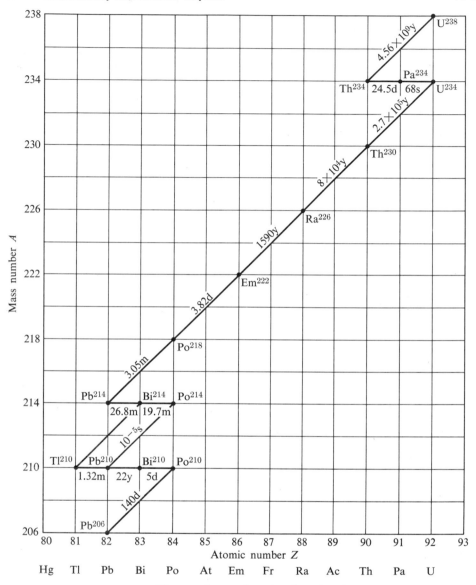

Fig. 44–6. The uranium series of radioactive elements.

expressed on a diagram such as that shown in Fig. 44–6. The mass number (the nearest whole number to the atomic mass) is plotted along the y-axis, and the atomic number (positive nuclear charge) along the x-axis. Unit increase of atomic number without change of mass number indicates emission of a beta particle; a decrease of two in atomic number accompanied by a decrease of four in mass number indicates emission of an alpha particle. The half-lives are given either in years (y), days (d), hours (h), minutes (m), or seconds (s). Figure 44–6, representing the uranium series of radioactive elements, is only one of three such series that exist.

44–7 Artificial nuclear disintegration

The nuclear disintegrations that have been described up to this point have consisted exclusively of a natural, uncontrolled emission of either an alpha or beta particle. Nothing was done to initiate the nuclear explosion, and nothing could be done to stop it. It occurred to Rutherford in 1919 that it ought to be possible to penetrate a nucleus with a massive high-speed particle such as an alpha particle and thereby either produce a nucleus with greater atomic number and mass number or induce an artificial nuclear explosion. Rutherford was successful in bombarding nitrogen with alpha particles and obtaining as a result an oxygen nucleus and a proton, according to the reaction

$$_2\text{He}^4 + {_7}\text{N}^{14} \rightarrow {_8}\text{O}^{17} + {_1}\text{H}^1. \tag{44–1}$$

In this symbolism, the number at the lower left corner represents the atomic number, and the upper right number represents the mass number. Thus, $_2\text{He}^4$ is an alpha particle and $_1\text{H}^1$ is a proton. Note that the sum of the initial atomic numbers is equal to the sum of the final atomic numbers, a condition imposed by the conservation of charge. The sum of the initial mass numbers is also equal to the sum of the final mass numbers, but the initial rest mass is not equal to the final rest mass. The difference between the rest masses is equal to the *nuclear reaction energy*, using Einstein's equation expressing the equivalence of mass and energy,

$$W = mc^2.$$

If the sum of the final rest masses exceeds the sum of the initial rest masses, energy is absorbed in the reaction. Conversely, if the final sum is less than the initial sum, energy is released in the form of kinetic energy of the final particles. (1 amu = 931 Mev.)

For example, in the nuclear reaction represented by Eq. (44–1), the rest masses of the various particles, in amu, are found from Table 44–1 to be:

$_2\text{He}^4 =$	4.00260	$_8\text{O}^{17} =$	16.99913
$_7\text{N}^{14} =$	14.00307	$_1\text{H}^1 =$	1.00783
	18.00567		18.00696

The total rest mass of the final products exceeds that of the initial particles by 0.00129 atomic mass unit, which is equivalent to 1.20 million electron volts. This amount of energy is absorbed in the reaction. If the initial particles did not have this much kinetic energy, the reaction would not have taken place.

On the other hand, in the proton bombardment of lithium and consequent formation of two alpha particles,

$$_1\text{H}^1 + {_3}\text{Li}^7 \rightarrow {_2}\text{He}^4 + {_2}\text{He}^4, \tag{44–2}$$

the sum of the final rest masses is smaller than the sum of the initial values, as shown by the following data:

$_1\text{H}^1 =$	1.00783	$_2\text{He}^4 =$	4.00260
$_3\text{Li}^7 =$	7.01601	$_2\text{He}^4 =$	4.00260
	8.02384		8.00520

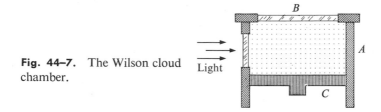

Fig. 44-7. The Wilson cloud chamber.

Since the decrease in mass is 0.01864 amu, energy of amount 17.3 Mev is liberated and appears as kinetic energy of the two separating alpha particles. This computation may be verified by observing the distance the alpha particles travel in air at atmospheric pressure before being brought to rest by collisions with molecules. The distance is found to be 8.31 cm. (One way of making such measurements is with the help of a cloud chamber, illustrated in Fig. 18–13 or 44–7.) A series of independent experiments is then performed in which the range of alpha particles of known energy is measured. These experiments show that in order to travel 8.31 cm, an alpha particle must have an initial kinetic energy of 8.64 Mev. The energy of the two alphas together is therefore $2 \times 8.64 = 17.28$ Mev, in excellent agreement with the value 17.3 Mev obtained from the mass decrease.

Alpha particles and protons are not the only particles used to instigate artificial nuclear disintegration. The nucleus of a deuterium atom, known as the *deuteron* and represented by the symbol $_1\text{H}^2$, may be speeded up tremendously. At high speed the deuteron is a very effective "atom smasher." In order that positively charged particles such as the alpha particle, the proton, and the deuteron can be used to penetrate the nuclei of other atoms, they must travel with very high speeds to avoid being repelled or deflected by the positive charge of the nucleus they are approaching. Obviously, the ideal bombarding particle is one which, besides being massive, has no charge and is therefore not affected by the electric field around a nucleus. A discussion of this particle, the *neutron*, will be given in Section 44–9.

44-8 Cosmic rays. The positron

If a charged electroscope is left standing, it will eventually lose its charge no matter how well it is insulated. Evidently the air is slightly ionized at all times, even in the absence of obvious causes of ionization such as x-rays, ultraviolet light, and radioactivity. Ionization of air inside a vessel is decreased slightly if the vessel is lowered into a lake, but increases considerably if the vessel is transported in a balloon high into the stratosphere. Hess suggested that the ionization is due to some kind of penetrating waves or particles from outer space, and called them *cosmic rays*. It is fairly certain that cosmic rays consist largely of high-speed protons with energies of the order of billions of electron volts. A collision between such a proton and the nucleus of a nitrogen or oxygen atom in the upper atmosphere gives rise to so many interesting secondary phenomena that the study of cosmic rays has become one of the richest sources of knowledge of the structure and properties of the nucleus.

An instrument devised by C. T. R. Wilson, called a *cloud chamber*, which is used extensively not only to study cosmic rays, but also to render visible the paths of the particles engaging in artificially produced nuclear reactions, was described in Section 18–8.

The principle of the cloud chamber is illustrated in Fig. 44–7. The space above the piston, called the expansion chamber, contains saturated water vapor. If this vapor is slightly compressed and then allowed to expand quickly (adiabatically), water droplets will condense on any particles which serve as nuclei of condensation. A massive particle moving rapidly in the water vapor creates many ions and electrons in its path. Water droplets condense on these ions and electrons and thus make visible the path of the ionizing particle. Cloud chambers are sometimes made several feet in diameter, and when illuminated on the side, are photographed from above, at times with the aid of two cameras in order to obtain stereoscopic pictures. Very often the cloud chamber is placed in a magnetic field so that the ionizing particle travels perpendicular to the field. If the ionizing particle is charged, it will be deflected, and by measuring the radius of curvature of the path its momentum may be determined, provided the charge is known.

In recent years, the *bubble chamber*, which was also described in Section 18–8, has proved even more useful than the cloud chamber for studying ionizing particles. The bubble chamber makes use of a superheated liquid, rather than a supersaturated vapor. When ions are produced in a superheated liquid, it boils in the vicinity of an ion and forms a tiny bubble of vapor. The track of an ionizing particle is thus marked by a line of vapor bubbles rather than of liquid droplets. The advantage of the bubble chamber is that the molecules of a liquid are much closer together than those of a gas, so that there is a greater probability of an encounter between a molecule and an ion.

Tracks of particles passing through a bubble chamber in a magnetic field are shown in Fig. 30–6.

The positive electron was first observed during the course of an investigation of cosmic rays by Dr. Carl D. Anderson in 1932, in the cloud chamber photograph reproduced in Fig. 44–8. The photograph was made with the cloud chamber in a

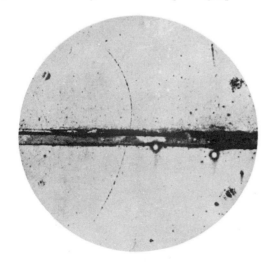

Fig. 44–8. Track of a positive electron traversing a lead plate 6 mm thick. (Photograph by C. D. Anderson.)

magnetic field perpendicular to the plane of the paper. A lead plate crosses the chamber and evidently the particle has passed through it. Since the curvature of the track is greater above the plate than below it, the velocity is less above than below and the inference is that the particle was moving upward, since it is difficult to see how it could have gained energy going through the lead.

The density of droplets along the path is what would be expected if the particle were an electron. But the direction of the magnetic field and the direction of motion are consistent only with a particle of positive sign. Hence Anderson concluded the track had been made by a positive electron or *positron*. Since the time of this discovery many thousands of such tracks have been photographed and the positron's existence is now definitely established. Its mass is the same as that of a negative electron and its charge is equal but of opposite sign.

Positive electrons have only a transitory existence and do not form a part of ordinary matter. There are two known processes which result in positive electrons. They are ejected from the nuclei of certain artificially radioactive materials, and they spring into existence (along with a negative electron) in a process known as "pair production" in which a γ-ray is simultaneously annihilated. Charge is conserved in the process, since the particles have charges of opposite sign.

44–9 Neutrons and mesons

In 1930, Bothe and Becker in Germany observed that when beryllium, boron, or lithium was bombarded by fast alpha particles, the bombarded material emitted something, either particles or electromagnetic waves, of much greater penetrating power than the original alpha particles. Further experiments in 1932 by Curie and Joliot in Paris confirmed these results, but all attempts to explain them in terms of γ-rays were unsuccessful. Chadwick in England repeated the experiments and found that they could be satisfactorily interpreted on the assumption that *uncharged* particles of mass approximately equal to that of a proton were emitted from the nuclei of the bombarded material. He called the particles *neutrons*. The emission of a neutron from a beryllium nucleus takes place according to the reaction

$$_2\text{He}^4 + {}_4\text{Be}^9 \rightarrow {}_6\text{C}^{12} + {}_0\text{n}^1,$$

where $_0\text{n}^1$ is the symbol for a neutron.

Since neutrons have no charge, they produce no ionization in their passage through gases. They are not deflected by the electric field around a nucleus and can be stopped only by colliding with a nucleus in a direct hit, in which case they may either undergo an elastic impact or penetrate the nucleus. It was shown in Chapter 8 that if an elastic body strikes a motionless elastic body of the same mass, the first is stopped and the second moves off with the same speed as the first. Since the proton and neutron masses are almost the same, it follows that fast neutrons may be slowed down by performing collisions with the hydrogen atoms in hydrogenous materials like water or paraffin. The usual laboratory method of obtaining slow neutrons is to surround the fast neutron source with water or blocks of paraffin.

TABLE 44–2

NUCLEAR PARTICLES

Nucleus	Mass number (total number of nuclear particles), A	Atomic number (number of protons), Z	Neutron number, $N = A - Z$
$_1\text{H}^1$	1	1	0
$_1\text{D}^2$	2	1	1
$_2\text{He}^4$	4	2	2
$_3\text{Li}^6$	6	3	3
$_3\text{Li}^7$	7	3	4
$_4\text{Be}^9$	9	4	5
$_5\text{B}^{10}$	10	5	5
$_5\text{B}^{11}$	11	5	6
$_6\text{C}^{12}$	12	6	6
$_6\text{C}^{13}$	13	6	7
$_7\text{N}^{14}$	14	7	7
$_8\text{O}^{16}$	16	8	8
$_{11}\text{Na}^{23}$	23	11	12
$_{29}\text{Cu}^{65}$	65	29	36
$_{80}\text{Hg}^{200}$	200	80	120
$_{92}\text{U}^{235}$	235	92	143
$_{92}\text{U}^{238}$	238	92	146

Once the neutrons are moving slowly, they may be detected by means of the alpha particles they eject from the nucleus of a boron atom, according to the reaction

$$_0\text{n}^1 + {}_5\text{B}^{10} \rightarrow {}_3\text{Li}^7 + {}_2\text{He}^4.$$

The ejected alpha particle then produces ionization which may be detected in a Geiger counter or an ionization chamber.

The discovery of the neutron gave the first real clue to the structure of the nucleus. Heretofore it had been thought that the total mass of a nucleus was due to protons only. Now it is believed that a nucleus consists of both protons and neutrons (except

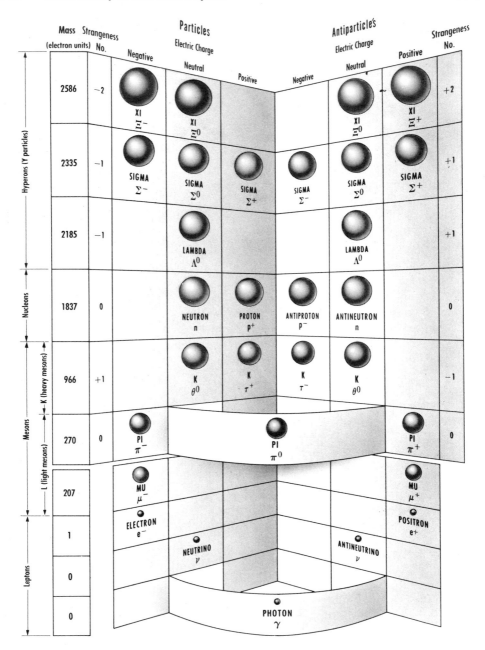

Fig. 44-9. The mirror symmetry of elementary particles. Of the 30 particles shown, a full 16—the 4 K's and the 12 hyperons—were unsuspected a dozen years ago. Only 7 of the 30 are intrinsically stable: photons, protons, electrons, neutrinos, antineutrinos, antiprotons, and positrons. The last two, however, share the usual fate of antiparticles that wander into this world: they are annihilated when they meet their counterparts. Antineutrinos may possibly be an exception to this rule. Photons and neutral pi-mesons commute freely be-

hydrogen, whose nucleus consists only of one proton) and that (1) the mass number equals the total number of nuclear particles and (2) the atomic number equals the number of protons only. The number of neutrons in a nucleus is therefore the difference between the mass number and the atomic number, as shown in Table 44–2, where a few representative elements are listed.

In 1935, the Japanese physicist Hideki Yukawa inferred the existence of a particle of mass intermediate between that of the electron and the proton from theoretical equations derived from the assumption of very short-range nuclear forces between constituents of the nucleus. A particle of intermediate mass, but not identical with that predicted by Yukawa, was discovered one year later by Anderson and Neddermeyer as a component of cosmic radiation. This particle is now known as a *mu meson* (or *muon*). It has a mass 207 times as large as that of an electron, a mean lifetime of 2.2×10^{-6} sec, and decays into an electron, a neutrino, and an antineutrino. A particle more nearly like the one predicted by Yukawa is called a *pi meson* (or *pion*). It has a mass 273 times that of an electron, a mean lifetime of about 2.6×10^{-8} sec, and decays into a muon and a neutrino. Muons and pions may have either negative or positive charges. Neutral pions with a lifetime of about 2×10^{-16} sec have also been discovered. When they disintegrate they form two gamma-ray photons.

The interaction of both muons and pions with protons, neutrons, and nuclei has been studied most extensively both experimentally and theoretically. The experimental results and their theoretical interpretation constitute a perplexing and difficult part of modern physics. Some insight into the complexity of the subject will be obtained from an inspection of Fig. 44–9.

44–10 Nuclear stability

Of about 1000 different isotopes now known, only about one-quarter are stable. The others are radioactive, with lifetimes ranging from a small fraction of a second to many years. The stable nuclei are indicated on the graph in Fig. 44–10, where the neutron number N is plotted against the proton number Z. Since the mass number A is the sum $N + Z$, a curve of constant A is a straight line perpendicular to the line $N = Z$. In general, lines of constant A pass through only one or two stable nuclei (see $A = 20$, $A = 40$, $A = 60$, etc.), but there are four cases when such lines pass through three stable isotopes, namely at $A = 96$, 124, 130, and 136. It is also an interesting fact that only four stable nuclei have both odd Z and odd N: $_1H^2$, $_3Li^6$, $_5B^{10}$, $_7N^{14}$.

---

tween both worlds, since each is its own antiparticle—although the neutral pi-meson has little time for traveling because it is the second shortest-lived of all the known particles. A neutron is stable if bound in an atomic nucleus; otherwise it has a half-life of 13 min, decaying into a proton, an electron, and a neutrino. Similarly, all unstable particles decay, directly or indirectly, into two or more of the 7 stable ones. Their mean lifetimes range from a few millionths to less than 10^{-15} second. (Adapted by permission from *Fortune Magazine*, copyright 1957 by Time, Inc.)

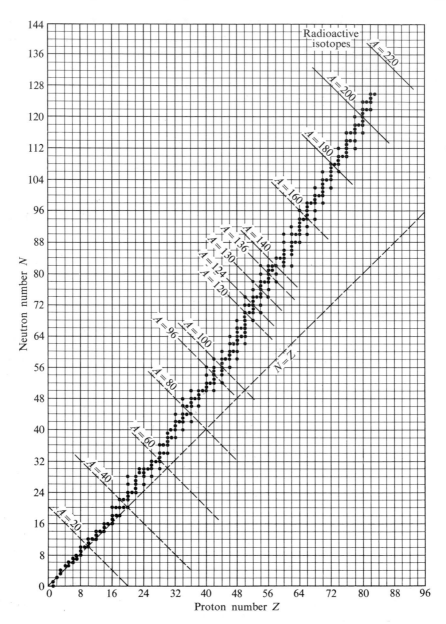

Fig. 44–10.   Neutron-proton diagram of stable nuclei.

It is seen that the points representing stable isotopes define a rather narrow stability region. For low mass numbers, $N/Z = 1$. This ratio increases and becomes about 1.6 at large mass numbers. Points to the right of the stability region represent nuclei that have an excess of protons or a deficiency of neutrons. They usually decay by emitting a positron or capturing an electron. To the left of the stability region are the points representing nuclei with an excess of neutrons or a deficiency of protons. Their most probable method of decay is by negative beta-particle emission, but the emission of neutrons or alpha particles is also possible.

It is not well understood why a neutron-proton ratio different from that within the stability region should give rise to radioactive emission, but at least one can predict, with the aid of Fig. 44–10, what the direction of the radioactive change will be.

44–11 Nuclear fission

Up to this point, all nuclear reactions considered have involved the ejection of relatively light particles, such as alpha particles, beta particles, protons, or neutrons. That this is not always the case was discovered by Hahn and Strassman in Germany in 1939. These scientists bombarded uranium ($Z = 92$) with neutrons, and after a careful chemical analysis discovered barium ($Z = 56$) and krypton ($Z = 36$) among the products. Cloud-chamber photographs (see Fig. 8–11) showed the two heavy particles traveling in opposite directions with tremendous speed. The uranium is said to undergo *fission*. Measurement showed that an enormous amount of energy, 200 million electron volts, is released when uranium splits up in this way. Since the rest mass of a uranium atom exceeds the sum of the rest masses of the fission products, it follows from the Einstein mass-energy relation that the extra energy released during fission is transformed into kinetic energy of the fission fragments. Uranium fission may be accomplished by either fast or slow neutrons. Of the two most abundant isotopes of uranium, $_{92}U^{238}$ and $_{92}U^{235}$, both may be split by a fast neutron, whereas only $_{92}U^{235}$ is split by a slow neutron.

When uranium undergoes fission, barium and krypton are not the only products. Over 100 different isotopes of more than 20 different elements have been detected among fission products. All of these atoms are, however, in the middle of the periodic table, with atomic numbers ranging from 34 to 58.

Discovery of the fact that 200 million electron volts of energy were released when uranium underwent fission, although of great interest to physicists, appeared to be of little importance in everyday life. The phenomenon took on a different aspect when it was discovered that during fission other neutrons were liberated from the uranium nucleus. This immediately suggested the possibility of a chain reaction, that is, a self-sustaining series of events which, once started, will continue until all the uranium in a given sample is used up (provided the sample stays together). In the case of a uranium chain reaction, a neutron causes one uranium atom to undergo fission, during which a large amount of energy and several neutrons are emitted. These neutrons then cause fission in neighboring uranium nuclei, which also give out energy and more neutrons. The chain reaction may be made to proceed slowly and in a controlled manner, and the device for accomplishing this is called an *atomic pile* or a *nuclear reactor*. If the chain reaction is fast and uncontrolled, the device is a bomb (called an *atomic bomb*), whose destructive ability is many thousands of times that of previously existing bombs.

The first experiments on an atomic pile were performed at Columbia University by Fermi, Szilard, and Zinn. The work was then continued in Chicago, where these physicists succeeded in establishing a controlled chain reaction in a huge structure composed of graphite in which rods of uranium were embedded. The principles of pile construction, operation, and control constitute a fascinating branch of modern applied physics. It would take too much space to go into details, but it is worth while to list the important uses for an atomic pile:

1. To produce the element plutonium from $_{92}U^{238}$ for explosive purposes.

2. To produce a neutron beam of high intensity for nuclear bombardment studies.

3. To produce artificially radioactive isotopes for medical use and for biological research.

4. To generate power for the propulsion of ships, submarines, and possibly aircraft and space vehicles.

44–12 Thermonuclear reactions

There are two types of nuclear reactions in which large amounts of energy may be liberated. In both types, the rest mass of the products is less than the original rest mass. The fission of uranium, already described, is an example of one type. The other involves the combination of two light nuclei to form a nucleus which is more complex but whose rest mass is less than the sum of the rest masses of the original nuclei. Examples of such energy-liberating reactions are as follows:

$$_1H^1 + {_1}H^1 \rightarrow {_1}H^2 + {_1}e^0,$$

$$_1H^2 + {_1}H^1 \rightarrow {_2}He^3 + \gamma\text{-radiation},$$

$$_2He^3 + {_2}He^3 \rightarrow {_2}He^4 + {_1}H^1 + {_1}H^1.$$

In the first, two protons combine to form a deuteron and a positron. In the second, a proton and a deuteron unite to form the light isotope of helium. For the third reaction to occur, the first two reactions must occur twice, in which case two nuclei of light helium unite to form ordinary helium. These reactions, known as the *proton-proton chain*, are believed to take place in the interior of the sun and also in many other stars which are known to be composed mainly of hydrogen.

The positrons produced during the first step of the proton-proton chain collide with electrons; annihilation takes place, and their energy is converted into γ-radiation. The net effect of the chain, therefore, is the combination of four hydrogen nuclei into a helium nucleus and γ-radiation. The net amount of energy released may be calculated from the mass balance as follows:

Rest mass of 4 hydrogen atoms	= 4.03132 amu
Rest mass of 1 helium atom	= 4.00260 amu
Difference in mass	= 0.02872 amu
	= 26.7 Mev

In the case of the sun, a gram of its mass contains about 2×10^{23} protons. Hence, if all of these protons were consumed, the energy released would be about 55,000 kwh. If the sun were to continue to radiate at its present rate, it would take about 30 billion years to exhaust its supply of protons.

Temperatures of millions of degrees are necessary to initiate the proton-proton chain. A star may achieve such a high temperature by contracting and consequently liberating a large amount of gravitational potential energy. When the temperature gets high enough the reactions occur, more energy is liberated, and the pressure of the resulting radiation prevents further contraction. Only after most of the hydrogen has been converted into helium will further contraction and an accompanying increase of temperature result. Conditions are then suitable for the formation of heavier elements.

Temperatures and pressures similar to those in the interior of stars may be achieved on earth at the moment of explosion of a uranium or plutonium fission bomb. If the fission bomb is surrounded by proper proportions of the hydrogen isotopes, these may be caused to combine into helium and liberate still more energy. This combination of uranium and hydrogen is called a "hydrogen bomb."

Attempts are being made at this time all over the world to control the fusion of hydrogen isotopes and to utilize the resulting energy for peaceful purposes. The reactions whose control is being studied are the following:

$$_1H^2 + {}_1H^2 \rightarrow {}_1H^3 + {}_1H^1 + 4 \text{ Mev}, \tag{1}$$

$$_1H^3 + {}_1H^2 \rightarrow {}_2He^4 + {}_0n^1 + 17.6 \text{ Mev}, \tag{2}$$

$$_1H^2 + {}_1H^2 \rightarrow {}_2He^3 + {}_0n^1 + 3.3 \text{ Mev}, \tag{3}$$

$$_2He^3 + {}_1H^2 \rightarrow {}_2He^4 + {}_1H^1 + 18.3 \text{ Mev}. \tag{4}$$

In the first, two deuterons combine to form tritium and a proton. In the second, the tritium nucleus combines with another deuteron to form helium and a neutron. The result of both of these reactions is the liberation of 21.6 Mev of energy. Reactions (3) and (4) represent another pair that is about equal in probability to reactions (1) and (2) and which would be attended by the liberation of the same amount of energy. No one has as yet succeeded in producing these reactions under controlled laboratory conditions.

Answers to

Odd-Numbered Problems

CHAPTER 1

1–3. (a) 19.3 lb in a direction mid-way between the 10-lb forces
(b) 8.46 lb in a direction mid-way between the 10-lb forces

1–5. 15 lb, 53° above the x-axis
26 lb, 28° below the x-axis

1–7. 25.7 lb, 30.6 lb

1–9. (a) 18.5 lb (b) 9.2 lb

1–11. 308 lb, 25° above the x-axis

1–13. (a) 7 lb, 2.9 lb (b) 7.6 lb (c) 11 lb

1–15. $F_x = 430$ lb, W; $F_y = 973$ lb, N

1–17. (a) 14 lb, same direction, 1.7 ft from the 10-lb force between A and B
(b) 6 lb, direction of 10-lb force, 4 ft to the right of B.

CHAPTER 2

2–3. (a) 10 lb (b) 20 lb

2–5. (a) 150 lb in A, 180 lb in B, 200 lb in C
(b) 200 lb in A, 280 lb in B, 200 lb in C
(c) 550 lb in A, 670 lb in B, 200 lb in C
(d) 167 lb in A, 58 lb in B, 125 lb in C

2–7. (a) Parts (b) and (c) can be solved
(b) In part (a) another side or angle is needed

2–9. 630 lb

2–11. (a) 20 lb (b) 30 lb

2–13. (a) $w/(2 \sin \theta)$ (b) $w/(2 \tan \theta)$

2–17. 22 lb

2–19. (a) 76 lb (b) 24 lb (c) from 15.4 to 84.6 lb

2–21. (a) Held back (b) 144 lb

2–23. (a) 3 lb (b) 4 lb (c) 5 lb

2–25. (b) 10 lb (c) 30 lb

CHAPTER 3

3–3. (b) 5 ft (c) 5. 75 ft

3–5. 25 lb, 20 lb to the right, 5 lb up

3–7. (a) -6 lb, 10 lb (b) $\frac{5}{3}$ (c) 11.7 lb
(d) 2 ft from right end

3–9. (a) 54 lb (b) 24 lb

3–11. (a) 65 lb, 75 lb (b) 45 lb
(c) 47 lb (d) 173 lb

3–13. (a) arctan 0.3 (b) 24 cm (c) 0.53

3–17. (a) 43 lb (b) 37 lb (c) 59 lb

3–19. (a) 20 lb (b) 0.2 ft to right of c.g.
(c) 1.25 ft

3–23. About 3000 mi from the center of the earth

CHAPTER 4

4–1. (a) 12.5 cm/sec^2 (b) 7840 cm

4–3. (a) 300 ft (b) 60 ft/sec

4–5. (a) 24 ft/sec, 29 ft/sec, 34 ft/sec
(b) 2.5 ft/sec^2 (c) 21.5 ft/sec
(d) 8.6 sec (e) 23 ft (f) 1 sec
(g) 24 ft/sec

4–7. (a) 32 ft/sec (b) 2.83 sec
(c) 16 ft (d) 22.6 ft/sec
(e) 16 ft/sec

4–9. (a) 8.7 sec (b) 75 ft
(c) $v_A = 52$ ft/sec,
$v_T = 35$ ft/sec

4–11. (a) 94 ft/sec (b) 124 ft
(c) 53 ft/sec (d) 150 ft/sec^2
(e) 1.96 sec (f) 93 ft/sec

4–13. 39.4 ft

4–15. (a) 48 ft/sec (b) 36 ft (c) Zero
(d) 32 ft/sec^2, downward
(e) 80 ft/sec

4–17. (a) 32 ft (b) 13 ft/sec, -32 ft/sec^2
(c) -51 ft/sec, -32 ft/sec^2
(d) 37 ft/sec

4–19. (a) 36 ft (b) 0.5 sec
(c) 32 ft/sec, -32 ft/sec^2,
-16 ft/sec, -32 ft/sec^2
4–21. (a) 4 m/sec^2 (b) 6 m/sec
(c) 4.5 m
4–25. (a) $t \approx 1$ min (b) $y \approx 100$ mi
4–27. (d) $k = 3.33 \times 10^{-3}$ ft^{-1}
(e) -1.33 ft/sec^2
4–31. 6.55 knots
4–33. (a) 50 mi/hr, 53° S of W
(b) 30° N of W
4–35. (a) 5 mi/hr, 53° E of N
(b) 0.75 mi (c) 15 min
4–37. 11.6 mi/hr, 59° N of E
4–39. 0.88c
4–41. (a) 37° (c) 1.28×10^{-6} sec
(d) 1.25×10^{-7} sec (e) 80 m
(f) No; E_1 occurs earlier than E_3

CHAPTER 5

5–1. (a) 0.102 kgm (b) 0.00102 gm
(c) 0.0312 slug
5–5. (a) 0.5 slug (b) 500 ft
5–7. (a) 1.62×10^{-10} dyne
(b) 3.33×10^{-9} sec
(c) 1.8×10^{17} cm/sec^2
5–9. 6.2×10^{27} gm
5–11. 6.32 ft/sec^2
5–13. (a) 59.0 n (b) const. velocity
(c) 6.25 m/sec
5–15. (a) 40 lb (b) 4 ft/sec^2 downward
(c) zero
5–17. 240 ft
5–19. $W = 2wa/(g + a)$
5–21. (a) 37° (b) 6.4 ft/sec^2 (c) 2.5 sec
5–23. (a) 6 lb (b) 8 ft/sec^2
5–25. (a) 2 lb (b) 1.9 lb
5–27. (a) 196 cm/sec^2 (b) 314,000 dynes
5–29. (a) to left (b) 2.13 ft/sec^2
(c) 43.3 lb
5–31. 1.33 lb
5–33.

	a_1	a_2
(a)	0	0
(b)	0	0
(c)	0	16 ft/sec^2
(d)	4 ft/sec^2	28 ft/sec^2
(e)	16 ft/sec^2	48 ft/sec^2

5–35. (a) 4.4 ft/sec^2 (b) 1.2 lb
5–37. 127.5 lb
5–39. g/μ
5–43. (a) 133 lb (b) 33 lb (c) 33 lb
5–45. (c) $v_T = \sqrt{ma_0/k}$
(d) $t_R\sqrt{m/ka_0}$
(e) $v = v_T \dfrac{e^{2t/t_R} - 1}{e^{2t/t_R} + 1}$

CHAPTER 6

6–1. (a) 0.5 sec (b) 12 ft/sec
(c) 20 ft/sec, 53° below horizontal
6–3. (a) 20 sec (b) 6000 ft
(c) $v_x = 300$ ft/sec
$v_y = 640$ ft/sec
6–5. (a) 100 ft (b) 200 ft
(c) $v_x = 80$ ft/sec
$v_y = 80$ ft/sec
$v = 113$ ft/sec, 45° below
horizontal
6–7. (a) 40 sec (b) 55°
6–9. (a) 8 ft (b) 19°, 71°
6–11. 100 ft
6–13. Yes. Ball clears fence by 10 ft
6–15. 1.98 sec, 157 sec
6–17. 1300 ft
6–19. $R = 2v_0^2 \sin(\theta_0 - \alpha)\cos\theta_0/g\cos^2\alpha$
6–23. (a) About 28° above horizontal
(b) About 650 mi
(c) About 10,000 mi/hr
(d) About 875 mi (e) About 5 min
6–25. (a) 6.5 cm/sec, 25° E of N
(b) 3.25 cm/sec^2, 25° E of N
6–27. (a) 66,700 mi/hr (b) 0.0193 ft/sec^2
6–29. 22 m/sec
6–31. (a) 0.43 (b) To the very end
6–33. (a) 6.4 sec (b) No
6–35. (a) 52° (b) No
(c) The bead would remain at the bottom
6–37. (a) 33° (b) 1.45 mi (c) 0.65
6–39. (a) 1530 ft (b) 1440 lb
6–41. (a) 0.37 (b) 4.3 sec
(c) Twice his actual weight
(d) He would strike the ground at a point 30 ft from the center of the wheel

6–45. 36,000 km above the earth
6–47. (a) 98 min   (b) 26.5 ft/sec^2
6–49. 9.8 oz

CHAPTER 7

7–1. 63.4 $\times$ 10^6 ft·lb
7–3. 9850 ft·lb
7–5. (a) 6 lb   (b) 48 lb   (c) 22.5 ft·lb
7–7. (a) 55,000 ft·lb   (b) 4 times
7–9. 4.5 $\times$ 10^{-10} erg
7–11. 9.8 joules
7–13. (a) 5 lb, 10 lb, 20 lb
      (b) 1.25 ft·lb, 5 ft·lb, 20 ft·lb
7–15. (a) 33 ft·lb   (b) about 13 ft·lb
7–17. (a) 160 ft·lb   (b) 160 ft·lb
7–19. (a) 3300 ft·lb   (b) 1300 ft·lb
      (c) 1500 ft·lb   (d) 500 ft·lb
      Goes into heat.
      (e) $b + c + d = a$
7–21. (a) 42 lb   (b) 105 ft·lb
7–23. (a) 40 ft/sec   (b) 19 ft/sec
7–25. 10 cm
7–27. (a) 0.25   (b) 3.5 ft·lb
7–31. 1.81 m/sec
7–33. (a) 24.6 ft/sec   (b) 27.2 ft/sec
      (c) 22.5 lb   (d) 10 ft/sec
7–39. 154 hp
7–41. $1.29
7–43. (a) 250 lb   (b) 5 hp, 80 hp
7–45. (a) 8200 joules   (b) 8200 joules
      (c) 0.55 hp
7–47. (a) 6300 lb   (b) 30 ft/sec
      (c) 68,000 ft·lb   (d) 220,000 ft·lb
      (e) 250 hp
7–49. (a) 250 lb   (b) 39 hp   (c) 16 hp
      (d) 10.5% grade

CHAPTER 8

8–1. (a) 28,000 slug·ft/sec
     (b) 60 mi/hr   (c) 43 mi/hr
8–3. (a) 8 $\times$ 10^5 m/sec^2
     (b) 4 $\times$ 10^4 n   (c) 5 $\times$ 10^{-4} sec
     (d) 20 n·sec
8–7. (a) 1 ft/sec   (b) $\frac{2}{3}$ of original E_k
     (c) 1.5 ft/sec
8–9. 780 ft/sec
8–11. 30 cm

8–13. (a) 0.39 ft   (b) 1950 ft·lb
      (c) 3.9 ft·lb
8–15. 3.3 cm
8–17. 17 mi/hr 53° E of S
8–19. (a) 10 cm/sec   (b) 0.14 joule
      (c) -70 cm/sec, 80 cm/sec
8–21. 5 cm/sec, -25 cm/sec
8–23. (a) 50 cm/sec 53° below the x-axis in
      the fourth quadrant
      (b) 380,000 ergs
8–27. (a) $v_A = 58.5$ ft/sec,
      $v_B = 41.5$ ft/sec
8–29. (a) 58,700 ft   (b) 18 $\times$ 10^4 m ft·lb
8–31. (a) 7.20 ft/sec   (b) 375
8–33. (a) 18 ft/sec   (b) 125
8–35. 1.82 ft/sec
8–37. (a) 149° from direction of electron
      (b) 10.6 $\times$ 10^{-16} gm·cm/sec
      (c) 14.5 $\times$ 10^{-10} erg
8–39. 4.22 lb
8–41. (a) 25 $\times$ 10^6 dynes, 250 n
8–45. (a) 1.8 $\times$ 10^{14} joules
      (b) 1.8 $\times$ 10^{14} megawatts
      (c) 2.5 $\times$ 10^{10} lb or 4 $\times$ 10^8 ft^3
8–47. (a) 0.89   (b) 1.56

CHAPTER 9

9–1. 16, 31, 47 ft/sec; 600, 1800, 5400
     rev/min
9–3. 20 rad/sec^2
9–7. (a) At the bottom of the wheel
     (b) 178 ft/sec^2
9–9. (a) 135°
     (b) 2.36 ft/sec^2, 11.1 ft/sec^2
9–11. 164,000 rev/min
9–15. (a) A smallest   (b) D largest
9–17. (a) 2.56 $\times$ 10^{30} slug·mi^2
      (b) 2530 mi
9–19. (a) $mb^2/12$,   (b) $mb^2/3$
9–21. 0.47
9–23. (a) 19.1 kgm·m^2 (b) 2 n·m
      (c) 91.6 rev
9–25. (a) 63 m   (b) 38 newtons
      (c) 185 newtons
9–27. (a) 0.0625 slug·ft^2
      (b) 12 lb, 4 lb
9–29. (a) 2 rad/sec^2 (b) 8 rad/sec
      (c) 240 ft·lb   (d) 7.5 slug·ft^2

9–31. (a) 4400 lb·ft
(b) 5900 lb   (c) 190 ft/sec
9–33. 69 mr^2
9–35. 1.1 slug·ft^2
9–37. (a) 2×10^7 joules   (b) 18 min
9–39. (a) 4 rad/sec^2 (b) 14 rad/sec
(c) 32,000 ft·lb
9–41. 1.45 joules
9–43. (a) 24 slug·ft^2/sec   (b) 6 rad/sec
(c) 24 ft·lb, 72 ft·lb
9–45. 1 ft
9–47. (a) 6 rev/min   (b) 6 rev/min
9–49. 4500 ft·lb
9–51. 0.15 rad/sec in same direction
9–53. (a) 1.8 hr   (b) 130,000 lb·ft
9–55. 2.5 rad/sec
9–57. (a) 5 lb upward
(b) 7.4 lb up, 2.6 lb up
(c) 16.5 lb up, 6.5 lb down
(d) 0.087 rev/sec

CHAPTER 10

10–1. 25×10^6 lb/in^2
10–3.   (b) 14×10^6 lb/in^2
(c) 0.016×10^6 lb/in^2
10–5.   (a) 27.5 lb   (b) 0.028 ft
10–7.   0.0287 in.
10–9.   (a) 2.18 ft (b) 30,000 lb/in^2 in steel,
12,000 lb/in^2 in copper
(c) 1.03×10^{-3} in steel, 7.5×10^{-4}
in copper
10–15. Steel, 0.64×10^{-6} atm^{-1}
Water, 50×10^{-6} atm^{-1}
Water is 78 times more compressible
10–17. 5.1 in.

CHAPTER 11

11–3.   (a) 9470 cm/sec^2, 377 cm/sec
(b) 5680 cm/sec^2, 301 cm/sec
(c) 0.0368 sec
11–5.   (a) 2400 π^2 ft/sec^2
(b) 740 lb   (c) 43 mi/hr
11–7.   23.2 lb
11–9.   (a) 9 vib/sec   (b) 20×10^6 lb/in^2
11–11. (a) 4 lb
(b) 2.59 in. below equilibrium, moving upward   (c) 5.2 lb
11–13. (a) 31 cm/sec   (b) 49 cm/sec^2
(c) 0.33 sec   (d) 100 cm

11–15. 0.79 sec
11–17. (a) 5.6 lb   (b) 13.6 lb, 8 lb, 2.4 lb
(c) 0.62 ft·lb, 0.077 ft·lb
11–19. (a) $k = k_1 + k_2$
(b) $k = k_1 + k_2$
(c) $\dfrac{1}{k} = \dfrac{1}{k_1} + \dfrac{1}{k_2}$
(d) $\sqrt{2}$
11–21. (a) 1.4 sec, 3.5 cm
11–23. 0.817 ft
11–25. (a) 93.3 cm   (b) -2×10^{-4}
11–27. (a) 6.9 in.   (b) 0.70 rad/sec
11–29. (a) 81 ft
11–31. 67 cm

CHAPTER 12

12–1.   21 lb/in^2
12–5.   (a) 1.09×10^6 dynes/cm^2
(b) 8 cm of mercury
(c) 109 cm of water
12–7.   (a) 9.8×10^6
(b) 1.95×10^5 dynes
12–9.   34.8 ft^2
12–11. 270,000 ft^3, 9.3 tons lift, using helium
12–13. (a) 5 cm   (b) 4900 dynes/cm^2
12–15. (a) 100 lb/ft^3 (b) E will read 5 lb,
D will read 15 lb
12–19. (a) 4500 lb   (b) 10,000 lb
(c) 230 lb
12–21. 100.87 gm
12–23. (b) 4 lb   (c) 1 ft^3
12–25. 0.781 gm/cm^3
12–29. 6.25×10^4 lb·ft
12–31. (a) 4.17×10^7 lb·ft
(b) 5×10^7 lb·ft
12–33. (a) la/g (b) $\omega^2 l^2 /2g$

CHAPTER 13

13–3. 13,720 dynes/cm^2
13–5. (a) 70.7 cm of Hg
(b) 71.2 cm of Hg   (c) 11 cm
13–7. 4.3 cm

CHAPTER 14

14–1. (a) 36 ft/sec   (b) 0.2 ft^3/sec
14–3. (a) 10 cm   (b) 11 sec
14–5. 39.6 ft/sec

14–7. (a) 0.056 ft^3/sec (b) 3 ft
14–9. (a) 16 ft/sec (b) 0.79 ft^3/sec
14–11. 56.7 lb/in^2
14–13. (a) 12 lb/in^2 (b) 12 ft^3/sec
14–15. 0.91 ft^3/min
14–17. 12 ft^3/min
14–19. 26.8 ft^3/sec
14–21. 3.88 × 10^3 cm/sec
14–25. (a) 0.44 cm/sec (b) 1.05 cm/sec
14–27. 325 ft/sec
14–29. (a) Turbulent (b) 5.3 1/sec
14–31. (a) Yes (b) No

CHAPTER 15

15–1. 600.45°K
15–5. About 7%
15–7. 235 cm
15–9. 20 cm, 10 cm
15–11. About 250 ft
15–13. (a) About 1C°
15–15. 270,000 lb
15–17. 9.35 × 10^8 dynes/cm^2
15–19. (a) 3 × 10^{-4} (b) 9000 lb/in^2
       (c) 450,000 lb (d) 21,000 lb/in^2
       (e) 105°F
15–21. (a) 893 atm (b) 36.2°C
15–23. 494 atm

CHAPTER 16

16–1. (a) Yes (b) No
16–3. 4.0 Btu
16–5. 370 years
16–7. (a) 64.5
16–9. (a) 1:0.093:0.031
       (b) 1:0.83:0.35
16–11. 0.1 Btu/lb·F°
16–13. (a) 0.092 cal/gm·C°
16–15. (a) 72°C
16–17. (a) Higher (c) 0.72 cal/gm·C°
16–19. 35,300 cal
16–21. 0.023 cal/mole·K°,
       0.555 cal/mole·K°
16–23. 100 gm
16–25. 0°C with 0.2 gm of ice left
16–27. 539 cal/gm
16–29. 24°C
16–31. 40°C
16–33. 1.84 kgm

CHAPTER 17

17–1. (d) 31.4 C°/cm
       (e) 29 cal/sec
       (f) zero
       (h) 10 C°/sec
17–3. (a) 1.8 cal/sec (b) 20 cm
17–5. (a) 1.13 cal/sec
       (b) 4% through steel
17–7. 0.20 Btu·in./hr·ft^2·F°
17–9. 110°C
17–11. (a) $\sqrt{R_1 R_2}$
17–13. 84.2 C°
17–15. (a) 7.32 × 10^5 cal (vertical)
       (b) 8.05 × 10^5 cal (horizontal)
17–17. 15.2
17–19. (a) 460 watt/m^2
       (b) 4600 kw/m^2
17–21. 1.78 watts
17–23. 20.03°K

CHAPTER 18

18–1. 3.6 lb/in^2
18–3. (a) 0.75 atm (b) 2 gm
18–5. $\rho = pM/RT$
18–7. 3.25
18–9. (a) 82 cm^3 (b) 0.33 gm
18–11. When the piston has descended
       13.12 in.
18–13. 0.0023 gm
18–15. (b) 600°K (c) 4 atm
18–19. (a) Meniscus goes down
       (b) Meniscus goes up
       (c) Meniscus stays approximately in
           the same place
18–23. 16%
18–25. (a) 12°C (b) 10 gm/m^3
18–27. 1.3 lb/hr

CHAPTER 19

19–1. (a) Yes (b) no (c) negative
19–3. (a) No (b) yes (c) yes
       (d) Work done on the resistor equals
           the heat transferred to the water.
19–5. 10.8 ft^3
19–7. $U_1 = U_2$
19–9. (a) 59,300 ft·lb, 76 Btu
       (b) 870 Btu

19-11. (a) 1.1×10^{-2} ft^3
(b) 650 ft·lb (c) 1800 Btu
(d) 1.4×10^6 ft·lb

19-13. $K \ln (V_2 - b)/(V_1 - b)$
$-(a/V_1 - a/V_2)$

19-15. (b) 830 j (c) on the atmosphere
(d) 2110 j (e) 2940 j
(f) Same as (b)

19-19. 267°C

19-21. (a) When piston is 3.13 inches from
bottom (b) 477°K

19-23. (a) $p_1 = 1$ atm, $V_1 = 2.46$ l
$p_2 = 2$ atm, $V_2 = 2.46$ l
$p_3 = 1$ atm, $V_3 = 3.74$ l
(b) 49.4 j

19-25. 18%

19-27. (a) 320°K (b) 20%

19-29. (a) 900 cal (b) 1600 cal
(c) 400 cal

19-31. (a) 10^5 cal (b) 312 cal/K°
(c) 50°C (d) 312 cal/K° before,
165 cal/K° after.

CHAPTER 20

20-1. (a) About 3×10^{-7} cm
(b) About 10 times as great

20-3. 6.32×10^{-12} cm^3

20-5. 1700 ft/sec

20-7. (a) 6.2×10^{-14} erg
(b) 1.03×10^{-13} erg
(c) 1490 cal

20-11. (a) 51.5°K (b) 100°K

20-13. (a) 0.114 mm
(b) 0.57×10^4 rad

CHAPTER 21

21-1. (b) 320 m/sec

21-3. (a) 2 cm (b) 30 cm
(c) 100 cy/sec (d) 3000 cm/sec

21-5. 6320 cm/sec

21-7. (a) 0.5 cy/sec (b) π rad/sec
(c) $\pi/100$ cm^{-1}
(d) $y = 10 \sin [(\pi x/100) - \pi t]$
(e) $y = -10 \sin \pi t$
(f) $y = 10 \sin [(3\pi/2) - \pi t]$

(g) 10π cm/sec
(h) $y = 5\sqrt{2}$ cm,
$v = -5\pi\sqrt{2}$ cm/sec

21-9. 48×10^{-6} atm^{-1}

21-11. Argon: 322 m/sec
hydrogen: 1320 m/sec

21-13. (a) 132 cy/sec (b) 1320 cy/sec
(c) 13,200 cy/sec

21-15. (a) 0.58 m/sec (b) No

21-17. (a) $S = Mv^2/L$ (c) SL (d) $SL/2$
Ans. to (b) and (e) not given.

CHAPTER 22

22-1. (a) 200 cy/sec (b) 49th overtone

22-3. (a) 3600 cm/sec
(b) 6.5×10^6 dynes

22-5. 1.28

22-7. (a) 5000 m/sec (b) 340 m/sec

22-9. Diatomic

22-11. (a) 1140, 2280, 3420, 4560,
5700 cy/sec
(b) 570, 1710, 2850, 3990,
5130 cy/sec (c) 16, 17

22-13. (a) 420 cy/sec (b) 415 cy/sec

CHAPTER 23

23-1. (a) 9 times (b) 4 times

23-3. (a) 60 db (b) 77 db

23-5. 10^{-6} watt

23-7. (a) π rad
(b) $I_A = 4 \times 10^{-10}$ watt/cm^2
$I_B = 12 \times 10^{-10}$ watt/cm^2
(c) 2.1×10^{-10} watt/cm^2, 63.2 db

23-9. (a) 0.029 m (b) 21 cm
(c) 455 cy/sec

23-11. 24 mi/hr

23-13. (a) 2.06 ft (b) 2.46 ft
(c) 548 cy/sec (d) 460 cy/sec
(e) 572 cy/sec (f) 439 cy/sec
(g) 2.12 ft, 2.40 ft, 547, 458, 572,
and 437 cy/sec

23-15. (a) 454 cy/sec (b) 462 cy/sec
(c) 8 beats/sec

23-17. (a) 11 ft (b) 1 ft
(c) about 15 waves (d) 1100 ft/sec
(e) 0.47 ft

CHAPTER 24

24-1. (a) Zero
  (b) $2kq^2[x/(a^2 + x^2)^{3/2}]$
  (d) $x = \pm a/\sqrt{2}$

24-3. (b) 0.41a to the right of q_2, 0.77 a above q_2

24-5. (a) 4×10^6 electrons
  (b) 4.9×10^{-17}

24-7. (a) About 115,000 lb
  (b) About 326,000 lb

CHAPTER 25

25-1. (a) 4 n/coul upward
  (b) 6.4×10^{-19} n downward

25-3. (a) 1010 n/coul
  (b) 2660 km/sec

25-5. (a) 1.42 cm
  (b) 9.8 cm

25-7. -25×10^{-9} coul

25-9. (a) 1.8×10^4 n/coul, negative x-direction
  (b) 8×10^3 n/coul, positive x-direction
  (c) 3.3×10^3 n/coul, 70°, second quadrant
  (d) 6.4×10^3 n/coul negative x-direction

25-11. 41°

25-13. 8.85×10^{-10} coul

25-15. (a) 2400 n·m²/coul
  (b) Zero
  (c) 100 n/coul in the negative x-direction

25-17. (a) kq/r^2
  (b) kq/r^2

CHAPTER 26

26-1. (a) $-15 \mu j$
  (b) 10^5 n/coul

26-3. (b) 0.667 mm

26-5. (a) 3m (b) 0.2 μ coul

26-7. (e) $\pm a\sqrt{3}$

26-15. (b) 2.30×10^6 m/sec

26-17. (a) 3.54×10^{-10} coul
  (b) 15.9 volts

26-21. (a) Outside $-2\lambda k \ln (r/R)$
  Inside $(\rho/4\epsilon_0)(R^2 - r^2)$

26-23. (a) 4.34×10^{-4} m/sec
  (b) 2.74×10^{-4} m/sec upward

26-25. (a) 1.61×10^{-6} m
  (b) 1.41×10^{-14} kgm
  (c) 0.23

26-27. (a) $v = \sqrt{2qV/m}$
  (b) 5.93×10^5
  (c) 2.24×10^7 m/sec

26-29. (a) 12,700
  (b) 0.9999999969
  (c) 4.8×10^{10} m/sec

26-31. (a) 0.047 Mev
  (b) 0.294 Mev
  (c) 7.2, 4.0

26-33. (a) 0.704 cm
  (b) arc tan 0.352
  (c) 4.92 cm

26-35. 10.8 hp

CHAPTER 27

27-1. (a) 1000 volts (b) 2000 volts
  (c) 0.5 mj

27-3. (a) 0.38 μcoul
  (b) 7600 volts
  (c) 1.43 mj
  (d) 1.35 mj

27-5. (a) $1\mu f$ (b) .900 μcoul
  (c) 100 volts

27-7. (a) 800 μcoul, 800 volts;
  800 μcoul, 400 volts
  (b) 533 μcoul, 533 volts; 1070 μcoul, 533 volts

27-9. 1.30 mj

27-11. (a) 66.7 volts
  (b) 100 volts
  (c) 300 μcoul

27-13. (a) 0.226 m²
  (b) 1250 volts

27-15. (b) 1770 pf

27-17. (a) 26.6 μcoul/m²
  (b) 17.7 μcoul/m²
  (c) 17.7 μcoul/m²
  (d) 26.6 μcoul/m²
  (e) 13.3 joules/m³

CHAPTER 28

28-1. (a) 20 ma
  (b) 2.75×10^{-6} m/sec

28–3. 1.3×10^5 electrons/mm^3

28–5. (a) 10^{-4} coul/sec

(b) 4×10^{-6} coul/m^2

28–7. 2.07×10^{-14} sec

28–9. (a) 0.106 coul   (b) Zero

(c) 12.7 amp

28–11. (a) 2.01 amp

(b) 71.1 n/coul

(c) 1.01 amp

28–13. (a) Yes; 4.36 ohms

(b) No

28–15. 1.52 volts, 0.1 ohm

28–17. (a) -3.75 volts

(b) 3.75 volts   (c) 4.1 volts

28–19. (a) 0.05 ohm   (b) 0.15 ohm

(c) 0.006 ohm

28–21. (a) 22 ohms   (b) 5.5 amp

(c) 157 cal/sec

(d) 550 watts

28–23. (a) +   (b) 1000 amp

(c) 9.9 ohms   (d) 13 volts

(e) 1120 watts   (f) 990 watts

(g) 120 watts   (h) 6.7 cents

28–27. 22 thermocouples

CHAPTER 29

29–3. (a) 8 ohms

(b) 12 volts

29–5. 27 watts

29–7. 90 watts

29–9. (a) 8 ohms

(b) 72 volts

29–11. (a) -12 volts

(b) 3 amp

(c) -12 volts

(d) 12/7 amp from b to a

(e) 4.5 ohms

(f) 4.2 ohms

29–13. (a) 18 v

(b) Point a

(c) 6 volts

(d) 36 μcoul

29–15. $\mathcal{E}_1 = 18$ volts

$\mathcal{E}_2 = 7$ volts

$V_{ab} = 13$ volts

29–17. (a) 1200 ohms

(b) 30 volts

29–19. 10.9 volts, 109.1 volts

29–21. (a) 99.1 volts

(b) 0.0527

29–23. 4.97 ohms

29–25. 2985 ohms, 12,000 ohms,
135,000 ohms; 3000 ohms,
15,000 ohms, 150,000 ohms

29–29. (a) 1450 ohms

(b) 4500, 1500, 500 ohms

(c) No

29–31. 55 ohms

29–35. (b) 10^{-2} joules

CHAPTER 30

30–1. (a) Zero

(b) $I_D = qv/d$

(c) $d\sqrt{1 - v^2/c^2}$

(d) $d/\sqrt{1 - v^2/c^2}$

(e) $qv^2/dc^2\sqrt{1 - v^2/c^2}$

(f) $F_{eA} = \dfrac{2kqq'v^2}{rdc^2\sqrt{1 - v^2/c^2}}$

(g) $I_A = I_D/\sqrt{1 - v^2/c^2}$

(h) $F_{mA} = \dfrac{2kqq'v^2}{rdc^2\sqrt{1 - v^2/c^2}}$

(i) Zero

30–3. (a) 0.24 weber   (b) Zero

(c) 0.24 wcber

30–5. (a) 2.9×10^7 m/sec

(b) 4.3×10^{-8} sec

(c) 8.7×10^6 volts

30–7. 0.5 w/m^2 downward parallel to
y-axis

30–9. 3640

30–11. (a) **E** and **B** downward

(b) **E** upward, **B** downward

(c) **E** and **B** upward

30–13. (a) 1.7×10^8 m/sec

(c) 0.48 m

30–15. 0.1248 cm

30–19. (a) 4.58×10^7 reversals/sec

(b) 5.03×10^7 m/sec

(c) 1.32×10^7 volts

CHAPTER 31

31–1. $F_{ab} = 1.20$ n in negative z-direction

$F_{bc} = 1.20$ n in negative y-direction

$F_{cd} = 1.70$ n, $45°$ up, $\parallel$ to yz-plane
$F_{de} = 1.20$ n in negative y-direction
$F_{ef} = 0$

31–3. 6.85×10^{28} electrons/m^3

31–5. (a) 16,000 dynes, 83,000 dyne·cm
(b) 16,000 dynes, 48,000 dyne·cm
(c) Same torque

31–7. (a) 2.82×10^{-15} m
(b) No
(c) 2.90×10^{-60} kgm·m^2
(d) 1.82×10^{25} rad/sec

31–9. (a) 14.0 Gc/sec
(b) 21.4 Mc/sec

31–11. $30°$

31–13. 5.76×10^{-18} kgm^2·m^4/sec^2

31–15. (a) 0.5 amp   (b) 4 amp
(c) 108 volts   (d) 60 watts
(e) 48 watts   (f) 540 watts
(g) 71%

CHAPTER 32

32–1. (a) 20 μw/m^2 (b) 7.1 μw/m^2
(c) 20 μw/m^2 (d) Zero
(e) 5.4 μw/m^2

32–3. (b) $B = 4k'Ia/(a^2 + x^2)$
(d) Zero

32–5. (a) $4k'I/a$
(b) $\frac{4}{3}k'I/a$
(c) Zero
(d) $\frac{8}{3}k'I/a$

32–7. (a) 0.192 n/m down
(b) Same, up

32–9. 1.02 cm

32–11. 7.2×10^{-4} newton

32–15. 16 turns

32–17. 6.91 mw/m^2

32–19. (a) $2k'I/r$
(b) Zero

CHAPTER 33

33–1. (a) 2 volts/m, upward
(b) 2 volts/m, downward
(c) 3 volts
(d) 3 volts; upper end

33–3. (a) 2 volts/m   (b) 3 volts
(c) 15 amp   (d) 1.5 volts/m in left
end, 0.5 volt/m in remainder

(e) 2.25 volts
(f) 11.25 n   (g) 45 watts

33–5. (b) FR/B^2l^2
(c) $v = v_T(1 - e^{-(B^2l^2/Rm)t})$

33–9. (a) 0.2 volt   (b) Zero
(c) 0.2 volt

33–11. (a) $\pi r_1^2 \dot{B}$ (b) $r_1 \dot{B}/2$
(c) $BR^2/2r_2$
(e) $\pi R^2 \dot{B}/4$
(f) $\pi R^2 \dot{B}$
(g) $\pi R^2 \dot{B}$

33–13. (a) Circles, clockwise
(b) 0.005 volt/m,
3.14 mv
(c) 1.57 ma
(d) Zero
(f) 3.14 mv

33–15. (b) zero   (c) 4 mv
(d) 2 ma   (e) 1 mv

33–17. (a) Downward
(b) Upward
(c) Zero

33–19. (a) $2k'i/r$
(b) $2k'il\,dr/r$
(c) $2k'il \ln (r_2/r_1)$

33–21. (a) a to b (b) b to a (c) b to a

33–23. (a) 10^{-5} coul

33–25. (a) $B = mv/qR$
(b) $\mathcal{E} = A\,(dB/dt)$

33–31. (a) 0.05 amp   (b) 1 amp/sec
(c) 0.5 amp/sec   (d) 0.23 sec
(e) 0.0197, 0.0317, 0.0389, and
0.0433 amp

33–33. 0.326 amp to right

33–35. (a) 2.39 mh
(b) 4.41 pf

CHAPTER 34

34–1. 0.113 deg

34–3. (a) 2000 amp/m
(b) 795,000 amp/m
(c) 398
(d) 318×10^3 amp
(e) 399

34–5. (c) diamagnetic
(d) 10 amp, opposite
(e) it is repelled

34–9. 8 amp

34–11. 13.6 amp/m

34–13. (a) 70 amp
(b) 175 amp/m
(c) 6.2×10^{-3} w/amp·m
(d) 1.29×10^5 amp/w
(e) 54.2×10^{-5} w

CHAPTER 35

35–1. (a) 5 ma (b) 0.05 amp
(c) 0.5 amp
35–3. (a) 0.05 amp (b) 5 ma
(c) 0.5 ma
35–7. (a) 583 ohms (b) 0.0858 amp
(c) 25.8 volts, 43.0 volts
(d) 59°, lead
35–11. $V_1 = 30/\sqrt{2}$ volts,
$V_2 = 90/\sqrt{2}$ volts,
$V_3 = 50/\sqrt{2}$ volts,
$V_4 = 40/\sqrt{2}$ volts,
$V_5 = 50/\sqrt{2}$ volts
35–13. (b) 1.5 watts
(c) at $t = 2.04 \times 10^{-3}$ sec
$v = 44.6$ volts,
$i = 0.0899$ amp
35–15. (b) 1.10 watts
(c) at $t = 1.06 \times 10^{-3}$ sec,
$v = 43.8$ volts,
$i = 0.0750$ amp
35–17. (b) 745 rad/sec (c) 1
(d) $V_1 = 50/\sqrt{2}$ volts,
$V_2 = 112/\sqrt{2}$ volts,
$V_3 = 112/\sqrt{2}$ volts,
$V_4 = 0, \quad V_5 = 50/\sqrt{2}$ volts
(e) 745 rad/sec (f) $0.5/\sqrt{2}$ amp
35–19. (a) 121 ohms
(b) 0.757 amp
(c) 0.178 amp
(d) 516 ohms
35–21. (a) 0.0316 (b) 3.16 volts

CHAPTER 36

36–1. (a) $\epsilon_0 ctw/l$ (b) $\mu_0 ctl/w$
(c) $\epsilon_0 ctwV^2/2l$
(d) $\mu_0 ctlI^2/2w$
36–3. (a) 5.30 amp/m
(b) 3.53×10^{-5} joule/m^3
(c) 1.06×10^4 joule/sec·m^2
36–5. (a) $\rho I/\pi a^2 \parallel$ to wire
(b) $Ir/2\pi a^2 \perp$ to wire
(c) $\rho I^2 r/2\pi^2 a^4$

36–11. 0.11 volt/m,
2.80×10^{-4} amp/m

CHAPTER 37

37–1. (a) 1.5×10^{-9} m,
1.5×10^{-3} μ,
1.5 nm, 15 A
(b) 5.37×10^{-7} m, 0.537 μ, 537 nm,
5370 A
37–3. 16.6 min
37–11. 1.732
37–13. (a) 32°
(b) Does not depend on it

CHAPTER 38

38–1. (a) 2×10^8 m/sec
(b) 333 nm
38–3. 1.87
38–7. No
38–9. (b) 90°
38–11. 1.89
38–15. 1.02 cm
38–17. 30°
38–19. 12.2°

CHAPTER 39

39–1. (b) Half the observer's height
39–5. (a) 9.88 cm (b) 5 cm
39–7. 3
39–9. 0.643 in., 0.143
39–11. (a) 45° (b) 0.53 in.
39–13. 3.0 cm
39–15. 1.35
39–17. $s' = 30, m = -1$
39–19. 0.667 cm

CHAPTER 40

40–1. $4R$ from center of sphere
40–3. (a) The first image
(b) 30 cm (c) Real (d) At ∞
(e) Infinite
40–5. 50 cm
40–7. 1.5 cm
40–11.

R_1	R_2	f
10 cm	20 cm	40 cm
10 cm	−20 cm	13.3 cm
−10 cm	20 cm	−13.3 cm
−10 cm	−20 cm	−40 cm

40–13. (a) 6 cm and 12 cm from the object
(b) -2, -0.5

40–15. 60 cm to right of third lens

40–17. -7.2 cm

40–19. (a) 20.0 cm   (b) 18.7 cm

40–21. (b) 12 cm

40–23. $t = 0.375$ in.

40–25. 0.67 in. to left of first lens,
0.67 in. to right of second lens

40–27. (a) 7.14 cm   (b) 3.5 mm

40–29. 1/400 sec

40–31. (a) 14.4 in.   (b) 15 in.

40–33. (a) 842$\times$ (b) 50$\times$

40–35. 380$\times$

40–37. 20$\times$

CHAPTER 41

41–1.   1 mm

41–5.   480 nm

41–7.   0.045 mm

41–9. 2.945×10^{-4} rad

41–11. 2.79 mm

41–13. 1.06×10^{-4} mm

41–15. 0.5 mm

41–19. 12.5°

41–21. 500 nm

41–23. 2000 ft

CHAPTER 42

42–1.   35°32′

42–3.   (a) 37°   (b) Horizontal

42–5.   67°22′

42–7.   (a) 0.75   (b) 0.50
(c) 0.25

42–13. (b) 5.82×10^{-5} cm

42–15. Linearly polarized, rotated 90°

CHAPTER 43

43–3.   (a) 88 ma   (b) 130 volts

43–5. $hf_0 = \phi$

43–7. 1.72×10^8 cm/sec

43–9.   (a) 4.58×10^{14} cycles/sec
(b) 6540 A
(c) 1.90 ev
(d) 6.62×10^{-34} joule·sec

43–11. 0.34 volt greater

43–13. (a) 1.04 ev
(b) 11,900 A
(c) 2.52×10^{14} cycles/sec
(d) 4.14×10^{-7} ev
(f) no

43–15. 1.41×10^{19} quanta/sec

43–19. (a) 6.16×10^{14} cycles/sec
(b) 4861 A
(c) 2.06×10^6 m^{-1}

43–23. 4866.4 A, 4865.1 A, 4864.7 A

43–25. 1.79 A

43–27. 0.868 A

43–29. (a) 1.80×10^5 ev
(b) 12.3×10^{-31} kgm
(c) 2.02×10^8 m/sec
(d) 1.30×10^{11} coul/kgm
(e) 2.52×10^8 m/sec

NATURAL TRIGONOMETRIC FUNCTIONS

Degree	Radian	Sine	Cosine	Tangent	Degree	Radian	Sine	Cosine	Tangent
0°	.000	0.000	1.000	0.000					
1°	.017	.018	1.000	.018	46°	0.803	0.719	0.695	1.036
2°	.035	.035	0.999	.035	47°	.820	.731	.682	1.072
3°	.052	.052	.999	.052	48°	.838	.743	.669	1.111
4°	.070	.070	.998	.070	49°	.855	.755	.656	1.150
5°	.087	.087	.996	.088	50°	.873	.766	.643	1.192
6°	.105	.105	.995	.105	51°	.890	.777	.629	1.235
7°	.122	.122	.993	.123	52°	.908	.788	.616	1.280
8°	.140	.139	.990	.141	53°	.925	.799	.602	1.327
9°	.157	.156	.988	.158	54°	.942	.809	.588	1.376
10°	.175	.174	.985	.176	55°	.960	.819	.574	1.428
11°	.192	.191	.982	.194	56°	.977	.829	.559	1.483
12°	.209	.208	.978	.213	57°	.995	.839	.545	1.540
13°	.227	.225	.974	.231	58°	1.012	.848	.530	1.600
14°	.244	.242	.970	.249	59°	1.030	.857	.515	1.664
15°	.262	.259	.966	.268	60°	1.047	.866	.500	1.732
16°	.279	.276	.961	.287	61°	1.065	.875	.485	1.804
17°	.297	.292	.956	.306	62°	1.082	.883	.470	1.881
18°	.314	.309	.951	.325	63°	1.100	.891	.454	1.963
19°	.332	.326	.946	.344	64°	1.117	.899	.438	2.050
20°	.349	.342	.940	.364	65°	1.134	.906	.423	2.145
21°	.367	.358	.934	.384	66°	1.152	.914	.407	2.246
22°	.384	.375	.927	.404	67°	1.169	.921	.391	2.356
23°	.401	.391	.921	.425	68°	1.187	.927	.375	2.475
24°	.419	.407	.914	.445	69°	1.204	.934	.358	2.605
25°	.436	.423	.906	.466	70°	1.222	.940	.342	2.747
26°	.454	.438	.899	.488	71°	1.239	.946	.326	2.904
27°	.471	.454	.891	.510	72°	1.257	.951	.309	3.078
28°	.489	.470	.883	.532	73°	1.274	.956	.292	3.271
29°	.506	.485	.875	.554	74°	1.292	.961	.276	3.487
30°	.524	.500	.866	.577	75°	1.309	.966	.259	3.732
31°	.541	.515	.857	.601	76°	1.326	.970	.242	4.011
32°	.559	.530	.848	.625	77°	1.344	.974	.225	4.331
33°	.576	.545	.839	.649	78°	1.361	.978	.208	4.705
34°	.593	.559	.829	.675	79°	1.379	.982	.191	5.145
35°	.611	.574	.819	.700	80°	1.396	.985	.174	5.671
36°	.628	.588	.809	.727	81°	1.414	.988	.156	6.314
37°	.646	.602	.799	.754	82°	1.431	.990	.139	7.115
38°	.663	.616	.788	.781	83°	1.449	.993	.122	8.144
39°	.681	.629	.777	.810	84°	1.466	.995	.105	9.514
40°	.698	.643	.766	.839	85°	1.484	.996	.087	11.43
41°	.716	.658	.755	.869	86°	1.501	.998	.070	14.30
42°	.733	.669	.743	.900	87°	1.518	.999	.052	19.08
43°	.751	.682	.731	.933	88°	1.536	.999	.035	28.64
44°	.768	.695	.719	.966	89°	1.553	1.000	.018	57.29
45°	.785	.707	.707	1.000	90°	1.571	1.000	.000	∞

COMMON LOGARITHMS

N	0	1	2	3	4	5	6	7	8	9
0	....	0000	3010	4771	6021	6990	7782	8451	9031	9542
1	0000	0414	0792	1139	1461	1761	2041	2304	2553	2788
2	3010	3222	3424	3617	3802	3979	4150	4314	4472	4624
3	4771	4914	5051	5185	5315	5441	5563	5682	5798	5911
4	6021	6128	6232	6335	6435	6532	6628	6721	6812	6902
5	6990	7076	7160	7243	7324	7404	7482	7559	7634	7709
6	7782	7853	7924	7993	8062	8129	8195	8261	8325	8388
7	8451	8513	8573	8633	8692	8751	8808	8865	8921	8976
8	9031	9085	9138	9191	9243	9294	9345	9395	9445	9494
9	9542	9590	9638	9685	9731	9777	9823	9868	9912	9956
10	0000	0043	0086	0128	0170	0212	0253	0294	0334	0374
11	0414	0453	0492	0531	0569	0607	0645	0682	0719	0755
12	0792	0828	0864	0899	0934	0969	1004	1038	1072	1106
13	1139	1173	1206	1239	1271	1303	1335	1367	1399	1430
14	1461	1492	1523	1553	1584	1614	1644	1673	1703	1732
15	1761	1790	1818	1847	1875	1903	1931	1959	1987	2014
16	2041	2068	2095	2122	2148	2175	2201	2227	2253	2279
17	2304	2330	2355	2380	2405	2430	2455	2480	2504	2529
18	2553	2577	2601	2625	2648	2672	2695	2718	2742	2765
19	2788	2810	2833	2856	2878	2900	2923	2945	2967	2989
20	3010	3032	3054	3075	3096	3118	3139	3160	3181	3201
21	3222	3243	3263	3284	3304	3324	3345	3365	3385	3404
22	3424	3444	3464	3483	3502	3522	3541	3560	3579	3598
23	3617	3636	3655	3674	3692	3711	3729	3747	3766	3784
24	3802	3820	3838	3856	3874	3892	3909	3927	3945	3962
25	3979	3997	4014	4031	4048	4065	4082	4099	4116	4133
26	4150	4166	4183	4200	4216	4232	4249	4265	4281	4298
27	4314	4330	4346	4362	4378	4393	4409	4425	4440	4456
28	4472	4487	4502	4518	4533	4548	4564	4579	4594	4609
29	4624	4639	4654	4669	4683	4698	4713	4728	4742	4757
30	4771	4786	4800	4814	4829	4843	4857	4871	4886	4900
31	4914	4928	4942	4955	4969	4983	4997	5011	5024	5038
32	5051	5065	5079	5092	5105	5119	5132	5145	5159	5172
33	5185	5198	5211	5224	5237	5250	5263	5276	5289	5302
34	5315	5328	5340	5353	5366	5378	5391	5403	5416	5428
35	5441	5453	5465	5478	5490	5502	5514	5527	5539	5551
36	5563	5575	5587	5599	5611	5623	5635	5647	5658	5670
37	5682	5694	5705	5717	5729	5740	5752	5763	5775	5786
38	5798	5809	5821	5832	5843	5855	5866	5877	5888	5899
39	5911	5922	5933	5944	5955	5966	5977	5988	5999	6010
40	6021	6031	6042	6053	6064	6075	6085	6096	6107	6117
41	6128	6138	6149	6160	6170	6180	6191	6201	6212	6222
42	6232	6243	6253	6263	6274	6284	6294	6304	6314	6325
43	6335	6345	6355	6365	6375	6385	6395	6405	6415	6425
44	6435	6444	6454	6464	6474	6484	6493	6503	6513	6522
45	6532	6542	6551	6561	6571	6580	6590	6599	6609	6618
46	6628	6637	6646	6656	6665	6675	6684	6693	6702	6712
47	6721	6730	6739	6749	6758	6767	6776	6785	6794	6803
48	6812	6821	6830	6839	6848	6857	6866	6875	6884	6893
49	6902	6911	6920	6928	6937	6946	6955	6964	6972	6981
50	6990	6998	7007	7016	7024	7033	7042	7050	7059	7067
N	0	1	2	3	4	5	6	7	8	9

COMMON LOGARITHMS

N	0	1	2	3	4	5	6	7	8	9
50	6990	6998	7007	7016	7024	7033	7042	7050	7059	7067
51	7076	7084	7093	7101	7110	7118	7126	7135	7143	7152
52	7160	7168	7177	7185	7193	7202	7210	7218	7226	7235
53	7243	7251	7259	7267	7275	7284	7292	7300	7308	7316
54	7324	7332	7340	7348	7356	7364	7372	7380	7388	7396
55	7404	7412	7419	7427	7435	7443	7451	7459	7466	7474
56	7482	7490	7497	7505	7513	7520	7528	7536	7543	7551
57	7559	7566	7574	7582	7589	7597	7604	7612	7619	7627
58	7634	7642	7649	7657	7664	7672	7679	7686	7694	7701
59	7709	7716	7723	7731	7738	7745	7752	7760	7767	7774
60	7782	7789	7796	7803	7810	7818	7825	7832	7839	7846
61	7853	7860	7868	7875	7882	7889	7896	7903	7910	7917
62	7924	7931	7938	7945	7952	7959	7966	7973	7980	7987
63	7993	8000	8007	8014	8021	8028	8035	8041	8048	8055
64	8062	8069	8075	8082	8089	8096	8102	8109	8116	8122
65	8129	8136	8142	8149	8156	8162	8169	8176	8182	8189
66	8195	8202	8209	8215	8222	8228	8235	8241	8248	8254
67	8261	8267	8274	8280	8287	8293	8299	8306	8312	8319
68	8325	8331	8338	8344	8351	8357	8363	8370	8376	8382
69	8388	8395	8401	8407	8414	8420	8426	8432	8439	8445
70	8451	8457	8463	8470	8476	8482	8488	8494	8500	8506
71	8513	8519	8525	8531	8537	8543	8549	8555	8561	8567
72	8573	8579	8585	8591	8597	8603	8609	8615	8621	8627
73	8633	8639	8645	8651	8657	8663	8669	8675	8681	8686
74	8692	8698	8704	8710	8716	8722	8727	8733	8739	8745
75	8751	8756	8762	8768	8774	8779	8785	8791	8797	8802
76	8808	8814	8820	8825	8831	8837	8842	8848	8854	8859
77	8865	8871	8876	8882	8887	8893	8899	8904	8910	8915
78	8921	8927	8932	8938	8943	8949	8954	8960	8965	8971
79	8976	8982	8987	8993	8998	9004	9009	9015	9020	9025
80	9031	9036	9042	9047	9053	9058	9063	9069	9074	9079
81	9085	9090	9096	9101	9106	9112	9117	9122	9128	9133
82	9138	9143	9149	9154	9159	9165	9170	9175	9180	9186
83	9191	9196	9201	9206	9212	9217	9222	9227	9232	9238
84	9243	9248	9253	9258	9263	9269	9274	9279	9284	9289
85	9294	9299	9304	9309	9315	9320	9325	9330	9335	9340
86	9345	9350	9355	9360	9365	9370	9375	9380	9385	9390
87	9395	9400	9405	9410	9415	9420	9425	9430	9435	9440
88	9445	9450	9455	9460	9465	9469	9474	9479	9484	9489
89	9494	9499	9504	9509	9513	9518	9523	9528	9533	9538
90	9542	9547	9552	9557	9562	9566	9571	9576	9581	9586
91	9590	9595	9600	9605	9609	9614	9619	9624	9628	9633
92	9638	9643	9647	9652	9657	9661	9666	9671	9675	9680
93	9685	8689	9694	9699	9703	9708	9713	9717	9722	9727
94	9731	9736	9741	9745	9750	9754	9759	9763	9768	9773
95	9777	9782	9786	9791	9795	9800	9805	9809	9814	9818
96	9823	9827	9832	9836	9841	9845	9850	9854	9859	9863
97	9868	9872	9877	9881	9886	9890	9894	9899	9903	9908
98	9912	9917	9921	9926	9930	9934	9939	9943	9948	9952
99	9956	9961	9965	9969	9974	9978	9983	9987	9991	9996
100	0000	0004	0009	0013	0017	0022	0026	0030	0035	0039
N	0	1	2	3	4	5	6	7	8	9

PERIODIC TABLE OF THE ELEMENTS

The atomic weights, based on the exact number 12 as the assigned atomic mass of the principal isotope of carbon, are the most recent (1961) values adopted by the International Union of Pure and Applied Chemistry. (For artificially produced elements, the approximate atomic weight of the most stable isotope is given in brackets.)

Period	Series	I	II	III	IV	V	VI	VII	VIII			O
1	1	1 H 1.00797										2 He 4.0026
2	2	3 Li 6.939	4 Be 9.0122	5 B 10.811	6 C 12.01115	7 N 14.0067	8 O 15.9994	9 F 18.9984				10 Ne 20.183
3	3	11 Na 22.9898	12 Mg 24.312	13 Al 26.9815	14 Si 28.086	15 P 30.9738	16 S 32.064	17 Cl 35.453				18 A 39.948
4	4	19 K 39.102	20 Ca 40.08	21 Sc 44.956	22 Ti 47.90	23 V 50.942	24 Cr 51.996	25 Mn 54.9380	26 Fe 55.847	27 Co 58.9332	28 Ni 58.71	
4	5	29 Cu 63.54	30 Zn 65.37	31 Ga 69.72	32 Ge 72.59	33 As 74.9216	34 Se 78.96	35 Br 79.909				36 Kr 83.80
5	6	37 Rb 85.47	38 Sr 87.62	39 Y 88.905	40 Zr 91.22	41 Nb 92.906	42 Mo 95.94	43 Tc [99]	44 Ru 101.07	45 Rh 102.905	46 Pd 106.4	
5	7	47 Ag 107.870	48 Cd 112.40	49 In 114.82	50 Sn 118.69	51 Sb 121.75	52 Te 127.60	53 I 126.9044				54 Xe 131.30
6	8	55 Cs 132.905	56 Ba 137.34	57–71 Lanthanide series*	72 Hf 178.49	73 Ta 180.948	74 W 183.85	75 Re 186.2	76 Os 190.2	77 Ir 192.2	78 Pt 195.09	
6	9	79 Au 196.967	80 Hg 200.59	81 Tl 204.37	82 Pb 207.19	83 Bi 208.980	84 Po [210]	85 At [210]				86 Rn [222]
7	10	87 Fr [223]	88 Ra [226.05]	89–Actinide series**								

*Lanthanide series:	57 La 138.91	58 Ce 140.12	59 Pr 140.907	60 Nd 144.24	61 Pm [147]	62 Sm 150.35	63 Eu 151.96	64 Gd 157.25	65 Tb 158.924	66 Dy 162.50	67 Ho 164.930	68 Er 167.26	69 Tm 168.934	70 Yb 173.04	71 Lu 174.97
**Actinide series:	89 Ac [227]	90 Th 232.038	91 Pa [231]	92 U 238.03	93 Np [237]	94 Pu [242]	95 Am [243]	96 Cm [245]	97 Bk [249]	98 Cf [249]	99 Es [253]	100 Fm [255]	101 Md [256]	102 No	103

FUNDAMENTAL CONSTANTS

Largely based on values in the *American Institute of Physics Handbook* (1963). The probable error for each value has been omitted here; it should properly be considered part of the datum.

Name of Quantity	Symbol	Value
Velocity of light in vacuum	c	2.9979×10^8 m/sec
Charge of electron	q_e	-1.602×10^{-19} coul $=$ -4.803×10^{-10} statcoul
Rest mass of electron	m_e	9.109×10^{-31} kgm
Ratio of charge to mass of electron	q_e/m_e	1.759×10^{11} coul/kgm $=$ 5.273×10^{17} statcoul/gm
Planck's constant	h	6.625×10^{-34} j·sec
Boltzmann's constant	k	1.380×10^{-23} j/°K
Avogadro's number (chemical scale)	N_0	6.025×10^{23} molecules/mole
Universal gas constant (chemical scale)	R	8.314 j/mole·°K
Mechanical equivalent of heat	J	4.185×10^3 j/kcal
Standard atmospheric pressure	1 atm	1.013×10^5 new/m^2
Volume of ideal gas at 0°C and 1 atm (chemical scale)		22.415 liter/mole
Absolute zero of temperature	0°K	-273.15°C
Acceleration due to gravity (sea level, at equator)		9.78049 m/sec^2
Universal gravitational constant	G	6.673×10^{-11} new·m^2/kgm^2
Mass of earth	m_E	5.975×10^{24} kgm
Mean radius of earth		6.371×10^6 m $= 3959$ mi
Equatorial radius of earth		6.378×10^6 m $= 3963$ mi
Mean distance from earth to sun	1 AU	1.49×10^{11} m $= 9.29 \times 10^7$ mi
Eccentricity of earth's orbit		0.0167
Mean distance from earth to moon		3.84×10^8 m $\doteq 60$ earth radii
Diameter of sun		1.39×10^9 m $= 8.64 \times 10^5$ mi
Mass of sun	m_S	1.99×10^{30} kgm $= 333{,}000 \times$ mass of earth
Coulomb's law constant	C	8.98×10^9 new·m^2/coul^2
Faraday's constant (1 faraday)	F	96,500 coul/mole
Mass of neutral hydrogen atom	m_{H^1}	1.008145 amu
Mass of proton	m_p	1.007596 amu
Mass of neutron	m_n	1.008986 amu
Mass of electron	m_e	5.488×10^{-4} amu
Ratio of mass of proton to mass of electron	m_p/m_e	1836.11
Rydberg constant for nucleus of infinite mass	R_∞	109,737 cm^{-1}
Rydberg constant for hydrogen	R_H	109,678 cm^{-1}
Wien displacement law constant		0.2898 cm·°K

Numerical constants: $\pi = 3.142$; $e = 2.718$; $\sqrt{2} = 1.414$; $\sqrt{3} = 1.732$

CONVERSION FACTORS

LENGTH:

1 m = 100 cm = 1000 mm
1 km = 1000 m = 0.6214 mile
1 m = 39.37 in.; 1 cm = 0.3937 in.
1 ft = 30.48 cm; 1 in. = 2.540 cm
1 mi = 5280 ft = 1.609 km
1 A = 10^{-8} cm; 1μ (micron) = 10^{-4} cm

AREA:

1 cm^2 = 0.155 in^2; 1 m^2 = 10^4 cm^2 = 10.76 ft^2
1 in^2 = 6.452 cm^2; 1 ft^2 = 144 in^2 = 0.0929 m^2

VOLUME:

1 liter = 1000 cm^3 = 10^{-3} m^3 = 0.0351 ft^3 = 61 in^3
1 ft^3 = 0.0283 m^3 = 28.32 liters; 1 in^3 = 16.39 cm^3 = 7.5 gal

VELOCITY:

1 cm/sec = 0.03281 ft/sec; 1 ft/sec = 30.48 cm/sec
1 mile/min = 60 mi/hr = 88 ft/sec

ACCELERATION:

1 cm/sec^2 = 0.03281 ft/sec^2 = 0.01 m/sec^2
30.48 cm/sec^2 = 1 ft/sec^2 = 0.3048 m/sec^2
100 cm/sec^2 = 3.281 ft/sec^2 = 1 m/sec^2

FORCE:

1 dyne = 2.247 $\times$ 10^{-6} lb = 10^{-5} newton
1.383 $\times$ 10^4 dynes = 0.0311 lb = 0.1383 newton
4.45 $\times$ 10^5 dynes = 1 lb = 4.45 newtons
10^5 dynes = 0.2247 lb = 1 newton

MASS:

1 gm = 6.85 $\times$ 10^{-5} slug = 10^{-3} kgm
453.6 gm = 0.0311 slug = 0.4536 kgm
1.459 $\times$ 10^4 gm = 1 slug = 14.59 kgm
10^3 gm = 0.0685 slug = 1 kgm

PRESSURE:

1 atm = 14.7 lb/in^2 = 1.013 $\times$ 10^6 $dynes/cm^2$

ENERGY:

1 joule = 10^7 ergs = 0.239 cal; 1 cal = 4.18 joule
1 ev = 10^{-6} Mev = 1.60 $\times$ 10^{-12} erg = 1.07 $\times$ 10^{-9} amu
1 amu = 1.66 $\times$ 10^{-24} gm = 1.49 $\times$ 10^{-3} erg = 931 Mev

Index

Abcoulomb, 804
Aberrations of lenses, 881
Absolute humidity, 404
Absolute pressure, 283
Absolute zero, 437
Acceleration, angular, 213
  average, 68
  centripetal, 136
  constant, 74
  of gravity, 76, table, 150
  in harmonic motion, 261
  instantaneous, 68
  radial, 136
  variable, 80
Accelerometer, 73, 113
Accommodation, 883
Achromatic prism, 848
Action, 25
Adaptation, 883
Adhesive force, 305
Adiabatic process, 416
  of ideal gas, 422
Adiabatic wall, 335
Airspeed indicator, 317
Alpha particle, 531, 983
Alternating current, 783
Ammeter, 615, 654
Ampere, 615
Ampere's law, 715
Amplification, 956
Amorphous solid, 470
Amplitude, 258
  angular, 271
  pressure, 510
Angle, of departure, 130
Angstrom, 3, 829
Angular acceleration, 213
Angular amplitude, 271
Angular displacement, 212
Angular frequency, 261, 783
Angular harmonic motion, 271
Angular impulse, 227
Angular magnification, 884
Angular momentum, 227
  conservation of, 230
Angular velocity, 211
  of precession, 233
Anisotropic substance, 472
Anode, 954

Antinode, 497
Archimedes' principle, 288
Atmosphere, 285
Atom, 530
Atomic bomb, 999
Atomic mass, 688
Atomic number, 531
Atomic pile, 999
Avogadro's number, 449

Balance, Cavendish, 104
  equal-arm, 107
  spring, 6
Ballistic galvanometer, 702
Ballistic pendulum, 189
Balmer series, 961
Band spectrum, 974
Banking of curves, 140
Bar, 285
Barkhausen effect, 769
Barometer, mercury, 284
Barometric equation, 393
Beats, 521
Bernoulli's equation, 313
Beta particles, 986
Betatron, 739
Binding energy, 193
Binocular, 889
Biot's law, 709
Biot-Savart law, 710
Birefringence, 937
Blackbody, 378
Blue light, of the sky, 943
Bohr atom, 531, 961
Boiling point, 340
Boltzmann constant, 381, 454
Boltzmann equation, 973
Boundary layer, 327
Boundary surface, 296
Boyle's law, 391
Brackett series, 961
Brehme diagram, 86
Brewster's law, 936
British engineering system, 102
British thermal unit, 353
Brownian motion, 450
Bubble chamber, 407, 993
Bulk modulus, 250

Caloric, 352
Calorie, 353
Calorimeter, 355
Calorimetry, 355
Camera, 885
Capacitance, 594
Capacitor, 594
Capillarity, 306
Carbon arc, 825
Carnot cycle, 433
Cathode, 954
Cathode-ray tube, 583, 662
Cavendish balance, 104
Celsius scale, 343
Center, of gravity, 27, 54
  of oscillation, 272
  of percussion, 273
Centigrade scale, 343
Centimeter, 3
Centipoise, 320
Centrifugal force, 140
Centrifuge, 137
Centripetal acceleration, 136
Centripetal force, 138
Cesium clock, 4
cgs system, 102
Characteristic impedance, 809
Charge-to-mass ratio, 681
Charging, by contact, 532
  by induction, 533
Chromatic aberration, 881
Circle of confusion, 885
Circuit, electric, 649
  magnetic, 779
Circuit equation, 626
Circular motion, 135, 141
Circular polarization, 944
Circulation, flow, 324
Clausius equation of state, 469
Cloud chamber, Wilson, 406, 680, 992
Coefficient, convection, 374
  dielectric, 606
  of linear expansion, 347
  of performance, 432
  of sliding friction, 35
  of static friction, 34
  of stiffness, 169
  temperature, of resistance, 619
  of viscosity, 319
  of volume expansion, 345
Coercive force, 771
Coercivity, 771
Coherent sources, 896
Cold reservoir, 427
Collision, elastic, 187, 190
  inelastic, 187, 188
Collision cross section, 463
Colloidal particles, 450
Components, of vector, 12
Compressibility, 250

Compression, 245
Compression ratio, 428
Compression stroke, 428
Compressive strain, 247
Compressive stress, 245
Concurrent forces, 21
Condensation, heat of, 362
  wave, 478
Conduction, of electricity, 533, 618
  of heat, 368
Conductivity, electrical, 533
  thermal, 369
Conductor, electrical, 533
Conical pendulum, 140
Conservation, of angular momentum, 230
  of energy, 163, 415
  of linear momentum, 186
Conservative force, 171
Contact angle, 305
Continuity, equation of, 311
Continuous spectrum, 977
Convection, 372
Convection coefficient, 374
Convergent polarized light, 949
Coolidge x-ray tube, 975
Cosmic rays, 992
Coulomb, 536, 712
Coulomb's law, 535
Couple, 12, 57
Critical angle, 844
Critical point, 398
Critical pressure, 398
Critical specific volume, 398
Critical temperature, 299, 398
Cross product, 47
Crystals, 470
Curie constant, 763
Curie law, 763
Current, electric, 530, 614
Current-voltage diagram, 634
Curvature of field, 857
Cyclotron, 688

Dalton's law, 404, 457
Dam, 290
Damping, of galvanometer, 736
Decay of radioactivity, 988
Deceleration, 69
Declination, magnetic, 777
Deformation, plastic, 249
Degree of freedom, 458
Density, 280
  surface, 546, 558
Depth of field, 885
Detergent, 306
Deuterium, 966
Deuteron, 992
Deviation of a prism, 845
Dew point, 405
Diamagnetism, 759

Diathermic wall, 335
Dichroic crystal, 939
Dielectric, 533
Dielectric coefficient, 606
Dielectric strength, 572
Diesel engine, 429
Diffraction, 519
    of light, 895
Diffraction grating, 923
Diffusion pump, 285
Diode, 634, 954
Dip, magnetic, 777
Dipole, electrical, 577, 603
Direct-current circuits, 649
Direct-vision prism, 848
Dispersion, 847
Dispersive medium, 488
Displacement, 608
    angular, 212
    linear, 65
Dissipative force, 171
Distortion of a prism, 845
Domains, magnetic, 768
Domino rule, 907
Doppler effect, 521
    relativistic, 524
Dot product, 158
Double refraction, 937
Ductile metal, 249
Dulong and Petit law, 358
Dynamic lift, 323
Dynamic pressure, 317
Dynamics, 99
Dyne, 102
Dyne·centimeter, 157
Dyne·second, 183

Earth's magnetic field, 777
Eddy currents, 737
Efficiency, of Carnot engine, 437
    thermal, 427
Efflux, speed of, 313
Einstein, Lorentz-Einstein transformation
        equations, 91
    mass-energy relation, 201
    mass-velocity equation, 198
    relative time, 89
Elastic collisions, 187, 190
Elastic force, 169
Elastic hysteresis, 249
Elastic limit, 248
Elastic modulus, 249
Elastic potential energy, 168
Elastic restoring force, 169, 256
Elasticity, 244
Electric eye, 958
Electric field, 540
Electric intensity, 540
Electromagnetic pump, 704
Electromagnetic spectrum, 830

Electromagnetic wave, 720, 804
Electromotive force, 625
    induced, 730
Electron, 530
Electron microscope, 968
Electron volt, 582
Electronics, 953
Electroscope, 532
Electrometer, 532, 570
Electrostatic force, 537
Elliptic polarization, 944
Energy, binding, 193
    conservation of, 163, 415
    electrical potential, 568
    internal, 414
    kinetic, 157, 161, 225
    mechanical, 163
    potential, 162
    radiant, 375
    surface, 299
Engine, Carnot, 433
    diesel, 429
    gasoline, 428
    heat, 425
    steam, 429
Enthalpy, 418
Entropy, 438
    principle of increase of, 440
Epoch angle, 260
Equal-arm balance, 107
Equation of state, 389
    Clausius, 469
    of ideal gas, 451
    van der Waals, 470
Equilibrium, 20
    first condition of, 22
    neutral, 24
    of particle, 26
    phase, 339
    second condition of, 22, 48
    stable, 24
    thermal, 335, 383
    unstable, 24
Equipartition of energy, 458
Equipotential surface, 570
Equipotential volume, 570
Equivalence, principle of, 147
Erg, 158
Etalon, 2
Event, 85
Excited state, of atom, 964
Exhaust stroke, 428
Expansion, linear, 347
    volume, 345
Eye, 881
Eyepiece, 885

Fahrenheit scale, 343
Farad, 594
Faraday's ice-pail experiment, 554

Faraday's law, of induction, 730
Ferromagnetism, 765
Field, electric, 540
    magnetic, 671
Films, interference in, 911
First law, of Newton, 20, 23
    of thermodynamics, 414, 419
Fission, 999
Fixed point, 340
Flow, circulation, 324
    homogeneous, 310
    laminar, 318
    line of, 309
    plastic, 249
    stationary, 309
    steady, 309
Flow tube, 309
Fluid, 280
    ideal, 309
Fluorescent lamp, 826
Flux, 552
    magnetic, 678
Flux density, 678
Focal length, 861
Focal plane, 876
Focal point, 861
Foot·pound, 158
Force, adhesive, 305
    centrifugal, 140
    centripetal, 138
    conservative, 171
    dissipative, 171
    elastic, 169
    electrostatic, 537
    frictional, 34
    gravitational, 103
    impulsive, 183
    normal, 33, 34
    restoring, 169, 257
    transverse, 202
Force constant, 253, 256
Force diagram, 27
Fraunhofer diffraction, 919
Free-body diagram, 27
Free fall, 76
Fresnel diffraction, 919
Frequency, 258
    angular, 261
    fundamental, 499
    natural, 747
Friction, 33
    coefficients of, 34
    sliding, 35
    static, 34
Fundamental frequency, 499
Fusion, heat of, 361

g, 76
    and earth's rotation, 148
    variations in, 150

Galilean-Newtonian transformation
    equations, 82
Galvanometer, 615, 654, 699
Gamma rays, 987
Gas constant, universal, 390
Gas thermometer, 339
Gaseous electrical discharge, 952
Gasoline engine, 428
Gauge pressure, 284
Gauss, 678
Gaussian surface, 549
Gauss' law, 549
Gay-Lussac's law, 394
Geiger counter, 983
Generator, alternating current, 732
    direct current, 733
Geometrical optics, 895
Glow discharge, 952
Gradient, potential, 575
Gram, 5, 102
Gram-mole, 354
Gravitation, Newton's law of, 103
Gravitational constant, 103
Gravitational potential energy, 162
Gravity, acceleration of, 76
    center of, 27, 54
    and earth's rotation, 148
    force of, 103
    specific, 281
Grid, 956
Gyration, radius of, 224
Gyroscope, 231

Half-life, of atom, 989
    of circuit, 661
Half-wave plate, 945
Hall effect, 695
Harmonic, 499
Harmonic motion, 256
    angular, 271
    simple, 257
Harmonic series, 499
Heat, 252
    of condensation, 362
    of fusion, 361
    mechanical equivalent of, 354
    of solidification, 362
    of sublimation, 362
    of transformation, 362
    of vaporization, 361
Heat capacity, 354, 357
    of crystal, 473
    of ideal gas, 420
Heat current, 369
Heat engine, 425
Helium atom, 531, 984
Henry, 742
Hole conduction, 696
Homogeneous flow, 310
Homogeneous substance, 472

Hooke's law, 169, 248, 249
Horsepower, 175
Horsepower·hour, 175
Hot reservoir, 427
Humidity, 404
Huygen's principle, 838
Hydraulic press, 283
Hydrodynamics, 309
Hydrostatic paradox, 283
Hydrostatic pressure, 246, 281
Hydrostatics, 280
Hyperboloid, 897
Hysteresis, 249, 769

Ice-pail experiment, 554
Ideal fluid, 309
Ideal gas, 390
    adiabatic process of, 422
    equation of state of, 451
    heat capacity of, 420
    molecular definition of, 447
Image distance, 853
Impedance, 789
    characteristic, 809
Impulse, 182
    angular, 227
Impulse-momentum principle, 183
Impulsive force, 183
Inclination, magnetic, 777
Indefinables of mechanics, 1
Index of refraction, 834
Induced emf, 730
Inductance, 741
Induction, electrostatic, 533
    magnetic, 674
Induction coil, 730
Inductor, 744
Inelastic collisions, 187, 188
Inertia, moment of, 218, 220
Inertial mass, 108
Inertial reference system, 23
Infrared, 824
Initial velocity, 74
Insulator, electrical, 533
Intake stroke, 428
Intensity, electric, 540
    of light, 902
    magnetic, 674
    wave, 510
Intensity level, of sound wave, 512
Interference, of light, 495, 895
    of longitudinal waves, 501
Interference fringes, 2, 896
Interferometer, Michelson, 2, 905
Internal energy, 414
    of gas, 419
Internal potential energy, 173
Internal reflection, 844
Internal resistance, 627
Inverse photoelectric effect, 977

Ion, 530
Irreversible processes, 431
Isobaric process, 395, 417
Isochoric process, 416
Isochronous motion, 260
Isolated system, 415
Isothermal process, 397, 416
Isotopes, 686
Isotopic substance, 472

Joule, 157
Joule effect, 419

Kelvin scale, 435
Kerr effect, 947
Kilogram, standard, 101
Kilowatt, 175
Kilowatt·hour, 176
Kinematics, 64
Kinetic energy, 157, 161, 225
Kinetic friction, 35
Kinetic theory of gases, 447
Kirchhoff's law, 379
Kirchhoff's rules, 652

L-C circuit, 746
Laminar flow, 318
Laminated core, 738
Laser, 974
Lateral magnification, 884
Leaf electroscope, 532
Leakage flux, 778
Length, standard, 2
Length contraction, 92
Lens, 873
Lens aberrations, 887
Lensmaker's equation, 875
Lenz's law, 731
Lewis-Tolman experiment, 195
Leyden jar, 601
Lifetime of an excited state, 971
Light, 823
    velocity of, 89
Limit, elastic, 248
    proportional, 248
    of resolution, 930
Linear conductor, 618
Linear expansion, 347
Linear momentum, 182
    conservation of, 186
Lines of force, electrical, 548, 614
    magnetic, 678
Line spectrum, 959
Lissajous figures, 268
Lloyd's mirror, 904
Long-range order, 447
Longitudinal mass, 204
Longitudinal wave, 477
    adiabatic character of, 485
    velocity of, 484

Loop, 497
Lorentz-Einstein transformation, 88
Loschmidt's number, 451
Loudness, 513
Lyman series, 961

Macroscopic cross section, 464
Magnetic circuit, 779
Magnetic field, 671
  of earth, 777
Magnetic flux, 678
Magnetic hysteresis, 249
Magnetic induction, 674
Magnetic intensity, 674, 762
Magnetic moment, 697
Magnetic pole, 671
Magnetism, 671
Magnetization, 761
Magnetomotive force, 779
Magnification, angular, 884
  lateral, 884
Magnifier, 884
Magnus effect, 325
Malus' law, 942
Manometer, 284
Maser, 974
Mass, 99
  of electron, 531
  and energy, 199
  gravitational, 108
  inertial, 108
  longitudinal, 204
  of neutron, 531
  of proton, 531
  relativistic change of, 195
  standard, 2
  and weight, 105
Mass number of an atom, 687, 988
Mass spectrometer, 686
Mathematical pendulum, 267
Maxwell, 678
Maxwell-Boltzmann distribution function,
  460
McLeod gauge, 392
Mean free path, 464
Mechanical energy, 163
Mechanical equivalent of heat, 354
Megawatt, 175
Melting point, 340
Meniscus, 306
Meson, 994
Metastable state, of atom, 974
Meter, standard, 2
Michelson interferometer, 2, 905
Michelson-Morley experiment, 88, 907
Microgram, 5
Micron, 3, 829
Micropoise, 320
Microscope, 887

Microscopic collision cross section, 464
Millibar, 285
Millikan's oil-drop experiment, 580
Minimal surfaces, 302
Minimum deviation, 846
Mirror, plane, 852
  spherical, 855
mks system, 101
Modulus, bulk, 250
  elastic, 249
  of rigidity, 250
  shear, 250
  stretch, 249
  torsion, 250
  Young's, 249
Molar heat capacity, 354, 357
  of gas, 456
Molecular diameter, 468
Molecular speed, distribution of, 459
  experimental measurement of, 461
Molecular theory of matter, 446
Molecules, nonpolar, 603
  polar, 603
Moment, of couple, 58
  of a force, 44, 218
  of inertia, 218
  of momentum, 229
Moment arm, 45
Momentum, 182
  angular, 227
  linear, 182
Monochromatic aberrations, 881
Motion, accelerated, 68
  circular, 135, 141
  harmonic, 256
  oscillatory, 258
  periodic, 258
  in plane, 124
  rectilinear, 64
  rotational, 211
  wave, 477
Motor, 702
Muon, 997
Muzzle velocity, 130

Nanometer, 3, 829
Nanosecond, 5
Neutron, 530, 992
Newton, 102
Newton·meter, 157
Newton·second, 183
Newton's first law, 20, 23
Newton's law of cooling, 384
Newton's law of gravitation, 103
Newton's rings, 912
Newton's second law, 99
  applications of, 108
Newton's third law, 24
Nicol prism, 939
Node, 497

Nonconcurrent forces, 26
Normal force, 33, 34
Normal state, of atom, 964
Normal stress, 245
Nuclear disintegration, 989
Nuclear fission, 999
Nuclear reaction energy, 991
Nuclear reactor, 999
Nucleus, 530, 986

Ocular, 885
Ohm, 621
Ohmmeter, 658
Ohm's law, 618
Oil-drop experiment, 580
Oil diffusion pump, 285
Optic nerve, 882
Optical activity, 949
Optical pyrometer, 338
Organ pipes, 505
Oscillation, 258
    center of, 272
Oscillatory motion, 258
Overtone, 499

Pair production, 680
Parallel forces, 53
Parallel-plate capacitor, 595
Paramagnetism, 760
Particle, 27, 531
Pascal's law, 282
Paschen series, 961
Peltier effect, 641
Pendulum, ballistic, 189
    conical, 140
    physical, 272
    simple, 267
Percentage polarization, 941
Percussion, center of, 273
Period, 258
Periodic motion, 258
Periodic table, 531, 1016
Periodic time, 258
Permanent set, 249
Permeability, 764
Permittivity, 606
Perrin's experiment, 450
Perverted image, 855
Phase, change of, 360
Phase angle, 260
Phase equilibrium, 339
Phosphor, 826
Photoelasticity, 947
Photoelectric effect, 957
Photon, 824, 958
Photronic cell, 959
Physical optics, 895
Physical pendulum, 272
Pinch effect, 713
Pion, 997

Pitch, 514
Pitot tube, 316
Pivoted-coil galvanometer, 701
Planck's constant, 537
Planck's law, 380
Plane mirror, 852
Plasma, 953
Plastic deformation, 249
Plastic flow, 249
Plasticity, 248
Pohl's experiment, 901
Poise, 320
Poiseuille's law, 321
Polarization, of a dielectric, 603
    of light, 934
Polarizing microscope, 949
Polarizing ring sight, 949
Polaroid, 940
Poles, magnetic, 671
Porro prism, 845
Porous plug experiment, 417
Positron, 992
Potential, electrical, 569
Potential difference, 569
Potential energy, elastic, 168
    gravitational, 162
    internal, 173
Potential gradient, 575
Potentiometer, 643, 659
Pound, force, 102
    mass, 5
Pound-second, 183
Power, in AC circuit, 793
    electrical, 636
    mechanical, 175, 226
Power factor, 796
Power stroke, 428
Poynting vector, 813
Prandtl tube, 317
Precession, 233
Presbyopia, 883
Pressure, absolute, 284
    critical, 389
    dynamic, 317
    gauge, 284
    hydrostatic, 246, 281
    partial, 404, 457
    static, 316
    across surface film, 300
    vapor, 401
Pressure amplitude, 510
Pressure gauges, 284
Pressure gradient, 322
Principle of superposition, 495
Prism, 844
Projectile, 129
Projection lantern, 886
Propagation constant, 480
Proportional limit, 248
Propulsion, rocket, 194

Proton, 530
Proton-proton chain, 1000
Pulsing sphere, 515
Pump, electromagnetic, 704
pVT-surface, 394, 395

Quality of sound, 514
Quantum, 380
Quantum mechanics, 967
Quantum number, 963
Quarter-wave plate, 945

R-C series circuit, 659
R-L circuit, 745
R-L-C circuit, 748
Radial acceleration, 136
Radial heat flow, 372
Radian, 211
Radiant emittance, 379
Radiant energy, 375
Radiating efficiency, of sound source, 519
Radiation, 375
   electromagnetic, 987
   heat transfer, 383
   from piston, 515
Radiation damping, 515
Radiator, complete, 378
Radioactive decay, 988
Radioactivity, 982
Radius, of gyration, 224
Rainbow, 848
Ramsden ocular, 885
Range, horizontal, 133
Rankine cycle, 430
Rankine scale, 343
Rarefaction, 478
Reactance, 785
Reaction, 25
Recoil, 192
Rectangular components, of acceleration, 127
   of force, 13
   of vector, 12
   of velocity, 125
Rectangular resolution, 14
Rectilinear motion, 64
Rectifier, 634
Reference level, 162
Reference system, 23
Reflected wave pulse, 494
Reflection, of light, 832
Refraction, of light, 833
Refrigerator, 431
Regelation, 403
Relative emittance, 379
Relative humidity, 405
Relative permeability, 764
Relative permittivity, 606
Relative velocity, 81

Relativistic force transformation, 202
Relativity, 81
Reluctance, 779
Remanence, 771
Resistance, 621, 627
Resistance thermometer, 338
Resistivity, 617
Resistor, 621
Resolving power, 928
Resonance, acoustical, 500
   electrical, 796
Resonance radiation, 971
Resonant frequency, 797
Restoring force, 169, 257
Resultant, 11
   of antiparallel forces, 11
   of parallel forces, 11, 53
Retentivity, 711
Reversible process, 434
Reynolds number, 327
Rheostat, 621
Rocket propulsion, 194
Rotary oil pump, 285
Rotating vector, 264
Rotation, 211
Rotation-translation analogy, 219
Rotor, 264
Rowland ring, 758
Rutherford's experiment, 984

Satellite, 145
Saturated liquid, 398
Saturated vapor, 398, 405
Scalar, 8
Scalar product, 158
Scattering of light, 942
Schroedinger equation, 968
Search coil, 735
Second law, of Newton, 99
   of thermodynamics, 430, 433, 440
Seeback effect, 640
Self-inductance, 743
Semiconductors, 618
Series in spectra, 961
Shear modulus, 250
Shearing strain, 248, 318
Shearing stress, 245, 319
Short-range order, 447
Shunt, 655
Simple harmonic motion, 257
Simple pendulum, 267
Single-slit diffraction, 920
Skin effect, 784
Sliding friction, 35
Slug, 102
Snell's law, 834
Solenoid, 697
   field of, 716
Solidification, heat of, 362
Sound, velocity of, 479

Sound wave, 510
Sources of light, 896
Space charge, 954
Space lattice, 447
Specific gravity, 281
Specific heat capacity, 354
    experimental values of, 357
Specific volume, 395
    critical, 398
Spectral emittance, 381
Spectrum, band, 974
    continuous, 977
    line, 959
    x-ray, 976
Speed, 66
    of efflux, 313
Sphere of exclusion, 468
Spherical aberration, 856
Spherical mirror, 855
Spherical wave, 515
Spring balance, 6
Spring constant, 169
Stagnation point, 310
Statcoulomb, 804
State coordinate, 334
Static friction, 34
Static lift, 323
Static pressure, 316
Stationary flow, 309
Stationary wave, 477, 495, 502, 817
Statistical mechanics, 473
Steady flow, 309
Steady state, 368
Steam engine, 429
Stefan's law, 382
Stiffness coefficient, 169
Stokes' law, 323
Strain, 247
Streamline, 309
Stress, 244
    thermal, 348
Stretch modulus, 249
Sublimation, heat of, 362
Sublimation point, 340
Superconductivity, 620
Superheated liquid, 407
Superposition, principle of, 895
Supersaturated vapor, 406
Surface, equipotential, 570
    gaussian, 549
Surface energy, 299
Surface tension, 296
Susceptibility, 605
Sweep circuit, 663
Systems of units, 101

Tangential stress, 245
Telescope, terrestrial, 888
Temperature, 334
    critical, 299, 398

Temperature gradient, 368
Temperature scale, 339
    celsius, 343
    fahrenheit, 343
    kelvin, 436
    rankine, 343
Tensile strain, 247
Tensile stress, 245
Tension, 26, 244
    surface, 296
Tensors, 245
Terminal velocity, 323
Terminal voltage, 627
Thermal conductivity, 369
Thermal efficiency, 427
Thermal equilibrium, 335, 383
Thermal stress, 348
Thermionic emission, 954
Thermistor, 620
Thermocouple, 338, 640
    fundamental equation, 641
Thermodynamics, 411
    first law of, 414, 419
    second law of, 430, 433, 440
    third law of, 437
    zeroth law of, 336
Thermoelectricity, 640
Thermometer, 337
Thermometric properties, 339
Thermopile, 640
Thin films, interference in, 911
Third law, of Newton, 25
    of thermodynamics, 437
Thomson effect, 641
Threshold frequency, 957
Throttling process, 417
Thrust, 315
Thyratron, 663
Time, dilation, 93
    standard, 2
Time constant, of circuit, 661
Toroid, field of, 717
Torque, 45, 218
Torque constant, 271
Torricelli's theorem, 314
Torsion modulus, 250
Total internal reflection, 844
Trajectory, 129
Transformation, heat of, 362
    relativistic force, 202
Transformer, 799
Transient, 783
Translation-rotation analogy, 219
Transverse force, 202
Transverse mass, 204
Transverse wave, 477
    velocity of, 482
Triode, 956
Triple point, 340, 401
Tropical year, 2

Tube, of flow, 309
  Pitot, 316
  Prandtl, 317
  Venturi, 315

Ultraviolet, 826
Unit, 2
Units, systems of, 101
Universal gas constant, 390
Uranium series, 990

Vacuum pump, 285
Van de Graaff generator, 588
van der Waals equation of state, 470
van der Waals forces, 469
Vapor, 399
Vapor pressure, 401
Vaporization, heat of, 361
Variation, magnetic, 778
Varignon's theorem, 45
Vector, 8
Vector analysis, 8
Vector difference, 16
Vector product, 47
Vector sum, 9
Velocity, angular, 211
  average, 65
  in harmonic motion, 260
  initial, 74
  instantaneous 65
  of light, 89
  of longitudinal wave, 484
  muzzle, 130
  precessional, 233
  relative, 81
  of sound, 479
  terminal, 323
  of transverse wave, 482
Velocity gradient, 319
Vena contracta, 314
Venturi meter, 316
Venturi tube, 315
Vernal equinox, 2
Vibration, 258
  of organ pipe, 505
  of rod, 506
  of string, 498
Virtual image, 854
Virtual object, 873
Viscosity, 317
  coefficient of, 319
  of gas, 466
Volt, 569

Volta potential, 569
Voltage, 569, 627
Voltmeter, 570, 654
Volume, equipotential, 570
Volume expansion, 345
Volume strain, 248
Vortices, 327

Water, density of, 346
  heat capacity of, 354
  volume of, 346
Water calorimeter, 355
Watt, 175, 638
Wave, electromagnetic, 720, 804
  longitudinal, 477
  sound, 510
  spherical, 515
  stationary, 477, 495, 502
  transverse, 477
Wavefront, 827
Wavelength, 478
Wave mechanics, 967
Wavemeter, 819
Weber, 678
Weight, 27, 54, 105
  apparent, 112, 147, 148
Weightlessness, 113, 147
Wet- and dry-bulb thermometer, 406
Wet steam, 430
Wheatstone bridge, 657
Wien's displacement law, 382
Wilson cloud chamber, 406, 680, 992
Work, 157, 226
  and heat, 413, 425
  internal, 172
  in thermodynamics, 411
  in volume change, 412
Work-energy principle, 157
Work function, 955
Working stroke, 428
World line, 85

X-ray, 927
X-ray diffraction, 927
X-ray spectrum, 976

Yield point, 248
Young's experiment, 898
Young's modulus, 249

Zero, absolute, 437
Zero-point energy, 343
Zeroth law of thermodynamics, 336